PRINCIPLES OF MICROBIOLOGY
AND IMMUNOLOGY

PRINCIPLES OF

HARPER & ROW, PUBLISHERS

New York, Evanston, and London

MICROBIOLOGY
AND
IMMUNOLOGY

BERNARD D. DAVIS

Head, Department of Bacteriology and Immunology
Harvard Medical School

RENATO DULBECCO

Resident Fellow, Salk Institute for Biological Studies

HERMAN N. EISEN

Head, Department of Microbiology
Washington University School of Medicine

HAROLD S. GINSBERG

Chairman, Department of Microbiology
University of Pennsylvania School of Medicine

W. BARRY WOOD, JR.

Director, Department of Microbiology
The Johns Hopkins University School of Medicine

PRINCIPLES OF MICROBIOLOGY AND IMMUNOLOGY

CONTENTS

v

PREFACE

This book is an unusual publishing venture: it is an excerpt from a recently published textbook, "Microbiology," by the same authors. The parent volume was designed primarily for medical students and physicians, and was published by Hoeber Medical Division of Harper & Row, Publishers, Incorporated. Because of the recent and growing prominence of microbes in the study of molecular genetics and cell physiology it seemed to us advisable to emphasize strongly the molecular and genetic aspects of the subject. As a result, we found that the parts of the book concerned with general properties of microbes, molecular genetics, and immunology might also provide a suitable textbook for graduate students, advanced college students, and biologists desiring a review of modern developments in these fields. We are therefore delighted that cooperative arrangements have been made for the College Department of the same publishing firm to bring out this excerpt volume, whose decreased bulk and expense should increase its usefulness for the non-medical audience.

The chapters on bacterial physiology and most of those on immunology and virology are identical with the corresponding chapters of the parent volume, except for a few corrections. The chapter on Hypersensitivity has been markedly condensed, while the chapters on Pathogenic Properties of Bacteria (19), Selected Bacteria (20), Fungi (21), and Viral Immunology and Pathogenesis (27) contain material selected from appropriate chapters of the parent volume. Students interested in antimicrobial defenses of the host and in pathogenic bacteria, fungi, and viruses should of course consult the parent volume. We have also added Supplementary References, with the expectation that graduate students, in particular, may wish to pursue such additional leads into the scientific literature. As in the original volume, material that seemed not essential for introductory courses, but still likely to interest many readers, has been printed in small type.

The book concentrates on the general properties of microbes, including considerable emphasis on animal virology; there is only brief coverage of the geochemical activities of microbes, or of aspects of microbiology that are primarily of industrial or agricultural interest. Nevertheless, we hope that the volume will be a useful text, together with suitable outside reading, in those general microbiology courses that emphasize metabolic, genetic, and cellular rather than ecological and descriptive aspects of the subject. In this connection we would like to emphasize our conviction that a text should illustrate the scientific method as well as transmit a body of information. We have therefore briefly reviewed the history of many major discoveries in order to show how scientific advances may depend on new concepts or technics, or on ingenious experiments, or on alertness to the significance of unexpected observations. Moreover, we have endeavored throughout to indicate the nature of the evidence underlying the conclusions presented—for otherwise the student sees only the shadow and not the substance of science.

The portion devoted to immunology is quite sufficient for a separate course in this subject—one that has rapidly developed independent status in biology, apart from its relation to infectious disease. Since most students of either microbiology or immunology have some interst in both subjects, and since the price of two separate volumes would have been substantially higher, we have elected to keep the excerpt book as a single volume.

The preparation of this volume has been a truly cooperative effort: the chapters drafted by each author have been critically reviewed by most or all of the others. We are deeply grateful for the education and for the warm friendships that have resulted.

A new book of this size will inevitably contain many errors and weaknesses. We shall welcome corrections and suggestions for future editions.

B. D. DAVIS
R. DULBECCO
H. N. EISEN
H. S. GINSBERG
W. B. WOOD, JR.

ACKNOWLEDGMENTS

We are deeply indebted to the many professional colleagues who have critically reviewed various portions of the manuscript. The number is too large to list, but those who have made particularly extensive and important suggestions include: Elmer Becker, Albert H. Coons, Julian Fleischman, Dan Fraenkel, Howard Goldfine, James G. Hirsch, Rollin D. Hotchkiss, Francois Jacob, Elvin A. Kabat, Manuel Kaplan, George Kobayashi, Irwin Lepow, Hans Muller-Eberhard, Milton R. J. Salton, William D. Sawyer, John G. Scaife, and Aaron E. Szulman.

We wish to acknowledge the patient contributions of the publisher's staff to this enterprise which has occupied us all for a period of nearly five years. We also want to express our deep appreciation for the efforts of our several secretaries, who toiled without complaint over the innumerable revisions resulting from our cooperative authorship. In addition, we are very much indebted to the Marine Biological Laboratory at Woods Hole, Massachusetts, for the hospitality of its library, where much of this work was written.

Many investigators and publishers have provided illustrations or permission to utilize previously published material. We are most grateful for all these generous contributions, whose sources are noted in the legends to the Figures and Tables.

There are similarities between the diseases of animals or man and the diseases of beer and wine. . . . If fermentations were diseases one could speak of epidemics of fermentation. L. PASTEUR

1 EVOLUTION OF MICROBES AND OF MICROBIOLOGY

EVOLUTION OF MICROBIOLOGY

The First Microscopic Observations

To account for the rather obvious spread of certain diseases from one person to another, thoughtful men since ancient times postulated the existence of invisible, transmissible agents of infection. Thus in the prescient and rationalistic poem *De Rerum Natura* Lucretius (96?–55 B.C.) intuitively recognized not only the atomistic nature of matter but also the existence of "seeds" of disease. Microscopic organisms (microbes) were not seen, however, until Antony van Leeuwenhoek (1632–1723) made microscopes with sufficient magnification: the science of microbiology began with his letter in the *Philosophical Transactions of the Royal Society of London* in 1677.

Even in an age when science was still in the hands of gifted amateurs, Leeuwenhoek was unusual for his isolation from the learned world and his lack of formal education. A cloth merchant in the town of Delft, Holland, with a political sinecure as custodian of the Town Hall, he spent much of his leisure time in grinding tiny lenses of high magnification (probably up to 300✕), with which he made simple (one-lens) microscopes (Fig. 1-1). With these instruments this patient and curious man discovered an incredible variety of hitherto unseen structures, including the major morphological classes of bacteria (spheres, rods, and spirals; (Fig. 1-2), as well as the larger microbes (protozoa, algae, yeasts), erythrocytes and spermatozoa, and the capillary circulation. Leeuwenhoek's discoveries were described in a flow of letters to the Royal Society of London, whose distinguished members he apparently never met.* Moreover, by keeping secret the methods of constructing and using his instruments, he remained throughout his long and productive lifetime the sole occupant of the field that he had created.

Since no other observers succeeded in using single lenses as effectively as Leeuwenhoek, further advances depended on the perfection of the compound microscope, which had already been invented but suffered from serious optical aberrations. Following the improvement of this instrument further descriptive observations on microbes accumulated; and though Linnaeus in 1767 distinguished only 6 species in assigning microbes to the class "*Chaos*," 600 types were figured in Ehrenberg's *Atlas* in 1838.

Fig. 1-1 A Leeuwenhoek microscope, viewed from the back (1) and in diagrammatic section (4). The specimen, on a movable pin, is examined through a minute biconvex lens (l), held between two metal plates. (From C. Dobell. *Antony van Leeuwenhoek and His "Little Animals."* Dover, New York, 1960.)

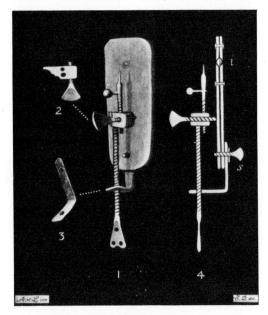

* Leeuwenhoek's letters have a charming colloquial style, no longer seen in scientific communications. For example, he describes the following observations on a decayed tooth, which emphasize that motility was then the only available criterion for considering a microscopic object alive. "I took this stuff out of the hollows in the roots, and mixed it with clean rainwater, and set it before the magnifying-glass so as to see if there were as many living creatures in it as I had aforetime discovered in such material: and I must confess that the whole stuff seemed to me to be alive. But notwithstanding the number of these animalcules was so extraordinarily great (though they were so little withal, that 'twould take a thousand million of some of 'em to make up the bulk of a coarse sand-grain, and though several thousands were a-swimming in a quantity of water that was no bigger than a coarse sand-grain is), yet their number appeared even greater than it really was: because the animalcules, with their strong swimming through the water, put many little particles which had no life in them into a like motion, so that many people might well have taken these particles for living creatures too."

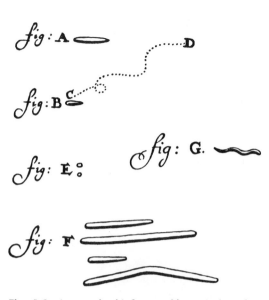

Fig. 1-2 Leeuwenhoek's figures of bacteria from the human mouth, from letter of 17 September, 1683. Dotted line between B and D indicates motility. (From C. Dobell. *Antony van Leeuwenhoek and His "Little Animals."* Dover, New York, 1960.)

An experimental science of microbiology, however, emerged only slowly, and required the development of a special methodology. The key was the use of sterilized materials and aseptic technics; for while the chemist defines purity in terms of percentage of contaminating material, in microbiology a single contaminating cell can ruin an experiment. Only after learning to avoid such contamination could investigators recognize the existing variety of microbes, their distribution, and their major roles. The development of reliable methods was very much stimulated by a prolonged and intense controversy over an issue with religious overtones: the spontaneous generation of life. This topic therefore occupies a prominent place in the early history of microbiology.

Spontaneous Generation

Until recent centuries it was widely believed that living organisms can arise spontaneously in decomposing organic matter. For visible organisms this notion was dispelled in the seventeenth century, when Redi demonstrated that maggots no longer appeared in decom-

posing meat if it was protected from the deposition of eggs by flies. However, the idea of spontaneous generation persisted for the new world of microbes, whose relation to the rest of biology was far from clear.

The question would appear to have been settled in the eighteenth century by the careful experiments of Spallanzani (1729–1799), who introduced the use of sterile culture media: he showed that a "putrescible fluid," such as an infusion of meat, would remain clear indefinitely if boiled and properly sealed.* Moreover, in 1837 Schwann elegantly showed that similar results could be obtained even when air was allowed to reenter the cooling flask before sealing, provided the air passed through a heated tube. Skeptics could claim, however, that the absence of decomposition in these sealed vessels was due to the limited supply of air rather than to the exclusion of dustborne living contaminants. To answer this objection Schroeder and von Dusch introduced the use of the cotton plug, which is still widely used today to exclude airborne contaminants from culture media.

Nevertheless, the controversy continued, for some investigators were unable to reproduce the alleged stability of dust-free sterilized organic infusions. Louis Pasteur (1822–1895) then entered the lists because of his conviction that microbes were the cause rather than a product of fermentation (see below). He showed that boiled medium could remain clear in an unsealed "swan-neck" flask, open to the air through a sinuous horizontal tube, in which dust particles would settle (or be trapped by moisture of condensation), as air reentered the cooling vessel (Fig. 1-3). Pasteur also demonstrated that in the relatively dust-free atmosphere of a quiet cellar, or of a mountain top, sealed flasks could be opened and then resealed with a good chance of escaping contamination.

---

* Indeed, the soundness of this discovery was confirmed in the early nineteenth century, when a Parisian confectioner, Appert, competing for a prize offered by Napoleon, developed the art of preserving food by canning.

Fig. 1-3 Pasteur's "swan-neck" flasks. After use in his studies on spontaneous generation these flasks were sealed, and they have since been preserved, with their original contents, in the Pasteur Museum. (Courtesy of Institut Pasteur, Paris.)

Pasteur's experiments were among the public sensations of his day; and his style may be illustrated by the following quotation from a lecture delivered at the Sorbonne in 1864.

"I have taken my drop of water from the immensity of creation, and I have taken it full of the elements appropriate to the development of microscopic organisms. And I wait, I watch, I question it!—begging it to recommence for me the beautiful spectacle of the first creation. But it is dumb, dumb since these experiments were begun several years ago; it is dumb because I have kept it sheltered from the only thing man does not know how to produce; from the germs which float in the air, from Life, for Life is a germ and a germ is Life. Never will the doctrine of spontaneous generation recover from the mortal blow of this simple experiment!"

The Problem of Spores. Though Pasteur's contributions were in principle no more decisive than those of his predecessors who had also achieved stable sterility, his zeal and skill

as a polemicist were largely responsible for laying the ghost of spontaneous generation. Yet it turned out that his accusations of technical incompetence on the part of his opponents did not really explain why their infusions stubbornly refused to remain clear. The key fact was that they used infusions of hay, and Pasteur preferred other materials (sugar plus yeast extract) for his culture media.

The most important experimental step in finishing the controversy was taken when various materials were compared by the British physicist John Tyndall, who became engaged in the problem through his interest in the optical effects of atmospheric dust. Tyndall found that after he had brought a bale of hay into his laboratory he could no longer repeat his earlier successes in achieving sterility by boiling various kinds of extracts; but he could repeat them in a separate room. He finally concluded that the hay had contaminated his laboratory with **an incredible kind** of living organism: one that could survive boiling for hours. In the same year (1877) Ferdinand Cohn demonstrated the resistant forms as small, refractile **endospores** (Ch. 5), and showed that they were stages in the life cycle of the hay bacillus (*Bacillus subtilis*). Even the most resistant bacterial spores, however, are readily sterilized in the presence of moisture at 120°; hence the autoclave, which reaches this temperature through the use of steam under pressure, became the hallmark of the bacteriology laboratory.

Once the biological continuity of microbes was recognized, it soon became apparent that there are different kinds, which occupy different ecological niches and have different actions. Microbiology then developed largely through interest in three different groups of microbes, responsible, respectively, for fermentations, for much of the cycle of organic matter in Nature, and for diseases of man as well as of lower animals and plants. These developments gave rise to the corresponding applied fields of industrial, agricultural, and medical microbiology. The study of fermentations came earliest, and provided much of the impetus for the development of other areas in microbiology, as well as the development of biochemistry.

The Role of Microbes in Fermentations

We have seen that practical men proceeded to preserve foods while the savants continued to dispute spontaneous generation. Useful fermentations* have an even longer history of achievement without a theoretical foundation: lost in antiquity are the origins of leavened bread, wine, or the fermentations that preserved food through the accumulation of lactic acid (soured milk, cheese, sauerkraut, ensilage).

In the 1830s, with the development of microscopes of sufficient resolving power, Schwann, Cagniard-Latour, and Kutzing concluded independently that the sediment of microscopic globules accumulating in an alcoholic fermentation consists of tiny, growing plants, whose metabolic activities are responsible for the fermentation.† However, the leading chemists of the day considered that fermentation was a chemical process, due to a self-perpetuating instability of the grape juice initiated by its exposure to the air. The amorphous sediment would thus be a by-product of the fermentation, analogous to the frequent crystalline precipitates of tartaric acid. In particular, the distinguished Liebig, father of biochemistry, advanced this view with such vehemence that Schwann's excellent evidence on the nature of fermentation was essentially discarded for two decades.‡

Pasteur's Contributions. Liebig's authority was eventually refuted by an equally forceful personality, Louis Pasteur: a crusader who sought not only to discover the truth but also to overwhelm its enemies. Because of this drive, as well as his experimental skill and intuitive genius, Pasteur was for the nineteenth century, in Dubos' words, ". . . not only the arm but also the voice, and finally the symbol, of triumphant science."

Educated as a chemist, Pasteur became interested in fermentations through discovering optical isomerism as a property of certain fermentation products (isoamyl alcohol, tartaric acid). A combination of biological and chemical studies then led him to recognize the specificity of different agents of fermentation. In 1857, in his first paper on fermentation, he showed that different kinds of microbes were associated with different kinds of fermentation: spheres of variable size (now known as

---

* In general usage the term **fermentation** refers to the microbial decomposition of vegetable matter, which contains mostly carbohydrates; while **putrefaction** refers to the formation of more unpleasant products by the decomposition of high-protein materials, such as meat or eggs. (For a more rigorous definition of fermentation see Chapter 3.) The etymology of the word ferment (L. *fervere*, "to boil"), and its figurative use today, reflect the heating and bubbling that are generated in a vat of fermenting grape juice.

---

† Within 2 years Schwann was also to propose one of the most important unifying principles of biology, the cellular structure of the tissues of higher organisms.

‡ Indeed, in 1839 Liebig and Wohler published an anonymous, scatological hoax in which they reported the microscopic visualization of an animal, shaped somewhat like a distilling apparatus, that took in sugar at one end and excreted alcohol at the other, while its large gonads released bubbles of CO_2.

yeast cells) in the alcoholic fermentation, and smaller rods (lactobacilli) in the lactic fermentation.*

In the course of establishing the nature of fermentation Pasteur founded the study of **microbial metabolism** and developed profound insight into many of its problems. Thus in proving that living organisms are responsible for fermentations Pasteur also emphasized that **life is possible without air.** He recognized the existence of both obligatory anaerobes, which are inhibited by air, and facultative anaerobes, which can grow either with or without air; and he showed that fermentation yields much less growth than respiration per unit of substrate consumed.

Selective Cultivation. Since the nature of a specific fermentation depends on the organism responsible, how can a given kind of substrate, when not deliberately inoculated with a particular microbe, regularly undergo a given kind of fermentation? Pasteur recognized that the explanation lay in the principle of selective cultivation: various organisms are ubiquitous, and the one that eventually predominates in a mixed culture is the one best adapted to the environment. For example, the high sugar concentration and low protein content (i.e., low buffering power) of grape juice leads to a condition, now recognized as low pH, that favors the outgrowth of acid-resistant yeasts and thus yields an alcoholic fermentation; while neutralization of the acid by the high protein content of milk favors the outgrowth of faster-growing but more acid-sensitive bacteria, which cause a lactic fermentation.

An excess of the wrong organism in the starting inoculum, however, can grow out sufficiently to cause formation of a product with a poor flavor; hence specific microbes

play a role in "diseases" of beer and wine, as well as in different normal fermentations. This finding led Pasteur to make the fruitful suggestion that specific microbes would probably also prove to be causes of various diseases of man.

With an eye always to practical as well as to theoretical problems, Pasteur developed the procedure of gentle heating (pasteurization) to prevent the spoilage of beer and wine by undesired contaminating microbes. Many years later this process was extended to prevent milkborne diseases of man.

Soil Microbiology: Geochemical Cycles. Pasteur was concerned with pathways of carbohydrate metabolism that subsequently proved very similar to those of mammalian "physiological" chemistry, thus leading eventually to the concept of the **unity** of biology at a molecular level. In contrast, toward the end of the Pasteurian era other investigators, notably Winogradsky in Russia and Beijerinck in Holland, began exploring the microbiology of the soil, and discovered an astonishing **variety** of metabolic patterns by which different kinds of bacteria, adapted to different ecological niches, make their living. These organisms were isolated by the use of a systematic extension of Pasteur's principle of selective cultivation: **enrichment cultures,** in which only a particular energy source is provided, and growth is thus restricted to those organisms that can use that source. Some of the unusual patterns of bacterial energy production, ranging from the oxidation of sulfur to the formation of CH_4 from CO_2 and H_2, are described in Chapter 3.

With the development of soil microbiology it became clear that the major role of microbes in Nature is **geochemical:** mineralization of organic carbon, nitrogen, and sulfur (i.e., conversion to CO_2, NH_3 or NO_3^-, $SO_4^=$ or $S^=$), so that these elements can be used cyclically for generation after generation of growth of higher plants and animals, rather than being tied up in dead organic matter. In addition, marine algae, and to a much smaller extent photosynthetic bacteria, are responsible

---

* As in many scientific disputes, the losing argument possessed at least a grain of truth. The view of fermentation as a chemical rather than a vital process was ultimately vindicated in 1897, though in a profoundly modified form, when Edouard Buchner accidentally discovered that a cell-free extract, made by grinding yeast cells with sand, fermented a concentrated sugar solution added to preserve the extract.

for a considerable fraction of the other half of the geochemical cycle: the formation of organic matter from CO_2 by photosynthesis.

The beneficent geochemical role of microbes is worth emphasizing, since the prominent historical connection between infectious disease and microbiology has given rise to the popular image of a malignant and hostile microbial world. In fact, human pathogens constitute only a small fraction of the recognized bacterial species, and an infinitesimal fraction of the total mass of microbes on the earth: most microbes attack organic matter only after it is dead and buried.

The development of soil microbiology led to the recognition that soil fertility is enhanced by the bacteria that convert atmospheric nitrogen, or the ammonia from organic decay, into the nonvolatile form of nitrate. Of even greater economic importance was the extension of fermentations, in industrial microbiology, from the production of foods and beverages to that of valuable chemicals, such as glycerol, acetone, and later vitamins, antibiotics, and alkaloids. In these applications, just as in the study of cell physiology, successful developments have depended largely on the possibility of selecting microbial mutants with desired metabolic properties.

Microbiology and Medicine

The Germ Theory of Disease

Among the major classes of disease infections have undoubtedly presented the greatest burden to mankind. Since many infectious diseases kill the young even more frequently than the old, their social impact has been even greater than would be indicated by their numerical position among the leading causes of death. Moreover, by their epidemic nature they have often disabled and terrorized communities and determined the fate of armies and nations. Small wonder, then, that the discovery of the causes of infectious diseases, and the development of methods for their control, have been hailed as the most dramatic achievement of medical science; the men most responsible for developing the re-

quired methodology, Pasteur in France and Robert Koch (1843–1910) in Germany, were enshrined as national heroes.

Epidemiological Evidence. The discovery of infectious agents was long preceded by the concept of **contagious** disease, i.e., one initiated by **contact** with a diseased person or with objects contaminated by him. Thus even though the ancient Hebrews viewed pestilences as punishments visited on peoples by the Lord, the Mosaic code also contains numerous public health regulations, including the isolation of lepers, the discarding of various unclean materials, and the avoidance of shellfish and pork as foods. Later shrewd observers, such as Lucretius and Boccaccio, explicitly recognized the contagious nature of certain epidemic diseases.

In 1546 Fracastorius of Verona presented an impressive body of evidence in *De Contagione*. This book founded the science of **epidemiology,** which analyzes the distribution in human populations of events affecting health. After carefully studying epidemics of several diseases, including plague and syphilis, Fracastorius concluded that these diseases were spread by **seminaria** ("seeds"), transmitted from one person to another either directly or via inanimate objects. But like later writers, for some time to come, he presented a curious mixture of common sense and superstition: though it seemed prudent to avoid exposure to patients, or to plagued communities, as sources of "seeds" of disease, it also seemed reasonable to believe that outbreaks of these agents had the same supernatural and/or telluric origin that had long been held for the diseases themselves.

The epidemiological evidence for the germ theory of disease was not generally taken seriously, and a century after Fracastorius even as distinguished a physician as William Harvey rejected his conclusions. Most physicians continued to follow the views of Hippocrates and Galen, who ascribed epidemics to **miasmas,** i.e., poisonous vapors, created by the influence of planetary conjunctions or by disturbances arising within the earth.

Part of the difficulty arose from the existence of many communicable diseases that are not contagious in a strict sense. We now know that these are transmitted by less obvious routes than direct contact, such as air, water, food, and insects; and it is easy to see how an airborne disease could logically be ascribed to poisoned air until the particulate nature of the agent was demonstrated. Moreover, the idea that living organisms too small to be seen could exist, and could mortally harm large animals, was more radical and contrary to common sense than we can readily appreciate today. Thus even the recognition of transmissible "seeds of disease" did not quite hit the mark: the notion of seed was taken literally, the actual *contagium vivum* within the diseased body being considered something more complex derived from the seed. Experimental evidence was required, and it accumulated slowly, from several directions: transmission of infection, its prevention, and finally identification of the agents.

Transmission of infection was demonstrated boldly in the eighteenth century by the renowned surgeon John Hunter, who inoculated himself with purulent material from a patient with gonorrhea; unfortunately, both for him and for the understanding of etiology, he transmitted at the same time a much more serious disease, syphilis. The use of experimental animals in such studies was introduced later: for example, in 1865 Villemin so transmitted tuberculosis, though the nature of the responsible agent in the infectious material was not established until 20 years later.

The role of **indirect** transmission from one person to another was emphasized in the 1840s by Ignaz Semmelweis in Vienna, and by Oliver Wendell Holmes (perhaps better known as a poet than as a physician) in Boston, who shockingly (but unsuccessfully) asserted that obstetricians, moving with unwashed hands from one patient to the next, were responsible for the prevalence in hospitals of puerperal sepsis, a frequent cause of maternal death. More detailed evidence for the communicability of a disease was provided in 1854 by John Snow in London, who traced a localized epidemic of cholera to the now famous Broad Street pump, and deduced that this enteric disease was spread by a water supply contaminated with fecal material.

Preventive measures also lent support to the germ theory. In 1796 Edward Jenner, observing that milkmaids rarely came down with smallpox, introduced **vaccination** (L. *vacca,* "cow") against this disease by inoculating material from lesions of a somewhat similar common disease of cattle, cowpox; yet the theoretical implications of this finding with respect to the infectious origin of the disease were not appreciated. In the 1860s,

however, Joseph Lister (later Lord Lister) introduced **antiseptic surgery** on a much firmer theoretical foundation. Impressed by Pasteur's evidence for the ubiquity of airborne microbes and their importance in the contamination of sterile culture media, Lister reasoned that similar contamination might be responsible for the very frequent development of pus in tissues exposed by surgery or by wounds. He found that direct application of a disinfectant, phenol (carbolic acid), markedly reduced the incidence of serious infections. It is noteworthy that this major advance was achieved a decade before any specific agent of human infection was identified. Emphasis later shifted from antiseptic to **aseptic surgery.**

Recognition of Agents of Infection

The epidemiological evidence for communicability, though logically convincing, did not carry the weight of a direct demonstration of the postulated agents of infection. The first microbial pathogens to be recognized were **fungi,** which are larger than bacteria: in 1836 Agostino Bassi demonstrated experimentally that a fungus was the cause of a disease (of silkworms), and 3 years later Schönlein discovered the association of a fungus with a human skin disease (favus). Pathogenic fungi were soon also recognized in plant pathology, where they have become even more prominent than in medicine. In 1865 Pasteur entered the field of pathogenic microbiology with the discovery of a **protozoon** that was threatening to ruin the European silkworm industry.

The etiological role of **bacteria** in a disease was unequivocally established by Robert Koch for anthrax, in 1876, and was confirmed by Pasteur and his medical colleague, Joubert. This disease offered the investigator several advantages: the bacillus of anthrax is unusually large, and is readily identified morphologically; the disease, primarily one of cattle and sheep, is readily experimented on and may be conveniently transmitted to small animals; and unusually dense bacterial populations may appear in the blood. Indeed, Davaine in 1850 had already seen rod-shaped bodies in the blood of sheep dying of anthrax, and had later transmitted the disease by inoculating as little as 10^{-6} ml of blood. However, this evidence, though highly suggestive, did not prove that these bodies were the cause rather than a result of the disease, especially since the rods could not always be seen in infectious blood.

Koch, then a rural physician, solved the problem by isolating the anthrax bacillus in pure culture and showing that such cultures could transmit the disease to mice. In addition, though only vegetative rods were found in the blood, he found that cultures eventually developed spores, recognized by virtue of their refractility, which were highly resistant to sterilization (Fig. 1-4). This finding accounted for the puzzling observation that fields once inhabited by anthrax-infected animals could infect fresh herds years later.

Pure Cultures. The key to the identification of bacteria as pathogens was the isolation of pure cultures. The necessity of this step had been pointed out as early as 1840 by Koch's teacher of pathology, Henle, following Schwann's identification of the agents of

Fig. 1-4 Spore formation in *Bacillus anthracis,* as independently described and simultaneously published by Robert Koch ("Fig. 5a") and Ferdinand Cohn ("Fig. 5b"). (Courtesy of Koch Museum, Berlin.)

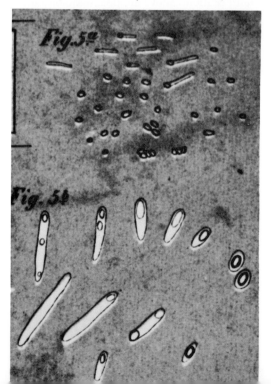

fermentation as living organisms. (Pasteur, in working on specific fermentations, had depended not on pure cultures but on recognizing the different predominant organisms selected under different conditions.) Lister showed that pure cultures could be obtained by the method of **limiting dilutions,** in which the source material is diluted until the individual inocula each contain either one infectious particle or none; but this method is awkward. Koch meticulously perfected the technics that are used today, including the use of **solid media,** on which individual cells in the inoculum give rise to separate colonies, and the use of **stains,** which proved important for identifying organisms much smaller than the anthrax bacillus. Koch's genius is perhaps best reflected in his patient modifications of his own methods that led to the identification of the tubercle bacillus, in 1882: because this organism grows very slowly the usual 1 to 2 days of cultivation had to be extended to several weeks, and because it is so impervious the usual few minutes of staining had to be extended to 12 hours.

The powerful methodology developed by Koch introduced the "Golden Era" of medical bacteriology. Between 1879 and 1889 various members of the German school isolated (in addition to the tubercle bacillus) the cholera vibrio, typhoid bacillus, diphtheria bacillus, pneumococcus, staphylococcus, streptococcus, meningococcus, gonococcus, and tetanus bacillus. Studies naturally followed on the mechanisms of pathogenicity of these organisms, the host responses, and methods of prevention and treatment.

Curiously, Pasteur, despite his early start with anthrax, did not enter the race to identify pathogens. Uninterested in the problems of isolating and classifying organisms, and ever alert to novel fundamental principles and to their practical applications, he devoted his later years to the development of **vaccines.** By accident he found that chickens injected with an old culture of the bacterium of chicken cholera were subsequently resistant to a fresh, virulent culture. Having earlier emphasized the constancy of the organisms responsible for different fermentations, he quickly recognized that this observation suggested an important **variability** as well. Within the incredible space of 4 years, and before the development of any understanding of the nature of the immune response, Pasteur discovered four methods of "attenuating" organisms and thus converting them to useful vaccines: aging of the culture (chicken cholera), cultivation at high temperature (anthrax), passage through another host species (swine erysipelas), and drying (rabies). As we shall see in later chapters, this "attenuation" comprises two distinct processes: selection of less virulent mutants, and killing of virulent organisms with retention of their immunizing activity.

Koch's Postulates. After identifying the tubercle bacillus Koch formalized the criteria for distinguishing a pathogenic from an adventitious microbe, and these criteria have since become known as **Koch's postulates:** 1) the organism is regularly found in the lesions of the disease, 2) it can be isolated in pure culture on artificial media, 3) inoculation of this culture produces a similar disease in experimental animals, and 4) the organism can be recovered from the lesions in these animals. These criteria have proved invaluable in establishing pathogens, but they have limitations: some organisms cannot be grown on artificial media, and some are pathogenic only for man.

Koch's development of solid media also had important consequences for general bacteriology. The ready isolation of pure cultures finally dispelled the claim of the "pleomorphists" (based on the fluctuating properties of impure cultures) that the various bacterial cell types were merely different stages in the life cycle of a single organism. With this misconception out of the way, the classification of bacteria proposed by Ferdinand Cohn was generally accepted and has persisted, in its main features, to the present day.

Viruses

The term virus (L., "poison"), long used as a synonym for infectious agent, is now reserved for the true viruses. These were originally defined as infectious agents small enough to pass filters that retain bacteria, and were later characterized also by the requirement of a living host for their multiplication. Since these pathogens could not be cultivated on artificial media, Koch's criteria, as originally stated, could not be satisfied; but subsequent developments have provided other means of obtaining pure cultures and thus returning to the spirit of these criteria.

The first virus to be recognized as filtrable was a plant pathogen, tobacco mosaic virus, discovered independently by Iwanowski in Russia in 1892 and by Beijerinck in Holland in 1899. Filtrable animal viruses* were first demonstrated for foot-and-mouth disease of cattle by Löffler and Frosch in 1898, and for a human disease, yellow fever, by the U.S. Army Commission under Walter Reed in 1900. A third class of viruses (bacteriophages), which infect bacteria, were discovered by Twort in England in 1916 and by d'Herelle in France in 1917.

Viruses proved much more difficult to study than bacteria: they could be cultivated only in living hosts and detected only by their pathogenic effects on these hosts. Progress was therefore slow for the first third of this century, until sophisticated physical and chemical methods were developed for purifying and characterizing viruses and studying their multiplication. Above all, precise quantitative studies became possible with the development of monolayer cultures of host cells in which viruses can propagate and form discrete plaques, analogous to the bacterial colonies formed on solid media. Virology has accordingly flourished in recent years, and viruses are now known to be a special class of particles with a unique method of reproduction. With the development of rigorous criteria for distinguishing viruses from cells, certain filtrable agents long considered to be viruses have turned out to have a cellular organization; these groups (mycoplasmas, rickettsiae,

---

* It is curious that though the most dramatic part of Pasteur's work in the 1880s on the development of vaccines was performed with tissues containing rabies virus, he did not recognize the filtrability of the agent.

chlamydiae) are therefore classified in this book as bacteria.

The Host Response: Immunology

Vertebrates infected by a microbial parasite exhibit a **specific, "immune" response,** which contributes both to recovery from the disease and to protection against reinfection. The existence of such a response has long been known to sharp observers, since recovery from many diseases is associated with protection from a second attack. (Indeed, with diseases that are widespread, and that tend to be less serious when acquired at an early age, it has long been customary in many communities to deliberately expose children to infection.) Analysis of the immune response has given rise to the major field of **immunology,** which is concerned with 1) the process by which foreign materials (antigens) elicit the appearance of specific cells and circulating proteins (antibodies) with a high affinity for the antigens, and 2) the properties, interactions, and uses of these components.

As with other practical problems, the search for protection against infection resulted in successes that ran ahead of theory. Jenner's vaccination against smallpox in 1798, using the less virulent cowpox virus, was a remarkable achievement; and we have already noted that Pasteur developed several vaccines in the early 1880s, before the nature of the immune response was at all understood.

The Scope of Immunology. The concept of **immunity** involves all factors that affect resistance to infectious disease, including major nonspecific factors (i.e., not requiring specific elicitation by antigens), such as enzymes that attack the parasites and specialized **phagocytic** cells that engulf them. The science of immunology is thus in a sense more restricted, being concerned with only the specific aspects of immunity. But immunology is in another sense broader, since it extends into areas distinct from infectious disease; for the same responses are equally brought into play when foreign substances of nonmicrobial origin gain access to the tissues (e.g., pollens, insect stings, drugs, foreign serum or other proteins, transplanted tissues). In addition, immunological methods are being used increasingly in biochemistry as delicate tools for the study of macromolecular structure.

Immunology is thus, strictly speaking, a branch more of pathophysiology than of microbiology. Nevertheless, immunology is still inextricably connected with microbiology: not only are immune reactions of vital importance in host-parasite interactions, but immunological methods are indispensable for identifying and classifying various pathogenic microbes, and for identifying those individuals in a host population who have previously been infected with a given organism. Finally, infectious disease constitutes the principal selective force in the evolution of the immune response; and, conversely, this response has had great influence on the evolution of those microbes that are pathogenic for man and other vertebrates. Hence immunology constitutes a major section of this book.

Control of Infectious Diseases

As we have already noted, the identification of the agents of various infectious diseases soon led to several remarkably effective methods of control. 1) In technologically advanced countries environmental **sanitation** and improved personal **hygiene** have led to a striking reduction in incidence, and sometimes even to the elimination, of certain diseases, particularly those spread by water or food (e.g., typhoid, cholera) or by insects (e.g., typhus, yellow fever). However, a knowledge of these diseases is still essential for the physician, since they may at any time be reintroduced by travelers. 2) **Vaccination** has drastically reduced the incidence of several serious epidemic diseases (e.g., smallpox, diphtheria, whooping cough, poliomyelitis), and has been especially valuable for diseases transmitted by respiratory droplets, since this means of transmission is difficult to control. For many organisms, however, vaccination is not effective or feasible. 3) The development of effective antibacterial **chemotherapy** has dramatically reduced the seriousness of many infectious diseases and the incidence of some. Indeed, this development represents the most striking advance in medical bacteriology since the 1880s.

In principle it should ultimately be possible to **eradicate,** by one or more of these methods, those organisms that are **obligatory** human pathogens. However, this hope does not exist for those pathogens that can also be widely carried by man without causing disease, or those that have **reservoirs** in lower animals or in the soil.

The Impact of Microbiology on the Concept of Disease

Against a background of vague speculations on the causation of disease, the discovery of specific etiological agents for a number of infections represented a tremendous theoretical advance for medicine. But as often happens with a new principle, its limits were not promptly recognized. The success of the Pasteurian approach thus led to unwarranted confidence that a single cause was waiting to be discovered for every disease. Such an oversimplified view still appears today: some will argue, for example, with total irrelevance, that tobacco-smoking cannot be **the** cause of bronchogenic cancer since this disease occasionally arises in nonsmokers.

It has become increasingly apparent that the principle of multifactorial causation is applicable even to many infectious diseases. Thus even though the concept of the tubercle bacillus as the etiological agent of tuberculosis proved much more fruitful than the preceding concept of the "phthisical diathesis" (i.e., a constitutional tendency to develop this disease), tuberculin testing has shown that many more people are **infected** with tubercle bacilli than have the **disease.** Hence, the presence of the tubercle bacillus is a necessary but not a sufficient condition for the disease tuberculosis: other factors, involving genetic constitution and physiological state of the host, can be decisive. Studies on infectious disease are therefore focusing increasingly on these subtle host factors; and the development of such a molecular pathology must rest on the foundation of molecular biology, to which mi-

crobiology has contributed extensively (see next section).

The Development of Microbial Physiology and Molecular Genetics

Until relatively recently microbiology was largely an applied field, concerned primarily with learning to control the activities, whether beneficial or harmful, of various microorganisms. Microbiology therefore long remained largely separated from the rest of biology, in its goals as well as in its technics. Indeed, it was not until the 1940s that heredity in bacteria was found to have any relation to the science of genetics. However, microbes eventually proved to be especially suitable for studying many basic problems of cell physiology and genetics, and so these organisms have now come to occupy a central position in biology.

The course of this spectacular development will be outlined in later chapters. Here we may simply note that it was first necessary to recognize the **unity of biology at a molecular level,** as shown by the many close biochemical resemblances between microbial cells and those of higher organisms—in their building blocks, enzymes, and metabolic pathways, and in the structure and function of their genetic material. Microbes then proved especially valuable for studying many problems common to all cells, such as biosynthetic pathways (Ch. 4), molecular aspects of genetics (Ch. 8), and intracellular regulatory mechanisms (Ch. 9). The advantages of microbes include their relatively simple structure, homogeneous cell populations, and extremely rapid growth. But by far the greatest advantage lies in the possibility of easily cultivating billions of individuals and exploiting these huge populations, by appropriate selective methods, to yield rare mutants and rare genetic recombinants between these mutants.

Microbial mutants obtained in this way have provided unequivocal answers to many basic questions, and have revealed novel mechanisms, in various aspects of cell physiology. At the same time, biochemistry, reinforced by X-ray diffraction and other elegant physical technics, has converged with electron microscopy in the direct exploration of the structure and the biosynthesis of macromolecules. These several developments have given rise to an exciting interdisciplinary activity which is perhaps best termed **molecular genetics** (though it is often called **molecular biology**). As noted in the preface, we shall consider these aspects of microbiology in some detail in this volume, not only because of their importance for understanding the behavior of pathogenic microbes (particularly viruses) and for understanding the action of antimicrobial agents, but even more because of their growing relevance for human cells, and hence for aspects of medicine distinct from infectious disease.

Since the study of genetics is intimately linked with that of evolution we shall now consider some evolutionary aspects of microbiology.

MICROBIOLOGY AND BIOLOGICAL EVOLUTION

Over the past century biological thought has flowed in two major streams, **evolutionary** (genetic) and **mechanistic** (physiological), concerned respectively with the origin of various organisms and with the mechanisms by which they function. These streams have often flowed far apart, and medicine, in particular, has traditionally focused almost exclusively on the physiological approach, in considering the biological problems of the human species. However, with the development of molecular genetics the two streams have converged again: the study of a physiological function can now often be extended up to its controlling genes: and the study of genes is increasingly concerned with their functions in the living organism, and not simply with the formalities of their distribution among progeny. Hence human genetics is rapidly assuming increasing importance for medicine.

The study of genetics inevitably leads to an interest in evolution. Indeed, the rapid population changes that can be readily seen with microbes constantly remind the microbiologist that evolution is not a finished historical process but is still going on. For example, because bacteria grow so rapidly, and because the presence of a drug can apply extreme selective pressures on a bacterial population, one can demonstrate the natural selection of fitter (i.e., drug-resistant) mutants overnight in a laboratory culture, or in a few months or years in the flora of a drug-treated human population. We shall therefore frequently invoke evolutionary principles in this volume in considering the genetic adaptation of various microbes to various ecological niches.

In medical bacteriology, in particular, the existence of a large number of variants of certain pathogens, differing from each other only in the structure of their surface macromolecules (antigens), may at first appear chaotic. These variations become understandable, however, in evolutionary and immunological terms: in a host that has developed specific immunological means of attacking the original surface a mutation of the parasite to the formation of a different surface represents increased fitness. Conversely, widespread infection by a given agent will tend to select for increased resistance of the host species to that agent.

For example, myxoma virus, which produces a highly lethal disease of rabbits, was introduced into Australia to reduce its crop-destroying plague of these animals; and at first this biological warfare was dramatically effective. Within a few years, however, the rabbit population had recovered its initial density, and it could be shown to have shifted to strains with increased resistance to myxoma. (In addition, there was widespread infection by a milder form of the virus, which evidently outgrew the original form because it did not kill off its hosts too rapidly.)

Since hosts and parasites have thus evidently had a marked reciprocal effect on each other's evolution, it seems appropriate to dwell for a moment on the impact of microbes (and microbiology) on the human gene pool.

Role of Microbes in Human Evolution

It is generally considered that human evolution has moved continuously in the direction of increasing intelligence and manual dexterity—the features most responsible for man's dominating position. However, as Haldane has pointed out, when *Homo sapiens* shifted some 10,000 years ago from a social pattern of isolated family units to one based on larger and more freely intercommunicating groups, epidemic disease must have played an increasingly prominent role as a cause of death; and the resulting selection for increased resistance to various infectious diseases would automatically conflict with the selection for more interesting traits.*

As an index of the selective pressures present over the last few thousand years, we may note that a century ago in the United States (and still today in some parts of the world) at least 25% of children died, predominantly of infectious diseases, before reaching puberty. Today the improved control of most of these diseases has reduced this figure to well below 5%. And though medicine is sometimes blamed for exerting an undesirable (dysgenic) effect on the human gene pool by keeping alive people with various hereditary diseases, this effect may be more than outweighed by the subtle but widespread eugenic effect of eliminating most of the selection for resistance to infection. Unfortunately, however, the same advances in the control of infectious disease have been largely responsible for creating another, even more pressing world problem involving the human gene pool—its currently explosive growth, which has resulted from an abrupt decrease in the death rate, without balancing adjustments in the birth rate, in most parts of the world.

Molecular Individuality in Man. Evolution selects for survival of an interbreeding group (i.e., a species); and since such a group occupies varied, and often fluctuating, environments, it will be selected for a balance of fitness for various environments, rather than for the single type best fitted for a single environment. Encounters with various infectious agents constitute important variations in the environment, and no one human genotype is maximally resistant to all kinds of infectious disease. Selective pressures from a **variety** of infectious agents will therefore promote **genetic heterogeneity** (polymorphism) in the genes that influence resistance to these agents. The results of such selection can be clearly seen in a few instances: for example, sickle-cell hemoglobin, which protects against falciparum malaria, is prevalent in African tribes constantly exposed to this disease (even though the sickle-cell gene is strongly selected against in other environments because it causes, in the homozygous state, a serious disease, sickle-cell anemia). Other infectious agents must exert similar selective pressures, though the specific gene products that they select are as yet obscure.

This consideration suggests a solution to a puzzling problem: why the cells of a vertebrate species possess an extraordinary variety of specific surface antigens, differing from one individual to another. We recognize these antigens because they prevent successful organ transplantation between individuals (Ch. 18), but they can hardly have evolved for this function. An alternative explanation for such molecular individuality would be that a specific antigen promote resistance to a specific disease, just as different surfaces on microbial cells influence their virulence for different hosts. This view is supported by evidence that different allelic forms of the best-studied human antigens, the ABO blood group substances (Ch. 18), are associated with differences in resistance to major killers of the past, such as smallpox. Moreover, the geo-

---

* It is a well established principle that selection for one trait will interfere with the efficiency of selection for an uncorrelated trait. For example, a school may select its student body on the basis of both ability to pay tuition and personal qualities; but if scholarships are used to eliminate the first selection the second will become more effective because of the enlarged pool of applicants.

graphic distribution of these antigens is very uneven, and it shows some correlation with the historic distribution of certain major infectious diseases.

Evolution and Teleonomy

The convergence of the evolutionary and the mechanistic approaches to biology has had another important consequence: a wider acceptance of the relevance of **teleological** considerations. The essential feature of teleology is the principle that any structure or mechanism found in a living organism is likely to be valuable (i.e., to have a "purpose") for that organism; but Aristotle, in formulating this concept, also invoked an agency that had foreseen this "final" value. Hence, though biologists after Darwin could profitably employ the same concept in a modified form, substituting the hindsight of natural selection for divine providence, the use of teleology continued to be plagued by its earlier supernaturalistic connotations. Recently the term **teleonomy** has been introduced to circumvent these connotations: the new, purified word simply implies that an organism's genetic characters have been adapted to its environment, through the action of evolutionary rather than theurgic forces.

Teleonomical reasoning has long been held suspect in biochemistry, in part because the fragmentary nature of our knowledge made inferences concerning the "purpose" of a reaction quite unreliable, in contrast to the explicit characterization of the components of the reaction. However, the focus of biochemistry has shifted: the wilderness of metabolic reactions has been mapped to form complete, plausible sequences of reactions; mutants have unequivocally revealed the physiological consequences of deleting various enzymes; and the physiological roles of these enzymes are further revealed by the mechanisms that have been found to regulate them. Hence criteria are now available for distinguishing, for example, whether an enzyme has a biosynthetic or a degradative function.

Indeed, the chapter on regulatory mechanisms (Ch. 9) would be nearly meaningless unless one were willing to infer a purpose for these mechanisms, i.e., the increased efficiency of growth for which natural selection inexorably presses. Hence at the level of the individual cell we can once again emphasize the point of view of the physiologist, which is implicit in the etymology of the word "organism": an entity with unique properties derived from the interactions of its component parts. As we review, in the next few chapters, the intricate pattern of organization that has been revealed within a $1-\mu$ cell, we may well feel an old-fashioned sense of awe at the marvels of evolution, perhaps akin to Leeuwenhoek's feelings on discovering that the world was teeming with such organisms.

Microbial Taxonomy

Plants, Animals, and Protists

Men have long been accustomed to dividing the living world into two kingdoms: the nonmotile, photosynthetic plants, and the motile, nonphotosynthetic animals. Hence when the microbial world began to be systematically explored, in the early nineteenth century, efforts were made to fit the newly discovered organisms into this familiar pattern. Those single-celled organisms that were motile, like animals, and had a flexible cell integument, like animal cells, were considered the most primitive animals, or **Protozoa.** The **Algae,** on the other hand, were considered plants, since they were photosynthetic and had a rigid cell wall, like plant cells. The **Fungi** or **Eumycetes** (molds and yeasts), and the **Bacteria** (also called **Schizomycetes,** or fissionfungi, because they divide by transverse fission), were also lumped with the plants, though on vaguer grounds. This classification is still perpetuated in many introductory biology books; and, indeed, it is reflected in the omission from this volume of the protozoa, which are traditionally taken up in the medical curriculum along with the higher animal (metazoan) parasites.

Nevertheless, this Procrustean classification into plants and animals presented too many inconsistencies. Fungi and most bacteria are nonphotosynthetic; many bacteria are motile; some fungi and algae have motile spores (zoospores) which by themselves could be taken for protozoa; and the small group of slime molds were claimed by both zoologists and botanists. Moreover, Darwin's publication of the monumental *Origin of Species,* in 1859, showed that living organisms did not **have** to belong to one or another sharply separated group: transition forms were expected. Indeed, microbes strongly supported the theory of evolution by providing the required connection between the very disparate kingdoms of plants and animals. The microbes of today have apparently descended, perhaps with little change, from the primitive common ancestors of these kingdoms. The most logical solution therefore appears to be that proposed in 1866 by Haeckel, but long ignored: the establishment of a **third** biological kingdom, the **Protista** (Fig. 1-5), which are distinguished from animals and plants by their **relatively simple organization.**

Most protists are unicellular or coenocytic (multinucleate) throughout their life cycle, though some form large, multicellular, superficially plant-like structures, such as seaweeds (many marine algae) and mushrooms (the

basidiomycete group of fungi). However, the tissues of these organisms are essentially aggregates of similar cells, with only very primitive differentiation, whereas true plants and animals have highly differentiated multicellular adult forms, alternating with transient unicellular gametes.

Eucaryotes and Procaryotes

With the development of electron microscopy it has become possible to recognize a fundamental division among the protists, based on complexity of organization. The higher protists, which include protozoa, fungi, and most algae, have large, **eucaryotic** cells (Gr., "true nucleus"), much like those of plants and animals: they contain a nuclear membrane, multiple chromosomes within each nucleus, and a mitotic apparatus to ensure equipartition of the products of chromosomal replication among the daughter nuclei. In contrast, the lower protists, which include all bacteria and the small group of blue-green algae (*Cyanophyceae*),* are characterized by smaller, **procaryotic** cells, in which the "nucleus" is in fact a single naked chromosome, without a nuclear membrane. Procaryotic cells also differ from eucaryotes in lacking other membrane-bounded organelles, and there are chemical differences that will be described in the next chapter. (Viruses do not fit into this classification, since they are not cells at all.)

In view of these major differences the lower protists appear to be a distinct evolutionary group, stabilized at a primitive stage in the evolution of the cell. A wide evolutionary gap separates them from the eucaryotic protists, which have reached an advanced state of evolution and are organized much like the cells of the highest

Fig. 1-5 Probable evolutionary relations of the major groups. Postulated ancestral, extinct groups are encircled.

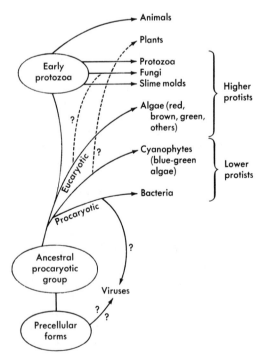

* Algae carry out photosynthesis by a mechanism that releases oxygen from water, just like the photosynthesis of higher plants; while the few bacteria that have also evolved the capacity for photosynthesis employ a more primitive mechanism, which does not liberate molecular oxygen (Ch. 3). The "blue-greens" were originally classified as algae because of their plant-like photosynthesis, but they are better grouped with the bacteria in the light of their typically procaryotic structure.

plants and animals. Further advances in evolution depended on aggregation, differentiation, and specialization of cells, but not on any radical change in cell design.

The classification of bacteria is considered in Chapter 2. We shall also discuss fungi (Ch. 21), which include pathogens, but not algae, which do not cause infectious disease (although some are extremely poisonous when ingested). For a broader introductory survey of bacterial and other microbial groups we recommend *The Microbial World,* by Stanier *et al.* (see Selected References).

Precellular Evolution and the Origin of Life

We have already seen that the problem of spontaneous generation was finally settled by the work of Pasteur and of Tyndall. But while life did not arise from nonliving matter under the experimental conditions that they employed, this result did not exclude the possibility that it could arise under other conditions, and given eons of time. Indeed, Darwin's theory of evolution (published within 2 years of Pasteur's first paper on spontaneous generation) logically required such an initial evolution of life, preceding the evolution of the contemporary living world. For a long time, however, speculations about this process remained fruitless. The problem is of particular interest to microbiologists since it concerns the development of the simplest living forms.

A satisfactory explanation, now widely accepted, was proposed around 1930 by Haldane in England and Oparin in the Soviet Union. According to this view the development of obviously living organisms was preceded by a period of **chemical, prebiotic evolution,** occupying perhaps the first 2 billion of the earth's 4 to 5 billion years. During this period bodies of water on the surface of the earth accumulated an increasing variety of organic compounds, formed with the aid of such agencies as ultraviolet light, lightning, volcanic heat, and inorganic surface catalysis. These substances could accumulate because the primitive earth lacked the two agents that make them so unstable under present terrestrial conditions: microbial cells and molecular oxygen. The former would be absent by definition; and there is geological evidence that free oxygen appeared in the earth's atmosphere rather late,

arising as a consequence of the biological evolution of photosynthesis and/or the inorganic splitting of water followed by loss of the light H_2 molecules from the gravitational field.

The thin "soups" resulting from this organic accumulation are believed to have developed systems that slowly catalyzed their own formation from simpler substrates. With the selection of improved catalysts, which permitted an increasingly complex system to be condensed in a smaller volume, chemical evolution would merge into precellular biological evolution, and would eventually yield the minimal unit of life that we can recognize: a genome-containing, membrane-bounded cell, within which a concentrated and efficient set of catalysts bring about both replication of the genetic material and synthesis of all the surrounding machinery.

A particularly interesting feature of this hypothesis is that **it eliminates the concept of a sharp division between the living and nonliving** —a concept that was useful for settling the problem of spontaneous generation as formulated a century or two ago, but is too primitive to apply to the problem of early evolution. For if the principle of evolution is extended backward to the origin of life, it follows that there was no moment in time at which the first living being suddenly began to stir, or at least to grow. Viewed in these terms, "life" cannot be defined in terms of a cellular pattern of organization, or even in terms of a given kind of molecule, but is defined in terms of self-replication from simpler substrates. And though the basis for this genetic continuity is admirably provided by nucleic acids in the organisms that we know today, the same function may originally have been provided, in a primitive form, in a system of catalytic molecules whose over-all capacity for self-replication was not concentrated in any special informational macromolecules.

The postulated precellular living systems have not been demonstrated. They would be difficult to recognize; and they would surely be completely displaced once a major evolutionary advance created the much more efficient cellular systems, which rapidly metabolize all accessible organic matter. Furthermore, while multiple primitive systems may well have arisen independently, in various localities, we would expect them to be displaced by spread of the first efficient, cellular system. This development would account for the apparently monophyletic origin of the present biological kingdom—an origin suggested by the construction of proteins only from L-amino acids, and not from the equally likely D-amino acids.

Viruses have been suggested as possible representatives of a precellular stage in evolution, since their organization is simpler than that of cells. Indeed, the first crystallization of a virus (tobacco mosaic virus), by Stanley in 1935, was widely hailed as having philosophical implications, because it apparently bridged the gap between the living and the nonliving. In reality, however, crystallinity simply reflects structural uniformity and surface complementarity of the particles, leading to orderly aggregation. Moreover, subsequent discoveries showed a special, intimate relation, rather than a simple nutritional dependence, between viruses and their host cells: in their method of multiplication viruses depend entirely upon the cell for biosynthetic machinery (Ch. 23); and some viruses can even exchange genes with the host cell (Ch. 24). It therefore seems quite possible that the viruses we know have evolved from host cell components, rather than from early precursors of cells.

Experimental Approaches. The Haldane-Oparin hypothesis received considerable support when Miller and Urey showed that various amino acids can be formed, in detectable amounts, by the action of an electric spark on a gas designed to simulate the atmosphere of the primitive earth (a mixture of water vapor, ammonia, methane, and hydrogen). Similar nonspecific reactions have yielded products as complex as nucleic acid bases, and have formed polynucleotides and polypeptides from their monomers. The problem of the origin of life has thus become a respectable area of experimentation, spurred on by the prospect of exploring for extraterrestrial life, in perhaps quite unfamiliar form.

SELECTED REFERENCES

BROCK, T. D. (*ed. and trans.*) *Milestones in Microbiology*. Prentice-Hall, Englewood Cliffs, N.J., 1961. Paperback. An excellent selection of classic papers, with helpful annotations; probably the best introduction to the history of the field.

BULLOCH, W. *The History of Bacteriology*. Oxford Univ. Press, London, 1960. A detailed account, with emphasis on medical bacteriology.

DOBELL, C. *Antony van Leeuwenhoek and His "Little Animals"*. Constable, London, 1932. Reprinted in paperback by Dover, New York, 1960.

DUBOS, R. J. *Louis Pasteur: Free Lance of Science*. Little, Brown, Boston, 1950.

LARGE, E. C. *Advance of the Fungi*. Cope, London, 1940. Reprinted in paperback by Dover, New York, (1962). An entertaining account of the development of the infectious microbiology of higher plants.

LECHEVALIER, H. A., and SOLOTOROVSKY, M. *Three Centuries of Microbiology*. McGraw-Hill, New York, 1965.

Microbial Classification (12th Symposium, Society for General Microbiology). Cambridge Univ. Press, London, 1962.

OPARIN, A. I. *The Origin of Life on Earth*, 3d ed. Academic Press, New York, 1957; or 2nd ed. (1938), reprinted in paperback by Dover, New York, 1953.

STANIER, R. Y. Toward a Definition of the Bacteria. In *The Bacteria*, Vol. V, p. 445. (I. C. Gunsalus and R. Y. Stanier, eds.) Academic Press, New York, 1964.

STANIER, R. Y., DOUDOROFF, M., and ADELBERG, E. A., *The Microbial World*, 2nd ed. Prentice-Hall, Englewood Cliffs, N.J., 1963. An excellent introduction to general microbiology.

VALLERY-RADOT, R. *The Life of Pasteur*. Constable, London, 1901. Reprinted as paperback by Dover, New York, 1960. This biography is detailed and chronological; that of Dubos (see above) is more interpretive.

WILSON, G. S., and MILES, A. A., *Topley and Wilson's Principles of Bacteriology and Immunology*, 3d ed., 2 vols. Williams & Wilkins, Baltimore, 1964. An excellent reference work on medical bacteriology, including its history.

BACTERIAL PHYSIOLOGY

2 STRUCTURE AND CLASSIFICATION OF BACTERIA

BACTERIAL STRUCTURE

As we have seen in Chapter 1, bacteria are considerably smaller than other cells. Their diameters are usually in the range of 1 μ, though the smallest spherical representatives (mycoplasmas, rickettsiae, and chlamydiae) have a diameter of about 0.4 μ, and the largest bacteria range up to several microns in diameter (and considerably greater in length). Bacteria are also morphologically less complex, inside the cell membrane, than the **eucaryotic** cells of higher organisms, and are classified as **procaryotic** cells because they lack a nuclear membrane, a mitotic apparatus, mitochondria, and a visible endoplasmic reticulum.

Another distinguishing characteristic of bacteria (except for the mycoplasmas) is the presence of a more complex surface structure than that of animal cells, with a **rigid cell wall** outside the cell membrane. The wall permits bacteria to tolerate an exceptionally wide range of environments: it protects against mechanical damage (including freezing); and it allows the maintenance of a much higher concentration of salts and metabolites within the cell than outside, without osmotic rupture. In addition, the wall is responsible for many of the taxonomically significant features of different bacteria: it determines their shapes and their major division into gram-positive and gram-negative organisms; and its finer chemical differences are responsible for antigenic specificities that are important in the interactions of pathogens with the host, and in microbial classification. We shall therefore consider wall structure and wall biosynthesis in considerable detail.

The development of bacterial cytology as a substantial discipline was long delayed, since the limited resolving power of the light microscope (0.2 μ) can reveal little detail in such small cells; hence bacteria were long regarded as essentially bags of enzymes, lacking any interesting organization. With the development of the electron microscope, however, the distinctive architecture of the procaryotic cell could be recognized, and we can now schematically represent the structure of a typical bacterium as in Figure 2-1. The **surface layers** (cell wall, membrane, and capsule) are often referred to together as the **integument** or **cell envelope,** while the flagella and pili are considered **appendages.** Within the membrane it is possible to differentiate several kinds of **cytoplasmic structures** (mesosomes, ribosomes, granular inclusions) and one or more **nuclear bodies.** Some of these components are essential for viability, while others, as we shall see, are optional.

Methodology

The light microscope has long been the hallmark of the bacteriologist, since classification has depended heavily on differences in size, shape, and staining properties. While unstained preparations can be observed, especially with the use of the phase-contrast microscope, medical bacteriologists have generally studied heat-fixed, stained preparations. For most organisms the Gram stain (perfected by the Danish bacteriologist Christian Gram in 1884) is preferred. Special stains used for certain organisms (e.g., mycobacteria, corynebacteria) will be described in chapters on these groups.

In the **Gram stain** the cells are first heat-fixed and stained with a basic dye (e.g., crys-

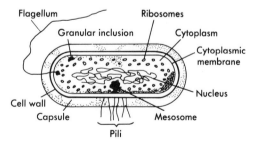

Fig. 2-1 Diagram of prototype eubacterial cell.

tal violet), which is taken up in similar amounts by all bacteria. The slides are then treated with an I$_2$-KI mixture to fix (mordant) the stain, washed with acetone or alcohol, and finally counterstained with a paler dye of different color (e.g., safranin). Gram-positive organisms retain the initial violet stain, while gram-negative organisms are decolorized by the organic solvent and hence show the counterstain. This empirical distinction between the two groups proved very useful, though its basis was long a mystery. However, recent advances have provided convincing evidence that the difference between gram-positive and -negative bacteria lies in the permeability properties of the cell wall (p. 34).

Special stains have also been used to demonstrate relatively large intracellular structures, including the nucleus and certain inclusion bodies. Since fixation and staining may introduce artifacts, the phase-contrast and the anoptral microscopes have been valuable in demonstrating the presence of these localized condensations in living cells. For this purpose it is useful to suspend the cells in a medium with about the same refractive index as the cytoplasm (e.g., 30% glycerol); intracellular bodies of different refractive index are then easily visualized. Another useful variant is **darkfield** microscopy, which uses reflected light and thus has increased resolving power. Finally, surface layers of low density (capsules) are best revealed by **negative staining** (i.e., suspending the bacteria in an opaque medium such as India ink, which provides contrast but not true staining.

The electron microscope has increased the available resolving power at least 200-fold (i.e., ca. 0.001 μ). However, the material ordinarily is fixed, and it is only gradually that resulting artifacts have been eliminated. Electron microscopy is used in bacteriology in several ways. 1) **Shadow casting** with metal has been valuable for studying surface appendages of intact bacteria (Figs. 2-3 and 2-5, below) as well as viruses (Ch. 22). 2) **"Nega-** tive staining"** is accomplished by drying in the presence of an electron-opaque solution (e.g., phosphotungstate), which forms thicker deposits in crevices. This procedure has made it possible to resolve subunits that are obscured in metal-shadowed preparations, e.g., the fine structure of flagella or of the surface of the cell wall. 3) The most important method is the study of **thin sections** (ca. 0.02 μ) of bacteria.

Successful electron microscopy of thin sections of bacteria required modification of the methods of fixation and embedding developed for animal cells. The method of Ryter and Kellenberger, which is one of the most widely used, employs osmium tetroxide fixation at a low pH (6.0), in the presence of polyvalent cations (e.g., Ca^{++}) plus amino acids to preserve nuclear structure, followed by embedding in a nonshrinking epoxy resin (e.g., Araldite) or polyester resin (e.g., Vestopal). Contrast is enhanced by treating the sections with heavy ions (lead salts, uranyl acetate, lanthanum nitrate). Different procedures are optimal for demonstrating different structures.

Physical fractionation of bacteria has made it possible to study the chemical composition and molecular organization of visible structures; and electron microscopy has been invaluable in establishing the identity and homogeneity of the morphological units to be analyzed. Because the wall is tough and the cells are small it has been necessary to develop special methods for disrupting bacteria.

Thus by violent agitation (e.g., in a Waring Blendor) it is possible to separate flagella and pili (Fig. 2-1) from bacteria. Shaking with glass beads disrupts the wall as well, releasing the cell contents; the wall fraction can be recovered by differential centrifugation (Fig. 2-8). Bacteria can also be disrupted by grinding as a wet paste with abrasives (e.g., alumina), by strong sonic or supersonic oscillation (sonication), or by explosive release of high pressure (e.g., release past a needle valve from a pressure of thousands of pounds per square inch in a French press). While these last methods yield rather heterogeneous particles, and thus have not been favored for morphological studies, they are very useful for producing extracts that contain ribosomes and a great variety of enzymes, in active form.

Protoplasts and Spheroplasts. A particularly valuable procedure consists in selectively eliminating the cell wall, e.g., by digestion with the enzyme lysozyme (see Cell wall, below). Weibull showed in 1953 that in a hypertonic medium (e.g., 20% sucrose or 0.5 M KCl) such treatment no longer lyses sensitive cells but instead releases the membrane and its contents as an osmotically sensitive **protoplast.** With sensitive gram-positive organisms this product appears to be free of wall constituents, by microscopic and chemical criteria. Gram-negative organisms, if suitably sensitized to lysozyme (see Gram-negative wall, p. 31), similarly yield osmotically sensitive spheres, but these retain adherent layers of fragments of wall; they are therefore called **spheroplasts,** to distinguish them from the presumably wall-free protoplasts. Spheroplasts can also be formed by growing cells either in the presence of an agent (e.g., penicillin) that inhibits synthesis of the rigid layer of the wall (Ch. 10) or in the absence of a compound specifically required for wall synthesis (e.g., diaminopimelate: see Ch. 4).

Osmotically sensitive spheres may be lysed by transfer to a hypotonic medium, or by adding reagents that dissolve the membrane (lipase, deoxycholate). The cell contents are thereby released with so little disturbance that very delicate structures, such as the chromosome (Ch. 8) or polysomes (Chs. 4 and 9), can be extracted without fragmentation. In addition, after osmotic rupture of washed protoplasts the "ghosts," i.e., the membrane fraction (including any firmly attached cell components), can be recovered by sedimentation. Because the DNA is released in relatively unfragmented threads such lysates are very viscous, in contrast to the extracts produced by grinding or sonication; hence treatment with DNase is helpful in the recovery of membrane fragments.

Other Methods. Radioautographic studies have occasionally been valuable, particularly for localizing DNA by means of radioactive thymidine. Cytochemical technics have included the use of specific antibodies tagged with a fluorescent dye, or coupled to a substance, such as ferritin, that forms a sharp image in electron micrographs. Such cytochemical procedures have had limited use in bacterial cytology because of the small dimensions involved, but they have been of great value in animal virology, as will be seen in later chapters. Cytochemical tests for electron transport systems are provided by the use of tellurite or of tetrazolium dyes, whose function as an oxidant yields insoluble, opaque reduction products.

We shall consider here the structures of only the typical or "true" bacteria (eubacteria); later chapters will deal with the less typical bacteria (including actinomycetes, spirochetes, mycoplasmas, rickettsiae, and chlamydiae), as well as with fungi and viruses.

Gross Forms of Bacteria

The light microscope reveals two principal forms of eubacteria: more or less spherical organisms known as **cocci** (Gr. and L., "berry") and cylindrical ones called **bacilli** (L., "stick").* Incompletely separated cocci may appear in a number of different patterns, depending upon the planes in which they divide: when predominantly in pairs they are known as **diplococci;** in chains as **streptococci** (Gr. *streptos,* "twisted"); and in clusters as **staphylococci** (Gr. *staphyle,* "bunch of grapes"). Cocci that remain adherent after splitting successively in two or three perpendicular directions, yielding square tetrads or cubical packets, are known as **sarcinae** (L., "bundles"). Bacilli when unusually short are referred to as **coccobacilli;** when tapered at both ends as **fusiform bacilli;** when growing in long threads as filamentous forms; and when curved as **vibrios** or **spirilla** (Fig. 2-2).

---

* The term "bacillus" is unfortunately used both as a general name for rod-shaped bacteria and as the name of a particular genus (capitalized and in italics).

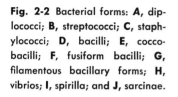

Fig. 2-2 Bacterial forms: **A,** diplococci; **B,** streptococci; **C,** staphylococci; **D,** bacilli; **E,** coccobacilli; **F,** fusiform bacilli; **G,** filamentous bacillary forms; **H,** vibrios; **I,** spirilla; and **J,** sarcinae.

Fine Structure

We have already presented the principal structural components of bacteria schematically in Figure 2-1. We shall now consider the fine structure of these components, proceeding from the appendages to the center of the cell.

Flagella

Flagella (*flagellum,* sing.; L., "whip"), when present, are responsible for the motility of eubacteria. Motile cells from which flagella are mechanically removed, without harming the cell proper, regain motility when the flagella regenerate. Motility can be recognized under the microscope in liquid medium (in a hanging drop or under a cover slip), where it must be carefully distinguished from brownian movement; it can also be revealed by the spread of visible growth in thin solid medium (e.g., 0.3% agar).

Flagella are long (3 to 12 μ), fine, wavy, filamentous appendages. Though readily vis-

Fig. 2-3 Flagella. **A.** Flagellated bacillus stained with tannic acid-basic fuchsin, a flagellar stain. **B.** Palladium-shadowed electron micrograph of bacillus showing peritrichous flagellation. ×13,000. **C.** Highly motile form of *Proteus mirabilis* ("swarmer"), with innumerable peritrichous flagella. (**A** from E. Leifson, S. R. Carhart, and M. Fulton, *J. Bact.* 69:73, 1955. **B** from L. W. Labaw and V. M. Mosley. *Biochim. Biophys Acta* 17:322,1955. **C** from J. F. M. Hoeniger. *J. gen. Microbiol.* 40:29, 1965.)

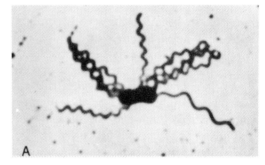

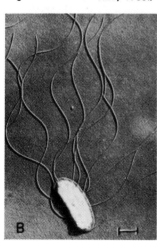

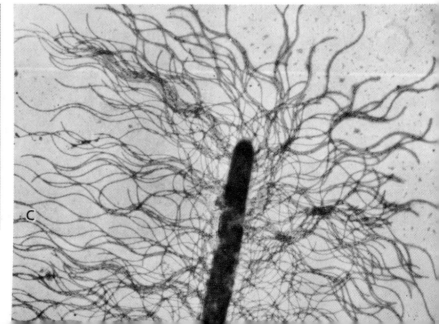

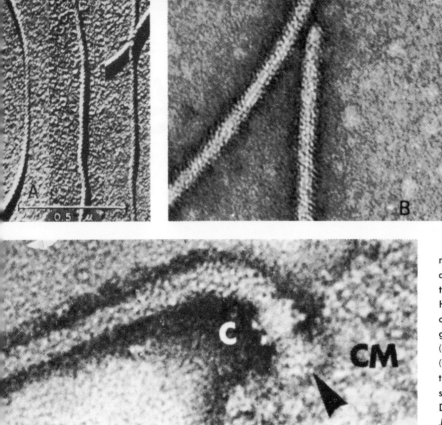

A

0.5 μ

B

C

CM

Fig. 2-4 Flagella: fine structure. **A.** Flagella of same bacillus as in Figure 2-3 **B,** metal-shadowed, ×77,000, showing helical structure. **B.** Flagellum of *Salmonella typhi* at higher magnification (×300,000), negatively stained with uranyl acetate, showing individual structural units. (Courtesy A. Klug) **C.** Hooked basal end of flagellum connected through constricted region (C) to spherical basal body (arrow) in cytoplasmic membrane (CM) of *Proteus vulgaris.* Negatively stained with phosphotungstate, ×280,000. (From Abram, D., Koffler, H., and Vatter, A. E. *J. Bact.* 90:1337, 1965.)

ualized by darkfield microscopy, they are too thin (100 to 200 A) to be seen by ordinary microscopy unless heavily coated with special flagellar stains containing a precipitating agent (mordant), such as tannic acid (Fig. 2-3A). It is now known, however, that this method often underestimates their number, since it not only thickens the filaments but also mats neighboring ones together. The wave length of the flagella, whether in live or in fixed preparations, is characteristic for a given bacterial strain.

In some species flagella are distributed at random over the cell surface (**peritrichous** flagellation; Gr. *trichos,* "hair") (Fig. 2-3), while in other species one or a few flagella are found only at one or both poles (**polar** flagellation. The pattern of flagellation is a genetically stable characteristic: strains that mutate to loss of flagellation revert to the original pattern. This pattern has thus provided the basis, in the present official classification of bacteria (see below), for the separation of a large fraction of the common bacteria into two orders, **Eubacteriales** (with

peritrichous flagellation) and **Pseudomonadales** (with **polar** flagellation).

Bacteria vary widely in the number of their flagella, which determines the vigor of their movement. Certain species (e.g., *Proteus,* Ch. 20) may produce huge numbers of flagella (Fig. 2-3C), especially when cell division is slowed; they thus acquire the ability to spread in a thin film ("swarm") on the surface of the usual moist agar media.

Fine Structure. Being much thinner than the cilia of vertebrate cells, or the flagella of protozoa, bacterial flagella do not contain the nine peripheral and two central subfibrils found in these structures. Rather, they appear on metal-shadowing to be wound in a tight spiral (Fig. 2-4A). While most of the flagellum appears uniform, it has a hook-like shape, and a slight constriction, in the region near its attachment to a **basal body** just beneath the cytoplasmic membrane (Fig. 2-4C).

At a high magnification negative staining reveals individual spherical subunits (Fig. 2-4B), whose arrangement is consistent with their mutual attachment in three parallel chains, wound to form a triple helix. This structure can be correlated with chemical studies on preparations of purified flagella, which are obtained by mechanical agitation followed by differential centrifugation. Such preparations can be dissociated at relatively mild acidity, yielding a homogeneous soluble protein, called **flagellin,** with a molecular weight of about 20,000.*

Movement. In view of the simple structure of the bacterial flagellum its motion cannot be ascribed to metabolic activities within the filament itself; rather, the motion must

---

* A novel amino acid, ϵ-N-methyl-lysine, has been found in flagellin. Since the protein-synthesizing machinery is not able to code for such additions to the standard list of 20 amino acids (Ch. 8), this compound is presumably formed by modification of lysine **after** its incorporation into protein. The development of this modification in procaryotes may well have preceded in evolution the development in vertebrates of the similar ability to modify another structural protein, collagen, by converting proline residues to hydroxyproline.

be imparted by mechanical changes in its basal body. When studied by darkfield microscopy flagella appear to impart motility by a longitudinal wave-like action; hence the waves seen in fixed preparations are not rigidly built into the structure.

Certain bacteria use other means of locomotion. In **spirochetes** the cell proper forms a helix around a relatively rigid axial filament, and some form of contraction of the cell relative to the filament causes the cell to bend and thus to move. Certain **myxobacteria** (slime bacteria), and some blue-green algae, exhibit a slow **gliding** movement on solid surfaces; its mechanism is not understood.

Pili (Fimbriae)

With many gram-negative bacilli the electron microscope unexpectedly revealed a group of still finer filamentous appendages, called pili (L., "hairs") or fimbriae (L., "fringe"). They are shorter and straighter than flagella (Fig. 2-5), and on the same cell

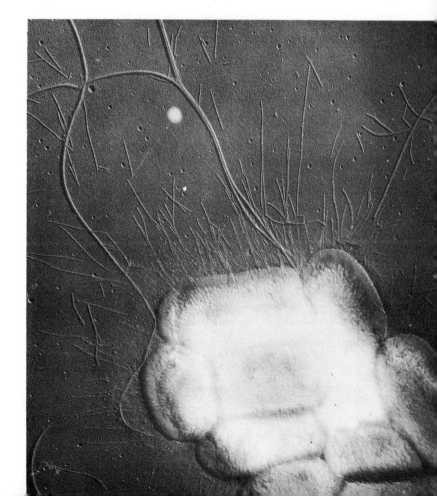

Fig. 2-5 Pili. Piliated strain of *Escherichia coli,* grown in liquid medium without aeration. Each cell possesses hundreds of pili (diam. 70A), and their presence promotes aggregation. Many isolated, broken pili are also seen. A few flagella, much longer and of larger diameter (140A), extend from the cells to the edge of the photograph. Platinum shadowed, ×45,000, reduced. (Courtesy Charles C. Brinton, Jr.)

they vary in thickness (ca. 75 to 100 A) and length (up to several microns). Like flagella, they appear to arise from basal bodies in the cytoplasmic membrane, and they have been found to consist only of protein.

As we shall see in Chapter 7, in bacterial conjugation the male cell carries one or two special hollow pili that apparently form a bridge with the female cell, through which DNA is transferred. The same male cell, however, may carry hundreds of other pili whose function is unknown. Thus in mutants that can no longer form them the only significant change observed has been a decreased tendency to adhere to red blood cells; and cells mechanically deprived of pili rapidly form them again, without having lost viability.

surrounding medium; these properties blur the distinction between a highly viscous excretion product and a cellular structure.

Some mutants that have lost the ability to make a visible capsule make a microcapsule with unchanged specificity. This material is detectable immunologically, and under the electron microscope it is sometimes seen as a thin layer outside the denser wall. The thickness of the capsule also varies with growth conditions.

The substances responsible for the immunological specificity of most capsules are relatively simple polysaccharides, containing repeating sequences of two or three sugars; uronic acids, which are not found in the wall, are often present. Homopolymers of D-glutamic acid have also been found. The biosynthesis of capsular polymers will be discussed in Chapter 4.

Capsules

The bacterial capsule is a loose, gel-like structure, which varies widely among strains in thickness, density, and adherence to the cell wall. Capsules are most easily demonstrated in India ink suspensions, where they are recognized as a clear zone between the opaque medium and the more refractile (or stained) cell body. They can also be rendered visible by exposure to specific anticapsular antibodies, which increase their refractility, or by special stains. Capsules in pathogenic bacteria often play a major role in determining virulence because they protect the cells from phagocytosis (Ch. 19, Antiphagocytic capsules). A given bacterial species may include strains of different antigenic types, which produce immunologically distinct capsules.

As would be expected of a gel, the capsular layer usually does not reveal any structural detail in electron micrographs. True capsules have a well defined border (Ch. 19, Fig. 19-1A) and may require enzymatic attack for removal from the cell, although soluble capsular substance can often be detected immunologically in culture filtrates. Some "capsules" have no definite border, and their outermost portions can be seen to diffuse into the

Cell Wall

The presence of a rigid cell wall, outside the cytoplasmic membrane, may be demon-

Fig. 2-6 Plasmolysis of *Bacillus megaterium*. The cells on a slide were successively treated with ether vapor (which loosens the attachment of membrane to wall), air-dried and then post-fixed with Bouin's fluid (which cause contraction of the protoplast), and stained with Victoria blue (which enhances the visibility of the membrane enclosing the protoplast). (Courtesy of C. Robinow.)

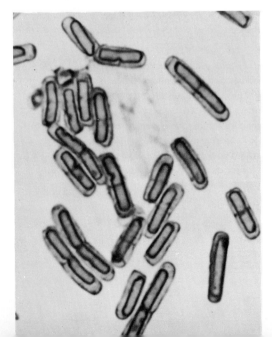

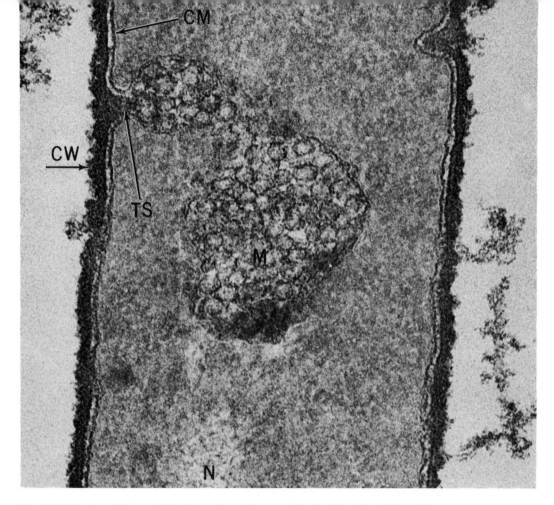

Fig. 2-7 Electron micrograph of thin-sectioned gram-positive bacillus *(B. subtilis)*. Note relatively thick cell wall (CW) and thin cytoplasmic membrane (CM); mesosome (M) arising at site of beginning transverse septum formation (TS) connects cytoplasmic membrane with nucleus (N). (From van Iterson. *Bact. Rev. 29:299,* 1965.)

strated by plasmolysis, i.e., exposure of bacterial cells (especially of gram-negative species) to a hypertonic solution, which causes the membrane and its contents (the protoplast) to contract and shrink away from the wall (Fig. 2-6). Moreover, in bacterial preparations subjected to mechanical damage (e.g., crushing) many of the cells lose much refractility, from loss of their intracellular contents, but leave a pale ghost which retains the characteristic shape of the original cell; and the distribution of refractility under phase contrast shows that this ghost is an empty wall. Walls can also be demonstrated by special stains.

The Gram-Positive Wall. Electron microscopy of thin sections reveals the walls of gram-positive organisms as a relatively thick (150 to 800 A), uniform, dense layer, with the cytoplasmic membrane closely apposed to its inner surface (Fig. 2-7). By mechanical disruption of the cells, followed by differential centrifugation, Salton obtained cell wall preparations that were free of other visible cell components under the electron microscope (Fig. 2-8); the wall could thus be shown to constitute 10 to 25% of the dry weight of the cell. On hydrolysis such preparations yielded relatively few constituents: several amino acids, including D as well as L isomers, and a few sugars, including a novel sugar, **muramic acid** (L. *murus,* "wall"), which was found to be the 3-O-lactyl ether of glucosamine.

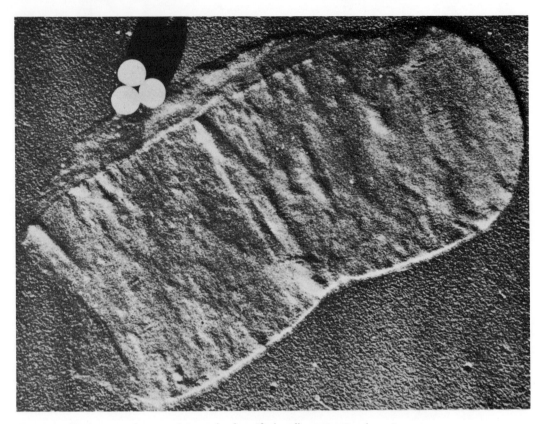

Fig. 2-8 Shadow-cast electron micrograph of purified wall preparation from *B. mega-terium*. Note flattened structure compared with intact cell (Fig. 2-3B). Latex balls: diam. 0.25 μ. (From M. R. J. Salton and R. C. Williams. *Biochim. et biophys. acta* 14:455, 1954.)

The arrangement of these components was worked out by methods to be described in Chapter 4. The results are summarized in

Fig. 2-9 Diagram of repeating units of glycopeptide (mucopeptide) of *Staphylococcus aureus*. Moderate variations in structure are seen in other species. The tetrapeptide and pentaglycine [(Gly)5] cross-link the polysaccharide chains, which consist of alternating residues of acetylmuramic acid (MurAc) and N-acetylglucosamine (GNAc). (For further details see Ch. 4.)

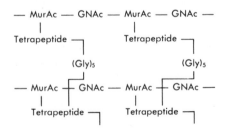

Figure 2-9, in which we see a network of polysaccharide chains containing alternating N-acetyl muramic acid and N-acetylglucosamine, connected by polypeptide cross-links; this network is called the **glycopeptide** or **mucopeptide** layer of the wall. Very similar glycopeptides containing N-acetylmuramic acid have been found in almost all bacterial species studied,* and muramic acid appears to be unique to the bacterial kingdom (including blue-green algae).

The glycopeptide or **basal** wall layer is covered in most species by additional layers, whose specific macromolecules are exposed

---

* Exceptions are 1) the mycoplasmas, which lack a characteristic shape, and 2) certain **halophilic** bacteria (Ch. 5), whose evolutionary adaptation to a high external salt concentration has evidently eliminated the need for a glycopeptide layer to maintain their shape.

on the cell surface, and are therefore readily detected by immunological methods. In some gram-positive bacteria these specific surface groupings are provided by various substituents on **teichoic** acid (Gr. *teichos,* "wall"), a polymer of polyhydric alcohols (usually ribitol or glycerol), connected in a chain by phosphodiester bonds (Ch. 4) and covalently attached to the glycopeptide. Some streptococci also have an external protein antigen (M protein).

The glycopeptide layer is responsible for the **rigidity** of the bacterial cell wall. Thus lysozyme (also called muramidase), a bacteriolytic enzyme found in such biological fluids as egg white, tears, and saliva, dissolves the rigid layer of the wall, releasing a spherical protoplast; and with purified wall preparations lysozyme can be shown to attack one of the alternating linkages in the polysaccharide chain of the glycopeptide, ultimately releasing peptide-substituted disaccharides.*

Several features of the glycopeptide are of structural interest. The successive units in the polysaccharide are joined in β-1,4 linkage. The same repeating linkage, between other hexoses, is found in chitin (a poly-N-acetylglucosamine) in fungal cell walls and crustacean exoskeletons, and in cellulose (a polyglucose) in plants; it provides a particularly compact, strong polymer. Moreover, the alternating D and L amino acids in the side chain may have a similar advantage: in synthetic polypeptides this alternation (which causes successive R groups to stick out from the same side of the chain) provides a stronger polymer than that resulting from either the L or the D monomer alone (in which alternating side chains protrude in opposite directions). Finally, the glycopeptide cannot be solubilized without partial hydrolysis; and it seems possible that the entire glycopeptide layer of a cell is one giant, bag-shaped, covalently linked molecule ("murein").

The Gram-Negative Wall. In those gram-negative bacteria that have been studied the basal wall is thin (ca. 100 A) compared with gram-positive organisms, but at the same time the entire wall is more complex. It contains a good deal of **lipopolysaccharide,** which appears to require Ca^{++} for its stability; and this layer is external to the glycopeptide.

This location has been established in several ways. 1) In many gram-negative bacteria the glycopeptide appears to be entirely covered by a protective outer layer, since it is not accessible to **lysozyme** action unless this layer is damaged, either physically (by freezing and thawing the cells) or chemically (by exposure to dilute alkali or to a metal-chelating agent, such as Versene (= ethylenediamine tetraacetic acid = EDTA); the latter reagent has been shown to liberate much of the lipopolysaccharide from the cell. 2) The immunological specificity of intact cells of Enterobacteriaceae, which must depend on groups exposed on the cell surface, is the same as the specificity of the purified lipopolysaccharide. 3) The lipopolysaccharide does not appear to be covalently linked to the glycopeptide, or trapped within this layer, since it can be extracted by reagents that would not be expected to break covalent bonds, such as phenol or EDTA. (The latter reagent breaks only ionic cross-links, presumably provided by Mg^{++} and Ca^{++}.) 4) While most electron micrographs have not revealed multiple layers in the cell wall of gram-negative bacteria, one study has shown a heavier band on the inner than on the outer border of the sectioned wall, and lysozyme was found to dissolve this band (Fig. 2-10).

Gram-negative cell walls are reported also to contain **lipoproteins** (as shown by the presence of a full complement of amino acids, plus lipid components, in their hydrolysates). However, the position of the lipoproteins, and even their presence in wall, is not certain; for despite the ease of separation of wall and membrane by plasmolysis of the intact gram-negative cell, it is quite possible that in homogenates lipoprotein membrane fragments may be adsorbed onto wall

---

*Spirochetes, whose motility involves considerable flexibility of the cell, also contain a glycopeptide layer, as shown by their sensitivity to lysozyme and to penicillin. Hence the rigidity conferred by this wall layer is only relative.

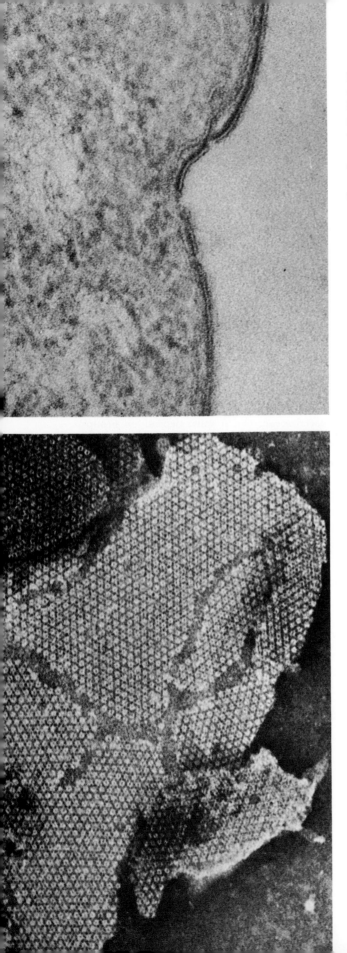

Fig. 2-10 Partial dissolution of glycopeptide layer of cell wall of *Escherichia coli* by light treatment with lysozyme. Prolonged fixation was used to increase density of glycopeptide layer, which is seen as a thick, dense band, between membrane and outer wall layer, along part of section; along the rest of the section this band has largely disappeared. In cells not treated with lysozyme no such discontinuity was seen. ×203,000, reduced. (Courtesy of R. G. E. Murray. See *Canad. J. Microbiol.* 11:547, 1965.)

fragments. Moreover, no suitable enzymes are available for digesting away all of the wall in these organisms, and so clean membrane preparations (see below) have not been available to provide a basis for estimating the contamination of wall with membrane. At least some lipoprotein appears to be located outside the lipopolysaccharide, since the receptor for phage T5, which must be on the surface, has been purified and identified as lipoprotein. On the other hand, there cannot be a continuous external lipoprotein layer, since the lipopolysaccharide is readily accessible to antibodies.

Surface Topography. Though sections of fixed preparations give the impression of a uniform wall thickness, in both gram-positive and gram-negative organisms, surface photographs sometimes reveal considerable structural detail. Metal-shadowing of some gram-negative cells and their isolated wall preparations reveals a surface layer of regular, hexagonally packed spherical subunits of 80 to 120 A (Fig. 2-11), analogous to a tile wall. The walls of some other bacteria and of fungi, in contrast, have a matted, irregular fibrous texture, analogous to a thatched wall.

Studies of **unfixed** gram-negative bacilli (*Escherichia coli, Veillonella*) by negative staining have revealed an unexpectedly convoluted surface (Fig. 2-12). These differentiations of the surface are apparently restricted

Fig. 2-11 Regular hexagonal array of granules on outer surface of isolated cell wall of a *Spirillum*. Similarly regular rectangular arrays are found on many gram-positive bacteria, but the layer bearing the pattern is easily lost in preparation. Negatively stained. ×204,000, reduced. (Courtesy of R. G. E. Murray.)

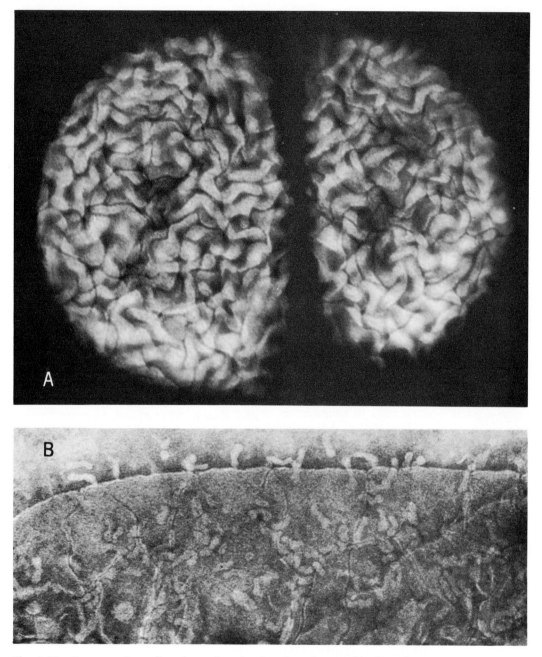

Fig. 2-12 Gram-negative cell surface. Convoluted surface (presumably lipopolysaccharide) of freeze-dried, unfixed cells of gram-negative bacteria, negatively stained with silicotungstate. **A.** *Veillonella,* a diplococcus closely resembling *Neisseria.* ×104,000. **B.** *Escherichia coli:* portion of wall after unfixed cell had been disrupted in frozen state to permit extrusion of cytoplasm. Negative staining reveals protrusions from surface, presumably resulting from distortion of convolutions; in addition, deep channels in the underlying layer are seen as dark lines. (**A.** from H. A. Bladen and S. E. Merganhagen. *J. Bact.* 88:1482, 1964. **B.** From M. E. Bayer and T. F. Anderson. *Proc. Nat. Acad. Sc.* 54:1592, 1965.)

to the superficial layers (lipopolysaccharide and possibly lipoprotein), since extraction by a lipid-dissolving detergent (phenol or dodecylsulfate) leaves a much smoother surface. The function of these irregularities is not certain.

Permeability of the Wall. It is generally assumed that the permeability of a bacterial cell is determined entirely by its membrane (see below), and not by the looser lattice of its wall. The membrane certainly plays this role for many small molecules (see below); for example, a cell that admits glucose may exclude the very similar compound galactose, though both can undoubtedly traverse the wall equally well. However, it is striking that the rather large molecule of the drug actinomycin (Ch. 10) can penetrate regularly into gram-positive but not into gram-negative bacteria; and treatment of the latter group with EDTA, which removes much of the lipopolysaccharide (as noted above), renders the cell permeable to the drug. Furthermore, gram-negative bacteria tend to be more resistant than gram-positive to ionic detergents, which lyse the cell by attacking the cell membrane (Ch. 11). These results suggest that the lipid-containing layer of the gram-negative wall, which apparently keeps the enzyme lysozyme from reaching the basal layer, also keeps various smaller molecules from reaching the membrane.

Even though the wall covers the membrane completely enough to provide strong mechanical protection, and perhaps even to prevent the flow of certain moderately large molecules into the cell, it does allow certain macromolecules to reach the membrane in very restricted amounts (a few molecules per cell), and perhaps in only a few loci on the surface. For example, DNA molecules penetrate in genetic transformation (Ch. 7), and bacteriocins must attack the membrane to exert their lethal effect (Ch. 24). In the infection of bacteria by viruses (bacteriophages) the cell wall plays a more positive role by providing specific receptors to which the viruses first attach (Ch. 23).

Mechanism of the Gram Stain. We have noted (p. 22) that the mechanism of the empirically discovered Gram stain was long a mystery. After many unsuccessful efforts to explain it in terms of differential stainability of various cell components, the discovery of a consistent difference in cell wall composition of gram-positive and gram-negative bacteria focused attention on the wall. Its role in retaining the dye-I_2 complex was already suggested by the observation that mechanical damage (e.g., crushing between two slides) converted cells from positive to negative; and a similar effect was later observed on converting cells to protoplasts. Salton has further shown that the gram-positive wall is not stained itself but presents a permeability barrier to elution of the dye-I_2 complex by alcohol.

These experiments also suggested that a dehydrating effect of the organic solvent on the gram-positive wall may increase its impermeability, since gram-positive (but not gram-negative) cells showed less elution of metabolites by 95% than by 50% ethanol. However, the molecular basis of this difference is not known: though the glycopeptide layer is regularly thicker in gram-positive than in negative walls, the difference may be small. Hence other properties of the wall (e.g., the presence of lipid) may increase permeability and thus contribute to gram-negativity. But whatever the intimate mechanism, this general explanation also accounts for another important feature of the Gram reaction: the tendency of gram-positive cells to become negative in aging cultures (in which autolytic enzymes attack the wall).

Cytoplasmic Membrane

We have already noted that a distinct cytoplasmic membrane (cell membrane, plasma membrane, plasmalemma), internal to the cell wall, has been demonstrated by plasmolysis, by the formation of protoplasts, and by electron microscopy of thin sections of bacteria and protoplasts. The high osmotic pressure within bacterial cells, relative to their usual media, would be expected to press the membrane against the surrounding wall; and in sectioned cells the membrane is indeed found to be closely adherent to the wall. The profile of the membrane, fixed by the usual methods, is that of a typical "unit membrane," i.e., two dark bands separated by a light band, with a total width of about 75 A (Figs. 2-7 and 2-11).

A reasonably pure membrane fraction can be obtained from gram-positive cells by lysis of protoplasts, as noted on page 24. With gram-negative bacteria, however, the methods used for eliminating the glycopeptide layer to form spheroplasts leave lipid-containing wall components attached to the membrane. The presence of these components in the **spheroplasts** of gram-negative organisms can be demonstrated not only chemically, but through the presence of surface antigens and phage receptors characteristic of the intact cell.

The composition of bacterial membranes is roughly similar to that of mammalian cell membranes: about 40% lipid and 60% protein, with small amounts of carbohydrate. However, bacterial membranes (except those of certain mycoplasmas) **contain no sterols.** Furthermore, though the lipids in both classes of membranes consist largely of phosphatides, the composition of the phosphatides is quite different (Ch. 4, Complex lipids): for example, very few bacteria contain phosphatidyl choline (lecithin).

The bacterial cell membrane has several functions:

1) It provides an **osmotic barrier** that is essentially impermeable to ionized substances, and to nonionized molecules larger than glycerol. This barrier retains metabolites, and it excludes most exogenous substances other than those that can be carried by one of the transport systems present in the cell.

2) The membrane contains many different **transport systems** for various mineral ions, sugars, amino acids, etc. Each kind of transport system is specific for a given compound, or for a structurally related group of compounds. Since the function of these systems requires that they traverse the entire thickness of the membrane, the latter cannot be simply a uniform bimolecular leaflet of lipoproteins, as is sometimes inferred from its appearance and composition; it must possess an extensive topographic differentiation.

The properties of these membrane transport systems will be discussed in Chapter 5. Here we may simply note that they possess not only **specificity** but also the capacity for **active transport.** This property has evidently evolved, in such primitive cells as bacteria, to provide two major functional advantages: the ability to scavenge nutrients efficiently from very dilute media, and the ability to maintain a relatively constant intracellular ionic environment through an enormous range of external concentrations.

3) The isolated membrane fraction can be shown to contain the components of the **electron transport system** of bacteria: cytochromes, quinones, carotenoids, respiratory enzymes, etc. The bacterial cytoplasmic membrane is thus responsible for the functions that are performed in eucaryotic cells by the mitochondrion (which the whole bacterium resembles in size). In addition, the inner (cytoplasmic) surface of the membrane is densely studded with small spherical structures attached by thin stalks (Fig. 2-13), which closely resemble in appearance the **oxysomes** of the inner mitochondrial membranes. In both systems these structures appear to contain, and to coordinate in function, the enzymes of electron transport and oxidative phosphorylation (Ch. 3).

4) The membrane must transport outward not only small molecular waste products but also the larger building blocks that are incorporated into wall polymers (Ch. 4, Repeating heteropolymers), and the protein exoenzymes excreted by certain bacteria (Ch. 5). Some of these transfers are known to involve intermediate attachment to membrane lipids.

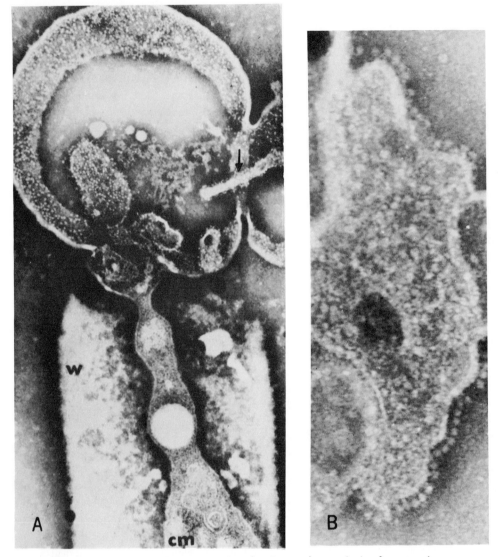

Fig. 2-13 Bacterial cell membrane. **A.** Cytoplasmic membrane (cm) of ruptured protoplast emerging from lysozyme-treated cell wall (w) of gram-positive bacillus (*B. stearothermophilus*). Note electron-lucid (light) particles. Where the membrane is folded (arrow) particles can be seen in rows. Negatively stained. ×90,000. **B.** Enlargement (×200,000) of folded surface of membrane. (From D. Abram. *J. Bact. 89:855*, 1965.)

Mesosomes and Other Endoplasmic Membrane

Thin sections of bacteria (especially gram-positive species) often show one or more large, irregular, convoluted invaginations of the cytoplasmic membrane, which are called **mesosomes** (plasmalemmosomes, chondrioids, peripheral bodies; Fig. 2-7). Though these sometimes appear as isolated bodies sur-

rounded by cytoplasm, serial sections always reveal a connection with the cytoplasmic membrane. In some species the mesosomes are vesicular (Fig. 2-7); in others they appear as concentric, lamellar whorls (Fig. 2-14). In either form they increase the total membrane surface of the cell. The lamellar type disappears on protoplast formation, evidently uncoiling and being drawn back into the cytoplasmic membrane as the latter is stretched.

Fig. 2-14 Section of *B. subtilis*. Separation from neighboring cell is not complete, while new septum is beginning to form in equatorial ring. Note well defined plasma membrane, continuous with small vesicular mesosome at one portion of septum and at each pole of cell. Also note large, concentric lamellar mesosome in lower nuclear region. (Courtesy of A. Ryter.)

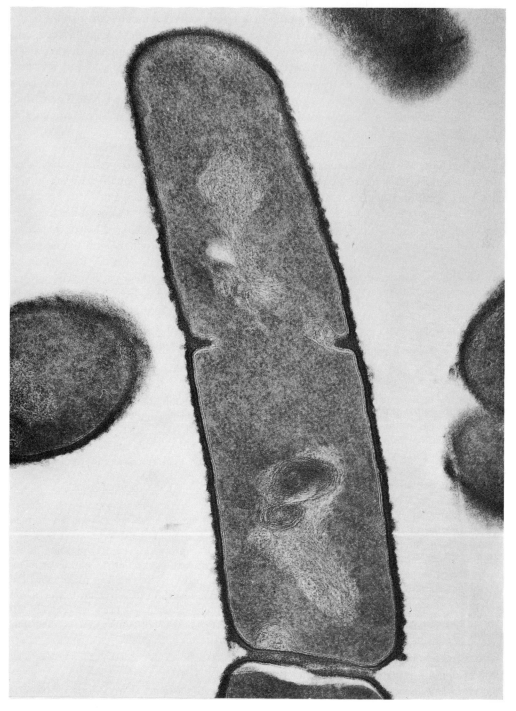

This finding confirms the continuity of the mesosomes with the cytoplasmic membrane (Fig. 2-18).

Mesosomes may have more than one function. They are frequently found to be attached to the nuclear body and to the region of membrane that invaginates in septum formation; hence their most important functions may well be connected with wall synthesis and with the segregation of nuclei to the daughter cells in cell division (see below). Mesosomes also provide an increased membrane surface area for supporting oxysomes and possibly transport systems.

Although no endoplasmic reticulum can be seen in sectioned bacteria, there are reasons to believe that some sort of fine **reticulum** is present but is concealed by the very dense packing of the cytoplasm with ribosomes (see next section).

Thus the amount of material recovered in the "membrane fraction" of lysed protoplasts (up to 30% of the dry weight of the cell) far exceeds what might be expected from the thin layer seen in sections of bacteria. Moreover, when cells (rather than protoplasts) are disrupted by osmotic explosion (e.g., by equilibration with glycerol, which penetrates freely, and then sudden transfer to water, which penetrates faster than the glycerol can escape), the membrane is somewhat protected by the residual wall, and sections reveal more membrane than can be accounted for by separation of the cytoplasmic membrane alone. Further evidence is provided by the large amount of recoverable membrane-bound ribosomes (see next section).

A highly differentiated membranous reticulum, either lamellar or in the form of vesicular chromatophores, is seen in photosynthetic bacteria and blue-green algae. It is obviously homologous to the more elaborate chloroplasts of photosynthetic eucaryotes (algae and higher plants).

Ribosomes

In electron micrographs of sectioned bacteria the cytoplasm, visualized under moderate magnification, exhibits a finely granular appearance (Figs. 2-7, 2-10, and 2-14), which is due to the presence of ribosomes. These are roughly spherical objects with a diameter of ca. 180 A (Ch. 4, Fig. 4-36). Bacterial ribosomes (M.W. ca. 2.8×10^6) are somewhat smaller (ca. 35% by weight) than those from eucaryotic cells. Ribosomes are readily recovered from homogenates by high-speed centrifugation (100,000 g), and are found to contain about 60% ribonucleic acid and 40% protein; they constitute up to 40% of the cell's dry weight and 90% of its RNA. Their function in protein synthesis will be considered in Chapter 4.

In a cell that is synthesizing protein the ribosomes are mostly grouped in chains called **polysomes** (Ch. 9). Though these are identifiable in extracts (Ch. 9, Fig. 9-10) they cannot be recognized in sectioned bacteria because of the close packing. The concentration of ribosomes varies widely with the nature of the growth medium (Ch. 9, Regulation of macromolecule synthesis): in a cell grown on a rich medium, which supports rapid growth, the concentration is high, and the average distance between ribosomes is about equal to the diameter of a ribosome.

Because of this density it is also impossible to see directly whether or not ribosomes are attached to membranes in the bacterial cell, as they are in the "rough" endoplasmic reticulum of many eucaryotic cells. However, cell fractionation yields a substantial proportion (ca. 20%) of the total ribosomes in the membrane fraction of gently lysed protoplasts of *Bacillus megaterium;* and the attached ribosomes do not appear, on electron microscopy, to be simply trapped in the artificial vesicles that are formed on fragmentation of the membrane (Fig. 2-15). This finding provides evidence for some as yet unseen structural connection (? fibrous or membranous) between the plasma membrane and distant ribosomes; for it is evident, from electron micrographs of sectioned bacteria, that far less than 20% of the ribosomes are immediately adjacent to the membrane.

Granular Inclusions

The cytoplasm of many kinds of bacteria often contains relatively large granules, com-

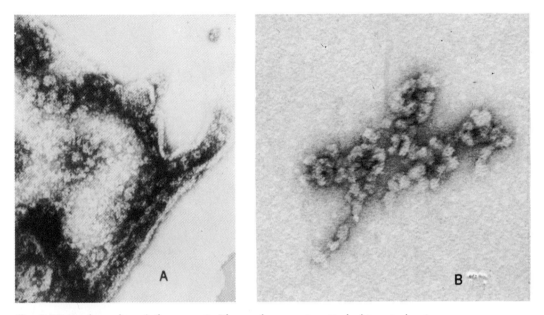

Fig. 2-15 Membrane-bound ribosomes. **A.** Ribosomal aggregates attached to cytoplasmic membrane of protoplast ghosts from gram-positive bacillus (*B. megaterium*). Negatively stained. ×100,000. **B.** Aggregates apparently bound to a nonmembranous reticulum. Negatively stained. ×150,000. (From D. Schlessinger, V. T. Marchesi, and B. K. W. Kwan. *J. Bact.* 90:456, 1965.)

posed of cellular storage materials, in amounts that vary widely with nutritional conditions. **Polymetaphosphate** granules $(PO_3^-)_n$ are stained metachromatically (i.e., with a change in color) by such dyes as methylene blue or toluidine blue; they are traditionally called **volutin** granules.* Lipophilic stains (e.g., Sudan black) reveal **lipids** (e.g., poly-β-hydroxybutyric acid), while iodine reveals the characteristic red of **glycogen** in some bacteria, and the blue of a starch-like granulose in others. The high molecular weight polymers of these granules enable bacteria to store relatively large quantities of nutrients without further increasing the osmolarity of the cytoplasm.

Nucleus (Nucleoid)

In mammalian cells a variety of basic dyes can be used to reveal the chromosomes: they stain nucleic acids, and the DNA of the nuclei then stands out because it is ordinarily more densely aggregated than the RNA of the cytoplasm. In bacteria, in contrast, this procedure fails to differentiate any nucleus, because the cytoplasm is densely packed with RNA and hence is at least as basophilic as the nucleus. However, discrete nuclear bodies in bacteria can be recognized under the light microscope through special procedures: 1) the use of a DNA-specific stain, such as the Feulgen (fuchsin-sulfite) stain or the fluorescent dye acridine orange; 2) selective hydrolysis of the RNA (in fixed cells) by HCl or RNase, followed by staining with a basic dye (Fig. 2-16); or 3) suspension of live cells in a medium of the same refractive index as the cytoplasm, which permits the nuclei to be recognized under phase contrast as areas of different refractility. Most bacilli contain two or more such bodies per cell, since cell division lags behind nuclear division.

The electron microscope made possible

---

* So named because they are particularly common in the species *Spirillum volutans.* Because they stain with basic dyes they have often been confused with nuclei.

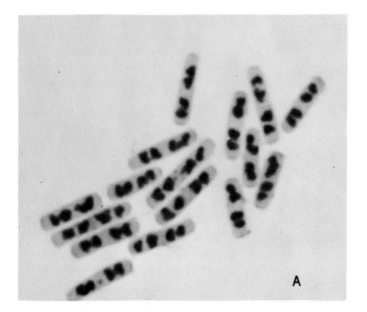

A

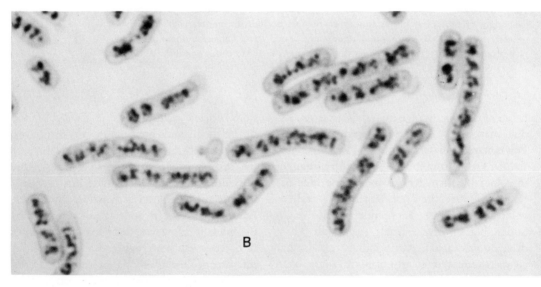

B

Fig. 2-16 Bacterial nuclei. Demonstration of "chromatin bodies" by a basic stain (Giemsa), after hydrolysis of the RNA by treatment with HCl. **A.** *Bacillus cereus,* in which the bodies appear compact. **B.** *B. megaterium,* in which the bodies are more dispersed and granular. Both ×3600. (Courtesy of C. Robinow.)

more detailed study of these bodies, which established the concept of bacteria as procaryotic cells, lacking the discrete chromosomes, mitotic apparatus, nucleolus, and nuclear membrane of the nuclei of eucaryotic cells. Hence the nuclear region in bacteria is referred to by some as the **nuclear body, nuclear equivalent, nucleoid,** or **chromatin body.** However, since this body is homologous in function to the eucaryotic nucleus, though more primitive, we shall refer to it as the bac-

terial nucleus. In contrast to eucaryotic nuclei, bacterial nuclei contain no histones, as tested either cytochemically or by fractionation of cell extracts.

The nuclear region in bacteria is less dense to the electron beam than the cytoplasm, even after the DNA is stained with uranyl or lanthanum ion. Different methods of fixation yield strikingly different pictures: a few coarse, dense bodies, which are undoubtedly artificial coagulates, against an empty background; or a homogeneous pale area, in which the fibers are too fine to be resolved (diameter of DNA double helix = 20 A); or a mass of relatively fine fibers, often arranged in parallel, curved bundles (Fig. 2-17). In the last type of preparation, which is the most useful, each visible fiber is apparently an aggregate of a few parallel DNA chains, since the fibers seen in the serial sections of a nucleus provide in toto only a fraction of the known length of the bacterial chromosome. (The latter, as we shall see in Chapter 8, can be extracted and spread out, and can then be shown by radioautography to be a circle of double-stranded DNA about 1000 times as long as the bacterium.)

The bacterial chromosome thus appears to have, in all stages of cell growth and division, the diffuse state characteristic of the interphase nucleus of higher forms. Presumably the unknown forces that keep the DNA chains more or less evenly spaced are also responsible for maintaining a sharp border, without a membrane, between nucleus and cytoplasm (Figs. 2-14 and 2-17). The loose packing of the bacterial nucleus presumably allows ready diffusion of soluble metabolites and enzymes (but not of ribosomes, Fig. 2-17) to all regions of the chromosome. The inference of a relatively wide spacing between DNA chains is supported by two further observations: the bacterial nucleus occupies about 10% of the cell's volume, while the DNA represents only 2 to 3% of its weight; and in virus particles, in which the DNA is metabolically inactive, the same electron micrographic methods reveal a much denser DNA-containing region.

Though the nucleus is well defined, and regularly occupies a predominantly central position in the cell, its shape is often quite irregular, and sections may cut through lobulations and give the illusion of isolated small bodies. Serial sections, however, show that all such regions are continuous with a larger body, and that this body is regularly attached to the cytoplasmic membrane, often via one or two mesosomes deeply embedded in the nucleus. The function of this connection in nuclear division will be discussed below.

The nucleus is large enough to contain a complete genome, which fits the genetic evidence (Ch. 7) that all the genes in a bacterium are linked in a single chromosome. It might be

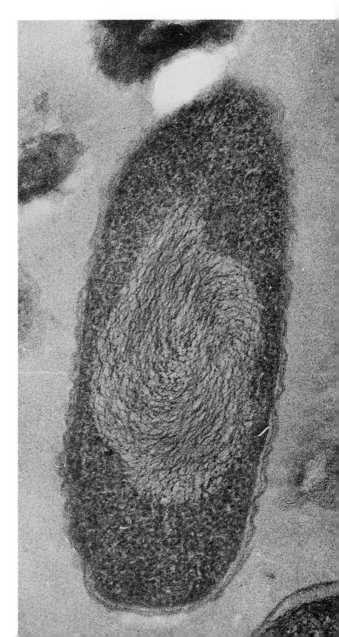

Fig. 2-17 Section of *Agrobacterium tumefaciens*. Special fixation to bring out fine fibrillar structure of nucleus. (Courtesy of A. Ryter.)

further noted that the size of the nucleus is not constant: since the DNA of a cell is ordinarily replicating at a constant rate through most of a cycle of cell division (Ch. 9), the nuclei vary in size between one genome (when recently divided) and two (when on the verge of division).

Cell Sap and Cytoplasmic Organization

Bacterial cell volumes can be determined from measurements of the volume of packed wet cells, corrected for intercellular space (ca. 20%) by the use of a labeled macromolecule that does not penetrate or adsorb to the bacteria (e.g., hemoglobin, or isotopically labeled dextrin or albumin). Dry weight determinations then show that an average bacterium (e.g., *E. coli*) contains about 25% dry weight and 75% water. Since the wall is dense, and contributes a substantial fraction of the cell weight, the cytoplasm (including the nuclear region) is about 80% water. It contains a great variety of small molecules (the metabolite pool) and inorganic ions.

The intracellular pool can be recovered for chemical estimation by transferring cells to boiling water, or to cold 5% trichloroacetic acid; these procedures disrupt the cytoplasmic membrane and precipitate the macromolecules, thus freeing the contents of the pool into the fluid. The cells must be washed, or filtered free of extracellular fluid, before disruption, and this step should be rapid in order to minimize metabolic alteration of the pool. For this purpose nitrocellulose membrane filters of high porosity but small pore size have proved invaluable, since they retain bacteria quantitatively but allow fluid to pass quickly.

The high osmotic pressure of the bacterial cell shows that the components of the metabolite pool are largely in a free state of solution (except for ions balancing charges in macromolecules). This osmotic pressure can be estimated by determining at what point increasing external osmolarity causes an abrupt decrease in cell volume (i.e., plasmolysis). The values observed are about 20 atmospheres in some gram-positive organisms and about 5 atmospheres in thinner-walled gram-negative organisms. (It will be recalled that a 1-M solution of a nonelectrolyte ideally has an osmotic pressure of 22.4 atmospheres.)

Most kinds of enzymes in bacteria appear to be "soluble" (i.e., in solution in the cell fluid),

since on mechanical disruption of the cells, followed by high-speed centrifugation to sediment the ribosomes and other particles, these enzymes are found in the supernatant. Other enzymes, however—particularly those concerned with oxidative phosphorylation and with wall polymer synthesis—are firmly bound to the membrane, since they are found in the "particulate" fraction, i.e., the fraction that sediments in centrifugation at ca. 100,000 g. However, the distribution of enzyme activities between particles and supernate varies somewhat with the method of fractionation, indicating that bound enzymes are not all bound equally firmly. Furthermore, there is evidence, from differences in the fate of an endogenous and an exogenous supply of the same metabolite, that even some "soluble" enzymes may be bound, though weakly, in preferential locations. Hence the bacterial cell may possess a greater degree of topographical organization than is apparent.

Some highly basic enzymes (e.g., certain ribonucleases) are found in the ribosome fraction. However, they may well be simply adsorbed during cell fragmentation by the highly acidic ribosomes, for some of these enzymes are known to lie between the cell wall and membrane (Ch. 5, Exoenzymes), since they are lost when the cells are converted to spheroplasts.

Cell Division

The problems of cell division are intimately connected with cell wall biosynthesis (Ch. 4), cell growth (Ch. 5), and the regulation of DNA synthesis (Ch. 9). However, it seems convenient to consider the morphological aspects of cell division in the present chapter.

Wall Growth and Separation

Bacteria generally divide by **binary fission,** producing two daughter cells of equal size.* Electron micrographs show that bacterial division is visibly initiated by the ingrowth of cytoplasmic membrane, often in association with a mesosome (Fig. 2-18). This process is accompanied by ingrowth of wall and eventu-

---

* Yeasts generally divide by a process of **budding,** resulting in the separation of a small daughter cell from the larger mother cell (Ch. 21).

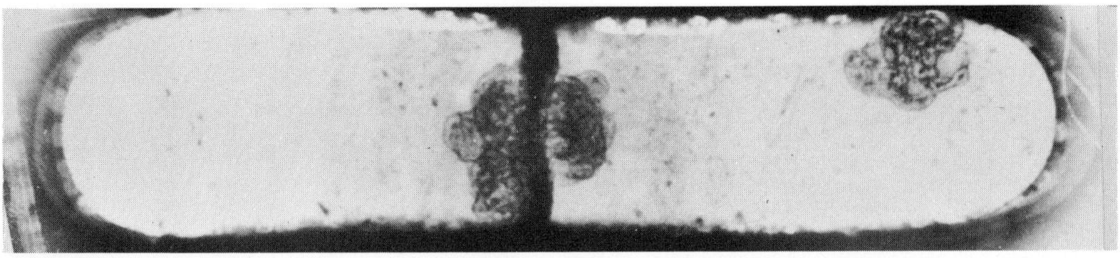

Fig. 2-18 Negatively stained mesosomes at site of transverse septum during cell division of gram-positive bacillus (*B. stearothermophilus*), and also near pole of one cell. Penetration of opaque stain permits visualization of mesosomes in the unsectioned, intact cell, and demonstrates their continuity with the exterior. ×46,000. (From D. Abram. *J. Bact.* 89:855, 1965.)

ally leads to the formation of a complete transverse septum (cross-wall), which is thicker than the ordinary cell wall (Figs. 2-7, 2-14, and 2-18). Cell separation begins by cleavage of the septum, progressing from its periphery toward its center.

Differences in the details of this separation are responsible for characteristic differences in bacterial shape and arrangement. Chains of cocci are formed by incomplete cleavage of septa, rather than by the presence of an agglutinating substance; and prolonged delay in the cleavage of bacilli (often seen under conditions of impaired growth) results in the pathological formation of long filaments.

In some organisms cleavage of the peripheral region of the septum begins while the inner region is still advancing, resulting in cell constriction; while in cells that form long rods the septum is completed, and may persist for some time, before its split begins. The mechanisms that regulate the partial enzymatic lysis of the cell wall in cell division, specifying its location and its extent, are a mystery. Cell types that tend to adhere as they divide produce colonies with a rough surface, while those that slip into more compact configurations produce smoother colonies (Ch. 5, Colonial morphology).

Division of Cells with Defective Walls. The important role of the wall in orderly cell division is illustrated by the inability of lysozyme-induced protoplasts to divide, although they can increase their protoplasm several-fold. Mycoplasmas, how-ever, and the spheroplasts formed by gram-negative eubacteria, can divide, though they lack a rigid wall. Division occurs more readily in the depths of agar than on the surface or in liquid medium, and it has been suggested that the fibers of the agar may help to pinch off daughter cells. The cells formed are much more variable in size and shape than are eubacteria. Indeed, electron micrographs show that there are no mesosomes and no septa; and the process of pinching off and separating daughters is so irregular, without a rigid wall, that bags of cytoplasm without a nucleus are often formed.

The influence of wall synthesis on growth rate and cell shape is also illustrated by a curious bacterium, *Lactobacillus bifidus,* which predominates in the feces of breast-fed infants. This organism apparently has difficulty in forming one of the constituents of its wall: in ordinary media it grows slowly and forms somewhat branched (bifid) cells, like abortive fungal filaments. However, human milk contains a factor (a glycoside of N-acetylglucosamine) that permits faster growth and formation of normal bacilli, presumably by contributing to glycopeptide synthesis.

Sites of Wall Addition. If the entire basal wall is a single bag-shaped molecule it must grow by adding monomers across the membrane interstitially, i.e., in microscopic "open" areas. These areas can be located, on a rather gross scale, by staining the whole cell surface with fluorescent antibodies (Ch. 13) and then

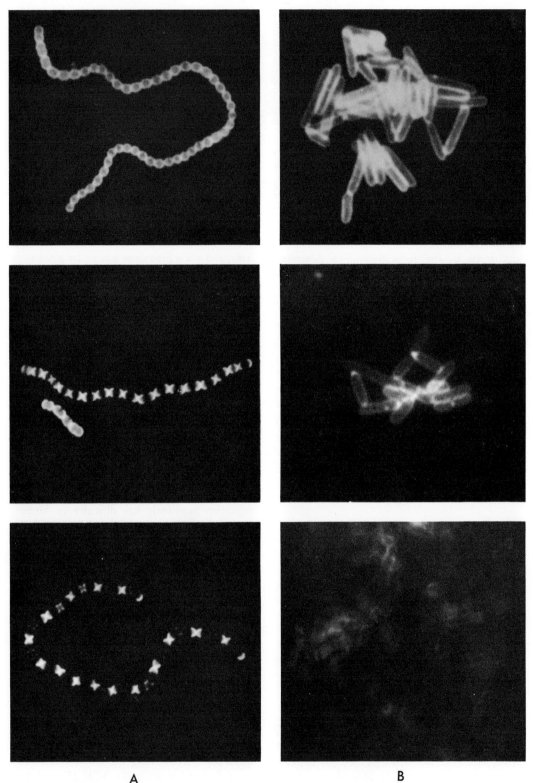

A   B

allowing further growth. The newly synthesized wall, if sufficiently localized, then stands out as unstained areas. Several patterns have been seen. Gram-positive streptococci lay down their new wall in an **equatorial zone** (in relation to the axis of the chain of cells), in which septum formation and finally cell division take place (Fig. 2-19). Gram-positive

Fig. 2-19 Site of cell wall addition. Demonstrated by staining with fluorescent antibody specific for cell antigen (Ch. 13, Immunofluorescence). **A.** Cells of a gram-positive streptococcus (*S. pyogenes*), whose chain maintains cell orientation along an axis during cell division, were exposed to fluorescein-labeled antibody; as is shown in the photograph on the top, the entire cell surface was fluorescent when exposed to ultraviolet light. The next two samples, taken after 15 and 30 minutes of growth in the absence of antibody, show the deposition in each cell of fresh, unstained wall in an equatorial ring, which separates the older stained wall into two portions. Each portion remains adherent to the similar older portion of the adjacent cell, thus forming an "X." (When the cells were stained with unlabeled antibody first, and with labeled antibody during growth, the expected complementary pattern of staining was seen.) **B.** Cells of a gram-negative bacillus (*Salmonella typhosa*), treated in the same way, showed diffuse loss of initial stain rather than localized separation. **C** and **D.** Diagrammatic representation of modes of cell division. (R. M. Cole. *Bact. Rev.* 29:326, 1965.)

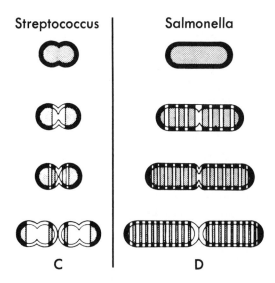

Streptococcus | Salmonella

C | D

bacilli also appear to synthesize new wall only at the sites of septum formation.

In gram-negative Enterobacteriaceae, in contrast, the same technic fails to show any demarcation between old and new wall, but rather suggests growth by **diffuse intercalation** (Fig. 2-19). The difference between the localized synthesis in the gram-positive and the dispersive synthesis in the gram-negative organisms may well be related to the much more regular and prominent mesosomes attached to septa in the former, noted above. This difference therefore suggests that mesosomes may be sites of rapid wall synthesis.

Fungi, consisting of branching filaments, show still a third pattern: **terminal addition** to the growing tips of the filaments.

Nuclear Division

The bacterial cell does not require a mitotic spindle because it does not have a set of chromosomes to be segregated to the two daughter cells. Nevertheless, the daughters of the single bacterial chromosome must be regularly segregated.

Jacob and Ryter have provided evidence that this process does not depend simply on chance migration toward the two poles of the cell before septum formation. Rather, serial sections showed that the nuclei in a bacillus are regularly attached to the cytoplasmic membrane, often via a mesosome (Figs. 2-7 and 2-18). It was therefore suggested that the mesosome divides along with the attached nucleus; then in cell division the two progeny mesosomes, through their attachments to the plasma membranes, migrate in opposite directions from the site of septum formation, carrying the two nuclei with them (Fig. 2-20). In this way **the cytoplasmic membrane serves as a primitive mitotic apparatus,** with mesosomes substituting for the mitotic spindle. Moreover, since mesosomes are associated also with septum formation, migration of a nucleus and mesosome to the middle of each daughter cell might be related to the initiation of septum formation at that site at the next cell division.

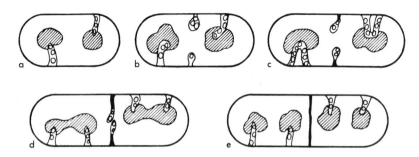

Fig. 2-20 Nuclear division and segregation. Diagrammatic representation of the role of mesosomal attachments to the cell membrane in nuclear division and segregation, as well as in septum formation. (A. Ryter and F. Jacob. *Ann. Inst. Pasteur,* 107:384, 1964.)

Spores and L Forms

Under certain circumstances some bacilli cease dividing and instead undergo a complex process of differentiation, which yields highly refractile, dehydrated spores. This process, and the structure of spores, are discussed in Chapter 5.

We have noted above that the rigid mucopeptide layer of the wall can be eliminated, yielding spheroplasts or protoplasts in osmotically protective media. This conversion occurs in Nature as well as in the laboratory, and the products can often multiply indefinitely as pleomorphic **L forms.**

BACTERIAL CLASSIFICATION

Since we cannot communicate meaningfully about things unless we can identify them, it is a matter of practical necessity to develop a nomenclature for any objects of study, and to classify them on the basis of their similarities and differences. With the discovery of biological evolution, however, the ordering of living organisms has developed an additional goal: that of going beyond a systematic, purely descriptive classification to a "natural" taxonomic classification, which tries to arrange groups of organisms in a pattern reflecting their lines of evolutionary descent.

With higher animals and plants, through the study of morphological, physiological, and developmental homologies, as well as through study of the fossil record, we now have taxonomic schemes that are generally accepted as reflecting natural, phylogenetic relations. A keystone in this classification is the definition of a **species** as a group of individuals capable of continued fertile interbreeding. Indeed, despite the continuity of evolution it has proved feasible to divide the world of plants and animals, with few exceptions, into hundreds of thousands of such discontinuous groups, whose reproductive separation places some limits on the range of gene flow, and thus has the evolutionary advantage of minimizing the production of unworkable combination of genes. In contrast, the higher levels of classification (genus, tribe, family, order, class) lack such a clean, operational definition as the species, and so their assignments have been more arbitrary.

With bacteria the situation is quite different: the number of characteristics available is much more limited; there is no ontogeny to recapitulate phylogeny; there is no fossil record; and reproduction is ordinarily not sexual. Hence the many efforts to create a true taxonomy have failed, for lack of an adequate basis for determining which characters were acquired by an organism earlier and which later. For example, the morphological subdivision of bacteria into spheres, rods, and spirals would appear to reflect a fundamental and stable trait, settled early in evolution; and the same might be thought of the major energy-yielding patterns, such as various specific fermentations, oxidative metabolism, or photosynthesis. Yet each of these metabolic patterns is found in each of the morphological groups, and the decision to subordinate one of these criteria to the other is arbitrary. It is therefore hardly surprising that in the most extensive cooperative effort at classification (*Bergey's Manual of Determinative Bacteriology*), which is widely used as a guide in the United States, the shape of the taxonomic tree should change substantially with each of the seven successive editions, between 1923 and 1957.

But however speculative the proposed **taxonomic** relations, such a classification is useful as a **determinative key,** i.e., for **identifying** an unknown organism and relating it to previously described organisms. In this way, and by reference to collections of "type cultures" (i.e., standard strains) that are maintained in several countries, bacteriologists can communicate meaningfully with each other.

In the Linnaean* tradition of zoology and botany, each "species" of bacterium is assigned an official Latin binomial, with a capitalized genus followed by an uncapitalized species designation: this name is printed in italics to indicate the foreign language. Unitalicized vernacular or colloquial names may be derived from, or may be identical with, the official name (e.g., pneumococcus = *Diplococcus pneumoniae;* salmonella = *Salmonella* spp.). Unfortunately, international codes of nomenclature were developed late, have not always been adhered to, and have

undergone frequent change as opinions concerning the relations between various organisms changed. Hence the same organism can be encountered in the literature under several names: e.g., *Bacillus typhosus, Bacterium typhosum, Eberthella typhosa,* and *Salmonella typhi.* In virology, which developed later and emphasized molecular properties, the connection with systematic botany and zoology has been weak, and a proposed binomial system has not been generally adopted.

The Present Classification. For purposes of general orientation some of the major "families" of bacteria are described in Table 2-1. This classification, and the more detailed descriptions of various organisms to appear in later chapters, may be best regarded as simply a convenient way of identifying organisms and grouping them in terms of shared properties. Many properties have been used for this purpose: visible properties (including shape, size, color, staining, motility, flagellar pattern, capsule, and colonial morphology); energy-yielding pattern; formation of characteristic chemical products; nutrition (including both growth requirements and ability to utilize various sugars and other foods); presence of characteristic surface macromolecules (usually detected immunologically, but more recently also chemically); and ecological relations (including the ability to parasitize higher organisms and to cause disease).

From the point of view of the systematic biologist ecological criteria are highly unreliable; for if he wishes to know what environments an organism can inhabit he cannot use the habitat to define the organism. He would thus object to creating separate genera for *Escherichia,* a major inhabitant of the vertebrate gut, and *Erwinia,* which is found in rotting plants; for the two groups are essentially identical (except that the latter contain enzymes to attack pectin, a cement substance of plants). However, for purposes of an arbitrary classification, to be used in the applied fields of medical and agricultural bacteriology, the mutually exclusive habitats of these organisms constitute a major taxonomic difference, even though based on minor physiological differences.

---

* Carolus Linnaeus (Carl von Linné) (1707–1778), Swedish botanist and professor of medicine.

TABLE 2-1.   MAIN GROUPS OF BACTERIA

		1. Gram-positive eubacteria		
Cell shape	Motility	Other distinguishing characteristics	Genera	Families
Cocci	Nearly all permanently immotile	Cells in cubical packets	Sarcina	MICROCOCCACEAE
		Cells irregularly arranged	Micrococcus Staphylococcus	
		Cells in chains, lactic fermentation of sugars	Streptococcus Diplococcus	LACTOBACILLACEAE
			Leuconostoc	
Straight rods	Nearly all permanently immotile	Lactic fermentation of sugars	Lactobacillus	LACTOBACILLACEAE
		Propionic fermentation of sugars	Propionibacterium	PROPIONIBACTERIACEAE
		Oxidative, weakly fermentative	Corynebacterium Listeria Erysipelothrix	CORYNEBACTERIACEAE
	Motile with peritrichous flagella, and related immotile forms	Endospores produced Aerobic	Bacillus	BACILLACEAE
		Anaerobic	Clostridium	

(Continued)

The Arbitrary Definition of a Species

Even if we settle for the limited goal of a descriptive classification, bacteria still present problems. First, the grouping of individual strains into the same "kind" or "species" of bacterium had to be settled initially without benefit of the interfertility test used in higher organisms; and even with the more recent development of bacterial genetics (Ch. 6), the interfertility test has not proved very useful (see below). Moreover, the mutability and the rapid growth of bacteria, combined with strong selection pressures from changes in the environment (Ch. 6), often lead to striking changes in the heritable properties of a strain during its cultivation in the laboratory (though many of these variants might not be able to survive under the conditions encountered in Nature). The "art" of the systematic bacteriologist therefore lies in distinguishing secondary details from the more stable properties of bacteria, which presumably depend on large numbers of genes, or on genes whose mutations are lethal or are strongly selected against in Nature. Surprisingly, some properties, such as the ability to utilize lactose or other sugars, have proved very useful in classification even though they may be lost by a single mutation.

We thus find that a bacterial species usually includes a continuum of organisms with a relatively wide range of variation in many properties. In the Enterobacteriaceae in particular, which appear to undergo much genetic recombination in Nature, a large fraction of the strains encountered are intermediate in properties rather than identical with one or another type culture; the species thus represents a cluster of biotypes, more or less resembling a strain that is maintained as the type culture of the species, but without the

TABLE 2-1. (Continued)

II. Gram-negative bacteria, excluding photosynthetic forms

Cell shape	Motility	Other distinguishing characteristics		Genera	Families
Cocci	Permanently immotile	Aerobic		Neisseria	NEISSERIACEAE
		Anaerobic		Veillonella	
				Brucella	BRUCELLACEAE
				Pasteurella	
				Hemophilus	
				Bordetella	
Straight rods	Motile with peritrichous flagella, and related immotile forms	Facultative anaerobic	Mixed acid fermentation of sugars	Escherichia Erwinia Salmonella Shigella	ENTEROBACTERIACEAE
			Butylene glycol fermentation of sugars	Aerobacter Serratia	
		Aerobic	Free-living nitrogen fixers	Azotobacter	AZOTOBACTERIACEAE
			Symbiotic nitrogen fixers	Rhizobium	RHIZOBIACEAE
	Motile with polar flagella	Aerobic	Oxidize inorganic compounds	Nitrosomonas Nitrobacter	NITROBACTERIACEAE
				Thiobacillus	THIOBACTERIACEAE
			Oxidize organic compounds	Pseudomonas Acetobacter	PSEUDOMONADACEAE
		Facultative anaerobic		Photobacterium Zymomonas Aeromonas	
Curved rods	Motile with polar flagella	Comma-shaped	Aerobic	Vibrio	SPIRILLACEAE
		Spiral	Anaerobic	Desulfovibrio Spirillum	

III. Other major groups

Characteristics	Genera	Orders (-ALES) or families (-ACEAE)
Acid-fast rods	Mycobacterium	ACTINOMYCETALES
Ray-forming rods (actinomycetes)	Actinomyces	
Ray-forming rods (actinomycetes)	Nocardia	
Ray-forming rods (actinomycetes)	Streptomyces	
Spiral organisms, motile	Treponema Borrelia Leptospira Spirocheta	SPIROCHETALES
Small, pleomorphic; lack rigid wall	Mycoplasma	MYCOPLASMATACEAE
Small intracellular parasites	Rickettsia Coxiella	RICKETTSIACEAE
Small intracellular parasites, readily filtrable	Chlamydia	BEDSONIA (CHLAMYDOZOACEAE)
Intracellular parasites; borderline with protozoa	Bartonella	BARTONELLACEAE

Modified from R. Y. Stanier, M. Doudoroff, and E. A. Adelberg. The Microbial World. Prentice-Hall, Englewood Cliffs, N.J., 1963.

sharp boundaries that we are accustomed to in higher organisms.

Medical bacteriologists are especially interested in those properties of bacteria that influence their interactions with man, including their resistance to host defenses. Since such resistance depends heavily on the cell surface, the immunological characterization of antigenic surface macromolecules plays a much larger role in medical bacteriology (and medical virology) than in general microbiology. Hosts that are resistant to one strain may be susceptible to an otherwise identical strain with a different kind of surface polysaccharide; and in an extreme emphasis on this ecological relation, and on the arbitrariness of grouping, investigators of *Salmonella* have become "splitters" rather than "lumpers": a new species name has been assigned to every isolate with a novel antigenic pattern, even though these "species" may differ from each other by only one or a few mutations. In contrast, comparable variants in the pneumococcus or the streptococcus are defined as "types," with different numbers assigned, within the same species.

In this connection it might be emphasized that the deeper layers of the wall, and the cell membrane, tend to change much less readily than the surface layers of the cell, which are subject to much greater selection pressure from agents that attack the surface (antibodies, enzymes, bacteriophages, etc.). Hence immunological or chemical characterization of these deeper components provides a relatively satisfactory basis for recognizing natural relations.* With the recent and continuing advance of bacterial cytology and chemistry we may expect increasing reliance on this approach, which has already been extensively used with viruses.†

Numerical Taxonomy. To avoid the arbitrary weighting of characters, some investigators, with the aid of computers, have revived an approach to taxonomy introduced in the eighteenth century by the French biologist Adanson. In this system a large number of characters are determined for each strain, and groups are established on the basis of the proportion of characters shared, without giving any characters more weight than others. The approach is laborious, but it may lead to significant regrouping of certain classes of organisms.

Taxonomy Based on DNA Homology

Since we now know that genetic information is encoded in DNA, we can define the concept of the evolutionary relatedness of organisms in more precise and operational terms: the **degree of homology of their DNA.** For as organisms drift further and further apart in evolution, through the accumulation of mutations, their genes not only code for different structures and functions but also differ increasingly in their base sequences. Indeed, the interfertility test for a species in higher organisms depends on just this homology: the ability of essentially any region in any chromosome of one parent to replace the corresponding region of the other parent and to carry out its essential functions (Ch. 8, Table 8-1).

As we have noted, the interfertility test in bacteria is not very useful for this purpose. One reason is that genetic recombination has so far been restricted to relatively few kinds of bacteria, because the transfer of DNA requires special features of the bacterial surface (Ch. 7). Moreover, in addition to such surface incompatibility there may be incompatibility

---

* However, since only a finite number of repeating polysaccharides are possible (in contrast to the virtually unlimited variety of proteins), the phylogenetic significance of shared polysaccharide antigenic determinants is inevitably limited by the occasional appearance of the same determinant in widely separated organisms. For example, the surface of *E. coli* type 0-86 cross-reacts with blood group substance B of human red cells.

† The attitude of many bacterial physiologists toward problems of classification is reflected in Duclaux' story of a clever microscopist, who pointed out to Pasteur that an organism which he had taken for a coccus was in reality a small bacillus. The reply was, "If you only knew how little difference that makes to me!" However, as the study of bacterial variation has developed into bacterial genetics and then into molecular genetics, and as the study of visible structure has merged with that of chemical structure, the gap between the taxonomist and the physiologist has narrowed a good deal.

of the DNA, even of closely related strains: each strain can modify its DNA in specific chemical ways that render it resistant (while foreign DNA is susceptible) to the action of nucleases in the cell (Ch. 23, Host modification of viruses).

The **chemical study of DNA,** however, now offers a **direct** approach to the measurement of the relatedness of different organisms. Thus, though the base composition of the DNA is found to be essentially the same in all vertebrates (ca. 40 mole % guanine + cytosine [=GC] and 60% adenine plus thymine), in the bacterial kingdom it varies remarkably, from about 30 to 70 mole % GC (Table 2-2). Moreover, the chromosome of a bacterium is strikingly homogeneous in this respect, as shown by its behavior on sedimentation after fragmentation into small segments

(Ch. 8). Thus the DNA base composition of an organism is evidently a stable characteristic, settled over a long period of evolution.

The base compositions presented in Table 2-2 in general confirm previously accepted ideas concerning close relations. For example, a similar composition (38 to 40% GC) is observed for various streptococci, pneumococci, and lactobacilli, which have traditionally been grouped together as lactic acid bacteria because of their characteristic fermentation. On the other hand, *Lactobacillus bifidus* is far removed (56% GC).

Similarly, though *Proteus* is traditionally grouped with the Enterobacteriaceae, and some species have the same GC content (50 to 52%) as the majority of this "family," others are far removed (38 to 40%). We also see considerable spread within other large groups that have been

TABLE 2-2.   DNA BASE COMPOSITIONS OF REPRESENTATIVE BACTERIA

Mole % guanine plus cytosine	Organism
28–30	*Spirillum linum*
30–32	*Clostridium perfringens, C. tetani*
32–34	*C. bifermentans, Leptospira pomona, Staphylococcus aureus*
34–36	*Bacillus anthracis, other bacilli, Clostridium kluyveri, Leptospira pomona, Mycoplasma gallisepticum, Pasteurella aviseptica, Staphylococcus albus, Streptococcus faecalis, Treponema pallidum*
38–40	*Bacillus megaterium, Hemophilus influenzae, Diplococcus pneumoniae, Lactobacillus acidophilus, Leuconostoc mesenteroides, Streptococcus pyogenes, other streptococci, Proteus vulgaris, Sporosarcina ureae*
40–42	*Bacillus laterosporus, Leptospira biflexa, Neisseria catarrhalis*
42–44	*Bacillus subtilis, B. stearothermophilus, Bacteroides insolitus, Coxiella burneti*
46–48	*Bacillus licheniformis, Clostridium nigrificans, Corynebacterium acnes, Pasteurella pestis, Vibrio cholerae*
48–50	*Neisseria gonorrheae, other neisseriae*
50–52	*Bacillus macerans, Escherichia coli, other escherichiae, Erwinia spp., Neisseria meningitidis, Proteus morgani, Salmonella spp., Shigella spp.*
52–54	*Aerobacter-Klebsiella spp., Corynebacterium diphtheriae, Erwinia spp.*
54–56	*Aerobacter-Klebsiella spp., Alcaligenes faecalis, Azotobacter agile, Brucella abortus*
56–58	*Corynebacterium spp., Lactobacillus bifidus*
58–60	*Agrobacterium tumefaciens, Corynebacterium spp., Serratia marcescens*
60–62	*Azotobacter vinelandii, Pseudomonas fluorescens, Rhodospirillum rubrum, Vibrio spp.*
64–66	*Desulfovibrio desulfuricans, Pseudomonas spp.*
66–68	*Pseudomonas aeruginosa, Mycobacterium tuberculosis*
68–70	*Pseudomonas saccharophila, Sarcina flava*
70–80	*Micrococcus lysoideikticus, Mycobacterium smegmatis, Nocardia spp., Sarcina lutea, Streptomyces spp.*

Modified from J. Marmur, S. Falkow, and M. Mandel. Ann. Rev. Microbiol. 17:329 (1963).

considered a single genus primarily on morphological grounds, e.g., *Bacillus, Corynebacterium, Pseudomonas*. Finally, the weakness of gross morphology as a major taxonomic criterion (cf. whales and fishes) is well illustrated by the anomalous position of *Sporosarcina ureae*, the only coccus that sporulates: this organism has a base composition (38 to 40% GC) close to that of the sporulating rods (*bacilli* and *clostridia*), and very far from that of other sarcinae (70 to 80% GC).

Similarity of base composition represents only a minimal basis for genetic relatedness, since organisms with a similar composition can have very different sequences. In a more refined comparison, **homology of DNA sequence** can now be measured quantitatively by determining the ability of DNA strands from two different sources to form molecular hybrids with each other in vitro (Ch. 8, Hybridization of DNA). With this development we can hopefully look forward to the growth of a firmly based, rational taxonomy of bacteria. Moreover, since base sequences are ultimately translated into amino acid sequences in proteins, evolutionary relation will surely also be illuminated by analysis of the amino acid sequences of homologous proteins (e.g., cytochromes, various enzymes) in various microbes, just as the analysis of hemoglobins has yielded interesting results with vertebrates. Meanwhile, the nomenclature and the groupings employed in this book will have to depend on the conventional classification developed by earlier methods.

SELECTED REFERENCES: STRUCTURE

Books and Review Articles

COLE, R. M. (ed.). Symposium on the fine structure and replication of bacteria and their parts. *Bact. Rev.* 29:277 (1965).

GLAUERT, A. M. The fine structure of bacteria. *Brit. M. Bull.* 18:245 (1962).

GUNSALUS, I. C., and STANIER, R. Y. (eds.). *The Bacteria,* vol. I, *Structure.* Academic Press, New York, 1960.

KELLENBERGER, E., and RYTER, A. Selected Applications of the Electron Microscope in Bacteriology. In *Modern Developments in Electron Microscopy,* p. 335. (B. M. Siegel, ed.) Academic Press, New York, 1964.

SALTON, M. R. J. *The Bacterial Cell Wall.* Elsevier, New York, 1964.

Specific Articles

BAYER, M. E., and ANDERSON, T. F., The surface structure of *Escherichia coli. Proc. Nat. Acad. Sc.* 54:1592 (1965).

BRINTON, C. C., JR. Contributions of Pili to the Specificity of the Bacterial Surface. In *The Specificity of Cell Surfaces.* (B. D. Davis and L. Warren, eds.) Prentice-Hall, Englewood Cliffs, N.J., 1966.

DUGUID, J. P., and WILKINSON, J. F. Environmentally Induced Changes in Bacterial Morphology. In *Microbial Reaction to Environment* (11th Symposium, Society for General Microbiology), p. 69. Cambridge Univ. Press, London, 1961.

RYTER, A., and LANDMAN, O. E. Electron microscope study of the relationships between mesosome loss and the stable L state (or protoplast state) in *Bacillus subtilis. J. Bact.* 8:457 (1964).

SELECTED REFERENCES: CLASSIFICATION

Books and Review Articles

Bergey's Manual of Determinative Bacteriology, 7th ed. (R. S. Breed, E. G. D. Murray, and N. R. Smith, eds.) Williams & Wilkins, Baltimore, 1957. 1094 pp.

MARMUR, J., FALKOW, S., and MANDEL, M. New approaches to bacterial taxonomy. *Ann. Rev. Microbiol.* *17*:329 (1963).

Microbial Classification (12th Symposium, Society for General Microbiology; G. C. Ainsworth and P. H. A. Sneath, eds.). Cambridge Univ. Press, London, 1962.

SKERMAN, U. B. D. *A Guide to the Identification of the Genera of Bacteria.* Williams & Wilkins, Baltimore, 1959. 217 pp.; a useful set of diagnostic keys, intended as a companion to *Bergey's Manual.*

Symposium: La notion d'espèce bacterienne à la lumière des découvertes récentes. *Ann. Inst. Pasteur* *94*:137 (1958).

VAN NIEL, C. B. Classification and Taxonomy of the Bacteria and Blue-green Algae. In *A Century of Progress in the Natural Sciences.* California Academy of Science, San Francisco, 1955.

The immediate principles of living bodies would be, to a degree, indestructible if, of all the organisms created by God, the smallest and apparently most useless were to be suppressed. And because the return to the atmosphere and to the mineral kingdom of everything which had ceased to live would be suddenly suspended, life would become impossible. LOUIS PASTEUR

3 ENERGY PRODUCTION

From man's point of view the most interesting function of a given microbe may be to cause a disease, or to form a desired chemical compound. From its own point of view, however, the basic function of a microbe is simply to grow, in one or another environment. In thus filling all possible ecological niches the microbial world has evolved members that thrive on the most remarkably different diets; and by thus attacking all manner of compounds microbes play an essential geochemical role in the cycle of organic matter. But whatever the fuel used, the useful energy derived from its consumption is converted into the universal currency of metabolic energy transfer, adenosine triphosphate (ATP); hence the study of energy metabolism is the study of ATP production.

As was noted in Chapter 1, in biological evolution fermentation preceded the more efficient process of respiration,* which yields several times as much ATP per mole of substrate; respiration could evolve only after the appearance of oxygen in the terrestrial atmosphere. The less efficient fermentative way of life persists, however, in many microbes, because microbes in general must have an aqueous environment for growth—and in a body of water only a thin surface layer can receive a rapid supply of oxygen from the atmosphere. Hence long before bacteriologists developed the technology necessary to ensure strict anaerobiosis in the laboratory, prescientific men discovered the occurrence of fer-

* The term fermentation here refers to an energy-yielding rearrangement of the atoms of organic substrates, without net oxidation, while respiration refers to the net oxidation of substrates at the expense of molecular oxygen. Modified uses of the terms will be noted below.

mentation in the depths of sugar-rich fluids such as grape juice.

While respiration, when complete, yields only uninteresting products (CO_2 and H_2O), fermentations yield various organic compounds in large amounts. As noted in Chapter 1, these differ from one organism to another; and their identification, starting even before Pasteur, was the first stage in the study of microbial metabolism. Only much later (after 1930) were methods developed for dissecting the individual enzymatic reactions of both fermentation and respiration. These methods involved simplification of the experimental system, progressing from growing cultures to nongrowing (resting) cells; then cells with damage to their membranes (e.g., toluene-treated) to remove permeability barriers; then cell-free extracts (prepared by grinding with abrasives, sonic oscillation, explosion by sudden release of pressure, or enzymatic attack on the wall); and finally fractionation of the extracts to yield isolated (often crystalline) enzymes. Fortunately, many enzymes are just as active in the artificial extracellular environment as in the cells, and a wealth of results has generated confidence in the physiological significance of the properties of enzymes seen in solution.

In this chapter we shall focus on the variety of energy-yielding patterns that have evolved, and on the key reactions that provide metabolically useful energy; for further details the reader is referred to a textbook of biochemistry. We shall find that organisms of medical interest, which grow in the same environments as mammalian cells, also have the same central pathways (glycolysis and terminal respiration). To broaden acquaintanceship with the microbial world we shall also consider briefly certain other energy-yielding pathways, essential for maintaining the biosphere, that are seen only in nonpathogens (e.g., photosynthesis, chemosynthesis).

FERMENTATIONS

Pasteur defined fermentation as **life without air;** and he recognized that metabolic energy is derived, in this remarkable process, by the organism's "property of performing its res-

piratory functions, somehow or other, with the oxygen existing combined in sugar." This chapter will be largely concerned with the "somehow or other." But first we should note that a more sophisticated definition of fermentation is now required because of the later discovery of **anaerobic respiration,** a mode of metabolism that depends on a fundamentally respiratory mechanism but is anaerobic, O_2 being replaced by another inorganic electron acceptor such as nitrate or sulfate. Fermentation is therefore now better defined as **metabolism in which energy is derived from the use of organic compounds as both the electron donors and the electron acceptors.**

A fermentation must balance: since there is no net oxidation, the number of moles of C, H, and O must be the same in the products as in substrates (including water, and with a small correction for assimilation into cell constituents). For example:

$$C_6H_{12}O_6 \longrightarrow 2\,C_3H_6O_3 \quad (CH_3CHOHCOOH)$$

Glucose　　　　　　　　　　　Lactic acid

or

$$C_6H_{12}O_6 \longrightarrow 2\,CH_3CH_2OH + 2\,CO_2$$

Ethanol

The anaerobic conditions required for fermentation are easily achieved with liquid media. In the laboratory it is convenient to use bottles completely filled and provided with loose glass stoppers, to allow venting of any gas that may be produced. In industry deep vats, incubated without agitation, provide sufficient anaerobiosis; oxygen at the surface does not penetrate far, and in the gas phase above the surface it may be displaced by the heavier CO_2 evolved. (In industrial jargon the term fermentation is loosely extended to any large-scale process catalyzed by microbes, even when the process involves strong aeration, as in antibiotic production.)

The Source of Energy in Fermentation

The energetics of fermentation may be considered from several points of view. In **thermodynamic** terms fermentations proceed because the product(s) have a lower energy content than the substrates. Thus the molar free energy content of glucose exceeds that of its fully oxidized products (6 CO_2 + 6 H_2O) by 688 Kcal, while the difference be-

tween glucose and 2 moles of lactic acid is 58 Kcal. The latter difference would theoretically be sufficient to allow the generation of about 7 moles of high-energy (ATP) phosphate from ADP + P_i (inorganic phosphate) (ΔF = ca. 8 Kcal) per mole of glucose.

In terms of **chemical bond energy** fermentations are generally based on the regrouping of H and O atoms, from hydroxyl and carbonyl groups, to yield the lower-energy carboxyl group. This may be retained in an organic acid, as in the lactic fermentation, or freed as CO_2 (HOCOOH), as in the ethanol fermentation.

The oxidation and the reduction of a fermentation may occur in different parts of the same molecule, as in these examples; or they may occur in different molecules, as in the fermentation of glycerol plus fumarate. In the latter process the glycerol is oxidized successively to triose phosphate, pyruvate,* and acetate plus CO_2, at the expense of reduction of fumarate to succinate:

$$HOCH_2\text{-}CHOH\text{-}CH_2OH + H_2O \longrightarrow \longrightarrow$$

$$CH_3COOH + CO_2 + 6\,[H]$$

$$3\,HOOC\text{-}CH{=}CH\text{-}COOH + 6\,[H] \longrightarrow$$

$$3\,HOOC\text{-}CH_2\text{-}CH_2\text{-}COOH$$

Finally, from the point of view of **intermediate metabolism** one might say that the function of a fermentative reaction sequence is to concentrate enough of the over-all energy drop in a single enzymatic reaction to allow linkage with the generation of ATP. Three classes of reactions are widely used for this purpose. The simplest (class 1) is the conversion of a low-energy phosphate ester to an enol-phosphate, whose hydrolysis to a free carbonyl group releases enough energy to per-

---

* For organic acids terms such as pyruvic acid and pyruvate will generally be used interchangeably in this volume; and for the sake of simplicity the formula will be generally written as the free acid, though at the usual pHs organic acids are largely ionized.

mit transfer of the phosphate to ADP. Thus in the glycolytic pathway:

$$CH_2\text{-}CH\text{-}COOH \xrightarrow{-H_2O} CH_2 = CH\text{-}COOH$$

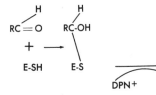

2-P-glycerate*   P-enolpyruvate

$$ATP + CH_3\text{-}C\text{-}COOH$$
$$\phantom{ATP + CH_3\text{-}}O$$

Pyruvate

The other two classes of reaction involve oxidation of a carbonyl to a carboxyl group. The key to the formation of a high-energy group is the preliminary reaction of the carbonyl with an -SH group, which can form a low-energy thiohemiacetal and then be oxidized to a high-energy thioester.

In the oxidative step of the glycolytic pathway (class 2), in which an aldehyde is oxidized, the enzyme (E = aldehyde dehydrogenase) provides the -SH group.

$$\textcircled{P}OCH_2\text{-}CHOH\text{-}CHO + P_i + DPN^+ \longrightarrow$$

3-P-glyceraldehyde

$$\textcircled{P}OCH_2\text{-}CHOH\text{-}COO\textcircled{P} + DPNH + H^+$$

1,3-DiP-glyceric acid

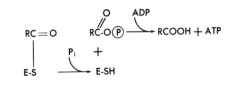

Aldehyde Thiohemiacetal

Thioester   Acid anhydride   Acid

The thiohemiacetal first formed is converted to a thioester by transfer of 2[H] to DPN, which has been adsorbed to an adjacent site on the enzyme; and because the thioester has about the same high-energy level as an acid anhydride, it can be phosphorolyzed by inorganic phosphate (P_i) to yield 1,3-diP-glyceric acid. This compound, in turn, can transfer the phosphate from its phosphate-carboxyl anhydride to ADP, forming a phosphate-phosphate anhydride in ATP.

The third class of reactions for creating a $\sim$P involves conversion of a ketone to a carboxyl group. In this reaction the carbonyl carbon must, of course, be split from an adjacent carbon. α-Keto acids are activated for this purpose by combining with thiamine pyrophosphate (TPP). In some organisms pyruvate (complexed with TPP) is split through the action of the enzyme **pyruvate transacetylase,** which transfers the acetyl group to (CoA)-SH (coenzyme A) and frees the remainder as formic acid:

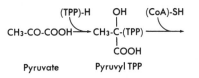

Pyruvate   Pyruvyl TPP

$$CH_3\text{-}CO\text{-}S(CoA) + HCOOH + (TPP)\text{-}H$$

Acetyl CoA   Formate

Here the -SH group of CoA functions like the -SH group of the enzyme in the preceding reaction, forming a high-energy bond when the initial thiohemiacetal of the complex is oxidized (not depicted) to the thioester, acetyl CoA. Phosphorolysis of this compound by P_i, as in the preceding reaction, yields a $\sim$P in acetyl phosphate, which is then transferred to ADP to yield ATP.

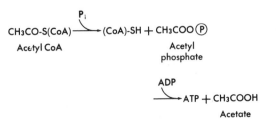

Acetyl CoA   Acetyl phosphate

Acetate

In some organisms, however, such as *Escherichia coli,* this **phosphoroclastic reaction,** in which pyruvate is in effect split by phosphate to yield acetyl phosphate and formate, appears to occur by an incompletely understood mechanism which does not involve CoA.

In another sequence, observed in other fermentative organisms (and regularly in oxidative metabolism), pyruvyl TPP is oxidized by **pyruvate oxidase** to acetate and CO_2. This process involves a larger number of steps. Elimination of CO_2 leaves "active acetaldehyde" attached to TPP; this two-carbon fragment is oxidized by lipoic acid; and the resulting acetyl group is transferred to CoA. The acetyl CoA yields ATP as above, and the reduced lipoic is reoxidized by DPN, the electron acceptor for this oxidation.

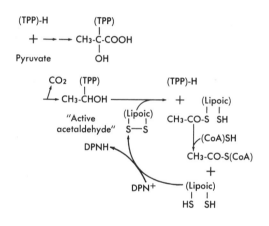

Coenzymes; Ferredoxin

The reactions of bacterial fermentations and respiration employ a variety of cofactors (coenzymes) identical with those found in mammalian tissues. These substances, of relatively low molecular weight and high thermostability, were initially distinguished from enzymes because they could often be removed from extracts by dialysis, with consequent loss of enzymatic activity; and activity could be restored to the "resolved" enzymes by supplying the coenzyme-containing supernatant from an extract in which the enzymes had been denatured by boiling (Kochsaft). Such familiar cofactors include coenzyme A for acyl transfer; thiamine pyrophosphate for transferring groups derived from a ketone (e.g., decarboxylation of α-keto acids, or the transketolase reaction of ketoses described in

Ch. 4); biotin for CO_2 transfer; lipoic acid, DPN, TPN, riboflavin derivatives, and cytochromes for hydrogen or electron transfer; and, of course, ATP for phosphate and energy transfer. In addition, various biosynthetic reactions (Ch. 4) employ pyridoxal phosphate for amino acid transamination, decarboxylation, and racemization; tetrahydrofolate for 1-carbon group transfer; and cobamide (from vitamin B_{12}, cobalamin) in methyl group transfers and certain reductions.

These cofactors could not account for those reactions that occur at a very low redox (oxidation-reduction) potential: for example, the release of H_2 gas by certain anaerobes (clostridia) or the utilization of H_2 as a fuel for respiration by other bacteria (Autotrophic metabolism, below). These processes evidently require biological catalysis of the reaction of the hydrogen electrode:

$$2H^+ + 2\textcircled{e} \rightleftharpoons H_2$$

The mechanism was revealed when Mortenson, in 1962, discovered a new iron-containing cofactor, **ferredoxin**, with a remarkably low standard redox potential (-417 mv), similar to that of the H_2 electrode. The addition of ferredoxin made possible the utilization and the formation of H_2 by appropriate extracts. And though ferredoxin was discovered in connection with rather specialized reactions of anaerobic bacteria, similar coenzymes have now been found in many bacteria and in higher plants. They have been shown in vitro to participate in various fundamental processes, including photosynthesis and nitrogen fixation (see below).

The ferredoxins are small proteins, M.W. 5,000 to 10,000. The Fe is complexed with a labile form of S, which readily yields H_2S; and this attachment to such a strongly reducing group evidently contributes to the low redox potential. As we shall see below, in cytochromes the Fe of heme exhibits a variety of redox potentials, up to that of O_2 when attached to different proteins. Nature has thus adapted the $Fe^{++} \rightleftharpoons Fe^{+++}$ system to the entire range of

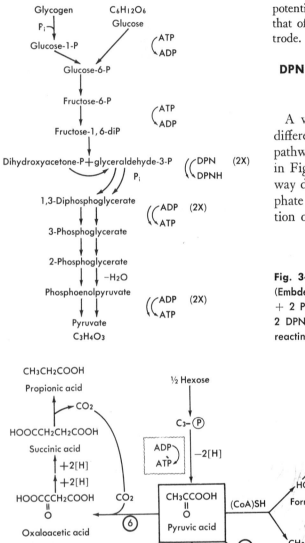

potentials encountered in aqueous systems, from that of the H_2 electrode to that of the O_2 electrode.

DPN Regeneration and the Key Role of Pyruvate

A variety of fermentations, yielding quite different products, are based on the glycolytic pathway, which is presented, up to pyruvate, in Figure 3-1. ATP generation in this pathway depends on the oxidation of triose phosphate to an acid, at the expense of the reduction of DPN^+. Since the total DPN in the

Fig. 3-1 The glycolytic formation of pyruvate (Embden-Meyerhof pathway). Sum: Glucose + 2 ADP + 2 Pi + 2 DPN^+ ⟶ 2 Pyruvate + 2 ATP + 2 DPNH + $2H^+$. Double arrows signify two moles reacting per mole of glucose.

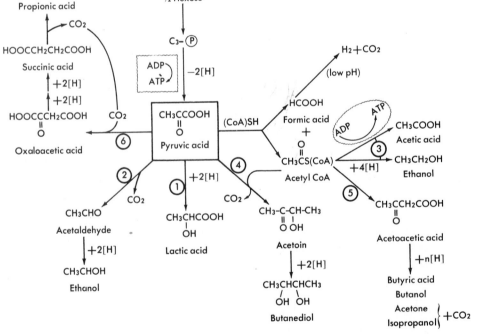

Fig. 3-2 *Key role of pyruvate in principal fermentations.* **Principal fermentations. 1.** Lactic (*Streptococcus, Lactobacillus*) **2.** Alcoholic (Many yeasts, few bacteria) **3.** Mixed acid (*Enterobacteriaceae* including *Aerobacter*) **4.** Butanediol (*Aerobacter*) **5.** Butyric (*Clostridium*) **6.** Propionic (propionic acid bacteria).

cell is very limited, fermentation would cease very rapidly if the reduced form of DPN were not reoxidized in a further reaction of pyruvate. Microbes have evolved a variety of pathways for this purpose, some of which also yield additional ATP. These pathways are illustrated in Figure 3-2.

Lactic Fermentation. This is the simplest fermentation: a one-step reaction, catalyzed by a DPN-linked lactic dehydrogenase (really a pyruvate reductase), reduces pyruvate to lactate, and no gas is formed. Since 2 ATPs are consumed in the formation of hexose diphosphate from glucose, and since 4 ATPs are subsequently produced, the net yield is two ATP per hexose. This fermentation is identical with the glycolysis of mammalian cells.

This **homolactic** fermentation, which forms only lactate, is characteristic of many of the lactic acid bacteria (e.g., rods such as *Lactobacillus casei;* cocci such as *Streptococcus cremoris*). Other members of this group carry out a rather different, **heterolactic** fermentation (Phosphogluconic fermentations, below), which converts only half of each glucose molecule to lactate. These lactic fermentations are responsible for the souring of milk and certain other foods; and such acidification, achieved at the expense of some carbohydrate energy, preserves food from further decomposition as long as it is kept anaerobic. The accompanying changes in flavor also add to the economic importance of these fermentations. Examples include cheeses, sauerkraut, and ensilage. The homolactic fermentation occurs in certain pathogens, the streptococci and pneumococci, which are included by taxonomists among the lactic acid bacteria.

Alcoholic Fermentation. Pyruvate (activated by TPP) is converted by pyruvate decarboxylase to CO_2 (retained in some beverages) plus acetaldehyde, which is then reduced to ethanol in a DPN-linked reaction. This fermentation is characteristic of yeasts; as a major pathway it is uncommon in bacteria. Its economic and social value in the leavening of bread, as well as in the formation of beverages, has been recognized for millennia.

Propionic Fermentation. This pathway illustrates a method for extracting even more energy from a given amount of substrate. Pyruvate is carboxylated to yield oxaloacetate, which undergoes two reductions to yield succinate; and this compound is decarboxylated (after activation by CoA) to yield propionate.* The over-all process takes up 4[H] per pyruvate. Since only 2 are required to balance the oxidation of triose to pyruvate, 2 are left over to balance a further oxidation. Hence for each 2 pyruvates reduced to propionate a third pyruvate can be formed from triose ($-2[H]$) and then oxidized to acetate and CO_2 ($-2[H]$ more). This oxidation is associated, as noted above, with the generation (via acetyl CoA) of an ATP.

Organisms possessing this pathway can eke out a living by fermenting lactate, the end-product of another fermentation. The lactate is first oxidized to pyruvate; part is then reduced to propionate and the rest oxidized to acetate and CO_2.

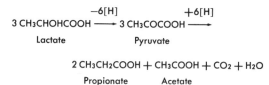

This arduous process of extracting energy from lactate, by the over-all conversion of 3 hydroxyls to 1 carboxyl, yields only 1 ATP per 9 carbons fermented. Hence propionic acid bacteria, which are closely related morphologically and metabolically to the corynebacteria (such as the diphtheria bacillus), grow slowly. In Swiss cheese their late formation of CO_2, after the completion of the lactic fermentation of milk by other organisms, is responsible for the formation of the holes, while the propionic acid formed contributes to the flavor.

The mixed acid fermentation noted immediately below also involves reduction of pyruvate to succinate, but not the subsequent decarboxylation to proprionate. To ferment lactate, however, this decarboxylation is essential; if 2 succinates

---

* The decarboxylation is accomplished via a novel, cobamide-linked reaction, in which succinyl CoA is rearranged to form the less stable methylmalonyl CoA [CH₃ CH(COOH)CO—CoA]. This compound is then split to yield propionyl CoA and CO_2.

were formed instead of 2 propionates there would be a deficit of CO_2. The precious CO_2 is efficiently conserved in the propionate fermentation by the use of a novel enzyme, transcarboxylase, which does not free the CO_2 derived from the dicarboxylic acid but instead transfers it directly to pyruvate (Fig. 3-2). The evidence for such transcarboxylation is that radioactivity from carboxyl-labeled succinate fails to mix with a free CO_2 pool.

Mixed Acid (Formic) Fermentation. This fermentation is characteristic of most enteric bacteria, as well as many related species found on vegetation. While these organisms dispose of part of their substrate through a lactic fermentation, most of it usually goes through a fermentation characterized by the splitting of pyruvate to an acetyl group and formate (p. 58). By releasing acetyl groups as acetate (via acetyl CoA and acetyl P) an extra ATP is generated. However, this reaction does not absorb the 2[H] released in forming that pyruvate; and to achieve fermentation balance an equal amount of pyruvate is reduced by pathways absorbing more [H]. (a) Part is reduced, via acetyl CoA, to ethanol; and (b) part is reduced, after carboxylation, to succinate (as in the propionic fermentation).

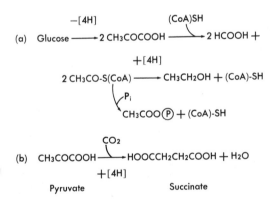

Either process consumes 4[H] per pyruvate reduced. The formic fermentation thus yields 3 ATP per glucose fermented (compared with 2 in the lactic fermentation).

While the formate from this fermentation

may remain as such if the pH is kept alkaline, most fermentations become acidic; and at a pH of 6 or less *E. coli* is induced to form an enzyme system, **formic hydrogenlyase,** which converts formic acid to CO_2 and H_2, thus producing copious gas.

$$HCOOH \longrightarrow H_2 + CO_2$$

This reaction is the source of the gas formed in most bacterial fermentations in the laboratory and in the gut. CO_2, being highly soluble in water, is readily removed in the body; but H_2 is quite insoluble, and is accumulated in the tissues in the gas gangrene caused by certain clostridia.

Butylene Glycol (Acetoin) Fermentation. This is a variant of the formic fermentation, observed in *Aerobacter*. A pyruvate takes up 2[H] to yield formate plus a 2-carbon fragment at the oxidation level of "active acetaldehyde." This fragment condenses with a second pyruvate, and the endproduct undergoes decarboxylation to yield acetoin, followed by reduction (by DPNH) to 2, 3-butylene glycol (butanediol). The total of 4[H] absorbed balances the 2 pyruvates consumed.

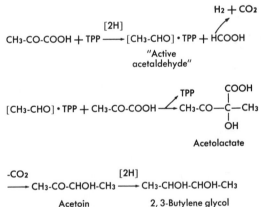

This fermentation, like the alcoholic fermentation, yields only neutral products and produces 2 ATP per glucose. It is often called the acetoin fermentation because exposure to air oxidizes some of the butylene glycol to acetoin, which is readily recognized by a specific color test (Voges-Proskauer). This test is of considerable diagnostic value (Ch. 20), for in sanitary engineering it is of prime importance to discriminate between *E. coli,* primarily from the mammalian gut, and *Aerobacter,* primarily from vegetation.

The formation of neutral rather than acidic products permits the fermentation of larger amounts of carbohydrate and therefore the production of more gas; hence the name *Aerobacter aerogenes.*

Butyric-Butylic Fermentation. This represents still another way of achieving the reduction of pyruvate. Following a scission that yields H_2 two 2-carbon fragments are condensed, not head-to-head as in acetoin, but head-to-tail as in fatty acid metabolism. The resulting acetoacetyl CoA is decarboxylated and/or reduced, yielding acetone, isopropanol, butyric acid, and *n*-butanol, in varying proportions.[*]

Mixed Amino Acid Fermentations. These lack the economic importance of the above fermentations, and they have accordingly received less attention. They are prominent, however, in putrefactive processes, including the gangrene associated with anaerobic wound infections. In these fermentations, which occur where there is considerable proteolysis, certain amino acids (or their deamination products) serve as electron donors and others as acceptors. For example:

$$CH_3\text{-}CHNH_2\text{-}COOH + 2\,CH_2NH_2\text{-}COOH + 2\,H_2O \longrightarrow$$

   Alanine   Glycine

$$3\,CH_3\text{-}COOH + CO_2 + NH_3$$

              Acetate

---

[*] The use of this fermentation for the industrial production of acetone was developed by Chaim Weizmann in England in 1915. This scientific contribution, which solved an urgent problem in explosives manufacture in World War I, is said to have promoted the Balfour Declaration, and thus contributed eventually to the founding of the state of Israel, with Weizmann as its first president.

Accompanying decarboxylations increase the volatility of the products, which include such malodorous nitrogenous compounds as indole (from the breakdown of tryptophan) and even more mephitic -SH compounds derived from cysteine and methionine. More pleasant, empirically selected fermentations of minor constituents are responsible for the characteristic flavors of various wines and cheeses; while on the other hand the toxic effect of poorly fermented wines is largely due to longer-chain aldehydes (fusel oil) derived from amino acids.

Phosphogluconic Pathways. The use of glucose labeled in specific carbon atoms confirmed the Embden-Meyerhof pathway for many organisms by showing that the CO_2 (or the -COOH group of lactate) came from C-3 and C-4 of glucose (Fig. 3-3, pathway A). Not all fermentations, however, proceed via this pathway. For example, the **heterolactic** (see p. 61) fermenters (e.g., *Leuconostoc mesenteroides*) yield approximately equimolar quantities of lactate, ethanol, and CO_2. This proportionality was explained by isotopic evidence that the CO_2 is derived from C-1 of glucose, the ethanol from C-2,3, and the lactate from the rest. Enzymatic studies then revealed pathway B of Figure 3-3, in which the CO_2 is formed by the decarboxylation of P-gluconate, and the ethanol is formed by the reduction of acetyl phosphate.

The acetyl phosphate is formed by an unusual reaction, catalyzed by phosphoketolase plus thiamine pyrophosphate, in which the C-1,2 (a ketol) of a pentose phosphate is cleaved and rearranged, with the uptake of inorganic phosphate.

Many pseudomonads have developed still another fermentative pathway, (Entner-Doudoroff pathway), whose existence was revealed by the novel distribution of isotopes in the fermentation products: oxidation of glucose-6-P to 6-P-gluconate is followed by conversion to *2-keto-3-deoxy-6-P-gluconate,* which is then cleaved to yield pyruvate and triose-P pathway C, Fig. 3-3). This pathway also appears in some organisms (e.g., *E. coli*) when growing on gluconate (which is first converted to 6-P-gluconate), but not on hexoses. This fermentation of cactus juice by the bacterium *Pseudomonas lindneri* was put to use by Mexican Indians even before the Aztecs to make the beverage pulque.

Pentose phosphate formation by oxidation of P-gluconate (the first part of pathway B, Fig.

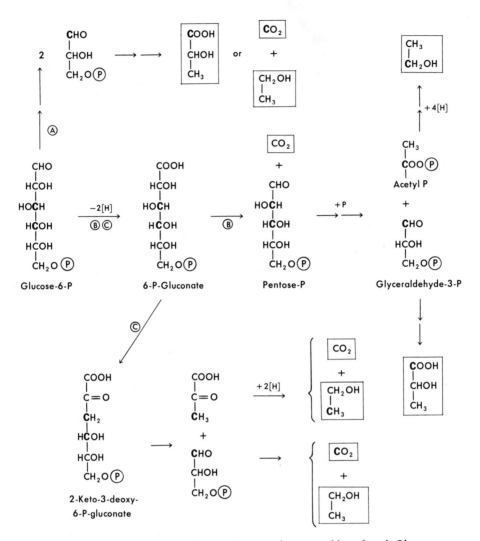

Fig. 3-3 Alternative ways of metabolizing glucose to lactate and/or ethanol. Glucose-3,4-14C yields alcohol labeled in neither C atom (Embden-Meyerhof pathway, **A**), or in the CH_2OH (heterolactic pathway, **B**), or in the CH_3 (Entner-Doudoroff pathway, **C**).

3-3) also provides the nucleic acid pentose in most organisms (Ch. 4); and as we shall see below, in autotrophic organisms a pentose phosphate cycle is responsible for CO_2 fixation (Fig. 3-6). Moreover, in many organisms some of the pentose phosphate molecules derived from hexose are converted to fructose phosphate by a series of transfers of 2-C and 3-C fragments (the reverse of those shown in Fig. 4-20). With labeled hexose this auxiliary pathway (*"hexose monophosphate shunt"*) modifies the isotope distribution expected from the Embden-Meyerhof pathway.

The Adaptive Value of Various Fermentations

The central role of the glycolytic pathway in many different fermentations illustrates the unity of biology at a molecular level, and reflects the evolutionary principle of selection for the most effective mechanism possible. The diversity of final products of these fermentations, on the other hand, reflects the variety of ecological opportunities available, which select for different variants of the basic mechanism. The basis of this selection can perhaps be understood if we consider the kinds of selective media provided in Nature.

We have already considered in Chapter 1 the factors, some of which were recognized by Pasteur, that are responsible for the outgrowth of yeasts in grape juice and lactic acid bacteria in milk. Grape juice is much richer in sugar but poorer in protein (i.e., buffering power) and in amino acids. Lactic acid bacteria will not proceed very far in the fermentation of grape juice, since they are sensitive to the low pH that is soon produced, and they may run out of the numerous amino acids that they require. Hence they are outgrown by the slower-growing yeasts, which are less sensitive to acid and also nutritionally less fastidious. In milk, however, the faster-growing bacteria can continue to outgrow the yeasts until the exhaustion of the sugar ends the fermentation.

Enteric organisms show a similar adaptation to their environment. The gut is largely anaerobic; and since its absorptive properties leave only a dilute solution of amino acids and sugar in its lower regions, it should select for an organism that has no specific growth requirements and that extracts as much energy as possible from its fermentation. These are the properties of *E. coli.* In contrast *Aerobacter,* which grows primarily on vegetation, can ferment larger concentrations of carbohydrate than *E. coli* before reaching a limiting pH, but with a less efficient energy yield. It is evident that Nature selects for a variety of fermentative talents, which might be compared with sprinters and long-distance runners.

RESPIRATION

Aerobic and Anaerobic Metabolism

Bacteria fall into several groups with respect to the effect of oxygen on their growth and their metabolism.

1) **Obligate aerobes** (e.g., the tubercle bacillus and some spore-forming bacilli) require oxygen and lack the capacity for substantial fermentation.

2) **Obligate anaerobes** (e.g., clostridia, Propionibacter) can grow only in the absence of oxygen. A subgroup, called **microaerophilic,** can tolerate or even prefer O_2 at a low tension, but not at that of air.

3) **Facultative organisms** can grow with or without air. (These are often called facultative anaerobes, but they could equally well be called facultative aerobes.) In the presence of air some (e.g., most lactic acid bacteria) continue to maintain an essentially fermentative metabolism, while others (e.g., many yeasts and Enterobacteriaceae such as *E. coli*) shift to a respiratory metabolism.

We shall consider later some special groups that depend on autotrophic metabolism or on anaerobic respiration.

While it is not certain why the addition of oxygen prevents anaerobes from continuing to ferment and grow, the probable mechanism is the maintenance of certain enzymes in an oxidized state which prevents them from carrying out an essential reductive reaction. For example, succinate is required for the biosynthesis of several amino acids, and in facultative organisms this compound is synthesized under aerobic conditions by the oxidation of α-ketoglutarate in the tricarboxylate cycle; but anaerobically succinate is made by reduction of fumarate, through reversal of part of the cycle (as we have seen in the propionic and the succinic fermentations, Fig. 3-2). In an *E. coli* mutant that has lost α-ketoglutarate oxidase anaerobic growth is still normal, but the addition of oxygen immediately stops growth unless succinate or its biosynthetic products are provided. Oxygen thus "poisons" the flavoprotein fumarate reductase, presumably by keeping it too completely oxidized.

Since organisms well adapted to anaerobic life would have no use for a full tricarboxylic acid cycle they presumably resemble the *E. coli* mutant in making succinate only by the reductive route; hence they are inhibited by O_2.

Some obligate anaerobes (especially clostridia) not only are inhibited but actually are killed by the presence of oxygen. The reason is not certain; since anaerobes generally lack catalase they may be poisoned by accumulated hydrogen peroxide, formed by their flavoproteins in the presence of air.

Respiratory Components. Obligate aerobes, and those facultative organisms that shift in air to a respiratory metabolism, contain a complete **electron transport** chain in which electrons flow from DPNH (or directly from very few substrates, such as succinate or lactate) to a flavoprotein, and thence via several cytochromes to oxygen; ATP is generated in the accompanying process of **oxidative phosphorylation.** The cytochromes are absent, however, from the strict anaerobes that depend on fermentative metabolism, as well as from those facultative organisms that remain essentially fermentative in the presence of air.

The latter organisms, nevertheless, carry out in the presence of air a limited repiration. *Lactobacillus delbrueckii,* for example, can oxidize glucose via glucose-6-phosphate to 6-phosphogluconic acid through a flavoprotein, which in turn is directly reoxidized by air. This short respiratory chain yields little or no ATP and hence is a far cry from true respiratory metabolism. However, such a pathway may serve to scavenge dissolved oxygen and thus to make anaerobic growth possible.

Oxygenases carry out a small class of oxidative reactions in which oxygen is transferred directly to the substrate. These reactions do not yield ATP; but they convert a refractory compound to one that is useful, either for structural purposes (e.g., saturated → unsaturated fatty acids, see Ch. 4) or for profitable further metabolism. An example of the latter is the utilization of various benzenoid compounds by pseudomonads via the reaction sequence:

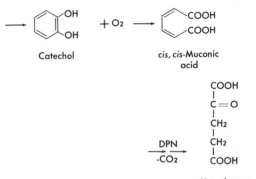

Catechol   cis, cis-Muconic acid

α-Ketoglutarate

Electron Transport and Oxidative Phosphorylation

In most bacteria, as in higher organisms, the respiratory utilization of glucose depends on the oxidation of pyruvate to acetyl CoA

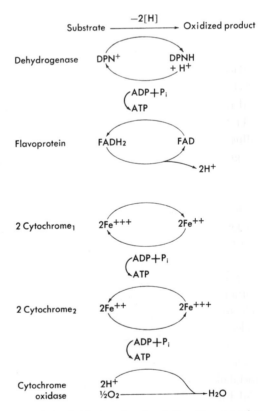

Fig. 3-4 Oxidative phosphorylation. The steps that produce oxidative phosphorylation in the electron transport chain (P/O = 3).

+ CO_2 by pyruvate oxidase (p. 59); the acetate is then oxidized to CO_2 and H_2O in one turn of the tricarboxylate cycle (Ch. 4, Fig. 4-6). Each oxidative reaction in these several processes, and in the preceding formation of pyruvate, is accomplished at the expense of the reduction of DPN to DPNH (except that succinate oxidation is coupled directly to reduction of a flavoprotein). Just as in fermentation, the DPNH must be regenerated to DPN if metabolism is to continue; and this is accomplished at the expense of the reduction of O_2 to H_2O. The large amount of energy thus released (effectively, that of burning H_2 gas) is used to form 3 molecules of ATP per 2[H] oxidized. This oxidative phosphorylation is believed to occur at three stages in electron transport, shown in Figure 3-4, which are each associated with a sufficient energy drop.

In a sense, every dehydrogenation represents electron transport; for DPN can be shown to accept directly only 1 of the 2 hydrogens removed from a labeled substrate, the other donating an electron and thus forming a hydrogen ion:

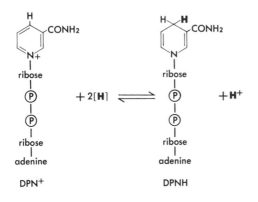

The pathway under consideration, however, involves pure electron transport, as no H can be accepted directly by the cytochromes; these are heme proteins which undergo a reversible 1-electron oxidation ($Fe^{++} \rightleftharpoons Fe^{+++} + e$).

The Cytochrome Sequence. The study of bacterial cytochromes rests heavily on earlier studies of the cytochromes from animal muscle. These were initially labeled a, b, and c by Keilin, being differentiated by the position of the peak in the absorption spectrum of the reduced form.

Cytochrome a was identified with cytochrome oxidase (i.e., the last member of the chain, which interacts directly with O_2), since its spectrum is immediately altered on addition of O_2 and its catalytic activity is inhibited by CO, a competitor of O_2. It contains a somewhat different porphyrin from the others. Cytochrome c is distinguished by being much more stable than the others, and hence more readily isolated; the porphyrin of its heme pigment, in contrast to the other cytochromes, is covalently attached to the protein. The electron transport sequence flavin-b-c-a-O_2 was established by measurements of redox potential of the separated units, and by the spectral responses of the mixture to inhibitors that selectively interrupted the chain at a given point. More refined studies have revealed additional components (e.g., c_1 before c, and a_3 after a in cytochrome oxidase).

It is now believed that the cytochromes in the chain have two kinds of functions: a pair with a large difference in redox potential may be geared to translate the energy drop into ATP production; while adjacent members of the chain, transferring electrons through a smaller potential difference, effect a smooth regeneration of the phosphorylating pair to the initial levels of oxidation. It may thus be helpful, though rather artificial, to view some members of the chain as substrates and others as enzymes.

The pattern in bacteria resembles that in mammalian cells, but with wide variation in the absorption spectrum and the redox potential of the individual cytochromes, and with generally fewer distinguishable components in a given organism. The same heme can possess a wide range of redox potentials, depending on the protein to which it is attached; and it seems quite certain that a given microorganism, possessing cytochromes at several potentials, creates the opportunity for tapping off phosphate-bond energy at an electron transfer step with a suitable potential difference. Furthermore, the successive members of a chain must have not only suitable potentials but also a suitable enzymatic (stereospecific) relation of their surfaces: in vitro, the extracted cytochrome oxidase of certain bacteria has been found to oxidize the cytochrome c of that species much more rapidly than the cytochrome c of beef heart or even that of other bacterial species.

The practice of continuing to name cytochromes as variants on the initial types has unfortunately resulted in a confusing terminology, with numbers up to a_4, b_7, and c_5. This development has depended not only on the temptation to take advantage of a conveniently measured spectrum, but also on the difficulty in precisely delineating the function of a given cytochrome. Thus, for example, an enzymologist isolating aldolase from *E. coli* and from pigeon breast muscle may find marked differences in kinetics, serological specificity, and composition, but the enzyme will be defined by the reaction that it catalyzes. Until the reactions of the individual members of the cytochrome chains of various organisms are more adequately defined, the terminology, with its implications of homology of function, will have an insecure basis.

Organisms carrying out **anaerobic respiration**, with NO_3^- or $SO_4^=$ as electron acceptor, have an extensive set of cytochromes, justifying this paradoxical extension of the term respiration. Ordinary obligate anaerobes lack cytochromes.

Oxidative Phosphorylation. Experiments with mitochondria, isolated from mammalian cells, have led to the estimate of 3 P_i incorporated into ATP per 1/2 O_2 consumed (P/O ratio = 3) (Fig. 3-4). Bacteria, however, do not contain mitochondria, but rather equal them in size; and since intact bacteria or protoplasts (unlike mitochondria) are impermeable to ATP,* they must be disrupted for any studies on oxidative phosphorylation. This fragmentation evidently damages the respiratory apparatus, since the observed P/O ratio, as with damaged mitochondria, rarely

exceeds 1.0. Hence for bacteria the value of 3.0 is inferred from the resemblance of individual components of the electron transport system to those of mammalian cells, rather than from direct observation.

The cytochromes and respiratory enzymes of disrupted bacteria are found in the particulate fraction, whereas most other enzymes are found in the soluble fraction; the two fractions are separated by high-speed centrifugation (e.g., 100,000 × g for 2 hours). The particles with respiratory activity vary widely and continuously in size, and they contain much phospholipid; they thus appear to be artificial fragments of the cell membrane.

Since in either bacteria or mitochondria phosphorylation depends on the spatial relation of components organized within the membrane, including membrane-bound particles, the resulting difficulties in fractionation and reconstitution have slowed the analysis of the mechanism linking electron transport and oxidative phosphorylation. The basic mechanism, however, is probably rather like that observed in the "substrate-level" phosphorylation of fermentation or of a-keto acid oxidation as noted above: spontaneous phosphorylation of a molecule at one level of oxidation in its redox cycle, followed by elevation of the phosphate energy level resulting from an increase in oxidation level of the compound, and then phosphate transfer to yield ATP. There is evidence that the reversibly reducible cofactors in this kind of reaction include a **naphthoquinone** of the **vitamin K** group, and a variety of **benzoquinones** called **ubiquinones** (coenzyme Q). Both groups of quinones are abundant in various bacteria, and both have a long alkyl side chain, which presumably contributes to their localization in the lipid-rich membrane.

Flavoprotein Linkage to O_2. This group of cofactors of oxidation was discovered by Warburg on the basis of simple observations on lactobacilli. Because these organisms lack the red cytochromes, the shift in absorption spectrum of their flavins (L. *flavus*, "yellow") on exposure to air causes the intact cells to become yellow. Pursuit of the yellow substance led to the isolation of glucose-6-phosphate dehydrogenase (originally called the "yellow enzyme"), and later

---

* An exception is provided by the rickettsiae, small intracellular parasites which appear to be able to use directly ATP provided by the host cell.

other flavoproteins were discovered in all kinds of biological material. Some enzymes were found to use riboflavin phosphate (FMP, flavin mono-phosphate) and others flavin adenine dinucleo-tide (FAD).

It is a general property of flavoproteins, in extracts, to be directly oxidizable by air, though those from fully respiring organisms are oxidized much more rapidly when connected to oxygen via the cytochrome chain. We do not know whether the energy-wasting direct bypass to oxygen is an in vitro artifact or whether it con-tributes to the metabolism of the cell under some circumstances. This short-circuited electron trans-port usually results in the reduction of O_2 to H_2O_2 (hydrogen peroxide) rather than to H_2O. While there are some enzymes (peroxidases) that can use H_2O_2 for valuable oxidations, in most biological systems this toxic material is immediately destroyed by catalase. The lactic acid bacteria characteristically lack catalase; and it has been inferred that their growth on aerobic plates is promoted by blood because of its con-tent of catalase. Some streptococci, called viri-dans (L., "green"), form a diagnostically im-portant ring of green pigment on blood agar plates, the color being due to oxidation of the porphyrin of hemoglobin to a bile pigment by H_2O_2.

A curious accompaniment of respiration in certain bacteria, as in some higher forms, is the production of **bioluminescence** by the oxidation of a flavoprotein by O_2 in the presence of an appropriate enzyme, luciferase. The social value of bioluminescence for a fish or a firefly is not hard to imagine, but one is tempted to conclude that in bacteria it must be a purely adventitious concomitant of a primitive respiratory system. Because light production will respond to even very low concentrations of O_2, luminescent bac-teria have proved useful as delicate detectors of O_2 in solution.

The Energetics of Respiration

The yield of useful energy from respiration is presented in Table 3-1. It is seen that res-piration is considerably more efficient than glycolysis: not only does it yield about 10 times as much free energy (ΔF) from glu-cose, but the fraction of the energy retained in ATP is also greater, resulting in 19 times as much ATP per mole of glucose metabo-lized. If we accept 8000 cal as the current market value for the ΔF of ATP $\rightleftharpoons$ ADP + P_i, cellular respiration exhibits rather high efficiency, converting about 45% of the total free energy released into the metabolically useful form of ATP, while fermentation con-verts about 25%. The rest, plus part of the

TABLE 3-1. ENERGETICS OF METABOLISM

Reaction	No. of ATP generated	$-\Delta F$ (cal)	$-\Delta F$/ATP
Glucose → 2 lactic acid	2	58,000	29,000
Glucose → 2 ethanol + 2 CO_2	2	57,000	29,000
Glucose + 6 O_2 → 6 CO_2 + H_2O Stages:			
—[4H] Glucose → 2 pyruvate (substrate)	2		
(2 DPN)	6		
—[4H] → 2 AcCoA + 2 CO_2 (2 DPN)	6		
—[16H] → 4 CO_2 + 4 H_2O (8 DPN)	24		
Total	38	688,000	18,000

ATP energy subsequently used in biosynthesis, appears as heat. Indeed, dissipation of heat is one of the major problems of large-scale fermentation; if inadequate, a fermentation may sterilize itself.

Because of this difference in $\sim$ P yield, a facultative organism grown on a limited amount of glucose will exhibit a larger growth yield (dry weight of bacteria/weight of substrate metabolized) under aerobic than under anaerobic conditions; but the increase will be close to 3- to 5-fold, rather than the 19-fold that might superficially be expected from the data of Table 3-1. The major reason is that part of the substrate taken up is assimilated rather than used to yield energy: in fermentation the growth yield represents an almost negligible fraction ($<10\%$) of the substrate consumed, whereas in respiration it may reach, with yeast, as much as 2/3.

Even with cells that are not growing (for lack of a N source) this **oxidative assimilation** may take up 1/3 or more of the substrate, which is converted to **storage materials.** These are predominantly fat or carbohydrates, depending on the species and conditions; and such storage is more prominent in yeasts than in bacteria. Many bacteria form a unique storage product, **poly-β-hydroxybutyric acid,** which is an incompletely reduced, highly polymerized equivalent of fat. This substance is intermediate in composition $(C_2H_3O_2)_n$, and in energy content, between fat and carbohydrate $(CH_2O)_n$; it is presumably more readily available than fat as a reserve material.

2n CH₃-C-S(CoA) → → (—OCH—CH₂—C—)ₙ

Acetyl CoA   Poly-β-hydroxybutyrate

Respiratory patterns of metabolism are influenced by the tendency of some organisms to carry out the early stages faster than the late ones. *E. coli,* for example, growing aerobically on glucose, will at first oxidize this substance only as far as acetate and CO_2, yielding about 40% of the possible ATP; only after acetic acid is heavily accumulated will it begin to be metabolized via the TCA cycle. The reasons for this preferential utilization of glucose are not clear.

The Pasteur Effect. Pasteur discovered that though the admission of air increased the rate and the yield of growth of yeast on glucose, and though it should obviously increase the completeness of the conversion of the substrate to CO_2, it actually decreased the **rate** of evolution of CO_2 and of glucose utilization. This apparently paradoxical observation has been the subject of a large literature, and the problem is still not entirely settled. In modern terms we would say that it represents a reasonable control mechanism: the shift from fermentation to respiration so enormously increases the ATP yield per glucose molecule that a smaller rate of glucose utilization saturates the cell's capacity to use it effectively. The actual mechanisms may be multiple, but the most important one is probably a decrease in the ADP/ATP ratio. Glycolysis requires a supply of ADP for substrate-level phosphorylation, e.g., for accepting phosphate from 1,3-diphosphoglyceric acid (Fig. 3-1); and respiration, by supplying an additional source of phosphorylation, will tend to keep the ATP level high and the ADP low. This explanation is supported by an observation of Meyerhof: when electron transport in yeast is uncoupled from phosphorylation by the addition of dinitrophenol, the aerobic utilization of glucose increases.

Growth and Energy Production. Microbes invariably consume fuel more rapidly when growing than when growth is prevented by lack of some required material (usually a nitrogen source). The explanation is presumably similar to the above: in the absence of growth ATP will not be consumed for biosynthetic purposes, and so ATP will accumulate and ADP will decrease. Since growth exerts this stimulatory effect on respiration as well as on fermentation, it appears that the electron transport chain also requires a supply of ADP in order to permit continued utilization of substrate. The fact that nongrowing cells do ferment or respire at all probably reflects several processes: use of ATP for maintenance and for synthesis of storage materials; a background level of ATPase activity in the cell; and imperfect coupling of electron transport with phosphorylation.

Incomplete Oxidations

By and large the products of respiration—mostly CO_2—did not interest the early students of microbiology as much as did the products of fermentation. However, just as men discovered how to make wine and cheese long before the role of microbes was known, so they learned that wine trickled repeatedly over wood shavings (to provide a large surface) became vinegar. This aerobic process of oxidation of ethanol to acetic acid has been repeatedly rediscovered by impecunious students who kept an opened bottle of wine too long! The process is due to a group of organisms called *Acetobacter;* some of these can oxidize ethanol to acetate much faster than they can oxidize the acetate, while others (e.g., *A. suboxydans*) are incapable of going beyond acetate.

The number of commercially valuable microbial suboxidations is increasing constantly; a few examples will be noted. The citric acid used widely in carbonated beverages is derived more cheaply from *Aspergillus* cultures than from citrus fruits or from chemical synthesis. The reduction product of glucose, sorbitol, is oxidized by an *Acetobacter* to the previously rare sugar sorbose, which has made possible the inexpensive synthesis of ascorbic acid; and microbial oxidation of C-11 of the steroid nucleus has similarly facilitated the synthesis of steroid hormones and their analogs. Antibiotics and certain vitamins, obtained from well aerated cultures, are the most valuable products of microbial technology today. Finally, bacterial mutants are increasingly used for the commercial production of a few amino acids, including glutamate and lysine. When we learn how to make amino acids, or palatable protein, cheaply from petroleum or wood, the contribution of microbial technology to the world food supply may rival that of agriculture.

AUTOTROPHIC METABOLISM

Chemoautotrophy and Photosynthesis

The metabolic patterns described above are observed in those microorganisms that grow on organic compounds, which are formed in Nature by animals or plants. This mode of metabolism is called **heterotrophic** (feeding on others). Various other microbes, however, do not depend on organic compounds but tap quite different sources of energy, and use this energy to reduce CO_2 to the organic compounds needed for growth. Table 3-2 presents examples of such **autotrophic** (self-feeding) metabolism. A number of these processes were discovered before 1900 by the Russian soil microbiologist Winogradsky.*

Autotrophic processes can be divided into two classes. 1) **Photosynthesis** derives energy from the absorption of visible light, and is found in algae and a few bacteria, as well as in higher plants. Microbial photosynthesis in the upper layers of the ocean and lakes, mostly by algae, accounts for about half the total terrestrial photosynthesis. 2) **Chemoautotrophy** (chemosynthesis) derives energy from the respiration of **inorganic** electron donors; it is found only in certain bacteria, which are also known as **lithotrophs** (Gr. *lithos*, "stone"). In their electron transport some of these organisms use O_2 (class I, Table 3-2), while others use other electron acceptors (class II).

Those autotrophic bacteria that oxidize H_2 can often similarly utilize simple carbon compounds, such as CO, CH_4, HCHO, HCOOH, or CH_3OH. Since these compounds are, by definition, organic, their utilization does not conform to the original definition of autotrophy; but the fundamental mode of metabolism is the same: energy is used to reduce CO_2. It is therefore necessary to redefine **autotrophy** in metabolic rather than nutritional terms: **the utilization of**

---

* Winogradsky (1856–1953) had a remarkable history. After studying with Pasteur he returned to Russia, where he established the fundamentals of soil microbiology; but then tiring of struggles with bureaucracy, he retired at about 1900 to his family estate. Driven out by the Revolution, he returned to laboratory work, in France, at the age of 65; and after contemptuously reviewing the mediocre state of his field, he began a long period of further important contributions.

TABLE 3-2. AUTOTROPHIC MODES OF METABOLISM

Organism or group	Source of energy	Remarks
I. Aerobic lithotrophs		Inorganic (litho-) electron donors
Hydrogen bacteria	$H_2 + 1/2\ O_2 \rightarrow H_2O$	
Sulfur bacteria (colorless)	$H_2S + 1/2\ O_2 \rightarrow H_2O + S$ $S + 1.5\ O_2 + H_2O \rightarrow H_2SO_4$	} Can produce H_2SO_4 to pH as low as 0
Iron bacteria	$2\ Fe^{++} + 1/2\ O_2 + H_2O \rightarrow 2\ Fe^{+++} + 2\ OH^-$	
Nitrifying bacteria		
Nitrosomonas	$NH_3 + 1.5\ O_2 \rightarrow HNO_2 + H_2O$	} Convert soil N to nonvolatile
Nitrobacter	$HNO_2 + 1/2\ O_2 \rightarrow HNO_3$	form, used by plants
II. Anaerobic respirers		Most can also use organic electron donors
Denitrifiers*	$nH_2 + NO_3^- \rightarrow N_2O,\ N_2,$ or NH_3	Cause N loss from anaerobic soil
Desulfovibrio	$nH_2 + SO_4^= \rightarrow S$ or H_2S	Odor of polluted streams, mud flats
Methane bacteria	$4\ H_2 + CO_2 \rightarrow CH_4 + 2\ H_2O$	Sewage disposal plants
Clostridium aceticum	$4\ H_2 + 2\ CO_2 \rightarrow CH_3COOH + 2\ H_2O$	
III. Photosynthesizers		
Purple sulfur bacteria	$4\ CO_2 + 2\ H_2S + 4\ H_2O \xrightarrow{light} 4\ (CH_2O) + 2\ H_2SO_4$	} $H_2(A)$ = various electron donors
Nonsulfur purple bacteria	$CO_2 + 2\ H_2(A) \xrightarrow{light} (CH_2O) + H_2O + 2\ (A)$	
Algae	$CO_2 + 2\ H_2O \xrightarrow{light} (CH_2O) + 1/2\ O_2$†	"Plant" photosynthesis

*Anaerobic respiration, with the use of nitrate instead of O_2, is also common for the oxidation of the usual organic substrates by heterotrophs (e.g., E. coli). This metabolism bears no resemblance to autotrophy, as the energy is used for biosynthesis from organic compounds rather than from CO_2.
† The O_2 is derived directly from H_2O, and not from CO_2.

CO₂ as a major source of organic compounds. (Minor incorporation of CO_2, in several biosynthetic reactions, occurs in all organisms; these reactions are described in the next chapter.)

Bacterial Photosynthesis

In photosynthesis the absorption of a quantum of visible light by chlorophyll causes the displacement of an electron, which creates a positive (oxidizing) and a negative (reducing) region in the chlorophyll. The positive charge is promptly neutralized by taking up an electron from a closely linked cytochrome molecule ($Fe^{++} \rightarrow Fe^{+++}$) of high redox potential, while the negative charge is transferred from the chlorophyll to a cofactor of very low redox potential, ferredoxin (Ch. 4). These two factors, with a wide potential difference between them, constitute the ends of an electron transport chain,

through which this potential difference is used to create energy and reducing power in metabolically available form (ATP and TPNH, respectively).

The electron transport system functions in two different ways, which permit the proportions of ATP and TPNH formed to be varied as needed. In **cyclic photophosphorylation** (Fig. 3-5) the electron is transported from the reduced factor to the oxidized cytochrome through a chain of quinones and cytochromes, much as in respiratory electron transport (Fig. 3-4), and ATP is similarly generated. The companion process of **noncyclic photophosphorylation** produces useful reducing power as well as ATP (Fig. 3-5). In this process the electron at the reducing end of the chain is trapped by being used to reduce DPN or the parallel coenzyme TPN (NADP). To complete the electron transport, therefore, an electron must be supplied from another source.

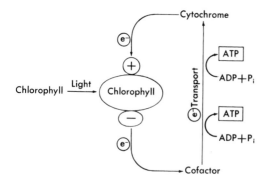

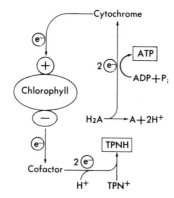

Cyclic photophosphorylation

Noncyclic photophosphorylation

Fig. 3-5 Electron flow in photosynthesis. In plants and algae H_2A is H_2O; in photosynthetic bacteria it is H_2, H_2S, or various organic compounds.

Plants and bacteria differ in the source of this electron. In plants (and algae) it is derived from the oxidation of water:

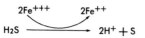

$$H_2O \longrightarrow 2H^+ + \tfrac{1}{2}O_2$$

In bacteria, however, the photosynthetic system is apparently too primitive to generate the very high potential necessary for this oxidation; hence a more readily oxidized donor of electrons than water must be available, such as H_2S:

$$H_2S \longrightarrow 2H^+ + S$$

Bacterial photosynthesis thus never releases O_2; but in the purple sulfur bacteria an equivalent formation of S is seen.

Some photosynthetic bacteria show the property, remarkable in so small an organism, of **phototaxis**: a gradient of light intensity elicits differential flagellar activity in different parts of the cell, resulting in motion toward the light. This mechanism represents perhaps the most primitive antecedent of a nervous response.

Autotrophic Fixation and Reduction of CO₂

With the use of the energy and the reducing power supplied by photosynthesis, or by chemosynthesis, an autotrophic cell makes more of itself from CO_2. Although this process of CO_2 assimilation is fundamentally biosynthetic, it is so intimately linked with autotrophic energy metabolism that it will be presented here rather than in the next chapter.

The elucidation of the major pathway of CO_2 reduction, largely by Calvin and Horecker, has been one of the triumphs of modern biochemistry. It turns out to involve surprisingly few novel enzymes, in addition to enzymes already present in universal pathways of carbohydrate metabolism (including pentose synthesis). The basic mechanism for the initial fixation of CO_2 is:

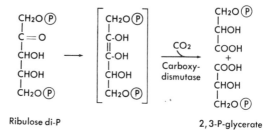

Ribulose di-P   2, 3-P-glycerate

At this stage the assimilated carbon is still at the fully oxidized, carboxyl level. To reduce it, so that it can serve as a source of all carbon in the cell, TPNH (or DPNH) is then used, with further energy from ATP, in the ribulose diphosphate cycle. The over-all pattern of this cycle is presented in Figure 3-6. The 3-P-glyceric acid, formed as above, is reduced to triose-P; of 6 such trioses, 5 are used to regenerate the pentoses of the cycle, while 1 represents the net gain. (The over-all process by which 5 trioses can become 3 pentoses is presented later: Ch. 4, Pentose biosynthesis).

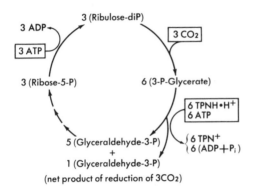

Fig. 3-6 The ribulose-diphosphate cycle for CO_2 fixation and reduction.

The Nitrogen Cycle; Nitrogen Fixation

Microbes play an essential role in the geochemical **nitrogen cycle.** Since some of the chemoautotrophic bacteria listed in Table 3-2 participate, this cycle will be briefly considered here.

The N in decomposing organic matter is at first largely converted to NH_3; this volatile compound is then stabilized in the soil by oxidation, through the action of **nitrifying** bacteria, to nonvolatile nitrate, which can be reduced by plants to organic amino compounds. However, some NH$_3$ is lost immediately to the atmosphere, and additional amounts are lost, from anaerobic regions of the soil, through the action of denitrifying bacteria, which reduce nitrate to N_2 and NH_3. Maintenance of the biosphere therefore requires constant **fixation of atmospheric N_2.**

Biological N_2 fixation is accomplished only by bacteria and algae, of which the quantitatively most important group appears to be the genus *Rhizobium* (Gr. *rhizo,* "root"). These bacteria infect the roots of leguminous plants, leading to formation of symbiotic nitrogen-fixing nodules. Nitrogen can also be fixed, however, by many other bacteria, including the photosynthetic purple sulfur bacteria (e.g., *Rhodospirillum rubrum*). These remarkably self-sufficient organisms can therefore derive all their major atoms (C, H, N, and O) from the atmosphere and water.

The processes of N_2 fixation, nitrification, and denitrification involve several different valence levels of N. It is interesting that enzymes in two of these processes have been shown to contain molybdenum, which can also occupy several valence levels, and the reduction of N_2 to NH_3 can be accomplished in vitro with the aid of the recently discovered powerful reductant, ferredoxin (p. 59).

ALTERNATIVE SUBSTRATES

Genotypic Adaptation (Selection of Organisms)

Evolution has produced, as we have noted, a variety of fermentation patterns, adapted to different environments. Even greater differences among organisms can be seen in their ability to utilize different foodstuffs. Indeed, it is axiomatic that every compound in the organic world can be metabolized by some microbe; otherwise the grand cycle of organic matter in Nature would come to a halt, since the conversion of decaying organic matter to atmospheric CO_2 (mineralization) is just as essential for this cycle as is the fixation of CO_2 into living matter by photosynthesis (see Pasteur quotation at head of chapter).* Indeed, if the atmospheric reservoir of CO_2 were not replenished it would last only 20 years.

In even a single small sample of soil many different kinds of organisms are present, and they play different roles in the process of mineralization. As was noted in Chapter 1, a general microbiologist will sort out these organisms by using the procedure of **enrichment**

---

* It is perhaps not surprising that the present microbial population does not always attack so readily those products of the organic chemist that have first reached the soil recently. Indeed, increasing problems are being created by the persistence in the soil of toxic pesticides, which can be concentrated by plants and animals; and synthetic detergents create problems in sewage disposal. **Biodegradable** substitutes for the offending compounds are therefore being sought.

culture, or elective enrichment, which exaggerates, in the laboratory, the selective pressures present in Nature. For this purpose a sample of soil or mud is incubated in a flask of medium containing a given compound as sole carbon source, under aerobic or anaerobic conditions, etc. While many organisms have only a narrow range of possible foodstuffs, as many as 80 effective carbon sources have been recorded for a single strain of *Pseudomonas*, a particularly versatile soil scavenger. As glucose is much the most widely distributed sugar in higher plants (being the monomer of cellulose and starch), it is not surprising that most bacteria can attack this compound, which is therefore considered the typical substrate for the Embden-Meyerhof pathway.

Adaptation to Aerobiosis and Anaerobiosis. Since the initial stages of decay of animal and plant tissues generally occur in anaerobic environments, the early stages of metabolism of most organic constituents are usually fermentative. The products formed diffuse toward a surface and are then oxidized by a different group of organisms.

A facultative organism can make both those special enzymes required for a fermentation and those required for respiration. The existence of obligate aerobes and obligate anaerobes, however, suggests that when the habitat permits prolonged dependence on only one of these sets of enzymes there is selective advantage in dispensing with the genes for the other set. It is of interest that yeasts, which tend to grow both on the surfaces of living fruits and within the juices of crushed or decaying fruit, are generally facultative. The closely related molds, which form fluffy aerial growths (mycelia) on surfaces, tend to be strictly aerobes, but many can also differentiate into a yeast phase, which grows in the depths of fluids and is facultative.

Fatty compounds are too highly reduced to be readily fermented, and so the surface of their insoluble globules tends to be attacked by aerobes with a lipophilic surface, generally mycobacteria. Petroleum probably represents the ultimate in fermentation. It is formed when large amounts of organic matter decay below deep water, which ensures perpetual anaerobiosis; the hydrocarbons

remain when all the oxygen has left the system, in the form of water-soluble organic compounds, CO_2, and H_2O.

The Specific Pathways for Less Common Substrates. We have already described the almost universal central metabolic pathways (glycolysis and TCA cycle), which account for energy production from such common substrates as glucose, lactate, or acetate. The metabolism of a great variety of other compounds depends on enzymes that convert the compound to some intermediate in a central pathway. Usually this specific connecting pathway is quite short. For example, a single step will convert fructose to fructose-6-phosphate; a one-step hydrolysis will yield glucose from sucrose or from lactose; three enzymatic reactions are necessary to convert galactose to glucose-1-phosphate (see Fig. 4-24); and two steps will convert glycerol to glyceraldehyde phosphate.

Some bacteria, including the meningococcus, utilize sucrose very efficiently by means of the enzyme **sucrose phosphorylase**, which catalyzes the reaction:

$$Sucrose + P_i \rightarrow Glucose\text{-}1\text{-}P + Fructose.$$

As a result of this saving of $\sim$P energy these organisms grow more rapidly on sucrose than on either glucose or fructose.

Incidentally, an organism that can use a given compound is often referred to as "fermentation-positive" for that compound, since this action is most conveniently recognized through the formation of acid; but under aerobic conditions facultative organisms may actually combust rather than ferment the compound. Highly reduced compounds (e.g., fatty acids, certain amino acids) cannot be fermented, and are generally converted to acetate or to members of the TCA cycle, which are then metabolized in the usual way.

Phenotypic Adaptation (Selection of Enzymes)

Not only do organisms differ in their inherent capacity, genetically controlled, to metabolize a given substrate, but the cells of a competent strain may or may not possess the enzymes required, depending on their im-

TABLE 3-3. ADAPTIVE FORMATION OF "CARBOHYDRASES" BY THE LACTIC ORGANISM *LEUCONOSTOC MESENTEROIDES*. Cells grown on the sugar indicated (plus a source of amino acids and vitamins) were freed from the medium, resuspended in the presence of various sugars, and tested for the formation of detectable acid within the next 3 hours. (Note that hydrolysis of lactose yields galactose and glucose.) (From Karström, H. Ph.D. Dissertation, Helsinki, 1931.)

Sugar in growth medium	Sugar tested for fermentation				
	Glucose, fructose, sucrose	Maltose	Lactose	Galactose	Arabinose
Glucose	+	0	0	0	0
Sucrose	+	0	0	0	0
Maltose	+	+	0	0	0
Lactose	+	0	+	+	0
Galactose	+	0	0	+	0
Arabinose	+	0	0	0	+
None	+	0	0	0	0

mediate past history. Thus the cells that grow out in an enrichment culture not only are genotypically adapted but also are phenotypically adapted to attack the substrate provided.

This aspect of the metabolic versatility of bacteria was first demonstrated in 1931 by Karström in Finland, through a fundamental modification in the test for fermentative abilities: instead of simply testing the utilization of various sugars by growing cells, he grew the organism on one sugar and tested the ability of "resting" cells (i.e., cells not growing for lack of a N source) to form acid from various sugars. The results (Table 3-3) showed that with the particular organism used the enzyme system for utilizing glucose or sucrose was formed regardless of C source, while enzymes essential for fermenting certain other sugars were absent unless the cells had been grown on these compounds. The former group of enzymes were called **constitutive** and the latter **adaptive**.

While modern studies have made this distinction less sharp, it has provided a valuable point of view for studying bacterial metabolism. The constitutive group includes not only the enzymes for introducing a favored C source, such as glucose, into a central pathway, but also the enzymes

of that pathway. The adaptive group includes not only enzymes concerned with optional or alternative substrates, but even the components of the electron transport chain (which are often not formed under anaerobic conditions).

More recent investigations, focusing on mechanism rather than on biological function, have led these enzymes to be called **inducible** rather than adaptive, since their formation may be induced by compounds which are not substrates and therefore are not adaptively used (Ch. 9). However, from the ecological point of view, stressed in this chapter, the concept of adaptive enzyme formation is useful. It ordinarily refers, of course, to phenotypic adaptation; this must be superimposed on the genotypic adaptation that originally gave rise to the capacity to make the required enzyme.

Diauxie. The adaptive response of a growing culture to an added substrate may be blocked by the presence of a more favored substrate, which supports faster growth. This mechanism, which promotes metabolic economy, was discovered in 1940 in Kluyver's laboratory in Holland in experiments with *Micrococcus denitrificans*. This organism can use either O_2 or nitrate as electron acceptor, but in the presence of O_2 nitrate can no longer induce the cells to form nitratase, the enzyme

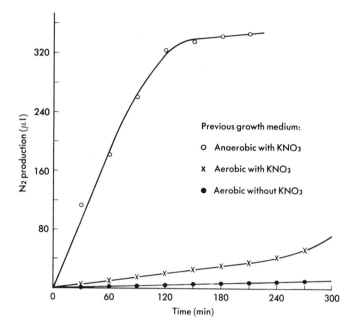

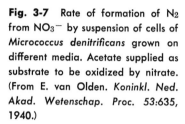

Fig. 3-7 Rate of formation of N_2 from $NO_3{}^-$ by suspension of cells of *Micrococcus denitrificans* grown on different media. Acetate supplied as substrate to be oxidized by nitrate. (From E. van Olden. *Koninkl. Ned. Akad. Wetenschap. Proc.* 53:635, 1940.)

that connects nitrate with the electron transport pathway (Fig. 3-7). Similarly, this organism can use either H_2 or organic compounds as electron donor; but in the presence of organic compounds H_2 fails to induce formation of the enzyme hydrogenase, required for its utilization.

In 1942 Monod in France found that such selectivity extends also to alternative carbon sources. Thus *E. coli,* growing on glucose plus almost any other carbon source, consumes all

the glucose first and then, after a lag of half an hour or so, resumes growth (Fig. 3-8). Later analysis of this **diauxie** (diphasic growth curve) showed that glucose represses the induction of the enzymes and membrane transport systems required for the utilization of the other substrates. Such regulation of the formation of β-galactosidase, in particular, has been intensively studied as a model for the regulation of enzyme formation; this work will be presented in Chapter 9.

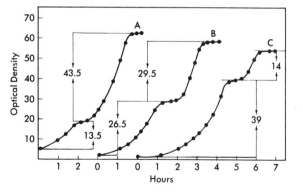

Fig. 3-8 Diauxic growth of *E. coli* on glucose and sorbitol in the proportions 1/3 (**A**), 2/2 (**B**), and 3/1 (**C**). Minimal medium; inoculum grown on glucose. (From J. Monod, *La croissance des cultures bactériennes.* Hermann, Paris, 1942.)

SELECTED REFERENCES

Books and Review Articles

GUNSALUS, I. C., and STANIER, R. Y., eds. *The Bacteria,* vol. II. Academic Press, New York, 1961. Especially Cyclic Mechanisms of Terminal Oxidation (Krampitz), Survey of Microbial Electron Transport Mechanisms (Dolin), Cytochrome Systems in Aerobic Electron Transport (Smith), and Fermentation of Carbohydrates and Related Compounds (Wood).

KLUYVER, A. J., and VAN NIEL, C. B. *The Microbe's Contribution to Biology.* Harvard, Cambridge, Mass., 1956. A thought-provoking set of lectures, providing perspective on the unity of biology and the evolutionary aspects of microbiology.

LEHNINGER, A. L. *Bioenergetics.* Benjamin, New York, 1965.

MORTENSON, L. E. Nitrogen fixation: Role of ferredoxin in anaerobic metabolism. *Ann. Rev. Microbiol.* *17*:115 (1963).

RACKER, E. Mechanisms of synthesis of adenosine triphosphate. *Advances Enzymol.* 23:323 (1961).

THIMANN, K. V. *The Life of Bacteria,* 2nd ed. Macmillan, New York, 1963. Includes a detailed account of the various fermentations.

VALENTINE, R. C. Bacterial ferredoxin. *Bact. Rev.* 28:497 (1964).

WHITE, A., HANDLER, P., and SMITH, E. L. *Principles of Biochemistry,* 3rd ed. McGraw-Hill, New York, 1964, Ch. 17–20.

4 BIOSYNTHESIS

Years after the main energy-yielding pathways had been analyzed in microbes and in higher organisms, biosynthesis still remained largely a mystery. Several reasons may be noted. 1) Each individual biosynthetic pathway metabolizes relatively little material, and so its enzymes are present in small amounts. 2) Many biosynthetic reactions are endergonic, and hence they could not be studied outside the cell until their coupling with the exergonic breakdown of ATP* was appreciated. 3) Biosynthetic intermediates are normally present in the cell in quantities too small to detect; and no selective inhibitors to promote their accumulation were found, comparable to fluoride or iodoacetate in glycolysis.

An effective approach was provided in 1941, when Beadle and Tatum isolated auxotrophic mutants of a microbe and showed that these strains could be used to reveal biosynthetic intermediates. This approach, and the use of isotopically labeled precursors, have opened many biosynthetic pathways to enzymatic analysis; and the pattern observed has proved remarkably uniform throughout the biological kingdom. The resulting building blocks are polymerized into macromolecules, whose synthesis has recently also become amenable to biochemical analysis.

Since the reader is assumed to have some familiarity with biochemistry this chapter will review the subject of biosynthesis rather selectively, with emphasis on its fundamental principles and methodology, on the connections between the various pathways, on the significance of these pathways for cell function, and on those sequences that have been revealed primarily in microbes.

---

*In this chapter the following abbreviations are used: ATP, adenosine triphosphate; TCA, tricarboxylic acid; DPN, diphosphopyridine nucleotide (= NAD, nicotinamide adenine dinucleotide); TPN, triphosphopyridine nucleotide (= NADP); DPNH, TPNH, the reduced forms of DPN, TPN; CoA, coenzyme A; PRPP, 5-P-ribose-1-PP; DAP, diaminopimelate; THF, tetrahydrofolate; PEP, phosphoenolpyruvate; GNAc, 2-N-acetylglucosamine; UMP, CMP, GMP, AMP: the ribonucleotide of uracil, cytosine, guanine, and adenine, respectively; dUMP, etc.: deoxyuridine monoP, etc.; UDP, UTP, etc.: uridine diP and uridine triP, etc.

Microbial Composition and the Unity of Biochemistry

We have already noted that many microorganisms can synthesize all their organic constituents from a single carbon source—even, in autotrophs, from CO_2—whereas other microorganisms, including many pathogens adapted to animal tissues, will not grow unless supplied with a rich medium. It was long taken for granted that nutritional simplicity reflected biochemical simplicity. However, when the specific growth requirements of various microbes were later defined an extensive and overlapping variety of nutritional patterns was revealed, involving various amino acids, purines, pyrimidines, and vitamins. These patterns defied classification, and they did not make sense until Lwoff in France, and Knight in England, recognized in the 1930s the distinction between **essential nutrients** and **essential metabolites.** They proposed that in all cells growth depends on the presence of much the same set of building blocks and cofactors (essential metabolites). What the organisms differ in is their ability to make these metabolites, and the essential nutrients are simply those that cannot be made endogenously.

This reinterpretation of nutritional requirements, as reflecting different deficiencies in a common metabolic pattern, has provided strong support for the growing concept of the **unity of biochemistry.** This concept had already been formulated by the Dutch microbiologist Kluyver, in 1926, on the basis of the similarity of the classes of enzymatic reactions (hydrolyses, dehydrogenations, etc.) found throughout the biological kingdom; and the extent of this unity had become more impressive when studies of the glycolytic pathway revealed precisely the same intermediates and reactions in yeast cells and in mammalian muscle. The further extension of the concept, to include a universal set of essential metabolites, was finally established directly, following the development of suitable analytic methods: the proteins, nucleic acids, and cofactors of the most varied cells were found to be made of the **same building blocks.** For example, such a metabolic eccentric as *Thiobacillus,* deriving its energy by converting sulfur to H_2SO_4, is not made of brimstone: its protoplasm contains the same constituents as that of other organisms, with no excess of sulfur except in the pool of metabolites.

This unity lends general interest to the elucidation of biosynthetic pathways in microbes.

Methods of Analyzing Biosynthetic Pathways

Auxotrophic Mutants. Nutritionally simple microbes offer several advantages over animal tissues for biosynthetic studies: more rapid growth and biosynthesis; the ability to synthesize all the cell components; and homogeneity of the cell population. An even greater advantage was provided, as noted above, when Beadle and Tatum discovered a genetic method for causing such organisms to accumulate previously undetectable intermediates. From the common red bread mold, *Neurospora crassa,* these investigators isolated a variety of auxotrophic mutants, which had each lost the ability to make a single biosynthetic enzyme, and which therefore required for growth the product of the blocked pathway.[*] Most of these mutants were found to accumulate and excrete the substrate of the blocked reaction in large amounts, often exceeding the weight of the cells.

With bacteria similar mutants have proved even easier to isolate and to study quantitatively. A convenient method for their selection, based on the use of penicillin, will be described in Chapter 6.

Auxotrophic mutants have another useful property: they can grow not only on the endproduct of the blocked sequence, but often

also on intermediates between the block and the endproduct. Hence strains blocked in different reactions in the same sequence often exhibit cross-feeding (**syntrophism**), the strain with the later block accumulating an intermediate to which the other can respond (Fig. 4-1). This nutritional response not only can reveal the accumulation of an interesting compound, but it also provides the basis for a quantitative bioassay of that compound (Ch. 5), which is helpful in its isolation.

Indeed, the growth response of mutants to already known compounds has sometimes provided a shortcut to the identification of an intermediate. Thus, in the complex pathway of biosynthesis of aromatic amino acids and vitamins the key was provided by the isolation of mutants requiring a mixture of these compounds for growth, followed by the finding that some of these mutants can alternatively grow on a single

Fig. 4-1 Cross-feeding between different bacterial mutants blocked in the same pathway. The mutants are labeled in terms of the enzyme that they can no longer make:

Note that a streak of mutant A, growing slightly on medium containing a trace of arginine, stimulates growth of adjacent streaks of mutants C and O, while C similarly stimulates O but not A. (From B. D. Davis. *Experientia* 6:41, 1950.)

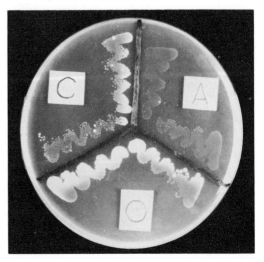

---

[*] Also called "biochemically deficient" mutants, or, individually, "serineless," etc. The latter terminology has become misleading, however: these cells **contain** normal amounts of serine, whereas true deficiencies in content can be achieved for certain substances (e.g., deficiencies in cell wall; substitution of analogs).

compound, the rare plant product shikimate, while others accumulate it (p. 98). (The similar accumulation of shikimate by the shikimi tree in Japan, like that of citrate in citrus fruits and malate [L., "apple"] in apples, reflects quantitative variation in the function of a widespread pathway.) Many intermediates cannot be detected by such a nutritional response, since they cannot penetrate into cells.

Other Methods. This use of mutants opened to exploration many pathways, including those to essentially all the amino acids. Once some intermediates in a pathway were available it became possible also to characterize, in cell extracts, the enzymes that connected them, and to use the classic approach of **enzyme fractionation** to find those intermediates that had not been revealed by mutant accumulation.

The use of **isotopes,** in two ways, has also contributed substantially to the analysis of biosynthetic pathways in bacteria, as in mammals. One approach is **isotopic competition.** For example, when an isotopically labeled possible precursor (glycine) is supplied in competition with an unlabeled general carbon source (glucose) the purines recovered from the cells by hydrolysis are found to be heavily labeled, showing that glycine has served as a direct precursor. In another approach the organism is supplied with a single carbon source (e.g., glucose) **selectively labeled in a specific atom;** an endproduct is then isolated and is degraded in a way that permits determination of the isotope concentration (specific activity) in its individual atoms. Since we know how the individual atoms of a fuel are arranged in the products of the central pathways, the results can often indicate whether a given biosynthetic pathway branched off from a glycolytic intermediate, or acetate (Fig. 4-2), or a tricarboxylate cycle intermediate.

In the extension of the study of biosynthesis to complex macromolecules (proteins, nucleic acids, or heteropolymeric polysaccharides) the amounts of product formed in vitro have generally been too small to detect by ordinary analytical methods. The indispensable method for measuring these reactions has therefore consisted in the incorporation of radioactive precursors into polymers, followed by the use of reagents (e.g., trichloroacetic acid) that precipitate the polymers but not the substrates.

Criteria for a Biosynthetic Intermediate

The incorporation of an exogenous compound by a cell can thus be established by showing either 1) the assimilation of isotopically labeled molecules or 2) activity as a growth factor for an auxotroph. By definition, such an incorporated substance is serving as a **precursor.** However, though any metabolic utilization of a compound is of biochemical interest, it does not necessarily follow that the compound serves in the cell as an **intermediate** between a general nutrient and a cell component. The distinction is significant for cell physiology; and while most precursors have also turned out to be intermediates, there are exceptions.

For example, the α-keto acids corresponding to tryptophan or histidine serve well as precursors, supporting growth of the corresponding amino acid auxotrophs; but their activity depends on transaminases of rather broad specificity, rather than on enzymes of the biosynthetic pathways to these amino acids. In a more intricate example, histidine provided in the medium induces *Aerobacter* to form degradative enzymes that convert its 5-carbon chain to α-ketoglutarate; hence it can serve as a source of glutamate (p. 91). However, the level of histidine formed **endogenously** in the cell is not sufficient to induce its own degradation, and histidine biosynthesis has no connection with normal glutamate biosynthesis.

These considerations have led to the formulation of the following criteria: A and B are **obligatory intermediates** in the biosynthesis of product P

$$\rightarrow \ \rightarrow A \ \rightarrow B \ \rightarrow \ \rightarrow P$$

if 1) compounds A and B can each give rise to P (in the cell or in extracts); 2) a single enzyme converts A to B; and 3) loss of that enzyme (e.g., by mutation) results in a requirement for P. These criteria exclude, for example, free purines as intermediates, even though they may be excreted by certain mutants and used by others; the biosynthetic pathway to purines proceeds at the level of nucleotides (see below), and the enzyme that forms a nucleotide from a purine is not obligatory for biosynthesis. Such pathways, utilizing added precursors that are not true intermediates, are called **salvage pathways.**

Catabolic, Anabolic, and Amphibolic Pathways

When the major energy-yielding pathways of glycolysis, pyruvate oxidation, and the tricarboxylate (TCA) cycle were discovered they were considered purely catabolic or degradative. The energy thus derived from some molecules of glucose was assumed to be used, in the then unknown pathways of anabolism, to cause the atoms of other molecules of glucose to flow through quite a different set of intermediates. This view was supported by the fact that in "resting" cells, whose bio-

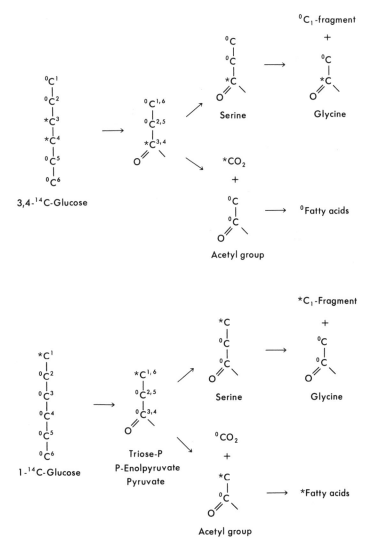

Fig. 4-2 Example of use of selectively labeled glucose in analysis of biosynthetic pathways. $*C$ (radioactive); $^0C = {}^{12}C$ (nonradioactive).

synthesis was prevented by lack of a nitrogen source, the catabolic pathways remained active. However, it turned out that the various pathways of biosynthesis branch off from quite a variety of the intermediates in the so-called "catabolic" pathways. A number of these connections are summarized in Figure 4-3.

Since the glycolytic and the TCA pathways thus function just as directly and indispensably in biosynthesis as in energy production, their original designation as catabolic pathways is no longer adequate, and they are better designated as **amphibolic** (Gr., *amphi,* "either") pathways. The purely **anabolic** or **biosynthetic** pathways would then be those

Fig. 4-3   Relation of amphibolic to anabolic pathways. Amphibolic pathways have heavy arrows.

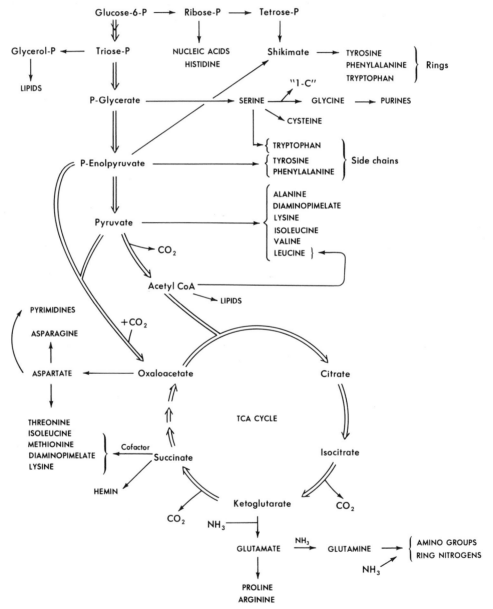

that branch from amphibolic intermediates to endproducts, while the term **catabolic** would be restricted to the short sequences that convert amphibolic intermediates to fermentation endproducts.* The optimal use of a foodstuff will require a proper balance between the anabolic and the catabolic drains on its amphibolic flow.

Nature has obviously achieved a substantial sparing of genes and enzymes by selecting biosynthetic and catabolic pathways that share intermediates. This pattern illustrates the evolutionary pressure for **metabolic economy,** which will receive additional support when we consider regulatory mechanisms in a later chapter. Indeed, it seems probable that this principle is a major factor underlying the unity of biochemistry: the presence of identical pathways in the most diverse organisms may reflect not only a

common ancestry, but also retention of these pathways because of their efficiency.

Conversion of Amphibolic to Biosynthetic Pathways

Under a variety of conditions, which are no less "normal" than aerobic growth on glucose, parts of the central, amphibolic pathways become purely biosynthetic. For example, under anaerobic conditions there is no terminal respiration of acetate, and the TCA cycle no longer functions as a cycle. Nevertheless, net synthesis of oxaloacetate, α-ketoglutarate, and succinate is still required, since these compounds serve as essential biosynthetic intermediates (Fig. 4-3). Under these conditions the TCA cycle is modified to form a branched biosynthetic pathway from oxaloacetate: one branch leads, by reductive reversal of the usual pathway, to succinate, while the other leads, by the usual oxidative pathway, to α-ketoglutarate (Fig. 4-4).

---

*It has been suggested that pathways difficult to classify (or perhaps those difficult to memorize) be designated as diabolic.

Fig. 4-4 Biosynthesis of TCA intermediates in **anaerobic** growth on glucose. The TCA cycle becomes split into a reversed reductive branch and a normal oxidative branch.

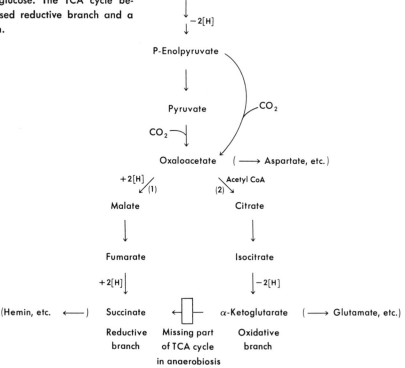

The persistence of the oxidative pathway under anaerobic conditions is evidently due to the irreversibility of the oxidative decarboxylation of α-ketoglutarate: i.e., this compound cannot be formed directly from succinate and CO_2 (see exception under Ferredoxin, below).

A different reversal of flow is seen when a cell grows aerobically on succinate (or another component of the TCA cycle), which undergoes oxidation to oxaloacetate, then decarboxylation to pyruvate or P-enolpyruvate, and oxidation via acetate and the TCA cycle (Fig. 4-5). Under these circumstances the glycolytic pathway no longer functions catabolically; yet flow of carbon through this pathway, in the reverse of the familiar direction, is essential to provide various cell components (e.g., sugars for cell walls and nucleic acids). Still another pattern is exhibited by cells growing on glycerol (which is readily converted to triose-P): the lower part of the glycolytic pathway is then used amphibolically and the upper part, in reverse, biosynthetically.

Thus, since anabolic branches arise from both the glycolytic and the TCA pathways, growth on any single carbon source will require net flow of carbon from one of these pathways to the other (C3 + C1 ⇌ C4), to keep pace with the biosynthetic drains. The reactions that connect the two pathways will be discussed below (Fig. 4-7). In mammals, of course, metabolic flow patterns are similarly affected by the use of different fuels (e.g., gluconeogenesis), but the cells cannot be as rigidly restricted to a single fuel for purposes of investigation.

Biosynthesis from 2-C Compounds: The glyoxylate cycle

The pathways that have been reviewed can account for the ability of organisms to grow on many compounds: sugars (or substances convertible to them), 3-C monocarboxylic acids, 4- to 6-C di- or tricarboxylic acids, and even CO_2 in autotrophs (Ch. 3). These pathways, however, do not account for the ability of many bacteria to grow on acetate, and hence on fat, as the sole C source; for though pyruvate is readily decarboxylated to acetate, the reverse reaction, like the reversed decarboxylation of α-ketoglutarate noted in the preceding section, does not occur (except in some photosynthetic organisms: see below).

Fig. 4-5 Pathway of metabolic flow in aerobic growth on succinate. The glycolytic intermediates would be included, but are not specified, in the box.

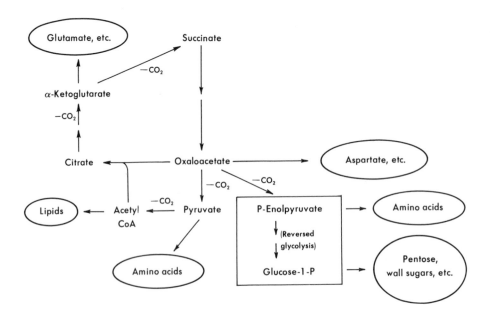

Moreover, acetate cannot condense with itself "back-to-back" yield succinate. This inability of acetate to replace the biosynthetic drain on the TCA cycle is largely responsible for the acidosis of a diabetic mammal forced to consume fat (via acetyl CoA) without carbohydrate. The problem is how bacteria can thrive on such a diet.

The answer, discovered in 1957 by Hans Kornberg, in Krebs' laboratory, is a bypass or epicycle on the Krebs cycle, involving two additional enzymes that had been known but whose function had been sought. These enzymes catalyze reactions (1) and (2):

The succinate and malate formed in (1) and (2) can be used to regenerate isocitrate through familiar reactions of the TCA cycle (summed as reaction 3), yielding a **glyoxylate cycle.** This cycle shares part of the enzymes of the classic TCA cycle but bypasses its two decarboxylative reactions (Fig. 4-6); acetate is thus used for net synthesis of 4-C compounds rather than burned to CO_2.

The two enzymes of the glyoxylate bypass have been found in a variety of organisms grown on acetate as sole C source, but their formation is repressed by the simultaneous supply of a more rapidly used substrate, such as glucose or

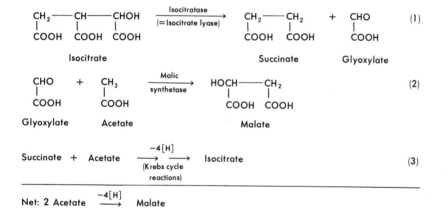

Fig. 4-6 The Krebs tricarboxylic acid cycle, and within it the "glyoxylate bypass." The circled compounds represent sources of biosynthetic drain, and in an organism growing on acetate alone the glyoxylate cycle provides net C-4 (and thus C-3) synthesis to the extent required to replenish this drain. (Since this cycle involves two oxidative steps, linked to electron transport, it also provides some energy; but most of the required energy is derived from the simultaneous oxidation of other acetate molecules via the Krebs cycle.)

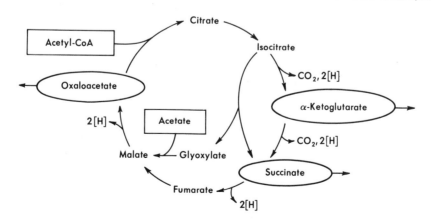

succinate. This response resembles the diauxic response to different sugars, noted at the end of the last chapter.

Ferredoxin and Acetate Reduction. We have seen that the need for the glyoxylate cycle arises from the irreversibility of the oxidative decarboxylation of pyruvate to acetyl CoA and CO_2, as observed with enzymes from a variety of microbes and higher organisms; the similar decarboxylation of α-ketoglutarate to succinyl CoA and CO_2 is also irreversible in most systems. The irreversibility means that the **standard** potential of the redox cofactor involved is not low enough to achieve significant reversal of the reaction, even when the **actual** potential of the system is lowered by providing a high ratio of reduced to oxidized cofactor.* However, the recently discovered cofactor of very low redox potential, **ferredoxin** (Ch. 3), permits extracts of photosynthetic bacteria and certain anaerobes to form pyruvate, and in some cases also α-ketoglutarate, by a reductive carboxylation. This evolutionary adaptation promotes the efficient use of acetate for biosynthetic purposes under anaerobic conditions, where the glyoxylate cycle cannot be used.

Promotion of Unidirectional Flow

Reversible and Irreversible Reactions. As we have noted, in the cell some over-all sequences (e.g., glycolysis) may exhibit net flow in either direction, depending on circumstances. For some steps in this reversal the same enzyme appears to be used reversibly. For example, aldolase catalyzes either the conversion of two molecules of triose-P to one hexose-di-P or the reverse, depending on whether the C source is glycerol or glucose. However, for other steps, which are also reversible in vitro, cells have developed a somewhat different reverse reaction, presumably because the equilibrium constant of the first

---

* The **standard** redox potential (E'_0) is that observed with a 1:1 ratio of oxidized to reduced form of the cofactor, under standard conditions of pH, etc. The **actual** potential of the system is modified by shifts in this ratio: the greater the proportion of reduced form, the lower the potential.

reaction is too unfavorable for physiological reversal of this reaction.

For example, the "clockwise" flow of the TCA cycle is favored by the release of acyl-CoA energy in the reaction of the citrate condensing enzyme:

Acetyl-CoA + Oxaloacetate $\rightleftharpoons$ Citrate + CoA

In contrast, without the participation of CoA the equilibrium strongly favors cleavage; and organisms fermenting citrate start with this reaction, employing the inducible enzyme citratase:

The oxaloacetate can then be fermented by dismutation, some molecules being oxidized via pyruvate and others being reduced to fumarate.

In many biosynthetic routes sequences of reversible reactions can flow only in the desired direction because of the presence, early in the sequence, of a virtually irreversible reaction (usually ATP-linked). This reaction functions rather like the initial, power-driven climb in a rollercoaster, followed by spontaneous fall past several peaks of decreasing energy level. It is therefore not surprising that the pathways of degradation of amino acids or nucleotide bases, which must flow downhill, have not overlapped much with their pathways of biosynthesis.

For some reactions flow in the desired direction is further promoted by release of pyrophosphate (PP) rather than phosphate. In the use of ATP the **standard** free energy drop (i.e., at unit concentration of all components) is essentially the same for PP release as for P release. However, the cell has a substantial P concentration, whereas the steady-state concentration of PP is negligible because of the presence of pyrophosphatase. The **actual** free energy drop is therefore greater for PP than for P release, and the reaction costs two high-energy bonds rather than one.

The same principle is applied in the biosynthetic use of ribose-5-P. Here PP from ATP is used to create a stable high-energy intermediate, 5-P-ribose-1-PP (PRPP), whose subsequent condensation is the reverse of a pyrophosphorolysis:

$$PRPP + XNH_2 \rightleftharpoons XNH\cdot RP + PP_i;$$
$$PP_i \rightarrow 2\ P_i$$

Because early studies on enzymes focused on in vitro reversibility, many enzymes (e.g., glutamic dehydrogenase, pyrophosphorylases) are unfortunately named for what we now know to be the reverse of their physiological reactions.

Alternative Pathways. A number of enzyme sequences have been discovered, in extracts of the same organism, that appear to offer alternative routes for converting one compound to another. However, the pathways of biosynthesis of a great variety of compounds must be unique: otherwise mutants lacking an enzyme in one of these pathways would not require its product. Moreover,

there is obviously widespread selection against synthesis of superfluous enzymes, such as the phenotypic loss of the electron transport system in the anaerobic growth of facultative organisms, or the genotypic loss of many biosynthetic enzymes in organisms adapted to grow in a rich environment. These considerations suggest that the apparently alternative pathways in other areas of metabolism are likely to be adapted to different circumstances, rather than to provide simultaneous duplicate pathways.

An excellent example is seen in the several different carboxylation and decarboxylation reactions, reversible in vitro, that can mediate carbon flow between the glycolytic and the TCA pathways (Fig. 4-7). The existence of enzymes for more than one of these reactions, within the same species, now seems rational, since recent evidence indicates that these enzymes are formed adaptively in response to the use of different carbon sources, each reaction providing an exer-

Fig. 4-7 Carboxylation and decarboxylation reactions connecting the glycolytic and the TCA pathways under various conditions and in different organisms.
Carbon source
Glucose: Carboxylation by reaction 1 in E. coli (using energy of PEP), or by reaction 2 in *Pseudomonas* (using energy of ATP).
Lactate: Carboxylation by reaction 2, or by reaction 3 (using energy from favorable equilibrium of TPN-linked reduction).
TCA component (such as succinate): Decarboxylation by reaction 4 to high-energy PEP (using energy of GTP) for biosynthetic needs, and also by reaction 3 or 5 (spontaneous) to lower-energy pyruvate for amphibolic purposes.

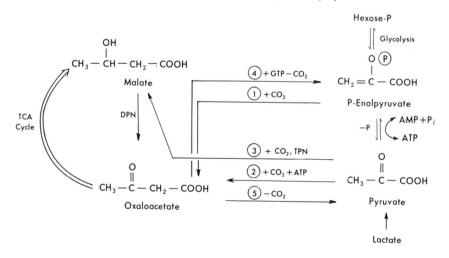

gonic process for the flow required by that source.

Redox Cofactors: The Roles of DPN and TPN.

Redox cofactors play a major role in directing metabolic flow. In order to ensure a smooth flow and to promote economy of energy, the cell contains several cofactors of different redox potential, increasing in the order ferredoxin, lipoic acid, DPN and TPN, flavins, and cytochromes. (Since flavins and hemes are firmly bound to their enzymes their potentials can vary from one complex to another.)

An example of control by these cofactors is provided by the reduction of pyruvate to lactate, and its reversal, by various lactic dehydrogenases. The DPN-linked reduction, seen in the lactic fermentation (Ch. 3), is reversible in vitro; but the equilibrium strongly favors lactate.* Hence to oxidize lactate various cells employ a quite different, flavin-linked lactic dehydrogenase, thus ensuring flow in the desired direction. It may be noted that energy is thereby sacrificed, since the step between DPN and flavoprotein in electron transport would yield an ATP (Ch. 3).

The necessity of ensuring a given direction of flow also explains the presence in the same cell of both DPN and TPN, which are very similar not only in structure but also in redox potential. A few dehydrogenases can apparently be linked with either, but most are specific for one or the other. In the earlier study of catabolic sequences it was not clear why such similar cofactors should both be present. However, the analysis of many biosynthetic reactions involving these pyridine nucleotides now supports the generalization that **those enzymes catalyzing an oxidative biosynthetic reaction are DPN-linked** (e.g., histidinol → histidine), **while those catalyzing a reductive biosynthetic reaction are TPN-linked** (e.g., α-keto glutarate → glutamate; fatty acid biosynthesis from acetate). Furthermore, in steady-state metabolism the TPN in a cell is mostly in the reduced form, and the DPN in the oxidized form; and these ratios would promote the functions just noted. Evidently two distinct cofactors of similar potential are present in the same cell because it must be able, for biosynthetic purposes, to oxidize some intermediates and reduce others at the same time.

Just as the constant reduction of DPN in fermentation requires its constant regeneration, so the oxidation of TPNH in biosynthesis requires its regeneration in some other reaction. While glycolysis, as we have seen, does not perform this function, it is accomplished in three other sets of reactions: 1) the oxidation of glucose-6-P to 6-P-gluconate and then to pentose-P and CO_2 (Fig. 4-19); 2) the oxidation of isocitrate to α-ketoglutarate and CO_2 (Fig. 4-6); and 3) the oxidation of malate to pyruvate and CO_2 by malic enzyme (reaction 3, Fig. 4-7). These reactions all have a larger energy drop than most other dehydrogenations; hence they can establish a very low TPN/TPNH ratio, which would support the reductive biosynthetic function of TPNH. Furthermore, the flow through these reactions is not rigidly coupled to over-all energy metabolism but can be adjusted precisely to meet the TPNH requirement for biosynthetic purposes; for though the cell requires the product of each of these reactions for other purposes, it can also make these products by alternative reactions that do not involve TPN. Thus pentose-P can be synthesized (from hexose-P) by a nonoxidative reaction employing transketolase (Fig. 4-20), α-ketoglutarate by a DPN-linked isocitrate dehydrogenase paralleling the TPN-linked one, and pyruvate from malate by DPN-linked oxidation to oxaloacetate, followed by decarboxylation (Fig. 4-7).

---

* At 37° and pH 7.0 the reaction pyruvate + DPNH ⇌ lactate + DPN has a value of −ΔF of 5000 cal., corresponding (ΔF = −RTlnK) to an equilibrium constant, K, of about 10^4 [K = (lac)(DPN)/(pyr)(DPNH)]. Hence at a DPN/DPNH ratio of 1.0 the equilibrium ratio of lac/pyr would be about 10,000. Though the DPN/DPNH ratio in aerobic cells exceeds 1.0, it is not high enough to ensure a good flow over this energy barrier.

AMINO ACIDS

Most of the steps in the biosynthesis of the amino acids are now known. We shall note selected reactions to illustrate the variety of patterns that have evolved.

The Glutamate Family

The reductive amination of α-ketoglutarate,

$$HOOC-CH_2-CH_2-\underset{\underset{O}{\|}}{C}-COOH \xrightarrow[\text{TPNH}]{\text{NH}_3}$$

α-Ketoglutarate

$$HOOC-CH_2-CH_2-\underset{\underset{NH_2}{|}}{CH}-COOH$$

L-Glutamate

yields glutamate. In most bacteria, as in higher organisms, glutamate serves as the source, by **transamination,** of the α-amino group of all the other amino acids, and of N atoms in many other cell components. Glutamate also takes up NH₃ (with the utilization of ~P)

to form **glutamine** [H₂NCOCH₂CH₂CH-(NH₂)COOH], and the resulting amide group in turn serves as a source of N, at a higher energy level, in the biosynthesis of various compounds (amino sugars, purines). Finally, glutamate provides the C skeleton as well as an N atom in **proline,** and in **ornithine,** a precursor of **arginine.** Ornithine also provides a part of the **polyamines** spermidine and spermine. These pathways are outlined in Figure 4-8.

The conversion of glutamate to **proline** requires reduction of the γ-carboxyl-group to an aldehyde. The next step is the cyclization of glutamic γ-semialdehyde, which occurs spontaneously between the appropriately spaced carbonyl and amino groups, much like the formation of the analogous O-containing furanose ring in sugars. The product of cyclization, a pyrroline derivative, is then reduced to yield proline. Bacteria do not contain hydroxyproline, which is generally absent also from mammalian cells (but present in collagen).

Arginine synthesis also involves a semialdehyde, but the spontaneous cyclization of glu-

Fig. 4-8 Biosynthesis of glutamate derivatives.

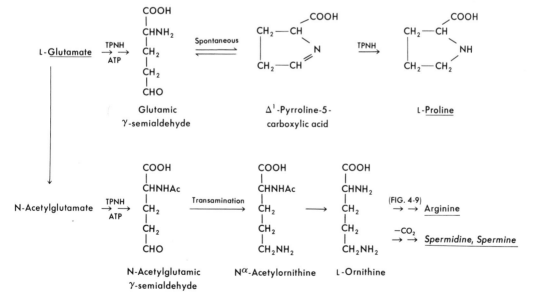

tamic semialdehyde would interfere with the further reduction of the open chain; this cyclization is prevented by first blocking the α-NH$_2$ group of glutamate with an acetyl group, just as one would do in a laboratory synthesis. In some bacteria the acetyl group is subsequently eliminated by simple hydrolysis; but in others, in an interesting variant of this pathway, the acetyl group is instead transferred directly from acetylornithine to glutamate, and is thus recycled without loss of energy. The later reactions, from ornithine to citrulline to arginine (Fig. 4-9), involve use of ATP to incorporate CO_2 and NH_3 via carbamyl phosphate, followed by condensation with aspartate as a means of accepting its amino group.

This pathway is extended in mammalian liver by the addition of arginase, which hydrolyzes arginine to ornithine and urea. The result is the Krebs-Henseleit cycle of urea formation, which was discovered long before the arginine pathway but undoubtedly evolved much later. The arginine pathway has been extensively used to study regulatory mechanisms in bacteria.

The Aspartate Family

Aspartate is synthesized by transamination of oxaloacetate. Like glutamate, it can be directly converted to its amide, **asparagine,** and can be reduced to its semialdehyde. This reduction, in contrast to that of glutamate, has been successfully analyzed enzymatically: it is made possible energetically by prior phosphorylation of the carboxyl by ATP (as in the reduction of P-glycerate to P-glyceraldehyde in the reversal of glycolysis) (Fig. 4-10). The resulting aspartic β-semialdehyde undergoes further reduction to homoserine, which yields the 4-C chains of **methionine** and **threonine.** Threonine in turn, by deamination to α-ketobutyrate, provides a 4-C precursor of **isoleucine.**

Aspartic β-semialdehyde also contributes 4 carbons to a 7-C dicarboxylic acid which is converted to **diaminopimelate** (DAP). This compound serves both as a component of wall mucopeptide in many bacteria and as the source of **lysine** in all bacteria. Aspartate is also a direct precursor of the pyrimidine

ring (see below); and the amino group of aspartate is the source of N atoms in several biosyntheses: the purine ring, the amino group of adenine, and the guanido group of arginine.

Methionine derives its S from cysteine by the following mechanism, involving the intermediate formation of a thioether, cystathionine:

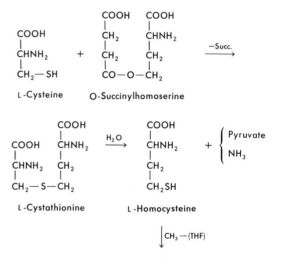

Homocysteine obtains a methyl group by transfer from 5-methyl-THF; the formation of this group, by reduction of a hydroxymethyl group derived from serine, is described below (Fig. 4-15). Vitamin B$_{12}$ has a role in this reduction and transfer, as was indicated by the early observation that an *E. coli* mutant blocked in the synthesis of vitamin B$_{12}$ can grow on either this compound or methionine. This finding illustrates the ability of an endproduct to spare the requirement for a cofactor in its own synthesis.

A high-energy precursor of methionine in this sequence, **S-adenosylmethionine,** serves also as the source for a variety of **methylations,** whose products include a minor fraction of the bases in DNA and RNA, branched-chain fatty acids, the cyclopropane ring in some fatty acids, and cobamide. S-adenosylmethionine also provides the —(CH$_2$)$_3$NH$_2$ portion of **spermidine** [H$_2$N-(CH$_2$)$_4$-NH-(CH$_2$)$_3$-NH$_2$] and **spermine** [H$_2$N-(CH$_2$)$_3$-NH-(CH$_2$)$_4$-NH-(CH$_2$)$_3$-NH$_2$].

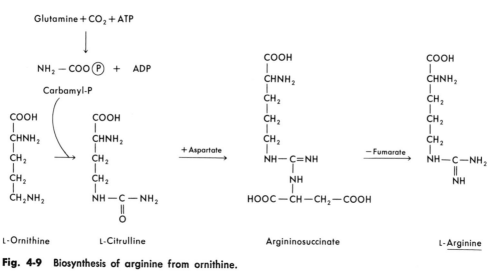

Fig. 4-9 Biosynthesis of arginine from ornithine.

Diaminopimelate and Lysine. In this pathway (Fig. 4-11), analyzed largely by Gilvarg, aspartic semialdehyde condenses with pyruvate, and a succinyl group is temporarily attached to the amino group, presumably to prevent cyclization (as in the addition of an acetyl group in ornithine biosynthesis, Fig. 4-8). After suitable transformations removal of the succinyl group

Fig. 4-10 Biosynthesis of the aspartate family.

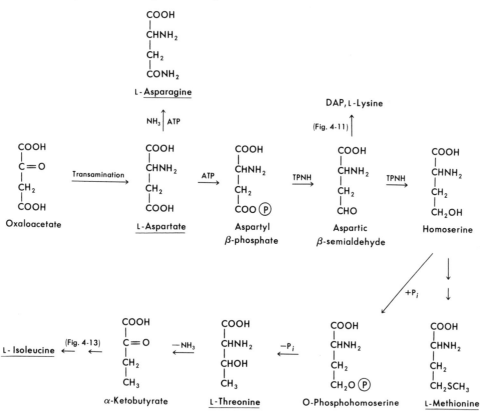

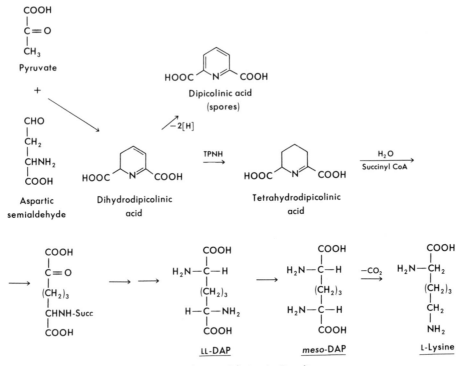

Fig. 4-11 Biosynthesis of diaminopimelate and lysine in *E. coli.*

yields L, L-DAP. A few bacterial species incorporate this compound into wall, but more use its derivative, the symmetrical, optically inactive *meso*-DAP, which contains a D-amino group. A specific decarboxylase eliminates the COOH group adjacent to this D-amino group, yielding L-lysine.

A mutant blocked before DAP cannot grow, for lack of both DAP and lysine; but if given lysine it will lyse, because it can carry out protein synthesis and growth but cannot form adequate wall. (Lysine was named, however, 60 years before the discovery of this property.)

An early intermediate in the DAP pathway also yields dipicolinate (Fig. 4-11), a prominent constituent of bacterial spores (Ch. 5).

Lysine is the only amino acid for which quite **different biosynthetic routes** have been found in different organisms.* In most fungi

it is synthesized by a route involving the 6-C α-aminoadipate (Fig. 4-12), rather than the 7-C DAP (Fig. 4-11).

It is tempting to speculate that the two routes to lysine have evolved in association with differences in the biosynthesis of cell walls: DAP is present in the walls of many bacteria, and α-aminoadipate is present in antibiotics (which may be wall derivatives, see Ch. 10) from some molds. In higher plants, in which neither precursor has been demonstrated as a structural component, the DAP pathway is found.

The Pyruvate Family: The Aliphatic Amino Acids

Alanine is usually derived, like aspartate, by a one-step transamination of the corresponding α-keto acid, pyruvate.† Pyruvate also

---

* Variation is also seen in the salvage reaction by which phenylalanine is converted to tyrosine: this reaction is found in mammals and a few bacteria, but not in those bacteria that can synthesize these amino acids de novo, by the pathway described below.

† The properties of certain mutants, however, indicate that some members of the genus *Bacillus* form alanine by reductive amination, and then use alanine, instead of glutamate, as the source of the amino group in **transamination**.

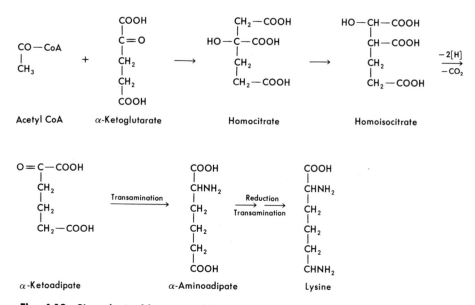

Fig. 4-12 Biosynthesis of lysine in molds. Note the precise homology between this pathway and that to glutamate (Fig. 4-3), the 5-C, lower homolog of α-aminoadipate.

serves as the starting point for formation of the longer-chain aliphatic amino acids: **isoleucine, valine,** and **leucine.** These pathways, analyzed by Umbarger, exhibit an unusual feature: a single set of enzymes catalyzes two parallel sequences of reactions, the substrates differing by a -CH_2- group (Fig. 4-13).

Specifically, "active acetaldehyde" from pyruvate (i.e., hydroxyethyl-TPP) condenses with

Fig. 4-13 Biosynthesis of isoleucine and valine.

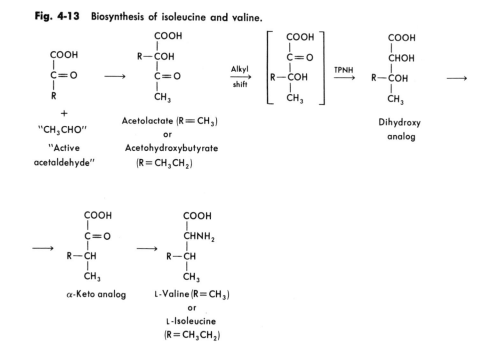

pyruvate, to yield acetolactate, or with α-keto-butyrate, to yield the homolog α-aceto-α-hydroxy-butyrate. The subsequent transformations of these compounds include a biochemically un-usual rearrangement of the carbon skeleton (alkyl shift), ultimately yielding isoleucine and valine.

Acetolactate is also an intermediate in the butylene glycol fermentation of *Aerobacter* (Ch. 3, Fig. 3-2). Umbarger has shown that this spe-cies can form two acetolactate synthetases, which act on the same substrates and apparently con-tribute to the same pool of acetolactate. In Chap-ter 9 (Isozymes, under Endproduct inhibition) we shall discuss evidence, from differences in the properties and the regulation of these en-zymes, that one functions primarily in biosyn-thesis and the other in degradation.

Leucine formation involves elongation of the chain of valine by 1 C atom, through addition of an acetyl group to "ketovaline," followed by oxidative decarboxylation (Fig. 4-14). This series of reactions, like the formation of lysine in plants (Fig. 4-12), is precisely analogous to a familiar series in the TCA cycle, which con-verts oxaloacetate to its higher homologue, α-ketoglutarate (Fig. 4-6).

The 5-C chain of "ketovaline" also takes up a hydroxymethyl group, via tetrahydrofolate, to yield **pantoate**, a component of CoA (Fig. 4-14).

The Serine Family: 1-C Fragments

Serine, which is derived from 3-P-glycerate, gives rise to glycine, cysteine, the side chain of tryptophan, and a transferable "1-C" frag-ment (in the form of hydroxymethyl-tetra-hydrofolate, $HOCH_2$-THF). The pathway to

Fig. 4-14   Biosynthesis of leucine and pantoate.

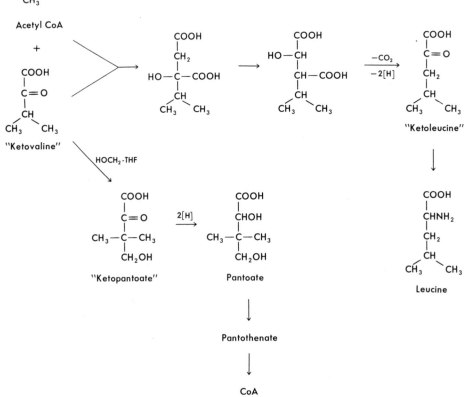

serine, glycine, and HOCH₂-THF is the following:

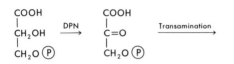

3-P-Glycerate 3-P-Hydroxypyruvate

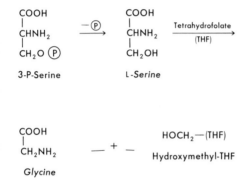

which accepts the 1-C fragment from serine or glycine, has the following structure:

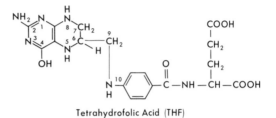

Tetrahydrofolic Acid (THF)

The initial fragment, which is at the hydroxy-methyl (= aldehyde) level of oxidation, condenses with THF to form 5,10-methylene-THF. To create 1-C fragments at other levels of oxidation this compound is reduced to 5-methyl-THF, and oxidized to 10-formyl-THF, as indicated in Figure 4-15. Also noted are the biosynthetic sequences that take up these fragments, to form the purine ring (and thence the imidazole ring of histidine), the methyl group of methionine (and thence many derivatives: see p. 92), the methyl group of thymine, and (not shown) the HOCH₂-group of pantoate and a 1-C fragment of thiamine.

Interconversion of Glycine and Serine. The split of serine described above forms equimolar amounts of glycine and 1-C fragments. The cell, however, will ordinarily require these products in a different proportion. Economy in biosynthesis is achieved by an additional reaction, which generates a 1-C fragment from glycine; the two reactions together convert the carbon of serine to two 1-C fragments + CO_2, without leaving an excess of glycine. Moreover, since the conversion of serine to glycine + 1-C is reversible, the cleavage of glycine has a further advantage: the formation of 1-C from glycine permits the cell to use exogenous glycine for the net synthesis of serine as follows:

Glycine + (THF) ⟶ HOCH₂—(THF) + CO_2 + NH_3

HOCH₂—(THF) + Glycine ⇌ Serine + THF

_____

Net: 2 Glycine ⟶ Serine + CO_2 + NH_3

1-C Transfer. Tetrahydrofolic acid (THF),

Cysteine is formed by replacing the -OH group of serine with an -SH from H_2S.

COOH
|
CH₂NH₂ —Acetyl CoA→ COOH
| |
CH₂OH   CH₂NH₂ —H₂S→
                              |
L-Serine   CH₂OAc

                              O-Acetyl
                              L-Serine

                              COOH
                              |
                              CHNH₂ + AcOH
                              |
                              CH₂SH

                              L-Cysteine

Sulfate Reduction. The usual inorganic S source in bacteriological media is sulfate rather than sulfide. Most bacteria can form sulfide from sulfate on a small scale for biosynthetic purposes, apparently by the same pathway that is used on a large scale for energy production by _Desulfovibrio_ (Table 3-2). In this pathway sulfate is activated by the use of two ATP molecules to yield 3'-phosphoadenosine-5'-phosphosulfate:

Adenine-ribose-3'-Ⓟ-5'-Ⓟ-OSO₃H

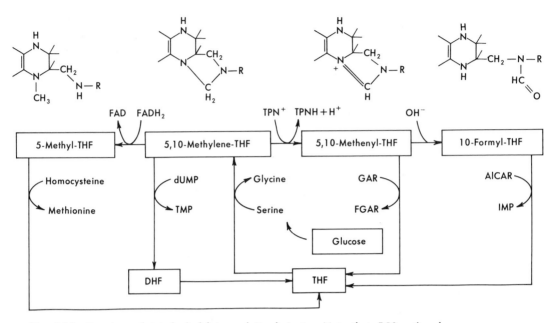

Fig. 4-15 Reactions of tetrahydrofolate and its derivates. Note that 5,10-methenyl-THF and 10-formyl-THF are at the same level of oxidation; the formyl group from one closes the imidazole ring; and that from the other closes the six-membered ring, in purine biosynthesis (Fig. 4-22). DHF=dihydrofolate. (After J. M. Buchanan. Medicine 43:697, 1964.)

Histidine

The biosynthesis of histidine (Fig. 4-16), largely worked out by Ames, is unique in several respects. A 5-C chain is furnished by ribose-5-P; and whereas the carboxyl of all other amino acids derives from the preexisting carboxyl of an amphibolic precursor, that of histidine is formed by the oxidation of an intermediate aminoalcohol (histidinol). Furthermore, both steps in this oxidation (histidinol to histidinal to histidine) are catalyzed by the same enzyme.

The early stages of this sequence involve a remarkable reaction in which ATP serves as more than an energy donor. Ribose-5-P (from PRPP) is condensed with ATP; and in the subsequent cleavage the N^1-C^2 fragment of ATP is contributed to a histidine precursor to form (with the addition of NH_3) the imidazole ring. The residue of the ATP in this cleavage is the nucleotide of 5-aminoimidazole carboxamide, which is a normal intermediate in purine biosynthesis and hence is reconverted to ATP. Thus a cycle, grafted onto the pathway of purine biosynthesis, serves for the generation of an N-C portion of histidine.

Aromatic Biosynthesis

Since aliphatic compounds are generally difficult to aromatize in the organic chemical laboratory, the mechanism of this process in biological systems has considerable biochemical interest. Moreover, the same pathway is used in both bacteria and higher plants; and in the latter it yields the enormous amount of aromatic material polymerized in lignin, which has probably been the major source of the aromatic components of petroleum and hence of the aromatic products of the chemical industry. This biosynthetic pathway was elucidated, largely by Davis and Sprinson, with the aid of mutants of *E. coli;* and as has been noted above, the key was provided by the finding that certain mutants, which require a mixture of aromatic compounds (**tyrosine, phenylalanine, tryptophan,** and certain trace factors), can also grow on shikimic acid

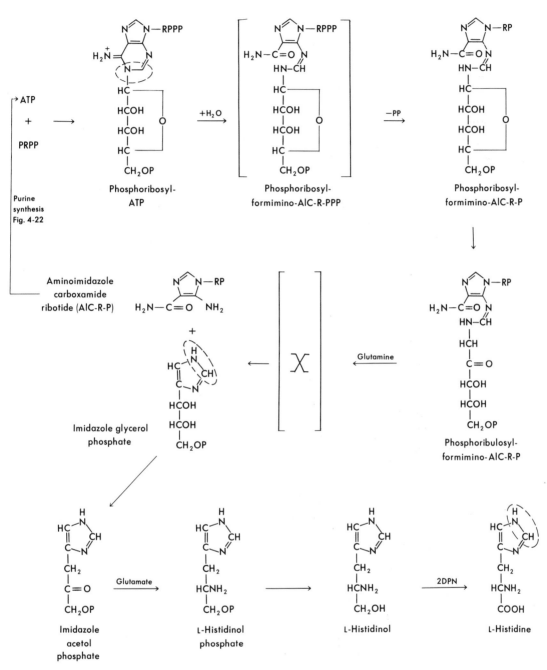

Fig. 4-16 Biosynthesis of histidine. The N-C fragment donated by ATP is circled by a dashed line; the remainder of the ATP molecule becomes a normal intermediate in the purine nucleotide pathway. (After B. N. Ames and P. E. Hartman. Cold Spring Harbor Symp. Quant. Biol. 28:349, 1963.)

(Fig. 4-17), a hydroaromatic compound from a higher plant.

As is shown in Figure 4-17, aromatic bio-

synthesis is initiated by aldol condensation of erythrose-P with P-enolpyruvate (PEP). The resulting 7-C straight-chain compound is readily cyclized and then reduced to shikimate, which

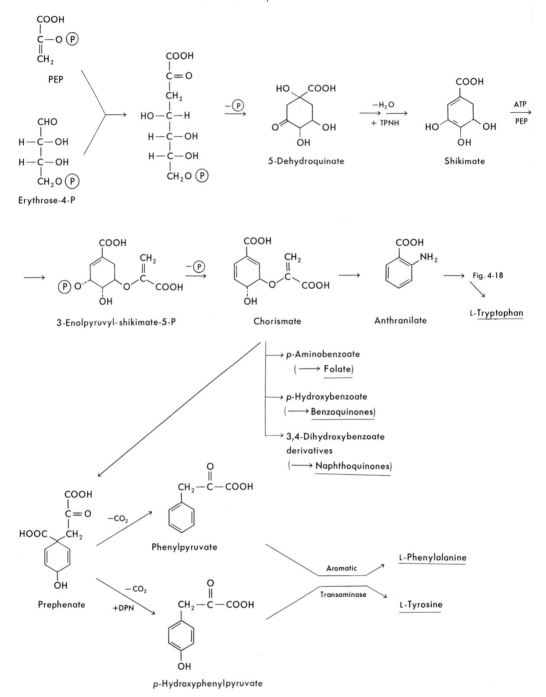

Fig. 4-17 The aromatic pathway: synthesis of tyrosine, phenylalanine, tryptophan, and aromatic vitamins.

becomes phosphorylated and takes up another PEP. The resulting highly reactive compound undergoes a biochemically novel shift of its 3-C side chain from an enol-ether to a stable C-C attachment to another carbon of the ring. The ring then develops a second double bond by dehydration, which labilizes it for **aromatization.**

Chorismic acid (Gr., "fork") is the major

branch point in this pathway. In some branches aromatization is accompanied by loss of the carboxyl group, which has activated preceding reactions; such decarboxylative aromatization, accompanied by dehydrogenation or by dehydration, yields the α-keto acid precursors of tyrosine and phenylalanine, respectively. In other aromatization reactions, which yield the tryptophan precursor anthranilate (*o*-aminobenzoate), or the folic acid precursor *p*-aminobenzoate, the carboxyl group is retained and the pyruvic side chain is discarded. Still other branches yield *p*-

hydroxybenzoate, a precursor of benzoquinones (ubiquinones), and 3,4-dihydroxybenzoate derivatives that serve as precursors of naphthoquinones (vitamin K).

In the conversion of anthranilate to **tryptophan** (Fig. 4-18) the first step is condensation with ribose-5-P (from PRPP). Subsequent transformations, including loss of the shikimate carboxyl and formation of a second ring, yield indoleglycerol-P. This compound is a precise analog of imidazoleglycerol-P, described above as a precursor of histidine. However, instead of

Fig. 4-18 Biosynthesis of tryptophan, branching from the common aromatic pathway.

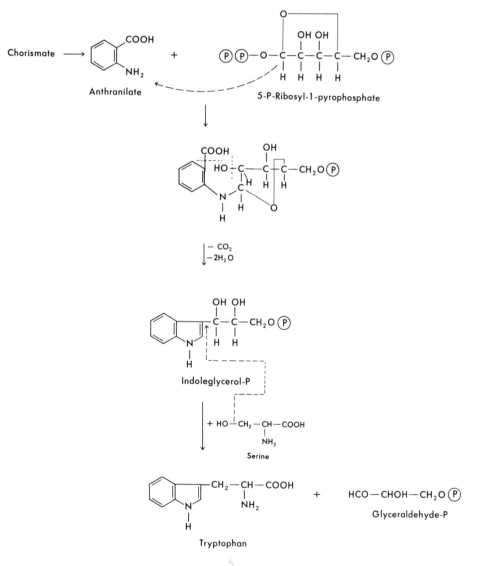

retaining and oxidizing the 3-C side chain, as in histidine biosynthesis, indoleglycerol-P exchanges this chain for the 3-C chain of serine, to yield tryptophan in a single step. This biosynthetic short-cut is apparently made possible by the fact that the indole ring labilizes the side chain to electrophilic attack much more strongly than does the imidazole ring.

Genetic alterations in the enzyme of this last step, tryptophan synthetase, have been intensively investigated by Yanofsky, and these studies have contributed decisive evidence that the nucleotide sequence of a gene is translated into the corresponding sequence of a polypeptide (Ch. 8).

D-Amino Acids

All bacteria studied contain D-amino acids in polypeptides in their cell wall, and sometimes in capsules and antibiotic products as well. The synthesis of D-amino acids has been shown, in some organisms, to involve a racemase that acts on alanine, plus a special transaminase that can transfer the D-amino group to various keto acids, as follows:

$$\text{L-Alanine} \underset{}{\overset{\text{Racemase}}{\rightleftharpoons}} \text{D-Alanine}$$

$$\text{D-Alanine} + \alpha\text{-Ketoglutarate, etc.} \underset{}{\overset{\text{D-Transaminase}}{\rightleftharpoons}} \text{D-Glutamate, etc.} + \text{Pyruvate}$$

NUCLEOTIDES

Purine and pyrimidine nucleotides have several functions: they are 1) building blocks of nucleic acids; 2) components of many coenzymes; and 3) activators for the transfer and transformations of sugars, wall peptides, and complex lipids, and for the activation of amino acids. The biosynthesis of the several purines involves a common pathway, which branches at hypoxanthine ribonucleotide to yield adenylate and guanylate. Pyrimidine nucleotides are similarly synthesized via a single pathway, which branches at uridylate (UMP).

These pathways were to a large extent elucidated first in animal tissues, by the use of isotopic and enzymatic methods. One stage in purine biosynthesis, however, was revealed in bacteria very early, through the finding that sulfonamide-inhibited cultures accumulate 5-amino-4-imidazole carboxamide (for structure see Fig. 4-22, below).

Many bacteria, like mammalian cells, can use exogenously supplied free purines and pyrimidines, or their nucleosides, as sources of nucleotides. Nevertheless, these precursors are not normal biosynthetic intermediates, and we shall not review the reactions involved. The wide biological distribution of these "salvage" enzymes probably reflects the presence of nucleosides and free bases wherever cells are degraded, and their ready penetration, in contrast to the corresponding nucleotides,* into living cells.

We shall also not discuss the kinases that increase the level of phosphorylation of various nucleoside phosphates, except to note one feature that is important for the specificity of DNA synthesis. Uracil and thymine pair equally well with adenine (Ch. 8); and DNA polymerase (see below), given dUTP in vitro, can utilize it in place of dTTP, forming a DNA of abnormal composition. However, in E. coli no dUTP is formed by the deoxyribonucleotide kinases present, which convert the other deoxyribonucleotides to the triphosphates. This mechanism ensures the exclusion of U from DNA.

Pentoses

Ribose-5-P can be formed in two ways: oxidatively from glucose-6-P (Fig. 4-19), and nonoxidatively by the transfer of C-1,2 of fructose-6-P to triose-P (first reaction, Fig. 4-20). Furthermore, in the latter process the residue from the fructose-6-P, erythrose-4-P, can also be converted to ribose-P by the subsequent reactions listed in the figure. The net result is the conversion of 2 hexoses + 1 triose to 3 pentoses.

---

*An exception is found in the rickettsiae. These small obligate intracellular parasites are permeable to nucleotides, which abound in their natural habitat.

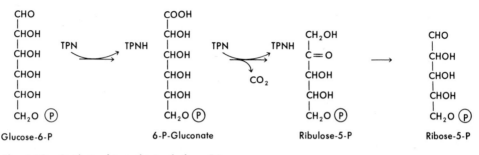

Fig. 4-19 Oxidative biosynthesis of ribose-5-P.

The presence of both the oxidative and the nonoxidative pathways to ribose in the same organism (e.g., *E. coli*) may reflect the possibility of both aerobic and anaerobic growth. Probably even more important, however, is the problem posed by the double function of the oxidative pathway, which both synthesizes pentose and regenerates TPNH from TPN (see p. 90 for the biosynthetic function of TPNH). Since the two products are not necessarily required in the proportions formed, additional pathways to and from pentose are required to maintain metabolic economy. Thus a need for pentose exceeding that for TPNH could be met by employing the nonoxidative pathway; and conversely, any excess of pentose could be converted to triose-P and hexose-P by reversal of the reactions of Figure 4-20.

The latter modification of the oxidative pathway, resulting in conversion of glucose-P to CO_2 and triose-P, is known as the "shunt" pathway, since it provides a mechanism for glucose utilization that bypasses part of the glycolytic pathway. However, in line with the principle that apparently alternative pathways do not ordinarily serve the same function in the cell (p. 89), it seems likely that the shunt pathway has a biosynthetic and not an amphibolic function.

Deoxyribose. After ribose-5-P is incorporated into purine and pyrimidine nucleotides via its high-energy derivative PRPP (see be-

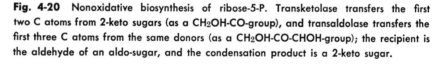

Fig. 4-20 Nonoxidative biosynthesis of ribose-5-P. Transketolase transfers the first two C atoms from 2-keto sugars (as a CH₂OH-CO-group), and transaldolase transfers the first three C atoms from the same donors (as a CH₂OH-CO-CHOH-group); the recipient is the aldehyde of an aldo-sugar, and the condensation product is a 2-keto sugar.

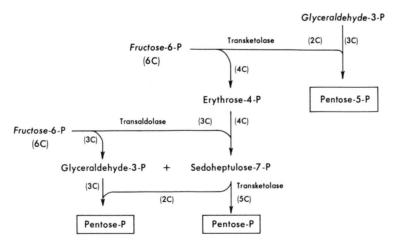

low), the **deoxyribose** residue is formed by TPNH-linked reduction of the ribose of the several ribonucleotides.

This reduction involves a novel small-protein cofactor, **thioredoxin,** in which a pair of -SH groups undergo reversible oxidation to -S-S-, just as in the function of lipoate. In other respects, however, this pathway is not uniform in all bacteria. In *Lactobacillus leichmannii* the reduction takes place at the nucleoside **triphosphate** level of phosphorylation, and it involves the B_{12} coenzyme, cobamide. In *E. coli,* in contrast, the substrates are the nucleoside **diphosphates,** and cobamide does not participate. This difference in the requirement for cobamide explains an early nutritional observation: various deoxyribonucleosides can replace vitamin B_{12} as a growth factor for the *Lactobacillus,* but not for mutants of *E. coli* that require the vitamin. Incidentally, this utilization of the deoxyribose residue appears to involve a salvage pathway, much like the utilization of free purines or pyrimidines or their ribonucleosides.

Purines

The synthesis of the purine ring is highly endergonic, requiring at least 3 $\sim$P. The origin of its atoms is summarized in Figure 4-21, and the major reactions are presented in Figure 4-22.

The first step is the condensation of ribose-5-P (from PRPP) with the amide of glutamine to yield 5-P-ribosylamine (i.e., the ribotide of am-

Fig. 4-21 Origin of purine ring atoms. The origin of C-2 and C-8 from 1-C fragments was first indicated through the incorporation of isotopically labeled formate, in a mammalian system. However, the condensation of formate with tetrahydrofolate is not a physiological process; there is evidence that even in bacteria whose fermentations yield formate the biosynthetic formyl group is derived entirely from serine.

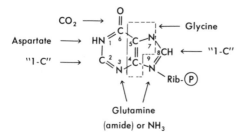

Glutamine
(amide) or NH_3

monia). This compound then forms an imide by condensation with glycine; and two steps later the addition of another -NH₂ from glutamine converts the imide to a substituted amidine [-C(=NH)NH-]. Addition of a formyl group, from THF (Fig. 4-15), to the amino group derived from glycine, is followed by a further condensation to close the imidazole ring. Further additions form a carboxamide group; and closure of the second ring is effected by insertion of another formyl group from THF. The product is the ribonucleotide of hypoxanthine (6-ketopurine nucleotide, inosinic acid, IMP).

Adenylate (6-aminopurine nucleotide) is formed from IMP by transfer of the amino group from aspartate. This unusual reaction involves not transamination but formation of a stable condensation product with aspartate, just as in the formation argininosuccinate in arginine biosynthesis (Fig. 4-9). Furthermore, the energy source for the condensation is GTP rather than ATP, which cleverly prevents any deficiency of adenylate from interfering with its own replenishment. Finally, the same condensing enzyme also performs a similar reaction in the formation of an earlier intermediate (the carboxamide) in the same pathway.

Guanylate formation from IMP involves oxidation by DPN to xanthylate (2,6-diketopurine nucleotide). The 2-keto group is then replaced by an amino group, derived in bacteria from NH_3; $\sim$P is consumed.

Adenylate and guanylate production from IMP each involve a virtually irreversible reaction. Nevertheless, either adenine or guanine furnished exogenously can give rise, to a varying extent in different organisms, to both nucleotides. This conversion of either base to the other involves enzymes distinct from the normal biosynthetic ones.

As was noted earlier, in histidine biosynthesis ATP donates its $N^1 - C^2$ fragment (Fig. 4-16), thus forming as a byproduct 5-amino-4-imidazolecarboxamide ribotide (Fig. 4-22), a normal intermediate in purine biosynthesis.

Pyrimidines

In contrast to the purines, the pathway to the pyrimidine ring is rather simple, and it does not involve the attachment of ribose-P until a late stage. It starts with the addition of a carbamyl group to aspartate. The reactions are depicted in Figure 4-23.

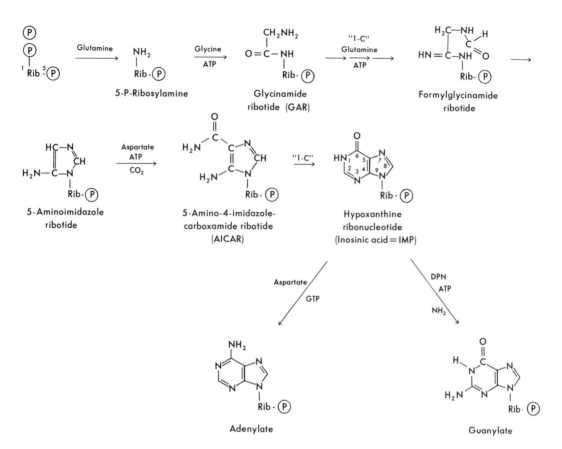

Fig. 4-22 Biosynthesis of purine nucleotides.

The source of the carbamyl group is carbamyl phosphate, which, as we have seen, donates the same group in the formation of citrulline from ornithine (Fig. 4-9). Hence mutants blocked in the formation of carbamyl phosphate (from ATP, CO_2, and NH_3 or glutamine) require both a pyrimidine and arginine (or citrulline). The carbamyl aspartate (= ureidosuccinate) formed in the pyrimidine pathway is directly cyclized and then dehydrogenated by a flavoprotein to yield orotic acid, a substituted pyrimidine. (This dehydrogenation closely resembles that of succinate, which is also linked to a flavin cofactor.) Orotic acid then adds ribose-P to form the first nucleotide in this pathway, which is decarboxylated to yield uridylate (UMP).

UMP serves as the source of the other pyrimidine nucleotides. After conversion to the triphosphate (UTP) it forms **cytidine triphosphate** (CTP) by adding an amino group; and after conversion to its deoxyribose derivative (dUMP) it takes up a methyl group from 5-methyl-THF

(Fig. 4-15) to form **thymidylate** (5-methyluracil deoxyribonucleotide). Finally an unusual pyrimidine, **hydroxymethylcytosine,** is present instead of cytosine in the DNA of certain bacteriophages (Ch. 23), and it is formed from dCMP (Fig. 4-23).

While bacteria use NH_3 (and ~P energy) in the amination reactions that convert UTP to CTP and xanthylate to GMP, animals use the amide of glutamine instead. This difference evidently reflects the prevalence of ammonia in the habitats of bacteria, contrasted with its toxicity to animal cells.

As noted above, a minor fraction of the various bases of RNA and DNA are methylated. These methylation reactions, in contrast to the formation of thymidylate described above, occur with the completed nucleic acid, rather than in the course of nucleotide biosynthesis; and the methyl donor is S-adenosylmethionine (p. 92) rather than methyl-THF.

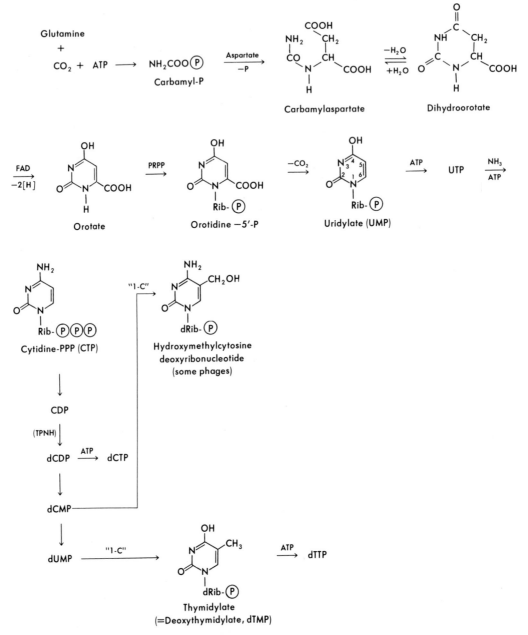

Fig. 4-23 Biosynthesis of pyrimidine nucleotides.

OTHER PATHWAYS

Sugars

Free sugars are fuels but are not metabolic intermediates within the bacterial cell (or the mammalian cell): on entering a cell a sugar is immediately phosphorylated. The phosphate group is provided usually by ATP, but in some reactions by PEP (via a small phosphate-carrier protein). Conversion into other sugars sometimes takes place at this phosphorylated level (cf. pentoses, Fig. 4-20; fructose, Fig. 3-1). However, most conversions of sugars occur at the level of **sugar nucleotides** (nucleoside diphosphate sugars), which were discovered in 1949 by Leloir and shown to be formed by specific pyrophosphorylases:*

$$\text{Nucleoside-P} \vdots \text{P-P} + \text{Hexose-1-P} \rightleftharpoons$$
$$\text{Nucleoside-P-P-hexose} + \text{P-P}$$

The utilization of such a nucleoside-diphosphate "handle" in the conversion of glucose to galactose (and vice versa) is depicted in

---

* The reaction, though reversible, normally flows in the direction opposite to pyrophosphorolysis, for reasons discussed on p. 89: pyrophosphate is released from the triphosphate, whose remaining phosphate condenses with that of the sugar.

Figure 4-24. In addition to undergoing such alterations of configuration, sugars attached to nucleotides may also undergo more extensive conversions, e.g., amination, reduction to deoxysugars, or oxidation to uronic acids. Moreover, nucleotide sugars are the donors in the transglycosylation reactions of wall polysaccharide formation (see below), just as in the formation of glycogen in animals or starch in plants.

Intermediates in bacterial sugar synthesis have often been discovered, just like those in amino acid biosynthesis, through their accumulation by appropriately blocked mutants. Such mutants, lacking one or another enzyme required for polysaccharide biosynthesis, sometimes contain large amounts of precursors of the missing polysaccharide, each

Fig. 4-24 Epimerization of galactose and glucose. The anabolic sequence from glucose to galactose (**A**) evidently employs the same isomerase as the pathway for the amphibolic utilization of galactose (**B**), for a gal⁻ mutant that lacks this enzyme has lost the ability both to use galactose as a carbon source and to make a galactose-containing wall polysaccharide from glucose. (These two sequences are also found in mammalian cells.)

(A) Biosynthetic formation of galactose from glucose

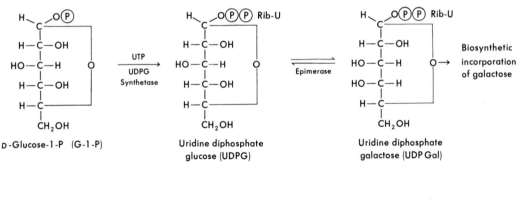

(B) Utilization of galactose (Gal) as carbon source

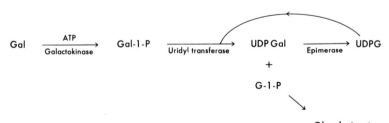

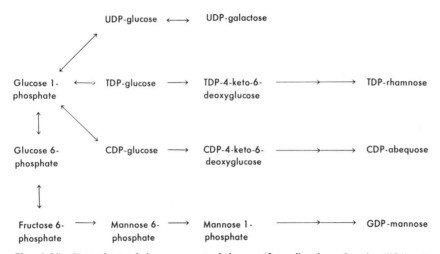

Fig. 4-25 Biosynthesis of the precursors of the specific wall polysaccharides ("O" antigen) of group B *Salmonella*. (From H. Nikaido, K. Nikaido, and P. M. Mäkelä. J. Bact. 91:1126, 1966.)

sugar being attached to a different nucleotide (guanosine-diphosphate mannose, deoxythymidine-diphosphate rhamnose, etc.). An example of such a set of related pathways, worked out in this manner, is presented in Figure 4-25.

Over 60 nucleotide sugars have now been isolated. Some of the known wall precursors are the following:

UDP-D-glucose (G)
UDP-D-acetylglucosamine (GNAc)
UDP-D-galactose (Gal)
UDP-D-galacturonate
GDP-D-mannose
GDP-L-fucose (6-deoxy-L-galactose)
GDP-D-rhamnose (6-deoxy-D-mannose)
GDP-colitose (3,6-dideoxy-L-galactose)
GDP-D-glycero-D-mannoheptose
dTDP-D-galactose
dTDP-L-rhamnose
dTDP-D-fucose
dTDP-6-deoxy-D-glucose
dTDP-GNAc
dTDP-GalNAc
CDP-tyvelose (3,6-dideoxy-D-mannose)
CDP-abequose (3,6-dideoxy-D-galactose)
CDP-glycerol ⎱ Reduced sugar (polyol) pre-
CDP-ribitol ⎰   cursors of teichoic acids

The advantage of using several different nucleotide carriers may conceivably lie in improving the specificity of the enzymes that incorporate sugars into polymers. However, there may be a more fundamental advantage: the attachment of glucose to different nucleotides permits it to be converted to different sugars with a minimum of mutual interference between their pathways, thus broadening the range of polysaccharides that can be evolved. The possibility of such interference is suggested by the observation that various capsular polysaccharides of *Aerobacter* contain mannose or fucose, but never both. Since fucose is derived (as GDP-fucose) from GDP-mannose, the presence of the enzymes for its formation may lower the level of GDP-mannose in the cell, and thus interfere with the incorporation of mannose into the polysaccharide.

Lipids

Though the lipids of the "waxy" coat of mycobacteria have been known since the 1920s to contain unusual components, systematic analysis of the structure of bacterial lipids, and of their biosynthesis, has begun only recently. The current rapid advance has depended on the development of chromatographic technics (including gas chromatography) that facilitate the separation and analysis of these water-insoluble, previously "smeary" compounds.

Interest in lipid biochemistry has grown

recently, not only because of the availability of precise analyses, but also because of increasing interest in the structure and function of the cell membrane. (In gram-positive bacteria this is the only known lipid-containing structure.) Since differences in structure should eventually be correlated with their effect on function, bacterial lipids are of particular interest because they differ so strikingly in their composition from those of other cells: bacteria lack both steroids and polyunsaturated fatty acids.

In gram-negative bacteria and mycobacteria lipids are also responsible for part of the surface specificity, being found in the cell walls in covalent linkage with other major components (lipopolysaccharides, lipoproteins). Lipids also appear to be an essential constituent of the important group of bacterial **endotoxins,** whose chemical structure is not yet well defined. Bacteria do not contain storage fats (triglycerides), but many of them convert acetate to a less completely reduced storage material, poly-β-hydroxybutyrate.

Fatty Acids

The apolar components of bacterial lipids are predominantly long-chain (C_{14} to C_{18}) saturated and monounsaturated fatty acids, much as in higher organisms, but without polyunsaturated chains. There are also a number of unusual fatty acids containing methyl branches, cyclopropane rings, or extremely long chains (e.g., mycolic acids with two long branches totaling C_{88} in tubercle bacilli.

The biosynthesis of fatty acids in bacteria, as in animals, proceeds by addition and reduction of successive acetyl units. The reactivity of the methyl group of acetyl CoA is first increased by the addition of CO_2 to form malonyl CoA:

$$CH_3-CO-S(CoA) \;+\; Biotin-CO_2 \longrightarrow$$

Acetyl CoA

$$HOOC-CH_2-CO-S(CoA) \;+\; Biotin$$

Malonyl CoA

In the course of the subsequent condensation this CO_2 is released.

In extracts from yeasts or from animal cells the enzymes responsible have not been separable from particles, but in *E. coli* extracts Vagelos has separated these enzymes and has demonstrated the key role of a small **acyl carrier protein** (ACP). The initiating acyl group, and the subsequent malonyl groups, are each transferred from the —SH of CoA to the —SH of a prosthetic group on ACP (4-phosphopantetheine, a component of CoA), and the entire process of chain extension occurs on molecules attached to this protein (Fig. 4-26).

Fatty acid synthesis is usually initiated by an acetyl group, leading to the formation of the predominant even-numbered, straight-chain fatty acids. However, odd-numbered straight-chain fatty acids can be formed by starting with a propionyl group, and those with a subterminal methyl branch are formed by starting with a short branched-chain acid (derived from the pathways to leucine or valine).

Fig. 4-26 Mechanism of elongation of fatty acids. (ACP)–SH = acyl carrier protein; RCO— = initiating acyl group.

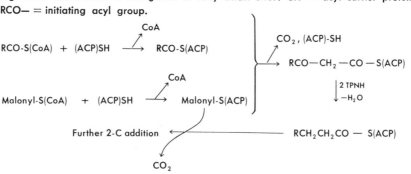

Like fungi and animals, a few aerobic bacteria can form unsaturated fatty acids by an aerobic mechanism, employing molecular oxygen to directly desaturate long-chain fatty acids. In addition, bacteria have a unique mechanism, not employing O_2, which produces unsaturated fatty acids by failing to reduce one of the double bonds formed (by dehydration) in the course of chain elongation. As a result, the predominant C_{18} monounsaturated fatty acid of many bacteria, vaccenic acid, differs from oleic acid in the position of its double bond.

Complex Lipids

The complex lipids of bacteria consist largely of glycerol with two hydroxyls attached to hydrocarbon chains, through either ester, vinyl ether (plasmalogen), or saturated ether linkages; the third hydroxyl is attached to a more polar moiety (either phosphate or a sugar). The phosphate in turn is linked either to a nitrogenous compound such as serine or ethanolamine, or to a polyol such as glycerol. Lecithin (phosphatidyl choline), an important phospholipid of higher organisms, is rarely found in bacteria.

Steps leading to the synthesis of phosphatidyl ethanolamine and phosphatidyl glycerol in *E.*

coli are shown in Figure 4-27. Phosphatidyl glycerol, in turn, gives rise in certain bacteria to a recently discovered additional class of complex lipids, lipoamino acids, in whose synthesis an amino acid is transferred from its transfer RNA (see below) to one of the free hydroxyls of phosphatidyl glycerol.

In eucaryotic cells, in which ACP is particle-bound, the acyl residue, synthesized as acyl-ACP, is transferred to complex lipids via acyl-CoA. In bacteria, however, in which ACP is not tightly bound to particles, the transfer is direct.

As noted above, bacteria do not contain steroids, which are synthesized in yeasts and higher organisms from acetyl CoA via **mevalonic acid** (β, δ-dihydroxy-β-methylvaleric acid); but many bacteria do contain carotenoids, which are synthesized via the same intermediate. Indeed, the requirement of a bacterium, *Lactobacillus acidophilus,* for mevalonic acid provided the first clue to the existence of this compound.

Environmental Influences. The composition of bacterial lipids varies markedly with conditions of growth. At lower temperatures, for example, cells form a larger proportion of unsaturated fatty acids, which have a lower melting point and hence presumably help maintain the

Fig. 4-27 The biosynthesis of phosphatides in *E. coli*. Only phosphatidyl ethanolamine and phosphatidyl glycerol accumulate in this organism; the other phosphatides are short-lived intermediates.

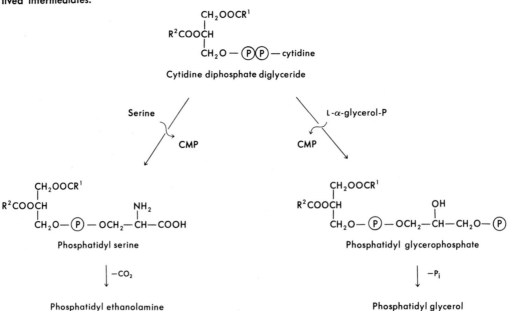

desired physical properties of the membrane at this temperature. Furthermore, as cells grow from the exponential to the stationary phase (Ch. 5) a number of changes occur: most of the unsaturated fatty acid molecules are often converted to cyclopropane fatty acids, by addition across the double bond of a 1-C fragment from S-adenosylmethionine; and the phospholipids tend to become more complex by the addition of an amino acid, or a second phosphatidic group, to the glycerol of phosphatidyl glycerol. These changes may well "toughen" the membrane and increase the chances of cell survival through a period of starvation.

Vitamins and Cofactors

The biosynthesis of **tetrapyrroles** (precursors of the **heme** components of many oxidative enzymes) proceeds in bacteria as in mammalian cells, from glycine and succinyl CoA via δ-aminolevulinate. The biosynthesis of most coenzymes, however, has not yet been worked out in detail, since the amounts of material synthesized are very limited. It is evident from the structures of these compounds that their pathways involve a large number of enzymes, and therefore of genes.

We shall not review these pathways. It is interesting to note, however, a rare exception to the unity of biosynthesis: nicotinamide (a component of DPN and TPN) is synthesized in fungi from tryptophan, but in bacteria via quite a different pathway, starting with aspartate and a 3-C glycolytic intermediate.

The conversion of p-aminobenzoate into folate will be discussed later, in connection with sulfonamide inhibition (Ch. 10).

Selected Features of Small-Molecule Biosynthesis

Certain interesting generalizations emerge from the pathways that we have just reviewed.

Heterotrophic CO$_2$ Fixation

For decades autotrophs, which derive their carbon from CO_2, were sharply distinguished from heterotrophs, which derive their carbon from organic matter. It was therefore a major surprise when Wood and Werkman, in 1935, discovered CO_2 fixation by a heterotroph fermenting glycerol to propionate.

On reviewing the propionic fermentation (Ch. 3) it is readily seen that the C in glycerol would ordinarily be quantitatively converted to propionate, with no CO_2 fixation. Wood and Werkman found, however, that with an excess of CO_2 present some of the succinate produced was not decarboxylated to propionate, and the fermentation yielded **more** C than was present in the glycerol supplied. Within a few years radioactive CO_2 became available and made it possible to show that **all heterotrophs (including mammals) assimilate** CO_2; but in the over-all stoichiometry of metabolism this process is ordinarily masked by the production of more CO_2 than that fixed.*

The subsequent analysis of biosynthetic pathways revealed multiple mechanisms for heterotrophic CO_2 fixation, resulting in assimilation into purines, pyrimidines, and several amino acids. The following reactions have been demonstrated:

1) Carboxylation of pyruvate or PEP (Fig. 4-7). In this reaction CO_2 yields one of the carbons of oxaloacetate (or malate), and thus of **aspartate, glutamate,** and their numerous derivatives. This is the largest route of heterotrophic CO_2 fixation.

2) Formation of carbamyl phosphate, which contributes both the guanido C of **arginine** (Fig. 4-19) and C$_2$ of the **pyrimidine** ring (Fig. 4-23). (C$_4$ of pyrimidines also arises from CO_2, via aspartate.)

3) The addition of CO_2 to 5-aminoimidazole ribotide, contributing C$_6$ of the **purine** ring (Fig. 4-22).

---

* In fact, despite this masking, as early as 1921 a Russian microbiologist, Lebedev, reported that heterotrophs must fix CO_2, since the mold *Aspergillus* failed to grow in a current of CO_2-free air. This evidence does not constitute proof by contemporary standards; but the interpretation was bold and reasonable. In a moving introduction he apologized for the lack of specific data; his notebooks had been destroyed in the Revolution, and he was publishing a general account because he "did not know what the morrow will bring." Unfortunately, this important discovery was buried in the Journal of the Don Academy of Sciences.

The carboxylation of pyruvate not only **fixes** CO_2 (by definition) into a carboxyl group, but leads, through subsequent anabolic reactions, to its **reduction** to the alkyl level: see, for example, the conversion of aspartate, via aspartic semi-aldehyde, to several amino acids (Fig. 4-10). However, in contrast to autotrophic CO_2 fixation (Fig. 3-5), this limited ability of heterotrophs to reduce CO_2 is unable to provide net synthesis of an amphibolic intermediate, and hence cannot be used for general biosynthesis.

Nonassimilative CO_2 Fixation. The biosynthetic reactions that fix CO_2 explain certain earlier **nutritional** observations: 1) bacteria require an appreciable CO_2 tension in the atmosphere for growth on a minimal-glucose medium; and 2) the CO_2 can be largely replaced by a mixture of succinate (or aspartate or glutamate), purines, and pyrimidines. However, even with these additions growth can be prevented by measures that further reduce the CO_2 tension in the vessel. The explanation was provided by the discovery of yet another biosynthetic carboxylation, the conversion of acetyl CoA to malonyl CoA in fatty acid synthesis (see above). Since lipids cannot ordinarily be supplied from without, **any growing cell has an absolute requirement for an adequate pCO_2** even though the CO_2 involved in fatty acid synthesis is recycled rather than assimilated.

Role of biotin. Certain carboxylases (e.g., pyruvate carboxylase, malonyl CoA synthetase), and the transcarboxylase of propionate synthesis (Ch. 3), employ biotin as a cofactor. Its function involves the formation of **carboxylated biotin,** which has been isolated.

Transcarboxylation. An unusual variation on carboxylation is seen in the propionic fermentation (Ch. 3), in which carboxylation of pyruvate eventually leads to decarboxylation of methylmalonyl CoA. The cycling of the CO_2 evidently involves its direct transfer, by a transcarboxylase, since radioactivity in this CO_2, derived from carboxy-labeled pyruvate (via carboxy-labeled succinate), fails to mix with a free CO_2 pool.

Transcarboxylase, as well as certain carboxylases (e.g., pyruvate carboxylase, malonyl CoA synthetase), have biotin as a cofactor; and **carboxylated biotin** has been isolated as an intermediate.

Prevalence of Ionized Intermediates

With the elucidation of a great many metabolic reactions a curious general property has emerged: although nonionized compounds may be excreted from the cell (e.g., ethanol), or may circulate between cells in higher organisms (e.g., glucose), **all known biosynthetic and amphibolic intermediates in bacteria contain one or more groups that are largely ionized at physiological pH.** These groups are generally either phosphate (as in glycolysis) or carboxyl (as in the TCA cycle). Their apparent importance is exemplified by a comparison of the purine and the pyrimidine pathways. Thus, from the first reaction of purine biosynthesis the intermediates are attached to ribose-P; otherwise several of them would be un-ionized (Fig. 4-22). In contrast, at the start of pyrimidine biosynthesis (Fig. 4-23) aspartate provides a carboxyl that is retained until ring formation; at this stage ribose-P (containing an ionized P) is added, and the carboxyl is immediately eliminated. Similarly in glycolysis the two Ps that are added to hexose from ATP, and are then recovered from PEP, contribute no net energy; but without them many intermediates would be un-ionized.

The function of these ubiquitous dissociable groups is not certain. Ionization is known to promote the retention of a compound by a cell; in addition, since ionized groups can interact strongly with oppositely charged groups of proteins, they may improve the efficiency or the specificity of enzyme action.

Economy in Mammalian Biosynthesis

We have stressed, earlier in this chapter, the evolutionary pressure on a cell for economy in biosynthesis. The same principle can now explain the curious fact that man can synthesize about half his amino acids but is an auxotroph for the other half. A survey of the pathways in *E. coli* reveals that the 9 amino acids also synthesized in man arise by pathways of 1 to 3 enzymes each; while the 11 amino acids nutritionally essential in man have individual path lengths of 6 to 13 en-

TABLE 4-1. THE NUMBER OF ENZYMES INVOLVED IN THE BIOSYNTHESIS OF THE AMINO ACIDS

Amino acid	Number of enzymes	Amino acid	Number of enzymes	Plus shared enzymes
Alanine	1	Arginine	8	1
Aspartate	1	Histidine	9	
Asparagine (f. aspartate)	1	Threonine	5	1
Glutamate	1	Methionine	5	9
Glutamine (f. glutamate)	1	Lysine	7	
Proline (f. glutamate)	2	Isoleucine	4	6
Serine	3	Valine	1	9
Glycine (f. serine)	1	Leucine	3	9
Cysteine (f. serine and S^{--})	2	Tyrosine	10	
		Phenylalanine	2	8
Total	13	Tryptophan	6	7
		Total	60	

The enzymes counted are those of the anabolic pathways, after they have branched off from amphibolic pathways. For branched anabolic pathways the enzymes of a shared portion are counted for the first end product cited, and are listed as "shared" for subsequently cited products.
Modified from B. D. Davis. Cold Spring Harbor Symp. Quant. Biol. 26:1 (1961).

zymes (Table 4-1). Totaling the results, one sees that the human species has spared itself genes for about 60 enzymes by losing the pathways to 11 amino acids, while the pathways to the other 9 amino acids are relatively inexpensive, involving only 13 enzymes in all.

REPEATING (PERIODIC) POLYMERS: CAPSULES AND CELL WALLS

Capsular Polysaccharides

Most bacterial capsules are heteropolymers (i.e., contain more than one kind of monomer). They are formed from sugar nucleotides by transglycosylation reactions, similar to those described below for wall polysaccharides. Examples will be given in the discussion of pneumococci.

Certain lactic acid bacteria (e.g., *Leuconostoc*) form a **homopolymer** from exogenous sucrose (glucose-1,2-fructoside) by a curious, simple reaction, in which the energy of the glycoside bond of sucrose is used to polymerize one of its two residues. Some species free the fructose moiety and polymerize the glucose (= dextrose),

$$n \text{ Sucrose} \rightarrow (\text{Glucose})_n + n \text{ Fructose}$$

yielding a high molecular weight **dextran**. Others free the glucose and polymerize the fructose (levulose) to a **levan**. These polymers contain primarily α-1,6 linkages, in contrast to the predominant α-1,4 of starch or glycogen.

The polymerization appears to be catalyzed by an enzyme on the outer surface of the cell. In the absence of added sucrose no capsule is formed, but in its presence the colonies become very mucoid. The freed hexose is available as a food, but no function is known for the polymer.

Cellulose (poly-β-1,4-glucose), indistinguishable from that of higher plants, is formed by some members of the bacterial genus *Acetobacter*. It appears to be synthesized within the cell and excreted as separate macromolecules to the exterior, where it crystallizes into a mat which enmeshes the cells. This synthesis has an evident function for these cells, which are obligate aerobes: the mat traps bubbles of CO_2 and thereby floats the cells to the surface of the culture.

Glycogen (poly-α-1,4-glucose) is stored by many bacteria. It is formed, as in mammals, from UDPG (Fig. 4-24), and is utilized via phosphorolysis:

$$\text{Glycogen} + n\text{P}_i \rightarrow n \text{ Glucose-1-P}$$

Homopolymeric Polypeptides

Some species of the genus *Bacillus* form a capsule of poly-D-glutamic acid, or a mixture of this material and poly-L-glutamic acid, in which the units are linked by a γ-**peptide** bond (in contrast to the α-peptide of proteins). The molecular weight may reach 250,000. The process of polymerization is quite different from that of protein synthesis (see below); it can be accomplished in vitro by an enzyme plus ATP, without RNA.

The formation of such a polyglutamic acid capsule is essential for the virulence of *Bacillus anthracis*. In cultures most strains do not form capsules unless given a high CO₂ tension, which presumably promotes the carboxylation of pyruvate (or P-enolpyruvate) required to provide the extra glutamate from glucose (Fig. 4-3).

Heteropolymers of Cell Wall

The Basal Wall (Glycopeptide)

The rigid basal wall of all bacteria, as noted in Chapter 2, consists mostly of a glycopeptide (mucopeptide)* layer, in which the backbone chains are formed of alternating residues of N-acetylglucosamine (GlcNAc) and its O-3-lactyl ether (N-acetylmuramate: MurNAc; Fig. 4-28). A tetrapeptide side chain is attached to the —COOH of the lactic group of MurNAc, and a bridge, whose composition varies in different species, connects the terminal carboxyl group of each side chain with the free amino group (of lysine or diaminopimelate) of another side chain. Since these cross-links can connect side chains arising from different backbones, forming a two- and possibly three-dimensional network, the entire glycopeptide of a cell may well constitute one enormous molecule (murein). The growth of such a network from within obviously requires open areas, and it is suspected that the formation of such openings may be the function of the variety of autolytic enzymes that are found in small amounts in bacteria, and that can attack various specific linkages in the walls of their own cells.

The chemical identification of this large and complex structure has been intimately linked with the study of its biosynthesis, and with the study of chemotherapeutic agents that interfere with this process (Ch. 10).

Determination of Structure. The analysis of the basal layer of bacterial cell walls began, as was noted in Chapter 2, with the development in the 1950s of procedures for isolating purified walls. When such material from some gram-positive species (e.g., *Micrococcus lysodeikticus*) was converted by acid hydrolysis to its monomers a rather simple composition was revealed: glucosamine, muramic acid, and four or five amino acids, some in the D-configuration. Subsequently, the enzyme lysozyme was found to hydrolyze a specific glycoside bond in the polymer, and structural analysis of the resulting disaccharide, as well as of the tetrasaccharide resulting from incomplete hydrolysis, showed that the two sugar residues alternate in the backbone of the polymer and are joined in β-1,4 linkage. Later the use of some 20 additional bacteriolytic enzymes from different sources, each specific for a different linkage within the wall, permitted the isolation of a variety of small fragments; these revealed the linkages between the various monomers, and thus made it possible to infer the structure presented in Figure 4-28.

---

* The term "muco" (in mucopolysaccharide or mucopeptide) refers to any polymer containing aminosugars; the original members of this class, which were found in mucoid secretions, form solutions of a very high viscosity. Since other members of the class have now been found in nonmucoid substances, such as bacterial cell wall, some authorities prefer the more general term glycopeptide, which refers to any covalent association of peptide and carbohydrate.

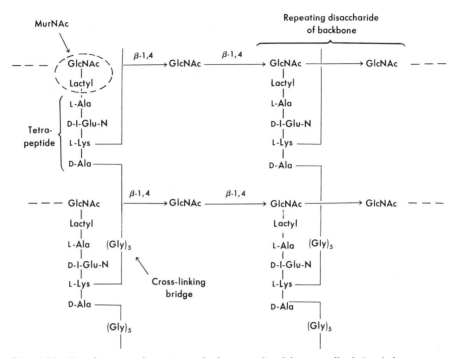

Fig. 4-28 Two-dimensional structure of glycopeptide of basal wall of *Staphylococcus aureus*. The backbone linear polysaccharides can be regarded as homopolymers of N-acetylglucosamine (GlcNAc) linked β-1,4. (However, these chains are usually considered as repeating polymers of alternating GlcNAc and N-acetyl muramic acid (MurNAc) since the lactic ether of the latter provides a very stable bond, which is retained in most methods of hydrolysis.) The lactic-tetrapeptide side chains appear regularly on alternate GlcNAc residues; but it is not known whether the cross-linking pentaglycine chains form a regular, parallel array of bridges between successive pairs of tetrapeptides along two parallel polysaccharides, or whether they form a less regular felt.

The D-glutamic component is linked via its γ-carboxyl group, and its α-carboxyl is amidated; hence it is a D-isoglutamine residue (D-I-Glu-N).

Studies on wall glycopeptide biosynthesis, which began even before any direct studies on its structure, showed that this process occurs in four stages: 1) synthesis of soluble complex building blocks; 2) attachment to a membrane lipid, followed by further additions; 3) formation of linear polymers outside the membrane; and 4) cross-linking of these polymers.

Biosynthesis of Soluble Precursors. First of all, penicillin-inhibited staphylococci were shown by Park to accumulate within the cells uridine nucleotides of MurNAc, in which the carboxyl of the lactic acid moiety was attached to peptides of varying length, up to a pentapeptide (Fig. 4-29). (Moreover, when the cells were deprived of lysine—a component of the complete peptide—a muramic nucleotide containing only a dipeptide was accumulated.) Since the peptides of increasing length undoubtedly represented sequential steps in the synthesis of a wall precursor, the sequence of these reactions could be inferred.

This sequence was confirmed, and additional intermediates were detected, by in vitro enzymatic studies of Strominger (Fig. 4-30). In this work nucleotides with incomplete peptides served as invaluable reagents, to which isotopically labeled amino acids could be transferred enzymatically (much like the use of intermediates accumulated by auxotrophic mutants to work out the biosynthesis of amino acids). Fif-

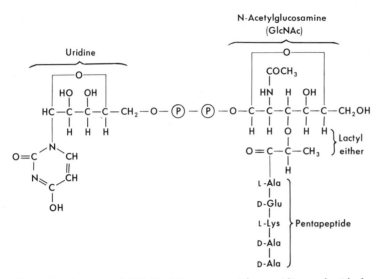

Fig. 4-29 Structure of UDP-Mur-NAc-pentapeptide, a uridine nucleotide from penicillin-treated *S. aureus*.

teen enzymes are required for the synthesis of the complete UDP-acetylmuramic-pentapeptide wall precursor from the usual metabolites of the cell. These enzymes are soluble, suggesting that the precursor is synthesized in the interior of the cytoplasm and not on the membrane.

Each successive addition of an amino acid is catalyzed by a different enzyme, whereas protein synthesis employs a template on which the same enzyme apparently transfers all the different amino acids (see below). Furthermore, protein synthesis involves the splitting of PP from ATP and the formation of an AMP-amino acid intermediate,

while wall polypeptide synthesis involves the less exergonic split of P_i from ATP, without detectable formation of an activated amino acid intermediate.

Biosynthesis of Lipid-Attached Precursors. Further enzymatic studies with radioactive precursors, by Strominger and by Park, showed that UDP-MurNAc-pentapeptide plus UDP-GlcNAc can be polymerized in vitro by particulate enzyme preparations which contain lipids, and are presumably de-

Fig. 4-30 Pathway of biosynthesis of the UDP-muramic-pentapeptide wall precursor in *S. aureus*. The individual amino acids are added with the use of energy from ATP. The sites of action of various inhibitors, which have been useful in working out this pathway, are indicated. (After J. L. Strominger and D. J. Tipper. Am. J. Med. 39:708, 1965.)

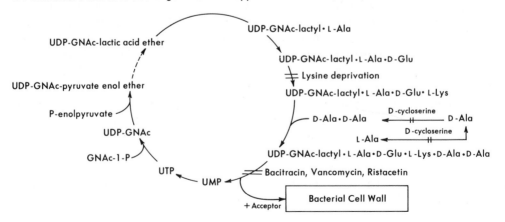

Fig. 4-31 Lipid cycle in cell wall biosynthesis in *S. aureus*. The acceptor is presumed to be the free end of a polymer, consisting of repeating units of the substituted disaccharide that is transferred in this scheme. At some stage during attachment to the lipid (not shown) the free α-COOH of the D-glutamic acid is amidated to form isoglutamine. The lipid has been shown to be a polyisoprene chain with a terminal pyrophosphate. (After M. Matsuhashi, C. P. Dietrich, and J. L. Strominger. Proc. Nat. Acad. Sc. 54:-587, 1965.)

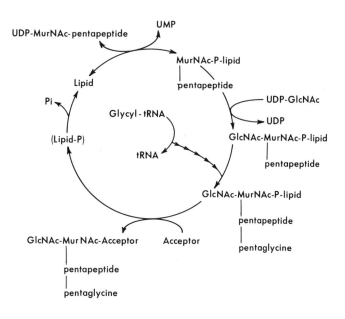

rived from the cell membrane. A labeled lipid is readily separated by chromatography from the lipid-free polymer, and through analysis of the kinetics of labeling it could be shown that the MurNAc-pentapeptide is first transferred, with its adjacent P, from its nucleotide to the lipid, via covalent attachment to the glycerol of a glycerophosphatide. Further additions then occur. First GlcNAc is added by transfer from its UDP carrier, forming a **disaccharide** wall precursor. In *S. aureus* the precursor is then completed by two further reactions, demonstrable in extracts: amidation of the D-glutamic residue, and addition of a pentaglycine tail (NH₂-terminal) to the free amino group of the pentapeptide (Fig. 4-31). It is notable that the glycine residues are derived from glycyl tRNA, which was previously known to function only in protein synthesis.

Polymerization. In the polymerization reaction the completed disaccharide is transferred from the lipid carrier to the growing end of a glycopeptide polymer, with loss of free P_i; the carrier is thus regenerated (Fig. 4-31). In the cell this lipid is presumably oriented in the membrane, accepting the addition of residues on the cytoplasmic side and

then transferring the completed precursor to polymer on the outer side.

Cross-Linking. The terminal stage in glycopeptide synthesis consists in the cross-linking of the polypeptide side chains. Since this step occurs outside the cell membrane it cannot draw on intracellular ATP for the creation of a peptide bond, which is an endergonic reaction. Instead, the energy source is built into the polymer by providing one more amino acid (in the pentapeptide) than is finally retained (in a tetrapeptide). The link can then be formed by an energetically neutral **transpeptidation** reaction (Fig. 4-32), in which the free NH₂ group of the pentaglycine displaces the terminal D-alanine of a nearby side chain, releasing that residue and forming a bridge to the subterminal D-alanine.

This step was first defined with intact cells, through the use of penicillin, which specifically blocks the reaction (Ch. 10). In the presence of this inhibitor labeled glycopeptide precursors are still polymerized by the cell, but these products are not cross-linked. The absence of cross-linking can be demonstrated in several ways: 1) there is a large accumulation of NH₂-terminal glycine (which can be identified by reagents that label free

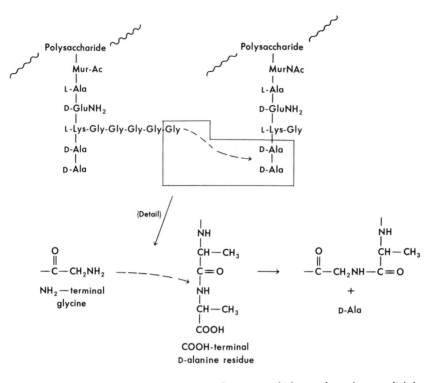

Fig. 4-32 The transpeptidation reaction in *S. aureus,* which completes the cross-link between different peptide side chains: the D-ala ⟶ D-ala peptide bond (CO ⟶ NH) is replaced by a similar D-ala ⟶ gly bond. Some species use other cross-links than the pentaglycine bridge.

NH$_2$ groups); 2) an excess of labeled D-alanine is retained in the polymer; and 3) the polymerized product is much more soluble than that in uninhibited cells. The transpeptidation reaction has since also been accomplished with extracts (from *E. coli*); the enzyme is particulate and is presumably bound in the cell to the outer surface of the membrane.

Species Differences. In different species the structure of the wall glycopeptide varies in some details from that described for *S. aureus.* In many species (e.g., *E. coli, Corynebacteria, Bacillus cereus*) *meso*-diaminopimelate replaces lysine in the pentapeptide; and in some species groups other than an amide cover the carboxyl of the D-glutamic residue. The cross-linking bridge may consist of alanine and threonine instead of glycine; and in some species (*E. coli, Micrococcus lysodeikticus*) the subterminal D-

alanine of one pentapeptide gets linked directly with the L-lysine or diaminopimelate of another, without an intervening bridge.

Teichoic acids are polyol-phosphate polymers, discovered by Baddiley, which are attached to a muramic acid of the glycopeptide via a phosphodiester bond. Since this bond is readily hydrolyzed by dilute acid the teichoic portion of the basal wall is more readily solubilized than the glycopeptide. In *S. aureus* the backbone of the teichoic acid is a **ribitol phosphate** polymer, while in some other species it is a polymer of **glycerol phosphate,** or a polymer in which the phosphate-linked residues are alternately ribitol and a sugar.*

Ribitol teichoic acid is formed from CDP-

---

* Besides being present in the cell wall of certain organisms, the same type of polymer has been observed in the supernatant fraction of all the gram-positive bacteria so far examined ("intracellular" teichoic acid); its function is unknown.

ribitol, and glycerol teichoic acid from CDP-glycerol.

$$n[\text{Cytidine-P-P-ribitol}] \longrightarrow$$

$$\left[\begin{array}{c} \text{O}-\text{CH}_2-\text{CH}-\text{CH}-\text{CH}-\text{CH}_2-\text{O}-\text{(P)} \\ \quad\quad\quad | \quad\quad | \quad\quad | \\ \quad\quad\quad \text{OH} \quad \text{OH} \quad \text{OH} \end{array} \right]_n$$

Teichoic acid backbone
(polyribitol phosphate)

+

n(CMP)

This reaction is unusual in transferring a P along with the organic residue from the nucleotide "handle." Since the enzyme is particulate in extracts it is presumably membrane-bound in the cell.

In various *S. aureus* strains different sugars, and an amino acid (D-alanine), are added to the teichoic acid in various patterns to provide specific surface macromolecules, which are detected immunologically; the enzymes responsible can be detected in extracts.

Lipopolysaccharides

In gram-negative bacteria the glycopeptide basal layer is covered with a lipopolysaccharide (LPS) layer, constituting 20 to 30% of the cell wall. The lipid is covalently attached to a polysaccharide, from which it may be separated by mild acid hydrolysis. The polysaccharide is unusually complex, and the elucidation of its structure and biosynthesis, by the application of genetic and immunological as well as biochemical technics, has been a major recent advance.

The polysaccharide consists of a "core" with attached side chains. The core appears to be uniform in all salmonellae, as shown chemically and immunologically; a somewhat different core is present in other major groups of Enterobacteriaceae. The terminal portions of the side chains ("whiskers") vary widely in composition and configuration in different strains, thus providing the many dozens of specific **O-antigen** determinants that are responsible for the surface specificity of these organisms. These antigens will be discussed in Chapter 20.

These polysaccharides closely resemble in structure certain human blood group substances (Ch. 18), with which, indeed, some O antigens cross-react immunologically. Hence the elucidation of O-polysaccharide biosynthesis in bacteria provides an interesting model system for the formation of mammalian cell surface antigens.

Evidence for a Core Plus Specific Side Chains. The first step toward determining the structure of these complex polysaccharides consisted of isolating the lipopolysaccharide (e.g., by extraction with a hot phenol-water mixture) and identifying the monomers released by complete acid hydrolysis.[*] In this way Westphal discovered that the lipopolysaccharides of all salmonellae contain a common set of four sugars (heptose, glucose, glucosamine, and galactose), while strains with different O-antigen specificities contain various additional sugars (some previously unknown). Moreover, the usual strains found in Nature, which form "smooth" (S) colonies, readily give rise to mutants that form "rough" (R) colonies (Ch. 5); and these **R mutants** were found to yield a smaller amount of lipopolysaccharide, which contained the "common" sugars but had lost the variable ones. It could therefore be inferred that the common sugars form a **core** polysaccharide, to which the three or four specific residues of any given S strain are added.

Analysis of the molar ratios of strain-specific residues to core residues, and determination of the linkages present, suggested that 1) the specific residues are present as side chains, and 2) all these residues are present in each chain as a group that is repeated several times. The sequences and configurations of the sugars in these side-chain repeating units were determined not

---

[*] When the phenol-water mixture separates into two phases, on cooling, lipopolysaccharides are found in the aqueous phase: these complexes thus contain enough polysaccharide to render them water-soluble. In contrast, **glycolipids** (obtained, for example, from the walls of mycobacteria) contain a higher proportion of lipid to carbohydrate and are soluble in lipid solvents rather than in water.

only by the usual chemical methods (identification of partial hydrolysis products and derivatives), but also by immunological studies with disaccharides and glycosides: these small molecules, of known structure, competitively inhibit the reactions (with specific antibodies) of those macromolecules that contain the same groups (Ch. 13, Hapten inhibition).

The Variety of R Mutants. Having revealed the existence of the core polysaccharide, R mutants then proved indispensable in working out its detailed structure, as well as its biosynthesis and that of the specific side chains. These mutants, as noted above, are readily recognized. Detailed genetic and biochemical analysis showed that different R strains are mutated in different genes and are correspondingly deficient in different enzymes. Some mutants form a complete core, and are blocked at some step in the formation or attachment of the specific side chain. Other mutants are blocked at some step in the formation of the complete core but have all the enzymes for forming the specific side chain. (The latter component then accumulates abnormally in the cell as a soluble polysaccharide with the immunological specificity of the normal O antigen.) In both groups two kinds of blocks can be demonstrated: some R mutants are blocked in the biosynthesis of a sugar nucleotide precursor, whose absence prevents addition of any of the subsequent sugars in the chain; while other R mutants have a complete set of sugar nucleotides, and are therefore inferred to be blocked instead in a specific transferase (i.e., a polymerizing enzyme).

That a defect in the biosynthesis of one sugar can block the incorporation of other sugars is an important principle, which was discovered in studies of Fukasawa and Nikaido on a gal⁻ mutant. This organism turned out to lack UDP-galactose-4-epimerase. Since this enzyme functions in the degradation of galactose (Fig. 4-24) the cells could not grow on galactose as sole carbon source. Moreover, the missing enzyme is also required for the synthesis of galactose from glucose (Fig. 4-24); hence when grown on glu-

cose this strain formed rough colonies. However, on glucose **plus** galactose it formed smooth cells, with a normal O polysaccharide, since the enzymes required for converting exogenous galactose to UDP-galactose were present. With this lead other R mutations could be traced to similar blocks in the synthesis of other sugars.

Many R mutants accumulate, in the cells, various sugar nucleotides, whose transfer is prevented by the genetic block. As in amino acid biosynthesis, the identification of these compounds, together with their use in enzymatic reactions, has revealed such biosynthetic pathways as those of Figure 4-25.

The Core Polysaccharide. R mutants blocked in various steps in the formation of the core polysaccharide have yielded a set of polysaccharides with different degrees of simplification. Their analysis has shown that the complete core (Fig. 4-33) consists of a backbone of repeating heptose-P units with side chains, at regular intervals, comprising a rather intricate sequence of heptose, glucose, GlcNAc, and galactose residues. To this **connecting** side chain of the core the O-specific **repeating** part of the side chain is attached. The backbone also contains an 8-C sugar-acid (3-deoxyoctulosonic acid), which apparently attaches it to the lipid, since 1) the reducing group of this sugar is freed when the polysaccharide is split from the lipid by mild acid, and 2) extreme R mutants have been obtained which contain this sugar but no other core sugars.

O-Polysaccharide Biosynthesis. The R mutants have provided still another advantage: their defective polysaccharides proved to be invaluable reagents for studying the biosynthesis of the side chains, since the incomplete mutant side chains could accept sequential transfer in vitro of the missing sugars, catalyzed by extracts of strains without the same genetic block. The enzymes are particulate, and the O-specific repeat unit is built up in covalent attachment to a lipid. It appears that the intracellular synthesis of prefabricated units, with subsequent transfer across the membrane for polymerization, follows a pattern very similar to that described above for the glycopeptide polymer of the wall. Curiously, though the different sugars of the repeat unit are transferred from different nucleoside diphosphates (Fig. 4-24), the different sugars of the core are all transferred from their UDP derivatives.

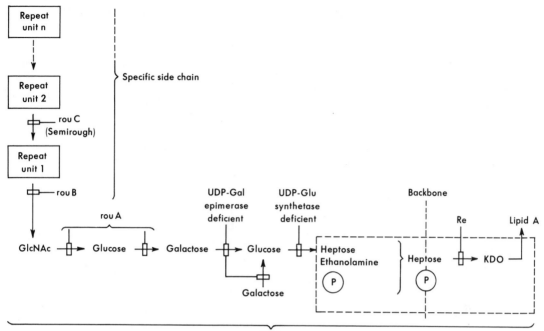

Fig. 4-33 Structure of unit of *Salmonella* O polysaccharide. [Hep = heptose (L-glycero-D-mannoheptose); KDO = 2-keto-3-deoxyoctulonic acid (= octulosonic acid).] A large number of such units are joined by phosphodiester bonds in a -Hep-P-Hep-P-backbone. Chemical analyses show that the average number of repeat units per side chain is 6, but the uniformity of this length is unknown. The side-chain sugars are attached with their reducing groups toward the core (1 ⟶ 4, 1 ⟶ 6, etc.); hence there are no free terminal reducing groups. The connections within the dotted rectangle have not yet been ascertained.

Various classes of R (rou) mutants are indicated; each lacks the material to the left of the block. Mutants lacking any of the transferases for forming the core are found to map in a cluster (the rou A "locus"); incomplete core formation can also be caused, as noted in the diagram, by mutations preventing the synthesis of a required sugar. Mutants blocked in the synthesis of the repeat unit (whether for lack of a sugar synthetase or of a transferase) all map in another cluster (the rou B "locus").

Semirough Mutants. Further light is shed on the biosynthesis of the lipopolysaccharide by the isolation of "semirough" mutants, which possess specific O antigen in a reduced amount (as shown by their reduced capacity for binding the corresponding antibody). One of these groups, the **rou C** mutants, expose only this antigen; the underlying R antigen is therefore entirely covered, presumably by a layer of single, unrepeated O-specific units. This pattern suggests that the enzyme for transferring the first O-specific unit to the connecting side chain differs from the enzyme for subsequent transfers, which must recognize a different acceptor group (Fig. 4-33); the mutant presumably lacks the second of these enzymes.

Another kind of semirough mutant, **rou D**, has a similar small amount of O antigen but does expose the underlying R antigen as well. This mutant is believed to have a **few** specific side chains of **normal length;** presumably some early transfer enzyme is defective but still somewhat active ("leaky" block). These findings provide evidence that in the normal O antigen the side chains are uniformly attached along the core.

INFORMATIONAL MACROMOLECULES: NUCLEIC ACIDS AND PROTEINS

The Discovery of Templates

As was noted above, the short specific sequences of amino acids in wall glycopeptide or in glutathione are formed by classic enzymatic processes, a different enzyme being responsible for adding the correct amino acid at each stage in the growth of the polypeptide chain. However, attempts to explain protein synthesis along similar lines ran into an infinite serial regression: if each amino acid addition were determined by the specificity of a particular enzyme, that recognized both that amino acid and the sequence to which it was to be added, each of these enzymes would in turn require a further large number of enzymes to account for its specific sequence. The paradox was resolved by the discovery of a new biochemical principle: the use of a specific, aperiodic* macromolecule as a **template** in the biosynthesis of other aperiodic macromolecules. The template serves neither as a catalyst nor as a substrate, but as a source of **information** determining the sequence of the different monomers in the macromolecule being synthesized.

The idea of a template found its first significant support when Watson and Crick, in 1953, proposed the double-stranded structure of DNA: the complementarity of the two strands (Ch. 8) immediately suggested that each strand serves, in DNA replication, as a direct template for the synthesis of its complement. In vitro confirmation of this prediction came in 1958, when A. Kornberg discovered and characterized DNA polymerase in extracts of *E. coli*: this enzyme requires not only a mixture of the four deoxyribonucleoside triphosphates of DNA, but also some "primer" DNA, whose composition is faithfully replicated. Following this germinal discovery a rather similar RNA polymerase, which can synthesize RNA in vitro on a DNA template, was recognized independently in 1961 by three investigators: Hurwitz, Stevens, and Weiss.

The similar employment of a template in protein synthesis was suggested when Zamecnik in 1954, on first achieving protein synthesis in extracts of mammalian cells, discovered that this process requires RNA as well as enzymes and substrate. The many components of this system were then separated and identified over a period of years. The fraction that was sedimentable at 100,000 g was subsequently recognized as **microsomes,** consisting of **ribosomes** attached to membrane fragments (derived from the extensive endoplasmic reticulum seen in animal cells by electron microscopy). The membrane component could be eliminated, by treatment with deoxycholate, without destroying the activity of the ribosomes, which were then found to consist only of RNA plus protein. In bacteria the bulk of the ribosomes are not bound to membranes; they may be obtained directly by grinding cells followed by appropriate centrifugal isolation.

The supernatant ("soluble") fraction was shown by Hoagland to contain enzymes that activate the amino acids, and also a "soluble RNA" (sRNA) fraction, to which the enzymes transfer the activated amino acids. The sRNA in turn transfers the amino acids into a position on the ribosome where they can be incorporated into a growing polypeptide. Finally, it was shown with a bacterial system in 1961, primarily by Jacob and Monod, that the information for the amino acid sequence of a protein is carried by a third, previously unrecognized fraction of cellular RNA, which they called **messenger RNA** (mRNA). This discovery will be discussed in detail in Chapter 9. Since mRNA is "soluble," it now seems better to redesignate the original sRNA more specifically as **transfer RNA** (tRNA).

We thus see that protein synthesis involves

---

* By referring to nucleic acids (and proteins) as aperiodic macromolecules we are emphasizing the absence of regular repeating units in their **sequences**. These macromolecules, however, often do exhibit marked periodicity with respect to general **structure** (i.e., helicity), as revealed by X-ray crystallography.

an elaborate machinery, in which various tRNAs serve as "adaptors" for the various amino acids, mRNA serves as an **indirect** template recognized by the adaptors, and the ribosome provides a "workbench" on which the several components can achieve the required positions and movement. DNA and RNA synthesis, in contrast, occur through relatively simple reactions, in which a single enzyme polymerizes monomers that have spontaneously paired with the **direct** DNA template.

We shall review here only the enzymological aspects of the synthesis of nucleic acid and of proteins. Since these problems merge with that of gene action, and are of great importance in the regulation of protein synthesis, they will be considered further in the chapters on molecular genetics (Ch. 8) and on regulatory mechanisms (Ch. 9).

DNA Synthesis

DNA polymerase, whether from bacteria or from mammalian cells, catalyzes a pyrophosphorolytic reaction:

$$n(B_{1-4} \cdot dR\text{-}PPP) \xrightarrow[\text{DNA primer}]{\text{Enzyme}} (B_{1-4} \cdot dR\text{-}P)n \ + \ n(P\text{-}P)$$
$$\downarrow$$
$$2n(P_i)$$

(B_{1-4} represents the four bases of DNA; dR is deoxyribose.) Because the pyrophosphate is rapidly hydrolyzed in the cell this reaction costs $2 \sim P$ per nucleotide incorporated and thus ensures a large energy drop in the biosynthetic direction.

As was noted above, the action of this enzyme requires all four deoxyribonucleoside triphosphates as well as primer DNA. As in native DNA, the phosphodiester links in the product connect the 5'-carbon of the deoxyribose of one nucleotide with the 3'-carbon of its neighbor; and the base composition of the product is identical with that of the primer, suggesting a template function for the latter.

A template mechanism is further supported by evidence that the primer DNA determines the sequence as well as the composition of the product. Though direct analysis of giant DNA molecules for their nucleotide sequence is not feasible, specificity of sequence can be demonstrated by "nearest neighbor" analyses. Thus by using in the DNA synthesis a monomer with radioactive 5'-P, and then recovering the labeled P as the 3'-P of the neighboring nucleotide (Fig. 4-34), it could be shown that templates of different biological origin, even when similar in gross composition, yield products with different patterns of nearest neighbor frequency. In contrast, synthetic DNA of known nearest neighbor frequency, when used as template, leads to the production of DNA with the same pattern. The enzymatic process seen in vitro thus appears to replicate the sequence of the template, and therefore can be considered closely related to DNA formation in the cell.

Presumably the action of DNA polymerase involves separation of the two complementary strands of the primer at the growing point of DNA replication. The enzyme then forms 5'-3' diester bonds between adjacent nucleoside triphosphates that have spontaneously paired with their complementary bases in each template strand (Ch. 8). Since the two strands of DNA are antiparallel (Ch. 8), simultaneous replication of both strands in the same direction along the DNA requires extension of one nascent chain at its 3' end and the other at its 5' end. The known DNA polymerase, which has been highly purified from *E. coli*, can be shown to carry out the first of these reactions (A in Fig. 4-35), but the reaction proposed for extending the other nascent chain (B in Fig. 4-35) has not been demonstrated.

The in vitro system can form DNA, of specific sequence and high molecular weight, in amounts many times the template provided. Nevertheless, the system differs in important ways from that in the cell. 1) It has yielded no increment of biological activity, as judged by the activity of the product in bacterial transformation (Ch. 7), or by infectivity when viral DNA was the template. (The enzyme has, however, repaired damaged primer DNA in vitro and thus increased its activity.) 2) Electron microscopy has shown that synthetic DNA is extensively branched, whereas natural DNA is linear. 3) The strands

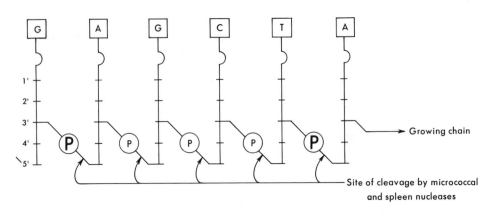

Fig. 4-34 Principle for determining nearest neighbor frequency. One species of nucleotide (e.g., dAMP) containing radioactive P (indicated by a heavy letter) is incorporated into synthetic DNA by using as substrates radioactive dATP plus nonradioactive dGTP, dCTP, and dTTP. Each P forms a phosphodiester bridge between the 5' position of its parent nucleotide and the 3' position of its nearest neighbor. Hydrolysis by specific enzymes ruptures the 5' bond and releases the residues as 3'-nucleotides; thus each P is shifted from the 5'-OH of its parent nucleotide to the 3'-OH of its nearest neighbor. By separating chromatographically the four different 3'-nucleotides in the hydroylsate, and determining the total radioactivity in each, it is possible to calculate what fraction of the A is connected 5'→3' to another A, what fraction to G, etc. In the segment shown radioactive dAMP would give rise to one radioactive D-guanosine-3'-P and one radioactive D-thymidine-3'-P. By performing similar experiments with separate labeling of each of the four monomers, the characteristic nearest neighbor frequency for a given primer DNA can be determined.

Fig. 4-35 DNA replication: two different reactions are required for simultaneous replication of both strands in the same direction. The pyrophosphate (PP) released is indicated by a surrounding dotted line. Reaction A has been established. Reaction B is inferred, but the resulting chains with a terminal triphosphate have not been demonstrated.

A. Nucleotide addition at the 3'-terminal end of the chain

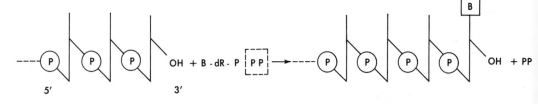

B. Nucleotide addition at the 5'-terminal end of the chain

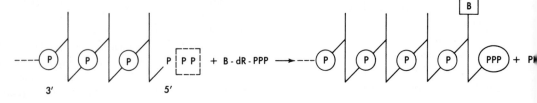

of synthetic DNA accordingly tend not to separate completely on denaturing treatments, but readily resume a helical configuration (Ch. 8). 4) The synthesizing activity is often greater with denatured than with native DNA as template. 5) Finally, modifications of the DNA template can markedly affect the rate of DNA synthesis. Thus the repair of partially single-stranded templates proceeds at a more rapid rate than does the replication of a native DNA. Moreover, the introduction of 3'-OH end groups into DNA molecules (by nuclease and phosphatase action) increases their capacity to serve as templates, presumably by providing additional sites for the initiation of synthesis. In contrast, synthesis in vivo proceeds at only one or two growing points per bacterial chromosome (Ch. 8).

The branching might be due to inability of the enzyme in vitro to copy both strands simultaneously in the same direction. Thus $5' \to 3'$ additions along one strand would leave its antiparallel complementary strand free, and a hairpin turn in the nascent chain could then extend its growth back, in the $5' \to 3'$ direction, along the antiparallel strand, creating a branch.

From the results summarized above it can be concluded that the in vitro synthesis of DNA at present resembles the natural process for short distances, which is a great achievement, but the product suffers from extensive artificial branching. Hence on a larger scale the product is abnormal to a degree that renders it genetically nonfunctional.

RNA Synthesis and Turnover

RNA polymerase closely resembles DNA polymerase in many respects. The reaction requires all four ribonucleoside triphosphates, as well as DNA.

$$n(B_{1-4} \cdot R \cdot PPP) \xrightarrow[\text{DNA template}]{\text{Enzyme}} (B_{1-4} \cdot R \cdot P)n + n(P \cdot P)$$
$$\downarrow$$
$$2n(P_i)$$

The nucleotides are linked by $5' \to 3'$ phosphodiester bonds, as in native RNA, and the product has a high molecular weight and has the base ratio of whatever primer DNA is used (except, of course, that it contains uracil instead of thymine). The product formed has "biological" activity, in the sense that it has mRNA-like properties, i.e., it can stimulate amino acid polymerization in an in vitro system.

A major difference between DNA replication and RNA synthesis in the cell is that both strands of DNA are replicated, but only one strand (for a given segment) serves as the template for RNA synthesis. Most RNA-synthesizing systems in vitro, however, lack the unknown mechanisms that specify the normal sites of initiation and termination, and both strands serve as templates, as can be shown by DNA-RNA hybridization experiments (Ch. 8). Recently, however, systems have been obtained in which only one strand is copied.

The complementary DNA strand apparently serves to displace RNA from the template strand. Thus with double-stranded DNA as template only free RNA is formed, whereas with single-stranded DNA (which can also serve as template in vitro) a stable RNA-DNA hybrid is formed first.

Polynucleotide Phosphorylase. A kind of RNA synthesis can be carried out in vitro by a different enzyme, unrelated to RNA polymerase in biochemical properties and biological significance. This enzyme, polynucleotide phosphorylase, catalyzes the reaction:

$$(B_4 \cdot R \cdot P)n + nP_i \rightleftharpoons n(B_4 \cdot R \cdot PP)$$

Polynucleotide	Nucleoside diphosphate

This reaction does not have a large energy drop in the direction of polymerization, but is reversible; and its physiological function is almost certainly degradative rather than biosynthetic. Thus the polymerization does not exhibit specificity, since it does not require either a template or a complete set of nucleotides: the character of the product is determined by the composition of the nucleoside diphosphate mixture supplied. Moreover, though this enzyme was discovered by Grun-

berg-Manago and Ochoa through its formation of a polymer in the presence of a high
concentration of nucleoside diphosphate and
a low concentration of P_i, these concentration
relations, and therefore the direction of the
reaction, are almost certainly reversed in the
cell.

In the degradation of RNA the action of
polynucleotide phosphorylase provides the
economic advantage, compared with the hydrolytic action of ribonuclease, of retaining
(with the use of P_i) the energy of the phosphodiester bond of RNA, which it converts
to the P-P bond of nucleoside diphosphate
($B \cdot R \cdot PP$). Thus one of the two $\sim P$ bonds
that went into the polymerization of each nucleotide is recovered.

The obvious (but unproved) substrate for
polynucleotide phosphorylase in mRNA: since
the rate of turnover of mRNA in bacteria corresponds to about half the over-all synthesis of
RNA in the cell, it would clearly be of considerable advantage for the cell to use a phosphorolytic
mechanism for this purpose. Moreover, polynucleotide phosphorylase has been readily demonstrated in various bacteria, in which mRNA
has a very short life (Ch. 8), but not in mammals, in which mRNA is more stable. The several ribonucleases of the bacterial cell, in contrast, probably have other functions (e.g., the
breakdown of ribosomes under conditions of
starvation).

Synthetic Polyribonucleotides. Enzymatically
synthesized ribonucleotide polymers of several
kinds have proved invaluable in deciphering the
genetic code (Ch. 8). Polynucleotide phosphorylase has been used to synthesize both ribonucleotide homopolymers (i.e., containing only
one kind of monomer) and ribonucleotide copolymers of random sequence. RNA polymerase
has made possible even more sophisticated syntheses, since it can use short deoxyribonucleotide
polymers (of 6 to 12 nucleotides) as templates,
and by somehow shifting the growing chain
along the template it can form long chains on a
short template. Hence by providing synthetic
polydeoxyribonucleotides with known, repeating
sequences, Khorana has been able to synthesize
ribonucleotide copolymers of precisely defined,
repeating sequence.

Protein Synthesis

Protein synthesis involves essentially the
same mechanism in bacteria as in animal
cells: the ribosome serves as a frame on which
the specific nucleotide sequence of mRNA is
translated into the corresponding amino acid
sequence. Each amino acid species is activated by one or more specific enzymes, which
catalyze a pyrophosphorolytic reaction with
ATP to yield an enzyme-bound aminoacyl
adenylate.

Enzyme + Amino acid + ATP $\longrightarrow$

Aminoacyl AMP-Enzyme + PP

Aminoacyl AMP-Enzyme + tRNA $\longrightarrow$

Aminoacyl tRNA + AMP + Enzyme

Since such aminoacyl-phosphate anhydrides
are highly reactive compounds, the usefulness
of keeping them enzyme-bound may readily
be appreciated. The same enzyme (called activating enzyme, or aminoacyl RNA synthetase) then transfers the activated amino
acid to a corresponding specific transfer RNA
(tRNA, sRNA), which is then said to be
charged. The reaction is slightly exergonic,
proceeding from a carboxyphosphate mixed
acid anhydride (with AMP) to an ester (with
a hydroxyl of the tRNA). Hence the amino
acid remains in an activated state when esterified to tRNA (i.e., the free energy level of
this bond is higher than that of the subsequently formed peptide bond).

Each tRNA species (M.W. ca. 25,000) is
specific for a given transfer enzyme and for
one or more specific codons (nucleotide triplets) in the mRNA. The genetic code is thus
specified by the properties of two kinds of
"double-headed" molecules: the tRNA molecules serve as "adaptors" between a given
codon and its amino acid; and the activating
enzymes must specifically recognize both a
given tRNA and the corresponding amino
acid.

The bacterial ribosome, of sedimentation
constant 70S (M.W. 2.6×10^6), consists of
one 50S and one 30S subunit, which dissoci-

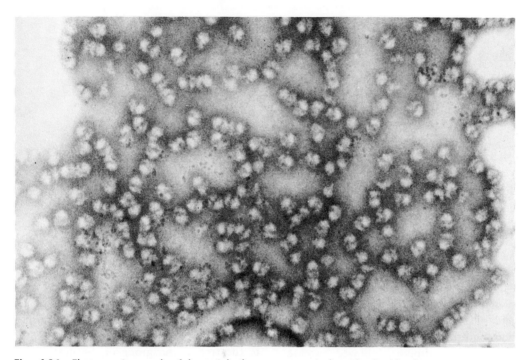

Fig. 4-36 Electron micrograph of bacterial ribosomes, negatively stained with phosphotungstic acid. Note that each 70S ribosome consists of a larger (50S) and a smaller (30S) portion, with a circumferential groove. (From H. E. Huxley and G. Zubay, *J. Molec. Biol.* 2:10, 1960.)

ate from each other at low Mg^{++} concentration (Fig. 4-36). Each subunit consists of about 60% RNA and 40% protein. On extraction with phenol and/or detergents (e.g., sodium dodecylsulfate), which denature protein but not RNA, the 50S particle yields a single RNA molecule of sedimentation constant 23S (M.W. 1.1×10^6), and the 30S particle yields a 16S RNA molecule, of half that molecular weight.

Though our knowledge of the structure of the ribosome is still rudimentary, it is believed that the mRNA fits in a groove that crosses the 30S subunit, while the tRNA molecules fit in slots that run perpendicularly from this groove across part of both subunits (Fig. 4-38). Effective attachment of a charged tRNA molecule must involve a double source of affinity: a nonspecific fit to the slot, plus the added specific interaction with a codon of the attached mRNA.

The roles of the 30S and 50S subunits are inferred from the results of binding studies in vitro. Thus labeled mRNA can be bound by 70S or 30S, but not by 50S, particles. Furthermore, such complexes (with a synthetic messenger polynucleotide) can bind the aminoacyl tRNA coded for by the polynucleotide; and the binding is weaker with the 30S-mRNA than with the 70S-mRNA complex. Finally, under ionic conditions that exaggerate its affinity for ribosomes tRNA can be bound (in the absence of mRNA) by the 50S or 70S, but not by the 30S, particles.

The structure of the **tRNA molecules,** which contain about 80 nucleotides, will be discussed in Chapter 8. Here we may note only that each must contain a specific "anticodon," which recognizes a corresponding codon in mRNA. Moreover, all species of tRNA contain the same terminal adenyliccytidylic-cytidylic (-CpCpA) sequence; in the charging of tRNA the amino acid is trans-

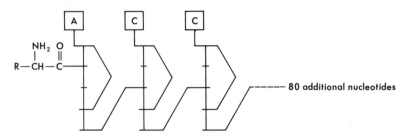

Fig. 4-37   Aminoacyl terminus of all charged tRNA species.

ferred to the 2'-hydroxyl of the terminal adenylate (Fig. 4-37). The uniformity of this terminal sequence presumably contributes to the ability of a single peptide-forming enzyme to polymerize all the different amino acids, bound to different tRNAs.

Polymerization. To determine the direction of polypeptide growth Dintzis exposed reticulocytes to labeled amino acids for brief periods and then subjected the globin to partial enzymatic hydrolysis, followed by chromatographic "fingerprinting" of the resulting peptides. Those peptides that were labeled early (i.e., the ones formed just before release of the completed chain from the ribosome) proved to be the peptides known, from the sequence of the protein, to lie at its carboxy-terminal end; hence **polypeptide chains must grow through amino acid additions at the C-terminal end.**

Goldstein later attacked this problem in bacteria by an ingenious approach that involved the total nascent protein in the cell, without requiring sequence analysis. A leucine auxotroph was starved of leucine, so that all the growing chains would be waiting for leucine addition as the next step. By cooling to 0° to lower the rate of chain extension drastically, and then adding ^{14}C-leucine, it could be shown that after 15 seconds 73% of the incorporated radioactivity was at or near the C-terminal end of the polypeptides, as determined by its release by carboxypeptidase. In contrast, in protein labeled in all its leucine only 17% was near enough to the C-terminal end to be released by the enzyme.

The nascent polypeptide chain remains firmly attached to the ribosome until its ter-

mination. However, **puromycin,** which serves as an analog of the aminoacyl adenosine terminus of charged tRNA (Ch. 10), can be transferred to the peptide, but it cannot stick firmly to the ribosome; hence the peptide, with covalently attached puromycin, is freed. This model reaction suggests that the polypeptide chain is covalently attached to a tRNA molecule, chain extension being accomplished by transfer of this peptide from its tRNA to the free amino group of the next amino acid in the sequence (Fig. 4-38). Since this amino acid is also attached to a tRNA, the growing peptide chain is constantly held on the ribosome via covalent attachment to a tRNA molecule.

The mechanism of release of the completed polypeptide is not known, beyond the fact that it is determined by certain codons (Ch. 8). It is encouraging, however, that this process occurs in the in vitro system, since polypeptides coded for by a natural messenger are largely freed from the ribosomes, whereas those coded for by synthetic messengers (lacking the terminator codons) remain attached to the ribosomes.

Aminoacyl Transfer Enzymes. The transfer of peptide to successive incoming aminoacyl tRNAs is well established, but the details are not so certain. According to the prevailing view two transfer enzymes bring about a cycle of movement of peptide between two positions on the ribosome, along with a linear movement of tRNA and mRNA, at the expense of energy furnished by GTP, from a peptide acceptor site (site 1) to a donor site (site 2) (Fig. 4-38). The net result is attachment of a charged tRNA to the ribosome, chain extension, loss of an uncharged tRNA,

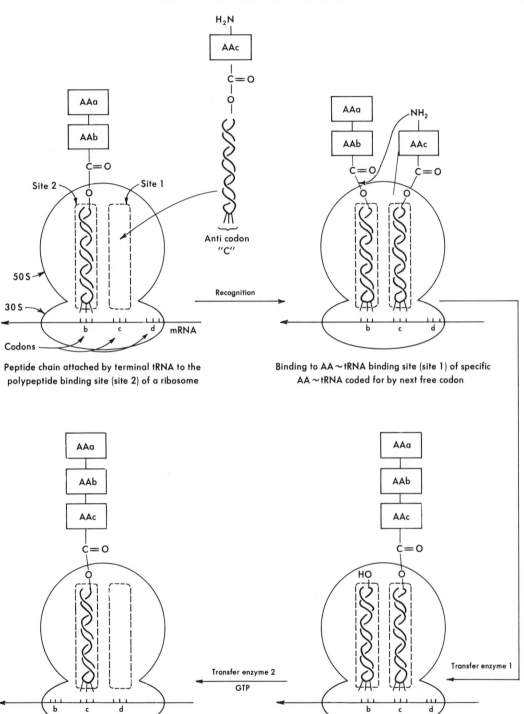

Fig. 4-38 Schematic representation of the addition of an amino acid to a growing polypeptide chain. (Modified from J. D. Watson. The Molecular Biology of the Gene. Benjamin, New York, 1965.)

and preparation for the addition of the next charged tRNA.

The evidence for this scheme is rather indirect. The ribosomes can be freed of transfer enzymes by high salt concentration, and among the supernatant factors required by these treated ribosomes two distinct enzymes can be separated. One is believed to form the peptide bond directly: it can complex in solution with aminoacyl tRNA (as shown by their effects on each other's stability), and it also is required for release by puromycin of nascent polypeptide previously formed on the ribosome. The second transfer enzyme is believed to cause the movement from site 1 to site 2. Thus the presence of this enzyme, along with GTP, increases the amount of aminoacyl tRNA bound (without peptide formation) by a ribosome, presumably because the initial binding site (1) has been freed to take up another aminoacyl tRNA. Moreover, at the same time the amino acid taken up initially gains the ability to be released by puromycin (in the presence of the first enzyme): this reaction apparently does not occur with aminoacyl tRNA in its initial binding position, and therefore requires movement to site 2. Finally, the second transfer enzyme has GTPase activity when complexed with the ribosome (but not when alone); and with a highly purified system the stoichiometry of the hydrolysis of GTP during protein synthesis supports the view that one molecule of GTP is split per peptide bond formed.

State of Ribosomes in the Cell. Though ribosomes were initially isolated as single units from cell extracts prepared by grinding or by sonic oscillation, gentler methods of extraction revealed that most ribosomes in cells (whether bacterial or animal) are located in **polysomes.** These consist of a variable number of ribosomes (monosomes) connected by a strand of mRNA (Ch. 9, Fig. 9-10), and in extracts they are more active in protein synthesis (without added mRNA) than is the monosome fraction. The formation of polysomes markedly increases the efficiency of utilization of mRNA, since a number of ribosomes are thereby permitted to "read" a given mRNA molecule simultaneously. Polysomes will be further discussed in Chapter 9.

In mammalian cells ribosomes are frequently attached (mostly as polysomes) to the endoplasmic reticulum, as is easily seen in electron micrographs. While comparable evidence is not available for the more closely packed bacterial cells, in bacterial extracts a substantial fraction of the ribosomes are also attached to membrane fragments (Ch. 2), from which they may be freed by treatment with deoxycholate. Moreover, these membrane-attached polysomes are reported to be more active in protein synthesis than the unattached fraction. The nature and the physiological significance of the attachment, however, are not yet clear.

It should be emphasized that while the available in vitro systems have thrown much light on the mechanism of protein synthesis, they represent but a shadow of the intracellular process. Thus in small-molecule metabolism the rates of most of the known enzymatic reactions in extracts are comparable to those observed in whole cells; but in extracted protein-synthesizing systems, even under optimal conditions, the rate of incorporation of labeled amino acids per ribosome is only 1% of that seen in intact cells. Furthermore, though synthesis of a defined protein can be accomplished in vitro by extracts containing a relatively homogeneous mRNA (e.g., reticulocytes, or bacterial systems provided with a bacteriophage RNA), the formation of specific enzymes by bacterial systems (with their very heterogeneous mRNA) has not been satisfactory. This limitation has hampered direct study, with extracts, of the mechanisms regulating the synthesis of specific proteins (Ch. 9).

SELECTED REFERENCES

Books and Review Articles

ARNON, D. I. Ferredoxin and photosynthesis. *Science 149*:1460 (1965).

DAVIES, D. A. L. Polysaccharides of gram-negative bacteria. *Advances Carbohydrate Chem. 15*:271 (1960).

ERWIN, J., and BLOCH, K. Biosynthesis of unsaturated fatty acids in microorganisms. *Science 143*:1006 (1964).

GINSBURG, V. Sugar nucleotides and the synthesis of carbohydrates. *Advances Enzymol. 26*:35 (1964).

GOLDFINE, H., and BLOCH, K. Oxygen and Biosynthetic Reactions. In *Control Mechanisms in Respiration and Fermentation.* (B. Wright, ed.) Ronald Press, New York, 1963.

GUNSALUS, I. C., and STANIER, R. Y., (eds.). *The Bacteria,* vol. III, *Biosynthesis.* Academic Press, New York, 1962. Especially Wood and Stjernholm, CO_2 Fixation by Heterotrophs (Ch. 2); Umbarger and Davis, Amino Acid Biosynthesis (Ch. 4); Magasanik, Nucleotide Biosynthesis (Ch. 6).

HURWITZ, J., and AUGUST, J. T., The role of DNA in RNA synthesis. *Progr. Nucleic Acid Res. 1*:59 (1963).

KATES, M. Bacterial lipids. *Advances Lipid Res. 2*:17 (1964).

KENNEDY, E. P. The metabolism and function of complex lipids. *Harvey Lect. 57*:143 (1961–62).

KORNBERG, A. *Enzymatic Synthesis of DNA.* Wiley, New York, 1962.

KORNBERG, H. L. Anaplerotic sequences in microbial metabolism. *Angew. Chem. (Eng.) 4*:558 (1965).

LEDERER, E. Glycolipids of acid-fast bacteria. *Advances Carbohydrate Chem. 16*:207 (1961).

LUDERITZ, O., STAUB, A. M., and WESTPHAL, O., Immunochemistry of O and R antigens of *Salmonella* and related *Enterobacteriaceae. Bact. Rev. 30*:192 (1966).

NIKAIDO, H. Bacterial Cell Wall—Deep Layers. In *The Specificity of Cell Surfaces.* (B. D. Davis and L. Warren, eds.) Prentice-Hall, Englewood Cliffs, N.J., 1966.

OSBORN, M. J., ROSEN, S. M., ROTHFIELD, L., ZELEZNEK, L. D., and HORECKER, B. L. Lipopolysaccharides of the gram-negative cell wall. *Science 145*:783 (1964).

PERUTZ, M. *Proteins and Nucleic Acids.* Elsevier, Amsterdam, 1962.

SYMPOSIUM: Molecular biology of gram-negative bacterial lipopolysaccharides. *Ann. New York Acad. Sci. 133*:279–763 (1966).

WATSON, J. D. Nobel lecture. *Science 140*:17 (1963).

Specific Articles

ANDERSON, J. S., MATSUHASHI, M., HASKIN, M. A., and STROMINGER, J. L. Lipid-phosphoacetyl muramyl-pentapeptide and lipid-phosphodisaccharide-pentapeptide: Presumed membrane transport intermediates in cell wall synthesis. *Proc. Nat. Acad. Sc. 53*:881 (1965).

MAJERUS, P. W., ALBERTS, A. W., and VAGELOS, P. R. The acyl carrier protein of fatty acid synthesis. *Proc. Nat. Acad. Sc. 51*:123 (1964).

NISHIZUKA, Y., and LIPMANN, F. Comparison of guanosine triphosphate split and polypeptide synthesis with a purified *E. coli* system. *Proc. Nat. Acad. Sc. 55*:212 (1966).

ROTHFIELD, L., TAKESHITA, M., PEARLMAN, M., and HORNE, R. W. Role of phospholipids in the enzymatic synthesis of the bacterial cell envelope. *Fed. Proc. 25*:1495 (1966).

When it is possible to catalogue the substances required by pathogenic bacteria for growth, it will probably be found that most of them are . . . important in animal metabolism, and . . . it is equally probable that some will be new. J. H. MUELLER, J. BACT. 7:309 (1922)

5 BACTERIAL NUTRITION AND GROWTH

NUTRITION

The early microbiologists learned how to grow various organisms reproducibly by using complex, empirically defined media—generally "broths" obtained by cooking animal or vegetable tissues. In 1922 Mueller, for reasons described in the above quotation, undertook a pioneering program aimed at defining bacterial growth requirements in precise chemical terms; and within a year he had discovered the previously unknown amino acid **methionine,** which subsequently proved essential in mammalian nutrition. It was not until about 1935, however, that progress in biochemistry made possible a systematic analysis of the nutritional requirements of microbes, and in the next 2 decades the requirements of many organisms were precisely defined in chemical terms. This development helped reveal the widespread unity of biochemistry; it also contributed extensively to the analysis of biosynthetic pathways (reviewed in the preceding chapter) and to the discovery of previously unknown metabolites (especially vitamins).

By now the study of microbial nutrition has receded in importance, but it still presents challenges; for example, we cannot cultivate the leprosy bacillus, the treponeme of syphilis, or rickettsiae in artificial media. Furthermore, the principles developed with bacteria are being applied, with increasing success, to the cultivation of mammalian cells.

Microbes with natural requirements have also lent themselves, like the auxotrophs described in the preceding chapter, to use in **quantitative bioassays** for growth factors. The simplicity of these assays, compared with those in animals, greatly facilitated the isolation of biologically active materials; hence a number of vitamins were first identified as microbial growth factors, and were only later found to be equally essential for mammals. A list is presented in Table 5-1. In addition, some bacteria require trace factors that are

TABLE 5-1. DISCOVERY OF VITAMINS

Vitamin	Microbe*	Animal
Discovered First in Animals		
Riboflavin	Lactic bacteria	Rats
Thiamine (B$_1$)	Yeasts; *Staphylococcus aureus*	Rats, man
Pyridoxine (B$_6$)	Yeasts; lactic bacteria	Rats
Discovered Independently or First in Microbes		
p-Aminobenzoic acid	Sulfonamide inhibition; *Clostridium acetobutylicum*	
Folic acid	*Lactobacillus casei; Streptococcus faecalis*	Chicks
Biotin	Yeast; *Rhizobium*	Chicks
Nicotinic acid	*S. aureus; Corynebacterium diphtheriae*	Canine blacktongue Pellagra in man
Pantothenic acid	Yeasts	Various; difficult to demonstrate
Lipoic acid	Lactic bacteria; *Tetrahymena geleii* (protozoon)	
Vitamin B$_{12}$	*Lactobacillus leichmannii; Lactobacillus lactis*	Pernicious anemia in man
Pyridoxal,-amine (physiological form of pyridoxine)	Yeasts; lactic bacteria	

The principles underlying microbiological assays are discussed on page 145.

more complex than the corresponding mammalian vitamin, e.g., coenzyme I, rather than nicotinic acid, for some *Hemophilus* species.

Since the observed effects of a nutritional deficiency are usually quite different in animals and in bacteria, investigations in the two fields have sometimes converged unexpectedly on the same compound. A dramatic example is provided by vitamin B_{12}, which was independently isolated in the same year (1948) through two programs, one based on arduous assays of the hematopoietic response of patients with pernicious anemia, and the other based on the purification of a growth factor for *Lactobacillus leichmannii*.

Physical and Inorganic Requirements

Temperature. Most bacteria can grow over a **temperature range** of 30° or more, but have quite a narrow range for optimal growth. Below the optimum the growth rate falls off with a Q_{10} of ca. 2 to 3 (i.e., that typical of enzyme reactions), over quite a temperature range, but then declines more rapidly, giving rise to a fairly well defined **minimal growth temperature** (Fig. 5-1). Above the optimum the growth rate decreases

Fig. 5-1 Effect of temperature on the generation time of a typical mesophile (*E. coli*) and a psychrophilic pseudomonad. (After J. L. Ingraham. *J. Bact.* 76:75, 1958.)

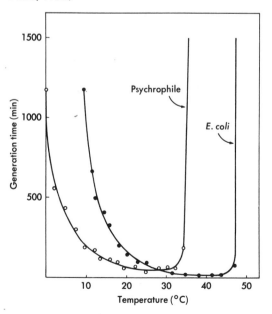

steeply with increasing temperature, giving rise to a sharply defined **maximum growth temperature.** Since heat killing begins at about this temperature, the slowness of growth just below it is probably due to competition between the biosynthesis and the denaturation of macromolecules.

The temperature range for growth of an organism is a stable characteristic, of considerable taxonomic value. Although one can isolate temperature-sensitive mutants with a narrowed range, attempts to extend the range have been generally unsuccessful, suggesting the adaptation of numerous gene products to the same limit.

It is customary to divide bacteria somewhat arbitrarily, in terms of their temperature ranges, into mesophiles, psychrophiles (or cryophiles), and thermophiles. Most bacteria are **mesophiles.** Those found in the mammalian body have a temperature optimum of 37 to 44°, but many others found in Nature (e.g., *Bacillus megaterium*) are inhibited by the conventional incubator temperature of 37°, and hence are generally grown at 30°. **Psychrophiles** (predominantly pseudomonads), despite the name, **tolerate** rather than prefer very low temperatures: their optima are rarely below 29° (Fig. 5-1), but they multiply at a substantial rate even at 0°. This property has ecological importance, psychrophiles being found especially in decomposing foods (or occasionally in transfusion blood) stored in a refrigerator, or in cold soil. **Thermophiles** (predominantly *Bacilli*) are what their name implies: their optimum temperatures may be as high as 50 to 55°, with tolerance to 75°. They are found especially in hot springs and compost heaps; infections of man with thermophilic strains of the mold *Aspergillus* have been rarely reported to arise from exposure to compost.

The contrast of the behavior of thermophiles with the usual lability of proteins simply tells us that our conceptions of protein stability are derived from organisms adapted to living at 37°. Nature, however, can produce proteins that function in quite a different temperature range. Thus certain temperature-sensitive mutants of mesophilic organisms have been shown to produce an altered enzyme: some of these enzymes function normally in solution at 20° but are denatured at slightly higher temperatures, while others, surprisingly, are inactivated by brief chilling. Presumably thermophiles have evolved by selecting numerous mutations that increased the thermal stability of their individual proteins.

Cold Shock. Though bacteria are often preserved successfully in the refrigerator, the sudden chilling of exponentially growing cells of some species (*E. coli, Pseudomonas*) from 37° to 0 or 10° results in substantial killing ($> 90\%$). This curious and unexplained phenomenon is not observed with gradual cooling or with stationary phase cells.

Water. In contrast to higher organisms, whose specialized integument provides for retention of water, the growth and the metabolism of microbes are immediately dependent on ambient water. Thus in regions of high humidity textiles and leather rapidly become moldy, reminding us that when man temporarily withdraws these organic materials from the geochemical cycle he must preserve them from moisture and hence from microbial attack. Indeed, armies bringing elaborate equipment into the tropics have had to provide fungicides even to protect glass lenses from attack by molds.

pH. The pH range tolerated by most microorganisms extends over 3 to 4 units, but rapid growth may be confined to 1 unit or less. *E. coli* cannot withstand a pH much above 8 or below 4.5 to 5.0, while pathogens adapted to tissues (pneumococci, neisseriae, brucellae) tend to have a narrower range. Vinegar-forming *Acetobacter* and sulfur-oxidizing bacteria can tolerate the acid that they produce up to 1 N (pH~O for sulfuric acid). In contrast, a few bacterial species (urea splitters, *Alcaligenes faecalis,* the cholera vibrio) thrive at a pH of 9.0 or more. Most yeasts and molds are highly acid-tolerant, and this feature is exploited in selective media for their cultivation.

The lower pH cutoff point is not fixed but depends in part on the concentrations of organic acids in the medium; a lower pH increases the concentration of the undissociated (and hence more permeable) form of an acid, and makes it more inhibitory. The physiological basis for the wide variation in tolerance to extremes of pH is not known.

A culture growing on a limiting amount of sugar often exhibits a fall of pH followed by a rise, as acid accumulates and then is utilized. To restrict pH changes during growth, media are often heavily buffered; and for fine control automatic continual titration is sometimes employed, the additions being controlled by a pH meter

attached to the culture. Incidentally, the concept of pH, which first clearly distinguished **extent** and **intensity** of acidity, was originally formulated by Sorensen in the course of determining what limited the growth of microbes in various media.

Oxygen. The effect of oxygen tension on growth has already been discussed in a comparison of aerobic and anaerobic growth (Ch. 3). Because of its low solubility the amount of oxygen present in solution is rapidly used up by aerobic bacteria even at a modest population density. The density attained by a culture is therefore often limited by the rate of diffusion of O_2 across the air-water interface, even when the culture is well aerated. Hence, such cultures, when fully grown, have often carried out the last portion of their growth under rather anaerobic conditions.

In a culture aerated by swirling of a flask the growth of an aerobe is often limited to around 1 to 2 mg dry weight per milliliter. Methods that increase the area of the liquid-air interface, such as rapid bubbling of air through a porous sparger, or recycled dripping of the culture, will support heavier growth. Since a shift from small- to large-scale cultivation may markedly alter the adequacy of aeration, it may lead to striking changes in composition of the cells and of the culture fluid. The difficulty of adequately aerating dense cultures also makes large-scale production of bacteria expensive, compared with yeasts, which respire more slowly (surface/volume ratio ca. 1/100 as great).

Anaerobiosis. The establishment of strict anaerobiosis for the cultivation of obligate anaerobes is difficult, since oxygen tensions as low as 10^{-5} atm can be inhibitory. Inclusion in the medium of a sulfhydryl compound, such as 0.1% sodium **thioglycollate** ($HSCH_2COONa$), markedly decreases sensitivity to oxygen through its ability to reduce O_2. With thioglycollate media even the strictest anaerobes, such as *Clostridium tetani*, can be grown in tubes exposed to air; it is helpful to add a layer of oil or paraffin to slow diffusion of oxygen, plus semisolid agar (0.2 to 0.3%) to prevent convection.

The difficulty encountered in cultivating strict anaerobes in the laboratory is increased by the desirability of studying pure cultures: in Nature mixed cultures are the rule, and the strict anaerobes may depend on neighboring facultative organisms to scavenge oxygen. For this reason pathogenic anaerobes tend to be found in mixed infections. Some organisms are **microaerophilic,** initiating growth well at reduced but not at fully aerobic O_2 tensions.

The conditions necessary for anaerobic growth are associated with a low **oxidation-reduction (redox) potential,** measured with a platinum electrode immersed in the culture. However, though extensive observations on this variable have been reported they are difficult to interpret. The somewhat similar measurements of hydrion potential have a definite meaning because all the dissociable acids and bases in a mixture come to instantaneous equilibrium with each other; their states are therefore all defined by the pH of the system and their individual pKs. Most oxidation-reduction systems, however, do not come to equilibrium with each other unless catalyzed, and so an observed redox potential in a complex mixture is the resultant of many competing reactions rather than an equilibrium state.

Carbon Dioxide. The role of CO_2 as a universally essential nutrient has been discussed in connection with CO_2-fixing biosynthetic reactions (Ch. 4). Some organisms (e.g., meningococcus, gonococcus), especially when first isolated from Nature, **initiate** growth better at a pCO_2 higher than that found in air (ca. 0.03% outdoors); they presumably have a lower affinity, rather than a special use, for CO_2. On reaching visible growth, however, all aerobic organisms provide an elevated pCO_2 in their own environment; but some fermentations, such as homolactic or formic (Ch. 3), do not yield CO_2. Elevated pCO_2 is conveniently provided in a **candle jar,** a closed vessel in which a candle is allowed to burn until it extinguishes itself. The accompanying lowering of pO_2, however, does **not** provide strict anaerobiosis.

The inorganic ions universally required in substantial quantity are PO_4^{---}, K^+, and Mg^{++}; in the absence of organic sources of nitrogen and sulfur, respectively, NH_4^+ (or NO_3^-) and SO_4^{--} (or a reduced product) are also required. Phosphate may alternatively be supplied as an organic phosphate that can be hydrolyzed by a phosphatase. K^+ appears to be especially important in protein synthesis: when the cellular K^+ content is progressively lowered, in a bacterial mutant lacking the K^+ transport system, protein synthesis is the first metabolic activity to disappear. Mg^{++} is important as a cofactor not only for many enzymes but also for ribosomal function: a high concentration of free Mg^{++} (10^{-2} M) is necessary in vitro to preserve the integrity of bacterial ribosomes; and when growing cells exhaust the Mg^{++} in the medium their ribosome content diminishes markedly.

Trace Elements. $Fe^{++(+)}$ is required for heme proteins and certain other oxidative enzymes, and Co^{++} for vitamin B_{12}. The requirements for other trace elements are less certain; all are usually supplied in adequate quantities as impurities in the major salts (even of reagent grade) of the medium and in distilled water. Hence the precise definition of trace element requirements is an exacting task. Indeed, the Co^{++} requirement has only been inferred from the presence of vitamin B_{12} in the cells.

Fe is required even by strict anaerobes (clostridia), for though these organisms lack heme proteins they have Fe-containing enzymes of a lower redox potential. Some organisms (e.g., *Serratia marcescens*) incorporate large amounts of Fe into red pigments of unknown function; and an excess of Fe inhibits formation of toxin by the diphtheria bacillus.

Ca^{++} is important for enzyme excretion by certain bacteria and is a major component of endospores (see below), but neither Ca^{++} nor Na^+ has the same general importance as in animals (where they apparently act predominantly on cell surfaces rather than on intracellular processes). Na^+, in fact, is for many bacteria a growth inhibitor, whose effect can be reversed by K^+. Zn^{++} is a component of alcohol dehydrogenase and several other enzymes; Cu^+ is a component of the tyrosinase that forms melanin in the black spores of some fungi; and Mo^{++} is especially important in N_2 fixation and nitrate reduction.

Ionic and Osmotic Concentrations

Most bacteria (other than obligate parasites) are likely to be exposed in Nature to a wide variety of environments and can grow, in contrast to mammalian cells, over a broad range of salt concentrations. But just as the deceptively simple nutritional requirements of certain bacteria concealed an internal metabolism similar to that of mammalian cells, so the flexible osmotic requirements of bacteria long hid the fact that their vital functions, too, need a constant *milieu interne.*

Their constant milieu, however, is found within the cells rather than around them. For example, the intracellular concentrations of K^+ and PO_4^{---} in growing bacteria remain essentially constant over a wide range of external concentrations; when a culture becomes stationary the intracellular K^+ content may drop rapidly, but in fresh medium it is restored before growth is resumed.

This constancy of intracellular ion concentration, even in the face of very low extracellular concentrations, implies the existence of specific active transport systems; these will be discussed below.

Halophiles. As was noted above, Na^+ and Cl^- are not widely required by bacteria, though moderate concentrations are generally tolerated. Most bacteria isolated from the ocean, however, are slight halophiles, requiring NaCl in a concentration approaching that of their natural habitat (3.5%). In addition, moderate and extreme halophiles, with NaCl requirements up to 20%, and with optima approaching saturation (slightly above 30%), are found in flats and lakes where salt water is evaporated, and in pickling fluids.

Although halophiles contain a substantial concentration of Na^+, the bulk of their unusually high salt content is K^+. Furthermore, many of their enzymes, and their ribosomes, are stimulated in extracts more by K^+ than by Na^+ Hence a major function of the external salt is probably purely osmotic, permitting the accumulation of a high intracellular K^+ concentration to which the enzymes of the cell are adapted. However, there is also a specific nutrient function of Na. Halophiles have an unusual cell integument, a high salt concentration being required not only to prevent lysis, and to preserve the function of the transport systems, but also to prevent disintegration of isolated wall fragments. Halophiles, like thermophiles, are of particular experimental interest because unusual structural features of the components that they have evolved can illuminate relations between macromolecular structure and function.

Organic Growth Factors

We have already noted that bacteria range in nutritional requirements from photosynthetic or chemosynthetic autotrophs (CO_2 plus inorganic salts; see Ch. 4), through nutritionally simple heterotrophs (single organic C source), to heterotrophs with requirements even more extensive than those of man. A **requirement** for a compound is distinct from the **ability to use** it as a general C, N, or energy source: different organisms may have one, the other, or both of these responses to the same compound.

Bacteria that are adapted to growth in animal tissues, on mucous surfaces, or in milk often require various groups of amino acids and nucleic acid bases, as well as vitamins. Yeasts and molds, in contrast, usually grow on higher plants, and many strains exhibit requirements only for vitamins, which plants often make in amounts far beyond their metabolic requirements.

Other compounds required by various microbes include inositol and choline (as components of phospholipids), vitamin K, hemin (or occasionally porphyrin), unsaturated fatty acids, and mevalonic acid (a precursor of isoprenoid compounds). The requirement of some neisseriae and pasteurella strains for polyamines (spermine, spermidine) can be eliminated by increasing the tonicity of the medium, suggesting that these bases play a role in strengthening the cell membrane. Steroids, required by many wall-deficient *Mycoplasma*, probably have a similar function.

Certain bacteria and molds respond to very small amounts of a novel group of Fe-containing compounds, called **ferrichromes** or **ferrioxamines,** which are produced by a wide variety of microbes; the function of these compounds is not yet known.

Practical Bacterial Nutrition

Though chemically defined media are often valuable in research, the traditional rich "soups" are still generally employed in diagnostic bacteriology: they are less expensive and often are more reliable in supporting initiation of growth by small inocula. These media are based primarily on **meat digest** (tryptic digest, peptone, nutrient broth), which is the soluble product of autolysis or enzymatic hydrolysis of meat or fish. Many types are marketed, differing in source material or in method of preparation, and often in suitability for cultivating specific organisms.*

To provide a better source of vitamins and coenzymes, mutant media are often further enriched with **meat extract (meat infusion)** or **yeast extract.** In contrast to the extracts of the enzymologist, in which denaturation is minimized, these nutritional extracts are prepared by boiling, to denature proteins and thus release small molecules from the cells and to concentrate the extract.

In **blood agar** a nutrient medium is enriched with whole blood, which not only serves as a further nutrient but also provides a diagnostically useful index of hemolysis. Various members of the *Hemophilus* group, named for their nutritional response to blood, require one or both of two factors, X and V, which have been identified as hemin and a nucleotide (coenzyme I, or DPN), respectively. Hemophilus is generally grown on **chocolate agar,** a medium enriched with blood and then heated sufficiently to release the hemin from the denatured hemoglobin and to denature an enzyme that hydrolyzes DPN.

Some organisms thrive best in media containing a high concentration of **serum** (e.g., 20%). One major function of this addition is to provide a **protective, nonnutrient growth factor, serum albumin,** which has an unusually versatile affinity for various small molecules, including fatty acids, cationic and anionic detergents, and various dyes and drugs. (In the animal this property of albumin permits various materials to be transported in the circulation without damaging cells.) In simple media small inocula of many bacteria (especially *Mycoplasma, Myco-*

bacterium, and *Neisseria*) are very sensitive to traces of detergents and heavy metal ions contaminating the glassware, and serum albumin (0.2 to 1.0%) is used to overcome this inhibition. Some diagnostic media for *Neisseria* include **starch** instead, which also has a high affinity for long-chain fatty acids.

Since individual amino acids are relatively expensive, **casein hydrolysate** is often used in preparing chemically defined, relatively rich media. In the usual acid hydrolysate (e.g., Casamino acids) the amino acids are all free, but tryptophan and glutamine have been destroyed. Enzymatic hydrolysate contains all the amino acids of protein, but mostly as small peptides.

Some facultative organisms (e.g., *E. coli*) require cystine to permit initiation of anaerobic growth in a minimal medium; cysteine is ineffective. Presumably strict anaerobiosis reduces some S-S bonds which are required for growth and are restored by cystine.

The composition of some representative media is given in Table 5-2.

TABLE 5-2. COMPOSITION OF REPRESENTATIVE BACTERIOLOGICAL MEDIA

Minimal medium for E. coli	
	Gm
K_2HPO_4	7.0
KH_2PO_4	3.0
Na_3citrate—$3H_2O$	0.5
$MgSO_4$—$7H_2O$	0.1
$(NH_4)_2SO_4$	1.0
Glucose*	2.0
H_2O	1000.0
pH adjusted to 7.0	

* Glucose is autoclaved separately, for when autoclaved in the presence of phosphate it produces discoloration and some toxicity.

Penassay broth (typical rich medium)	
	Gm
Peptone	5.0
Beef extract	1.5
Yeast extract	1.5
NaCl	3.5
Dipotassium phosphate	3.7
Monopotassium phosphate	1.3
Glucose	1.0
Water	1000.0

(continued)

---

* While the superiority of various digests is sometimes ascribed to their content of desirable **peptides,** the role of peptides in bacterial nutrition is obscure. Some organisms (e.g., certain streptococci) are stimulated by, though they do not require, various peptides; and some auxotrophic mutants respond better to peptides than to the corresponding amino acids. These responses reflect better penetration of the peptides rather than direct incorporation.

TABLE 5-2. (Continued)

B_{12} Assay medium for L. leichmannii

	Gm
Vitamin-free casein hydrolysate	15.0
Tomato juice	10.0
Glucose	40.0
Asparagine	0.2
Sodium acetate	20.0
Ascorbic acid	4.0
Monopotassium phosphate	1.0
Dipotassium phosphate	1.0
Sorbitan monooleate	2.0
$MgSO_4$	0.4
NaCl	0.02
$FeSO_4$	0.02
$MnSO_4$	0.02
L-Cystine	0.4
DL-Tryptophan	0.4
Adenine sulfate	0.02
Guanine hydrochloride	0.02
Xanthine	0.02
Uracil	0.02
	Mg
Riboflavin	1.0
Thiamine	1.0
Niacin	2.0
p-Aminobenzoate	2.0
Ca pantothenate	1.0
Pyridoxine	4.0
Folic acid	0.2
Biotin	0.008

Attack on Nonpenetrating Nutrients: Exoenzymes

Nutritional studies are concerned not only with what an organism **needs** but also with what it **can use.** Through specific transport systems, which will be discussed later in this chapter, microbes can take up foods of low molecular weight, up to oligopeptides, nucleosides, and small organic phosphates (e.g., glycerol phosphate); nucleotides generally cannot penetrate at a substantial rate.* To use macromolecular foods—the predominant form initially returned to the soil in dead plants and animals—preliminary extracellular hydrolysis is necessary, just as in higher animals. For this purpose various bacteria and fungi

---

* An exception is seen in the **Rickettsiae,** tiny intracellular parasites that apparently directly tap the energy metabolism of their host cells.

elaborate a variety of **exoenzymes.** Many of these are secreted into the medium (extracellular enzymes), while others remain attached to the cell (surface enzymes).

Extracellular enzymes include proteases and peptidases; polysaccharidases (amylase, cellulase, pectinase); mucopolysaccharidases (hyaluronidase, chitinase, lysozyme, neuraminidase); nucleases; lipases; and phospholipases. Some proteases are related from the cells as inactive zymogens. A number of these enzymes play an important role in pathogenesis by attacking tissue constituents.

The mechanism of secretion of enzymes (and protein toxins) is not well understood. Many appear only late in the growth of a culture, which originally suggested that they are released by cell lysis. However, the loss is highly selective for certain enzymes, and analysis of cell contents shows that rapid growth represses the synthesis of the enzymes and not simply their release. The enzymes are therefore apparently secreted across the highly impermeable membrane of a living cell, and the problem is essentially the same as that presented by the macromolecules of the cell wall. It has been proposed that such proteins may become attached to the inner surface of the cell membrane in regions that are then everted, or they may be incorporated into membrane as they are being synthesized on membrane-bound ribosomes. Flexibility of macromolecules may be important in their secretion: almost all the exoenzymes examined lack cystine, and hence have no cross-linking disulfide bonds. The secretion and the activity of some proteases require a relatively high concentration of Ca^{++}, which may conceivably serve as an alternative cross-linking agent to stabilize the protein in its active conformation.

Enzymes are frequently secreted by gram-positive but not by gram-negative bacteria. This difference may be related to the more prominent membranous invaginations of gram-positive organisms, or to the lipid-rich, and perhaps less permeable, wall of gram-negative organisms (Ch. 2).

Surface Enzymes. Among the cell-bound exoenzymes (surface enzymes), which sediment with the cells, are alkaline phosphatase in yeast and also in some bacteria. Such enzymes are presumably attached to membrane or to wall, or trapped between the two, since they 1) act on nonpenetrating substrates, 2) are sensitive to nonpenetrating inhibitors (including antibodies), and 3) are released into solution by lysis of the wall (by lysozyme) or by selective extraction with solutions (e.g., strong salt) that do not extract the bulk of the cellular protein. Some enzymes, such as penicillinase, are found in both an extracellular and a membrane-bound form in the same culture; their similar enzyme kinetics and specificity, and the kinetics of their appearance, suggest that the bound molecules are precursors of those in the medium.

Surface enzymes probably play a widespread and varied role in bacteria. A selective DNase, for example, which restricts the ability of some bacteria to be infected by certain bacteriophages, has been identified as a surface enzyme.

Some Macromolecular Substrates. The presence of various hydrolases is useful for taxonomic purposes: in diagnostic work the formation of extracellular protease is generally detected by the liquefaction of **gelatin** (denatured collagen),

which is susceptible to hydrolysis by a variety of proteases. The specificity and the variety of microbial hydrolases also offer considerable commercial promise, as in the tenderizing of meat. Moreover, some of these enzymes remove only a particular terminal polypeptide from a protein, and so they have been helpful in the analysis of protein structure. (For example, subtilisin, from *Bacillus subtilis,* converts ovalbumin to crystalline plakalbumin plus a specific peptide.)

While many bacteria and molds attack starch, few yeasts can. Hence in the fermentation of grain to yield **beer** germinating barley is used to convert the starch to the disaccharide maltose, which is then fermented by brewer's yeast (*Saccharomyces cereviseae*). The mold *Aspergillus oryzae,* however, is used in Japan in a one-step process that both splits and ferments starch.

The attack in the soil on the very insoluble, ubiquitous carbohydrate **cellulose** is a slow process. It is carried out in part by bacteria aptly named *Cytophaga* ("eating cell"), which remain adherent to the polysaccharide fibers and apparently have a surface cellulase that digests them. Bacteria are also responsible, in the rumen of herbivores and in the gut of termites, for converting cellulose to assimilable products.

GROWTH IN LIQUID MEDIUM

Methods of Measurement

Bacterial growth can be defined in terms of either **mass** of cellular material or **number** of cells. The two remain proportional under conditions of steady-state growth, but their ratio can vary with growth conditions. For biochemical studies the concentration of an enzyme or a compound is usually referred to the bacterial mass, while for studies of genetics or infection cell number is more pertinent.

Cell mass can be determined directly in terms of **dry weight** or indirectly in terms of packed cell volume or nitrogen content, but these measurements are inconvenient. By far the most useful index is **turbidity,** whose rapid measurement in a photoelectric colorimeter or spectrophotometer allows the density of a cul-

ture to be followed while it is still growing. At wave lengths of the visible range the absorption of light by colored cell constituents is negligible; most of the turbidity is due to light scattering, dependent on the high refractive index of the bacteria (ca. 25% solid compared with 1 to 2% in the medium).

Wave lengths between 490 and 550 mμ are generally used: the lower the wave length the greater the light scattering, but below 490 mμ absorption by yellowish products of autoclaving may become significant. Turbidity is linear with bacterial density between 0.01 mg dry weight per milliliter (ca. 10^7 cells/ml) and 0.5 mg/ml. The addition of a few per cent of a salt or sugar will cause appreciable shrinkage of bacteria; and though their cross section is decreased, their increased refractive index causes an increase in light scattering.

Cell Number. To determine the **viable number** of a culture a series of 10-fold or 100-fold dilutions is made in order to provide an inoculum that will yield discrete colonies when plated in, or on, a solid medium. In this method the number of units in the analyzed sample is so small that precision is limited by the statistical sampling error. The **standard deviation** (S.D.) is the square root of the number counted (e.g., in a count of 400, S.D. = 20, or 5%). Since reliable counts cannot be obtained with more than 400 colonies per Petri plate, it is customary in precise work to make several replicate plates per diluted suspension. This method is useful, of course, down to extremely low bacterial densities.

For some purposes, especially in studying antimicrobial action, it is desirable to measure not only viable count but **total cell count**; ordinarily the two are identical. Bacteria can be counted under the microscope in specially designed chambers, but it is more convenient to use the **Coulter counter,** an electronic particle analyzer widely used for counting blood cells. In this instrument a small, carefully measured volume (ca. 50 μl) of a dilute suspension flows past a pair of charged electrodes. The passage of each particle, detected through its effect on the electrical resistance of the system, is recorded electronically.

Cell number is difficult to determine with cells that tend to adhere to each other after division (e.g., streptococci); moreover, if changing conditions in a culture lead to aggregation the measurements of cell number and turbidity yield grossly misleading results, simulating lysis. The popularity of *E. coli* for physiological investigation is due in part to its freedom from aggregation under most circumstances.

Growth of bacteria in an adequate medium is characteristically **exponential,** i.e., the rate of increase in bacterial mass is proportional to the mass present. The consequences of this growth pattern are further considered in the next section. We may note here that in truly exponential growth cells are in a state of **balanced growth,** i.e., **every component of the growing system increases by the same factor.**

When cells from an exponentially growing culture in a rich medium are transferred to fresh, identical medium there is no lag in resuming growth. In experiments with minimal medium there may or may not be a lag; it is more likely to occur with small inocula (e.g., below visible turbidity). One factor promoting a lag is inhibition of growth by trace contaminants in the medium (e.g., soap or heavy metal ions). Another is the need to accumulate CO_2, which is required for several biosyntheses. Thus the lag may be decreased by the addition of these compounds (see Ch. 4).

The Stationary Phase. An exponentially growing culture eventually slows down and ceases growth, either because a required nutrient (often O_2) becomes limited or because inhibitory metabolic products (often organic acids or alcohol) accumulate. This process is referred to as the transition from the **log phase** to the **stationary phase** (Fig. 5-2). **In the approach to and during the stationary phase the cells become smaller** as a result of dividing faster than they grow, and they develop major changes in their macromolecular composition which will be discussed in Chapter 9 as a problem in regulation. A large loss in K^+ content has also been observed.

When such stationary phase cells are transferred to fresh medium a **lag phase** is regularly seen; it varies in length with the organism and the medium, and it is much more pronounced in minimal than in rich medium. To the early workers, who measured only viable number, the lag period seemed to be one during which growth was only preparing to get under way. Turbidimetric and chemical measurements reveal, however, that actual growth is proceeding, at an accelerating rate, through the log phase (Fig. 5-2); the cells are enlarging, and are shifting their composition toward that characteristic of the log phase, long before they begin to divide.

Exponential Growth

In the exponential phase of growth the rate of synthesis of bacterial substance at any time

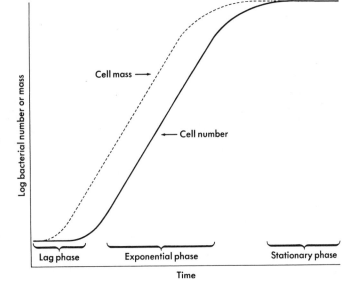

Fig. 5-2 Phases of bacterial growth, starting with an inoculum of stationary phase cells. Note that the classic phases, defined in terms of cell number, do not precisely coincide with the phases of changing growth in terms of protoplasmic mass.

is proportional to the amount of substance present at that time:

$$dB/dt = aB, \qquad (1)$$

where B is bacterial mass, t is time, and a is the **instantaneous growth rate constant** for that culture (i.e., the relative increase per unit time). Hence

$$dB/B = adt \text{ (or } d\ln B = adt). \qquad (2)$$

Integrating,

$$B_t = B_o e^{at}, \text{ and} \qquad (3)$$

$$\ln B_t/B_o = at, \text{ or } \ln B_t = \ln B_o + at. \qquad (4)$$

Hence a plot of the logarithm of B against time gives a straight line. This semilogarithmic plot (Fig. 5-2) is generally used for bacterial growth curves. Since the bacterial mass increases **exponentially** with time (equation [3]), which means that the **logarithm** of the mass increases linearly with time, this kind of growth is called either **exponential** or **log phase.**

It is sometimes convenient to convert the instantaneous growth rate constant a, which has the dimensions of time^{-1}, into the more familiar dimensions of time: $\tau = 1/a$. This **instantaneous generation time,** τ (Gr. tau), represents the time that would be required for a doubling of mass **if** the growth rate at

zero time, aB_o, continued unchanged. In exponential growth, however, the value of B, and hence of aB, is constantly increasing, and at the end of a doubling the rate of cell synthesis is twice what it was at the beginning. Hence in an exponentially growing culture the actual **doubling time,** t_D, is shorter than τ. The relation between the two is derivable by setting B_t at $2B_o$ (i.e., one doubling) in equation (4):

$$\ln B_t/B_o = \ln 2 = at_D$$
$$t_D = (1/a) \ln 2 = 0.69 (1/a) = 0.69 \tau,$$
$$\text{or } \tau = 1.45 t_D$$

Although the growth rate constant a is the key to understanding the kinetics of exponential growth, what is directly measured in the laboratory is the doubling time, t_D (also called the **mean generation time,** or **MGT**).* Hence growth rate is usually expressed in terms of t_D or its reciprocal, μ ($= 1/t_D$), which is the **exponential growth rate constant,** expressed as generations per hour.

These relations are shown graphically in Figure 5-3, which also demonstrates the curvature of exponential growth when plotted

---

* The doubling time is often also called the generation time, which can be confusing since this term, as noted above, has been applied to another useful function, τ.

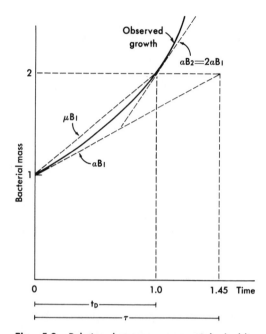

Fig. 5-3 Relation between exponential doubling time (t_D), growth rate constant (α), and linear (instantaneous) generation time $(\tau = 1/\alpha)$.

linearly, rather than logarithmically, against time. Precisely the same curve would be obtained if cell number were measured instead of cell mass. The reason is that ordinary bacterial cultures are **asynchronous,** the cells at any moment being randomly distributed with respect to stage in the division cycle: hence in exponential growth the rate of appearance of new cells rises continuously rather than discontinuously. The growth of a hypothetical perfectly synchronized culture is compared in Figure 5-4.

The linear relation between logarithm of number (or mass) and time obtains regardless of the base of the logarithm. Logarithms to the base 10 are most frequently used, but the base 2 is more pertinent since the unit of growth then represents a doubling (one generation). The conversion is made through the relationship:

$$\log_2 x = \log_{10} x / \log_{10} 2 = 3.3 \log_{10} x$$

It is convenient to remember that $2^{10} = 1024$, or about 10^3; i.e., 10 generations equal a thousandfold increase, 20 generations a millionfold, etc. Furthermore, in exponential growth plotted

in terms of the conventional $\log_{10}$, an increase of 0.3 units = 1 generation.

From these considerations it is evident that exponential growth must be more the exception than the rule in the life of bacteria. A bacterium that doubles in 20 minutes will yield 10 generations (10^3 cells) in 3.3 hours, and 10^9 cells in 10 hours; while a bacterium doubling every 60 minutes would require three times as long. (These are approximately the values for many bacteria on a rich and on a minimal medium.) Hence it is understandable that single cells yield grossly visible colonies (ca. 10^6 to 10^7 cells) in overnight cultures. Furthermore, since the volume of an average bacterium is 1 μ^3, or 10^{-12} cm^3, the volume of the earth (ca. 4×10^{27} cm^3) is equivalent to 4×10^{39} bacteria; and the progeny of our rapidly growing cell would reach this volume in only 45 hours if growth remained exponential. Fortunately, something becomes limiting earlier.

Linear Growth

The molecular basis of exponential growth is illustrated by observing the effect of adding certain **amino acid analogs,** whose substitution for

Fig. 5-4 Arithmetical plot of increase in **cell number** in asynchronous (solid line) and hypothetical synchronous (broken line) exponential growth. In either type of growth **mass** would follow the solid line.

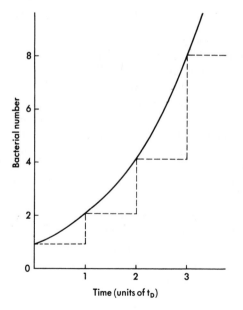

a normal amino acid in protein synthesis results in the formation of nonfunctional protein (Ch. 10). If an analog is used that does not directly slow protein synthesis growth continues at first at a normal rate; but the growth is now **linear** rather than exponential with time, and after the equivalent of a generation or so it ceases. Evidently in the exponentially growing culture the growth rate is limited by the content of at least one kind (and probably very many) of catalytic unit, and when this content is no longer being increased the growth rate is fixed, even though the mass of the cells increases.

Relation of Growth to Substrate Concentration

Bioassays with microbes are performed by adding limited amounts of a required factor to an otherwise adequate medium; after incubation until growth ceases the **amount of growth** is measured. In a satisfactory assay the response is strictly proportional to the amount of the limiting factor provided (Fig. 5-5); however, in the assay of complex material, such as food hydrolysates, the response may be modified by both the sparing and the inhibitory effects of other substances present. Bioassays played an important role in biochemistry (e.g., in establishing base ratios of DNA), but they have been largely superseded by chromatographic methods.

Concentration and Growth Rate. With a

Fig. 5-5 Growth curves (semilogarithmic plot) of auxotrophs given limiting amounts of a required building block (tryptophan) or a required cofactor (biotin).

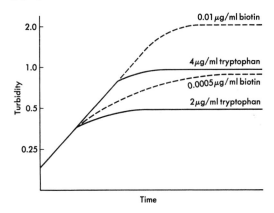

limiting supply of an essential nutrient growth ordinarily remains exponential until the concentration of that nutrient becomes low; growth then slows down and ceases. In other words, the **amounts** of various substances required to support a good growth yield involve **concentrations** that far exceed those required to saturate the corresponding uptake systems; only in the late stages of such a growth curve are the concentrations rate-limiting.

Specifically, the initial concentrations required for maximal growth yield of various auxotrophs of *E. coli* are of the order of magnitude of 5 to 50 $\mu g/ml$ of various amino acids, purines, or pyrimidines; 0.001 to 0.1 $\mu g/ml$ of various vitamins; and 0.2 to 0.5% of a carbon source (for aerobic growth in shaken flasks). Maximal growth **rate,** in contrast, is observed with limiting amino acids down to ca. 0.01 to 1.0 $\mu g/ml$, and with glucose down to ca. 40 $\mu g/ml$ (ca. 2×10^{-4} M). Hence with **building blocks,** or with general sources of cell material, **the transition from exponential growth to plateau is rapid** (ca. 1% of the range of visible growth; Fig. 5-5). (The turbidity of the growing culture, however, will not level off quite so abruptly, for though absence of tryptophan prevents any further net protein synthesis, the cell will continue for a while to synthesize wall polymers and storage materials.)

With limiting amounts of required **cofactors,** in contrast to building blocks, **the transition is more gradual** (Fig. 5-5); as the concentration of a required cofactor in the cell drops it ceases to saturate a biosynthetic enzyme, but that enzyme can still function, though at a decreasing rate.

The Chemostat

In diagnostic bacteriology the use of overnight cultures has been traditional, but in physiological studies more reproducible conditions are achieved by harvesting the cells in exponential growth. Even in this phase, however, the cells are growing in an ever-changing environment.

To obtain bacteria that have grown in a medium of truly constant composition Novick and Szilard, and Monod, devised the chemostat, which permits steady-state growth in a continuous-flow culture (Fig. 5-6). In this instrument fresh medium flows into a filled, stirred growth chamber at a constant, carefully controlled rate; each drop causes a drop of culture to overflow, and so the volume of growing culture is constant. A specific required growth factor is provided in the medium at a **concentration** low enough to limit growth, and thus to determine the **cell density** in the steady-state culture. Moreover, the rate of flow of the medium is set low, so that the cell population can expand fast enough to utilize fully the added medium; the **rate of growth** is thus determined by the **rate of flow.**

The chemostat thus permits indefinite growth of bacteria in a constant medium, with independent control of growth rate and population density. It has made possible very precise analysis of the mechanisms that regulate various processes in the cell (Ch. 6, Mutation rates, and Ch. 9, Regulation of enzyme formation).

Since the mass of growing bacteria remains constant in the steady state in a chemostat, growth of the culture is **linear** rather than exponential. The observed doubling time is therefore identical with the instantaneous generation time (τ), as previously defined (p. 143). Growth of the individual cell, however, is exponential, for as the cell gets larger it takes up a larger fraction of the constantly limiting nutrient.

In a specific example, a 50-ml chemostat is inoculated with a tryptophan auxotroph, and medium containing 2 μg/ml of tryptophan flows in at 25 ml/hour. The generation time is then 2 hours; and as a first approximation the cell density is the same as that produced by the same organism and medium in an ordinary culture. In fact, however, the culture fluid will contain free tryptophan at a low steady-state concentration, which just permits the transport units to take up tryptophan at the rate corresponding to the growth rate. If the generation time is further prolonged (by lowering the flow rate), the steady-state tryptophan concentration will drop lower. On the other hand, if the concentration of tryptophan supplied is reduced from 2 to 1 μg/ml and the flow rate is unchanged, the free tryptophan concentration and the growth rate will remain unchanged in the new steady state, but the **population density** will be approximately halved.

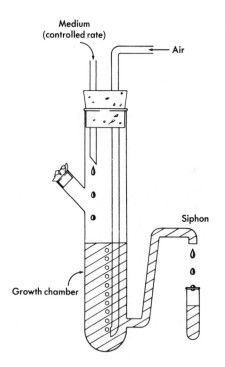

**Medium
(controlled rate)**

Air

Siphon

Growth chamber

Fig. 5-6 Simplified diagram of the chemostat. (For a detailed description see A. Novick and L. Szilard. *Proc. Nat. Acad. Sc.* 36:708, 1950.)

GROWTH ON SOLID MEDIUM

Solidifying Agents

The only method available at first for the enumeration of bacteria, or for the isolation of pure cultures (clones),* was **extinction dilution,** i.e., dilution up to loss of infectivity. An important advance was the introduction by Koch of **solid media.** The initial materials used were unsatisfactory: the cut surface of potato might permit confluent growth, while gelatin was solid only at relatively low temperatures and was liquefied by many organisms. The world is therefore much indebted to Frau Hesse, the wife of a German physician and amateur bacteriologist, for introducing agar, a Japanese domestic reagent with which she was familiar for thickening soups.

Agar (Malay, *"agar-agar"*) is an acidic polysaccharide derived from certain seaweeds (various red algae); it consists primarily of galactose, with 1 sulfate derivative per 10 to 50 residues. Because of the sulfate, agar introduces (and tends to bind) low molecular weight cations, especially Mg^{++} and Ca^{++}.† Agar proved to be an ideal substance for making solid media. It is nontoxic to bacteria, and very few attack it. At 1.5 to 2.0% agar provides a surface wet enough to support growth but dry enough to keep colonies separate. (Exceptionally motile organisms, such as proteus, require ca. 5% agar to prevent swarming.)

After melting at 80 to 100° agar solutions remain fluid at temperatures down to 45 to 50°, which most bacteria can withstand briefly; and after solidifying at room temperature they remain solid far above 37°. The fibrous structure of the gel is fine enough to prevent motility of bacteria within it, but coarse enough to permit diffusion even of macromolecular nutrients.

Being a material of natural origin, agar has the disadvantage, for refined nutritional investigations, of containing traces of various metabolites; hence many auxotrophs will yield microscopic colonies on minimal agar. Purer solid media can be made, though inconveniently, through the use of **silica gel,** formed by neutralizing dilute Na_4SiO_4 with HCl.

Uses of Solid Media

For **enumerating viable cells** known volumes of appropriate dilutions are conveniently spread on the surface of a prepared agar plate; greater accuracy may be obtained by using **pour plates,** in which the inoculum is added to melted agar medium at 45°, which is then immediately poured.

In **isolating pure cultures** on a selective medium an important precaution must not be overlooked. In a naturally occurring mixture the cells that can form colonies may be a minor proportion of the population; the more prevalent organisms not only may be present in the area of a colony but may be fed by it. These contaminants may then become predominant if the colony, isolated on a selective medium, is transferred to a richer medium for storage. Indeed, the literature is replete with results obtained with allegedly pure cultures that were mixtures isolated from a single plating. To isolate clones reliably a colony from the first plate should be streaked again to yield single colonies on **a second plate of the same medium;** one of these colonies can then be used to furnish the stock culture.‡

Solid media are used most widely for the **identification** of the variety of microorganisms present in an inoculum, including the detection of pathogens. A practiced eye can recognize a variety of species on a single throat culture, simply on the basis of size, color,

---

* A clone is defined as a group of cells derived by vegetative reproduction from a single parental cell. Thus any pure culture of bacteria is a clone, and the progeny of a mutant arising in it are a subclone.

† A sulfate-free fraction of agar, called **agarose,** is used for special purposes.

‡ Two successive platings are sufficient because of the diluting effect of each: if the originally predominant contaminant has become a minor component of a colony in the first plating, it will rarely contaminate colonies produced from dispersed cells on the second plate.

shape, opacity, and surface texture of the colonies; the presumptive diagnosis can then be confirmed by microscopic examination and by subculture onto special diagnostic media. Colonial morphology will be further considered below.

Because molecules can diffuse through agar while bacteria cannot, agar media have lent themselves to a variety of special applications.

1) **Nutritional activity** of spots of added substances can be detected on pour plates of inadequate medium heavily seeded with a test organism (10^2 to 10^4/ml); by adding known amounts of material on a disc of thick filter paper and measuring the zone of response, reasonably accurate bioassays (up to six per plate) can be performed. Moreover, paper chromatograms can be incubated on large seeded plates to detect the positions of growth factors.

2) Conversely, with nutritionally adequate plates a similar procedure provides a qualitative test or a quantitative bioassay for **antimicrobial agents** (Ch. 10, Fig. 10-2).

3) By streaking two strains close to each other on a medium that supports poor growth, it is possible to recognize **cross-feeding** of one by a growth factor released by the other (syntrophism). This phenomenon, originally recognized as **satellitism** on diagnostic plates, has proved invaluable in the recognition of biosynthetic intermediates excreted by auxotrophic mutants (Ch. 4, Fig. 4-1).

At the edge of a zone of inhibition growth may be heavier than at a greater distance; but this response is usually due to extra nutrient diffusing from the zone of inhibition, rather than to stimulation by subinhibitory concentrations of the antimicrobial agent.

Colonial Morphology

Surface Texture. One of the most important diagnostic features of a colony is the texture of its surface, ranging from rough (R) to smooth (S) to mucoid (M) (Fig. 5-7). **Rough** colonies have a dry and sometimes wrinkled surface; they are formed by cells that lack a capsule or other surface component promoting the compact cellular orientation associated with smooth colonies, or by cells growing in a filamentous manner. Different

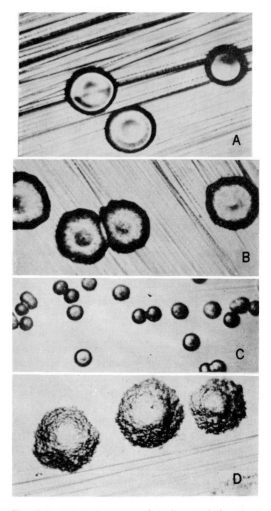

Fig. 5-7 Variations in colonial morphology of pneumococcus strains. **A.** Smooth colonies of capsulated, nonfilamentous cells. **B.** Rougher colonies of capsulated but filamentous variant. **C.** Nonfilamentous noncapsulated variant. **D.** Roughest variant, filamentous and noncapsulated. All photographs ×18, after 24 hours' incubation at 36° on blood agar. (From R. Austrian. *J. Exp. Med. 98:*21, 1953.)

degrees of roughness are possible within a species, and are often correlated with differences in virulence.

Thus with the tubercle bacillus mutations to **decreased** virulence are often associated with a decreased tendency of the cells to adhere to each other in serpentine cords, and hence with a **smoother** surface of the colonies, especially in the presence of a dispersing agent in the medium. With the pneumococcus and with salmonella, in contrast, the **virulent** strains form a surface antigen associated with a **smooth** colony; avirulent mutants lacking this antigen are rough. The basis for smoothness is not the same in all organisms. In the pneumococcus the R to S transition is associated with the acquisition of a capsule, while in *Salmonella* and other *Enterobacteriaceae* the S cells possess a wall polysaccharide absent in R cells, and the further addition of a capsule yields a **mucoid** or **glossy** colony.

Capsule formation, and therefore colonial morphology, sometimes depends on environmental as well as on genetic factors. Some nonmucoid *Enterobacteriaceae* become mucoid if grown at low temperature or in a medium with an excess of carbon source and a limitation of nitrogen or phosphorus. Mucoid colonies may be huge because of the volume of capsular material produced, and thus may contain relatively few cells per loopful transferred; in some cases they are liquid enough to run when the plate is tilted.

Size. The production of small colonies may be due either to a low growth rate or to the inability of the medium to support heavy growth; the two can be distinguished by prolonged incubation of plates containing well separated colonies. Indeed, colony size provides a more sensitive comparison of growth rate than does the most careful direct measurement of growth rate in liquid medium. Thus, it is not possible to detect directly a 1% difference in growth rate of two organisms. However, growth from 1 cell to the 10^7 cells of a colony involves about 23 generations; and if the differential of 1% is maintained through this period the faster grower should multiply through $(1.01/1)^{23} = 1.3$ times as many generations, and hence should yield a colony larger in volume by the same ratio.

Differential Media. Bacterial identification is often facilitated by the use of differential media which reveal specific characteristics. **Blood agar,** containing 5% sheep or horse blood, is used to reveal production of a hemolysin. In **fermentation plates** fermentation of the particular sugar provided is revealed by indicator dyes, such as an **eosin-methylene blue** (EMB) mixture. In the presence of acid this mixture not only changes color but precipitates, and so the colony itself is stained; precipitation is sufficiently localized to demarcate stained **sectors** in a colony that contains a mutant subclone (Fig. 5-8). Fermenta-

tion plates are used largely for facultative organisms; they are effective even when incubated in air, because such organisms convert sugars to organic acids faster than they can burn the latter to carbon dioxide.

A fermentation plate must, of course, contain other nutrients besides the test sugar, in order to permit growth of fermentation-negative organisms. When such negative colonies are fully grown they may give rise, on prolonged incubation, to positive **papillae** (Fig. 5-8) derived from

Fig. 5-8 **A.** Lac$^-$ (unstained) sectors in colony derived from an ultraviolet-irradiated lac$^+$ *E. coli* cell, plated on EMB-lactose medium (which stains only lac$^+$ cells). Note sharp demarcation of sectors, and adjacent lac$^+$ colony without lac$^-$ mutants. **B.** Lac$^+$ papillae, arising late in lac$^-$ colony incubated for several days on EMB-lactose medium. (**A** courtesy of H. B. Newcombe. **B** courtesy of V. Bryson.)

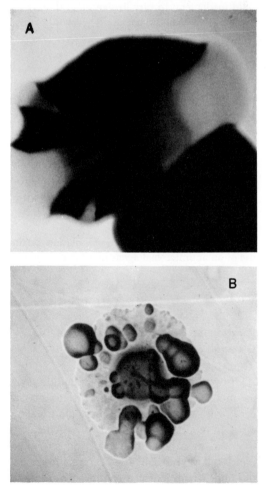

mutant cells arising late in the growth of the colony. Indeed, even on nondifferential media prolonged cultivation frequently gives rise to papillae that can grow on nutrients not adequate for the mother colony; hence colonies on old plates are frequently warty and irregular.

Crowding. In diagnostic bacteriology it is important to deal with well separated colonies. Crowded colonies will be too small to reveal characteristic morphology; they may not produce the localized high acidity required for detection of fermentation; and their extensive production of acid can cause diffuse nonspecific hemolysis. It is also important, of course, to inspect plates after a rather standard period of incubation (usually 18 to 24 hours).

The cells in different parts of a colony will differ in growth rate and in metabolic state, since they differ in access of oxygen from above and of nutrients from below. Hence cells from solid media tend to vary in size more than those obtained from an exponentially growing liquid culture.

Selective Media

Those cell types that predominate in a given microbial population can be readily isolated from a plate on which they can grow and be recognized. For the isolation of minor components, however, **selective** media are necessary. Selective **liquid** media provide **enrichment** (elective cultivation) of the population with respect to the desired organisms, while **solid** media permit direct **isolation.**

An extreme case of selective isolation is the use of an antimicrobial agent in a plate to permit quantitative recovery of the drug-resistant mutants that have developed in a population. One resistant cell in as many as 10^{10} inoculated cells may thus be selected. This number is about the maximum that should be inoculated per plate, since the cells consume nutrient even on a medium on which they cannot grow, and too large an inoculum may exhaust the medium before the resistant mutants can grow out.

Enrichment is based on several principles. Screening for the ability to utilize a given sugar is easily accomplished by making that compound the only carbon source. Selection of nonutilizers (nonfermenters), however, is more difficult. Similarly, the use of a minimal medium, or one containing few growth factors, will exclude fastidious organisms (polyauxotrophs); selection in the opposite direction is harder since media sufficient for exacting organisms will also support less exacting ones. Hence selection for fastidious organisms generally involves the introduction of **selective inhibitors** of the nutritionally simpler species (unfavorable pH, salts, specific inhibitors).

A variety of useful inhibitors have been empirically discovered, such as tellurite for selective growth of diphtheria bacilli in throat cultures, bismuth for selective growth of pathogenic salmonella and shigella in stool cultures, and various dyes (e.g., malachite green), as well as preliminary treatment with strong acid or alkali, to permit recovery of the slow-growing but hardy tubercle bacillus. In an extension of this principle, the selective suppression of bacterial growth in general, by the use of penicillin plus streptomycin, has converted the cultivation of animal cells from the realm of black magic to a simple routine.

CELL DIVISION AND SYNCHRONIZATION

Relation of Bacterial Cell Division to Growth

Growth is often considered essentially synonymous with cell division. This notion accords with the behavior of most mammalian cells, in which gradual cell enlargement is followed by a brief mitotic period and then rapid cell division. With bacteria. however, the final separation of a cell into two daughter cells, by the completion and cleavage of a septum (Ch. 2), is an arbitrary event, whose relation to nuclear division varies markedly with growth rate (Ch. 9, Table 9-2). (Nuclear division in growing bacteria is conveniently observed under the phase microscope in the presence of 20 to 25% gelatin or polyvinylpyrrolidone, which raises the refractive index of the medium to that of the cytoplasm.)

The uncoupling of cellular from nuclear division is seen in its extreme form in cells subjected to Mg^{++} starvation or to borderline concentrations of various inhibitors of growth (e.g., penicillin, various dyes, heavy metal ions, ultraviolet irradiation). Such cells give rise to long filamentous "snakes," sometimes extending across a microscopic field; these aberrant forms contain many nuclei but no septa. Apparently in a bacterial cell suffering various kinds of metabolic limitations the pressure to form a septum is somehow removed, and biosynthesis is channeled entirely into the formation of less dispensable cell components.

Synchronized Growth

In a growing bacterial culture the cells are distributed among all stages in their division cycle.* Hence chemical analyses yield only average values. But there are a number of things we would like to know about the properties of the individual cell in the course of its division cycle: the kinetics of any cyclic change (or lack of change) in the synthesis of its major components (particularly DNA synthesis in relation to cell and nuclear division); variations in mutability or stability of the genetic material; variations in interactions with the environment (including nutrient uptake); susceptibility to lethal agents; and competence for transfer of genetic material. Since it is not possible to study such problems with isolated cells, technics have been sought for synchronizing the growth of bacteria, i.e., for producing cultures in which all the cells would be in approximately the same part of the division cycle.

Synchronization by Temperature Shift or by Starvation. The first technic of synchronization, introduced by Hotchkiss in 1954 for genetic purposes, consisted of lowering the temperature of a pneumococcus culture to 25° for 15 minutes and then restoring it to 37°; a fairly well synchronized doubling of the cell number then occurred less than a generation time later (Fig. 5-9). Synchronization has also been achieved by depriving a thymine auxotroph of thymine, which prevents DNA synthesis but permits continued synthesis of all other cell constituents; on restoring thymine there is a lag followed by a synchronized cell division. Synchronization has also been observed to result from starvation for glucose followed by its restoration. All these methods, however, yield cells whose composition and state of balanced growth have been drastically altered; and such cells do not appear to provide reliable information on the regulatory mechanisms responsible for balanced growth.

Mechanical Selection. A more promising approach to physiological synchronization consists in **filtering** cultures through a number of layers of filter paper, which act as sieves: the smallest cells, resulting from recent divisions, are found in the effluent, while the larger cells, on the verge of dividing, may be recovered from the top layers. Under favorable circumstances either fraction gives syn-

Fig. 5-9 Synchronization of pneumococcal division by temperature shift. Time represents incubation at 37° following 15 minutes of exposure to 25°. (From R. D. Hotchkiss. *Proc. Nat. Acad. Sc.* 40:49, 1954.)

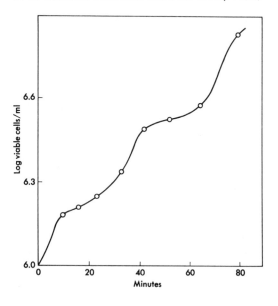

---

* Bacteriologists frequently speak of "old" cells in referring to cells from old cultures, which may mean either cultures in the stationary phase or those stored for a long time. However, the concept of age in a physiological sense is not useful for bacteria, since they undergo binary fission rather than a life cycle that includes senescence and death.

chronization, and it seems probable that balanced growth is resumed with little disturbance. An even simpler mechanical technic, recently introduced, is initiated by adsorbing (or wedging) cells in the **pores of a membrane filter;** subsequent reverse flow of fresh medium through the filter provides a continuous supply of newborn cells derived by fission from the permanently trapped cells.

During a synchronized doubling of cell size the synthesis of the major constituents proceeds exponentially (Fig. 5-10), except for DNA (see Ch. 9). This finding leads to the important conclusion that **exponential growth,** $dB/dt = aB$, **is a property of the**

growing cell, and not simply a statistical property of the culture: a cell on the verge of dividing has twice as many enzyme molecules and ribosomes as a cell just formed, and it grows twice as fast.

The **persistence of synchronization** has varied in the hands of different investigators, but little ordinarily remains after two to four generations. This finding is in harmony with early microscopic observations on the division time of single cells on solid media, which revealed a rather large standard deviation from the mean. This deviation may reflect the absence of a mechanism for ensuring precise equipartition of cytoplasm in cell division.

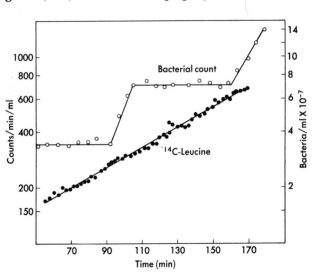

Fig. 5-10 Exponential synthesis of protein in an *E. coli* culture synchronized by filtration. Protein synthesis was measured in terms of incorporation of radioactive leucine from the medium into cell components precipitated with trichloroacetic acid. (Adapted from F. E. Abbo and A. B. Pardee. *Biochim. et biophys. acta* 39:478, 1960.)

SPORES

Certain gram-positive rods (aerobes of the genus *Bacillus,* and anaerobic clostridia) have developed a powerful, specialized mechanism for survival through hard times: the formation of **spores** (Gr., "seed"). These cells, like the seeds of higher plants or the cysts of protozoa, are in a state of **cryptobiosis** (latent life), with **no metabolic activity;** and they exhibit a marked increase in resistance to the lethal effect of heat, drying, freezing, deleterious chemicals, and radiation. Thus the survival of a vegetative culture on drying is

statistical, the survivors being a small fraction of the population and their number decreasing rapidly on storage. Bacterial spores, in contrast, survive drying **quantitatively,** and they die very slowly on storage. In fact, viable spores have been recovered from sealed soil samples stored at room temperature for 50 years.

Resistance to heat has been the most conspicuous property of spores, and spore-forming species are readily isolated from natural materials by pasteurizing the sample (i.e., heating to 65°) before inoculation.* However, resistance to drying may be ecologically at least as important. Fungi, for example, form spores which are only modestly resistant to heat, but are quite resistant to drying; since they are readily detached from the matted, mycelial colony, they evidently promote spread as well as survival.

Fungal spores are generally **exospores,** formed by budding. Bacterial spores, in contrast, are **endospores,** formed by a process (akin to internal budding) in which a vegetative cell gives rise within itself to another cell of novel structure and composition. Sporulation thus represents **differentiation** in an unicellular organism, and it is attracting increasing attention as a model for cell differentiation in general.

Spores are unusually dehydrated, highly refractile cells, whose refractility and physical density are close to those of fully dried protein. They also do not take ordinary stains (Gram, methylene blue) and they are resistant to disinfectants. These characteristics imply unusual properties of the cell envelope (integument).

Formation and Structure

In the light microscope the first visible stage in sporulation is the formation of a smooth area of slightly increased density, the forespore. This area gradually increases in refractility, and somewhat in size, until the mature spore is formed. At a later stage the spores are found partly or completely freed of the wall of the parent vegetative cell (sporangium). In a well sporulating culture most cells contain a spore.

The morphological features of various spores are constant enough to have taxonomic value. In most species they are smooth-walled and ovoid, but in some they are spherical or have characteristic ridges. In most bacilli the spores lie within the normal cell diameter, but in the slender clostridia they cause a con-

spicuous bulge which may be either terminal ("drumstick") or more central (Fig. 5-11).

The electron microscope has thrown much light on the process of sporulation. An early

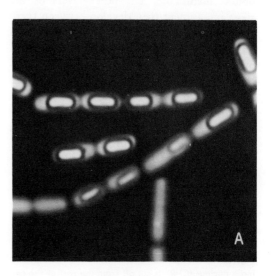

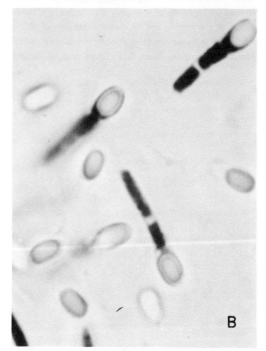

Fig. 5-11 Visualization of spores: light microscope. **A.** *Bacillus cereus:* elongated subterminal spores, nigrosin stain. **B.** *Clostridium pectinovorum:* large, terminal spores, and spores freed from parent cell (sporangium); cells stained with I₂ (which stains granulose). ×3600. (Courtesy of C. Robinow.)

---

* Indeed, as was noted in Chapter 1, the controversy over spontaneous generation was prolonged by the failure of boiling to kill spores present in the hay used to make culture media.

stage is revealed in Figure 5-12. First a nucleus assumes a condensed configuration at one end of the cell, and an invagination of cell membrane proceeds to enclose it in a **double membrane.** The other layers of the spore integument then develop between these two membranes, thus being synthesized on the surfaces corresponding to the original outer, wall-forming surface of the cell membrane. Meanwhile the protoplasm increases in density.

In the mature spore the electron microscope reveals a very thick envelope, which occupies nearly 1/3 the radius and 1/2 the volume of the spore (Fig. 5-13); several layers can be distinguished.

1) Surrounding the **core** (spore cytoplasm or contents) is the innermost layer, the thin **spore wall** or **membrane.** On germination it gives rise to the membrane and wall of the new vegetative cell; but in the spore it is much thinner and is usually difficult to resolve into a membrane and a wall component. 2) Next is the thickest layer, the **cortex;** when unstained it is less dense than the other layers, but the exposure to aqueous media during preparation of sections has probably removed much soluble material (see below). Staining with lanthanum reveals throughout the cortex a concentric laminated structure. 3) Outside the cortex are **two coats,** which frequently separate, in cut sections, to produce an artificial gap (Fig. 5-13B). The inner coat (called coat 1) appears to be a thin, laminated boundary of the cortex. 4) The outer coat (coat 2) is the densest structure of the unstained spore and is presumably responsible for its characteristic imperviousness. 5) Spores of some species are further loosely shrouded in a delicate **exosporium** of unknown function.

Fig. 5-12 Early stage in sporulation. **A.** The protoplasm at one end of the cell, containing a nucleus (CHR), is cut off from the rest of the cell by a transverse spore septum (SPS), formed by ingrowth of a double membrane and mesosome (M) from the protoplasmic membrane of the mother cell. **B.** Later extension of this invagination toward the tip of the cell encloses the forespore in a double membrane, which then detaches itself from the protoplasmic membrane. (From D. F. Ohye and W. G. Murrell. *J. Cell. Biol. 14*:111, 1962.)

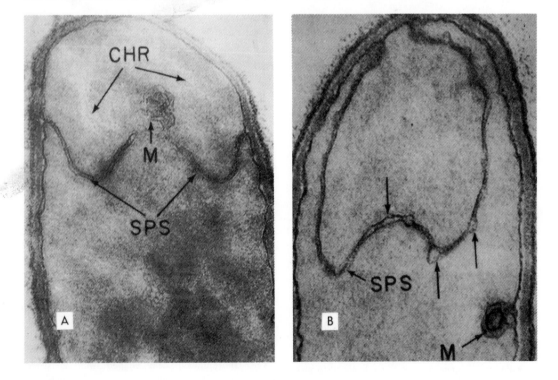

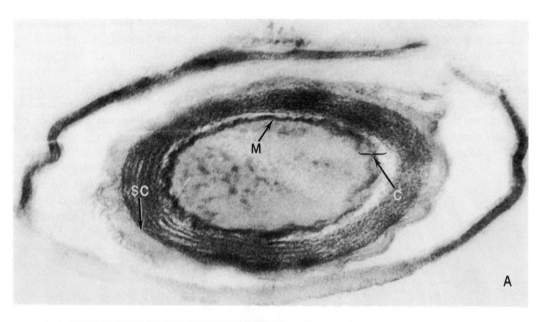

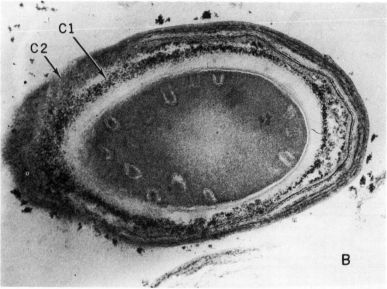

Fig. 5-13 Electron micrographs of sectioned spores. **A.** Fixed to bring out the laminated character of the thick cortex (C) surrounding the spore membrane (M); the spore coat (SC) is artificially separated from the cortex. **B.** Fixed to distinguish the thin inner coat (C1) and the thicker outer coat (C2). The spore membrane is also well preserved, but the cortex has been largely dissolved. (**A** courtesy of C. Robinow. **B** courtesy of D. F. Ohye and W. G. Murrell.)

Chemical Composition

The most striking chemical feature of spores is their **dehydration.** The mechanism for accomplishing the large thermodynamic work of eliminating the free water from the cell is a mystery.

Another unique feature of spores is a **huge content of Ca^{++}** and a roughly equivalent amount of **dipicolinic acid.** This compound constitutes from 5 to 12% of the dry weight of various bacterial spores; it has not been found in any other cells. The calcium dipicolinate is present in free form (though not necessarily in solution), since it immediately escapes into the suspending medium on mechanical damage to the spore. Its relation to heat resistance is discussed below.

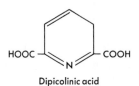

Dipicolinic acid

(Pyridine-2,6-dicarboxylic acid; for biosynthesis
see bacterial pathway to lysine, Ch. 4)

The novel biosyntheses involved in sporulation are emphasized by the fact that the spore surface shows **no immunological cross-reactivity** with the wall antigens of the parental cells. The composition of the integument has been studied by disrupting spores mechanically and recovering an insoluble fraction that corresponds, in the electron microscope, to the integument. In Table 5-3 this material is compared with the wall fraction of corresponding vegetative cells.

To correlate the chemical and the morpho-logical components of the spore, partial degradation products have been obtained by autolysis or by lysozyme. and these preparations have been both analyzed chemically and characterized under the electron microscope. It was found that **the more resistant layers ("coat" layers) consist largely or entirely of protein,** while the glycopeptide resides in the more readily autolyzed, laminated cortex and in the spore membrane (wall). Moreover, the coat protein has a very high content of **cystine,** which makes possible extensive cross-linking between adjacent polypeptide chains. Spores have thus developed an impervious, keratin-like skin surrounding a modified glycopeptide layer.

Enzymes. Spores have a quantitatively very different enzymatic composition from vegetative cells. In aerobes, for example, the cytochromes and the particulate enzymes of electron transport are reduced by over 95%, and a new, abbreviated electron transport system, containing a flavoprotein DPNH oxidase, appears. Those enzymes that have been carefully studied have appeared identical (including thermostability) whether from spores or from vegetative cells. Intact spores cannot attack most substrates, including glucose, and they exhibit no respiration; but since many enzymes resume activity on disruption of the spore, their dormancy in the cell is presumably due to a permeability barrier and/or the dehydrated state of the spore content.

Since spores can give rise to a vegetative cell they must contain a complete genome; and the corresponding amount of double-stranded DNA has been demonstrated. Moreover, since protein synthesis is resumed on germination it is not surprising that small amounts of ribosomes, transfer RNA, and amino-acid-activating enzymes are present; but the characteristically unstable messenger RNA appears to be absent. The RNA content rises rapidly during germination. Evidently some mechanism ensures that the compact spore contains at least a minimal amount of the enzymes and cofactors required to initiate energy production and biosynthesis.

Sporulation

Nutritional Stimuli. The use of labeled amino acids has shown that most of the pro-

TABLE 5-3. ANALYSES OF ENVELOPE FRACTIONS OF
BACILLUS SUBTILIS

	% Dry weight	
Constituent	Vegetative cell wall	Spore envelope
Total nitrogen	4.6	12.9
Total phosphorus	4.2	1.4
Hexosamine	10.7	2.2
Glucosamine	7.9	1.5
Muramic acid	2.3	0.6
Diaminopimelate	5.6	1.0
Lipid	0.7	3.0
Amino acids	Few	Many

Note that the spore integument contains a smaller proportion of mucopeptide components (e.g., glucosamine, muramic acid, diaminopimelate), a lower phosphorus content (i.e., less teichoic acid), a marked increase of lipid (probably adherent membrane), and protein.

From M. R. J. Salton and B. J. Marshall. J. Gen. Microbiol. 21:415 (1959).

tein of a spore is synthesized after formation of the forespore. It is therefore not surprising that sporulation is in general best induced by certain kinds of suboptimal nutrition, rather than by complete starvation.

Different organisms are induced by different kinds of imbalance. A limitation of carbon source, together with an excess of nitrogen source, often provides an effective stimulus. Some organisms also exhibit **endotrophic** sporulation, i.e., they sporulate when transferred to distilled water. This process depends on utilization of energy sources in the parent cell (e.g., poly-β-hydroxybutyrate, protein); the total protein content drops rapidly in a sporulating suspension.

Metabolic and Genetic Control. With some organisms the induction of sporulation can be correlated with preceding specific metabolic shifts (e.g., utilization rather than formation of poly-β-hydroxybutyrate; exhaustion of glucose followed by oxidation of its metabolic products accumulated in the medium). However, while these shifts themselves involve regulatory mechanisms of a familiar kind (Ch. 9), their link to the triggering of the complex, irreversible process of sporulation is not known.

Sporulation must involve the activation of a substantial number of genes, since novel enzymes must be formed to account for the surface antigens and other novel components of spores. Hence it is not surprising that recent genetic studies in bacilli have revealed a variety of loci at which mutations destroy the ability to form spores. Such **asporogenous** mutants are proving valuable in analyzing the mechanism and the regulation of sporulation. Some are blocked in early biochemical reactions, whose absence prevents any detectable formation of spore components. Others (morphological mutants) initiate sporulation but are blocked at various stages in its completion, and so they form incomplete spores which can be recognized in the electron microscope.

Germination

Dormancy and Activation. While the overall process of converting a spore to a vegetative cell has generally been called germination, more refined analysis of its kinetics has made possible the delineation of three stages: **activation, germination proper** (initiation), and **outgrowth.**

Thus, while some bacterial spores will germinate spontaneously in a favorable medium, others (especially if freshly formed) remain dormant unless they are first **activated** by some traumatic agent. Heat (65 to 100° for a few minutes, depending on species) is the agent most widely used in experiments, but **aging** with its multiple, undefined consequences is probably the most important one in Nature. Activation presumably damages an outer impermeable layer, since grinding with glass powder is also effective.

Dormancy has the same biological function in spores as in plant seeds. In many wild-type higher plants the seeds will not germinate until an outer coat has been damaged by some agent provided in the ecology of that plant: abrasion, chemical or bacterial attack, heat, freezing, light, maceration. Germination is thereby spread in time, promoting survival of the species by preventing uniform germination in response to conditions that are only temporarily favorable. Domesticated plants, in contrast, have been selected for uniformity of germination.

Germination and Outgrowth. An activated spore usually must be placed in a rich medium in order to **germinate.** This process of completing the breaking of dormancy involves an **uptake of water and a loss of solid content,** especially calcium dipicolinate and soluble glycopeptide;* the cell therefore loses refractility. It also becomes less heat-resistant and more stainable.

Various metabolites and inorganic ions (especially Mn^{++}) have been found effective as **germination agents** for various species. Such agents appear to activate a **lytic enzyme** that attacks the spore coat, thus leading to release of certain spore constituents and entry of water. The evidence for an enzymatic step is that activated spores must be exposed to a germination agent for a few minutes at a temperature permitting enzyme action; thereafter the loss of refractility can proceed at 0°, as would be expected of diffusion through a damaged barrier.

---

* It is in the material released from germinating spores ("spore peptide") that muramic acid was first found; its fundamental role in bacterial cell walls was discovered later.

Germination leads to **outgrowth,** in which the core of the spore grows, the inner membrane develops a vegetative cell wall (Fig. 5-15), and the vegetative cell eventually bursts out of the spore coat; several stages are depicted in Figure 5-14. Normally germination and outgrowth proceed at the same time. However, the two processes can be separated by adding an inhibitor of protein synthesis, such as chloramphenicol, which prevents the biosynthesis characteristic of out-growth; germination still goes to completion, causing the cell to lose all its calcium dipicolinate and much of its glycopeptide, to rehydrate and then swell, and to gain normal stainability and heat sensitivity.

The Basis of Resistance

Heat Resistance. The Ca^{++} and dipicolinate incorporated in spores can be decreased by lowering the Ca^{++} content or by varying

Fig. 5-14 Sequence of germination in *B. megaterium*, observed with light microscope. **A.** 5 minutes: all cells highly refractile. **B.** 50 minutes: most cells have lost refractility and begun to grow out of spore integument. **C.** 135 minutes: elongated cells still attached to refractile spore coat. **D.** 165 minutes: cells longer, some freed from spore coat. ×3600, reduced. (Courtesy of C. Robinow.)

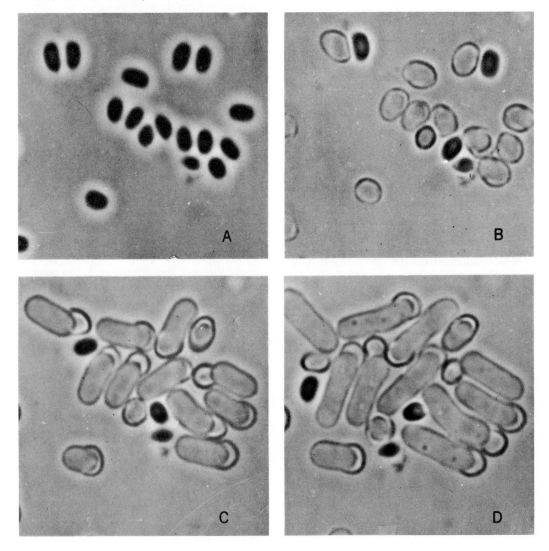

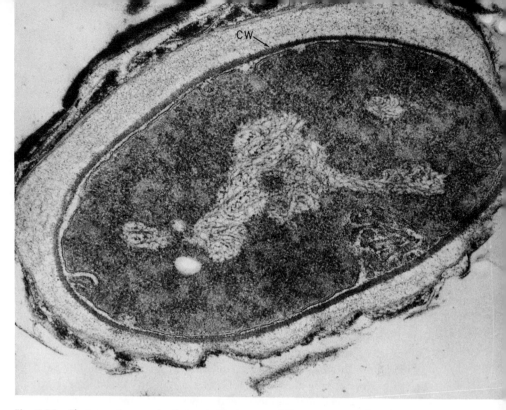

Fig. 5-15 Electron micrograph of germinating spore of *B. megaterium*. The cortex has lost its laminated appearance, and the coats have begun to disintegrate. Note deposition of vegetative cell wall (CW) outside cell membrane. Appearance of cytoplasm already closely resembles that of vegetative cell, with mesosomes, many ribosomes, and well demarcated nucleus. (Courtesy of C. Robinow and J. Marak.)

the organic constituents of the medium. Heat resistance is then seen to parallel calcium dipicolinate content (Fig. 5-16). The mechanism is not clear: conceivably ionic cross-linking by the enormous concentration of these divalent ions in the spore may stabilize proteins against the unfolding of denaturation.

Chemical Resistance. In contrast to the effect of calcium dipicolinate content on heat resistance, it does not influence resistance to killing by drying, to killing by membrane-lysing agents (phenol, octyl alcohol), or to staining. These properties evidently depend on the imperviousness of the spore integument, and not on the state of the cell contents.

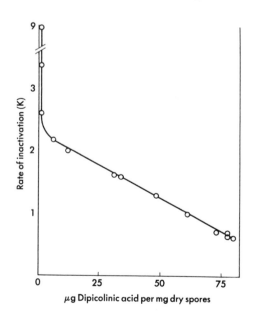

Fig. 5-16 Heat resistance of spores of *Bacillus cereus* with different dipicolinic acid content, resulting from growth in media of different composition. K is an index of the rate of exponential loss of viability at 80°. (From B. D. Church and H. Halvorson. *Nature* 183:124, 1959.)

Rate of inactivation (K)

μg Dipicolinic acid per mg dry spores

Radiation Resistance. Compared with vegetative cells, spores also exhibit moderately increased resistance to the lethal effect of ultraviolet and ionizing radiation. This property may depend on 1) imperviousness to radiochemical products formed in the medium, and 2) the ability of sulfur-containing compounds (which are unusually concentrated in the spore coat) to combine with free radicals (Ch. 11). In fact, during sporulation the radiation resistance increases simultaneously with disulfide content, whereas the calcium dipicolinate content and heat resistance increase later.

Summary

We have seen that bacterial endospores are differentiated cells formed within a vegetative cell; their function is to encase a genome in an insulating vehicle that permits subsequent germination in an appropriate medium. Spores are formed by the invagination of a double layer of cell membrane, which closes off to surround a chromosome and a small amount of cytoplasm. Between the two layers of membrane a multilayered integument is secreted; the thick middle layer of cortex contains much mucopeptide, while the thinner outer coat is a keratin-like protein, rich in cystine and therefore in disulfide cross-links. The stages of sporulation and germination are presented diagrammatically in Figure 5-17.

The characteristic features of spore physiology are beginning to be understood in terms of structure. We do not know the mechanism by which these cells become essentially completely dehydrated (and therefore highly refractile); but the keratin-like properties of the coat account for the resistance of these cells to rehydration, to staining, and to attack by deleterious chemicals. Germination is usually initiated by mechanical or chemical damage to the surface, followed by activation of a lytic enzyme that attacks the coat, thereby permitting uptake of water and loss of certain characteristic spore components. These include a large amount of calcium dipicolinate, which contributes strikingly, through unknown mechanisms, to the heat resistance of spores.

The spore illustrates the marvelous adaptation of biological structure, both chemical and morphological, to function. In its formation a number of genes are activated, with the resultant production of novel proteins, while other genes are repressed; and proteins are formed in the growing spore while the proteins of the sporangium are being degraded. The regulatory mechanisms involved in this microbial differentiation are being analyzed through the use of mutants blocked at various stages in the process.

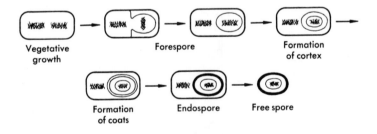

Vegetative growth   Forespore   Formation of cortex

Formation of coats   Endospore   Free spore

Fig. 5-17 Stages in sporulation.

MEMBRANE TRANSPORT

The Existence of Transport Systems in Bacteria

The model of a cell as a semipermeable bag of enzymes proved so useful in the analysis of metabolic pathways that it was taken too seriously. Bacteria in particular, because of their small size and presumed simplicity of organization, were long considered to lack selective membrane transport systems, despite highly suggestive evidence. Such components in bacteria were demonstrated in 1955, however, and they are now under intensive investigation, since the nature of cell membranes is one of the major challenges of present-day biology.

Two kinds of evidence pointed early to the existence of specific transport systems in bacteria. First, many substrates were found to be attacked by extracts of various bacteria but not by the corresponding intact cells; and this "**crypticity**" of certain enzymes suggested the presence of a **permeability barrier** (osmotic barrier) which excluded substances lacking a transport system. Second, when bacteria that had taken up an amino acid or inorganic ions from the medium were disrupted by various means (sonic oscillation, shaking with toluene, boiling), to release the permeant, its intracellular concentration was found to be many times greater than the extracellular concentration, suggesting the presence of structures performing **active transport*** across the osmotic barrier.

Each of these findings, however, also permitted an alternative explanation: the cryptic enzymes might be present in the cells in latent form; and the intracellular excess of a permeant or metabolite could conceivably be retained by binding to intracellular macromolecules.

Inducibility. Unequivocal evidence was finally obtained with the finding that the ability to take up various substances could be induced or repressed by alteration of the growth medium. Specifically, it was shown in the early 1950s that cells of various bacterial species grown on glucose cannot metabolize exogenous citrate; but after growth on citrate they can. Since citrate is an essential major metabolic intermediate, the **enzymes** for its utilization cannot be latent in the glucose-grown cells: not only are they **present,** as can be demonstrated with extracts, but they must be **active** in the cell. Hence the induction of intact cells to utilize exogenous citrate can be explained only by **increased access of the substrate to enzymes in the cell.** Because this increase in enzyme accessibility is specific for

citrate, it must involve formation of a specific transport system rather than a more general increase in membrane permeability.

Further evidence was provided by Cohen and Monod, who showed that the adaptive (inductive) response of *E. coli* to β-galactosides (Ch. 3, Diauxie) involves the simultaneous development of two new properties: the ability of the cells (and their extracts) to **hydrolyze** β-galactosides, e.g., lactose and o-nitrophenyl-β-galactoside (ONPG); and the ability of the cells to take up and **actively concentrate** nonmetabolizable analogs of these substrates, e.g., methyl-β-thiogalactoside (MTG). (For structures see Ch. 9, Table 9-1.) The induced cells therefore evidently form **both a new enzyme and a new specific transport system.** Moreover, there is abundant evidence that the same transport system is responsible for the entry of both the actively concentrated compounds and those that are metabolized.

For example, the two kinds of compounds competitively reduce each other's rate of entry. Furthermore, varying degrees of induction produce parallel increases in the rate of hydrolysis of ONPG and the rate of concentration of MTG. (The hydrolysis is limited by the rate of ONPG entry and not the amount of enzyme, as can be shown by comparing cells with extracts.) Finally, **cryptic** mutants, which can synthesize the enzyme but not the transport system, have lost both the ability to concentrate MTG and the ability of the cells to hydrolyze ONPG rapidly.

Other properties of this system provide further evidence that the intracellular excess of a permeant is actively concentrated, rather than bound to cell constituents. 1) **Stoichiometry:** Though an uninduced cell cannot concentrate MTG, within one generation of growth in the presence of inducer an inducible cell can concentrate this compound to an intracellular level as high as 5% of its dry weight. If induction were producing this effect by altering the composition of the cell interior to provide specific "hooks" for MTG, the number would have to be implausibly high—about 1 per 5,000 M.W. equivalent of cellular dry weight! 2) **Osmotic activity:** Spheroplasts swell on taking up MTG, indicating that the permeant is os-

---

* Active transport (or active concentration) can be defined as transport from a given external concentration (or, more precisely, chemical potential) to a higher level within the cell.

motically active and hence is not bound to intracellular macromolecules. 3) **Competitive displacement:** Though the analog thiodigalactoside has a lower maximal intracellular level than MTG, it can displace about six times its molar equivalent of MTG. This finding cannot be readily explained in terms of competition for intracellular binding sites, but it can be explained in terms of competition for active transport between compounds that differ from each other in affinity and in transport rate (see below).

Relation to Enzymes. Transport systems in bacteria resemble enzymes in a number of respects: 1) they exhibit striking stereospecificity; 2) their formation requires protein synthesis; 3) this formation is subject to induction, repression, and mutation; and 4) as will be shown below, these systems exhibit Michaelis kinetics (i.e., a mass-law interaction of the permeant with a rate-limiting, saturable reactant), rather than diffusion kinetics (in which the rate is not saturable but increases indefinitely with increasing concentration of permeant). The name **permease** has therefore been suggested for such systems, and has been widely used. However, this name should not obscure the fact that the transport systems in bacteria are indistinguishable from those long familiar in cells of higher organisms. Moreover, the "-ase" suffix implies that the system **is** an enzyme; but in studying the mechanism of active transport (see below) it cannot be assumed either that the systems are so simple or that the permeant must undergo enzymatic conversion to another compound in the course of transport. Hence though the term permease is useful in discussing regulation of the formation of specific proteins, it seems prejudicial in approaching the mechanism of specific transport.

Passive Transport Systems. Active transport requires the expenditure of energy, derived directly or indirectly from ATP. However, under conditions of "downhill flow" or in the absence of an energy supply, it appears that the systems capable of active transport become uncoupled from the energy supply but continue to shuttle back and forth; they then function as passive transport systems. (This kind of transport is often called **facilitated diffusion,** although the kinetics are not those of diffusion.) Systems capable of only passive transport of specific sugars are found in red blood cells and in many yeasts, which are evidently adapted to an environment

providing a high concentration of the sugar. The contrasting active transport of sugars in bacteria may reflect the evolutionary adaptation of these organisms to less opulent environments.

Kinetics of Active Transport

The study of membrane transport has been greatly facilitated by the use of radioactively labeled compounds. (To demonstrate active transport by this means it is essential to show that the accumulated radioactivity, recovered by lysing the cells, is in the same compound that was supplied.) Another advance has been the recovery of bacteria on a membrane filter, which permits very rapid washing prior to analysis. Thus earlier studies with cells washed by centrifugation led to the incorrect conclusion that amino acids can be concentrated by gram-positive but not by gram-negative organisms. We now know that washing eliminates accumulated pools much more rapidly from the latter.

With many metabolites, such as lactose, the rate of utilization is limited by the transport system and not by an enzyme; hence no active transport is ordinarily seen. To study active transport of such compounds it is necessary to interfere with their subsequent metabolism; for example, by mutation, or by the use of a nonmetabolizable analog of the metabolite.

β-Galactoside Transport. The most thoroughly studied bacterial transport system is that for β-galactosides, whose kinetics may be summarized as follows. When *E. coli* cells have been induced to form this transport system and then are suspended in a medium containing methyl-β-thiogalactoside and an energy supply (with or without the other ingredients required for growth), the **influx** of the permeant exhibits a constant rate. This influx is measured by adding radioactive permeant and then observing the **initial** rate of increase of cellular radioactivity; this initial value is important because the rate becomes progressively lower as the efflux begins to increase, balancing the influx.

The influx rate (V_{in}) varies with external concentration of permeant (C_{ex}) according to the mass-law kinetics of a saturable system with a characteristic dissociation constant (K_m). (This constant, like the Michaelis constant of an enzyme, represents the concentration yielding half the maximal uptake rate, the latter value (V_{in}^{max}) being obtained at a saturating concentration of permeant.) In contrast to the Michaelis kinetics of influx, the **efflux** rate at any time (in the presence of influx) is simply proportional to the internal concentration (C_{in}) of permeant; the exit rate constant is denoted as K. The cells come to equilibrium with the permeant after 2 to 3 minutes at 37°; the influx and the efflux rates are then equal, by definition, and there is no net uptake. The internal concentration is thus specified by the equation:

$$\text{Net uptake} = \text{Influx} - \text{Efflux}$$
$$dC_{in}/dt = V_{in}^{max} \, C_{ex}/(K_m + C_{ex}) - KC_{in}$$

Some quantitative characteristics of the β-galactoside transport system are presented in Table 5-4. It is seen that different permeants using the same system differ from each other independently in **affinity for the entry system,** in **maximal rate of entry,** and in **exit constant.** These permeants therefore also differ in the degree to which they can be concentrated (**maximal concentration ratio**): ratios of 100 or more are not uncommon with various transport systems.

Other Sugars. Specific transport systems have been demonstrated for several sugars; presumably a different one exists for each metabolizable sugar, or for each group of sugars that share a given stereospecific configuration.

Amino Acid Transport

Amino acids are actively concentrated by transport systems with the same general kinetic properties as those described above. In contrast to the systems described for most sugars, however, the amino acid systems are constitutive rather than inducible. Moreover, they have lower K_m values (which correlate with the smaller amounts of substrate generally encountered and transported), and they have broader specificity. Thus the aliphatic amino acids leucine, isoleucine, and valine are transported by a single system. In contrast to sugars, amino acid transport is often rapid enough (relative to metabolism) to exhibit active concentration even during normal metabolism; but the kinetics are simpler to study if protein synthesis is blocked (e.g., by adding chloramphenicol).

Competition for a shared transport system finally provided the explanation for the puzzling early observation that some normal amino acids

TABLE 5-4. PARAMETERS OF β-GALACTOSIDE TRANSPORT SYSTEM

Parameter	Thiomethylgalactoside	Thiodigalactoside	Thiophenylgalactoside	Lactose	o-Nitro-phenylgalactoside
Michaelis constant, K_m (mole/liter)	5×10^{-4}	2×10^{-5}	2.5×10^{-4}	7×10^{-5}	10^{-3}
Capacity Y (μmole/gm) at saturation	300 (14°) 160 (26°) 52 (34°)	40	32	550 (4°) — 125 (34°)	29 (14°) — 9 (34°)
Time for half-equilibrium, $t_{\frac{1}{2}}$ (min) at 25°	0.75	1.35	< 0.25	2.4	—
Maximal rate of uptake, V_{in}^{max} (μmole/gm/min)	148	20.4	> 86	158	—
Exit rate constant, K_{ex} (ml/gm/min)	0.82	0.59	> 2.7	—	—
Maximal concentration ratio, C_{in}/C_{ex}	65	400	26	1950	—

From A. Kepes and G. N. Cohen. In The Bacteria, *vol. IV, p. 179. Academic Press, New York, 1962.*

inhibit growth of certain auxotrophs (which must obtain the required amino acid from without), but do not inhibit the wild type (which can make it within the cell). For example, arginine inhibits the growth of lysine auxotrophs (in the presence, of course, of added lysine). The 10-year lag between this observation and its obvious explanation reflects the difficulty in conceiving that cells as small as bacteria could possess specific transport systems. Such competitive inhibition of transport must also be borne in mind in analyzing human diseases in which metabolites (such as phenylalanine) accumulate.

Mutants deficient in specific amino acid transport are readily obtained. One method is selection for resistance to inhibition of growth by an amino acid analog; for the uptake of both the normal metabolite and its analog is usually lost in a single step. Another method is to screen auxotrophic cells for derivatives that can no longer grow on the required amino acid, but can grow on its peptides (which are also transported by specific systems, and are hydrolyzed after entry into the cell).

The Exit Process

The exit of a permeant has generally been thought to depend on nonspecific diffusion through pores in the membrane, since the kinetics are those of diffusion—i.e., the rate is proportional to internal concentration. The existence of such pores is further indicated by observations on the effect of osmolarity on the capacity of cells for active transport: with decreasing osmolarity of the medium a saturating concentration of a permeant gives rise, at equilibrium, to a lower intracellular concentration. Since this effect can be shown to involve an increase in exit rate constant rather than a decrease in uptake rate, it suggests a general mechanism for regulating internal osmolarity: uptake of a permeant leads to osmotic uptake of water and thereby to slight swelling of the cell, which "stretches" the membrane and increases nonspecific exit.

The observed kinetics of exit, however, do not necessarily imply exit by "leakage"; for with specific transport systems, which exhibit Michaelis kinetics, the early part of the concentration/rate curve, well below saturation of the system, will also be linear. These kinetics would therefore equally fit exit via one or more transport systems for which the permeant had low affinity. Indeed, there is evidence for such a mechanism. Thus with many permeants induction increases not only the velocity of entry but also the exit rate constant, suggesting that the induced transport system participates in the exit as well as in the entry of the compound. It thus seems likely that the exit process involves the homologous transport system (and possibly heterologous systems) as well as nonspecific leakage through pores. The latter mechanism may well function primarily as a safety valve at high internal concentrations, limiting the difference in hydrostatic pressure between the inside and the outside of a cell.

Nonspecific Entry

Since the membrane exhibits very little "nonspecific" permeability to molecules of the size of sugars, it serves as an effective osmotic barrier that excludes most compounds (many of which would be useless and might be harmful. In addition, this barrier is essential for the retention of both endogenous metabolites and those that are actively concentrated.

Nonspecific entry is best studied in cryptic mutants, which have a large amount of an enzyme but no corresponding transport system. These mutants hydrolyze the substrate at a very low rate, compared with transport-positive strains; and the rate is directly proportional to extracellular concentration over the entire range studied, rather than saturable (Fig. 5-18). Like the exit process discussed above, whose rate is also linear with concentration, this nonspecific entry may represent true diffusion through pores (or through solution in the membrane), or transport through low affinity for systems designed to transport other compounds, or both.

Though nonspecific entry is ordinarily slow, this process nevertheless appears to be essential for the induction of transport units for a compound, since induction (see Ch. 9) evidently occurs at intracellular sites. Thus a higher concentration of an inducer is required for **initial** induction than for **maintenance** of induction: the transport system, once present, can concentrate MTG enough so that an initially inade-

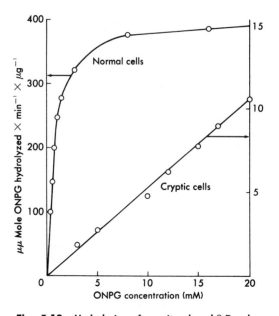

Fig. 5-18 Hydrolysis of o-nitrophenyl-β-D-galactoside (ONPG) by *E. coli* cells. Upper curve: induced wild type; lower curve: induced cryptic (permeaseless) mutant. Ordinates on left apply to upper curve, and ordinates on right (with expanded scale) to lower curve. (After L. A. Herzenberg. *Biochim. Biophys. Acta* 31:525, 1959.)

quate external concentration yields an adequate internal concentration (Ch. 9, Autocatalytic induction).

Active transport systems are found for compounds as small as pentoses and glycine. Glycerol, however, enters by true diffusion and hence equilibrates with the interior of the cell like water, but less rapidly. Bacteria may therefore be conveniently disrupted by suspension in a concentrated glycerol solution which is then rapidly diluted in water: the high osmotic pressure of the internal glycerol solution pulls in water faster than the glycerol can escape, and the cell bursts.

The saturability of specific transport systems, together with the low rate of nonspecific penetration, explains why spheroplasts can be protected by hypertonic solutions even of compounds that can enter the cell. Since relatively low extracellular levels saturate the transport system, higher levels will not further raise the intracellular concentration, and so will contribute to external hypertonicity.

Mechanism of Active Transport

The mechanism of active transport has resisted analysis at a molecular level—far more, for example, than even the mysteries of gene replication and gene action. One reason has been the difficulty in studying transport with isolated cell components: as soon as the cell membrane is disrupted one can no longer demonstrate its transport function, which is vectorial (directional) in character. But though transport systems have resisted direct biochemical analysis, it seems safe to infer that the cell membrane cannot be simply a uniform bimolecular leaflet of lipoprotein, as it appears to the morphologist: it must contain differentiated regions ("pumps") inserted at intervals. Each pump must have a stereospecific protein; but we cannot say whether the capacity to convert metabolic energy into osmotic work is built into this protein or depends on its attachment to additional, nonspecific components.

Biochemical Studies. For some years the only direct biochemical evidence on the mechanism of transport was the demonstration, first in red cell membranes and then in bacterial membranes, of an ATPase activity stimulated by major permeants, such as K^+ ion. This finding supports the assumption that ATP interacts with a membrane component to supply the energy for active transport; and it encourages the hope that the transport systems retain their activity, and hence can eventually be studied, in membrane fragments.

Recently Fox and Kennedy have initiated a new approach by separating a **specific transport protein** from the membrane of *E. coli*. Intact cells were reacted with an irreversible —SH reagent, N-ethylmaleimide, in the presence of a β-galactoside to protect any —SH groups on the active site of the β-galactoside transport system; then the permeant was removed and the uncovered groups were reacted with radioactive N-ethylmaleimide. The radioactive protein then recoverable from the membrane was largely specific for the β-galactoside transport system, since much less of this protein could be recovered from cells in which this transport system had not been induced. About 8000 molecules are found, per fully induced cell.

Models. In the absence of decisive evidence on the mechanism of active transport, several models continue to be entertained.

1) Enzymologists have tended to favor the involvement of **two stereospecific enzymes:** one at the outer surface of the membrane would use energy from ATP to link the permeant covalently to a diffusible carrier, and when this complex reached the inner surface by diffusion a second enzyme would release the permeant.

2) In a second model a single stereospecific protein is itself the **carrier** and is attached to a **contractile protein.** The latter would force the transport protein to shift from facing outward to facing inward, and this process would distort its conformation in a way that reduced its affinity for the permeant; hence the internal and external concentrations differ at equilibrium.

3) Finally, in a third model the stereospecific protein would **oscillate back and forth** freely as long as it was charged with permeant, and would have equal, high affinity for permeant on either side as long as no energy was applied (passive specific transport). However, on the inside a reaction utilizing energy from ATP would change the structure of the attachment site, so that the **affinity of the transfer protein for the permeant was lowered.** When the empty transport protein rotated outward in this altered state a release of the blocking effect would be triggered, and the protein would again have a high affinity for the permeant molecules outside the cell (Fig. 5-19).*

The first, enzymatic model cannot be directly applied to the transport of ions such as K^+ and Na^+, which cannot form covalent bonds; furthermore, it appears to require two specific proteins, whereas the evidence from mutation suggests the formation of only one type of specific protein per transport system. Hence the non-enzymatic models 2 and 3 seem more likely.

A choice between these models is suggested by the results of further studies on the exit process. When *E. coli* cells are equilibrated with an actively transported β-galactoside and then

* Although the arrows of Figure 5-19 seem to suggest "diffusion" of T from one side of the membrane to the other, the concept of diffusion is not strictly applicable to a solid membrane. Furthermore, the distance traversed by the binding site in its oscillation in a transport system may even be much shorter than the average thickness of the membrane. Hence the movement across this distance may simply be a hinge-like conformational change in a protein, fixed in the membrane, that allows the binding site to face either side.

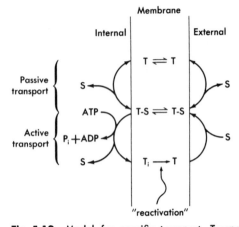

Fig. 5-19 Model for specific transport. T=specific transport protein; S=its substrate (permeant.) In passive specific transport (facilitated diffusion), without the application of energy, T moves back and forth reversibly, either unloaded (T) or loaded (T-S); the direction of net flow of S depends on whether the internal or external concentration of S is greater. When energy is applied, to bring about active transport, T is converted on the inner side of the membrane to a relatively "inactivated" form (T_i), with a much lower affinity for S. Hence T-S by conversion to T_i-S, can unload S within the cell even when the internal concentration is high; and T_i will return unloaded until that concentration becomes high enough to satisfy the high Michaelis constant of T_i (or to block its formation from T-S). During this cycle T_i, in a spontaneous, exergonic reaction, becomes T on the outer aspect of the membrane, and can thus again pick up external S at a low concentration.

are transferred to permeant-free medium the internal pool is lost only slowly. However, if the supply of energy is cut off by adding a metabolic poison, such as azide, the accumulated pool is now transported **outward** rapidly, with the same kinetics that characterized its initial inward transport in the presence of an energy supply. This effect favors model 3 (Fig. 5-19), in which the application of energy blocks exit (by lowering affinity of the transport system for the permeant within the cell), rather than model 2, in which the application of energy would act on the entry process. This model has the further advantage that the endergonic reaction occurs on the cytoplasmic side of the membrane, where ATP is available, rather than on the outer side.

Conformational responses of an oscillating transport protein might also account for an additional property of the amino acid systems: the ability under certain circumstances to **retain** permeants when they are no longer present in the outside medium. This feature could have economic advantage in promoting the retention of metabolites that can be made endogenously. For example, *E. coli* cells cannot concentrate an amino acid at 0°. However, if they have concentrated it at 37° and then are chilled they do not **lose** it for hours in the absence of the external compound, even though they can **exchange** it rapidly with added labeled compound. Evidently some kind of "ratchet" device, of unknown nature, allows this transport system to oscillate freely when occupied, but not to go out full and come back empty.

The Evolutionary Adaptation of Transport Systems

The adaptation of transport systems to the needs of bacteria is illustrated by several patterns.

1) As we have seen, inducible systems are provided for various sugars that may be encountered only occasionally; but for glucose, which is much the most widespread sugar in Nature, many bacteria have a constitutive system.

2) The systems for amino acids are generally constitutive. This property might have evolved because individual amino acids are useful to a cell (as building blocks) in small amounts compared with sugars, and at such low concentrations they might not be able to "force" sufficient nonspecific penetration to initiate induction of their transport systems.

3) Similar considerations may also explain why the transport systems for amino acids have lower Michaelis constants, by a factor of ca. 100, than those for sugars. Theoretical considerations, derived from enzyme kinetics, suggest that an increase in the tightness of fit of a substrate will result, other things being equal, in a decrease of turnover number. Indeed, this inverse relation between affinity and uptake rate is seen experimentally in mutants selected for a faster uptake of diaminopimelate: this increase in rate is accompanied by a decrease in affinity. Hence, though high turnover rate and high affinity both promote transport, one of these desiderata is evidently achieved at the expense of the other. It is therefore obviously advantageous for a cell to have systems tailored to fit the useful concentration ranges of various permeants.

SELECTED REFERENCES

Books and Review Articles

COHEN, G. N., and MONOD, J. Bacterial permeases. *Bact. Rev. 21:*169 (1957).

GUIRARD, B. M., and SNELL, E. E. Nutritional Requirements of Microorganisms. In *The Bacteria,* vol. IV, p. 33. (I. C. Gunsalus and R. Y. Stanier, eds.) Academic Press, New York, 1962.

HUTNER, S. H., and HOLZ, G. G. Lipid requirements of microorganisms. *Ann. Rev. Microbiol. 16:*189 (1962).

INGRAHAM, J. L. Temperature Relationships. In *The Bacteria,* vol. IV, p. 265. (I. C. Gunsalus and R. Y. Stanier, eds.) Academic Press, New York, 1962.

KEILIN, D. The problem of anabiosis or latent life: History and current concept. *Proc. Roy. Soc., London, S.B 150:*149 (1959).

KNIGHT, B. C. J. G. Growth factors in microbiology. *Vitamins & Hormones 3:*108 (1945).

MAALØE, O. Synchronous Growth. In *The Bacteria,* vol. IV, p. 1 (I. C. Gunsalus and R. Y. Stanier, eds.) Academic Press, New York, 1962.

MURRELL, W. G. Spore Formation and Germination as a Microbial Reaction to the Environment. In *Microbial Reaction to Environment* (11th Symposium, Society of General Microbiology). Cambridge Univ. Press, London, 1961.

NOVICK, A. Growth of bacteria. *Ann. Rev. Microbiol. 9:*97 (1955).

POLLOCK, M. R. Exoenzymes. In *The Bacteria,* vol. IV, p. 171. (I. C. Gunsalus and R. Y. Stanier, eds.) Academic Press, New York, 1962.

SUSSMAN, A. S., and HALVORSON, H. O. *Spores: Their Dormancy and Germination.* Harper & Row, New York, 1966.

SYMPOSIUM: Continuous Culture Methods and Their Application. In *Recent Progress in Microbiology* (7th International Congress of Microbiology, Stockholm, 1958). Thomas, Springfield, Ill., 1959.

Specific Articles

HITCHENS, A. P., and LEIKIND, M. C. The introduction of agar-agar into bacteriology. *J. Bact.* 37:485 (1939).

KENNEDY, E. P., and FOX, C. F. Specific labelling and partial purification of the M protein, a component of the β-galactoside transport system of *E. coli*. *Proc. Nat. Acad. Sc.* 54:891 (1965).

MONOD, J. La technique de culture continue: Théorie et applications. *Ann. Inst. Pasteur* 79:390 (1950).

NOVICK, A., and SZILARD, L. Experiments with chemostat on spontaneous mutations of bacteria. *Proc. Nat. Acad. Sc.* 36:708 (1950).

SCHAEFFER, P., IONESCO, H., RYTER, A., and BALASSA, G. La sporulation de *Bacillus subtilis*: Etude génétique et physiologique. In *Régulations chez les Microorganismes* (Colloque International du C.N.R.S. No. 124, Marseille, 1963). Editions du Centre National de la Recherche Scientifique, Paris, 1965.

WINKLER, H. H., and WILSON, T. H. The role of energy coupling in the transport of β-galactosides by *E. coli*. *J. Biol. Chem.* 241:2200 (1966).

6 BACTERIAL VARIATION AND POPULATION DYNAMICS

With the intensive exploration of the world of bacteria in the latter part of the nineteenth century the organisms encountered were found not only to vary widely in their morphological and physiological properties, but also to change extensively during cultivation in the laboratory. This apparent instability led some authorities (Naegeli, Büchner) to propose the doctrine of **pleomorphism,** according to which the wide range of bacteria encountered in Nature represented different stages in the life cycles of a relatively small number of species. However, after Koch introduced reliable pure culture technics in 1881 a wide variety of organisms were shown to maintain their differences through innumerable transfers. The opposing doctrine of **monomorphism** was thus successful, and for several decades the isolation and characterization of novel organisms became the major activity of microbiologists.

Genotypic and Phenotypic Variation

The success of the new pure culture methodology not only established the existence of a fantastic number of different kinds of bacteria, but also led to an exaggerated emphasis on the stability of their properties. It was gradually realized, however, that even an initially pure culture may yield, on repeated transfer in the laboratory, a mixture of progeny with various new properties. Their emergence is now adequately explained in terms of two processes fundamental to all living organisms: 1) **mutation and selection,** yielding new genotypes, and 2) **phenotypic variation** (physiological adaptation), yielding altered phenotypes within the range of potential of a given genotype. Yet the recognition of these principles came extraordinarily late in bacteriology, and inheritance in bacteria was widely believed to reside in some vague plastic properties of the entire cell, rather than in a genetic apparatus.*

---

*It is noteworthy that in 1900, within a few months after de Vries in Holland discovered mutations in higher plants, his countryman Beijerinck proposed that the same mechanism must be responsible for the heritable changes observed in cultured bacteria. But this idea was premature: for nearly half a century few biologists recognized any connection between the fields of bacterial variation and genetics.

Several factors contributed to this misconception. 1) The technical limitations of bacterial cytology led to the erroneous conclusion that bacteria have no nucleus or other form of localized chromatin. 2) Because bacteria produce enormous numbers of progeny in a short time, and their spontaneous mutants are often subject to strong selective pressures, inheritable changes may appear very rapidly: hence it seemed unreasonable to invoke the same mechanism responsible for the much slower changes seen in higher organisms. 3) Genetic recombination between nonidentical individuals is necessary for recognizing the existence of units of inheritance and for determining their linkage in chromosomes; and recombination was not discovered in bacteria until the 1940s. 4) The quantitative technics necessary to distinguish between genotypic and phenotypic variation were not developed until late, even though the criterion is basically simple: a **phenotypic adaptation** to an environmental change involves essentially **all** the cells in the culture, whereas a **genotypic adaptation** involves a **rare** mutant which is then selected (i.e., grows faster than the parental strain) because it is better adapted to the new environment. The enumeration of mutant **clones** (i.e., progeny derived from a single mutant cell) is thus crucial.

Mutant cells appearing in a liquid culture can often be detected and quantitated simply by plating on solid media: many kinds of mutants alter colonial morphology (Ch. 5), and others alter the ability to form a colony on appropriate media. In addition, mutants will appear among the cells newly formed during incubation of the inoculated plate, and the emergence of such a mutant subclone within a colony can often be recognized from the appearance of a **sectored colony.** Sectors may be seen, for example, with R-S (rough-smooth surface) variation, with color mutants, or with fermentation mutants (whose ability to ferment a sugar may be recognized by the resulting precipitation of a dye; Fig. 5-8).

Selective Pressures and Adaptation

Whatever the mechanism of their origin, some of the persistent (inheritable) changes in bacteria were obviously **adaptations**, increasing fitness to a new environment. For example, a pathogen that grows slowly when first isolated in a laboratory medium will frequently adapt to faster growth, and this process depends on selection of rare mutants appearing among the progeny. But these mutants, though able to grow faster in the artificial medium, are often less able to grow in the animal host: i.e., adaptation to laboratory cultivation is often accompanied by **loss of virulence (attenuation).** Conversely, virulence may in turn be restored by passage through an animal host, which again involves the selection of rare mutants by the new environment. In this process a large inoculum of an attenuated strain will be required to cause infection, but the organism subsequently recovered will be able to initiate infection with a smaller inoculum. Another common example of genetic adaptation is the selection of drug-resistant mutants during growth in the presence of an inhibitory compound, in vivo or in vitro.

Dissociation and Phase Variation

Certain frequent kinds of variation, in contrast, do not exhibit any obvious adaptive advantage; hence they were long considered to differ fundamentally from adaptation, and were given new names. Thus **dissociation** refers to the appearance of a novel colony type: the original, virulent isolate from a patient usually plates out homogeneously as smooth (S) or mucoid colonies; but after one or more passages in liquid medium it may yield mostly or entirely rough (R) colonies (Fig. 6-1). Furthermore, the phenomenon may be reversible on further cultivation. In the similar phenomenon of **phase variation** an enteric organism, with flagella of a given surface structure (recognized immunologically), abruptly shifts, during transfer in the laboratory, from this antigenic type (phase 1) to

Fig. 6-1 Rough (R) and smooth (S) colonies of *Brucella abortus*. Because of the difference in their reflection of light, the R colonies are considerably lighter in the photograph than the S colonies, as well as appearing more stippled. (Courtesy Werner Braun.)

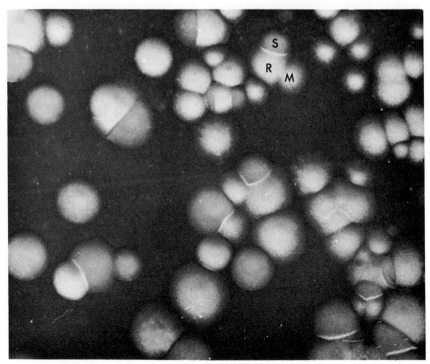

another (phase 2); and on further transfer the organism may shift back and forth between the two "phases."

The reversibility of these shifts caused them to be long regarded as manifestations of a **life cycle** in the bacteria. Quantitative analysis of the kinetics of the shifts, however, showed that they are due to **selection of spontaneous, inheritable variants;** and though the frequency of appearance of these variants **per unit time** seems high, **per cell generation** it is low enough to be consistent with a mutational origin. The apparently quixotic reversals in direction of the population shifts have two causes: the ready reversibility of the mutations involved, and the complexity of the selective pressures imposed by the environment. Thus not only does the initial transfer from natural habitat to laboratory cultivation provide a radically altered environment, but within a single growing culture the composition of the medium undergoes continuous changes that create new pressures.

The culture medium changes most rapidly as the population density becomes high and the culture approaches the stationary phase: the alterations include lowered concentration of nutrients, lowered pO_2, lowered pH, and accumulation of metabolic products. Hence the frequency and the reversal of phase variation and dissociation in laboratory transfers depend not only on the medium used but also on such details as the inoculum size and the duration of incubation. Indeed, a stable equilibrium can be reached if cultures are kept in prolonged exponential growth (Fig. 6-2); the value of the equilibrium depends on the mutation rates in the two directions. Since slow growth continues even on storage in a refrigerator, which introduces further new selective pressures, stock cultures are best preserved in the frozen or the dried (lyophilized) state, which prevents further multiplication.

The explanation for such populational shifts has been worked out with special care in reconstruction experiments with mixed R and S *Brucella* cells. In fresh medium S cells grow faster, but they excrete D-alanine. With increasing population density (i.e., "used" medium) the accu-

Fig. 6-2   Attainment of equilibrium between two phases of *Salmonella typhimurium* after prolonged exponential growth. Each initial culture contained cells of only one phase. Growth was kept exponential in a series of successive subcultures by transferring from each a small inoculum taken before the population density approached saturation. From these kinetics it can be calculated that the mutation rates were 5.2×10^{-3} per division for A→B and 8.8×10^{-4} for B→A. (After B. A. D. Stocker, *J. Hyg.* 47:398, 1949.)

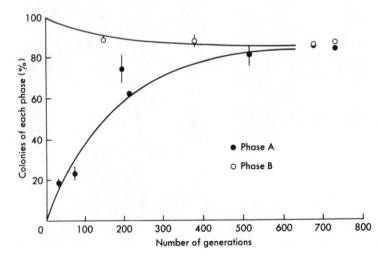

mulation of this substance, as well as the decrease in pO_2, cause S cells to grow more slowly than R cells and hence to be outgrown by them.

Periodic Selection. While mutation and selection tend at first to increase the genetic heterogeneity of a population, a related process of periodic or indirect selection tends to reduce this heterogeneity. In this process a variety of accumulated indifferent mutants (i.e., those with little or no effect on growth rate) are all eliminated by sharp selection for a new mutant with an increased growth rate.

For example, in a culture growing in the chemostat (Ch. 5) with limiting tryptophan the proportion of phage-resistant mutants increased with time for about 30 hours, and then rapidly declined and slowly rose again (Fig. 6-3). The decline was found to be due to the appearance of a new kind of mutant, with improved ability to utilize tryptophan at a very low concentration. Hence the rapid outgrowth of the new type resulted in indirect selection against the resistant cells—not because they were resistant, but because, purely on numerical grounds, their small population did not include any cells with the

mutation for faster growth. In the new population resistant mutants would appear again at the usual rate and again be wiped out by the appearance of a mutant with a further improvement in tryptophan utilization. Several such cycles of periodic selection could be followed.

The relevance of the population genetics of bacteria to problems of infectious disease will be noted repeatedly in later sections of this book, for the initial and the later stages of bacterial infection differ in selective pressures, much like fresh and aging cultures. Relevant factors include effects of high bacterial density on the composition of the surrounding fluid, as well as selective pressures from tissue defense reactions of the host, from the development of an immune response, and from the presence of chemotherapeutic agents. In an important application, attenuation of virulence on repeated transfer in artificial media, or in unusual hosts, has been used to develop useful live vaccines against various bacteria (e.g., those of tuberculosis and tularemia) and various viruses (e.g., those of smallpox and poliomyelitis).

Fig. 6-3 Periodic selection. In the population of a tryptophan auxotroph of *E. coli* growing in a chemostat under tryptophan limitation the fraction of phage T5-resistant mutants increases progressively, since existing mutant clones maintain a normal growth rate and fresh mutations continually add to their number. (The linear nature of the increase will be discussed below: see "Mutation rates".) The accumulated mutant population, however, is periodically almost wiped out when the entire population is displaced by the progeny of another kind of mutant, which can grow faster. (T5-resistant mutants were used in this study simply because they grow at a normal rate and are very easy to select, and therefore to count.) (Modified from Novick, A., and L. Szilard, *Proc. Natl. Acad. Sci.* 36:708, 1950.)

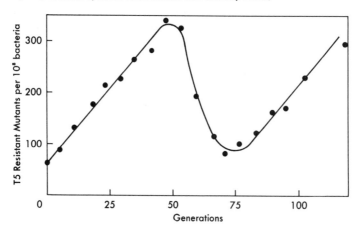

Random vs. Directed Mutation

In microbial cultures, as we have just seen, the rate of evolution is dramatically accelerated by three factors: the presence of extremely large numbers of individuals, the short generation time, and the effect of strong selective pressures. As a result, what looked superficially like excessive genetic instability turned out to be simply rapid selection—often literally overnight—of a hereditary variant, which appeared spontaneously during the multiplication of an originally homogeneous inoculum. Since the appearance of these variants was found to have much the same range of frequencies as the familiar spontaneous mutations in higher organisms (i.e., 10^{-5} to 10^{-10} per generation), the existence of a common mechanism for the two processes began to be considered seriously. Furthermore, the appearance of these variants was found to be accelerated by agents (ultraviolet light, X-ray) known to be mutagenic in higher organisms. Hence around 1940 bacteriologists began to refer to inheritable changes in bacteria as mutations, and to postulate the existence of units of inheritance—genes—instead of the vague plasticity proposed earlier.

The mutations of higher organisms, however, occur in germ cells, which are distinct from somatic cells and are protected from the environment; and it was largely the recognition of this distinction, in the late nineteenth century, that rendered untenable the lamarckian doctrine of the inheritance of adaptively acquired characteristics. The single bacterial cell, in contrast, is at the same time soma and gamete, and is fully exposed to the environment; hence an inhibitory compound that enters it, and thus reaches its genome, conceivably not only might select for resistant mutants but also might direct their appearance. To be sure, the appearance of resistance in only a tiny fraction of the population excludes the possibility of an ordinary phenotypic adaptation which, as noted above, would influence the whole population. Nevertheless, this finding does not rigorously exclude the possibility that the drug had a directive

hereditary influence with a low level of effectiveness; for all the cells are exposed to the drug in the course of detecting the resistant clones, and so these clones might have arisen during that exposure rather than spontaneously beforehand.

Fluctuation Analysis

Definitive evidence on this problem was furnished by a statistical approach, called fluctuation analysis, which was designed by Luria and Delbruck in 1943 to study resistance to bacteriophage; the same type of experiment was subsequently applied by Demerec to drug resistance (Fig. 6-4). Small inocula, containing no resistant mutants, were incubated in 100 identical 1-ml tubes of medium. When growth was complete the content of each tube was poured in a plate of medium containing the inhibitor, and after incubation the number of colonies (i.e., resistant mutants) was determined. If the resistant mutants arose only **during** exposure to the drug each plate should have received an identical, mutant-free inoculum, and the postulated interaction of drug and cell should have the same chance of producing resistant mutants in each plate; hence each should yield the same number of resistant colonies, except for a predictable statistical variation. If, on the other hand, the mutations had occurred in the liquid medium, **before** exposure to the drug, the individual tubes would differ from each other in the time of random appearance of the first mutant. They would then differ in the size of the clone derived from each mutated cell between its appearance and the cessation of growth in the tube. The number of resistant cells should therefore fluctuate widely from tube to tube.

Wide fluctuation was indeed observed, a few "jackpot" tubes (those with a very early mutation) having a large number of mutants. In contrast, in the control experiment in which 100 1-ml samples were plated from a single flask, rather than from separate tubes, the expected narrow statistical distribution about the mean was observed.

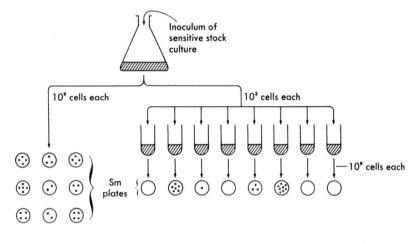

Fig. 6-4 Fluctuation analysis of mutation to streptomycin (Sm) resistance. A small number of sensitive cells were inoculated in a flask containing 100 ml of broth, and also in 100 tubes each containing 1 ml of the same medium. After full growth was reached 1 ml samples were inoculated in plates of medium containing the drug, and the number of Sm-resistant colonies appearing after overnight incubation was determined. The fluctuation in their number was much greater among the samples that had grown out in separate tubes than among those from the same flask. (Based on S. E. Luria and M. Delbruck, *Genetics 28:491,* 1943.)

In this ingenious experiment the separation of populations in tubes allowed the effect of an early spontaneous mutation to be amplified and thus detected. Lederberg subsequently used **separation on solid media** to achieve a more direct demonstration of the same effect: an inoculum of sensitive bacteria was grown on plates without drug to form a lawn, which was then **replica-plated** onto drug-containing medium. The results showed that the lawn contained resistant cells in localized clusters, which had been formed without exposure to the drug (Fig. 6-5).

Fluctuation analysis demonstrated conclusively that **drug-resistant mutants appear spontaneously,** before exposure to the drug, rather than being directed by the presence of the drug. This proof did much to overcome a widespread anthropomorphic reluctance to accept the overwhelming role of chance events in genetic adaptation.

Through the steps outlined above it was gradually recognized that inheritance in bacteria is governed by unit factors, indistinguishable from the genes of higher organisms. Bacterial genetics could not be studied in depth, however, until genes could be identified and manipulated by means of genetic recombination. The long sought classic sexual fusion was never found in bacteria; but between 1944 and 1951 various bacteria were found to employ three novel mechanisms for transferring genetic material: transformation, conjugation, and transduction. These will be considered in the next chapter.

Cytoplasmic Inheritance

Although the central role of chromosomal DNA in microbial heredity has been firmly established, there are a few well documented examples of nonchromosomal (cytoplasmic) mutations (using the term broadly to denote any abrupt hereditary change within an organism), which offer some formal resemblance to the lamarckian concept of directed inheritance. Thus acriflavine can "cure" bacteria of self-reproducing cytoplasmic genetic units called episomes (Ch. 24), and it can also destroy the capacity of yeasts to form mitochondria, and hence to respire (Ephrussi). Streptomycin can similarly cure algae of the ability to make chloroplasts, and hence to grow photosynthetically. There is evidence that all these examples involve elimination of DNA-containing cytoplasmic units.

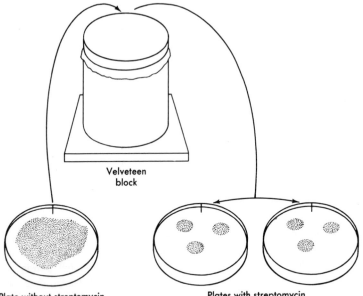

Velveteen
block

Plate without streptomycin
(confluent microcolonies)

Plates with streptomycin

Fig. 6-5 Use of replica-plating to demonstrate undirected, spontaneous appearance of streptomycin-resistant mutants. About 10^5 sensitive cells were spread on a plate of drug-free solid medium and allowed to reach full growth (10^{10}-10^{11} cells). Sterile velveteen, covering the flat end of a cylindrical block, was pressed lightly on this continuous heavy lawn ("master plate") and was then pressed successively on two plates of medium containing streptomycin, at a concentration that killed sensitive cells. A few colonies of resistant cells appeared on each plate, usually in coincident positions; and cells harvested from the corresponding positions on the master plate yielded a much larger proportion of resistant colonies than cells harvested from other parts of the plate. Evidently resistant clones, arising in the absence of drug on the master plate, were the source of most of the resistant colonies on the replica plates.

Moreover, mutations in these units in eucaryotes do not show mendelian segregation in genetic crosses, but rather exhibit "maternal" inheritance, i.e., the progeny of a zygote all inherit the allele present in the cell that provides the cytoplasm of the zygote.

DNA does not appear, however, to be involved in another example, in which penicillin converts bacteria quantitatively to wall-deficient, spherical L forms (Ch. 2) by interfering with wall synthesis (Ch. 10). While with some species these L forms will resume the normal bacterial form when grown in the absence of the drug, in others they are stable, i.e., they grow indefinitely without reversion, even in absence of the drug. Landman showed that penicillin can convert a very high proportion (over 25%) of the cells of one *Salmonella* species to viable,

stable L forms, which excludes the possibility that the drug simply selects rare spontaneous mutants. It therefore seems possible that a wall material, whose synthesis is disturbed by penicillin, is needed as a **primer** before more of the same material can be synthesized.

Since the wall-less L forms produced by penicillin are resistant to penicillin, this special case does indeed formally represent a directed, adaptive change in inheritance. It should be emphasized, however, that such an **irreversible loss** of a cytoplasmic component bears no resemblance, in mechanism or in scope, to the processes of genotypic and phenotypic adaptation, which can influence in either direction the expression of a great variety of genes.

Differentiation. A discussion of cellular heredity would be incomplete without reference to differentiation, which is a key problem in the biology of higher organisms. In this process **the environment directs** extensive differences in the activity of cellular genes, and these differences are then **stably inherited** by the resulting somatic cells, even though the genes have apparently not undergone mutation or loss. The possibility of a major role of cytoplasmic inheritance in differentiation was long considered seriously, but we shall discuss in Chapter 9 a more satisfactory model, based on the selective regulation of gene activity.

Haploid and Diploid Stages

Bacteria are almost always haploid, i.e., they possess only one representative of each genetic locus per nucleus. To be sure, more than one copy of a given gene may be present per cell, not only because one part of a bacterial chromosome replicates earlier than another, but also because the cell may be multinucleate. However, these multiple nuclei are not comparable to the pairs of homologous chromosomes in diploid eucaryotic cells: at cell division the former are segregated into different cells, whereas the latter remain paired. Hence when a mutation occurs in one nucleus of a multinucleate bacterium that cell becomes a heterozygous **heterokaryon;** but within a few divisions the progeny are all divided into a mutant and a nonmutant clone, each again genetically homogeneous.

Bacteria are thus comparable to the haploid gametes of higher organisms, except that in bacteria the haploid stage regularly undergoes vegetative division; normally a diploid stage in the life cycle (i.e., containing a pair of homologous chromosomes per nucleus) appears only rarely, is transient, and, as we shall see in the next chapter, is only a partial diploid. Since the problem of dominance does not arise in a haploid organism, it appears in bacteria only under the special circumstances that yield diploids or heterokaryons.

In all bacterial species studied thus far all the genetic loci are normally located in the same linkage group, indicating the presence of a single chromosome per nucleus. This inference has been confirmed by physical measurements of the length of the chromosome, which corresponds to the amount of DNA present per nucleus (Ch. 8).

Fungi, in contrast, have typical eucaryotic nuclei, with several different chromosomes enclosed within a membrane. In many of these organisms classic sexual reproduction has been observed, with a regular cycle of alternation between diploid and haploid stages. The genetic behavior of these organisms, including the interesting process of mitotic recombination, will be described in Chapter 21.

Detection and Selection of Mutants

The science of genetics is based on observable phenotypic differences resulting from alternative (**allelic**) forms of a gene: one must deal with mutant alleles in studying essentially any kind of genetic problem. Similarly, appropriate mutants provide powerful tools for studying such problems of cell physiology as metabolic pathways, metabolic regulation, or membrane transport. Hence the production, detection, and selection of various kinds of mutants are essential for both fundamental and applied genetics. The search for a given kind of mutant is ordinarily facilitated by the use of **mutagenic agents** (Ch. 8).

Wild-Type and Mutant Alleles. It is customary to refer to strains found in Nature, or to certain standard strains, as the **wild type,** and then to distinguish as mutants the altered strains derived from them, usually in the laboratory. This usage is obviously somewhat arbitrary, and one might indeed define a wild type as an organism whose most recent mutation was not observed by man. For many genes the wild type allele is recognized as the prevalent one for the species, while other genes are **polymorphic,** i.e., they have no single wild-type allele but rather two or more prevalent alleles (e.g., the genes determining eye color or blood group substances in man). Indeed, the various phenotypic effects of different mutations present a wide range of **selective pressures,** whose intensity depends on the environment. Thus mutations to **drug resistance** obviously increase fitness for a special environment, though presumably at the expense of fitness for the environment that had earlier selected the drug-sensitive wild type. Mutations to **auxotrophy** (defective biosynthesis), in contrast, put an organism at a disadvantage in many environments, compared with its parent or its **prototrophic** revertants (i.e., strains with the nutritional properties of the wild type). Mutations that alter the molecular structure of surface antigens (see Dissociation and phase variation, above) may be polymorphic, and they promote survival in the presence of antibodies to the initial structure.

The advantage of microbes for the study of many genetic problems arises first of all from the enormous **number** of individuals that can be studied in a limited time and space. This advantage, however, was long neglected, for geneticists dealing with higher organisms, such as the fruit fly (*Drosophila*) or maize, were accustomed to following genetic **"markers"** (i.e., detectable mutations) with grossly visible effects, and the variety of such morphological markers possible in single-celled organisms is very limited. The spectacular growth of microbial genetics was therefore largely based on the introduction of **biochemical markers.** To be sure, many geneticists had recognized that a simple enzymatic defect probably underlay certain well-known mutations in higher organisms, such as those involving pigmentation in plants, eye color in *Drosophila,* or albinism or alcaptonuria in man (Garrod); but Beadle and Tatum were the first to demonstrate, in 1941, the possibility of systematically isolating microbial mutants with specific enzymatic defects. (This study was undertaken primarily to provide an extensive set of markers for genetic studies of the mold *Neurospora;* the biochemical applications of these auxotrophic mutants, noted in Chapter 4, came as an unexpected dividend.)

Huge microbial populations would be of limited value were it not for a second advantage: the feasibility of **selecting** rare genotypes, whether produced by mutation or by recombination. For example, a fermentation mutation in bacteria, in either direction, can be readily **detected** on an appropriate plate containing a dye which will stain only fermentation-positive colonies (Fig. 5-8). However, since one can grow only a few hundred discrete colonies on a Petri dish, a rare mutant would be difficult to find by this method. On the other hand, if one inoculates a lactose-negative culture on a medium in which lactose is the sole carbon source, even 1 lactose-positive mutant in 10^9 cells can be selected.

Such quantitative, sensitive screening is possible for several classes of mutants: **fermentation-positive** (or similarly able to use a new source of N, S, etc.); **prototrophic; drug-resistant;** and **phage-resistant.** Some mutants, such as those involving **color, cell morphology, colonial morphology,** or **excretion** of various metabolites, are readily detected and quantitatively **scored,** but are not readily selected. Still others cannot be readily quantitated.

In scoring or selecting mutants on solid medium several precautions must be borne in mind. First, mutants that cannot grow on a given medium may nevertheless be metabolically active; hence an excessively dense inoculum can exhaust the available nutrients, preventing outgrowth of the mutants to be selected. Second, when prototrophs are selected from a predominantly auxotrophic population traces of nutrients in the agar may support substantial though invisible multiplication of the inoculated cells; hence "plate mutants," arising among new cells appearing on the plate, will be added to the prototrophs being selected and enumerated. Third, background growth of auxotrophic cells may be further increased by cross-feeding, resulting from excretion of a required metabolite by prototrophic revertants (or by a complementary mutant). Indeed, when cells of two nutritionally complementary mutants are mixed on a plate of minimal medium they may give the illusion of undergoing genetic recombination, because of the appearance of prototrophs that have actually arisen as revertants, owing to expansion of the background population by cross-feeding.

The method of **replica-plating** (Fig. 6-6) has proved to have general utility in scoring the clones in a mixed population (e.g., produced by mutation or by recombination) for their ability to grow on different media. Thus a plate containing 100 colonies, replica-plated onto 10 different selective media, can provide the same information that is obtained by 1000 repetitive transfers of cells from each colony, on a metal loop, to each medium.

Selection of Auxotrophs. Auxotrophic mutants have been especially valuable in studies of biosynthesis, as already noted, and in studying the fine structure of the gene (Ch. 8). Hence the development of efficient methods for their selection has been very helpful. The most widely used method depends on

Fig. 6-6 Detection of auxotrophic mutants by replica-plating. The master plate (A), containing enriched medium, was replicated by a velvet press (Fig. 6-5) onto a plate of enriched medium (B) and one of minimal medium (C). Arrows indicate colonies of auxotrophic mutants, which grow on B but not on C. (From J. and E. M. Lederberg, J. Bact. 63:399, 1952.)

E. coli culture

| Mutagen

Mixture of killed parental, live parental, and a few live mutant genotypes

| Intermediate cultivation in enriched medium

Phenotypic expression of mutant genotype

| Penicillin in minimal medium

Selective killing of parental cells

| Plate on enriched medium

Colonies from surviving cells, with parental type much decreased in frequency

| Parallel inoculation of each colony on minimal and enriched medium

Growth of parental clones on both media, auxotrophic mutants only on enriched medium

| Inoculation of mutant colony in minimal pour plate

Identification of growth requirement(s) of mutant by "spot tests" with growth factors

Fig. 6-7 Penicillin method for selecting auxotrophic mutants of bacteria.

the ability of penicillin to kill only growing cells, and thus to allow survival of auxotrophs in a minimal medium because they cannot grow in that medium (Fig. 6-7).

While this method produces marked enrichment for auxotrophs it does not permit their quantitative selection: the main limitation is the residual growth of auxotrophic cells, whether due to incomplete ("leaky") blocks, to stored metabolites, or to cross-feeding by the other cells present (especially since these are lysed by penicillin). Other agents that also kill only growing cells may be used in place of penicillin, with similar results: e.g., metabolite analogs that are incorporated, such as 8-azaguanine (Ch. 10), or

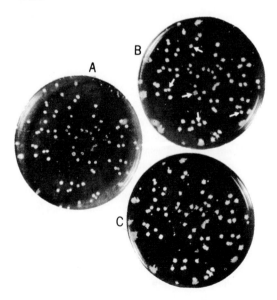

radioactive metabolites that are incorporated and are then allowed to disintegrate during prolonged storage.

Phenotypic Lag

A mutation is not phenotypically expressed until some time after it occurs. Thus when a suspension of cells is treated with a mutagenic agent and then plated on a selective medium the number of mutant colonies obtained may be very small, but it usually becomes much larger if the mutagenic exposure is followed by brief cultivation (one to two generations), on a nonselective medium, before subsequent selection, or if the selective medium supports a slight background growth (Fig. 6-8). Hence in the penicillin selection of auxotrophs, as noted above, such intermediate cultivation after irradiation is essential before exposure to penicillin.

There appear to be several reasons for this delayed appearance of mutants. The most important factor is a **delay in phenotypic expression,** which has two components. 1) **Nuclear segregation,** requiring cell division, is necessary for expression of a mutation yielding a recessive allele, e.g., a noncompetent biosynthetic gene, whose presence would be masked by a competent gene in a companion nucleus. 2) Growth is regularly required to overcome the **phenomic** lag: the delay before any mutagenic alteration in the genome of a cell is reflected in its phenome (i.e., everything in the cell other than the genome). This lag is found in both directions: an auxotrophic mutant is not phenotypically expressed until the enzyme molecules formed earlier by the gene are diluted out by further growth; and a prototrophic mutation (from an auxotrophic strain) cannot be expressed unless a trace of the missing building block (e.g., a given amino acid) is supplied (either exogenously or by turnover) to "prime the pump" (Fig. 6-8). This growth factor allows the restored gene to restore the first few molecules of the missing enzyme, following which the cell can resume formation of its product.

The effectiveness of a mutagenic treatment is also influenced by the extent to which **genetic damage is repaired** by enzymatic processes in the cell, and this extent depends in part on the lag between mutagenesis and resumption of

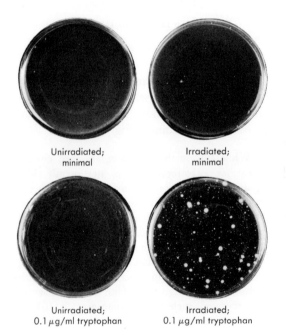

Unirradiated; minimal   Irradiated; minimal

Unirradiated; 0.1 μg/ml tryptophan   Irradiated; 0.1 μg/ml tryptophan

Fig. 6-8 Lag in phenotypic expression of induced mutations. Part of a culture of a tryptophan auxotroph was irradiated with ultraviolet to 0.1% survival, and equal numbers of cells, taken before and after irradiation, were plated on minimal medium to select for prototrophic mutants. Identical inocula were also plated on medium supplemented with 0.1 μg/ml of tryptophan, which permitted a few generations of growth of the large number of auxotrophic cells plated. It is seen that many back-mutants were induced, but very few of these initiated colony formation unless provided with a trace of the required growth factor. (B. D. Davis)

growth. This topic will be further discussed in Chapter 8.

Mutation Rates

Because mutants to either resistance or prototrophy are easy to select quantitatively from large populations, they can be used to measure with precision even low mutation rates. This development has revealed that the "spontaneous" mutation rate rises with increase in temperature, and also varies in some degree with almost any change in the culture medium. In addition, the detection of **weak mutagenic action** has expanded enormously the class of recognized mutagens, which even includes some normal components of our diet (e.g., caffeine).

Definition of Mutation Rate. Under ordinary circumstances, when growth is made faster or slower by shifting media the mutation rate (i.e., the probability of appearance of a given type of mutant) remains relatively constant **per cell division,** rather than per cell per unit time. Accordingly, it is customary to define mutation rate in these terms:

$$a = m/d$$

where a is the mutation rate, m the number of mutations, and d the number of cell divisions.

If one grows a population from a small inoculum the value of d essentially equals the final number of cells present, since the initial number is negligible and each division produces one additional cell. The value of m, on the other hand, cannot be determined simply by screening for the total number of, say, streptomycin-resistant mutants present; for one is then measuring the **mutant frequency** in that population, which may be quite different from the mutation rate just defined. As we have already seen from fluctuation analysis (see above), the total number of mutants in a population represents not only the fresh products of mutation in the most recent generation, but the multiplied progeny of mutations that occurred in earlier generations.

Hence the later a clone is harvested the greater may be the mutant frequency, though the mutation rate be constant.

Determination of Mutation Rate

1) The most precise and reliable method of determining the true mutation rate is to measure the slope of the increase in mutant frequency with continued growth, preferably in the chemostat (Ch. 5), which provides prolonged steady-state growth with a constant population size, and yields especially smooth linear curves (Fig. 6-3). This method is applicable only when the mutant multiplies at the same rate as the wild type.

2) Another method utilizes **mutation on solid medium,** in which the progeny of an early mutant can be held together in a colony. For example, 10^5 streptomycin-sensitive cells may be spread on a porous membrane on nonselective medium and allowed to grow to 10^9 cells (determined by enumerating the cells washed off a plate grown in parallel). When the membrane is then transferred to a drug-containing plate the progeny of each mutation to resistance, whether a single cell or a clone, will give rise to one colony.

3) A widely used **statistical** method is based on the Poisson distribution of random, chance mutations in a series of identically inoculated and incubated tubes of culture medium. The probability that x mutations occurs in a tube ($P_{(x)}$) depends on m, the average number of mutations per tube, averaged over all the tubes, and is:

$$P_{(x)} = (m^x/x!)e^{-m}$$

where e is 2.718, the base of natural logarithms. The value m cannot be measured directly, since, as we have seen, in any tube containing mutants their number does not measure the number of mutational events in that tube, owing to multiplication of mutants and to fluctuation. However, the number of tubes containing **no** mutants corresponds to the Poisson prediction, which reduces in this case to:

$$P_{(0)} = e^{-m}$$
$$\text{or} \quad \ln P_{(0)} = -m$$

Hence from a determination of the proportion of mutant-free tubes, $P_{(o)}$, one can calculate the average **mutation frequency** per tube, m. For example, an average of 1 mutation per tube yields $P_{(o)} = e^{-1} = 1/e = 0.37.$*

It might be noted that all determinations of spontaneous mutation rate probably slightly underestimate the true rate, since the phenotypic lag is not taken into account. Thus, if on the average one generation of growth is required before a resistant mutant will be sufficiently expressed to survive on the selective plate, the observed mutation rate will be half the true one.

* For a more extensive discussion of the Poisson distribution see Appendix, Chapter 22.

SELECTED REFERENCES

Books and Review Articles

ADELBERG, E. A. (ed.). *Papers on Bacterial Genetics.* Little, Brown, Boston, 1966. A collection of reprints of outstanding papers, with a valuable historical introduction and bibliography.

BEADLE, G. W. Genetics and metabolism in *Neurospora. Physiol. Rev.* 25:643 (1945).

EPHRUSSI, B. *Nucleo-cytoplasmic Relations in Microorganisms.* Oxford Univ. Press, New York, 1953.

SAGER, R. On Non-chromosomal Heredity in Micro-organisms. In *Function and Structure in Microorganisms,* p. 324. (15th Symposium, Society of General Microbiologists; M. R. Pollock and M. H. Richmond, eds.) Cambridge Univ. Press, London, 1965.

SAGER, R., and RYAN, F. *Cell Heredity.* Wiley, New York, 1961.

Specific Articles

LANDMAN, O. E., and HALLE, S. Enzymically and physically induced inheritance changes in *Bacillus subtilis. J. Molec. Biol.* 7:721 (1963).

LEA, D. E., and COULSON, C. A. The distribution of the numbers of mutants in bacterial populations. *J. Genetics* 49:264 (1949). In Adelberg collection.

LEDERBERG, J., and IINO, T. Phase variation in *Salmonella. Genetics* 41:743 (1956).

LEDERBERG, J., and LEDERBERG, E. M. Replica plating and indirect selection of bacterial mutants. *J. Bact.* 63:399 (1952).

LURIA, S., and DELBRUCK, M. Mutations of bacteria from virus sensitivity to virus resistance. *Genetics* 28:491 (1943). In Adelberg collection.

NOVICK, A. Experiments with the chemostat on spontaneous mutations of bacteria. *Proc. Nat. Acad. Sc.* 36:708 (1950).

With this discovery [of transformation] bacterial variation passes from the collector's box of the naturalist to the sophisticated atmosphere of the biochemical laboratory.

R. J. DUBOS. *Cold Spring Harbor Symposium. 1946.*

7 GENE TRANSFER IN BACTERIA

Evolution depends on genetic diversity, which is first created by mutations and then enormously amplified by genetic recombination. It is therefore hardly surprising that recombination should have evolved in microbes as well as in higher organisms. Indeed, sexual reproduction, as an occasional alternative to clonal, vegetative reproduction, was demonstrated relatively early with fungi.* For further decades, however, bacteria were believed to reproduce only clonally; and though it was sporadically claimed that conjugation had been observed, or genetic recombinants recovered, these reports were unconvincing. This unique position was not disturbing as long as bacterial variation was supposed to rest on a plasticity distinct from mutations (Ch. 6). In the early 1940s, however, as we have seen in the preceding chapter, the evidence for mutable genes in bacteria became overwhelming, and the search for recombination was renewed in a more sophisticated way. True zygote formation by cell fusion was not observed (though it does occur in fungi, with equally rigid walls); but other, novel mechanisms were discovered which produce merozygotes (Gr. *meros,* "part"): partial diploids, containing the entire genome (**endogenote**) of a recipient cell plus a genetic fragment (**exogenote**) transferred from a donor cell. The transfer can be accomplished by three distinct mechanisms: cell **conjugation** (mating), viral infection (**transduction**), or uptake of naked DNA (**transformation**).

One might expect that conjugation would be the most obvious of these mechanisms, since it is closest to the familiar fusion of gametes in higher organisms; while the most exotic would be transformation, since the naked DNA is so susceptible to enzymatic attack and so unlikely a candidate for penetration of the cell. In fact, however, transformation was the first to be recognized (though not through a deliberate attack on a genetic problem); and perhaps even more surprisingly, it was discovered in the pneumococcus, which is an exceptionally difficult experimental subject because of its ready autolysis and its unusually fastidious nutritional requirements. This curious historical development undoubtedly reflects the intensive investigation of the pneumococcus motivated by its outstanding position, until the advent of chemotherapy, as a cause of death in man.

TRANSFORMATION

Discovery of Transformation

Elucidation of the nature of bacterial transformation was a development of enormous importance: it revealed not only the possibility of gene transfer in bacteria, but also the function of DNA as the material basis of heredity. Hence it seems worthwhile to recall the circumstances leading to the fortuitous discovery of the phenomenon in 1928 by Griffith, a public health officer in England concerned with the epidemiology of pneumococcal pneumonia.

The work of Avery and Goebel had shown that all virulent pneumococci form smooth (S) colonies, owing to the presence of a carbohydrate capsule of one or another antigenic type. When such a strain is grown in the presence of its type-specific antiserum it loses the ability to make a capsule; hence it becomes avirulent and forms rough (R) colonies. Conversely, some R strains can revert to their parental, virulent S type when a large number of cells are inoculated in a mouse.

During the period of most intensive work on the pneumococcus the mutational origin of these shifts (Ch. 6) was not yet recognized.

---

* The essential features of sexual reproduction are the formation of haploid gametes from diploid parents by the process of **meiosis,** and the fusion of two gametes, one from each parent, to form a diploid **zygote.** Because meiosis is important in the genetics of fungi it is reviewed in Chapter 21.

To explain the recovery of virulence in the mouse Griffith postulated that R cells retained traces of S "antigen," which were liberated by the disintegrating cells and were then accumulated by a surviving cell to build up its full supply of this substance. With the intention of testing this hypothesis, he injected subcutaneously in mice a large number of **heat-killed S cells,** along with a small number of **live R cells** derived from them. The killed S cells did indeed appear to promote reversion. However, control mixtures revealed an unexpected transformation of type, which could not be accounted for in terms of reversion: heat-killed type 2 cells, mixed with live R cells derived from type 1, yielded live, virulent type 2 cells which killed the mouse (Fig. 7-1).

Griffith did not realize that this observation implied the existence of a chemical substance with the remarkable property of causing its own replication in a recipient cell. He referred to the transforming material from the killed S cells both as "S antigen" and as a protein "pabulum" required for capsule formation.

Identification of the Transforming Factor

Deeper analysis became possible when transformation was extended, a few years later, from mice to the test tube—first with heat-killed S cells (Dawson), and then with extracts of frozen and thawed cells (Alloway). (These studies were facilitated by adding antiserum specific for R cells, which agglutinates these cells; S cells are thus selected, since they grow diffusely in the medium above the sedimented aggregates of R cells.) The implications of type transformation for cell heredity, however, were apparently still not realized. The phenomenon had not aroused the interest of geneticists or biochemists, and the medical bacteriologists familiar with it hardly felt equipped to undertake the difficult biochemical work re-

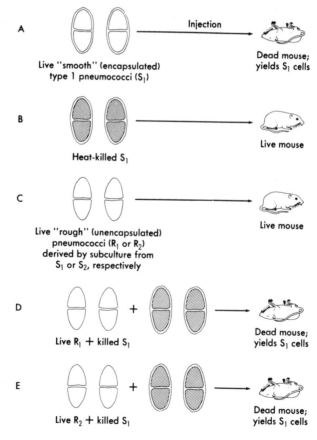

Fig. 7-1 The Griffith experiment. R cells not only were apparently reverted to S cells of their parental type by heat-killed S cells of the same type, but also were transformed to a different S type by heat-killed cells of that type.

A — Live "smooth" (encapsulated) type 1 pneumococci (S₁) — Injection — Dead mouse; yields S₁ cells

B — Heat-killed S₁ — Live mouse

C — Live "rough" (unencapsulated) pneumococci (R₁ or R₂) derived by subculture from S₁ or S₂, respectively — Live mouse

D — Live R₁ + killed S₁ — Dead mouse; yields S₁ cells

E — Live R₂ + killed S₁ — Dead mouse; yields S₁ cells

quired to identify the active substance. The problem was therefore largely ignored for more than a decade until 1944, when Avery, MacLeod, and McCarty, at the Rockefeller Institute, isolated the substance responsible for type transformation and identified it as deoxyribonucleic acid (DNA; Fig. 7-2).*

It is difficult today to appreciate how revolutionary was the identification of the transforming agent as DNA rather than protein. The presence of only four different bases in DNA had seemed to preclude the possibility of much specificity, compared with the 20 different amino acids of proteins. Moreover, in the samples of DNA then available the four bases were present in roughly equal proportions, suggesting a repeating tetranucleotide sequence rather than a variety of specific, aperiodic sequences. Finally,

---

* This discovery was the culmination of 30 years of work by Avery, devoted almost exclusively to the pneumococcus, which revealed the essential role of the capsular substance in the virulence of this organism, the carbohydrate nature of the substance, its immunogenicity (previously regarded as a sole prerogative of proteins), and finally a role of DNA in its formation.

it was only in the preceding few years that sufficiently undegraded samples of DNA were recovered even to permit its general recognition as a macromolecule. Hence, though cytologists recognized that DNA, as well as protein, is present in the chromosomes of animal and plant cells, it was universally assumed that genetic specificity resided in the protein. Indeed, for some years after Avery's report skeptics maintained that the transforming activity resided in traces of contaminating protein rather than in the DNA. However, the activity was destroyed by a trace of highly purified DNase, but not by a variety of purified proteases; and transforming DNA was later purified to the point where its protein content was less than 0.02%. (The active material is still frequently referred to by Avery's term "transforming principle"—a rather scholastic designation for an isolated, chemically defined substance.)

It took some time for investigators to realize that they now had in their hands the material stuff of heredity, rather than a mutagenic or an inducing agent. This conclusion was verified a few years later when Hershey and Chase, using radioactively labeled bacteriophage, showed that the DNA of the phage penetrated during infection of bacterial cells while most of the protein

Fig. 7-2   Transformation of R to S pneumococci by DNA from S cells. Left (1): Colonies on blood agar of an R variant derived from type 2 pneumococci. Right (2): Colonies from cells of the same strain that had grown in the presence of DNA from type 3 pneumococcus, plus antiserum to R cells (see text). (Type 3 forms especially glistening, mucoid colonies.) (From O. T. Avery, C. M. MacLeod, and M. McCarty. J. Exp. Med. 79: 137, 1944.)

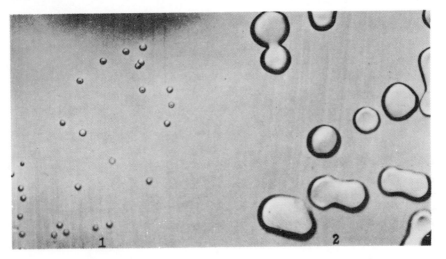

remained outside (Ch. 23); hence the DNA evidently contained the genetic information for making more bacteriophage.

Scope of Transformation

From the point of view of molecular genetics capsule production was a rather unsatisfactory marker. Its enzymatic basis remained entirely unknown for many years; and it did not yield the sharp selection that would be required for accurate studies of factors affecting its rate. Such studies became possible, however, when it was found that any selectable genes, such as those conferring drug resistance or fermentative ability, could also be transferred. (Auxotrophic mutants, so prominent in microbial genetics, have not been useful in studies with the pneumococcus because its fastidious growth requirements hinder the use of synthetic media.)

Transformation has been accomplished with only a few bacterial species, including *Hemophilus influenzae, Neisseria, Streptococcus,* the plant pathogen *Xanthomonas phaseoli,* and the nitrogen-fixing plant symbiont *Rhizobium.* Though these are all nutritionally fastidious, like the pneumococcus, the recent addition of *Bacillus subtilis* has provided an organism that is easily cultivated on a simple medium. Transformation has unfortunately not proved possible with DNA from *Escherichia coli* or other Enterobacteriaceae, in which so many well-studied mutants are available. (A special type of transformation of *E. coli,* however, requiring simultaneous infection with a phage, has been observed.)

Mechanism of Transformation

Ephrussi-Taylor demonstrated **reciprocal** transformations of type between two S strains of pneumococcus, e.g., type 2 as DNA donor and type 3 as recipient, and vice versa. Transformation must therefore involve **replacement** of part of the original bacterial genome through **recombination** with newly introduced DNA, rather than simple addition; otherwise both crosses in reciprocal transformation would be expected to lead to the same partial diploid with the same phenotype, instead of the different phenotypes observed.

(Rare transformants, however, do exhibit addition: e.g., strains forming both type 1 and type 3 polysaccharide.)

Quantitation. With markers that can be quantitatively selected (e.g., drug resistance), the number of transformants is found to be strictly proportional to the amount of DNA at low DNA/cell ratios; hence the **effectiveness** of DNA preparations can be compared. Conversely, at high DNA/cell ratios, saturating the cells, the number of transformants is independent of DNA concentration, and provides an index of the effectiveness of the DNA preparation and the state of **competence** of the cells to accept DNA (Fig. 7-3).

The use of drug resistance to study the kinetics of genetic recombination provides a special problem: it is necessary to plate the cells early in order to separate the transformants before they divide; but with bactericidal agents, such as penicillin or streptomycin, it is also necessary to allow time for phenotypic expression of resistance

Fig. 7-3 Transformation as a function of DNA concentration. **A.** Transforming DNA alone. **B.** Same DNA mixed with three equivalents of nontransforming DNA. A similar difference would be seen between two preparations of transforming DNA of different effectiveness. (After R. D. Hotchkiss. In *The Chemical Basis of Heredity.* Johns Hopkins, Baltimore, 1957.)

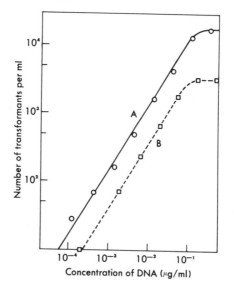

(Ch. 6; Phenotypic lag) before exposure to the selective agent. This dilemma was solved by a procedure in which the cells are exposed to DNA for a fixed period, DNase is added to stop further uptake, the suspension is poured into agar growth medium and incubated for several hours to permit phenotypic expression, and then a layer of medium is added containing the drug, which diffuses into the medium below and exerts the desired selective action.

Linkage. When a mixture of DNA from two strains, A^+B^- and A^-B^+, is used to transform A^-B^- cells, the frequency of double transformants (A^+B^+) is very low, as is expected if multiple molecules of DNA independently enter and transform the same competent cell. The same result was initially obtained with DNA from a single donor carrying both markers (A^+B^+), which suggested that each gene corresponded to a different molecule of DNA. With additional markers, however, Hotchkiss later observed **joint** transformation: DNA from a streptomycin-resistant (Sm^R) and mannitol-fermenting (Mtl^+) donor, applied to a Sm^SMtl^- recipient,* not only yielded single transformants for each gene but also yielded double transformants in a frequency (0.1%) well above the product of the frequencies of the singles (0.006%). Hence the Sm and Mtl genes must be so closely linked on the chromosome that they can both be carried on a single unit ("molecule") of transforming DNA. Further evidence was provided by studies on the kinetics of formation of single and double transformants (Fig. 7-4). This linkage of certain genes in transforming DNA is now readily understood, since the

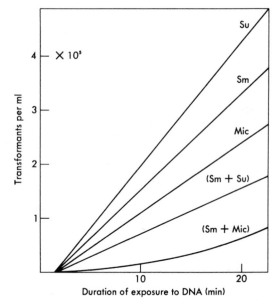

Fig. 7-4 Kinetics of formation of single and double transformants. Transforming DNA was obtained from pneumococcus resistant to streptomycin (Sm), sulfonamides (Su), and micrococcin (Mic). At the low concentration of DNA used the formation of transformants to single (Su, Sm, or Mic) resistance was linear through the experimental period. Double resistance to Sm and Su also was transferred linearly, indicating linkage in the same DNA particle. The lag in double transformation to (Sm+Mic) resistance, in contrast, indicates that this process requires entry of two particles. (After J. L. Kent and R. D. Hotchkiss. J. Molec. Biol. 9:308, 1964.)

"molecules" of this DNA, obtained by the usual methods, have been shown to be not individual genes but arbitrary fragments, consisting each of roughly 1/200 of the bacterial chromosome (Ch. 8).

Linkage made it possible to transform for **loss** as well as for gain of the same function; for though one cannot select directly for transformation from Mtl^+ to Mtl^-, the Mtl^- gene could be brought in as an unselected marker linked to the selected Sm^R gene. Thus DNA from a Sm^R Mtl^- donor, added to an $Sm^S Mtl^+$ recipient, yielded $Sm^R Mtl^-$ (as well as $Sm^R Mtl^+$) recombinants. This finding further supports the conclusion, noted above, that transformation ordinarily involves recombination rather than addition of genetic material.

Penetration. Transformation shows that huge

* In bacterial genetics superscripts R and S denote resistance and sensitivity, respectively, to an inhibitor or a phage, while the standard letters R and S refer to rough and smooth colonial morphology. The superscripts + and − denote ability and inability, respectively, to synthesize a required metabolite (prototrophy vs. auxotrophy), or to use a carbon source (fermentation-positive and -negative). In classic genetics, in contrast, mutants are named for visible deviations from the wild type: cin = cinnabar eye color, while cin+ = not cinnabar (i.e., wild type with respect to that character).

molecules of DNA (M.W. 10^6 to 10^7) can penetrate a bacterial cell. Such uptake was most unexpected, since the osmotic barrier of these cells will exclude even a small sugar unless a specific transport system is present. However, we must recognize that studies on transport of metabolites are concerned with the entry of thousands of molecules per cell, while transformation involves the entry of a single long-chain molecule. This entry appears to involve special sites, since with *Hemophilus* cells the maximal uptake of radioactive DNA is only 10 "molecules" per cell, suggesting the presence of about 10 entry sites.

DNA from distant species cannot transform, and studies with radioactively labeled material show that it cannot be integrated into the chromosome. Nevertheless, it enters the cell as well as does homologous DNA, and it can competitively inhibit penetration of transforming DNA (Table 7-1). This result accords with expectations, since in all DNA the double helix has the same exterior. Conversion to the **single-stranded** form, by heat denaturation, reduces sharply the ability of DNA to penetrate and therefore to transform (or to inhibit transformation).* It thus appears that the site of entry recognizes the external surface of any double-stranded DNA.

Eclipse.
Despite the importance of double-strandedness for entry it appears that the duplex does not enter as such but unwinds at the site of penetration.

Thus immediately after penetration there is an eclipse period of about 5 miuntes, during which markers characteristic of the transforming DNA cannot be extracted from the cells in a form that is still active in transformation. Moreover, labeled donor DNA recovered from the cells during this period has the physical characteristics of single-stranded DNA. Finally, there is evidence for hydrolysis of half the transforming DNA, which may be nonpenetrating strands.

---

*The residual transforming activity of denatured DNA, for the pneumococcus or for hemophilus, does not appear to be due to its slight renaturation during cooling, since the activity was retained in a single-stranded fraction separated by sedimentation (Ch. 8). Moreover, though the denatured DNA of *B. subtilis* should be subject to a similar degree of renaturation, this organism responds only to double-stranded DNA.

TABLE 7-1. INHIBITION BY NONTRANSFORMING DNA OF BOTH THE UPTAKE AND THE ACTION OF TRANSFORMING DNA

Ratio of competing to transforming DNA	Percentage inhibition	
	^{32}P-DNA uptake	Transformation
0	0	0
3	44	42
10	73	71
30	87	86

Hemophilus influenzae cells were exposed, under the usual conditions of transformation, to ^{32}P-labeled transforming DNA from a streptomycin-resistant mutant of the same organism, plus varying amounts of unlabeled DNA from another source. After several minutes the cells were treated with DNase to remove adsorbed DNA that had not penetrated, and the cells were analyzed for radioactivity and for the number of transformants to streptomycin resistance.

From P. Schaeffer. In Biological Replication of Macromolecules. Academic Press, New York, 1958.

Competence.
The competence of cells to be transformed depends on their physiological state, since in synchronized cultures the size of the competent fraction changes regularly during the cycle of cell division. Under optimal conditions, however, practically every cell even in a nonsynchronized culture is competent. Such conditions are restricted to a relatively short portion of the growth cycle of a culture.

A macromolecular activator has been obtained, from cultures in the optimal phase, that brings about competence when added to fresh cells. Presumably it changes the cell surface, since competence can be lost by washing. Competence is also lost when cells are grown briefly in fresh medium, or when a culture is grown too long (resulting in release of DNase). (Competence can be conveniently preserved by storing cells frozen in 15% glycerol.)

With improved technics it has become possible to transform about 5% of the cells for a given marker, compared with the fraction of 10^{-4} with which Avery worked. When pains are taken to keep the DNA relatively undegraded it is highly efficient in transformation: nearly one transformant for a given marker can be produced per genome-equivalent of DNA* taken up by the recipient culture.

Transformation is not easy to reproduce quantitatively; some batches of medium simply do not support it. The pneumococcus (but not some other species) requires serum albumin, which presumably influences the bacterial surface.

Integration. Integration of transforming DNA appears to consist of recombination with the bacterial chromosome. As was noted above, the introduced DNA is apparently single-stranded during the brief elcipse period. Fox and Hotchkiss has shown that this DNA then develops several properties at essentially the same time: 1) recovery of its transforming ability, implying double-strandedness; 2) genetic linkage to host genes, implying insertion into the chromosome; and 3) initiation of replication in synchrony with the chromosome. Furthermore, by the use of transforming DNA labeled with heavy isotopes (i.e., from cells grown on $^{15}NH_4Cl$, ^2H_2O, and ^{13}C-compounds) its firm linkage with unlabeled recipient DNA could also be demonstrated, since lysates of the posteclipse cells contained DNA fragments of intermediate density.

Significance of Transformation

Transformation may well be a significant mechanism of genetic recombination in Nature. It has been achieved with living cultures mixed in the test tube and also in the mouse peritoneum. Indeed, with pneumococcal strains of low virulence the mouse has been used to select for recombinants with increased virulence.[†]

In a process resembling bacterial transformation, the **extracted nucleic acids** of various **viruses** have been found to infect a variety of cells, including bacterial protoplasts (Ch. 23), animal cells (polyoma virus DNA, poliovirus RNA; Ch. 25), and plant cells (tobacco mosaic virus RNA).

The great promise of bacterial transformation (now including in this term infection by naked viral nucleic acid) lies in the possibility, with DNA altered or synthesized in vitro, of correlating structure with genetic activity. Thus, the action of mutagens on DNA in vitro, which avoids any complicating effects of bacterial metabolism, can be followed by biological tests; and transformation provides the only available test for the biological activity of DNA that has been synthesized by enzymes in the test tube (Ch. 4).

In species for which no other mechanism of gene transfer is available transformation has been very useful in study of the genetic control of a variety of bacterial functions. Transformation can also be used, but not very conveniently, for mapping genetic loci.

CONJUGATION

Discovery of Bacterial Conjugation

The isolation of a variety of auxotrophic bacterial mutants in the early 1940s provided a powerful tool for renewing the search for mating in bacteria: the wild-type alleles of these genetic markers could be efficiently selected, and hence could be used to test for the appearance of even very rare recombinants. Furthermore, when pneumococcal transformation was finally recognized as a special form of genetic recombination it provided a stimulus to reinvestigate the possibility of a more conventional recombination, between intact bacterial cells. Joshua Lederberg, a Ph.D. student of Tatum, seized on this combination of circumstances and made the dramatic discovery, in 1946, of a process resembling sex in bacteria.

Since the recombination initially observed occurred at a very low frequency, its discovery

---

* The amount present in a single nonreplicating bacterial nucleus.

† The production of different degrees of virulence, by mutation or recombination, is not surprising; for while most of the mutations discussed so far can be described in qualitative terms, virulence is a quantitative, **polygenic** character, i.e., one influenced by many genes.

depended on the ingenious use of **double auxotrophs** to discriminate between recombinants and revertants. Thus a mixture of singly auxotrophic parents, A^-B^+ and A^+B^-, yielded some A^+B^+ cells; but either parent, by a one-step back-mutation, yielded A^+B^+ revertants almost as frequently. However, a double auxotroph (A^-B^-) will not revert at a detectable rate to A^+B^+ (since such a reversion would require two independent mutations, each of low frequency). Lederberg therefore obtained from *E. coli* two double mutants (Fig. 7-5). When 10^8 cells of each were mixed and plated on minimal medium a few colonies appeared, whereas even 10^9 cells of either parent alone yielded none. These colonies represented recombinant genotypes, rather than cross-feeding mixtures, since their prototrophic behavior persisted in clones derived from single cells.

Recombination was found to require cell contact, rather than a soluble factor as in transformation. Thus filtrates of either parent did not transform cells of the other. Moreover, when the two strains were grown in the two halves of a U-tube divided by a sintered glass disc (permeable to macromolecules but not to cells), and fluid was rapidly forced back

and forth across the disc, no recombinants appeared; hence the possibility of even a very labile transforming factor was excluded.

The wild-type *E. coli* strain used in this work, labeled K12, had been carried for many years as a stock laboratory strain. Its choice was most fortunate, for in subsequent tests of a variety of *E. coli* strains, found in Nature or stocked in laboratories, only a small proportion were fertile (see discussion of fertility factors in Chapter 24).

Resemblance to Classic Zygote Formation

Linkage. A great variety of markers were all found to be **jointly transmitted,** suggesting transfer of the whole genome rather than of small segments as in transformation. Lederberg proceeded to develop the fundamentals of bacterial genetics by systematically studying this linkage in crosses involving a variety of multiply marked parents: certain markers in each parent were **selected** for, and among the selected recombinants the frequency of the two alleles of each **unselected** marker was determined. A typical cross is depicted in Table 7-2: among the recombinants selected for the T^+ marker from one parent, and for M^+ from the other, unselected marker L is encountered more frequently in the allele provided by the former parent; hence L is considered more closely linked to T than to M, according to the rules of classic genetics.

The linkage data obtained with a variety of markers indicated that the units of inheritance in *E. coli* are all physically connected with each other, apparently in a single chromosome. Moreover, the new genotypes produced by recombination were clearly haploid products of genetic exchange, rather than partial diploid products of genetic addition. Thus in a heterozygous diploid cell an auxotrophic marker would not be phenotypically expressed, since the effective (prototrophic) allele would make the missing enzyme, and hence would be dominant: but in fact, auxotrophic and prototrophic alleles were equally readily expressed in the recombinants. Furthermore, a diploid cell would be expected to

Fig. 7-5 Diagrammatic representation of the initial experiment of Lederberg and Tatum. The mutants, obtained by irradiation and selection, were cultivated in a medium that included growth factors A, B, C, and D; the test for recombination, and the control tests for reversion, were carried out in a minimal medium lacking these factors.

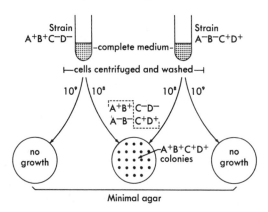

TABLE 7-2. RELATIVE FREQUENCY OF VARIOUS RECOMBINANTS

Parents

I			II	
$B^-M^-T^+L^+$		$\times$	$B^+M^+T^-L^-$	

Plates supplemented with	Selected markers	Unselected alleles found			
		Type	No.	Type	No.
Biotin (B)	$M^+T^+L^+$	B^-	10	B^+	60
Threonine (T)	$B^+M^+L^+$	T^-	9	T^+	37
Leucine (L)	$B^+M^+T^+$	L^-	5	L^+	51

Conclusions:
1) Unselected B is more often B^+ (from parent II) than B^- (from parent I); therefore B linked with M (the selected marker from parent II);
2) Similarly T^+L^+ more frequent than T^+L^- or T^-L^+; therefore T and L more closely linked with each other than with B or M.
After J. Lederberg. Genetics 32:505 (1947).

segregate occasional haploid progeny, with different combinations of the genes for which the parent was heterozygous; but no such segregants were obtained on further vegetative multiplication.

The Zygote. Because of the low frequency of mating its immediate products could not be studied directly, but could be characterized only in terms of the progeny observed many generations later. Nevertheless, to account for the observed results mating must have produced diploid cells which quickly yielded stable haploid segregants.

Indeed, Lederberg did isolate one persistent but unstable diploid (het), recognized as a **persistent heterozygote** because it spontaneously threw off a variety of stable segregants (frequency ca. 10^{-3} per division) containing different combinations of the several markers involved in the initial cross. This exception was evidently an unusually stable variant of the usually transient zygote.

The linked transfer of a wide variety of markers thus suggested that in sexual reproduction in bacteria, as in higher organisms, two haploid cells fuse to form a diploid zygote; the haploid recombinants would then arise by a process akin to meiosis. On the other hand, as an increasing number of markers were studied in various combinations it became increasingly difficult to trans-

late their linkage data into a consistent map, because the same pair of markers showed very different degrees of linkage in different crosses. Furthermore, the persistent heterozygote ("het" strain) noted above was found to be diploid for only part of the chromosome. However, since the unification of bacterial variation with genetics had been such a triumph, valiant efforts were made, by means of *ad hoc* assumptions (e.g., branched chromosomes, irregular chromosomal pairing), to preserve the concept of cell fusion, and the partial diploidy of the het strain was dismissed as an additional aberration of this atypical strain.

E. coli was thus forced, despite its unsatisfactory linkage relations, into a Procrustean bed of classic genetics. The first step toward clarification of the problem was the accidental discovery of two mating types.

Polarity in Bacterial Crosses

In some species of fungi, called **homothallic,** gametes from a single strain can fuse to form zygotes; whereas other species, called **heterothallic,** exist in two mating types (plus and minus, or male and female), and only gametes from strains of opposite type can mate. Since all the *E. coli* mutants described above were derived from the single K12 wild type and all were interfertile, it was naturally assumed that bacterial conjugation does not involve sexual differentiation, i.e., that bacteria are homothallic.

In a classic example of serendipity this assumption was found to be false by Hayes in London, who undertook in 1952 to study the kinetics of mating as a problem in bacterial physiology, rather than simply to score the products of the cross, as in formal genetics. Crosses were performed in liquid medium between a streptomycin-sensitive (Sm^S) and a resistant (Sm^R) parent, and at intervals the number of Sm^R recombinants was determined by plating samples on a selective medium. A control test, on the effect of streptomycin **during** mating, gave surprising results. When the $M^-T^+L^+$ parent was Sm^R and the $M^+T^-L^-$ parent was Sm^S, the presence of streptomycin prevented the formation of prototrophic ($M^+T^+L^+$) recombinants, as expected since Sm kills one of the parents; but when the Sm^S and Sm^R alleles were reversed in the two parents streptomycin had only a slight effect on the formation of prototrophs. Hence one of the parents could apparently serve as **donor** of genetic material even though killed by streptomycin, while the other parent appeared to serve as **recipient,** required to provide not only genetic material but also viable cells.

The F Agent

The explanation for the apparent separation of two mating types in Hayes' stock cultures was provided by the appearance, shortly thereafter, of a simpler example of the same phenomenon: some stock cultures were found to have lost their fertility with certain complementary stocks but not with others. This loss could have been due to an accidental purification of one of the mating types from a mixture of the two, particularly since such mixtures could well have been perpetuated by the standard practice of transferring stock cultures by means of large inocula. Accordingly, clones, freshly derived from single cells of various K12 mutant stocks, were tested for fertility by Hayes and by the Lederbergs.

These and subsequent studies led to the following picture. Cells of *E. coli* K12 exist in either of two inheritable mating types, called F^+ and F^-. $F^- \times F^-$ crosses are uniformly sterile, while $F^+ \times F^-$ crosses are fertile, with a relatively low frequency (10^{-5} to 10^{-6} recombinants per cell pair). The F^+ cells serve as genetic donors (males), since they can function even when killed by agents that do not lyse the cell (such as streptomycin or ultraviolet irradiation); the F^- cells serve as recipients (females). The process is thus evidently one of **conjugation** rather than cell fusion, resulting in the transfer of genetic material from male to female through some kind of conjugation bridge (see below).

The difference between F^+ and F^- cells is due to a sex factor (fertility factor), the **F agent,** whose presence can be demonstrated by its rapid **transmissibility.** Thus, when an F^+ and an F^- strain, carrying different genetic markers, are grown together for an hour (at population densities sufficient for frequent cell contact), up to 70% of the originally F^- cells are "converted" to F^+, while the originally F^+ cells remain F^+. This transmission requires cell contact. As might be expected from the ready infection of F^- cells by neighboring F^+ cells, the recombinants produced in such mixtures are also generally F^+.

The F agent can also disappear from a cell, which then becomes F^-; this loss is frequently observed during prolonged incubation in the stationary phase. Moreover, Hirota showed that **F^+ cultures can be regularly "cured"** of the F agent by incubation with **acridine dyes** (which are known to bind to nucleic acids and to be mutagenic). In Nature the loss of the F agent must occur readily, compared with its spread, since F^- strains are much more prevalent than F^+.

$F^+ \times F^+$ crosses are also fertile, but at a very low level. This behavior can be explained by two effects: conversion of some cells to the F^- genotype, as noted above; and the production of F^- "phenocopies" (i.e., cells that behave phenotypically, but not inheritably, as F^-). Such F^-

phenocopies are frequent in cultures grown to the stationary phase under strong aeration.

Asymmetric Genetic Contributions. The anomalies of the genetic linkage map in *E. coli* were clarified by the further discovery that the two parents make unequal **genetic** (as well as unequal **cytoplasmic**) contributions. Specifically, in the selected recombinants **the unselected markers tend to be derived much more frequently from the F⁻ than from the F⁺ parent.** It is therefore easy to see why earlier crosses, interpreted in terms of cell fusion and equal parental contributions, gave widely discordant linkage relations: distant unselected markers, which should be unlinked to either selected marker (i.e., derived 50% from either parent), are actually derived more often from the F⁻ parent, and thus appear to be linked to whatever marker is chosen for selection from that strain.

This asymmetric contribution suggested that the transient heterozygotes, postulated as intermediates in recombinant formation, were diploid for only part of the bacterial chromosome (merozygotes), just as had already been demonstrated for Lederberg's unusual persistent heterozygote. The next question was whether the missing part of the F⁺ chromosome failed to enter the zygote (**prezygotic** elimination), or whether it entered but could not participate in recombination (**postzygotic** elimination). The answer came with the development of sophisticated technics for studying directly the physiology of conjugation.

High-Frequency (Hfr) Recombination

The study of the physiology of conjugation took on new dimensions when Cavalli, in Milan in 1950, by chance isolated from an F⁺ strain a subclone with a 1000-fold increase in its rate of recombination with F⁻ strains. This strain, and subsequently isolated similar ones, are called Hfr (for "high frequency of recombination"). They are males, but in contrast to F⁺ strains they do not transmit the F agent to F⁻ recipients: the recombinants are F⁻. Thus the mutation from F⁺ to Hfr is associated with **loss of transmissibility of the F agent,** along with the gain in transmissibility of cellular genes. This mutation evidently involves an alteration in the state of the F agent: F⁻ cells, which lack the agent, never mutate to Hfr; and Hfr can revert to F⁺ but not directly to F⁻.

The mechanism responsible for these associated changes was brilliantly analyzed by Jacob and Wollman at the Pasteur Institute in Paris. By a novel mapping procedure, to be described below (Kinetics of Hfr × F⁻ mating), they showed that in Hfr strains the F agent has become **integrated** in the chromosome in some way. In that position the F agent still leads to conjugation; but whereas F⁺ cells (which contain an unintegrated F agent) transfer that agent alone, Hfr cells transfer the F-attached chromosome (Fig. 7-6). (We shall discuss later the failure of the Hfr chromosome to transfer the attached agent and thus to yield Hfr recombinants.) The integration of F into the chromosome explains the further observation that the Hfr state, in contrast to the F state, is not curable by acridine (which can selectively eliminate the F agent while sparing the chromosome; see above).

Role of Hfr in the Fertility of F⁺ Strains. The mechanism of conjugation was further clarified by evidence that the low-frequency fertility of F⁺ cultures depends partly on low-frequency mutations to Hfr. These mutants were demonstrated by replica-plating (Ch. 6) a lawn of F⁺ cells onto a thin lawn of a complementary F⁻ strain, seeded on a medium that would select for recombinants. A few recombinant colonies appeared on incubation, and from the corresponding regions on the stored F⁺ plate one could obtain Hfr clones. This indirect selection thus showed that crosses of F⁺ × F⁻ **cultures** involve crosses of Hfr × F⁻ **cells.**

This inference would seem to be contradicted by the production of F⁺ progeny in crosses of F⁺ × F⁻ cultures, in contrast to the F⁻ progeny of Hfr × F⁻ crosses. However, since F⁺

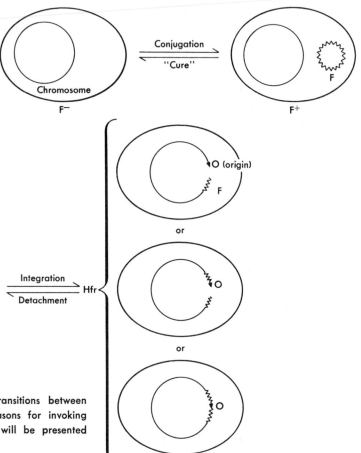

Fig. 7-6 Possible models for transitions between F⁻, F⁺, and Hfr cells. The reasons for invoking circularity appeared later, and will be presented below.

cultures contain many F+ cells per Hfr cell, and since the effective isolation of the rare recombinants from F⁺ × F⁻ crosses requires high cell densities, the zygotes or recombinants formed by an Hfr cell have a good opportunity for secondary contact with F⁺ cells, resulting in **multiple** conjugation. Crosses of purified Hfr × F⁻, in contrast, are carried out at low density and are not contaminated by F⁺ cells; hence a recipient rarely undergoes multiple conjugation, and even when it does it remains F⁻. Multiple conjugation can be demonstrated by mixing two different Hfr strains and an F⁻ at high density: recombinants are obtained that reflect **triparental inheritance.**

We can now also understand why **UV irradiation** stimulates the fertility of F⁺ strains: the integration of the F agent with the chromosome involves genetic recombination (see below), and UV is known to promote recombination (Ch. 8).

Kinetics of Hfr × F⁻ Mating

As long as bacterial conjugation was a rare event it could be studied only by observations on progeny many generations removed from the actual conjugants, and the major advances depended on ingenious exploitation of a series of accidental observations. The discovery of Hfr mutants, however, made it possible to study gene transfer directly and thereby to analyze the mating process systematically in terms of its component steps: cell pairing (bridge formation), chromosome transfer, and integration.

Interruption of Pair Formation

Jacob and Wollman studied the kinetics of mating in a cross in which a variety of alleles could be selected (prototrophic; fermentation positive; resistance to a drug or a bacteriophage) were transferred from the Sm^S Hayes Hfr strain (HfrH) to an $Sm^R F^-$ strain containing the complementary, nonselectable alleles (auxotrophic; fermentation negative; sensitive).* The presence of Sm in the medium "counter-selected" the male, and by other variations in the medium recombinants were readily selected with the Sm^R gene derived from the female and various other genes from the male. By mixing with a 20-fold excess of F^- cells, at a density of ca 10^8/ml, each Hfr cell was assured ample opportunity for effective contact. Samples of the mixture were taken at intervals, diluted to prevent formation of further mating pairs, and plated on various selective media to determine the numbers of recombinants containing various genes; their frequency of transmission was expressed in terms of percentage of input Hfr cells.

The number of recombinants of various types, which reflected the number of mating pairs, increased without a lag, until a plateau was reached at about 50 minutes (Fig. 7-7). Hence **effective contact,** firm enough to withstand the manipulations of dilution and plating, began at once; and all possible pairs had formed by 50 minutes (at the visible population density employed). Moreover, the **level of the plateau** differed for different markers: some were transmitted to the progeny with high frequencies (e.g., 18% of the Hfr cells for the closely linked T^+L^+ pair, and 5% for Gal^+, as illustrated), while others were transmitted with frequencies 1000-fold lower. Thus within a given set of paired cells

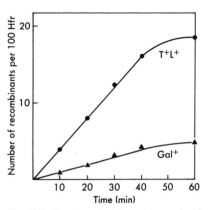

Fig. 7-7 Kinetics of conjugation, studied by interrupting further pair formation by dilution and immediate plating of samples taken at various times. Cross: HfrH $Sm^S thr^+ leu^+ gal^+ \times F^- Sm^R thr^- leu^- gal^-$. Exponential, broth cultures were mixed at time 0 (10^7 Hfr and 2×10^8 F^- cells per ml) and aerated in broth. At intervals samples were diluted and plated 1) on glucose minimal medium + streptomycin to select $thr^+ leu^+ Sm^R$ recombinants; and 2) on galactose minimal medium plus threonine, leucine, and streptomycin, to select $gal^+ Sm^R$ recombinants. (After E. L. Wollman, F. Jacob, and W. Hayes. *Cold Spring Harbor Symp. Quant. Biol.* 21:141, 1956.)

the markers could be arranged in a sequence, with a **gradient** of decreasing frequency of transmission to progeny. This gradient was presumed to reflect a decreasing probability of transmission of a gene with increasing distance from the origin of the entering chromosome.

Interrupted Transfer of the Chromosome

Mechanical Interruption. The inference of a gradient of gene transfer along the chromosome received the most direct possible demonstration through the introduction of a bold experimental procedure: the artificial interruption of mating (i.e., of transfer). Hayes showed that when bacteriophage was used to lyse a sensitive donor cell mating with a resistant recipient the merozygote remained viable. Wollman and Jacob then improved the procedure by using mechanical agitation (by means of a Waring Blendor, rapid pipetting back and forth, or strong vibration)

---

* In Hfr crosses, unlike the early crosses, the frequency of appearance of reversions is not significant relative to the high frequency of recombination; hence it was no longer necessary to employ double mutants, or unusually stable mutants, in the selection procedure.

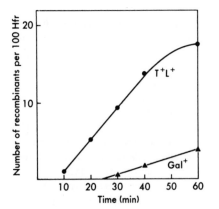

Fig. 7-8 Kinetics of conjugation, studied by interrupting further chromosomal transfer, as well as further pair formation, at various times. Same experiment as Figure 7-7 except that samples were agitated briefly in a Waring Blender before plating. (After E. L. Wollman, F. Jacob, and W. Hayes. *Cold Spring Harbor Symp. Quant. Biol.* 21:141, 1956.)

to separate the cells of the mating pair, instead of phage to kill one member: the timing was sharper and the rupture of the chromosome more certain. It thus became possible to distinguish the kinetics of chromosome transfer from the kinetics of cell pair formation.

When mating was interrupted at different times the effect on the transmission of various genes provided a measure of the **time of initial entry** of each gene (Fig. 7-8); and the increase in this time observed for various markers corresponded precisely to their sequence in the gradient of decreasing transmission to the progeny (Table 7-3). This orderly sequence indicated that all the cells of the Hfr strain start transferring their chromosome at the same locus (the **origin**), and as the transfer progresses the increasingly distal loci have a decreasing chance of reaching the progeny.

Zygotic Induction. The possibility of breaking the donor chromosome by artificial means reinforced the view that a similar spontaneous process was responsible for its usual incomplete transfer. However, it was also conceivable that the impairment occurred at the level of integration instead (i.e., postzygotic exclusion). This possibility was rigorously excluded by studies of the transfer of prophages (forms of bacterial viruses that are situated at characteristic loci on the chromosome; see Ch. 24): for prophage entry into a zygote is recognized without integration, since it is quite regularly followed by viral multiplication and cell lysis ("zygotic induction"). Different prophages were found to show different times of initial entry, and a correlated gradient of frequency of entry, just like markers that require integration.

Moreover, since the presence of a prophage in an Hfr donor caused lysis of the merozygotes receiving the prophage, the recovery (in recombinants) of genes distal to the prophage locus was drastically reduced. Genes closer to the origin, in contrast, showed a more normal frequency of recovery: their recombinants were evidently derived from zygotes that never received the prophage (because of spontaneous chromosome breakage during conjugation).

Protection of Mating Pairs. Further evidence for the role of spontaneous breaks in the "normal" gradient has been obtained more recently, with the finding that the breaks can be prevented, as well as increased, by external mechani-

TABLE 7-3. CORRELATION BETWEEN GRADIENT OF GENE TRANSMISSION AND TIME OF INITIAL ENTRY

Marker	Thr	Lac	Gal	His	Str	Met
Transmission to recombinants (% Hfr input)	46	36	30	6	1	0.1
Time of earliest transfer to zygote (min)	8	18	24	59	90	115

The time of initial entry of each gene was determined by interrupted mating, i.e., the intercept of each curve with the abscissas in Figure 7-8; and the per cent transmission is that observed without interruption, i.e., the plateaus of the same curves. (The F⁻ strain used in this cross permitted more frequent integration of Hfr markers than that observed in Figure 7-8, but the gradient of transfer [ratio of transmission of different markers] was very similar.) These data suggest a linear map in which thr is closest to the origin and met most distal.

From W. J. Hayes, F. Jacob, and E. Wollman. In Methodology in Basic Genetics. (W. J. Burdette, ed.) Holden-Day, San Francisco, 1963.

cal agencies: distal markers enter more frequently if the conjugating pairs are mechanically protected—e.g., plated in the depths of an agar medium, or, even better, forced by filtration into the pores of a membrane filter. Moreover, an unusual Hfr strain, called Vhfr (for very Hfr), has been found to transfer its distal segment with high frequency even without such help; it presumably forms an unusually stable conjugation bridge.

Interruption by ^{32}P Decay. Random breaks can be produced in DNA by growing cells in the presence of highly radioactive phosphate and then storing them in the frozen state to allow ^{32}P decay (which results in a chain break in the sugar-phosphate backbone). When such cells are used as donors their transmission of a locus near the origin is only slightly impaired, but the longer the period of ^{32}P decay the steeper the gradient of loss of transmission of more distal loci; hence continuity of transfer of the chromosome requires continuity of the DNA chain itself.

The use of donors containing labeled DNA has also verified previous genetic inferences by showing that a conjugating Hfr cell, under the usual conditions, transfers on the average about 1/5 of a chromosome.

Mapping by Interrupted Mating

The determination of times of initial entry made it possible to measure **physically,** in units of time, **map distances on a chromosome,** which previously could only be inferred from the relative frequency with which genes were linked in their appearance in recombinants. An early map that was obtained in this way is presented in Table 7-3. The last markers, which enter with a frequency of ca. 10^{-3} per Hfr (under ordinary conditions), require about 2 hours at 37°.

The **sequence** inferred from time of entry corresponds to that obtained from linkage studies. The **map distances** are also consistent when one examines the linkage of markers **proximal** to the selected marker (i.e., between the origin and that marker), since the entire segment up to the selected marker must be present in all zygotes receiving that marker. However, the apparent map distance of a marker **distal** to the selected marker is distorted, since an increase in distance not only increases the chance of crossing over (resulting in failure to be integrated), but also decreases the chance of entry.

The segment of chromosome transferred in 1 minute is found to correspond to about 20 recombination units (i.e., 20% crossing over). Since this length amounts to about 1% of the bacterial chromosome, the rate of transfer in conjugation is about 30 μ of double-stranded DNA, or 10^5 nucleotide pairs (Ch. 8), per minute. This estimate has been verified by the results of studies with ^{32}P-labeled DNA.

Mapping by interrupted mating is ideal for long distances in the chromosome (> 1 minute) and thus complements the use of methods based on linkage, which are necessary, and are only useful, for short distances.

Structure of the Chromosome and the F Agent

The Circular Chromosome

When a number of Hfr mutants were selected, by replica-plating (p. 194), from the same F$^+$ parent **different Hfr strains were found to differ in the sequence of genes injected.** However, the various sequences bore an orderly relation to each other: if the order of genes of one strain is denoted, from origin to distal terminus, as AB . . . YZ, other strains might be DEF . . . XYZABC, or KLM . . . HIJ. The sequence might also be reversed in orientation, as XWV . . . CBAZY. It was therefore inferred that **the E. coli chromosome is a circle, which can be interrupted at a variety of different points by integration of the F agent** (Fig. 7-9). This integration determines both the origin and the direction of transfer of the chromosome. Though the circularity of the *E. coli* chromosome remained for a number of years a purely formal genetic concept, eventually it was directly demonstrated (Ch. 8).

In Figure 7-9 the autonomous F agent is also represented as being circular, like the bacterial chromosome; the F agent thus becomes integrated by a single genetic crossover, which

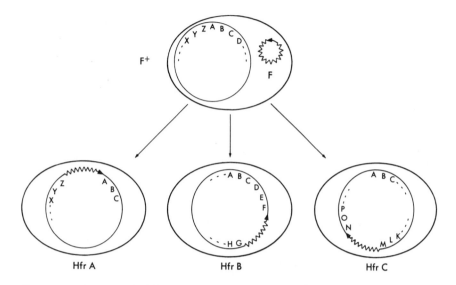

Fig. 7-9 Formation of different Hfr strains by integration of F agent at different locations on bacterial chromosome.

fuses it with the chromosome. Chapter 24 will present evidence supporting this model.

Though an open, linear structure, in contrast, was suggested for the Hfr chromosome by its linear transfer, the chromosome extracted from Hfr cells has also been found to be circular; hence a linear structure is apparently formed only during the special process of conjugation (see below). Moreover, when the entire Hfr chromosome enters the zygote the circle must close, perhaps rapidly, since genetic linkage can be demonstrated between very early and very late markers of the chromosome.

The Terminal Transfer of F. We have noted that recombinants from an Hfr × F⁻ cross are generally F⁻. However, those few recombinants that have incorporated a distal locus of the Hfr parent are usually found to be Hfr. Hence **in Hfr strains the F agent** (or at least an essential portion of it) **is located on the distal extremity of the entering bacterial chromosome.**

The model for integration presented in Figure 7-9 provides an explanation for this terminal transfer of the Hfr property, and unifies the behavior of F⁺ and Hfr strains. In either type the F agent causes the forma-

tion of a conjugation bridge and then enters it, starting at some characteristic site in F. In F⁺ strains the entire F agent enters, because its short DNA chain is rarely broken during conjugation. Hfr strains, on the other hand, are apparently formed by the fusion of two circles, and so the bacterial chromosome may be regarded as a huge insertion into the F agent. Hence a part of the agent may constitute the origin of the entering chromosome, and the rest of the agent would come in at the distal terminus of the chromosome and thus complete the requirement for producing an Hfr strain.

The Genetic Map of E. coli. Starting with the discovery of sexual polarity, the several novel features of recombination in *E. coli* were elucidated between 1952 and 1958. This development represents one of the triumphs of modern biology, and its success is attested to by the construction, at last, of a consistent chromosome map (Fig. 7-10). Indeed, with all the hidden complications that were present, it is perhaps remarkable that the early crosses gave sufficiently reproducible linkage data to be at all encouraging. On the other hand, we can now also understand how these crosses, which produced merozygotes, seemed

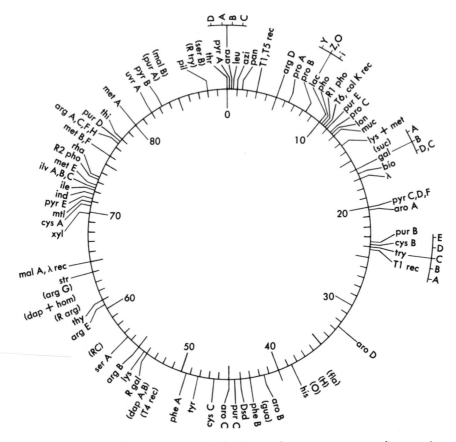

Fig. 7-10 Map of chromosome of *E. coli*. The numbers represent map distances in minutes required for transfer under the usual conditions (broth, 37°); zero is close to the origin of the first Hfr strain isolated, Hfr H (designated for Hayes). (From A. L. Taylor and M. S. Thoman. *Genetics* 50:659, 1964.)

at first to be producing classic zygotes by cell fusion: the presence of a variety of Hfr types in a stock culture could account for the usual recovery of all the markers in a given cross.

Modification of F Agent; F-duction

Recombination Between F and Chromosome. One item yet remained in the treasure-chest of genetic novelties in *E. coli* K12: **variation in F**, which is consistent with the picture of F as a small, supernumerary chromosome. The first variant was encountered when Adelberg, studying the mutation of Hfr strains to F⁺, isolated a mutant with properties of both Hfr and F⁺: this **intermediate donor** transfers the chromosome only

1/10 as frequently as its Hfr parent, but in the same sequence; but unlike that parent, it also transfers the sex factor with high frequency. Since these properties are passed on to the recipients of the factor, the hereditary alteration in this strain evidently resides in the F agent.

The properties of this mutant led to the inference that the integrated sex factor had incorporated an adjacent segment of the host chromosome in the course of being detached (Fig. 7-11). Other chromosomes in the same cell (and its progeny) would retain the region homologous to the one incorporated in the hybrid sex factor; and homology promotes genetic crossing over, which is evidently involved in both integration and

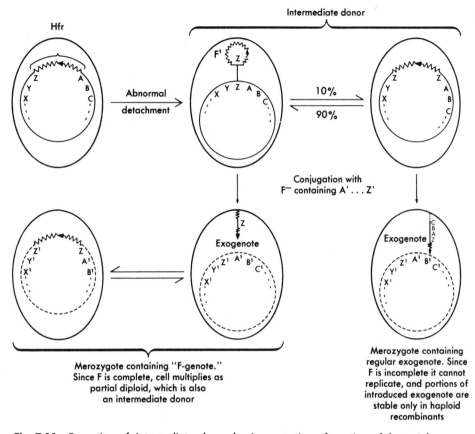

Fig. 7-11 Formation of intermediate donor by incorporation of portion of bacterial chromosome into detached F agent; and alternative mechanisms of gene transfer from this kind of donor.

detachment of the sex factor (Ch. 24). The intermediate donor property of this mutant is thus readily understood: because of strong homology with a region of the chromosome the hybrid sex factor alternates rather frequently between the autonomous and the integrated state, and it is in the latter in about 1/10 of the cells at any one time. Furthermore, because the autonomous hybrid factor possesses a structure that "remembers" the earlier site of its integration, it regularly returns to that site and forms the same kind of Hfr chromosome.

The inference of a genetic exchange between F and the chromosome is strongly supported by evidence that in donors of intermediate type the chromosome is sometimes altered in a reciprocal way. Specifically, when such a strain is cured of

its hybrid F by acridine it becomes F−, as expected; but when it is then "infected" with an **ordinary F agent** it becomes the same intermediate donor that it was before the cure, rather than the usual F+. **Evidently the chromosome now has a region of homology to which F preferentially attaches.** This region, which is called an sfa (sex-factor affinity) locus, presumably contains a segment of F.

F-duction. The presence of a bacterial segment in such hybrid F agents suggested the possibility of developing recognizable genetic markers in these agents; and bacterial strains with this property were ingeniously isolated by Jacob and Adelberg; they are called F′ (F-prime) or F-genote strains. The method of isolation was based on two expectations: the incorporated genes would come from loci adjacent to the site of F integration; and the F′ carrier of these genes, being much shorter than the bacterial chromosome, would transfer them early. Accordingly, recombinants were selected for the early transfer of a locus known to be near the distal terminus of an Hfr chromosome.

For example, when an Sm^S donor with terminal lac$^+$ is crossed with an Sm^R lac$^-$ recipient the usual mating process requires about 120 minutes to produce Sm^{R}lac$^+$ recombinants (in low frequency). However, when this cross was interrupted at 30 minutes such recombinants were still obtained, though in much lower numbers. The interruption had, as expected, prevented the transfer of lac$^+$ from occurring by the normal process; for while these recombinants had received the lac$^+$ gene from the Hfr parent, they had not received other Hfr markers that should normally have entered earlier. These results suggested the transfer of a hybrid F′ unit (F-lac$^+$) to the lac$^-$ cell, making it a **heterogenote** (i.e., a cell diploid and heterozygous for some region of the chromosome), of the type lac$^-$/F-lac$^+$ (e.g., Z/Z′ stable partial diploid of Figure 7-11).

This interpretation is supported by several additional properties of the new clone: 1) the cells had received the sex factor as well as the lac gene; 2) they were unstable, segregating stable lac$^-$ haploids with a frequency of about 10^{-3} per cell division; and 3) they were donors of intermediate type, which could convert lac$^-$ females to lac$^+$ heterogenotes indistinguishable from the donors.

Many types of F′ (F-gal, F-proline, etc.) have now been obtained. The size of an F′ can vary widely; some strains include as much as 1/3 of a bacterial chromosome (defined by genetic markers). Presumably any locus of the bacterial chromosome can become incorporated into the sex factor, from a suitable Hfr type, and can then be transferred with high efficiency. Since this process closely resembles transduction by bacteriophage, as will be seen in the next portion of this chapter, it has been called **F-duction** or **sexduction.** F-duction makes it possible to create stable

strains that are diploid for any desired genes, and these strains have proved especially valuable in studying regulatory interactions of genes (Ch. 9).

A **double male** strain, containing two F agents integrated in different positions on the chromosome, has been isolated by Clark (by using an F$^-$ phenocopy of an Hfr strain as recipient, and selecting for transfer of a distal terminal locus of a different Hfr donor). This strain behaves as though it had two different chromosomes: two unlinked groups of genes are each transferred at high frequency, any given recombinant usually receiving genes from only one group.

Significance of Conjugation

Conjugation undoubtedly contributes to bacterial variation in Nature: its importance in the recent spread of multiple drug resistance, for example, will be considered in Chapter 24. Conjugation has also been important for studies in many areas of bacterial physiology and genetics, by making it possible to create strains with different combinations of well-defined mutations.

In bacterial genetics the ability to create populations of partially diploid cells has widened the scope of studies on the functions and interactions of genetic determinants, and has contributed immensely to the analysis of regulatory mechanisms (Ch. 9). F′ is particularly valuable in studying the kinetics of the expression of newly introduced genes, since it can be transmitted rapidly to essentially all the F$^-$ cells in a mixture.

Most strains of *E. coli* are F$^-$ and can accept the F agent (and genes transferred by it); however, the level of fertility is often low, and because of restrictions in the compatibility of the DNA of different strains fertility is often even lower between different strains than within a strain. Gene transfer has been accomplished from *E. coli* to other Enterobacteriaceae, such as *Salmonella* and *Shigella;* it is considerably more effective with F′ than with Hfr donors because the former do not require integration of the transferred DNA. Indeed, F′ can even be transferred from *E. coli* to organisms with a grossly different DNA base composition, such as *Proteus, Pasteurella,* and *Vibrio.*

Other sex factors, differing in various ways from the F agent, have been found in various strains of *E. coli,* in *Pseudomonas aeruginosa,* and in the actinomycete *Streptomyces coelicolor.* The properties of sex factors, and particularly the mechanism of their integration and detachment, will be further discussed in Chapter 24, where sex factors are considered as members of the broader class of **episomes:** agents that can replicate either autonomously or as part of a chromosome.

Physiology of Conjugation

Bridge Formation

Conjugation requires that a male and a female cell possess complementary macromolecules, somewhere on their surface, whose mutual recognition leads to pairing; the presence of an F agent in the cell evidently induces the formation of the male component of this complementary pair. The presence of such distinct molecular patches (receptors) was independently established by the isolation of bacteriophages that can adsorb only to male or to female cells of *E. coli,* respectively.

In addition, gentle treatment with periodate (which attacks certain groups in carbohydrates and, less often, in proteins) had a "devirilizing" action—i.e., it rendered male cells (but not female cells) infertile, and fertility was recovered on further growth. Finally, immunological tests revealed a characteristic antigen in male cells, but it has proved too labile to isolate and identify chemically.

F-Pili. It was long assumed that formation of the bridge required an alteration in morphogenesis of the rigid cell wall, after initial adhesion of the two cells, to provide continuity between their walls. Indeed, impressive photographs of short, heavy bridges were obtained by electron microscopy of metal-shadowed preparations. However, the significance of these structures is not clear, and they may be artifacts, for an entirely different kind

of mating structure has been revealed by the use of phages that attack only male cells. Brinton, and Crawford and Gesteland, showed that when such phages are added in excess to F$^+$ or Hfr cells the small, spherical phage particles, unlike most phages (Ch. 23), do not adsorb to the cell wall, but rather adsorb along the entire length of two or three of the hundreds of rod-like pili, up to several microns in length (Ch. 2), that radiate from the cell surface (Fig. 7-12). The adsorption is highly specific for these **"F-pili"**: no phage is adsorbed to any other pili of the male cell, or to any of the pili on female cells.

The F-specific phage can thus serve as a specific "staining" reagent for F-pili. Its use has shown that **all** F$^+$ and Hfr strains tested possess F-pili; when the F agent is eliminated by acridine these pili are no longer formed; and when an F agent is introduced they soon appear. Moreover, when the pili are removed from a cell by mechanical agitation fertility is also lost, and when they have grown back fertility is restored. Hence, though the evidence is correlative rather than direct, it seems justified to conclude that the F-pilus is involved in the formation of the conjugation bridge, and may well be its only constituent.

Although the F-pili are long and narrow, their dimensions are suitable for a conjugation bridge. Electron micrographs of cross sections reveal an axial hole, and the dimensions of the tube (outer diameter ca. 70 A, inner diameter 20–25 A) are similar to those of the tails of certain phages, through which the phage DNA is known to be injected (Ch. 23). The properties of the F-pilus also explain certain features of mating: its ready spontaneous interruption; the failure of a bristling array of other pili to prevent cells from getting close enough to mate; and the absence of significant transfer of radioactively labeled cytoplasmic components. Finally, since conjugation does not require a specific change in wall morphogenesis following contact, but rather depends on a preformed, specialized structure, it is easy to understand why male and female spheroplasts, formed by the use of penicillin, can mate normally.

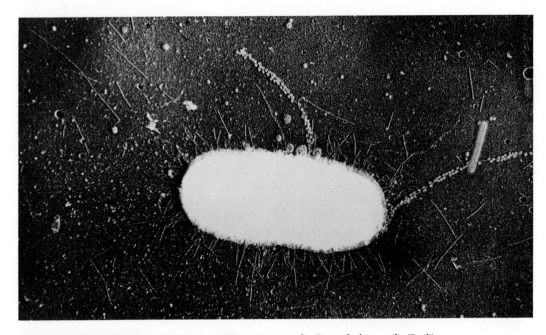

Fig. 7-12 *E. coli* cell of an Hfr strain, with numerous pili. Two of these pili (F-pili) have adsorbed particles of the male-specific MS-2 bacteriophage, which cover the entire surface of these pili. (Courtesy of C. C. Brinton.)

Transfer of DNA

It became possible to formulate a plausible mechanism for the transfer of DNA only when certain key features of chromosome replication were understood. 1) The replication of DNA, by synthesis of a new, complementary strand on each old, template strand (Chs. 4 and 8), is regulated by control over its initiation at a specific "replicator" site (Ch. 8), and the growing point thus initiated moves continuously along the DNA molecule until it reaches the replicator site again (Ch. 9). 2) Such a replicator site is required in any autonomous, self-replicating bloc of DNA (replicon), such as a chromosome or a sex factor. 3) The chromosome is attached to the plasma membrane, thereby ensuring orderly separation of the daughter chromosomes at cell division (Ch. 2).

Chromosome **replication** thus resembles chromosome **transfer** in being polarized, and in continuing progressively along the DNA molecule, starting at a fixed point. This simi-

larity led Jacob and Brenner to suggest a direct connection between the two processes. According to their model the F agent, whether integrated or autonomous, is attached at its replicator site to the cell membrane, at a location near a conjugation bridge (whose formation it induces). In ordinary cell division the agent (with or without an integrated bacterial chromosome) replicates and migrates with the growing membrane just like an ordinary chromosome. Cell pairing, however, in some unknown way triggers an extra initiation of replication, at the attachment site, and this replication then proceeds in a special manner: one of the double-stranded products goes into the conjugation bridge, and the other remains in the cell (Fig. 7-13). **The transfer of DNA thus requires its simultaneous replication;** and the energy of replication, derived from the pyrophosphorolysis of deoxyribonucleoside triphosphates (Ch. 4), might also provide the energy required to drive the transfer.

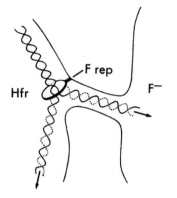

Fig. 7-13 Model for the mechanism of DNA transfer during conjugation: activation of a membrane-attached F agent results in initiation of DNA replication at a site in that agent, followed by direction of one of the two new DNA chains into the conjugation bridge (now tentatively identified as an F-pilus). (After F. Jacob, S. Brenner, and F. Cuzin. *Cold Spring Harbor Symp. Quant. Biol.* 28:329, 1963.)

Though the evidence has not all been consistent, several findings support this model. DNA transfer is inhibited by drugs that block DNA synthesis (novobiocin, nalidixic acid; Ch. 10), and not by inhibitors of wall or protein synthesis. Moreover, when the donor DNA was fully labeled with ³H-thymine **before** mating, or was labeled only **during** mating (to cells whose own

DNA synthesis was prevented by a genetic block), radioautography showed the transfer of similar amounts of radioactivity to the recipient cells. This is the result expected if the transferred DNA contains one strand synthesized before and one during mating. Also, replication is rapid enough for the Jacob-Brenner model, and is evidently slowed by association with transfer: an *E. coli* chromosome is normally replicated in about 50 minutes and is transferred in 90 minutes at 37°. Finally, there is direct evidence for the postulated synthesis of DNA at a site of attachment to the membrane, since the isolated membrane fraction of disrupted bacteria contains a small amount of DNA, including preferentially the part most recently synthesized (as determined by pulses of labeling at different times).

The mechanism of Figure 7-13 also explains other features of the F agent: its multiplication in synchrony with cell division under ordinary circumstances; its accelerated multiplication when spreading to F⁻ cells; and its inability to mediate gene transfer when the male (but not when the female) is deprived of its energy source. (It will be recalled that killing of the males by streptomycin, in contrast, does not have this effect; but the mechanism of action of streptomycin (Ch. 10) is now known to permit continued energy production and DNA synthesis long after killing.)

TRANSDUCTION

Transduction is a process of gene transfer in bacteria mediated by bacteriophage particles. Some bacteriophage strains mediate **generalized** transduction, in which any bacterial genes may be transferred, while others mediate **specialized** transduction, in which a particular phage strain can transfer only certain genes. Since an understanding of the mechanism of transduction requires a knowledge of bacteriophage physiology and genetics, detailed consideration of this topic will be deferred to Chapter 24. We shall consider here only the use of generalized transduction as a means for obtaining desired recombinants and for mapping the bacterial chromosome.

For this purpose it suffices to note that generalized transduction is akin to transformation in transferring only small fragments of bacterial DNA from a donor to a recipient strain. In transformation the DNA is naked, whereas in transduction it reaches the cell as a packet surrounded by the coat of the phage; but since the coat remains outside the cell and only the DNA penetrates, the intracellular events are much the same in transduction as in transformation. Transduction is available in a greater variety of species, and it also has certain advantages for mapping: the DNA is protected from the environment, which makes the process more readily reproducible; and the fragments transferred fill the phage coat and are therefore of rather uniform length (Ch. 24).

Mapping by Transduction

Mapping by transduction is based on the assumption that the population of phage particles released by the donor includes an assortment of segments, of the proper length, derived at random from the donor chromosome. Hence each bacterial gene should be represented with equal frequency, and it should be linked to variable lengths of chromosome, up to a fixed maximum, on either side (Fig. 7-14). The distance between two mutational sites within this maximal length can be estimated in two ways: from the frequency of their linked transduction, or from the frequency of recombination between them.

Fig. 7-14 Formation of transducing phage particles by phage-infected bacterium. The entry of the phage genome leads to its own replication, and to the formation of the components that are finally assembled into the phage coat. In this assembly the coat occasionally encloses a segment of bacterial DNA instead of the usual phage DNA.

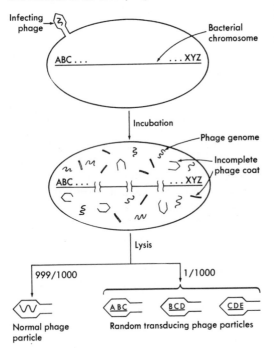

Frequency of joint transduction of closely linked loci (with distinct phenotypic effects) can be used to determine their **sequence** on a chromosome, since this frequency will decrease with the distance between the two markers. However, the relation of frequency to **map distance** is not simple: not only does increasing distance between two markers decrease the probability (as in classic genetics) that both will be integrated after being introduced, but it also decreases the probability that both will be introduced by a single phage particle. Indeed, as with transformation, markers separated by more than 1% of the chromosomes cannot be jointly transduced.

In the example provided in Table 7-4 the donor was wild-type *E. coli* B and the recipient was a mutant negative for leucine synthesis (leu⁻), threonine synthesis (thr⁻), and arabinose utilization (ara⁻). Transductants were selected separately, on appropriate media, for the wild-type allele of each marker. For example, selection for leu⁺, without selection for either allele of the other markers, was accomplished by plating on a medium lacking leucine but containing threonine and a carbon source other than arabinose. The selected colonies were then scored for the unselected markers (i.e., tested for arabinose utilization and for growth on medium **lacking** threonine). It is seen that thr is relatively distant from ara (6.7 and 4.3% linkage when one or the other was selected) and even more distant from leu (4.1 and 1.9% linkage), whereas leu and ara are closely linked (55 and 72% linkage). These results suggest the sequence thr-ara-leu, with ara considerably closer to leu than to thr, as diagrammed at the top of the table.

This sequence was verified by the results obtained by selection of pairs in a **three-factor cross,** shown in the same table. Selection for the two extremes (thr⁺ and leu⁺) yielded a very high frequency of unselected ara⁺ (80%), as would be expected if ara were the middle one of the three loci ("inside" marker). (The value was not 100% because an extra pair of crossovers occasionally occurred, from thr⁺ to ara⁻ and back to leu⁺.) In contrast, selection for the much closer ara⁺-leu⁺ pair (not shown) yielded a larger number of transductants, but with a

TABLE 7-4. JOINT TRANSDUCTION IN E. COLI BY PHAGE P1

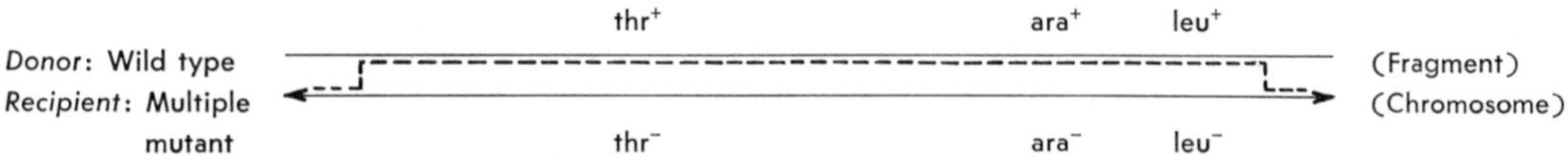

Selected marker	Number of transductants per phage P1 plated	Percentage of selected colonies that also have the following unselected marker		
		leu⁺	thr⁺	ara⁺
thr⁺	2.5×10^{-5}	4.1	—	6.7
leu⁺	5.0×10^{-5}	—	1.9	55.4
ara⁺	3.5×10^{-5}	72.6	4.3	—
thr⁺ leu⁺	1.0×10^{-7}	—	—	80.0

The dashed line in the diagram depicts the double crossover necessary to exchange the chromosomal segment containing all three markers. Crossovers in various other regions would result in transduction of one or two markers. After J. Gross and E. Englesberg. Virology *9:314 (1959).*

lower frequency of incorporation of the unselected, "outside" thr+ marker. The sequence thus established is the same as that obtained by conjugation.

Frequency of recombination is used for mapping sites within a gene (or in adjacent genes of similar function); it has thus been extremely valuable in **fine-structure genetics,** which is concerned with mapping sites at very close intervals (Ch. 8). Both donor and recipient must have the same phenotypic deficiency, and one selects for recombinants with the wild-type character.

In this procedure one compares the transduction frequencies obtained in parallel experiments with phage from various donors, added to the same or to different recipients. For example, different phage lysates, carrying genes from a series of independent ara⁻ mutants (ara_2^-, ara_3^-, etc.), may be used to transduce ara_1^- recipients (present in excess) to ara+. The frequency of transduction is expressed in relation to the number of phage particles supplied. This frequency is proportional to the map distance between the mutant sites in the donor and the recipient strain. Thus **low** frequency of appearance of recombinants is the index of closeness of linkage, whereas in joint transduction the index is **high** frequency of appearance of multiply transduced cells.

In such experiments different strains might vary in transduction efficiency (i.e., in the incorporation of bacterial genes into phage, or in the uptake of the phage); the observed recombinant frequencies would then no longer simply reflect map distances. To correct for this possibility the frequency of **recombination** between similar markers in each transduction is normalized against the simultaneous frequency of **incorporation** of an independent marker from the same donor. For example, in the recombinations between ara⁻ strains one might use leu+ donors and leu⁻ recipients; the proportion of leu+ cells produced would be determined, by a separate selection from that for ara+. Since the leu+ frequency provides an index of the transduction efficiency, the ratio ara+/leu+ provides a corrected measure of the distance between the two ara⁻ markers being recombined in each tube. The results obtained by this method are consistent: the mutant sites within a gene can all be fitted into a linear sequence, and the distance of any pair is approximately the sum of the distances of the intervening successive pairs. The order can be independently verified by determining which member of each pair is more closely linked to an adjacent locus (outside ara) on either side.

SELECTED REFERENCES

Books and Review Articles

ADELBERG, E. A. (ed.). *Papers on Bacterial Genetics*. Little, Brown, Boston, 1966. An excellent paperback reprinting of key articles, with a useful historical introduction and bibliography.

BRINTON, C. C., JR. Contributions of Pili to the Specificity of the Cell Surface, and a Unitary Hypothesis of Conjugal Infectious Heredity. In *Specificity of Cell Surfaces*. (B. D. Davis and L. Warren, eds.) Prentice-Hall, Englewood Cliffs, N.J., 1966.

CLARK, A. J., and ADELBERG, E. A. Bacterial conjugation. *Ann. Rev. Microbiol. 16*:289 (1962).

HAYES, W. *The Genetics of Bacteria and Their Viruses*. Blackwell, Oxford, 1964. A very readable and comprehensive review.

HAYES, W. The Structure and Function of the Bacterial Chromosome. In *Function and Structure in Microorganisms*, p. 294. (15th Symposium, Society of General Microbiologists; M. R. Pollock and M. H. Richmond, eds.) Cambridge Univ. Press, London, 1965.

JACOB, F., and WOLLMAN, E. L. *Sexuality and the Genetics of Bacteria*. Academic Press, New York, 1961.

SCHAEFFER, P. Transformation. In *The Bacteria*, vol. V. (I. C. Gunsalus and R. Y. Stanier, eds.) Academic Press, New York, 1964.

Specific Articles: Transformation

ALLOWAY, J. L. The transformation *in vitro* of R pneumococci into S forms of different specific types by the use of filtered pneumococcus extracts. *J. Exp. Med. 55*:91 (1932).

AVERY, O. T., MACLEOD, C. M., and MCCARTY, M. Induction of transformation by a desoxyribonucleic acid fraction isolated from pneumococcus type III. *J. Exp. Med. 79*:137 (1944).

DAWSON, M. H., and SIA, R. H. P. *In vitro* transformation of pneumococcal types. I. A technique for inducing transformation of pneumococcal types *in vitro*. *J. Exp. Med. 54*:681 (1931).

GRIFFITH, F. The significance of pneumococcal types. *J. Hyg. 27*:113 (1928).

HOTCHKISS, R. D. Genetic Structure of Transforming Units. In *Enzymes, Units of Biological Structure and Function*, p. 119. (O. H. Gaebler, ed.) Academic Press, New York, 1956.

KAISER, A. D., and HOGNESS, D. S. The transformation of *Escherichia coli* with DNA isolated from bacteriophage λdg. *J. Molec. Biol. 2*:392 (1960).

SPIZIZEN, J. Transformation of a biochemically deficient strain of *B. subtilis* by DNA. *Proc. Nat. Acad. Sc. 44*:1072 (1958).

Specific Articles: Conjugation

CAVALLI-SFORZA, L. L., LEDERBERG, J., and LEDERBERG, E. M. An infective factor controlling sex compatibility in *Bacterium coli*. *J. Gen. Microbiol. 8*:89 (1953).

GROSS, J. D., and CARO, L. Genetic transfer in bacterial mating. *Science 150*:1679 (1965).

HAYES, W. The mechanism of genetic recombination in *Escherichia coli*. *Cold Spring Harbor Symp. Quant. Biol. 18*:75 (1953). In Adelberg collection.

JACOB, F., BRENNER, S., and CUZIN, F. On the regulation of DNA synthesis in bacteria. *Cold Spring Harbor Symp. Quant. Biol. 28*:329 (1963).

LEDERBERG, J. Gene recombination and linked segregation in *Escherichia coli*. *Genetics 32*:505 (1947). In Adelberg collection.

LEDERBERG, J. Aberrant heterozygotes in *Escherichia coli*. *Proc. Nat. Acad. Sc. 35*:178 (1949).

WOLLMAN, E. L., JACOB, F., and HAYES, W. Conjugation and genetic recombination in *Escherichia coli*. *Cold Spring Harbor Symp. Quant. Biol. 21*:141 (1956). In Adelberg collection.

Specific Article: Transduction

HARTMAN, P. E., LOPER, J. C., and SERMAN, D. Fine structure mapping by complete transduction between histidine-requiring *Salmonella* mutants. *J. Gen. Microbiol. 22*:323 (1960).

8 MOLECULAR ASPECTS OF GENETICS

The preceding chapters have shown that genetic investigations with microbes have contributed extensively to our understanding not only of the biology of these organisms, but also of universal genetic mechanisms. Extensive recent work with in vitro systems has shed much additional light on various molecular aspects of genetics. Knowledge of these advances seems essential for understanding the behavior of the microbial cell, but the subject has become so large that we shall have to review it only briefly, omitting the experimental basis for many of the conclusions presented. Other topics in molecular genetics will be taken up later, particularly in discussions of regulation (Ch. 9) and of bacterial viruses (Chs. 23 and 24).

As we have already seen from experiments on bacterial transformation, DNA carries the **genetic information** of a cell: the instructions that cause their own replication and also determine the structure of the other highly specific macromolecules, whose activities are in turn responsible for the total structure, function, and growth of the cell. In viruses the genetic information has similarly been shown to reside in nucleic acid, which may be either DNA or RNA. This chapter will therefore be largely concerned with properties of nucleic acids that are relevant to the major functions of genes: 1) replication, 2) expression, 3) mutation, and 4) recombination.

Structure of Nucleic Acids

Extraction. Nucleic acids are extracted by using substances that denature and precipitate the proteins with which they are associated, e.g., the detergent sodium dodecyl sulfate (SDS) and water-saturated phenol. The conditions for extraction (temperature, ionic strength, and special additives) vary, depending on the type of nucleic acid (RNA or DNA) and on the nature of the material with which it is associated (e.g., whether containing lipids or not).

Constitution

The genetic information of all cells and many viruses is stored in double-stranded DNA; that of other viruses is in single-stranded DNA, single-stranded RNA, or rarely double-stranded RNA. All nucleic acids contain four main bases: guanine, adenine, cytosine, and either thymine in DNA or uracil in RNA. The DNA of certain bacteriophages contains 5-hydroxymethylcytosine in-

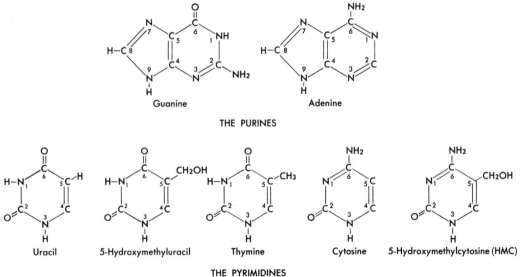

Fig. 8-1 The chemical structure of various purines and pyrimidines.

stead of cytosine, or 5-hydroxymethyluracil instead of thymine (Fig. 8-1).

Certain chemical substitutions occur in nucleic acid bases after the polynucleotide chains have been synthesized; most common in DNA is the **methylation** of cytosine and adenine residues to form 5-methylcytosine and 6-methylaminopurine (methyladenine). In addition, the DNA of some bacteriophages is glucosylated on hydroxymethylcytosine or hydroxymethyluracil. A great deal of methylation is introduced in tRNA to form 5-methylcytosine, thymine, methyladenine, 6-methylaminopurine, 6-dimethylaminopurine, 1-methylpurine, 2-methylamino-6-hydroxypurine, and 2-dimethylamino-6-hydroxypurine; other minor constituents include 5,6-dihydrouracil and pseudouridine (with the ribose attached to C-5 rather than N-1 of the ring). These substitutions do not affect the genetic information of the nucleic acids, but they are important either for function, as in tRNA, or for conferring resistance to nucleases, as in bacteriophage DNA (Ch. 23, Host-induced modification).

The salient feature of **double-stranded DNA,** as revealed by the classic work of Watson and Crick, is the presence of two **complementary** strands. Complementarity is determined by the steric relations of the bases in the nucleotide pairs, which can be either adenylic and thymidylic acid (AT pair), or guanylic and cytidylic acid (GC pair; Fig. 8-2). Since in double-stranded DNA the proportion of A equals that of T and the proportion of G equals that of C, the base ratios are given by the ratio of (A + T) to (G + C). The same relations apply to **double-stranded RNA,** with U substituting for T. In contrast, the proportions of the four bases of **single-stranded DNA and RNA** can vary independently because their bases are not paired, e.g., A need not equal T.

Each nucleic acid strand has a polarity, because phosphodiester bonds between nucleotide residues connect the 3′ position of one to the 5′ position of the next residue, leaving a free 3′ position at one end of the strand and a free 5′ position at the other end (Fig. 8-3).*

---

* Primed numbers in nucleotides refer to positions on the ribose or deoxyribose residue, and other numbers to positions in the purine or pyrimidine rings.

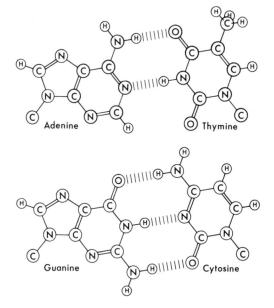

Fig. 8-2 Pairing of adenine with thymine and of guanine with cytosine in double-stranded DNA. Hydrogen bonds are shown as series of dashes.

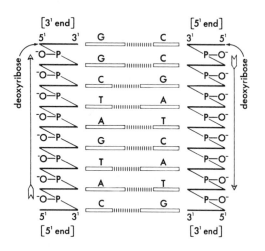

Fig. 8-3 Diagram of double-stranded DNA. Each strand has a polarity determined by the direction of the phosphodiester bonds. The two strands constituting the same molecule have opposite polarities.

These are referred to as the 3'-terminal and the 5'-terminal ends of the polynucleotide chain, respectively.

Nucleic acids have multiple negative charges, deriving from the primary phosphoric acid groups, which have pK_a about 1 and are therefore fully ionized under essentially all experimental conditions. In vivo the negative charges are neutralized either by inorganic cations (especially Mg^{++}) or basic organic molecules, such as histones in cells of higher organisms and polyamines in viruses (Ch. 22).

Shape and Size of Nucleic Acid Molecules

X-ray crystallography has demonstrated that in double-stranded nucleic acids the two strands are antiparallel, i.e., have inverse polarity and are regularly coiled around each other, forming a **double helix** with a diameter of about 20 A. The genetic information, which resides in the sequence of the bases, is on the inside of the molecules, near the axis of the helix; the outside of the helix contains the primary phosphoric acid groups and therefore has the character of a polyanion. Physical properties and electron micrographs show that the molecules of helical double-stranded nucleic acids are rather rigid. In contrast, molecules of single-stranded nucleic acids are very flexible and in solution form **random coils,** in which some bases pair at random with complementary bases of the same molecule. The proportion of paired bases of single-stranded nucleic acids (also called the **helical content**) varies with the base ratio and the sequential order of the bases.

DNA molecules are much larger than any other known molecules. Because of the molecules' fragility, most DNA preparations, including those used in genetic transformation experiments, consist of fragments. The size in Nature of the large DNA molecules can be determined only by methods that measure their length without purification and with a minimum of handling. These methods are electron microscopy and radioautography.

Electron Microscopy. Elegant electron micrographs of DNA are obtained by Kleinschmidt's method, which consists of spreading the molecules in a monomolecular film of a basic protein (such as cytochrome c) floating on water. The basic molecules adsorb to the primary phosphoric acid groups of the nucleic acid, increasing its thickness and therefore its visibility; the complexes are collected on a membrane and examined. This method reveals the length of the nucleic acid and its shape (i.e., whether linear or cyclic).

Radioautography. Tritium-labeled thymine of high specific activity is incorporated into replicating DNA. The molecules of the DNA, extracted by mild methods, are collected on membrane filters or glass surfaces, which are dried, overlaid with a photographic emulsion, and kept in the dark for several weeks or months. During this time β radiations from disintegrating tritium atoms cause the formation of silver grains along the DNA molecules. After photographic development and fixation the length and overall shape of the DNA molecules can be determined, and the molecular weight calculated, because it is known that under these conditions the nucleotide pairs are 3.4 A apart along the helix axis.

These methods have shown that bacterial and viral genomes each consist of a **single molecule of nucleic acid.** The molecules, which carry the **whole genetic information,** are extraordinarily long in comparison with the dimensions of the organism to which they belong. For instance, the DNA of *E. coli* (M.W. 2.8×10^9) is about 400 times longer than the long axis of the cell; that of bacteriophage T2 (M.W. 1.2×10^8) is more than 500 times longer than the capsid in which it is enclosed. RNA molecules of all kinds are much smaller, the largest (from a virus) having a molecular weight of about 10^7. DNA molecules are often cyclic, i.e., in the form of closed rings.

Physical Properties

Advances in technic have made possible a detailed description of the physical characteristics of nucleic acids, which are fundamental for understanding the structural basis of their activities and are also important as analytical tools. We shall briefly discuss the properties of particular biological interest.

Sedimentation Coefficient. The sedimentation coefficient $(s^0_{20, w})$ is the velocity of sedimentation in a centrifugal field in water at 20° and at very low nucleic acid concentration. Absolute values are determined in the analytical ultra-centrifuge; relative values can also be obtained in the preparative ultracentrifuge by **zonal centrifugation** through a **density gradient,** commonly of sucrose or CsCl, formed in a centrifuge tube by the appropriate mixing of two solutions of different specific gravity so that the denser part of the gradient is at the bottom of the tube (Fig. 8-4). A small sample containing

Fig. 8-4 Zonal centrifugation. A linear density gradient is prepared in a plastic centrifuge tube with an inert solute, as indicated in **A**; its purpose is simply to prevent convection. The sample is layered at the top of the gradient. After centrifugation the various components of the sample have moved different distances, depending on their sedimentation constants, and thus form **bands** as shown in **B**. The bottom is punctured with a fine needle and fractions are collected, in the form of drops, into a series of tubes, as shown in **C**; during this operation the bands maintain their relative positions because the density gradient prevents mixing. Different bands are therefore collected in different groups of tubes. When their contents are analyzed a diagram similar to that of **D** is obtained. In this technic components are separated on the basis of differences in their sedimentation constant, which depend on particle size, shape, and density.

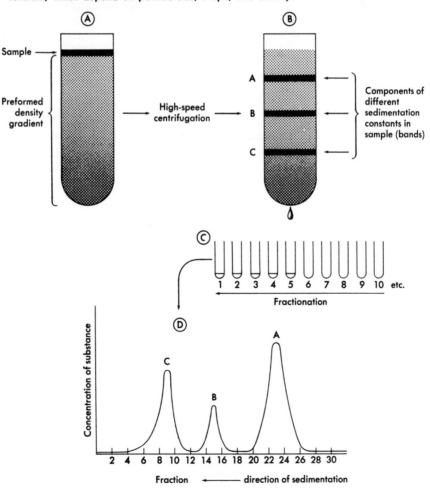

the nucleic acid is layered at the top of the gradient, and the tube is spun in an ultracentrifuge. Fractions are subsequently collected as drops after the bottom of the plastic tube has been perforated.

Sedimentation coefficients of proteins, nucleic acids, and viruses expressed in absolute units have very low values: for instance, that of ribo-nuclease is 1.6×10^{-13}, that of the polyoma virus DNA is 21×10^{-13}, and that of poliovirus RNA is 35×10^{-13}. The values are usually given after multiplication by 10^{13}, i.e., in Svedberg units (S). The sedimentation coefficient of nucleic acids is related to the molecular weight by empirical relations, which differ for single-stranded and double-stranded mole-

Fig. 8-5 Equilibrium density gradient centrifugation. The sample is mixed in a plastic centrifuge tube with a solution of a salt of high molecular weight (e.g., CsCl) to obtain a mixture of uniform specific gravity equal to that of a substance present in the sample, as shown in **A**. The tube is centrifuged at high speed for a long time (2 to 3 days), which causes the salt to form a concentration—and therefore a density—gradient. Each component of the sample accumulates at that position in the gradient where the density equals its own buoyant density, thus forming a band, as shown in **B**. Fractions are collected as in zonal centrifugation (Fig. 8-4).

The **location** of a band is independent of the size and shape of the particles; hence components are separated purely on the basis of differences in **density**. Diffusion tends to spread the band and the gravitational field tends to narrow it; at equilibrium the **band width** is inversely proportional to the square root of the **molecular weight**.

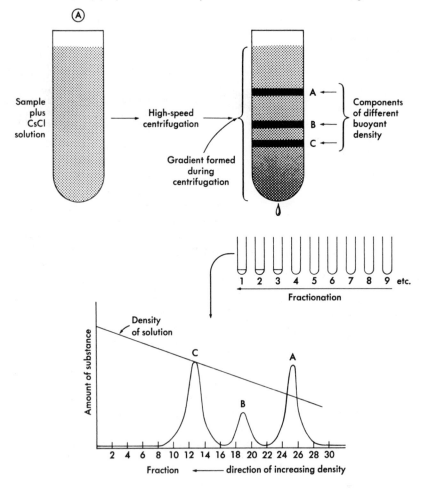

cules. For single-stranded molecules the S values are strongly affected by the degree of helical content, which differs in different nucleic acids and at different ionic strengths; these values are therefore not very useful for determining the molecular weight of this material.

Buoyant Density.* Buoyant density is determined by **equilibrium density gradient centrifugation,** either in the analytical or in the preparative ultracentrifuge. The sample is mixed with a solution of salt of high molecular weight (such as CsCl) at a concentration whose specific gravity is similar to the buoyant density of the nucleic acid. When the mixture is centrifuged at high speed for a prolonged period the salt eventually forms a stable linear density gradient by equilibration between sedimentation and diffusion, and the nucleic acid collects in a **band** at the level corresponding to its buoyant density (Fig. 8-5).

The buoyant density of nucleic acids at neutral pH depends on several characteristics of the molecules: 1) the sugar, whether ribose or deoxyribose; 2) strandedness; and 3) base ratio. RNA has a higher density than DNA of the same strandedness; single-stranded DNA is denser than double-stranded DNA of the same average base composition, owing to decreased hydration. The density of double-stranded DNA increases linearly with its proportion of guanine plus cytosine (Fig. 8-6). Since the buoyant density determination requires very little material, it is useful for analyzing the composition of DNA available only in small quantities. However, the presence of substitutions on the bases, especially glucosylation, alters the relation between base ratio and density.

Homogeneous nucleic acid molecules form a symmetrical band whose width is related to the molecular weight; since smaller molecules diffuse more rapidly, they give a wider band at equilibrium. Bacterial DNA from a given strain shows remarkable homogeneity in GC content, even when fragmented into quite small pieces. Mammalian species, however, contain DNA

---

* The buoyant density is determined from the density of a salt solution in which the macromolecules neither sediment nor float during centrifugation. This density is related to the specific volume of the macromolecules and to their state of hydration and ionization (and thus binding of ions of the salt).

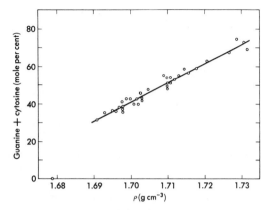

Fig. 8-6 Relation between buoyant density (ρ) and base ratio of double-stranded DNA. Each point refers to a DNA of different origin. (From C. L. Schildkraut, J. Marmur, and P. Doty. J. Molec. Biol. 4:430, 1962.)

with regions differing as much as 20% in GC content.

Denaturation and Renaturation; Melting Temperature (Tm). The two strands of helical (double-stranded) nucleic acid are held together by the hydrogen bonds of nucleotide pairs and other noncovalent bonds between bases; these bonds are individually weak, but through their large numbers they hold the two strands tightly together. The simultaneous disruption or **melting** of the hydrogen bonds causes the collapse of the helical structure (**denaturation**). The phenomenon is also referred to as **helix-coil transition.** Denaturation is caused by 1) high temperature, which dissociates the bonds; 2) alkaline pH, which causes loss of hydrogen atoms involved in hydrogen bonding; and 3) substances that compete with the basis for hydrogen bond formation, such as formamide ($HCONH_2$).

The change in reciprocal relations of the bases following denaturation causes an increase of the optical density of the nucleic acids at 2600 A, the peak of their absorption spectrum (OD_{260}). The extent of this **hyperchromic shift** is proportional to the change in the helical content; a complete helix-coil transition causes an increase of ca. 40%. A plot of the OD_{260} as a function of temperature yields as S-shaped curve whose slope is steep for helical nucleic acids, in which the shift from helix to random coil occurs rapidly in the whole molecule; the slope is shallow and variable for single-stranded nucleic acids, where individual helical segments melt independently of each other at temperatures that depend on their length and composition (Fig. 8-7). Denaturation also causes an increase in the buoyant density of nucleic acid.

The melting temperature (**Tm**) is defined as that at which 50% of the maximum increase in OD_{260} occurs. For double-stranded DNA the Tm is a strict function of the base ratio, since the triple hydrogen bond of GC requires a higher temperature for its rupture than the double hydrogen bond of AT. The G + C values obtained from Tm are similar to those obtained from buoyant density when the DNA contains only the four regular bases; if, however, unusual (e.g., glucosylated) bases are present, Tm and buoyant density no longer correspond. Small cyclic (i.e., ring-shaped) DNA molecules behave atypically (see below).

Heat-denatured DNA tends to re-form helixes (**renaturation**) on cooling, especially when it is made up of relatively small, homogeneous molecules, as is viral DNA. Renaturation is maximized by **annealing,** i.e., maintaining the denatured DNA at a temperature somewhat below that of melting, and at a high ionic strength (0.3 M NaCl) to decrease electrostatic repulsion between the molecules; once nucleation is initiated between two short homologous sequences the helical region extends by a process of one-dimensional crystallization. Renaturation is minimized by rapid cooling after heating (quenching), which permits secondary structure to be formed **within** a strand before complementary strands have time to pair. Crosslinks between complementary strands are produced by some cytocidal agents, and they can

be detected by renaturation experiments: they prevent the melted strands from separating completely and thus promote renaturation.

Under normal conditions helical DNA appears to "breathe" through the formation of melted segments which fluctuate in size and location; these melted segments confer flexibility on the molecules and probably play an important role in determining biological properties, such as recombination (see below) and transcription (Ch. 9). Small frayed segments are probably also present adjacent to discontinuities such as the ends of the molecules or single-stranded breaks.

The spontaneously melted segments, and especially the frayed segments at the ends of the molecules, appear to be starting points for melting of the helix as temperature is increased. Thus the small cyclic DNAs of certain viruses, lacking free ends, have a much higher Tm than would be expected from their base ratio.

Chromatographic Properties. DNAs can be fractionated on columns of methylated serum albumin adsorbed to diatomaceous earth. The methylation of the carboxyl groups, leaving the basic groups uncharged, transforms albumin into an anion exchanger, which holds the nucleic acids through their phosphate groups. Nucleic acids are separated on this material according to the number of strands, size, and base ratio, without alteration of their physical or biological properties.

Enzymatic Digestion. Enzymes are widely used for identifying the nucleic acids and for determining strandedness and details of structure. Pancreatic DNase hydrolyzes both double- and single-stranded DNA, attacking phospho-

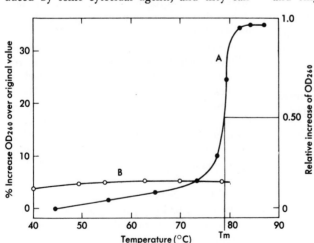

Fig. 8-7 Melting curves of two nucleic acids of the same length but of different structure. **A.** Double-stranded DNA of bacteriophage $\Phi \times 174$, which gives a sharp transition. **B.** Single-stranded DNA of the same phage, which gives a very flat curve. Tm is the melting temperature, i.e., the temperature where 50% of the hyperchromic effect of heating has appeared. For sample A, Tm is 79°. (From H. Chamberlin and P. Berg. Cold Spring Harbor Symp. Quant. Biol. 28:67, 1963.)

diester bonds inside the polynucleotide chain (endonuclease); pancreatic ribonuclease, also an endonuclease, hydrolyzes single-stranded, but not double-stranded, RNA. Snake venom phosphodiesterase, an exonuclease, hydrolyzes both DNA and RNA, double- or single-stranded, beginning at the end terminating with a 3'-OH group and yielding nucleoside 5'-phosphates. *E. coli* phosphodiesterase similarly hydrolyzes single-stranded DNA, but no other nucleic acid, from the 3'-OH end.

Homology: Hybridization

Since the genetic information is inscribed in the base sequence, the degree of similarity of the base sequences of two DNAs, which is called homology, reflects the similarity of their genetic information; it also provides the basis for the pairing of homologous chromosomes that precedes recombination, which will be discussed later.

Homology can be measured in vitro by **hybridization** between DNA molecules (Fig. 8-8). DNA molecules of two kinds are mixed and melted at high temperature; the resulting single strands are then annealed for several hours (e.g., at 65° in 0.3 M NaCl). Under these conditions the DNA molecules move past each other very rapidly. If two sufficiently long homologous segments come to face each other with their nucleotides in register they

Fig. 8-8 DNA hybridization experiment. DNA 1 is nonradioactive, DNA 2 is radioactive and broken in small pieces. Both are denatured by heat, and when they are incubated together at a high temperature, they form hybrid segments. The molecules carrying the radioactive hybrids still have over-all properties similar to those of denatured DNA 1.

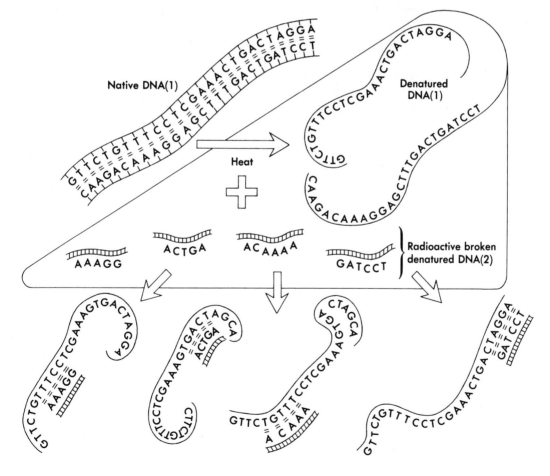

lock and form a helical segment, which immediately extends to the limit of the region of homology. Since long helical segments are stable at the incubation temperature they continue to increase in number during incubation until all homologous segments are paired. After the mixture has been cooled the helical regions are separated from the remaining random coils by methods that take advantage of a variety of properties: 1) enzymatic digestion, using *E. coli* exonuclease specific for single-stranded DNA; 2) equilibrium density gradient centrifugation, since helical and denatured DNA have different buoyant densities; and 3) chromatography through a column of methylated albumin.

To measure low degrees of homology the DNA of one species is radioactively labeled and is broken into small fragments (e.g., by sonic vibration), whereas the other is unlabeled and not sonicated. During annealing the short radioactive DNA strands form helixes with homologous regions of the long unlabeled strands. The hybrid labeled molecules have the physical properties of the long unlabeled strands and therefore can be retained by membrane filters, whereas the short unhybridized segments can pass. Alternatively, the long strands can be added to melted agar gel, which is then cooled and ground up and the granules used to form a column.

Homologous single-stranded DNAs in solutions passed through such a column under annealing conditions form helical segments with the trapped chains and are therefore retained. Not only do these methods measure the fraction of the DNA of one species that can pair with that of another, but by varying the conditions (e.g., salt concentration, temperature) it is possible to estimate the tightness of binding and thus the completeness of the homology.

Similar hybridization methods are used to measure complementarity between **RNA and DNA.**

Detection of homology between DNA molecules is important for many biological problems that will be dealt with in later chapters. It may be noted here that since homology between the DNAs of different microorganisms detects their genetic relatedness, it reveals significant **taxonomic** relations (Ch. 2). The experimental results listed in Table 8-1, for example, show that DNA homology detected by hybridization accompanies genetic homology detected by genetic recombination.

Organization of the Genetic Information

In the light of this correlation between frequency of genetic recombination and degree

TABLE 8-1. CORRELATION OF GENETIC RECOMBINATION AND HYBRID DNA FORMATION

Organisms	Recombination process		Extent of hybrid DNA formation
B. subtilis × B. natto	Transformation	++++	++++
B. subtilis × B. polymyxa	Transformation	+	+
B. subtilis × B. brevis	Transformation	−	−
E. coli B × E. coli K-12	Conjugation, transduction	++++	++++
S. dysenteriae × E. coli	Conjugation, transduction	++	++
S. typhimurium × E. coli	Conjugation	+	−
E. freundii X5610-52 × E. coli		?	−
E. freundii X17 × E. coli		?	+
E. carotovora × E. coli		?	−

From S. E. Luria. Recent Prog. Microbiol. 8:604 (1963).

of molecular homology, it is evident that the most important factor in recombination is the presence of large common sequences of nucleotides (**microhomology**) in the participating chromosomes, rather than the arrangement of the genetic loci for various functions in the same order, as revealed by conventional genetic mapping (**macrohomology**). In fact, *E. coli* and *Shigella,* in spite of extensive macrohomology, show little recombination, in agreement with their low microhomology. The reason for the significance of microhomology will appear below (Recombination).

It should also be pointed out that short homologous sequences may be found by chance among any DNAs. They explain important phenomena, such as the extensive secondary structure of single-stranded nucleic acids (which is based on such homologies within a molecule) and perhaps the very rare recombinations that lead to transfers of DNA, whether within a chromosome (inversions, deletions), between chromosomes of the same cell (translocations), or between viral and cellular DNA (Ch. 43, Transduction).

Significance of Double-Strandedness in Nucleic Acid

The double-strandedness of DNA has several consequences. 1) It provides a mechanism for self-replication, since each strand serves as a template on which its complement is formed. 2) It permits damages in one strand to be corrected by removal of the damaged piece and replacement with a new segment copied from the undamaged strand (see below, Lethal action of ultraviolet light). 3) Messenger RNA is formed on one strand of DNA, and its release appears to be promoted by the competitive reassociation of that strand with the complementary DNA.

A major contribution of molecular genetics to biology has been the concept of considering macromolecules in terms of the **information** contained in them, as well as in classic terms of their structure. Because the two strands of a DNA molecule ordinarily contain exactly the same information (though in complementary rather than in identical structures), this information is **redundant.** Hence heterozygosity ordinarily requires two homologous chromosomes. However, a mutation in one strand can cause heterozygosity within a DNA molecule, since the two strands are no longer complementary at the mutational site; and as we shall see in Chapter 23, recombination frequently produces a similar limited heterozygosity in certain phages.

Units of Information (Fig. 8-9)

Early in the development of genetics it was recognized that mutations affecting the same hereditary trait were usually located in the same position (**locus**) on a chromosome, distinct from loci whose mutations affected other traits. The positions of the different loci (genetic linkage) were determined by the frequency of their recombination in a genetic cross. These positions were confirmed in some cases by cytological observations, and were later directly confirmed in bacteria, as we have seen in Chapter 7, by interrupted mating experiments. Genetic loci, thus recognized by their mutations and located by recombination tests, were identified as the **units of genetic function** and were called **genes.** We have discussed above evidence for the generalization of Beadle and Tatum: "one gene–one enzyme" (see Ch. 7).

A specific form of a gene, as noted in Chapter 6, is called an **allele: wild-type** allele refers to the normal nucleotide sequence, whereas **mutant** allele refers to a sequence in which some portion has been modified by mutation. Since all genes have evolved by means of a succession of mutations the definition of normal is somewhat arbitrary; but the recognition of mutational differences, or alleles, is fundamental to all genetic studies.

Genes were at first treated as formal points connected by a line—the chromosome. Later the gene developed dimensions, when recombination was also observed to occur, at a low frequency, between mutational sites belong-

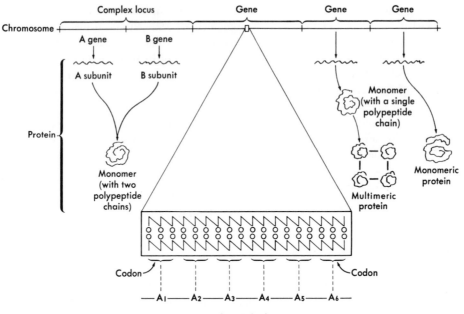

Fig. 8-9 Units of genetic information. Mutations that affect the same trait (i.e., production of the same protein) define a genetic locus. Often the protein contains only one kind of polypeptide chain, either as a monomer or as a multimer: in these cases the locus is identical with a gene (i.e., the genetic unit that specifies a polypeptide chain). When a protein contains more than one kind of polypeptide chain its locus is called complex; and the presence of more than one gene in that locus can be demonstrated by a complementation test (Fig. 8-10).

The current terminology for the different kinds of proteins formed is unfortunately confusing, for the term monomer is used both for proteins that contain one chain and for those that contain two different chains; moreover, in polymer chemistry monomer refers to the individual residues of a macromolecule, e.g., amino acids, rather than to a chain.

ing to the same gene; but because of the low resolving power of recombinational studies in higher organisms such intragenic recombination was observed only with a few special loci.

Fine-Structure Genetics. Microbial genetics had a tremendous impact on the theory of the gene by making it possible, through the use of huge populations and strongly selective technics, to detect recombinations at far lower frequencies, by several decimal orders of magnitude. Intragenic recombination was then found to be a general phenomenon. Moreover, Benzer showed, with the rII gene of bacteriophage T4, that **within a gene** mutations can occur at **many different sites,** distinguishable by recombination. The analysis of genetic **fine structure** was thus begun.

Locus and Gene: Complementation. Fine-structure studies with adjacent genes showed that recombination did not occur any more frequently at the boundary between the genes than at any sites within one of them. Hence the classic concept of the gene as a discrete unit of recombination (as well as of function) became obsolete. The chromosome could be mapped as a continuum of mutable sites that were distinguishable by crossing-over; and the boundaries of a gene now had to be defined more rigorously in terms of the sequence of those sites that all affect the same **function.** But this definition could also be ambiguous, since two mutants could appear to be altered either in the same or in different phenotypic functions, depending on the tests used. Thus mutants blocked in the same pathway, for example, have the same nutritional requirement but may be defective in different enzymes.

A more satisfactory, formal basis for distinguishing units of genetic function was developed in the form of the **complementation test,** which is applicable even where enzymatic studies are not possible. In this test two mutant genomes of similar phenotype are brought into the same cell. When the two mutations eliminate different enzymes of the same pathway the wild-type allele of each gene still functions, and the heterozygous cell is prototrophic (intergenic complementation). In contrast, mutants that are altered at different sites **within** the same gene in general do not complement each other (exceptions will be discussed later in this chapter, under Intragenic complementation).

The usefulness of the complementation test was most clearly brought out with the phage r_{II} locus, which specifies a single phage function but cannot at present be correlated with a known protein. Complementation was found to separate the mutants of this locus into two clearly distinct classes, A and B (Fig. 8-10): any mutant complemented members of the other, but not of its own, class. Moreover, the two sets of mutations occupied two adjacent, nonoverlapping parts of the

Fig. 8-10 Evidence for the existence of two r_{II} genes in bacteriophage T4. *E. coli* K-12 (λ) cells, which will not support multiplication of an r_{II} mutant, were infected simultaneously by two r_{II} mutants. The mutations were localized, by recombination tests, both in the A segment (1), both in the B segment (2), or one in each segment (3). In (1) only B protein is made; and in (2) only A protein; in neither is there viral multiplication (except for a small proportion of cells in which wild-type phage is produced by genetic recombination). In (3) both A and B proteins are made, and viral multiplication takes place in all cells. The A and B segments, therefore, are two separate genes.

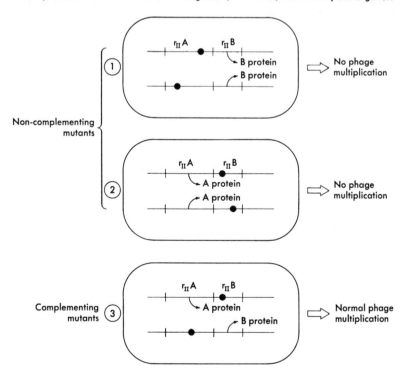

chromosome. It was concluded that this locus is made up of two subunits, which were called **cistrons.***

While the product of the phage r_{II} locus is not known, later studies by Yanofsky on the tryptophan synthetase locus of *E. coli* similarly revealed two cistrons, and with this system it could be shown that each cistron forms a distinct polypeptide. The earlier generalization about gene function could then be changed to "one cistron–one polypeptide chain." A number of such **complex loci** have now been recognized in bacteria, i.e., loci subdivisible into two or more cistrons.

Because it is now possible to identify the genetic unit of function in terms of a polypeptide, and not an enzyme, there has been a recent tendency to redefine the gene, making it equivalent to the cistron and abandoning the latter term. We shall therefore call **a gene the chromosome segment that specifies a polypeptide chain.** When a chromosome segment contains the sites of a cluster of mutations affecting a given trait, but does not (or has not yet been proved to) consist of a single gene, it will be referred to as a **genetic locus.** We shall therefore speak of an r_{II} or a tryptophan synthetase locus, each constituted of two genes.

Loci concerned with related functions are often clustered, and the cluster will appear to be a single locus until its phenotypic effects can be analyzed with sufficient refinement. For example, rough mutants of *Salmonella,* which have lost the ability to make the O polysaccharide of the normal cell surface, all map in a large O locus; but enzymatic analysis has recently shown that each of these mutants is blocked in one of a dozen enzymes, which are concerned with the biosynthesis, or with the transfer, of the several sugars of the O polysaccharide (Ch. 5). The O region of the chromosome is therefore now known to consist of a number of loci. The loci

concerned with the surface antigens of mammalian cells (Ch. 18) undoubtedly have a similar complexity.

Recent developments, to be discussed below, have shown that a **gene**—the unit of genetic function—contains numerous smaller units, the **codons,** made up of three nucleotides; each codon specifies an individual amino acid and is thus the unit of translation. The **nucleotide** is the smallest genetic unit—the **site** of point mutations and thus the unit of mutation. The book of information contained in the genome has thus been likened to paragraphs (loci), sentences (genes), words (codons), and letters (nucleotides).

Replication of DNA

Semiconservative Replication

The Watson-Crick structure of DNA suggests a model of reproduction called **semiconservative,** whereby each strand (i.e., **half-molecule**) serves as template for, and combines with, a new strand (Fig. 8-11), thereby being **conserved** in the new double helix (Fig. 8-12). This model takes advantage of the wonderful symmetry built into the DNA structure, and furthermore accounts, in a natural way, for the transmission of genetic information from parent to progeny molecules.

The semi-conservative model of DNA replication was verified by Meselson and Stahl in a classic experiment (Fig. 8-13), based on the fact that on equilibrium density gradient centrifugation, in CsCl solution, DNA containing ^{15}N ("heavy" DNA) and that containing ^{14}N ("light" DNA) form separate bands. In the experiment *E. coli* cells were grown with $^{15}NH_3$ as the sole nitrogen source and then transferred to $^{14}NH_3$-containing (light) medium; samples were taken at intervals, and the DNA was extracted and centrifuged. One generation after transfer all the DNA was found to have hybrid density, intermediate between the densities of the heavy (old) and the light (new) DNA; after two generations half of the DNA had hybrid density and half was light. In subsequent generations the amount of hybrid DNA remained constant

---

* The term was derived from the ability of two mutations in different units of function to complement each other (by virtue of the presence of their wild-type alleles) when on different chromosomes (**trans**), but not when on the same chromosome (**cis**).

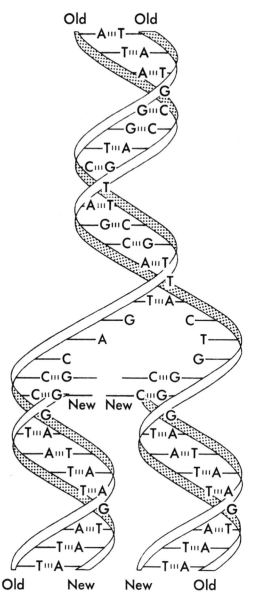

Fig. 8-11 The replication of DNA. (From J. D. Watson. *Molecular Biology of the Gene.* Benjamin, New York, 1965.)

Sequential Replication

Both radioautography and genetic observations have shown that replication of linear DNA molecules begins at one end and is completed at the opposite end; replication of circular molecules similarly proceeds around the circle and ends at the point at which it began.

Radioautography. Cairns examined by radioautography the DNA of *E. coli* cells exposed to ³H-thymine; the chromosomes were obtained from the cells as gently as possible by lysing protoplasts with detergents. Some of the molecules obtained after two generations of labeled growth (with both strands labeled) have twice the silver grain density of those obtained after one generation; the densities evidently reflect the labeling of both strands or only one.

The radioautographs clearly show, as was suggested earlier by the pattern of conjugation (Ch. 7), that the *E. coli* chromosome is cyclic (Figs. 8-14 and 8-15). Moreover, replication begins at the **initiation point,** without ring opening; the ring is doubled between initiation point and **growing point.** When the growing point reaches the initiation point, after going around the circle, the ring has been duplicated and the daughter molecules separate. This mode of replication raises the problem of how the molecule unwinds, which will be considered below.

Genetic Evidence. Genetic evidence on sequential replication is obtained by measuring the number of copies of bacterial genes situated at various places on the DNA, e.g., by determining in various DNA samples the proportion of transforming activity for several loci. In growing cultures the number of copies of a gene situated at the region of the chromosome where replication begins (i.e., on one side of the integrated F factor in Hfr strains) is found to be about double that of a gene situated at the other "end"; whereas in stationary-phase cultures the ratio is about unity. The reason is that in a culture grow-

whereas that of light DNA increased exponentially, verifying the predictions of the semiconservative model. Moreover, on fragmentation of the DNA chain the hybrid material did not change in density, indicating that its light and heavy halves were parallel rather than joined end to end.

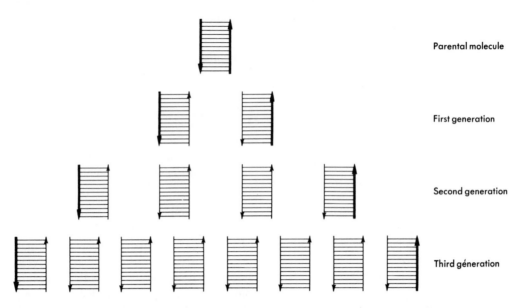

Fig. 8-12 Model of semiconservative DNA replication. The strands of the parental molecule (heavy lines) are found at any subsequent generation as half molecules in conjunction with a complementary, newly synthesized strand (thin lines).

ing nonsynchronously the chromosomes are growing in most cells, and so the initial genes have replicated whereas the terminal ones have not; while in a stationary culture each chromosome has become stationary after completing a round of replication (Ch. 9, Control of DNA synthesis).

The Problem of Unwinding. The two DNA strands are wound around each other in such a way that their separation, whether in denatura-

Fig. 8-13 Semiconservative replication of DNA. A diagrammatic representation of the results of Meselson and Stahl's experiment demonstrating the semiconservative replication of DNA. The DNA of a culture grown in^{15}NH$_3$ and then transferred to ^{14}NH$_3$ is extracted at various times after transfer and banded by equilibrium density gradient centrifugation in CsCl (Fig. 8-5); the bands formed are represented in the diagram. Before transfer the DNA is heavy (^{15}N), one generation after transfer it is hybrid (one strand ^{15}N, one strand ^{14}N), and at subsequent generations a constant amount of DNA per culture is hybrid and an increasing proportion is light (^{14}N). The hybrid band contains the DNA strands existing before transfer, which form double-stranded molecules together with a newly synthesized strand (Fig. 8-12).

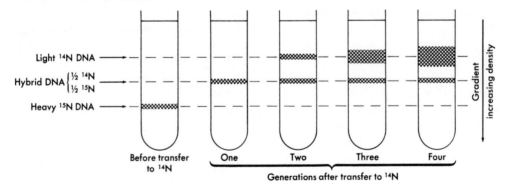

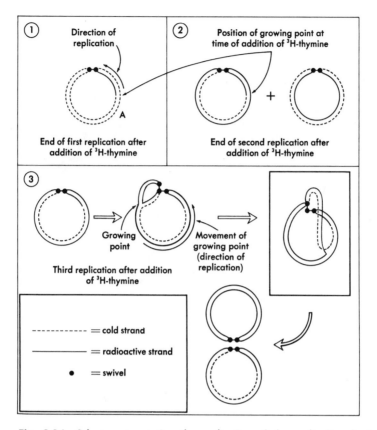

Fig. 8-14 Scheme representing the replication of the cyclic *E. coli* chromosome. It explains the features of the radioautograph of Figure 8-15, which was made when the chromosome was at the stage indicated in the box. ³H-thymine was added shortly before the chromosome had completed a duplication cycle, and therefore part of one strand, i.e., that replicated last, became immediately labeled, as shown in A. (Modified from J. Cairns. Cold Spring Harbor Symp. Quant. Biol. 28:43, 1963.)

tion or in semiconservative replication, requires unwinding of the helix. The unwinding presents a great mechanical problem owing to the length of DNA molecules.

The replication of a cyclic DNA molecule without ring opening, and therefore without free ends, suggests a way out of this difficulty, which can be represented through the model of a linear molecule whose ends are attached to a rigid support through a swivel (Fig. 8-16). Replication would start with a doubling of the swivel at the initiation end; as synthesis proceeds and the growing point moves distally, the unreplicated parts of the molecule rotate giving up turns of the helix, and the two replicated parts rotate taking them up. In this way there is no whipping around of loose ends and the rotation of the molecule can occur in a confined space, like the rotation of a flexible coaxial cable within its sheath. A cyclic molecule can replicate similarly if a swivel at the initiation point duplicates at the beginning of replication (Fig. 8-17).

It is still hard to see, however, how molecules of huge lengths can rotate neatly. Alternatively, the problem may be minimized by introducing additional swivel points along the replicating chains. The chemical nature of the postulated swivels is unknown: they could be made up of single covalent bonds, which have free rotation around the bond axis. Thus the internucleotide phosphodiester bond of one strand might act as swivel at any point where the other strand is broken. The role of single-strand breaks, while speculative, is made plausible by the known presence of enzymes able to heal such breaks

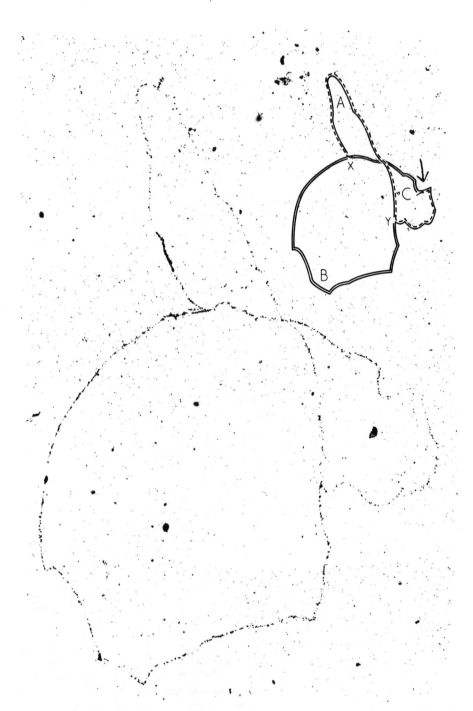

Fig. 8-15 Radioautograph of an *E. coli* chromosome corresponding to the box in Figure 8-14. Symbols of diagram are as in Figure 8-14: dashed line, unlabeled strand; solid line, labeled strand; A and B, the two parts of the chromosome already replicated; C, unreplicated part; arrow, position of the growing point at the moment of addition of ³H-thymine; Y, growing point; X, swivel. The marker shows 100μ. (From J. Cairns. Cold Spring Harbor Symp. Quant. Biol. 28:43, 1963.)

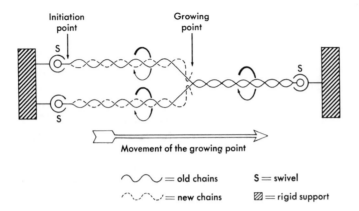

Initiation point   Growing point

Movement of the growing point

$\sim\sim$ = old chains   S = swivel

$\sim\sim$ = new chains   ▨ = rigid support

Fig. 8-16 Unwinding of DNA molecules during replication. As the growing point moves from left to right the unreplicated part of the molecule rotates, giving up turns of the helix, and the two parts already replicated also rotate, taking up turns. The attachment of the ends of all chains to fixed swivels does not impair replication.

(see below, Damage to Nucleic Acid by Radiation).

Properties of Replicating Enzymes. The properties of purified DNA polymerase, which synthesizes DNA in vitro, have been reviewed in Chapter 4, where we have seen that it is not altogether clear how this enzyme replicates DNA in vivo. We have no idea how replication is initiated: does the enzyme recognize a specific nucleotide sequence, or the swivel? Moreover,

Fig. 8-17 Unwinding and replication of a cyclic DNA, according to the model of Fig. 8-16.

Growing point

S = swivel $\sim\sim$ = old strand

$\sim\sim$ = new strand

the known enzyme attaches nucleotides only to the 3'-OH end of a polynucleotide chain; but replication in the cell must involve addition to the 3'-OH end of one chain and to the 5'-OH end of the other, since the two new chains are antiparallel and yet grow in the same direction. Possibly the DNA polymerase so far studied is only one of several enzymes that participate concurrently in DNA replication.

Transcription of DNA

The transfer of genetic information from DNA to RNA is called **transcription,** because both molecules use the same "language," i.e., a sequence of nucleotides capable of the same base-pairing. Apart from the multiplication of RNA viruses (Ch. 25) every RNA molecule appears to be the transcript of a DNA segment.

DNA-RNA Hybridization

Hybridization experiments, essentially identical to those between DNA molecules described above (Fig. 8-8), afford the evidence that base sequences of RNA are complementary to those of DNA in the same cell. Radioactive RNA is prepared by exposing the cells (i.e., *E. coli*) to a radioactive precursor (such as ^{32}P-phosphate); after the cells have been disrupted the RNA is extracted and purified.

Different conditions of labeling and extraction permit the study of one type of RNA at a time: mRNA is preferentially labeled by a brief period of incorporation, called a **pulse** (Ch. 9); rRNA is obtained from purified ribosomes and tRNA from the supernatant of the disrupted cells after the ribosomes have been removed.

Unlabeled DNA and radioactive RNA, both derived from cells of the same strain, are heat-denatured and mixed; the mixture is incubated at about 60° for several hours and then slowly cooled. Under these conditions complementary strands form double helixes, some consisting of two DNA strands and others of one DNA and one RNA strand (hybrid molecules). The hybridized RNA can be distinguished from unhybridized RNA because it is RNase-resistant. Furthermore, since the hybrid molecules usually contain small segments of RNA bound to long DNA strands, they have many physical properties of the DNA strands, such as buoyant density and retention by membrane filters or agar columns.

Such experiments show that every kind of cellular RNA hybridizes with the DNA of the same cells, but not with unrelated DNA (Fig. 8-18). The maximal amount of RNA that can be hybridized by a fixed amount of bacterial DNA varies for the various RNAs. The amount of mRNA is large, because it contains many different molecules corresponding to all the functional genes of the cell. Much smaller amounts of rRNA and tRNA can be bound, since they correspond to a small proportion of the genes. From these amounts the proportion of DNA coding for the various RNAs can be determined: in *E. coli* 0.4% of DNA is transcribed into rRNA and 0.025% into tRNA. A much higher but variable proportion is transcribed into mRNA; this proportion depends on the state of regulation of the various genes, as will be discussed in Chapter 9.

Properties of Transcribing Enzymes

The enzymology of transcription by **DNA-dependent RNA polymerase** has been re-

Fig. 8-18 Hybridization of rRNA with homologous DNA. A small amount of radioactive *E. coli* rRNA was melted and annealed with an excess of *E. coli* DNA and also with the unrelated DNA of bacteriophage T5. Equilibrium centrifugation in a CsCl density gradient separated hybridized RNA, which bands close to DNA, from unhybridized RNA, which has a much higher buoyant density. The points represent OD$_{260}$ (● - - - ●) or counts per minute (O——O), in fractions collected from the bottom of the tube. The results show the specificity of hybridization with *E. coli* DNA: there is no hybridization with T5 DNA. The high RNA counts toward the bottom of the tube (i.e., at the left of each diagram) are due to unhybridized RNA. (Modified from S. Spiegelman. Scient. Amer. 210:48, 1964.)

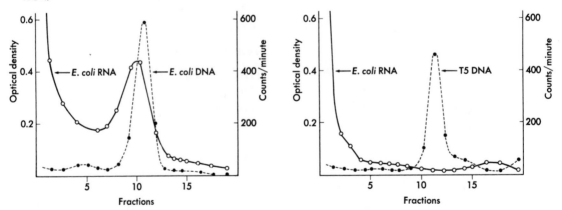

viewed in Chapter 4. Genetically, the most relevant aspect is the relation between template DNA and synthesized RNA. When intact molecules are transcribed, such as those of small cyclic viral DNAs, the RNA is complementary to only one of the two DNA strands (the template strand). In contrast, when broken or damaged DNA molecules are transcribed, both strands may be copied, probably owing to the initiation of transcription on the single strands at the frayed ends. These results suggest that transcription of helical DNA can begin normally only at special places; in fact, RNA polymerase molecules can be seen by electron microscopy to attach to a few sites in DNA. At these sites the DNA helix may be (temporarily?) unwound.

The synthesis of RNA on a double-stranded DNA template does not alter the DNA, which retains its biological activity (infectivity if viral, transforming ability if bacterial); the synthesized RNA does not remain bound to the template. Comparison between RNA synthesis on double-stranded and on single-stranded DNA in vitro provides evidence that the complementary DNA strand functions to displace the new RNA from the template DNA strand.

Actinomycin D is a powerful tool for investigating the transcription of DNA because it blocks this process at a much lower concentration than that required to affect DNA replication. Its mechanism of action will be discussed in Chapter 10.

Translation of Messenger RNA

The information contained in mRNA determines the sequence of amino acids in polypeptide chains. The transfer of information from RNA to protein involves a change from a "language" with 4 "letters" (the nucleotides) to one with 20 "letters" (the amino acids), and is therefore called translation. Translation involves two problems: a mechanical one, i.e., what are the **structures** effecting the translation; and a "linguistic"

one, i.e., what is the **genetic code** by which one language is translated into the other.

The main aspects of the synthesis of polypeptide chains are discussed in Chapter 4. Three structures are especially relevant to the genetic aspect of translation: 1) the **mRNAs**, which contain nucleotide sequences, **codons**, corresponding to the codons of the DNA, each characteristic for a given amino acid; 2) **amino acid–activating enzymes,** which recognize both a given amino acid and a corresponding tRNA; and 3) the **tRNAs**, which act as adaptors between amino acids and nucleotide sequences, each recognizing a codon through a complementary nucleotide sequence in the tRNA, the **anticodon,** and each recognizing an amino acid through the intermediation of its activating enzyme (Fig. 8-19). Furthermore, **ribosomes** provide the workbench on which the mRNA and the appropriate amino acid–carrying (charged) tRNAs are brought together in proper alignment for amino acid polymerization; ribosomes are also of genetic interest because their alterations have been shown to influence the fidelity of translation.

The affinity between a codon and its anticodon is not sufficient to cause detectable complexing of charged tRNA with mRNA alone; but when the mRNA is complexed with a ribosome this codon-anticodon affinity is added to the general affinity of all charged tRNA species for the ribosome (perhaps through the common sequence shown in Fig. 8-19), resulting in firm attachment of the tRNA. This interaction can be recognized in vitro by the use of radioactively labeled specific aminoacyl tRNA: in the presence of synthetic mRNA containing a high proportion of the correct codons, or even in the presence of the correct trinucleotide, the radioactivity sediments with ribosomes and is retained along with ribosomes by membrane filters.

The Genetic Code

Since 4 bases code for 20 amino acids, several bases must be used in translation to

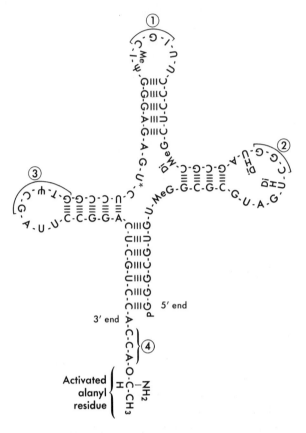

Fig. 8-19 The structure of alanine tRNA in one of several possible configurations. Note the considerable extent of base pairing, as well as the presence of single-stranded loops. One of the alanine codons is $^5{}'GCC^3{}'$, for which the anticodon would be $^3{}'CGG^5{}'$ if **antiparallel** polarity is required for binding. Such an anticodon is found at position 1 (I, inosine, is identical to G in coding properties). If **parallel** polarity is required, the anticodon would be in position 2. Note also the sequence 3, GTψCG, which has been found in all tRNAs examined, and may therefore establish a segment for fixation onto the ribosome. Sequence 4, CCA, is the common end to which the amino acid is attached. DiHU, dihydroxyuridine; DiMeG, 2-dimethylguanine; MeI, 1-methylinosine; Ψ, pseudouridine (5-ribosyluracil); U*, a mixture of U and DiHU; T, ribothymine. (From R. W. Holley, J. Apgar, G. A. Everett, J. T. Madison, M. Marquisee, S. H. Merrill, J. R. Penswick, and A. Zamir. Science 147:1462, 1965.)

specify 1 amino acid. The minimum possible number of nucleotides per amino acid is 3 (triplet code), which permits 64 (i.e., 4^3) different nucleotide combinations: 2 nucleotides per amino acid would produce only 16 combinations (4^2). In the investigations of the code it was thought that Nature would have developed by selection the most economical code, and many ingenious triplet codes were devised, which, by various *ad hoc* provisions, limited to about 20 the number of the acceptable nucleotide combinations. It turned out, however, that Nature adopted the simplest solution: a triplet code in which most of the 64 combinations correspond to some amino acid.

Several nucleotide combinations thus correspond to each amino acid, i.e., **the code is degenerate.** This conclusion is also supported by the presence for each amino acid of several tRNAs, which may be separated by chromatography or other procedures (Fig. 8-

20). **Degeneracy, however, does not cause ambiguity in translation:** although various codons may be used for specifying the same amino acid, under normal circumstances no codon specifies more than one amino acid.

Pattern of the Code. The code is now largely known, on the basis of experiments described immediately below. The catalog of three-letter code words is given in Fig. 8-21; its main features are the following. 1) The nucleotide on the 3′ end is the least significant. The meaning of many triplets is determined by the other two nucleotides alone; and for most of the remaining triplets either of the two purines in the 3′ position specifies the same amino acid, and either pyrimidine specifies another, thus providing a "2 1/2 letter" code. 2) Only three triplets have been identified with certainty as **nonsense,** i.e., do not correspond to any amino acid. 3) There is no signal to indicate the end of one codon and the beginning of another, i.e., the code is

Fig. 8-20 tRNA specificity. Two different tRNA molecules can accept leucine residues; through its anticodon each recognizes a different codon. The configuration of the tRNA indicated in dotted lines is arbitrary and merely reproduces the shape of the molecule of Figure 8-19. (Modified from J. D. Watson. *Molecular Biology of the Gene.* Benjamin, New York, 1965.)

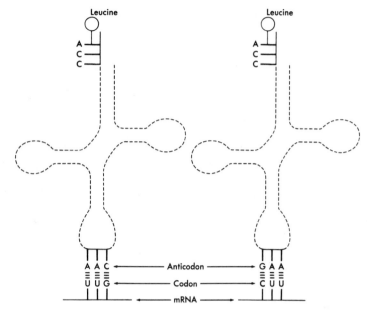

comma-less. The **reading frame** (the separation between triplets) is therefore established at the beginning of translation, and it is maintained by strictly reading three nucleotides at a time, in sequential order. 4) This organization, and the **polygenic** nature of many **messenger RNA molecules** (i.e., specifying several polypeptide chains: Ch. 9), stress the need for **punctuation** to ensure accurate positioning at the beginning of translation. Thus if the reading frame is shifted at any point, e.g., because a nucleotide is missing, the translation beyond that point is jumbled. Punctuation for **termination** of the growing polypeptide chain is provided by the three nonsense triplets, **amber** (UAG, **ochre** (UAA), and UGA, whose function will be further discussed below.

Fig. 8-21 Catalog of the genetic code. Code words read from 5′ end on the left, omitting the phosphoric acid residues. Codons UAA (ochre), UAG (amber), and UGA (in small boxes) cause termination of syntheses and detachment of the growing polypeptide chain; since they do not code for an amino acid they were designated as nonsense codons before they were recognized as terminators (see further discussion under Genotypic suppression, below.) Amino acids are designated by the three initial letters of their names with the exceptions ILEU=isoleucine, ASP-NH₂=asparagine, and GLU-NH₂ =glutamine.

Codon	Amino acid	Codon	Amino acid	Codon	Amino acid	Codon	Amino acid
UUU	PHE	UCU	SER	UGU	CYS	UAU	TYR
UUC	PHE	UCC	SER	UGC	CYS	UAC	TYR
UUA	LEU	UCA	SER	UGA	NONE	UAA	OCHRE
UUG	LEU	UCG	SER	UGG	TRYP	UAG	AMBER
CUU	LEU	CCU	PRO	CGU	ARG	CAU	HIS
CUC	LEU	CCC	PRO	CGC	ARG	CAC	HIS
CUA	LEU	CCA	PRO	CGA	ARG	CAA	GLU-NH₂
CUG	LEU	CCG	PRO	CGG	ARG	CAG	GLU-NH₂
AUU	ILEU	ACU	THR	AGU	SER	AAU	ASP-NH₂
AUC	ILEU	ACC	THR	AGC	SER	AAC	ASP-NH₂
AUA	ILEU	ACA	THR	AGA	ARG	AAA	LYS
AUG	MET	ACG	THR	AGG	ARG	AAG	LYS
GUU	VAL	GCU	ALA	CGU	GLY	GAU	ASP
GUC	VAL	GCC	ALA	GGC	GLY	GAC	ASP
GUA	VAL	GCA	ALA	GGA	GLY	GAA	GLU
GUG	VAL	GCG	ALA	GGG	GLY	GAG	GLU

In Vitro Evidence for the Code. The coding triplets were identified primarily by the study of **synthetic polynucleotides,** added to *E. coli* extracts containing ribosomes, tRNA, enzymes, an energy source, and various radioactively labeled amino acids. These studies began with the discovery, by Nirenberg and Matthaei in 1961, that poly U, a synthetic homopolymer of uridylic acid, causes the formation of polyphenylalanine: this result immediately suggested UpUpU (also designated as UUU) as the coding triplet for phenylalanine. This fortunate observation short-circuited the anticipated slow unraveling of the code through sequence analyses of naturally occurring proteins and their messengers. Polynucleotide phosphorylase (Ch. 4) was then used to synthesize many other polymers, including random heteropolymers containing two or three ribonucleotides in various combinations and proportions; and the specific incorporations directed by these artificial messengers soon revealed the general nature of the code and permitted the assignment of several triplets.

While this approach could reveal the **composition** of the three-letter codons it could not reveal the **ordering** and the **direction** of the letters. This problem was solved when Nirenberg and Leder showed that firm **attachment of aminoacyl tRNA** to ribosomes can be caused not only by long polynucleotide chains but also by trinucleotides of the form $B^1pB^2pB^3$ (where B stands for a base and p for a phosphate group); such compounds are written with the 5'-OH on the left. The specific interaction of each of the possible trinucleotides with a given species of tRNA soon led to an accurate determination of the entire "catalog."

Still further evidence for the pattern of the code has come from Khorana's synthesis of long polynucleotides with specific repeating sequences. (These compounds were made by using a synthetic short polydeoxyribonucleotide of known sequence as primer, on which DNA polymerase made a long copy; with this template RNA polymerase then formed the desired polyribonucleotides.) The coding properties of these products in vitro have unequivocally confirmed most features of the code. For example, with the repeating dinucleotide CUCUCU . . . , which codes for leucine (CUC) and serine (UCU), neither amino acid is extensively incorporated unless the other is also present. This result would be predicted from a comma-less triplet code, since any translation of CUC would have to be followed by a translation of UCU.

In Vivo Evidence for the Code. The triplet, comma-less nature of the code, strongly suggested by these in vitro experiments, was demonstrated in the cell by the consequences of frame-shift mutations induced in bacteriophages by **acridine** derivatives. These mutagens cause either the deletion or the addition of a nucleotide in DNA (Fig. 8-22), which results in coding for jumbled protein beyond the site of the mutation. If two acridine mutations occur at different points of the same gene, and if **one adds and the other removes a nucleotide,** the reading frame is reestablished after the more distal of these two mutations. This event can be recognized experimentally through restoration of function, in those mutants whose jumbled region has little effect on the function of the protein. For instance, in the lysozyme of bacteriophage T4 a jumbled length of 5 amino acids between two acridine mutations of opposite sign has been identified. The second mutation is described as an **intragenic suppressor mutation** in respect to the first, since it suppresses the mutant phenotype (see below).

Acridine mutations can be classified as + or − (it seems likely that + means addition of a nucleotide) by testing the effect of adding them. by genetic recombination, to a reference mutation; two mutations of opposite sign can suppress each other's effect. Moreover, the same result can be achieved if **three** mutations of the **same** sign are combined in the same gene. This striking result provides strong support for a comma-less triplet code.

Evidence on the code also derives from the

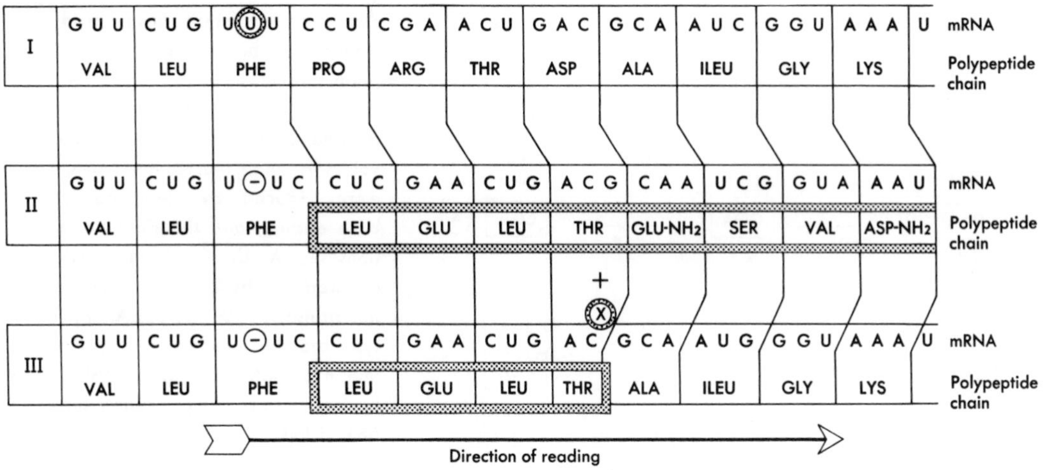

Fig. 8-22 Consequences of shifts of the reading frame. I. The normal correspondence between mRNA and polypeptide chain; the vertical lines indicate the reading frame. II. Deletion of a nucleotide, indicated as a circled dash, shifts the reading frame and causes production of a jumbled protein (hatched frame). The first amino acid (PHE) is not affected by the shift owing to the degeneracy of the code (both UUU and UUC code for PHE), but the subsequent amino acid residues to the right are totally different from those of the normal polypeptide chain. III. The addition of a second mutation of opposite sign (+) shifts the reading frame back to its correct order, and the amino acid sequence is again normal except for the region between the two mutations. The sequences are hypothetical.

study of **amino acid substitutions produced by mutations,** both in abnormal human hemoglobins and experimentally in the protein of tobacco mosaic virus and the tryptophan synthetase of *E. coli.* Missense mutations are expected to be substitutions of a single nucleo-

tide; and, indeed, most of the observed replacements are consistent with a change in a single nucleotide in one of the codons established in vitro (Fig. 8-23 and 8-24). Furthermore, as is shown in Figure 8-25, amino acid replacements produced by nitrous acid–in-

Fig. 8-23 Amino acid replacements in abnormal human hemoglobins caused by spontaneous mutations. Each replacement can be explained by a change of a single nucleotide in the assigned codons.

Original amino acid	Assigned codon	Amino acid in the mutant	Assigned codon	Replacement
Lysine	AAA ⟶	Glutamic Acid	GAA	A ⟶ G
Glutamic Acid	GAA ⟶	Glutamine	CAA	G ⟶ C
Glycine	GGU ⟶	Aspartic Acid	GAU	G ⟶ A
Histidine	CAU ⟶	Tyrosine	UAU	C ⟶ U
Asparagine	AAU ⟶	Lysine	AAA	U ⟶ A
Glutamic Acid	GAA ⟶	Valine	GUA	A ⟶ U
Glutamic Acid	GAA ⟶	Lysine	AAA	G ⟶ A
Glutamic Acid	GAA ⟶	Glycine	GGA	A ⟶ G
Valine	GUA ⟶	Glutamic Acid	GAA	U ⟶ A

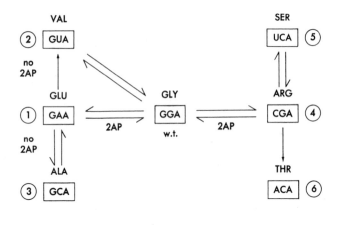

Fig. 8-24 Different amino acid substitutions at the same position in tryptophan synthetase of *E. coli.* Arrows indicate substitutions produced by a single mutational step. Each codon change involves a single nucleotide. Some steps were induced by 2-aminopurine, a base analog, and therefore are transitions $G \rightleftharpoons A$; $U \rightleftharpoons C$). Others could not be produced by 2-aminopurine and are not transitions ($U \rightarrow G$; $C \rightleftharpoons A$). w.t., wild type protein; numbers identify different mutants. (Data from C. Yanofsky. Cold Spring Harbor Symp. Quant. Biol. 28: 581, 1963.)

duced mutations are regularly consistent with a nucleotide substitution of $A \rightarrow G$ or $C \rightarrow U$, which are the base changes known to be produced by this agent (see below, Mutagenesis).

The Universality of the Code. These observations lead to the important additional conclusion that the code is universal: the same codon assignments apply to such different organisms as man, *E. coli,* and a plant virus.

The universality of the code suggests not only a common origin for all terrestrial life, but also

the impossibility of changing the code once life has achieved a certain degree of complexity. Mutations altering the genetic code, i.e., causing different amino acids to be associated with certain codons, would alter the synthesis of practically every protein and would invariably be lethal, if the codon is **always** translated in the wrong way. However, if the translation is wrong in only a proportion of readings (i.e., increased ambiguity) the mutations may not be lethal, but simply detrimental. Mutations of the latter type are known, and have a special significance that will be discussed below (Suppression).

The use of the code is known to vary, how-

Fig. 8-25 Amino acid replacements caused by nitrous acid—induced mutations in the coat protein of tobacco mosaic virus. All the replacements can be explained by the postulated chemical action of nitrous acid ($A \longrightarrow G$, $C \longrightarrow U$) on a single nucleotide in the assigned codons (see Fig. 8-33).

Original amino acid	Assigned codon	Amino acid in the mutant	Assigned codon	Replacement
Proline	CCC $\longrightarrow$ Serine		UCC	C $\longrightarrow$ U
Proline	CCC $\longrightarrow$ Leucine		CUC	C $\longrightarrow$ U
Isoleucine	AUU $\longrightarrow$ Valine		GUU	A $\longrightarrow$ G
Isoleucine	AUA $\longrightarrow$ Methionine		AUG	A $\longrightarrow$ G
Leucine	CUU $\longrightarrow$ Phenylalanine		UUU	C $\longrightarrow$ U
Glutamic Acid	GAA $\longrightarrow$ Glycine		GGA	A $\longrightarrow$ G
Threonine	ACA $\longrightarrow$ Isoleucine		AUA	C $\longrightarrow$ U
Threonine	ACG $\longrightarrow$ Methionine		AUG	C $\longrightarrow$ U
Serine	UCU $\longrightarrow$ Phenylalanine		UUU	C $\longrightarrow$ U
Serine	UCG $\longrightarrow$ Leucine		UUG	C $\longrightarrow$ U
Aspartic acid	GAC $\longrightarrow$ Glycine		GGC	A $\longrightarrow$ G

ever, in features that do not affect the dictionary: in bacteria, for instance, the proportion of G + C in DNA varies between 30% and 70% in different species. These differences fall within the limits of degeneracy of the code, and may be accounted for by selection toward the use of triplets with C or G rather than U or A at the less specific 3' end, or vice versa, for the same amino acid.*

While the code is universal, the specificity of the machinery for its translation is not; thus some tRNAs of yeast are not charged by *E. coli* enzymes. The evolution of such differences is understandable, for a change in the enzyme-recognizing region of a tRNA molecule does not alter the code itself and can be compensated for by a change in the enzyme.

The **number of tRNA species** is less than the number of codons, for while more than one kind of tRNA for certain amino acids (e.g., leucine) can be separated chromatographically from *E. coli* extracts, it has also been shown that the same tRNA can read codons that differ in the relatively unimportant third letter.

Evolution of the Code. The pattern of the present genetic code can easily be related to evolutionary needs. Thus a new gene probably arises first as a duplication of a preexisting gene, which is then modified by many mutations. With a degenerate code most nucleotide replacements yield a modified protein, which is useful in evolution because it can progressively change, by the addition of more missense mutations, until it improves its function or acquires and improves a new function. With a nondegenerate code, in contrast, most nucleotide replacements would give rise to a **nonsense** triplet, for which there is no amino acid; and nonsense mutations interrupt the evolution of the gene, since in the

absence of a protein its gradual improvement cannot be selected for.

The code seems to have evolved, in addition, in such a way as to minimize the phenotypic consequences of amino acid substitutions that result from incorrect base-pairing, whether in replication or in translation. A code capable of buffering the effects of such errors both stabilizes the phenotype and increases the reliability of gene expression. Such buffering can indeed be inferred from the particular pattern of degeneracy observed, which is far from random. Thus replacement of a base pair by the complementary pair (AT ⇌ GC) is probably the most frequent class of mutations; and as we have noted above, in all codons such a replacement in the 3' position would not change the amino acid specified (2 1/2-letter code). Moreover, when an amino acid has fourfold degeneracy its codons usually share the first two letters and are indeterminate with respect to the 3' position (Fig. 8-21); 1/3 of all mutations in such codons would therefore not change the protein.

Further inspection of the pattern of triplets reveals another source of buffering: chemically similar amino acids (e.g., the relatively nonpolar aliphatic group) tend to have similar codons; hence when a mutation (or misreading) does cause a change of amino acid it is likely to have little effect on protein structure and function. Such "connectedness" of codons (i.e., difference in only one nucleotide) is seen for such amino acid pairs as SER-CYS, THR-SER, and ALA-GLY.

In conclusion, it seems likely that very little of the code is due to chance; if terrestrial life had to start again it might end up developing nearly the same genetic code.

Relation of Sequence in Gene and Protein

Colinearity. The sites of mutations can be arranged in a linear sequence in the chromosome by recombination experiments; at the same time the amino acid replacements resulting from these mutations (within the same gene) can also be arranged in a linear sequence by analyses of the polypeptide chain. The two sequences have been shown to be identical, for both the tryptophan synthetase of *E. coli* (Fig. 8-26) and the head protein of bacteriophage T4 (Ch. 23). Both transcrip-

---

* DNA rich in G + C would have codons of the type XXG or XXC; (G + C)-poor DNA would have codons of the type XXA or XXU. In codons of the first type (assuming that in the first two positions all nucleotides occur with the same frequency) the proportion of G + C would be $(1/3 \times 1/2) + (1/3 \times 1/2) + 1/3 = 2/3$; in those of the second type it would be $(1/3 \times 1/2) + (1/3 \times 1/2) = 1/3$. These predictions are in good agreement with the experimental results.

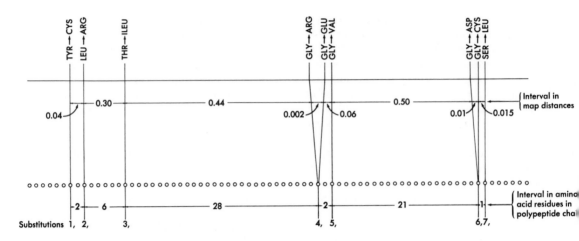

Fig. 8-26 Colinearity of gene and polypeptide. Colinearity of mutational sites in the gene and the corresponding amino acid substitutions in the A protein of tryptophan synthetase of *E. coli*. The map length of the whole A gene is 3.2 units; the protein contains about 280 amino acids. The map distances between mutational sites are related, but are not strictly proportional, to intervening numbers of amino acids in the polypeptide chain. In the amino acid substitutions in position 4 (and in 6) two mutational sites have been recognized: each mutation affects a different nucleotide of the same codon, and the two mutants can produce a recombinant. (Data from C. Yanofsky, B. C. Carlton, J. R. Guest, D. R. Helinski, and U. Henning. Proc. Nat. Acad. Sc. 51:266, 1964.)

tion and translation, therefore, proceed linearly from one end of the gene to the other.

Directions of Transcription and Translation. These directions are relevant to an understanding of certain aspects of the regulation of protein synthesis (Ch. 9). DNA, RNA, and protein molecules all have polarity, since nucleic acid strands have a 5' and a 3' terminal end, and proteins have an N-terminal and a C-terminal end. The polypeptide chain is synthesized in the N→C direction, as was shown in Chapter 4.

The synthesis of mRNA must go in the direction 5'→3', for the polymerase can be shown to add a nucleoside-5'-phosphate to a free 3'-OH group, which must therefore be present at the growing end. Translation of mRNA also proceeds in the 5'→3' direction, as was shown by analyzing the peptides specified in vitro by short nucleotide polymers. (For example, AAAUUU (5'→3') codes for lys-phe and not for phe-lys.) Since synthesis and reading of the mRNA thus begin at the same end, the first part of an

mRNA molecule can become attached to ribosomes and initiate protein synthesis while the other, growing end is still attached to DNA.

The direction of translation could also be inferred from a determination of the altered sequence of amino acids, in bacteriophage T4 lysozyme, in the segment that had a reading-frame shift between two acridine mutations (Fig. 8-23). Knowing the possible codons for the amino acids present before and after the frame shift, and knowing the direction of the connections between the nucleotides within these codons, the consequence of the reading-frame shift could be reconciled with a 5' → 3' but not with the opposite direction of reading of mRNA.

Punctuation

Though homopolymers, with only one kind of codon, can serve as messengers for the limited polypeptide synthesis that can be achieved in extracts, it seems likely that there are two special punctuation signs in translation in the cell: one **initiating** the formation of a polypeptide chain and one **terminating** it. An initiation sign is required to prevent the continual formation of useless polypeptide fragments, and a termination sign to end the individual polypeptide chains in polygenic messages.

Initiation. Methionine appears to have a special role in chain initiation in *E. coli*. Methionine attached to one of the methionine tRNAs can be N-formylated (by attaching a formyl group to the amino nitrogen). The formyl methionine cannot form a peptide bond, owing to blocking of the amino group; thus in polypeptide formation it could be inserted only at the beginning. Indeed, the polypeptide chains synthesized in vitro by an *E. coli* system in the presence of formylmethionyl tRNA have been shown to contain only formyl methionine at the N-terminal end.

In intact cells, however, the corresponding polypeptides do not begin with formyl methionine. For instance, when the polypeptide of the coat protein of the RNA phage R-17 is synthesized in vitro, with viral RNA serving as messenger, it begins with the following sequence:

N-formyl methionine-alanine-serine-asparagine—etc.

In contrast, that found in the infected cells is:

alanine-serine-asparagine—etc.

This difference is attributed to the removal of the terminal formyl methionine in the cells by a specific peptidase that is inactive in extracts. Similarly, the frequent presence of methionine as the end group in proteins could be attributed to the action of another enzyme, which removes only the formyl group.

In other systems the N-terminal amino acid is found to be acetylated rather than formylated. Apparently a general mechanism of chain initiation is the use of amino acids that cannot form a peptide bond because of a block of the amino group. In some proteins the blocking group persists; in others it is subsequently removed, either alone or together with one or more amino acids.

Further evidence for the initiating role of formyl methionine is provided by the results of polypeptide synthesis in vitro with repeating trinucleotides of the form ABCABC. . . . Such polymers ordinarily code simultaneously for three amino acid homopolymers, depending on whether the reading frame initiates the reading of ABC, BCA, or CAB on a given messenger. However, with the polynucleotide that contains repeating AUG, which is the codon for N-formyl methionine (or methionine), only methionine is polymerized, suggesting that this codon is used for initiation in vitro to the exclusion of the other two possible triplets, UGA or GAU.

Termination. The mechanism of chain termination is more problematic: what is coded for is unknown. There are two known chain-terminating codons, **amber** and **ochre** (Fig. 8-21). We shall discuss below (Genotypic suppression) evidence that of this pair only ochre is a regular chain terminator in the cell.

Failure of chain termination is brought about by deletions that remove the punctuation between two genes in the same messenger. Such a deletion has been found in the r$_{II}$ locus of bacteriophage T4, straddling the boundary between the A and B genes. In phages with this deletion the B function is partly preserved, showing that this particular deletion retains a normal reading frame. This deletion has been of great use in demonstrating the importance of the reading frame in translation.

Mutations

The term **mutation** applies broadly to all heritable changes in the genome, other than those due to the incorporation of genetic material from another organism. At the molecular level a mutation represents an alteration in the sequence of nucleotides in the genome. However, it is not at present possible to analyze long nucleotide sequences (in contrast to polypeptides), and so mutations can be recognized only through their modifications of the phenotype. This approach leaves many changes in nucleic acid sequence undetected, because a base substitution that produces a drastic phenotypic effect (e.g., inactivation of an essential enzyme) in one position on the chromosome may produce no detectable effect in another position. Hence there are many **silent** mutations.

Silent mutations include the following groups: 1) the changed triplet codes for the same amino acid as the original; 2) the change causes an amino acid substitution that does not appreciably modify the function of the protein; or 3) the change occurs in a gene that is not expressed, or whose protein is dispensable, under the circumstances of testing. 4) Another class of mutations are silent because of the simultaneous presence of a **suppressor** mutation. With this group, however, phenotypic expression can be achieved by deriving appropriate genetic recombinants (see below).

As a striking example of group 2 we may recall that the phenotypic effect of a shift of reading frame in phage T4 is sometimes suppressed by a second shift (in opposite direction) elsewhere in the same locus, even though the jumbled sequence between the two mutations causes the replacement of as many as 5 amino acids.

Detectable errors in the replication of DNA (spontaneous mutations) are normally rare— not more than one in 10^7 nucleotides at every replication. A random increase in mutation rate, however, can be induced by special **mutagenic agents,** as was first shown in 1927 by Muller, applying X-rays to the fruit fly *Drosophila*. X-rays, and also ultraviolet light, were subsequently used for producing mutant strains of bacteria, on which our present understanding of bacterial genetics is based. **Chemical mutagens** were discovered later; and since their effects on nucleic acids are easier to analyze than those of radiation, they have contributed greatly to our understanding of the molecular nature of mutations. We shall discuss the nature of mutations and the mechanisms of chemical mutagenesis here; radiation mutagenesis will be briefly considered at the end of the chapter.

Mutational Sites

By extensive fine-structure mapping of mutations in the above-mentioned rII genes of bacteriophage T4, Benzer showed that both **spontaneous** and **induced** mutations can occur at many different sites within a gene, separable by recombination. As is shown in Figure 8-27, different mutagenic agents tend to affect different sites, presumably depending on the chemical nature of the mutagens and the nucleotide composition of the various codons; and many of these sites are also sites of spontaneous mutation.

The large number of mutational sites within a gene suggested that mutations can be produced by a change in a single nucleotide. This conclusion was later confirmed when it became possible to correlate changes in codons with changes in the corresponding amino acids.

Figure 8-27 further shows that when a large number of mutations were mapped their frequency distribution among the various sites was found to be far from random: some sites in this system mutate at the lowest detectable frequency (ca. 10^{-8}); others (**hot spots**) at frequencies as high as 10^{-3}; and others at a variety of intermediate values. This continuum excludes the possibility that the frequency of mutation at a nucleotide pair is simply determined by the composition of that pair, for such a pattern would yield one frequency for all AT sites and another for GC. It is therefore necessary to infer a strong influence of as yet undetermined factors in the neighborhood of a nucleotide: e.g., flanking nucleotides, local structure of the DNA, and the presence of basic molecules neutralizing the negative charges.

Reversion and Suppression

In attempting to define the molecular changes in various mutations a powerful tool has recently been provided by the availability of several mutagenic agents with known, different actions; their ability to induce rever-

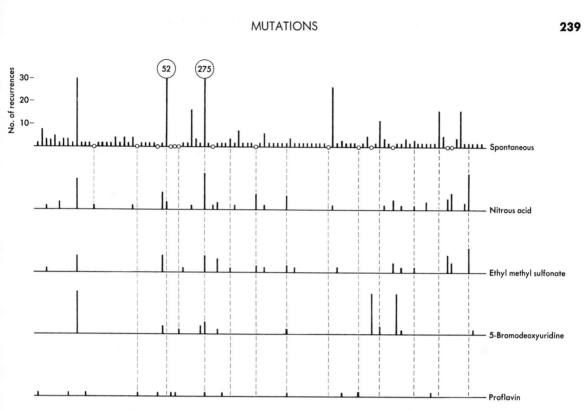

Fig. 8-27 Sites of occurrence of mutations in a segment of the rII B gene of the bacteriophage T4. Both spontaneous and induced mutations are mapped. Note the different distributions of mutational sites, and also the sites with very large numbers of recurrences of mutations (**hot spots**). Numbers in circles give the numbers of recurrences. Small circles on the base line in the distribution of spontaneous mutations indicate sites at which no spontaneous but only induced mutations occurred. (Data from S. Benzer. Proc. Nat. Acad. Sc. 47:403, 1961.)

sion of various mutations can be used to characterize these mutations.

Reversion refers to a return to the wild phenotype, which can be brought about not only by reversal of the original change (**true reversion**), but also by a change at a different site that phenotypically corrects the mutation (**suppression**). In using revertibility to analyze mutations it is important to distinguish true reversion from suppression. This distinction can be accomplished by crossing the revertant to the wild type: only suppressed mutants will yield recombinants in which the original mutated gene has been segregated from its suppressor and therefore again produces the mutant phenotype (Fig. 8-28).

Mutations causing suppression are of two main types, extragenic and intragenic. Some extragenic suppressors act at a **metabolic** level:

they may alter the level of a cofactor or inhibitor in a way that restores some activity to the mutant enzyme, or they may cause the production of an enzyme that can replace the mutant enzyme in the economy of the cell. This class of mutants is of more metabolic than genetic interest; it will not be considered further here. Recently another important group of extragenic suppressors has been found to act at quite a different level, altering the translation of the product of the mutated gene; this class will be discussed later in this chapter.

Intragenic suppressors compensate for the effect of a mutation by their presence in the same gene; they can be divided into several groups. 1) **Intracodon** suppressors cause the changed codon to be replaced by one that is less deleterious to protein function. 2) **Read-**

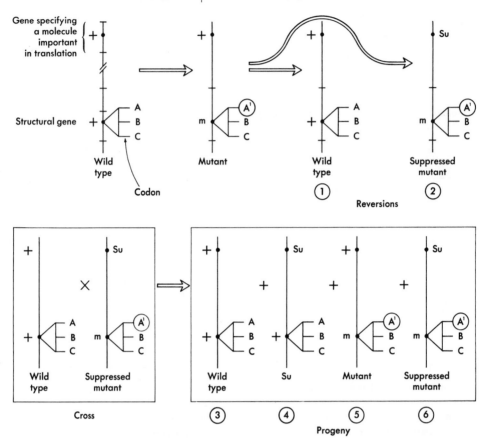

Fig. 8-28 Phenotypic reversions. Phenotype reversions caused either by true reversion of a mutation (as in 1) or by suppression (as in 2). A genetic cross between a suppressed mutant and a true wild type yields four types of progeny, in one of which (5) the primary mutation is expressed. (The recombinant carrying only the suppressive mutation [4] may or may not be phenotypically distinguishable from the wild-type.) A true reversion (1) would not produce mutant progeny in a similar cross. +, wild-type allele; Su, suppressor mutation; m, suppressible mutation; ABC, wild-type codon; A'BC, mutated codon.

ing-frame mutations add a shift in the frame opposite in direction to one already introduced in the gene, thus restoring normal reading except for the segment between the two mutations (Fig. 8-22). 3) Finally, intragenic suppression can result from **an amino acid substitution at some distance** from that caused by the primary mutation, provided the two new amino acids contribute to the folding of the finished protein in much the same way as the original pair. An example of the last group has been observed in the tryptophan synthetase A gene of *E. coli*: a primary mutation substituting glutamic acid for glycine was corrected by a second mutation 36 amino acid residues away, which substituted cysteine for tyrosine. Neither mutation alone allowed the synthesis of a functional protein.

Point Mutations and Deletions (Fig. 8-29)

Point mutations derive from changes affecting a single nucleotide. These changes consist of 1) **replacement** of a nucleotide by a different one, 2) **insertion** of an extra nucleotide, or 3) **loss** of a nucleotide. Point mutants are recognized by their ability to undergo true reversion and their ability to

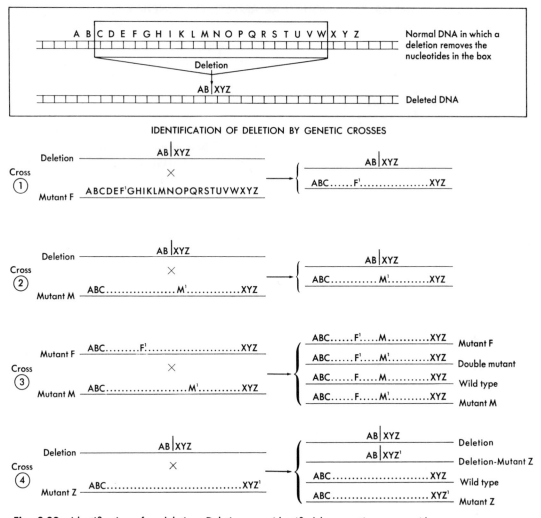

Fig. 8-29 Identification of a deletion. Deletions are identified by genetic crosses with selected point mutants. Cross 1 between the deletion mutant and point mutant F and cross 2 between the deletion mutant and point mutant M yield no wild-type recombinants; however, cross 3 between the two point mutants yields wild-type recombinants, showing that mutations F and M occur at different sites. The deletion mutant gives wild-type recombinants in cross 4 with point mutant Z, whose site is outside the deletion.

give wild-type recombinants with **all** other strains mutated in the same gene (except those in which the same nucleotide has been replaced and those in which it has been eliminated in a deletion).*

---

* While point mutations, as operationally defined here, include additions or deletions of a single nucleotide (reading-frame shifts), as well as nucleotide substitutions, frame shifts are a recent discovery; hence much of the earlier (and even current) literature uses the term point mutation (or simply mutation) as though equivalent to nucleotide substitution.

Nucleotide replacement occurs in two ways: in **transitions** a purine is first substituted for the other purine, or a pyrimidine for the other pyrimidine, leading to replacement of AT by GC or vice versa; and in **transversions** a purine-pyrimidine pair replaces a pyrimidine-purine pair, or vice versa (AT→CG or TA, etc.; Fig. 8-30).

Deletions consist of the loss of more than one nucleotide—often hundreds or thousands. They are recognized through two characteristics: 1) they do not give rise to reversions

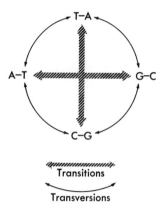

Fig. 8-30 Classes of nucleotide substitutions. Possible changes of base pairs in DNA as the consequence of a mutation that substitutes one nucleotide for another in a strand; at the next replication the new nucleotide is then paired to its regular partner. The resulting pair is represented. (Example: if in the upper T-A pair T is substituted by C, the resulting pair is the lower C-G pair.) Note that each base pair can undergo one kind of transition and two kinds of transversions.

(true reversions or suppressors affecting translation); and 2) they fail to give wild-type recombinants in pair-wise crosses with two or more point mutants altered at different sites within the region corresponding to the deletion. (The difference in sites of these test mutants is shown by their ability to produce wild-type recombinants among themselves: Fig. 8-29.)

Mechanism of Mutation

The chemical mutagens fall into several main groups, with different actions: 1) base analogs, 2) hydroxylamine, 3) nitrous acid, 4) alkylating agents, and 5) acridine derivatives. (In addition, other agents, of less significance for present purposes, are known, such as nitrosoguanidine, Mn^{++}, or formaldehyde.) The base analogs, the acridines, and Mn^{++} require replication for their action; the other mutagens, in contrast, are chemically reactive and thus can alter DNA even when it is not replicating.

On the basis of much work (especially with

bacteriophage T4), which cannot be reviewed in detail, **point mutations** can be subdivided into several groups, which can be distinguished by the agents that produce their reversion.

Group 1 Mutations: Transitions (see above). These mutations involve the substitution of AT for GC or vice versa. They are produced, for example, by the pyrimidine analog 5-bromouracil (5-BU) (which is more effective as its deoxynucleoside 5-bromodeoxyuridine, 5-BDU), and by the purine analog 2-aminopurine (2-AP). (Additional base analogs are known to be mutagenic but are less effective. Indeed, mutagenesis by a base analog was first observed with a weakly mutagenic naturally occurring purine, caffeine.)

The mode of action of the **base analogs** depends on their incorporation into new DNA in place of a normal base. Thus 5-BU closely resembles thymine (T): not only can it substitute for T in DNA quantitatively under certain circumstances (e.g., in an auxotroph starved for T), but its substitution for as much as 90% of the T in bacteriophages does not regularly prevent their subsequent normal replication. However, the presence of the analog in DNA introduces a chemical instability that occasionally leads to mutation. The instability arises because of the tendency of 5-BU to undergo a frequent but transient internal rearrangement (**tautomerization**) from the usual keto state to the rare enol state. (Tautomerization also occurs in T, but the enol form is much rarer.) Whereas in the keto state 5-BU pairs with adenine (A), in the enol state it pairs with guanine (G; Fig. 8-31). This explanation has been confirmed in DNA synthesis in vitro by the demonstration of increased ambiguity of pairing of 5-BU, compared with T. 2-Aminopurine is mutagenic in a similar way, being read as either A or G.

Mutagenesis by 5-BDU can occur in two ways (Fig. 8-32). An **instruction error** (or **replication error**) occurs when 5-BU, already incorporated into DNA in place of T, **occasionally** undergoes

Fig. 8-31 Regular and "Illegitimate" base pairing of 5-Bu. I. Regular base pairing of 5-Bu (in the common keto form) with adenine. II. "Illegitimate" base pairing of 5-Bu (in rare enol form) with guanine. The arrow in II indicates the displacement of the proton in the tautomerization of 5-Bu.

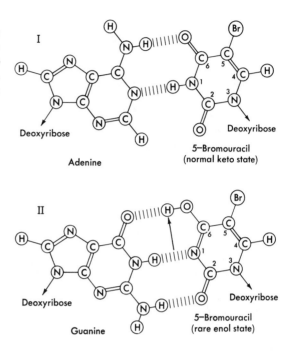

I

Deoxyribose
Adenine

Deoxyribose
5–Bromouracil
(normal keto state)

II

Deoxyribose
Guanine

Deoxyribose
5–Bromouracil
(rare enol state)

a keto-enol transition during replication, and G is consequently incorporated in place of A in the strand being synthesized. At the next replication the G pairs with cytosine (C), and the AT pair is thus changed into the GC pair. An **incorporation error** occurs when the triphosphate of 5-BDU is recognized, in its rarer enol form, as though it were the triphosphate of C, and hence is incorporated as partner in G. In the next replication the 5-BU in the usual keto form gives rise to an A-(5-BU) pair, which then **regularly** yields clones with an AT pair instead of the original GC pair.

Since a **replication** error may thus occur, and yield a mutant clone, any number of generations

after incorporation of the analog, DNA carrying the analog in place of AT exhibits increased genetic instability.

Group 1 mutations are defined operationally as those that can be induced by either 5-BDU or 2-AP to undergo true reversion. These mutations are identified as transitions, not only on the theoretical grounds outlined above, but because 5-BDU and 2-AP can induce the reversion of all the mutations that they produce. It therefore seems reasonable to use this test to identify the transitions among spontaneous mutants of unknown nature.

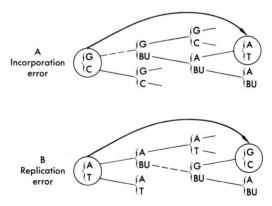

A
Incorporation
error

B
Replication
error

Fig. 8-32 Mutations induced by 5-Bu. The error is indicated by a dashed line. In either case a transition is produced.

Several **chemically reactive mutagens** induce **more selective transitions. Nitrous acid** (Fig. 8-33) oxidatively deaminates the amino-substituted bases: adenine is thus converted to hypoxanthine, which resembles G and pairs with C instead of with T; and C is converted to U, which resembles T and pairs with A.* **Hydroxylamine** is especially specific in its action: it deaminates C to a base able to pair with A instead of with G. Monofunctional **alkylating agents,** such as ethyl ethanesulfonate (EES), also produce transitions, but by a mechanism similar to that of base analogs. Thus EES alkylates G at the 7 position and thereby increases the probability of its ionization, which causes G to pair with T instead of with C (Fig. 8-34).

These rather specific mutagens have proved very useful, as noted above, for confirming the genetic code in vivo: the amino acid substitutions that they induce have been consistent, with

---

* Nitrous acid can also cause, through less obvious mechanisms, shifts of the reading frame and interstrand cross-links (see below).

few exceptions, with their known chemical effects on nucleotides in the codons assigned from in vitro studies (Fig. 8-25).

Group 2 Mutations: Reading-Frame Shifts. These mutations, as noted above, involve removal or insertion of a base. The clearest example is given by mutations induced by **acridine** derivatives (Fig. 8-22). These compounds can cause reversion of the mutations that they produce; but neither the mutagens nor the mutations of this group cross-react with those of group 1. Hence unknown mutations are considered frame shifts if they can be induced to revert by the acridine mutagens but not by base analogs.

The effects of acridines on the reading frame are based on a remarkable interaction with DNA. These polycyclic mutagens appear to intercalate noncovalently between the planar rings of successive nucleotide bases in DNA, as in-

Fig. 8-33 The oxidative deamination of DNA by nitrous acid and its effects on subsequent base pairing. **A.** Adenine is deaminated to hypoxanthine, which pairs with cytosine instead of thymine. **B.** Cytosine is deaminated to uracil, which pairs with adenine instead of guanine.

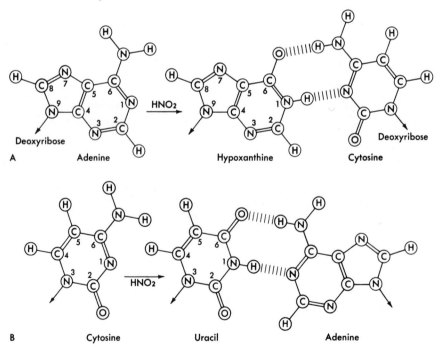

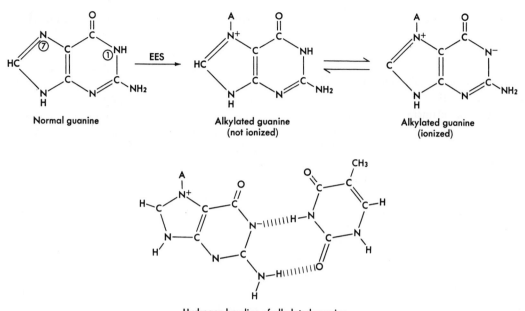

Hydrogen bonding of alkylated guanine
(in ionized state) with thymine

Fig. 8-34 Hydrogen bonding of alkylated guanine (in ionized state) with thymine. The alkylation of guanine at position 7 by ethyl ethanesulfonate (EES) leads to increased ionization of the nitrogen at position 1. The ionized guanine pairs with thymine instead of cytosine. A, alkyl group.

ferred from changes in its physical properties in solution. As a consequence, during replication an extra, uncoded nucleotide may be incorporated to match an acridine in the template; or an intercalation in the growing replica may cause it to skip a nucleotide. Through this symmetrical action acridine can correct the mutations that it has produced; but while the second mutation sometimes causes a true reversion of the first, more often it causes intragenic suppression by introducing, near the first shift of reading frame, a second shift of opposite direction (Fig. 8-22).

It appears that a base can occasionally also be directly removed (depurination), without interruption of the deoxyribose-phosphate backbone, by acid pH or high temperature. Monofunctional alkylating agents, such as EES, may also have such an effect, since G alkylated at position 7 is occasionally lost. Such a loss of a base could conceivably lead at the next replication to its random replacement by any base. However, all these mutations have thus far been found to be induced to revert by acridines; hence it appears that a lost base is not often spontaneously replaced during replication.

Group 3 Mutations: Transversions. Transversions constitute the third group of point mutations. The mechanisms responsible for their occurrence are not well known, compared with transitions and frame shifts, and no known mutagens produce them specifically or even frequently. Nevertheless, transversions are common among the spontaneous mutants of phage, and they are undoubtedly important in genetics.

For example, almost half the known abnormal human hemoglobins, which differ electrophoretically from normal hemoglobin A, involve amino acid substitutions that can be explained by single-base transversions (see Fig. 8-23). The high frequency of transversions among these mutations reflects the special requirements of the class: they must be missense mutations, in order to produce a useful protein; and the substituted amino acid must be quite dissimilar from the original since it differs in charge. As we have seen above (Evolution of the code), transition mutations tend to code for chemically similar amino acids; transversions have a much greater chance of introducing an amino acid with a different charge.

Group 4 Mutations: Deletions. Deletions in DNA can be induced by several agents: nitrous acid, bifunctional (cross-linking) alkylating agents, and ionizing irradiation (see below). Since these agents can link the two strands with each other, it appears that a segment of DNA around the cross-link is not replicated, and the segments on either side of it replicate regularly and join with each other. This joining may well involve the usual process of genetic recombination (see below), occurring very rarely because of the poor microhomology; the result would be excision of a defective loop of DNA.

A gene can be inactivated not only by deletion but by its obverse: the **insertion** within the gene of a foreign segment of DNA. For example, the integration of an episome into a bacterial chromosome (Chs. 7 and 43) involves the insertion of a bloc of DNA, by genetic recombination; and when the site of insertion is the middle of a gene the separated halves of that gene cannot form a useful product.

Spontaneous Mutations

Little is known about the origin of most spontaneous mutations. They no doubt arise in part from ever present mutagens in the environment; these include cosmic radiation, radioactive compounds, and naturally occurring base analogs (e.g., caffeine). However, the rate of spontaneous mutation in bacteria increases with increasing temperature of growth; hence it appears that these mutations can also arise as a consequence of thermal agitation (and heat can be considered a physical mutagen). Two mechanisms can reasonably be postulated: 1) occasional **breakage of a thermally activated bond** in a nucleotide in DNA (i.e., chemical decay); and 2) occasional **ambiguity of base-pairing in replication,** based on "wobble" of the interacting molecules. What is remarkable is not the

existence of such uninduced errors, but their rarity.

Such imperfection in base-pairing, without benefit of mutagens, is demonstrated by its exaggeration in mutants of phage T4, in which a **mutated DNA polymerase** has been shown to lead to a high frequency of mutations in general. It is thus evident that the polymerase can influence the fidelity of DNA replication, just as the ribosome can influence the fidelity of translation (see below); and different mutant polymerases differ in the sites of the mutations that they produce. The spontaneous mutation rate can also be affected by alterations in the supply of nucleotides in a cell (as shown by the mutagenic effect of thymine deprival) or conceivably by alterations in the mechanisms for correcting genetic errors (see below, Error Correction).

Little is known about the nature of spontaneous mutations. In phage T4 most of those detected are of the group 2 type. One reason may be that group 1 mutations so frequently code for a missense that permits the production of a functional, though altered, protein. In addition, this phage exhibits an exceptionally high rate of genetic recombination (Ch. 23), and imperfect pairing during this process can theoretically yield a frame shift.

Mutagenic vs. Lethal Action of Mutagenic Agents

Most mutagenic agents also kill microorganisms, both because they cause lethal mutations and because they produce changes in nucleic acid that upset its replication: e.g., intrastrand thymine dimers (see below) or cross-links between strands (produced especially by bifunctional alkylating agents such as nitrogen mustards or mitomycin). Nitrous acid appears to cause the mutagenic deamination of C and A, but its deamination of G is lethal because the product (xanthine) cannot be read.

Essentially devoid of killing action, in contrast, are certain base analogs (e.g., 5-BDU) and monofunctional alkylating agents (e.g.,

EES), which cause transitions. Thus, we have noted above (Fig. 8-31), when 5-BDU is incorporated in place of T it functions almost normally; and while it may throw off stable mutant clones by erroneous base-pairing, the progeny are predominantly nonmutant. The rarer incorporation of 5-BDU in place of C would, on the other hand, impair the function of an essential gene; but even here the occasional reading of 5-BDU as C rather than T, in both transcription and replication, could lead to slow growth and eventually the segregation of a nonmutant clone.

Significance of Chemical Mutagenesis

Chemical mutagenesis is important not only as a tool for studying the nature of mutations, but also because it is the closest step so far attained toward altering the genetic material of organisms in a predictable way. It is far, however, from achieving the desired goal of directed mutation, i.e., a predictable change of a certain gene: though we may be able to cause a predictable substitution of certain nucleotides, the substitution cannot be localized in a given codon of a given gene but will occur all over the genome.

Since most mutations are deleterious, **prevention of mutations** would also be desirable; but such protection does not seem feasible except in terms of minimizing exposure to mutagens. With bacteria an excess of normal bases has been observed to exert an antimutagenic effect on the action of base analogs, but the effect on the spontaneous mutation rate has been negligible.

Ambiguous Translation: Suppression

Although the translation mechanism is remarkably precise, it is not perfect. Misreading probably occurs now and then, causing the formation of abnormal proteins; but this process, being infrequent, is normally without appreciable consequences. Such ambiguity in translation becomes evident, however, when the error in translation can **correct** the consequences of a mutation, e.g., when the mutation produces a nonsense codon which by error is read as a sense codon.

Even a low frequency of correction can often restore a detectable level of function, since the reserve capacity of the cell to make a given enzyme often exceeds many-fold the normal steady-state level of that enzyme (Ch. 9, Fig. 9-23).

Corrections in translation fall into two different classes: 1) in certain types of **genotypic suppression** a second mutation alters some component of the translation mechanism; 2) in **phenotypic suppression** added substances alter translation without a genetic change.

Genotypic Suppression

In this type of correction, as noted above, the phenotypic consequence of a primary mutation is eliminated by a second mutation, called a suppressor mutation. **Intragenic suppressor** mutations have already been discussed. At least equally important are **extragenic** (or **external**) **suppressor** mutations, which are located in a different gene from the primary mutation. This gene may be at a distance on the same chromosome or even on a different chromosome, as in bacterial mutations that suppress the effect of certain mutations in an infecting bacteriophage. Suppressor mutations must therefore influence the expression of primary mutations through a cytoplasmic effect.

Suppressor mutations were revealed by early genetic studies, in higher organisms and then in bacteria, and they presented a major obstacle to acceptance of the one gene–one enzyme hypothesis as a general principle. The recent detailed analysis of gene action, however, has clarified the problem by showing that some of these mutations influence the **fidelity of the translation process.** Since the original mutation is thus corrected in only a fraction of the readings, suppressed mutations exhibit only partial restoration of function, as can be verified when the product of the mutated gene is examined quantitatively. Nevertheless, when the phenotype is observed simply in terms of growth rate it may be indistinguishable from true revertants. As noted above, suppressor mutations are identified by genetic crosses that separate them from, or combine them with, the primary mutations that they affect.

Suppressible mutations may be of either the missense or the nonsense type. Mutations of the first type cause the synthesis of an altered, nonfunctional (or poorly functional) protein; this protein is often recognizable immunologically as a cross-reacting material (CRM; Fig. 8-35), since most of the molecule is unchanged. Mutations of the second type cause termination of the growing polypeptide chain, which results in formation of incomplete chains; these fragments are sometimes recognizable by their amino acid sequences (e.g., in an infected bacterium that is synthesizing predominantly one species of phage protein). After suppression of either type of mutation a more functional protein is produced. Suppression of missense mutations may reinstate the original amino acid or may substitute one that is similar enough to restore function.

Since the translation of the mutated codon is characteristically **ambiguous** in external suppression, i.e., is altered in only a proportion of the acts of translation, the cells contain two types of protein from the mutant gene: a nonfunctional one expressing the uncorrected primary mutation, and a functional one expressing the corrected mutation. In the correction of missense mutations a low frequency of misreading is essential, because the process that corrects a given codon at a site of mutation will similarly affect the same codon in its **normal** positions throughout the chromosome, thus causing alteration of cellular proteins in general. Hence, if the translation mistake occurred too frequently it would be lethal. When the mistake is not frequent, however, a certain proportion of normal protein is made, allowing cell survival. Only those suppressor mutations that meet this criterion are recognized.

Molecular Mechanism of Suppression. Suppressor mutations may conceivably alter 1) a tRNA molecule, which sometimes recognizes a wrong codon or a wrong activating enzyme; 2) an activating enzyme, which sometimes recognizes a wrong tRNA; or 3) the ribosomes, whose structure influences the precision of fit of codon to anticodon. An example of the first type of mutation has been experimentally demonstrated in an *E. coli* strain suppressing an amber mutation in a bacteriophage: an altered serine tRNA can recognize the amber codon and frequently places serine at its site.

Amber and Ochre Suppressors. We have seen that suppression of missense mutations is difficult, requiring a balance between the beneficial effect of erroneous translation of the mutated codon and the harmful effect of similar translation of identical normal codons. Much simpler is the correction of a sense codon if this codon is absent from the nonmutant genome, since such ambiguity would affect the expression of few or no genes other than the mutated one. For these reasons most of our knowledge about ex-

Fig. 8-35 Demonstration of immunologically cross-reacting material. An antiserum is prepared to a bacterial extract containing the desired enzyme; specific antibody to that enzyme, present in the antiserum, will neutralize and precipitate the enzyme. In the experiment increasing amounts of the extract are added to constant amounts of the antiserum, and when the neutralizing capacity of the antiserum is exceeded enzyme activity can be detected in the supernatant (curve A). If an extract of a mutant that cannot make the enzyme (or its CRM) is first added to the antiserum the results are identical, since no protein in the extract will neutralize the specific antibody to the enzyme. However, if the antiserum is mixed with an extract of a mutant that makes a CRM for the enzyme the CRM ties up some of the specific antibody, and the neutralizing activity against the active enzyme is thereby reduced (curve B).

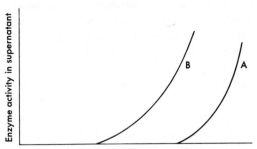

ternal genotypic suppression derives from the study of strains of bacteria or phage in which the primary mutated codon is one of the two that do not code for an amino acid: amber (UAG) or ochre (UAA) (Fig. 8-21).

The miscoding effect of a suppressor mutation can be studied with phage mutants altered in the formation of the coat protein, since that protein constitutes the bulk of the protein formed in an infected cell. By far the most common suppressible mutations in this locus are those due to an **amber** codon. A number of **different amber suppressor mutations** have been mapped, at widely separated loci, on the E. coli chromosome, and these cause various misreadings of this nonsense codon, with varying frequency. Thus some of these suppressors have been shown individually to cause the incorporation into the phage coat protein, at the amber (UAG) site, of an amino acid with a very similar codon: serine (UCG), glutamine (CAG), or tyrosine (UAU, UAC).

Since a given amino acid insertion at the amber position will restore functionality to some mutant proteins but not to others, each amber suppressor mutation will suppress only certain amber mutations; the amber class was established by the overlapping effect of various suppressor mutations on a number of primary mutations, in both bacteria and phage. Later the amber codon was identified as UAG by means of the pattern of codons to which it could mutate (or from which it could be formed) in one step; direct identification, of course, was impossible for lack of a known substance that this codon incorporated. Many amber suppressors can correct amber mutations with high efficiency, allowing certain mutated genes for the coat protein of bacteriophage T4 to complete between 30% and 63% (depending on the suppressor) of the polypeptide chains made.

Subsequently another class of nonsense mutations, not suppressible by amber suppressors, was discovered. They were named **ochre,** and were defined by a distinct set of suppressor mutations. The ochre codon (UAA) is structurally similar to amber (UAG). The efficiency of correction of most ochre mutations is low: 1 to 5% for mutations of the E. coli β-galactosidase gene. Hence these suppressor mutations could not be detected with coat protein mutants, whose products are required in large amounts; they were

discovered with mutations in genes for which slight restoration of activity was sufficient to restore growth (e.g., E. coli lac, or phage r_{II}).*

It is striking that amber suppressor mutations **do not** affect the growth rate of the bacteria that carry them, despite the high frequency with which they change the reading of an amber codon, wherever it occurs; yet ochre suppressor mutations appreciably slow the growth of their bacteria, even when the misreading frequency is only a few per cent. It therefore seems likely that amber and ochre have quite different functions in the code. While both are nonsense, as defined earlier in terms of not coding for an amino acid, **ochre** may be the **normal chain terminator,** and amber the only codon without an active function in normal coding. Even though ochre is thus reclassified, its random suppression throughout the chromosome is still likely to be more compatible with cell growth than suppression of an amino acid codon, since the terminator codon presumably appears much less frequently in the genome (i.e., only once per gene).

Phenotypic Suppression

Ambiguous Messengers. 5-Fluorouracil (5-FU), which is similar in structure to uracil (U) (Fig. 8-36), is incorporated extensively in place of the latter in RNA (Ch. 10, Biosynthetic incorporation of antimetabolites). The RNA can still function, since in RNA viruses a large proportion of the U can be replaced by 5-FU without affecting multiplication. The incorporation in the viral genome is mutagenic, however, which suggests that 5-FU is sometimes read at replication as C rather than as U, just as 5-BU in DNA may be read as C rather than T.

In mRNA the presence of 5-FU causes a comparable ambiguity of translation, which leads to errors in protein synthesis. Hence, as was shown by Benzer and Champe, at low

---

* Just as errors in transcription or translation are thus detected at a much lower frequency when amplified by the catalytic activity of the protein produced, so errors in replication are amplified still further by the process of reproduction. Hence mutations are detectable at extraordinarily low frequencies.

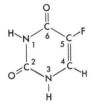

Fig. 8-36 5-Fluorouracil.

concentration 5-FU causes phenotypic suppression of some mutations, presumably those transitions that caused U to appear in the codon instead of C.

At high concentrations 5-FU causes the formation of mRNA that can no longer code for useful protein; it thus prevents further exponential growth (Ch. 5, Linear growth). This effect has been very useful in elucidating the role of mRNA in protein synthesis (Ch. 9, Messenger RNA). Similar effects have been obtained with 8-azaguanine, which replaces guanine in RNA but not in DNA.

Environmental Effects on Fidelity of Translation. Gorini and Kataja observed that streptomycin and related aminoglycoside antibiotics cause phenotypic suppression of certain auxotrophic mutations in *E. coli*. These drugs are known to act directly on ribosomes; and in polypeptide synthesis with synthetic polynucleotides in vitro they strikingly increase the ambiguity of translation. The effects on both the cells and the extracts are influenced by mutations that alter the ribosomes. These results show that ribosomes can influence the fidelity of translation. The effect of streptomycin will be analyzed further in Chapter 10.

Ambiguity of translation in vitro is also increased by many other environmental changes, such as altered cation concentration or pH, elevated temperature, and the presence of polyamines or organic solvents; these conditions probably all affect the configuration of the ribosomes. At least one of these changes (addition of 5% methanol) has been observed also to mimic streptomycin in restoring growth of certain cells.

Normal Ambiguity. Since mutations can alter the responsiveness of the ribosome to the induction of misreading by streptomycin, it is not surprising that such mutant ribosomes also vary in their background of **spontaneous misreading** in vitro. Indeed, it seems likely that a low frequency of error is also normal in transcription and translation in the cell, though such errors are much harder to identify than the comparable errors in replication, whose consequences are recorded in a clone of mutant progeny rather than in isolated "mutant" molecules. Such imperfection of gene expression may be responsible for some of the incompletely blocked ("leaky") auxotrophic mutants: these are generally considered to be forming an altered enzyme with low activity, but they may alternatively be forming a small amount of the fully active, normal protein along with much inactive, mutant protein.

Genetic Recombination

The formal aspects of the process of recombination of bacteria, leading to chromosome mapping, have been discussed in Chapter 7; and more will be said about recombination in bacteriophages in Chapter 23. We shall examine here the molecular aspects of recombination, i.e., how the interacting molecules pair (synapsis) and how they yield a product with genes derived from two different molecules.

First of all, it should be noted that genetic recombination is an **extremely precise process,** in which part of the nucleotide sequence of the product corresponds to that of one parent and part to that of the other, but normally without additions, losses, or substitutions of nucleotides. This conclusion could be drawn, even in early genetic studies, from the usual restoration of completely wild-type function in recombinants derived from two point mutants. The site of recombination has now been localized with the greatest possible precision, between **two adjacent nucleotides.** Thus a glycine in the tryptophan synthetase of *E. coli* is replaced in various mutants by **glutamic acid, arginine,** or **valine.** Crosses between certain pairs of these mutants yield a very low frequency of recombinants in which the glycine has been restored (Fig. 8-37). These results would have appeared extraordinary to geneticists and biochemists 10 years ago; now

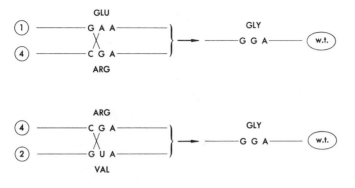

Fig. 8-37 Production of a new codon at site of recombination. Recombination within DNA codons in two crosses of mutants of the A protein of tryptophan synthetase of *E. coli.* The number on the left identifies the mutants and refers to Figure 8-24. The recombinants contain a different amino acid from that present in either parent at the same position. The amino acid shifts in the mutants, and the restoration of glycine in the recombinants, are consistent with the single nucleotide substitutions in known codons depicted above. As would be expected from the known codons, the cross of mutants 1 and 2 failed to restore glycine. (Data from C. Yanofsky. Cold Spring Harbor Symp. Quant. Biol. 28:581, 1963.)

they are easily understood as the consequence of rare recombination **within a codon.**

Molecular Mechanism of Recombination

As a biochemical process genetic recombination has remained mysterious until recently; even its most basic aspect—whether or not the exchange of genetic information between parental chromosomes is accompanied by a material exchange of parts of the chromosome (hypothesis of **breakage and reunion**)—remained obscure. An alternative mechanism, called **copy choice,** was widely held, whereby a recombinant DNA molecule would be synthesized by using as template first one and then the other of the parental molecules. However, after the discovery of the structure of DNA and its semiconservative replication the copy choice mechanism appeared highly unlikely, since the new DNA strand winds around the template on which it is being formed rather than simply copying and then leaving the template. Nevertheless, this hypothesis continued to be considered seriously.

The question of breakage was finally clarified by experiments of Meselson and Weigle with isotopically labeled bacteriophage λ. Bacteriophages offer a unique opportunity to study the possible exchange of the material of the parental DNAs together with their genetic markers because the DNA molecules are small enough to be isolated and studied without breakage. These studies showed that recombinants can be formed by exchanges of parts between unreplicated DNA molecules; hence breakage and reunion occur. Moreover, though the two recombining DNA molecules are exchanged for most of their length without replication, the incorporation of label suggested that the process involves demolition and resynthesis of **small parts** of the DNA. The details of these experiments will be given in Chapter 23.

The process of recombination in microorganisms—as well as in higher organisms—probably occurs as in the scheme of Figure 8-38; although not proved in all its details, this mechanism satisfactorily accounts for the known facts. Recombination first requires precise alignment of the corresponding nucleotides in a homologous region of the two DNA molecules, with each molecule contributing one strand to a new paired segment. The single strands become available at places where one of the DNA strands breaks and, as discussed above, the double helical struc-

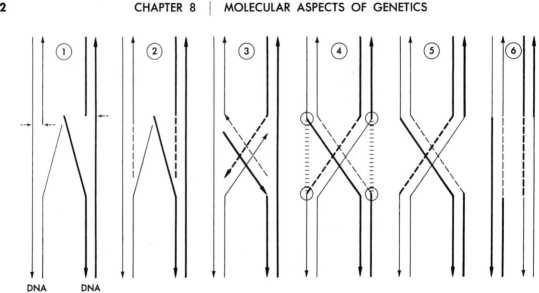

DNA   DNA
1   2

Fig. 8-38 Model of recombination by breakage and reunion between DNA molecules. Each strand of a DNA molecule is indicated by a line, whose arrow indicates its polarity. The hydrogen bonds between strands are not shown. **1.** Single-strand breaks occur in two homologous DNA molecules, on strands of opposite polarity, as indicated by the dashed arrows. The helical structures locally melt. **2.** The interrupted single strands are extended by new synthesis (dashed lines), copying the uninterrupted complementary strand. **3.** The newly synthesized segments peel off and pair with those that had peeled off in step 1. **4.** The remaining single strands are broken down hydrolytically (crossed) and the discontinuities (circles) are enzymatically closed. **5.** Two recombinant molecules are formed which are shown separately in **6.** Each recombinant has a heterozygous segment (one strand from one parent, heavy line; the other strand from the other parent, thin line). (Modified from H. L. K. Whitehouse and P. J. Hastings. Genet. Res. 6:27, 1965.)

ture melts locally. The exchange is then completed in a series of steps involving local synthesis and demolition of strands, and finally union of the free ends by some unknown mechanism.

The strict alignment of homologous segments appears to be the crucial step for the conservation of genetic information (i.e., neither loss nor gain) in normal recombination. As we have seen above (Mutations), errors in this process can account for important classes of mutations: frame shifts and deletions.

Support for this model in bacteria comes from the selection of **mutants that cannot recombine (rec⁻)**, and the finding that these mutants, which presumably lack one of the enzymes required for recombination, also lack the ability to

repair ultraviolet (UV) light damage in DNA.* As will be seen below, this repair is brought about by an error-correcting mechanism in which the damaged segment of a strand is hydrolytically removed and is subsequently resynthesized. Hence the double loss in these mutants strongly suggests that recombination and repair of UV damage involve at least one enzyme in common.

According to this model a recombinant molecule necessarily contains a short biparental segment, in which one strand derives from each parental DNA. As we shall see in Chapter 23, such segments, identified by markers that make them heterozygous, are regularly observed at the site of exchange in bacteriophage recombination.

---

* Such mutants were obtained by replicating F⁻ colonies onto an Hfr lawn on a selective medium that would allow outgrowth of recombinants but not of either parent. From several thousand F⁻ colonies two were unable to yield recombinants.

Gene Conversion. In the biparental segment the two strands may fail to pair properly in any region in which they are allelic, because they will have at least one nucleotide pair that is not complementary. An additional change, based on error-correction, may then occur. The imperfect pairing may cause a short segment to **loop out,** and one of the unpaired strands may be demolished and then resynthesized by copying the other strand, just as in DNA damaged by ultraviolet light (see below). The heterozygous region would thus lose one of its two allelic configurations, causing an abnormal segregation of alleles in the subsequent DNA replication. This asymmetrical segregation is called gene conversion. It can be formally explained by copy choice, and so it was earlier considered a reason for preferring that mechanism of recombination; but it can now be explained by the breakage and reunion model, as we have seen, through the inclusion of excision and repair.

Genetic Determination of Protein Structure

A hierarchy of structures can be recognized in proteins (Fig. 8-9); the **primary** structure, consisting of the sequence of amino acid residues in the polypeptide chain; the **secondary** structure, formed by regular and ordered helical regions of the polypeptide chain stabilized by hydrogen bonds; the **tertiary** structure, produced by one polypeptide chain (or two or more different polypeptide chains) into a more or less globular **monomer;** the **quaternary** structure, formed by assembling identical or different monomers. Tertiary and quaternary structures are stabilized by various types of noncovalent bonds, and in some proteins also by S-S bonds. The quaternary structures are usually less stable and can be dissociated without altering the tertiary structure of the monomers. Protein molecules constituted by a single monomer are called **monomeric,** e.g., pancreatic ribonuclease. Those made up of several monomers (whether or not identical) are called **multimeric,** e.g., *E. coli* β-galactosidase, which contains four identical monomers.

Secondary and Higher Order Structure. We have analyzed in preceding sections the genetic specification of the primary structure, and we shall now inquire into the specification of the structures of higher order. The following summary seems justified, although there is considerable uncertainty on many points.

Secondary and tertiary structures appear to arise spontaneously by progressive folding of the polypeptide chain as it is synthesized. For instance, β-galactosidase monomers must be almost completely folded before they leave the ribosomes, for while still attached to the ribosomes in the cell they can associate with other already formed monomers—which have no enzymatic activity—to constitute **ribosome-bound functional enzyme.** (Many other proteins, however, do not show this behavior, but take up their regular conformation only after dissociating from the polysome.) Moreover, with many proteins tertiary structure that has been destroyed in vitro can be reformed under proper conditions (reversible denaturation). It therefore seems certain that the tertiary and quaternary structures follow automatically from the primary structure and are thus indirectly defined by the genetic information. Indeed, the recognition of this fact—that **information encoded in a one-dimensional tape completely specifies complex three-dimensional structures**—constitutes one of the major triumphs of modern biology and is of the utmost significance for the problems of morphogenesis.

Since amino acids distant from the active site influence enzyme activity only through their effects on the folding of the protein, it is not surprising that in many positions an amino acid can be replaced by a chemically similar amino acid with little or no alteration of activity. Thus the tryptophan synthetase of *E. coli* remains functional when the glycine in one position is replaced by alanine, valine, serine, or threonine, but not when it is replaced by arginine or glutamic acid. It thus seems probable that **silent mutations** occur more frequently than those causing an obvious loss of function (see Mutations, above), and the accumulation of silent mutations accounts for the progressive changes in the amino acid sequence of those proteins (e.g., cytochromes) whose evolution can be traced across the biological kingdom. However, amino acid specificity is no doubt much more restrictive at certain critical positions in the protein sequence (e.g., the active site itself, S-S cross-links, the termination of helical regions, and sharp bends in the folded chain), and such restrictions may contribute to the much higher frequency of recognized mutations at certain sites in the gene (hot spots).

Although the structural gene evidently determines all the fundamental characteristics of a protein by specifying its primary structure, this structure is often compatible, especially in large protein molecules, with two (or perhaps more) similar configurations, which exhibit many small differences in bond lengths and bond angles. This plasticity is illustrated by the allosteric regulatory proteins, to be discussed in Chapter 9, and by intragenic complementation, which we shall now consider.

Intragenic Complementation

Complementation is the interaction of two sets of cellular (or viral) genes within a cell that permits the cell (or the virus) to function, although each set carries a mutated essential gene that is nonfunctional when in the haploid state. **Intergenic** complementation has been discussed above (Units of genetic information). We noted that it provided an operational basis for defining the gene or cistron, which was at first intellectually very satisfying; but this basis has been weakened by the discovery of intragenic complementation by Fincham and by Giles in 1957.

Intragenic (also called **interallelic**) complementation is the production of some degree of complementation between two sets of genes that have a mutation in the same gene, but in a different site (Fig. 8-39). It has appeared with only a small fraction of the pairs of alleles tested, and the process by which function results from collaboration of two nonfunctional proteins has been very puzzling.

A possible explanation was suggested by the observation that intragenic complementation is exhibited only by **multimeric** enzymes; and the mechanism was then revealed by the

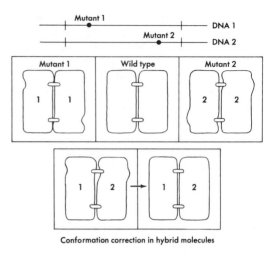

Conformation correction in hybrid molecules

Fig. 8-39 Intragenic complementation in a gene specifying a dimeric protein. Neither mutant alone produces functional dimers. The hybrid dimers, however, are functional because they mutually correct each other.

production of complementation with **extracts** of pairs of mutants that display intragenic complementation. Thus, by studying the conditions required for in vitro complementation of the dimeric alkaline phosphatase of *E. coli*, its intragenic complementation could be shown to involve the dissociation of the two nonfunctional proteins into monomers and then the reassociation of the monomers to form dimers. With β-galactosidase it could similarly be shown that mutant monomers from two inactive proteins are able to form functional tetramers. It could be concluded that intragenic complementation results from **formation of functional hybrid molecules from different nonfunctional mutant monomers.**

This result implies that mutual interaction of the monomers in the hybrid multimers can correct an abnormal conformation (Fig. 8-39). Thus the mutated monomers have minor abnormalities of the tertiary structure, which persist after assembly into nonfunctional multimers; but when two monomers with different structural abnormalities join to form a dimer by establishing reciprocal weak bonds, the resulting internal stresses can sometimes correct the configurational abnormalities and restore the precise apposition of monomers required to produce an active site on the enzyme.

This model accounts for the relative infrequency of the pairs of mutations that can produce intragenic complementation, since clearly only some very special abnormalities are capable of mutual correction.

The studies of intragenic complementation help answer a puzzling question: Why are multimeric proteins so common in Nature? A possible answer is that the tertiary structure, and therefore the function, of the monomers is modified in the multimers, and these changes may increase the possibility of delicately adjusting the active site. In addition, multimeric proteins are readily susceptible to functional regulation, as will be discussed in Chapter 9. Finally, the same polypeptide can apparently be incorporated into two different enzymes. Specifically, in yeast the enzyme that converts homocitrate to homoisocitrate (in the pathway to lysine: Ch. 4, Fig. 4-12) appears to share a polypeptide with the enzyme that converts citrate to isocitrate (in the tricarboxylate pathway); for though the enzymes are distinct, there are one-step mutants that inactivate both, as well as others that inactivate one or the other.

Damage to Nucleic Acid by Radiation

Ultraviolet (UV) light of wave lengths around 2600 A, and ionizing radiations such as X-rays, are useful tools for producing mutations. These agents also produce lethal damages in nucleic acid, which are exploited for sterilizing microbes (Ch. 11). The biological effects of ionizing radiations have been studied at the molecular level largely with microbes, and interest in this subject has been markedly stimulated by the increasing exposure of man to such irradiation.

Lethal Action of Ultraviolet Light

The most important recognized chemical effect of UV irradiation of nucleic acid is hydration of the pyrimidines at the 4:5 bond. In DNA this change also leads to formation of **dimers** between adjacent **thymine** residues

(Fig. 8-40), usually in the same strand but sometimes also between residues in different strands. In RNA uracil dimers are formed. Dimers block the replication of the nucleic acid because no normal base can pair with them; furthermore, when dimerization crosslinks different strands they cannot unwind and separate for replication.

Not all dimers formed during irradiation are lethal, because dimers can be removed by two mechanisms present in many kinds of cells: photoreactivation and dark reactivation.

Photoreactivation was discovered many years ago through a curious observation: when bacteria were exposed to a given dose of UV irradiation the viability counts obtained showed marked variation, depending on how long the inoculated plates remained on the laboratory bench, exposed to visible light, before being placed in a dark incubator. This ability of visible light to resuscitate apparently killed cells has recently been traced to an enzyme that combines specifically with thymine dimers but remains inactive in the dark; when the complex is irradiated with light of the long UV or short visible region the enzyme **cleaves** the dimer, restoring the original thymine residues and releasing the enzyme. Photoreactivation also occurs with UV-damaged RNA, but this effect has not been extensively studied.

The consequence of photoreactivation is to increase, sometimes enormously, the viable fraction of UV-treated bacteria, as if the effective UV dose had been reduced. After maximal photoreactivation, however, other lethal damages still remain. Viruses also show photoreactivation if the UV-irradiated virus particles are allowed to infect cells which are then exposed to white light; the particles themselves are not responsive to extracellular illumination because they do not contain the photoreactivating enzyme.

Dark reactivation is observed if a UV-irradiated suspension of bacteria is stored for a few hours in the cold, or in an inadequate medium, before being allowed to resume growth; the fraction of colony-forming cells

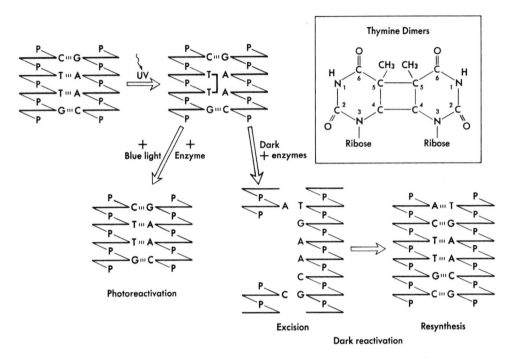

Fig. 8-40 Production of thymine dimers by UV irradiation of DNA. The dimers can be removed enzymatically in two ways: by photoreactivation, which restores the original nucleotides; and by dark reactivation, which first excises the dimers together with neighboring nucleotides, and then rebuilds the excised segment by copying the un-altered strand. The structure of the thymine dimer is given in box.

is seen to increase appreciably during this preincubation. In contrast to the dissociation of the thymine dimers catalyzed by the photo-reactivating enzyme, dark reactivation of DNA results from the **excision** of the dimers by a hydrolytic enzyme, which eliminates the nucleotides of the dimer-containing segment. The demolished segment is then rebuilt by a polymerase, which copies the complementary strand. This type of reactivation can occur only in double-stranded molecules; it there-fore accounts for the much greater resistance to UV of double-stranded compared with single-stranded phage nucleic acid, in cells containing the reactivating enzymes (Fig. 8-41).

Error Correction

The mechanism of dark reactivation just described is of extraordinary interest because

it may be a special case of a more general phenomenon of genetic error-correction, which removes and replaces improperly paired segments of DNA, and thus may vastly increase the stability of the genes. Similar mechanisms, involving the same enzyme, also participate in genetic recombination, as noted above; a mutant that has lost this enzyme is vastly more sensitive to UV ir-radiation and is unable to form genetic re-combinants.

Functional Inactivation of Genes

Damages in a gene induced by UV light prevent its transcription and therefore its function. In the same DNA molecule in which certain genes are damaged and non-functional other genes may be undamaged. The effect of irradiation on individual genes can be studied by a kind of complementation

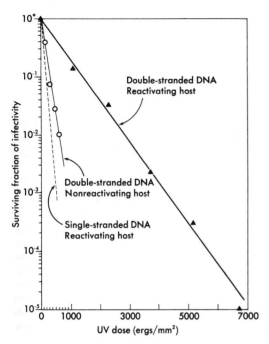

Fig. 8-41 UV inactivation of the single-stranded and double-stranded DNA of bacteriophage ϕX-174 (see Ch. 23). Each DNA in solution was exposed to increasing doses of UV light and then was assayed for infectivity on protoplasts of two *E. coli* strains, one capable and the other incapable of carrying out dark reactivation. The proportion of the residual titer is plotted versus the dose of irradiation. (Data from M. Yarus and R. L. Sinsheimer. J. Molec. Biol. 8:614, 1964.)

test in cells simultaneously infected with two different bacteriophages.

An example is the inactivation of the r_{II} genes in bacteriophage T4. As was noted above, the $r_{II}{}^+$ allele of this gene allows phage multiplication in a strain of *E. coli* K12(λ) that will not support multiplication of r_{II} phage. A bacterium infected by both $r_{II}{}^+$ and r_{II} phage supports multiplication of both viruses because the $r_{II}{}^+$ gene of one phage provides the required function for both. If the $r_{II}{}^+$ phage is UV-irradiated before infection, multiplication takes place only in bacteria receiving phage in which the function of the $r_{II}{}^+$ gene survives. The proportion of bacteria in which viral multiplication occurs measures the **functional survival** of the gene. As shown in Figure 8-42, the functional sur-

vival of the gene is much more UV-resistant than the survival of viability, because it requires only the integrity of the gene, whereas survival of viability requires integrity of the whole genome.

Mutagenesis

UV light induces point mutations. About half of them are induced to revert by base analogs and belong, therefore, to group 1; they appear to be produced mainly by UV damage to GC pairs and to consist, therefore, in GC $\rightarrow$ AT transitions. The other half are reverted by acridines and belong to group 2, i.e., consist in addition or deletion of a nu-

Fig. 8-42 Kinetics of UV damage to a gene and to a genome. Functional survival of the $r_{II}B$ gene (Fig. 8-10) compared with the entire genome of T4 bacteriophage particles irradiated with UV light. Survival of the genome was measured from the fraction of K12(λ) cells yielding phage after single infection by irradiated T4$r_{II}B^+$ particles (dashed line). Survival of the $r_{II}B$ gene was measured by simultaneously infecting the same cells with unirradiated $r_{II}B$ mutant phage, which cannot multiply in this host unless complemented with an undamaged $r_{II}B^+$ allele. As the UV dose is increased the function of the gene is inactivated much less than the ability of the phage to multiply. (Data from D. Krieg. Virology 8:80, 1959.)

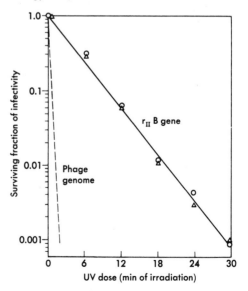

cleotide. The mechanism of UV mutagenesis is unclear but apparently sometimes involves the formation of thymine dimers, since a fraction of the mutations are photoreactivable. UV light does not cause deletions.

X-ray

X-irradiation causes two types of direct effects: 1) excitations of chemical groups in DNA, which lead to complex and poorly understood chemical alterations without a chain break and are most frequently lethal but can also produce point mutations; 2) production of highly reactive and short-lived radicals in the water surrounding the DNA, which cause hydration of thymine, deamination of cytosine, and other changes, resulting in point mutation. X-rays also cause breaks in the polynucleotide chain.

In double-stranded DNA a break sometimes affects a single strand and sometimes both strands; only breaks of the latter type are lethal. **Deletions** also arise when two double-stranded breaks are produced in the same molecule, and the two broken ends rejoin by some kind of internal recombination.

^{32}P Decay

^{32}P Decay is similar in its consequences to some damages produced by X-rays. When a ^{32}P atom decays it releases an electron and becomes an atom of ^{32}S. The sulfur atom has considerable recoil energy (as a gun at the moment of firing) and thus breaks the internucleotide bond in which it is located, fracturing the polynucleotide chain. Inactivation results if the nucleic acid is single-stranded but not if it is double-stranded, since the complementary strand may still give rise to a complete molecule. However, double-stranded nucleic acid is inactivated when the recoiling S atom also causes a break in the complementary strand. For these reasons the efficiency of inactivation per decay of a ^{32}P atom is about 100% for single-stranded nucleic acids but only about 10% for double-stranded nucleic acids.

When a lethal ^{32}P disintegration occurs in bacterial DNA the replication of the molecule stops, regardless of the localization of the decaying atom in respect to the growing point. Such a generalized effect of chain scission may occur through interference with unwinding, and thus provides evidence in favor of the view that replication involves rotation of the whole chromosome (see above, Replication of DNA).

APPENDIX

Quantitative Aspects of Killing by Irradiation

Certain mathematical relations between the dose of radiation and the effects obtained will be useful for understanding problems dealt with in later chapters of this book, involving the use of radiation both in research and for sterilization. These quantitative aspects of radiation biology will be considered here.

The inactivation or death of a microorganism is defined as the loss of its ability to initiate a clone; this effect is the consequence of a certain number of chemical **events,** each consisting, for instance, in the change of one chemical group or the breaking of one chemical bond. Organisms that have experienced a sufficient number of these events are inactivated; those that have not experienced them survive (i.e., retain their ability to multiply). The relation between the dose of radiation and the proportion of surviving organisms can be calculated as follows.

It is assumed that the events occur at random in the susceptible chemical groups or bonds in various individual organisms, with a probability (p), proportional to the dose. If there are n susceptible groups or bonds per organism each organism experiences, **on the average,** pn inactivating events. If a single such event is sufficient to inactivate the organism the proportion of surviving organisms (S) is, from the Poisson distribution (Ch. 22, Appendix), $S = e^{-pn}$. In turn $p = kD = krt$, where k is a constant that measures the probability of interaction of the radiation with the chemical group, D is the dose of radiation, r is the dose rate (i.e., the dose of radiation per unit time), and t is the time.

Thus, the basic equation of inactivation is $S = e^{-krtn}$. The equation is used in its logarithmic form: $\log S = -krtn \log e = {}^{-}Krtn$, where $K = k \log e$.

When the inactivation of bacteria or viruses by uv light, X-rays, or ${}^{32}P$ decay is followed by plotting the surviving fraction (S) versus time on semilogarithmic paper, the **survival curve** is seen to be **a straight line with a negative slope passing through the origin,** as in Figure 8-43A. Such a linear survival curve is called a **single-hit** curve, since it is generated by a process in which a single **event** in an organism, i.e., the change of a single chemical group or the breaking of a single bond, causes loss of viability.

The slope of the survival curve is equal to $-Krn$. Kn, the **target size** of the organism for that radiation, is proportional to the number (n) of susceptible chemical groups or bonds. If K is constant the slope is proportional to n; hence the ratio of the values of Kn for two different organisms, or **relative target size,** can be directly determined from the slopes of their survival curves. This procedure is the basis for radiation analysis of target size, which, as a first approximation, is proportional to the size of the genome if the proportion of repaired damages is constant. On the other hand, for organisms with genomes of similar size the target size is inversely related to efficiency of repair, which influences the value of K.

Other important types of survival curves are represented by curves B, C, and D in Figure 8-43, which have a shoulder near the origin, before becoming linear; they are called **multiple-hit** curves. Their shapes are generated by a process in which several events (hits) must accumulate before the organism is inactivated. To determine the number of events required for inactivation the straight part of the survival curve is extrapolated back to meet the ordinate axis. The position of the intersection measures the number of hits in logarithmic units. Curve B corresponds to 10 hits, curve C to 100 hits; curve D also corresponds to 10 hits, but has a different slope.

The slope of the straight part of a multiple-hit curve has the same meaning as for a single-hit curve, i.e., it is proportional to the target size of the organism. Thus, curves A, B, and C reflect the inactivation of organisms with the same target size. The different numbers of hits could

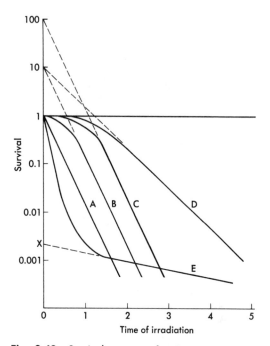

Fig. 8-43 Survival curves of microorganisms irradiated by UV light. **A,** a single-hit curve; **B,** a ten-hit curve; **C,** a hundred-hit curve, all with the same target size. **D,** a ten-hit curve for organisms with a smaller target size than that of B. **E,** a multicomponent curve produced by a population containing organisms with different target sizes. The dose rate is assumed to be constant.

be related, for instance, to the degree of clumping of the organisms, because the survival of a single organism is sufficient to maintain the colony-forming ability of a clump, and the curve is therefore measuring the inactivation of the last surviving individual in the clump. Curve A would then describe the inactivation of single organisms, curve B clumps of ten organisms, and curve C clumps of 100 organisms. Curve D would also reflect the inactivation of clumps of 10 organisms, but of smaller target size.

Multiple-hit curves are obtained whenever organisms, or parts of organisms, act cooperatively, i.e., when one susceptible component can replace another in the reproduction of the unit whose survival is being measured. For instance, when bacteria are infected by **several** UV-irradiated virus particles curves of this type describe the survival of the ability to yield active virus (Ch. 23, Multiplicity reactivation).

A third common type of survival curve is

represented by curve E: this is a **multicomponent curve,** generated by a population composed of organisms with different target sizes. Those with the larger target size, i.e., more sensitive, are inactivated first, while at the end only the most resistant ones survive. Thus the survival curve tails off into a line whose slope corresponds to the small target size of the more resistant or-

ganisms. The proportion of this group can be estimated by extrapolating back the final straight part of the curve to the ordinate axis (about 2×10^{-3} in Fig. 8-43). Curves of this type are commonly obtained when viruses are exposed to chemical inactivating agents (Ch. 26), and their recognition is most important in the preparation of safe vaccines.

SELECTED REFERENCES

Books and Review Articles

BALDWIN, R. L. Molecular Aspects of the Gene: Replication Mechanism. In *The Bacteria,* vol. V, p. 327. (I. C. Gunsalus and R. Y. Stanier, eds.) Academic Press, New York, 1964.

BENZER, S. The fine structure of the gene. *Scient. Am. 206*:27 (1962).

CRICK, F. H. C. The genetic code. *Scientific American 215*:55 (1966).

FINCHAM, J. R. S. *Genetic Complementation.* Benjamin, New York, 1966.

GORINI, L., and BECKWITH, J. R. Suppression. *Ann. Rev. Microbiol. 20*:401 (1966).

INGRAM, V. M. *The Biosynthesis of Macromolecules.* Benjamin, New York, 1965.

ORGEL, L. E. The chemical basis of mutation. *Advances Enzymol. 27*:289 (1965).

ROWND, R. Physical chemistry of transforming deoxyribonucleic acid. *Brit. M. Bull. 21*:187 (1965).

SONNEBORN, T. M. Degeneracy of the Genetic Code: Extent, Nature, and Genetic Implications. In *Evolving Genes and Proteins,* p. 377. (V. Bryson and H. Vogel, eds.) Academic Press, New York, 1965.

SPIEGELMAN, S. S. Hybrid nucleic acids. *Scient. Am. 210*:48 (1964).

STACEY, K. A. Intracellular modification of nucleic acids. *Brit. M. Bull. 21*:211 (1965).

Symposium on molecular action of mutagenic and carcinogenic agents. *J. Cell. & Comp. Physiol. 64,* Suppl. 1 (1964).

WACKER, A. Molecular mechanisms of radiation effects. *Progr. Nucleic Acid Res. 1*:369 (1963).

WATSON, J. D. *Molecular Biology of the Gene.* Benjamin, New York, 1965.

Specific Articles

BENZER, S., and CHAMPE, J. P. Ambivalent r_{II} mutants of phage T4. *Proc. Nat. Acad. Sc. 47*:1025 (1961).

BRODY, S., and YANOFSKY, C. Suppressor gene alteration of protein primary structure. *Proc. Nat. Acad. Sc. 50*:9 (1963).

CAPECCHI, M. R., and GUSSIN, G. N. Suppression in vitro: Identification of a serine-sRNA as a "nonsense" suppressor. *Science 149*:417 (1965).

CRICK, F. H. C., BARNETT, L., BRENNER, S., and WATTS-TOBIN, R. M. The general nature of the genetic code. *Nature 192*:1227 (1961).

DAVIES, J., GILBERT, W., and GORINI, L. Streptomycin, suppression, and the code. *Proc. Nat. Acad. Sc. 51*:883 (1964).

FINCHAM, J. R. S., and CODDINGTON, A. The mechanism of complementation between *am* mutants of *Neurospora crassa. Cold Spring Harbor Symp. Quant. Biol. 28*:517 (1963).

MESELSON, M. On the mechanism of genetic recombination between DNA molecules. *J. Molec. Biol. 9*:734 (1964).

MESELSON, M., and STAHL, F. W. The replication of DNA in *Escherichia coli. Proc. Nat. Acad. Sc. 44*:671 (1958).

NIRENBERG, M., LEDER, P., BERNFIELD, M., BRIMACOMBE, R., TRUPIN, J., ROTTMAN, F., and O'NEAL, C. RNA codewords and protein synthesis. VII. On the general nature of the RNA code. *Proc. Nat. Acad. Sc. 53*:1161 (1965).

SARABHAI, A. S., STRETTON, A. O. W., BRENNER, S., and BOLLE, A. Colinearity of gene with polypeptide chain. *Nature 201*:13 (1964).

SCHILDKRAUT, C. L., MARMUR, J., and DOTY, P. The formation of the hybrid DNA molecules and their use in studies of DNA homologies. *J. Molec. Biol. 3*:595 (1961).

SETLOW, R. B., and CARRIER, W. L. The disappearance of thymine dimers from DNA: An error-correcting mechanism. *Proc. Nat. Acad. Sc. 51*:226 (1964).

WATSON, J. D., and CRICK, F. H. C. A structure for deoxyribose nucleic acid. *Nature 171*:737 (1953).

WOESE, C. R. On the evolution of the genetic code. *Proc. Nat. Acad. Sc. 54*:1546 (1965).

9 REGULATORY MECHANISMS

Physiologists have long been concerned with the intricate mechanisms that govern the interactions **between** various cells and organs in animals; but recent observations have revealed an additional, underlying set of **intracellular** regulatory mechanisms. Progress in this area has been especially facilitated by several properties of bacteria: their ability to adapt to a wide variety of environments, the possibility of studying the kinetics of this adaptation in a homogeneous population of cells, and especially the production of mutants with altered regulatory mechanisms.

The mechanisms thus discovered have the broadest possible biological application. Since they occur in mammalian cells as well as in bacteria, their understanding will surely shed light on many aspects of disease. Furthermore, these advances have major implications for the molecular basis of other biological responses to stimuli, since they have revealed the widespread and fundamental role of reversible alterations in protein configuration. Finally, analysis of the regulation of gene expression has provided a long-sought model with which to approach the molecular mechanism of differentiation.

We shall discuss in detail three processes, which control 1) the synthesis of particular enzymes; 2) the activity of already existing enzymes; and 3) the over-all synthesis of DNA, RNA, and protein. The regulation of cell metabolism is known to involve two additional factors: membrane transport systems (Ch. 5), which control the rate of entry and the intracellular levels of exogenous metabolites; and the relative affinity constants of the competing enzymes that may channel a metabolite into alternative pathways. These processes will not be considered here, however, since their investigation has not depended especially on bacteria.

REGULATION OF SYNTHESIS OF SPECIFIC PROTEINS

Enzyme Induction and Repression

Enzyme Induction. We have already seen (Ch. 5) that bacteria can vary their enzymatic composition widely when grown in different environments. In particular, the specific enzymes required for the utilization of a given carbon or nitrogen source are usually made only during growth in the presence of that compound. Such responses were designated decades ago as **adaptive enzyme formation.**

This process has been studied intensively in *Escherichia coli* by Monod at the Pasteur Institute. The enzyme used as a prototype was β-galactosidase, which attacks lactose (glucose-4-β-D-galactoside), a sugar of particular importance in the identification of *E. coli*. This enzyme can also hydrolyze, and be induced by, a number of other galactosides (e.g., methyl-β-D-galactoside). With other compounds, however, the formation of the enzyme could be dissociated from its adaptive function. Thus phenyl-β-D-galactoside is a substrate for the enzyme but induces very poorly, while the sulfur analog, methyl-β-D-thiogalactoside, is a better inducer than lactose but is not a substrate at all (Table 9-1). To focus more sharply on the mechanism of this induction, rather than on its adaptive function, the process was renamed **induced enzyme formation.**

This shift of emphasis was associated with an important refinement in experimental design. Previous studies of the kinetics of induction, employing natural substrates, had suffered from the fact that the added compound exerted a double effect: it interacted directly with the regulatory system, and it could also influence enzyme synthesis indirectly by providing an increased supply of energy and biosynthetic precursors. By employing a nonmetabolized inducer, however, it became possible to study the mechanism of

TABLE 9-1. INDUCTION OF β-GALACTOSIDASE BY VARIOUS COMPOUNDS

Compound	Substituent	Relative induction*	Relative hydrolysis rate†	Relative affinity‡
β-D-galactosides	Glucose (product: lactose)	17	30	14
	Phenyl	15	100	100
β-D-thiogalactosides	Isopropyl	100	0	140
	Methyl	78	0	7
	Phenyl	0	0	100

* **Relative induction** *is the maximal enzyme concentration attained, after growth with a saturating concentration of inducer, relative to the value obtained with isopropyl-β-thiogalactoside (designated as 100).*

† *The* **hydrolysis rate,** *obtained at a saturating concentration, is given relative to that of phenyl-β-galactoside (100).*

‡ *The* **affinity** *is given relative to that of phenyl-β-galactoside (100); for substrates it is determined from the concentration giving half-maximal hydrolysis, and for nonsubstrates it is determined from the inhibitory effect of a given concentration on the hydrolysis of a substrate of known affinity.*

From F. Jacob and J. Monod. J. Molec. Biol. 3:318 (1961).

induction under **gratuitous conditions,** which eliminated the secondary effects.

With this approach it could be shown that within a few minutes, at a sufficient concentration of inducer, the rate of formation of the new enzyme (z) becomes a constant fraction (ca. 5%) of the rate of synthesis of either total protein or bacterial mass (B) (Fig. 9-1).

This **differential rate of synthesis** of an enzyme (dz/dB) proved a useful way of comparing efficiency of induction under various conditions. Furthermore, when radioactive precursors were used to label the protein formed by the cell during the period of induction, subsequent isolation and analysis of the induced enzyme showed that it had been

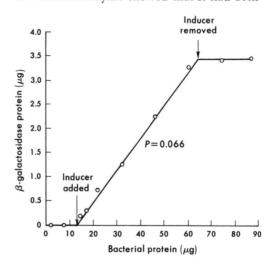

Fig. 9-1 Kinetics of induced enzyme synthesis. A differential plot expressing accumulation of β-galactosidase as a function of increase of mass of cells in a growing culture of *E. coli*. Since both coordinates are expressed in the same units the slope of the straight line gives galactosidase as the fraction (P) of total protein synthesized in the presence of inducer. (From F. Jacob and J. Monod. *J. Molec. Biol.* 3:318, 1961.)

formed entirely de novo from amino acids during the period of induction, and not by activation of a preexisting zymogen. The inducer thus stimulates synthesis of a specific protein.

Since the inducer had to be stereochemically similar to (and usually was identical with) the substrate of the induced enzyme, the notion was attractive that the inducer, by fitting the active site of the enzyme, helped mold it. However, various lines of evidence suggested that the inducer acts on some cell component differing in specificity from the enzyme itself. Thus certain substrate analogs can induce formation of an enzyme (Table 9-1), and others can antagonize its induction, without being able to bind to the enzyme (either as substrate or as inhibitor). Moreover, another, equally specific mechanism of regulation, enzyme repression, was discovered, which could not be accounted for by complexing with the active site of the enzyme, since it was elicited by compounds far removed in structure from the substrate.

Enzyme Repression was revealed by the finding that an added amino acid generally causes cells to cease forming the several enzymes of its biosynthetic pathway. Intermediates of the same pathway, in contrast, do not produce this effect when a genetic block prevents their conversion to the endproduct. The endproduct evidently plays a special role in regulating the synthesis of the enzymes of its own pathway, and this mechanism has become known as **endproduct repression.** Several years elapsed, however, before induction and repression were shown to be different manifestations of the same regulatory mechanism.

Inducible enzymes were earlier considered to be a small, special class, the remaining enzymes of a cell being **constitutive,** i.e., formed without exogenous induction, and hence presumably always present. However, this distinction could no longer be considered fundamental when constitutive enzymes were found to be generally repressible. Nevertheless, the term "constitutive" has remained useful to denote mutations that

eliminate the inducibility or repressibility of an enzyme.

Repression has been observed not only with the enzymes of amino acid and nucleotide biosynthesis, but also in a variety of other metabolic pathways. For example, alkaline phosphatase is formed in *E. coli* cells when various organic phosphorus compounds which it splits (e.g., glycerophosphate) are used as obligatory sources of phosphate; but the addition of a trace of inorganic phosphate (i.e., the endproduct) immediately represses formation of this enzyme. Similarly, many enzymes are induced and repressed in the shift of facultative organisms between aerobic and anaerobic conditions.

In pathways of amino acid biosynthesis the signal for repression is apparently not the intracellular level of the amino acid but rather a later endproduct, aminoacyl tRNA. Thus the addition of valine normally represses the enzymes of valine biosynthesis, but as Neidhardt has shown, a partial block in the activation of valine (achieved by raising the temperature of a culture of a mutant with a temperature-sensitive valine-activating enzyme) derepresses these enzymes and eliminates the response to added valine.

Catabolite Repression. We now know that induction and repression are different manifestations of the same regulatory mechanism, and can both be seen with the same enzyme. Indeed, even before the discovery of endproduct repression glucose was found to prevent formation of inducible enzymes (Ch. 3, Fig. 3-8). Eventually this effect was found to be indistinguishable from repression, the "endproduct" apparently being an intermediate in catabolism (i.e., a catabolite), whose steady-state level in the cell presumably rises when a rapidly utilized source of catabolism, such as glucose, is supplied. The "glucose effect" is therefore now called catabolite repression.

This interpretation is supported by the observation that the effect can be exerted not only by glucose but by any carbon source which can support more rapid growth than the inducer; and conversely, glucose fails to exert its characteristic effect when its entry (and therefore its metabolism) is slowed by a permeability muta-tion. Moreover, the steady-state level of an inter-mediate should be a function of its rate of utilization as well as its rate of formation; and even slowly utilized carbon sources have been found to exert a "glucose effect" when the utili-zation of their catabolic products is slowed. Such slowing can be achieved by impairing protein synthesis (e.g., through restricting the nitrogen supply or adding an inhibitor), thus reducing a major outlet for the expenditure of energy.

A change in carbon source no doubt causes the levels of many catabolites to change in parallel; and it is presumed that different ones serve as the "endproduct" repressors for different inducible enzymes. However, in contrast to bio-synthetic endproducts, these repressors are diffi-cult to define, since permeability barriers and the rapidity of catabolite turnover make it diffi-cult to influence specifically the intracellular level of various catabolic intermediates. Furthermore, studies of catabolite repression are complicated by the ability of a repressor not only to stimulate catabolite production but also to inhibit entry of an inducer into the cell. For example, galac-tose competitively inhibits β-galactoside trans-port.

Autocatalytic Induction: Inducible Transport Systems; Product Induction. Under gratuitous conditions, in which the inducer is not metabo-lized, it was expected that the cell would re-spond to a given inducer concentration with a constant differential rate of synthesis of the en-zyme relative to protein synthesized. While this pattern was observed at saturating concentra-tions of the inducer, at nonsaturating concentra-tions the response was found to be autocatalytic. This pattern was traced to the ability of β-galac-tosides to induce the formation not only of β-galactosidase but also of a **transport system** that can actively concentrate the inducer (Ch. 5). Moreover, because of this effect cells that are already induced can respond to a **maintenance concentration** of inducer considerably lower than that required to initiate induction effectively (Fig. 9-2). This phenomenon superficially re-sembles the differentiation of the cells of higher organisms: once parallel cultures of identical genotype have been grown in the presence and in the absence of preinduction, they can then be maintained as different phenotypes through many generations in an identical medium (i.e., one with a low concentration of inducer). In

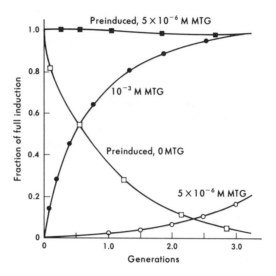

Fig. 9-2 Maintenance of induction of β-galac-tosidase by concentration of inducer too low to initiate induction effectively. Methyl thiogalactoside (MTG), a gratuitous inducer of β-galactosidase, was added at the indicated concentration to a culture of *E. coli* growing in the chemostat, and the concentra-tion of the enzyme (units/cell) was determined at in-tervals; the values are expressed in relative terms. The circles depict results obtained on inoculating uninduced cells; the squares depict results obtained on inoculating cells fully induced by previous growth in the presence of 10^{-3}M MTG.

It could be shown that the response of a cell to inducer is all-or-none: the slow response observed at low inducer concentration represents a slow in-crease in the fraction of induced cells, but each cell that begins to respond forms transport units that then ensure further induction at the full rate. (Adapted from A. Novick and M. Weiner. *Proc. Nat. Acad. Sc.* 43:553, 1957.)

contrast to true differentiation, however, this effect is readily reversible on shifting the en-vironment.

Another autocatalytic type of induction has been revealed with the recent discovery that **some enzymes are directly induced by their product,** rather than by their substrate. For ex-ample, glycerol is converted to α-glycerophos-phate by glycerol phosphokinase; and either compound can induce this enzyme, along with a transport system and the next enzyme in the pathway (glycerophosphate dehydrogenase). The direct inducer, however, appears to be glycerophosphate rather than the initial substrate in the sequence, for in a mutant that makes an inactive form of the phosphokinase glycerol cannot be converted to its phosphate, and is not an inducer; but glycerophosphate induces the full set of proteins.

Another basis for **persistent induction** is seen with **penicillinase.** In contrast to the rapid cessation of most induced syntheses on removal of the inducer, induction by penicillin persists for half an hour after its removal. The mechanism is not certain, but it seems possible that this rather reactive compound is converted in the cell to a chemical derivative that is not readily washed out.

Regulator Genes

The mechanism of regulation of enzyme formation, like many other cellular mechanisms, was revealed through its alteration by mutation. Indeed, without the application of formal genetics it is doubtful that the problem could have been solved.

Specifically, wild-type *E. coli,* inducible for β-galactosidase, gave rise to mutants that were constitutive* for this enzyme and to others (*lac⁻*) that could not form it. Analysis of these mutants showed that two different loci influence the formation of the enzyme. One of these clearly represents a **structural** gene (z), which directly controls the structure of the enzyme; for while some z^- mutants contain no detectable product of this gene, others contain an altered protein (**cross-reacting material, CRM**), which has lost enzyme activity but cross-reacts immunologically with β-galactosidase. The other locus is a **regulator** gene

---

* Constitutive *lac⁺* mutants can conveniently be isolated by virtue of the fact that they always contain β-galactosidase, even when grown on glucose, and hence can be stained by spraying with a chromogenic substrate (*o*-nitrophenyl-β-galactoside), which yields the yellow product *o*-nitrophenol on hydrolysis.

† This early work was done when attention was being focused on induction, rather than on regulation in general; hence the regulator locus for β-galactosidase was denoted *i*. However, since this locus governs the manufacture of a regulator, rather than that of an inducer, it seems best designated by the symbol (*R*), which has since been used for all other regulator loci.

(R—*lac*);† R^- mutations can cause the production of β-galactosidase to be constitutive, but do not appear to influence the structure of the enzyme. Since constitutive mutants (R^-z^+) can be readily crossed with mutants blocked in enzyme production (R^+z^-) to yield inducible recombinants (R^+z^+), two loci are evidently involved.

Similar regulator loci have been demonstrated not only for other inducible enzymes but also for repressible enzymes, such as those of amino acid biosynthesis. These R loci are recognized through their mutation to yield nonrepressible alleles, in whose presence the formation of the enzymes is no longer sensitive to addition of the endproduct repressor.

R⁺ Dominance; Trans Effect. The dominance of constitutivity versus inducibility was tested by Pardee, Jacob, and Monod in cells made heterozygous for the *lac* region. Tests were carried out in the transient merozygotes formed by *Hfr* × *F⁻* conjugation, and later in the stable merozygotes formed by F-duction (Ch. 7) with *F′-lac*. It was found that when a constitutive R^-z^+ genome is introduced into an inducible R^+z^+ cell the resulting R^+z^+/R^-z^+ merozygote is inducible. Similarly, an R^+z^-/R^-z^+ merozygote is inducible, whereas R^-z^-/R^-z^+ is constitutive. Two important, related conclusions follow: 1) **inducibility (R^+) is dominant to R-gene constitutivity (R^-);** 2) since the R^+ gene influences the expression of a z gene on a separate chromosome (*trans* effect), as well as on its own chromosome (*cis* effect), **the R gene must give rise to a diffusible cytoplasmic product** (Fig. 9-3). This product is designated as the **regulator** or **repressor.**

Repressors and Effectors. To explain the action of the R gene product in terms that can account for both inductive and repressive effects of added small molecules, Jacob and Monod have proposed a scheme in which **repression is fundamental, induction being a release of repression.** According to this model, the **repressor** produced by an R gene has a configuration that can be altered reversibly by complexing with a specific small-molecule

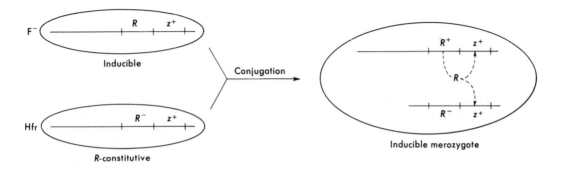

Fig. 9-3 Dominance of *lac* R^+ (inducible) over *lac* R^- (constitutive) allele. The dotted arrows indicate that the R^+ gene must yield a product that influences the activity of a *z* gene in a *trans* as well as in the *cis* chromosome.

will be active and can repress expression of the corresponding structural genes, but in another configuration the repressor will lack this activity.

In an **inducible** system three allelic classes are known for the *R* gene. 1) the R^+ allele would produce a repressor that is active in its "natural" configuration, and combination with the inducer would shift it to the inactive configuration. 2) R^- alleles presumably do not make an effective repressor, hence the inducer is not necessary for enzyme synthesis. 3) A third, superrepressive allele of the *R-lac* locus (R^s) apparently forms a permanently active repressor, since even in the presence of inducer this allele prevents expression of a z^+ gene (whether *cis* or *trans*).

In a system exhibiting endproduct **repression,** in contrast, the repressor would be inactive in its natural configuration, but would become active on combination with a specific effector (the corepressor).* In **catabolite** repression some catabolite presumably serves as a corepressor.

The catabolite corepressor and the inducer may well act on different aporepressors. Thus

glucose can repress β-galactosidase formation even in *lac*-constitutive (R^-) cells, and the reciprocal effect has been demonstrated by Magasanik with CR^- mutants (altered at quite a different locus from that of *R*), in which the *lac* enzymes have specifically lost catabolite sensitivity but remain inducible (R^+). However, it is possible that the *CR* gene affects the level of some catabolite rather than providing a second aporepressor for the *lac* locus.

The Nature of the Repressor. Since the regulation of enzyme formation has not been reproduced in vitro, the repressor has not been identified chemically. However, there are reasonable grounds for believing that it is a protein. Thus, 1) proteins are the only class of compounds known to be capable of complexing specifically with (and having their configuration altered by) a wide variety of ligand structures, such as are found among inducers and repressors. 2) Some mutants produce temperature-sensitive regulators, just as others produce temperature-sensitive protein enzymes. 3) Suppressor mutations, which alter the fidelity of translation of genetic information into protein (Ch. 8), can alter the function of some R^- mutants (i.e., can restore their repressibility). 4) A minor protein component that can bind β-galactosides has been isolated by Gilbert from strains R^+ for the *lac* locus, and it could not be found in R^- strains.

---

* Since the products of *R* genes were designated as repressors, this term could no longer be used for the small molecules whose addition brings about repression. These substances are therefore now called corepressors.

Operons and the Operator

Coordinate Synthesis of Enzymes. We have already noted that the addition of a single inducer can stimulate the formation of more than one specific protein (e.g., both β-galactosidase and the corresponding transport system). Indeed, long sequences of catabolic enzymes had been observed, many years earlier, to appear following the addition of certain substrates such as benzoate; but because of the emphasis then on the adaptive response to a substrate, it was believed that the substrate induced only the first enzyme, whose product induced the next, and so forth. However, such a sequential action could not account for the parallel repressive effect, discovered later, of an endproduct on a whole sequence of biosynthetic enzymes, and so it became apparent that a single metabolite

might directly influence the synthesis of several enzymes. A possible mechanism was suggested by an intriguing observation of Demerec and Hartman: in enteric bacteria the genes for a given pathway, such as those of histidine biosynthesis, are often adjacent and thus form a **cluster** in the chromosome.

Pursuing this lead, Ames found that the genes in the histidine pathway are **coordinately repressed:** when the levels of the enzymes are varied widely by growing a histidine auxotroph with different degrees of histidine limitation, **the ratio of each of these enzymes to the others remains constant** (Fig. 9-4). Similar coordinate repression has been observed with other closely related biosynthetic enzymes; and **coordinate induction** has been observed with groups of catabolic enzymes (e.g., *lac, gal, arabinose*). These observations suggested that the repressor might

Fig. 9-4 Coordinate synthesis of enzymes of the histidine biosynthesis pathway. Cells of several different histidine auxotrophs were harvested in different stages of derepression, caused by growth on a limited supply of histidine, and the levels of several enzymes were determined. Chart A shows that throughout the range of derepression two enzymes of the histidine pathway, histidinol phosphate (HP)-phosphatase and histidinol dehydrogenase, retained a constant ratio of concentrations. Similar constancy was observed with other enzymes of the pathway. In contrast, an enzyme not on the pathway, glutamic dehydrogenase, shows no constancy of ratio to HP-phosphatase (Chart B.) (From B. Ames and B. Garry. *Proc. Nat. Acad. Sc.* 45:1453, 1959.)

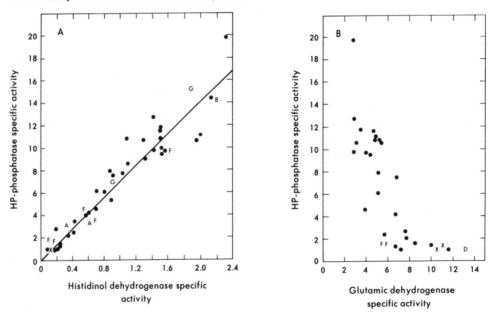

influence the activity of a structurally linked set of genes, functioning as a unit. However, it also could conceivably be acting separately on each of the genes of a cluster, rather than on a single controlling unit. Decisive evidence again came, as with the R gene, from the study of appropriate mutants.

Indeed, some pathways, such as those of arginine or of pyrimidine biosynthesis, were found to involve several scattered groups of genes which are nevertheless regulated by the same R gene. These scattered units, however, differ from each other in sensitivity to the regulator, causing imperfect coordination of enzyme synthesis in these pathways.

The Operator (O) Locus. A specific regulator must act on a specific receptor, which was defined by Jacob *et al.* as the **operator.** Whatever its nature, its specific structure must be genetically determined; hence there should theoretically exist strains in which a mutation in the operator (O) locus has resulted in constitutivity (i.e., in an operator that cannot respond to the R gene product). Moreover, such unresponsiveness to the repressor, in **operator-constitutive (O^c) mutants,** should logically result in **dominant constitutivity,** in contrast to the recessive constitutivity already seen (Fig. 9-3) with strains (R^-) that cannot make an effective repressor.

In accord with this prediction, strains were obtained with a mutation to constitutivity (O^c) that was dominant in heterogenotes (e.g., $O^c R^+ z^+/O^+ R^+ z^+$ strains were constitutive for β-galactosidase).* When the z alleles in such strains were varied it was found, as expected, that the O **locus acts only in *cis* position,** regulating the action of the z gene on its own chromosome but not that

on a homologous chromosome. Thus an $O^c z^+ R^+/O^+ z^- R^+$ heterogenote is *lac*-constitutive, but an $O^c z^- R^+/O^+ z^+ R^+$ heterogenote is inducible (Fig. 9-5). This local action of the O locus along its own chromosome contrasts with the diffuse action of the R gene via the cytoplasm (Fig. 9-3).

The Operon. The O locus was found to have the additional important feature of affecting the activity of a **group** of genes, previously noted to be coordinately induced and repressed. Specifically, O^c mutants are constitutive not only for β-galactosidase (z), but also for the β-galactoside transport system (permease; Ch. 5) and for an enzyme of unknown physiological function, β-galactoside-transacetylase. The genetic loci for these units map in a sequence adjacent to z (Fig. 9-6). **The O locus thus governs the expression of a sequence of structural genes,** and the whole complex is defined as an **operon.** In all the subsequently discovered operons, including those of biosynthetic pathways, the O locus, defined by O^c mutations, has always been found at one end of the sequence.

O^c mutations were originally assumed to be point mutations, like most z^- or R^- mutations. However, O^c mutations are not induced by chemical mutagens that alter a single nucleotide, and they do not revert to O^+. It therefore appears (Ch. 8, Mutations) that **all O^c mutations are deletions.** This finding is perhaps not surprising. When a single nucleotide substitution is translated into protein it can yield a product with a marked change in tertiary structure; hence such a substitution can understandably prevent the formation of an active enzyme. However, if the operator is a specific sequence of nucleotide units, which lacks tertiary structure, the replacement of a single unit might not be a large enough change to destroy the affinity for the repressor.

The Existence of an Intermediate Template Between DNA and Protein

To determine the level at which the repressor acts, in repressing the expression of an operon, it was necessary to analyze the

---

* To isolate such dominant operator-constitutive mutants, rather than the more frequent recessive regulator-constitutive mutants, ingenious use was made of their difference in dominance. A strain was obtained, by F-duction (Ch. 7), with two R^+ genes for the *lac* locus (i.e., an R^+/F-R^+ stable heterogenote). Mutations of either R^+ gene to R^- would be recessive and hence would not be expressed as constitutive in the heterogenote (R^+/R^-), but mutations of an O^+ to O^c would be so expressed.

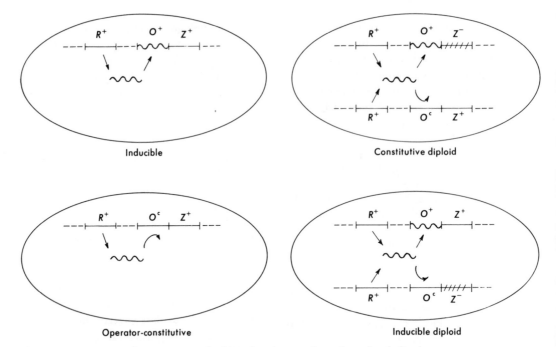

Fig. 9-5 Dominance of operator constitutivity. Attachment of regulator (symbolized as wavy line) to receptive form of operator (O$^+$) blocks expression of z$^+$ gene in *cis* but not in *trans* position. Regulator does not influence O^c allele of operator.

process of information transfer from DNA to protein. Studies on protein synthesis in vitro had already shown that this process requires the presence of ribosomes and transfer RNA (tRNA), as well as certain enzymes, but not DNA. It therefore seemed quite certain that the information is transferred from DNA to protein via **an intermediate RNA template.** As was noted in Chapter 8, the transfer of information from DNA to this template is called **transcription,** while the transfer from RNA is called **translation.**

For several years the intermediate templates were believed to be the ribosomes, which would thus have to vary widely in the specificity of their RNA, even though they appeared morphologically identical. However, in 1961 the templates were discovered, as will be shown below, to constitute a separate RNA fraction, called **messenger RNA** (mRNA).*

* Since mRNA, when not complexed with ribosomes, is soluble under the conditions that are used to precipitate or to sediment ribosomes, it may be included in the chemical fraction originally designated as "soluble" RNA; hence the functional component originally recognized in soluble RNA has been renamed "transfer RNA" (tRNA), though the abbreviation sRNA is still widely used.

Fig. 9-6 Map of the *lac* operon. Structural genes z, y, and a code respectively for β-galactosidase, the β-galactoside transport system, and β-galactoside transacetylase. The operator (O) locus is responsible for repressing expression of the adjacent sequence of structural genes. The regulator (R) gene appears to be adjacent to this operon, but this position is not obligatory, for in many other systems the two are separated by unrelated genes.

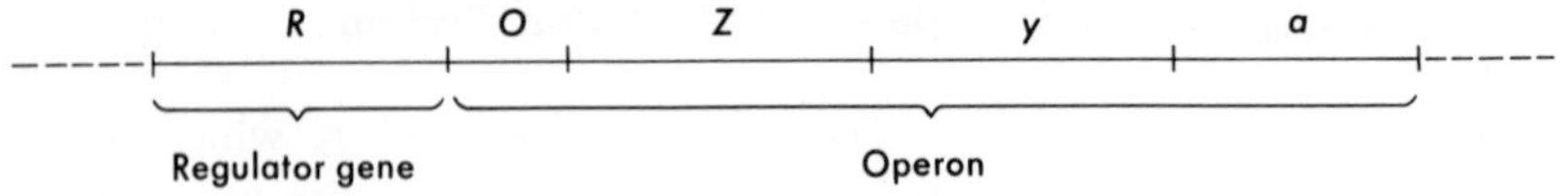

A wide variety of molecules of mRNA in a cell thus complex with a uniform (or relatively uniform) population of ribosomes.

Messenger RNA had previously been overlooked in chemical analyses for several reasons. 1) Under ordinary conditions of cell extraction it remains mostly complexed with the ribosomes. 2) It is ordinarily only a small fraction of the total RNA of the cell, and it is quite heterogeneous in molecular weight; hence even when dissociated from the ribosomes it usually does not form a visible peak in the ultracentrifuge. 3) Lacking the extensive double-strandedness of tRNA, and the complexing with protein that protects ribosomal RNA, it is especially susceptible to destruction by ribonuclease in the course of extraction.

The Discovery of Messenger RNA

Since the discovery of mRNA was intimately linked with the study of regulation in bacteria, we shall present the evidence here in some detail.

Kinetic Evidence. The existence of a rapidly turning over messenger was inferred by Jacob and Monod, and by Gros, on the basis of the extremely rapid response of β-galactosidase synthesis to various alterations in the system. Thus, when a z^+ gene is transferred, by conjugation, from repressed cells to z^- cells lacking repression, synthesis of the enzyme reaches its maximal rate within a few minutes of entry of the gene. Hence the newly formed intermediate template must **build up** to its steady-state level very rapidly; otherwise the rate of synthesis would continue to rise for a long time. Conversely, when the introduced chromosome fragment is heavily labeled with ^{32}P, and the cells are stored frozen (for periods of weeks) to allow the introduced genes to be inactivated by ^{32}P decay, the cells **lose** the ability to carry out continuous β-galactosidase synthesis at the same rate at which their z^+ genes are damaged (as detected in subsequent genetic recombination tests). Hence even though these cells had formed some intermediate template (as shown by enzyme synthesis) before the genetic decay, that template must be unstable.

The instability of the template can be measured more accurately by using 5-fluorouracil, **a base analog** whose incorporation into RNA causes errors in coding that result in the synthesis of inactive, altered forms of enzymes. Addition of this reagent blocks the synthesis of active enzymes (but not of protein) within a few minutes. Since this addition should influence the formation but not the destruction of the intermediate template, it appears that the template in a growing cell is degraded very rapidly.

The above evidence led to the conclusion that the intermediate templates of protein synthesis in *E. coli* turn over very rapidly, with a half life of around 2 minutes. However, the ribosomes do not turn over in growing cells: Davern and Meselson had already shown that when cells are grown for a generation with heavy isotopes and their extracts are subjected to equilibrium density centrifugation, the new, heavy ribosomes can be separated from the light ribosomes made in previous generations; no ribosomes of intermediate density are formed. It was therefore necessary to postulate a rapidly turning over "messenger" RNA fraction, distinct from the ribosomes.

Chemical Evidence. The novel RNA fraction inferred from these kinetic studies was soon demonstrated directly in several laboratories. In this work **bacteria infected with bacteriophage** proved especially useful. The metabolic effects of such infection will be described in detail in Chapter 23, but we may note here that the infecting virus completely dominates the metabolism of the host bacterium, so that the only net synthesis seen is that of bacteriophage DNA and proteins. But even though there is no **net** RNA synthesis in such infected cells, the incorporation of radioactive phosphate, and analysis of its distribution among the four ribonucleotides, had revealed earlier the synthesis of **a rapidly turning over RNA fraction with a base composition similar to that of phage DNA** (and different from that of bacterial DNA or RNA).

The function of this RNA remained obscure until the kinetic experiments described above suggested the concept of messenger. Brenner, Jacob, and Meselson then provided critical evidence for this function by growing cells with heavy isotopes to label their ribosomes, infecting them with phage, and incubating them without the heavy isotopes to permit recognition, by centrifugation, of new ribosomes. Radioactive isotopes were simultaneously provided to label new RNA and protein (Fig. 9-7). Analysis of the extracts showed that 1) as in uninfected cells, the previously synthesized ribosomes persist, but no new ribosomes are made; 2) new, labeled protein is found complexed with these old ribosomes; and 3) in this process newly formed, labeled RNA is also complexed with the ribosomes. Moreover, the labeled RNA and protein can be displaced from the ribosomes in the cells by a "chase," i.e., subsequent incubation of the cells with nonradioactive precursors; hence these complexes appear to be intermediates in protein synthesis.

In uninfected cells labeled mRNA is less readily detected because of the simultaneous synthesis of the other, stable forms of RNA. However, the actual **rate** of synthesis of

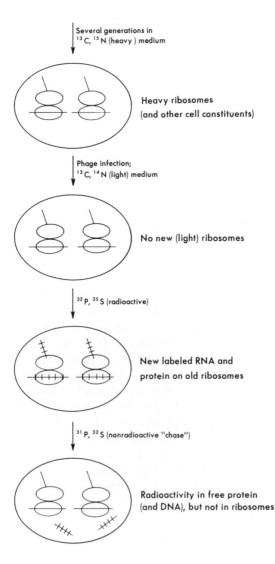

Several generations in
^{13}C, ^{15}N (heavy) medium

Heavy ribosomes
(and other cell constituents)

Phage infection;
^{12}C, ^{14}N (light) medium

No new (light) ribosomes

^{32}P, ^{35}S (radioactive)

New labeled RNA and
protein on old ribosomes

^{31}P, ^{32}S (nonradioactive "chase")

Radioactivity in free protein
(and DNA), but not in ribosomes

Fig. 9-7 Diagram of experiment of S. Brenner, F. Jacob, and M. Meselson (Nature *190:*576, 1961) on labeling of various components in phage-infected cells. Since there is no **net** synthesis of RNA in phage-infected cells the nucleotides released by mRNA breakdown would be reutilized in mRNA synthesis, and thus would prevent exogenous labeling of this fraction, were it not for the fact that the ribonucleotide pool is constantly being drained for the synthesis of precursors of phage DNA.

mRNA in balanced growth exceeds that of the other fractions—although they accumulate in time (i.e., exhibit much greater **net** synthesis), while the mRNA turns over instead. Hence the messenger fraction can be preferentially labeled by pulse-labeling cells: exposing them to labeled precursor ($^{32}PO_4$ or ^{14}C-uracil) for a period too brief (< 1 min) to allow much turnover of mRNA and synthesis of stable RNA.

Using this technic Gros *et al.* demonstrated, in **uninfected** cells, a rapidly labeled fraction with a DNA-like base composition.* Moreover, this pulse-labeled RNA had distinctive ultracentrifugal properties, which were also demonstrated by Spiegelman *et al.* for the phage-induced RNA. Thus at a sufficiently high Mg^{++} concentration (10^{-2} M) these mRNAs remain associated with ribosomes, and so both radioactivity (reflecting mRNA) and ultraviolet absorption (reflecting the bulk RNA) sediment with a peak at 70S (Fig. 9-8). At a low Mg^{++} concentration (10^{-4} M), however, the ribosomes dissociate into their 30S and 50S subunits and free the attached mRNA; the radioactivity is then found in a broad peak at 8 to 14S. (Larger mRNA molecules have since been obtained by minimizing degradation by RNase.)

Once the mRNA fraction was separated its function could be further demonstrated in vitro. 1) mRNA could be specifically hybridized with the corresponding DNA; hence the two have not only the same base composition but the same **base sequence,** which indicates that one served as the template for forming the other. 2) Furthermore, an in vitro **protein-synthesizing system** with a limiting supply of mRNA is best stimulated by those fractions of the extracted cellular RNA rich in the component centrifuging as mRNA. This effect also explains why the presence in extracts of DNA, which is a template for RNA formation, stimulates protein synthesis even though it is not essential. 3) Finally, as was shown in Chapter 8, the function of mRNA in a protein-synthesizing system can be replaced by various **synthetic single-stranded polyribonucleotides.**

The stability of the pulse-labeled RNA fraction can be studied with **actinomycin,** which specifically inhibits all DNA-dependent RNA synthesis but presumably does not influence the degradation of mRNA. As is seen in Figure 9-9, of the RNA labeled in a brief pulse in *Bacillus subtilis* about 80% undergoes decay, with a half life of about 2 minutes. Moreover, the decay of this labile RNA is closely paralleled by the decline in the rate of protein synthesis in the cells. These values for mRNA stability are in harmony with those obtained from the kinetics, noted above, of the inhibitory effect of a base analog on the synthesis of an active enzyme. These data suggest that a bacterial messenger molecule is used about 15 times before destruction.

Polysomes. The extracts used initially for studies on ribosomes were generally prepared by grinding the cells with abrasive. When gentler methods were introduced, such as osmotic lysis of protoplasts or of animal cells, a large fraction of the ribosomes in the cell were discovered to be present as polysomes (also called polyribosomes or ergosomes). These are seen under the electron microscope as a string of a variable number of ribosomes connected by a thread (Fig. 9-10), and they sediment more rapidly than the 70S "monosomes," yielding several peaks corresponding to different numbers of ribosomes. The connecting thread in a polysome is presumably simply mRNA, since it is extremely sensitive to scission by traces of

---

* The DNA-like composition of mRNA has helped in its recognition but is not logically necessary. Only one strand of the DNA is transcribed; and since that strand does not have to have the same composition as its complement, the mRNA could have a composition different from that of the average of the two strands of DNA. In fact, the DNA of certain bacteriophages, when denatured, yields strands of different density (and hence composition; Ch. 23). Nevertheless, bacterial chromosomes have empirically shown striking homogeneity in density when broken up into smaller fragments, whether double- or single-stranded.

While subsequent work has shown that the stable RNA components of a cell (rRNA and tRNA) are also synthesized by base-pairing on DNA, these DNA regions have a composition quite different from that of the average DNA. Hence the bulk RNA of a cell does not have a DNA-like composition.

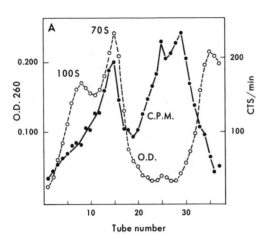

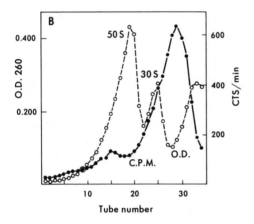

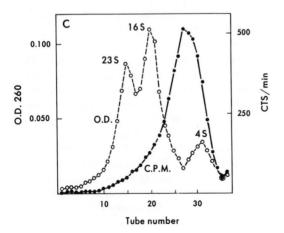

Fig. 9-8 Zonal sedimentation of pulse-labeled RNA. *E. coli* was grown for a very brief period (20 seconds) with ^{14}C-uracil to label the RNA. To stop further metabolism immediately the cells were poured on crushed ice and azide was added. Batches of cells were disrupted by grinding with alumina in various media. The extracts were subjected to zonal sedimentation in a gradient of 5 to 20% sucrose (Ch. 8) for the length of time necessary to separate the major RNA components. Fractions were collected through the bottom of the tube, and the RNA content (measured by optical density at 260 mμ) and radioactivity were determined.

A. Extract containing 10^{-2} M Mg^{++}, which preserves the integrity of the ribosomes and their association with mRNA. It is seen that some of the newly formed (labeled) RNA sediments with the 70S (ribosome) and the 100S (ribosomal aggregate) peaks, while the rest forms a broad slower peak. The separation of the latter material from ribosomes is largely an artifact of extraction, since gentler methods later yielded a much larger fraction associated with ribosomes. (The slowest peak of ultraviolet absorption, generally labeled 4S, contains the tRNA but is also contributed to by proteins.)

B. Extract containing 10^{-4} M Mg^{++}, which permits the ribosomes to dissociate into their 50S and 30S components. Almost all the labeled RNA has dissociated from these components and forms a broad peak between the 30S and the 4S peaks.

C. Extract purified with phenol to eliminate protein. The RNA components of the 50S and the 30S ribosome subunits, now RNA molecules in solution rather than ribonucleoprotein particles, form 23S and 16S peaks, respectively. The radioactive mRNA fraction sediments again as a broad, slower peak. (It is even slower than the corresponding peak in B, reflecting its partial fragmentation during the extra manipulations involved in preparing the extract.) (From F. Gros, H. Hiatt, W. Gilbert, C. G. Kurland, R. W. Risebrough, and J. D. Watson. *Nature* 190:581, 1961.)

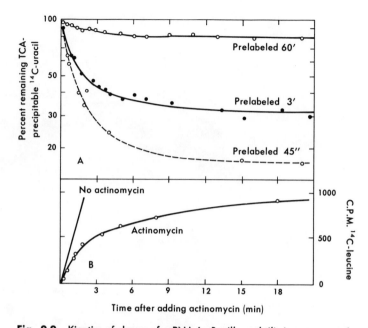

Fig. 9-9 Kinetics of decay of mRNA in *Bacillus subtilis* in presence of actinomycin.

A. Cells were grown in the presence of ^{14}C-uracil, to label the RNA, for 45 seconds, 3 minutes, and 60 minutes, and then (zero time) sufficient actinomycin D (10 μg/ml) was added to stop further RNA synthesis. Samples were taken at intervals during further incubation, and the labeled RNA was measured by washing the cells with 5% ice-cold trichloroacetic acid to remove nonpolymerized radioactive material, followed by drying and determination of radioactivity. It is seen that following the shortest pulse over 80% of the labeled RNA subsequently decayed (i.e., was depolymerized), reaching a plateau in about 10 minutes. The decaying material represents mRNA and probably also some incomplete rRNA and tRNA. Following the 60-minute exposure to ^{14}C-uracil, in contrast, most of the label was in the stable forms of RNA.

B. To two parallel batches of growing cells ^{14}C-leucine was added at zero time, and to one actinomycin D was also added. The amount of protein synthesized, in samples taken at intervals, was determined by the same technic used above to determine the survival of labeled RNA. It is seen that after addition of actinomycin protein synthesis decays with essentially the same kinetics as the decay of the unstable RNA fraction. (From C. Levinthal, D. P. Fan, A. Higa, and R. A. Zimmerman. *Cold Spring Harbor Symp. Quant. Biol. 28*:183, 1963.)

RNase; moreover, the polysome fraction, separated after sedimentation in a sucrose gradient, is more active in protein synthesis (without added mRNA) than is the monosome fraction.

The Length of the Messenger. The function of the operon as a unit of transcription suggests that it may produce an mRNA molecule of the same length as the corresponding segment of DNA, and that each molecule may code for several polypeptides, which are separated by a codon for punctuation. (Indeed, genetic evidence for the one-operon-one-messenger theory will be presented shortly.) It would follow that the mRNA molecules in a cell vary in length, as do the operons: the *lac* operon, for example, appears to contain 3 structural genes, and the histidine operon 10. Direct experimental evidence on mRNA length, however, suffers from the marked sensitivity of mRNA to the RNase in extracts. Hence the frequently observed polyribosomes that contain about five ribosomes, and correspond in length to about one protein, are probably degraded. Nevertheless, improved methods of preparation (including the use of

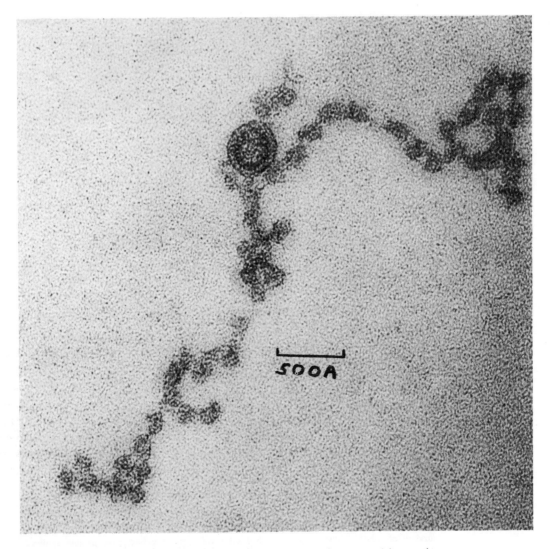

Fig. 9-10 Electron micrograph of a large polysome from *E. coli,* extracted by gently stirring penicillin spheroplasts with a nonionic detergent. Negative staining with uranyl acetate. (Courtesy Alexander Rich.)

rubber gloves to keep out the ribonuclease in traces of sweat) have yielded mRNA molecules large enough (30S, m.w. ca. 10^6) to code for several proteins, assuming one amino acid per nucleotide triplet of a molecular weight ca. 1000.

mRNA Turnover. While the rapid turnover of mRNA in bacteria was largely responsible for its discovery, in mammalian cells it is much more stable; hence reticulocytes can continue to synthesize hemoglobin for prolonged periods even though they lack a nucleus. The difference probably reflects a difference in enzymatic com-

position of the cells, but the enzyme responsible for the degradation of mRNA in bacteria has not been defined.

The Level of Action of the Repressor

We have already seen that induction of enzyme formation has essentially the same kinetics as the turnover of mRNA: the synthesis of β-galactosidase reaches its maximum rate within 3 to 4 minutes after addition of an inducer, and it ceases equally rapidly on removal of the inducer (Fig. 9-1). This close parallel strongly suggests that the regulator system acts by governing the **synthesis of mRNA,** rather than its activity.

This inference has been supported by experiments in which radioactively labeled mRNA corresponding to the *gal* operon was identified by hybridization with DNA rich in the *gal* region (i.e., DNA from the transducing phage λdg, Ch. 24). *Gal*-mRNA could be demonstrated in extracts of induced *gal*$^+$ cells but not of uninduced cells. The effect is small, however. Moreover, the absence of a given mRNA species in uninduced cells might alternatively be due to its rapid degradation when not being read: in extracts mRNA is known to be protected against RNase action by complexing with ribosomes.

Additional evidence has been obtained by carrying out the transcription and the translation of an operon at separate times. Specifically, an inducer of β-galactosidase was allowed to act on a culture of *E. coli* for several minutes in the presence of chloramphenicol, which blocks protein synthesis but permits RNA synthesis. The cells were then washed and resuspended in the absence of both the inducer and the chloramphenicol. The induced enzyme was then made for several minutes (Fig. 9-11), which indicates that the specific messenger had been formed, though not translated, in the presence of chloramphenicol and the inducer.

While there is thus good evidence that repressors act at the level of transcription, the possibility of an effect also at the level of translation has not been altogether eliminated. Definitive solution of the problem may require the attainment of repression in an extracted system.

Polarity Mutations

We have already seen that an operon functions as a unit. Further evidence on its function has been provided by the discovery of polarity mutations—a special class of mutations that not only alter the structure and function of the gene in which they occur,

but also decrease the activity of other genes of the same operon. In the *lac* operon, for example, polarity mutations in the *z* gene are z^- mutations (since they prevent β-galactosidase formation); but they have the additional effect of decreasing expression of the distal parts of the operon (*y* and *a*, Fig. 9-6). Polarity mutations in *y* similarly interfere with the expression of the distal gene *a*, but not with that of the proximal part of the operon (*z*). The degree of influence on the distal genes differs among these mutants; extreme (or complete) polarity mutations abolish all activity.

These effects lead to several conclusions: 1) **the operon is transcribed into a single messenger molecule;** 2) **the messenger molecule is translated in the direction away from the operator;** 3) certain mutations can inter-

Fig. 9-11 Induction of β-galactosidase messenger formation during inhibition of protein synthesis. *E. coli* cells were incubated with an inducer (isopropyl-β-thiogalactoside) for 4 minutes in the presence of chloramphenicol (50 μg/ml). The cells were then washed rapidly on a Millipore filter and resuspended in complete medium containing neither inducer nor chloramphenicol. The culture synthesized β-galactosidase for about 10 minutes, the amount formed being less than 1% of that seen in a fully induced culture. When the inducer was omitted from the incubation with chloramphenicol no enzyme was subsequently formed. (From D. Nakada and B. Magasanik. *J. Molec. Biol.* 8:105, 1964.)

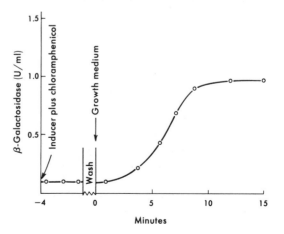

fere with the continuation of one of these processes beyond the site of the mutation.

Polarity mutations are point mutations, since they are revertible; and they can be eliminated by a small deletion, which restores an effective **connection** (though not a functional gene) between the operator and the distal genes. At first, it seemed possible that polarity mutations might code for a message that directly interrupted transcription. However, Beckwith found that the polarity effect can be overcome by a **suppressor** mutation, located in a distant region of the chromosome. Such suppressors are known to act on the translation rather than the transcription mechanism, canceling the effect of a point mutation through causing a certain frequency of error in reading the mRNA (Ch. 8, Suppression).

When a large number of auxotrophs in the histidine pathway were recently tested for revertibility by various mutagens, and for suppressibility by known suppressor genes, the polarity mutations among them (constituting the majority) were found to fall into two mutational classes: 1) those two codons that code for chain termination (nonsense), and are respectively suppressible by the **amber** or the **ochre** suppressors (Ch. 8, Genetic code); and 2) frame-shift mutations, which create a garbled sequence of distal codons that will sooner or later also turn up a codon for termination. In contrast, missense codons, which do not interrupt translation, did not have a polarity effect in this series.

Effect of Position on Polarity Mutations. The effect of a polarity mutation depends on its position in a gene: polar mutants with the same **amber** codon show a **decreasing** effect on distal genes the **closer** the mutation is to the distal end of its own gene. However, we do not know how the length of the dead space, between the mutation and the next gene, exerts this influence, nor do we know why the premature termination of a polypeptide should be associated with a block in further translation. One possibility is that continued transcription requires the presence of a ribosome on the nascent mRNA not far from its growing point, and that ribosomes normally fall off at the codon for polypeptide termination and attach at each codon for polypeptide initiation (Ch. 8).

Regulation of Translation: Modulation

We have already noted that the different enzymes of an operon, measured in terms of their activity, are formed in fixed **proportions** (coordinate synthesis). If the entire mRNA molecule were translated a certain number of times before its destruction these proportions would represent identical **molar amounts** of the individual polypeptides formed by the messenger. However, measurements of purified proteins have shown that a more distal gene in *lac* operon is expressed only about 1/10 as often as the gene adjacent to the *O* locus. These findings suggest **a gradient of protein synthesis along the messenger**, i.e., a cumulatively increasing chance of terminating translation before the ribosome reaches the far end of the messenger. This process, termed **modulation**, seemed likely to be a significant additional regulatory mechanism. However, its importance is now in doubt, since the various polypeptides of the long histidine operon have been shown to be synthesized in equal numbers.

The Mechanisms of Initiation and Repression of Transcription

Initiation. The effects of various deletions in the early part of the *lac* operon have indicated that for normal expression of the genes of the operon a small **initiating segment** must be present; it has been called the **promoter** (*p*). This segment, located at the border between *O* and *z*, may be a distinct locus, or it may also serve as the beginning of the *z* locus. Its function could conceivably relate to the attachment of RNA polymerase to DNA, or to the attachment of ribosomes to messenger RNA.

The evidence for this site of initiation is as follows. Deletions on the operator side of the *p* region, if confined to the *O* region or to the *O + R* regions of the operon, result in typical *O*c constitutivity, with synthesis at a normal level (group B, Fig. 9-12). Deletions on the other side of *p* (group A), if confined to the *z* region, result either in polarity mutations or in typical inducibility for the distal portion of the operon. In contrast, among the deletions originating in *z*, none could be isolated that termi-

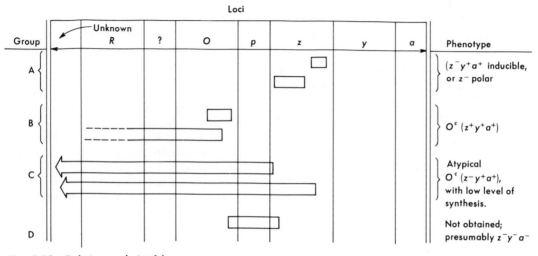

Fig. 9-12 Deletion analysis of *lac* operon.

nated anywhere in O and yet allowed y to be expressed. However, when the deletion beginning in z was very large and extended to the left into the domain of another operon, y could be active as an extension of that unknown operon (i.e., y was constitutive at a low level, and was no longer influenced by the compounds that normally regulate its activity). Jacob concluded that the region between O and z contains a site (p) that is essential for initiating transcription of an operon.

The inferred **fusion of operons** has been directly demonstrated by using a *lac*-containing episome, in which deletions, however large, would not eliminate genes vital for the cell. A mutant was thus isolated in which a long deletion fused the *lac* operon with a more distant operon for adenine synthesis, causing the *lac* genes to become repressible by adenine. The histidine operon has similarly been fused with a neighboring operon, and thus made unresponsive to regulation by histidine.

The Function of the Operator. It seemed possible at first that the O region, while having a special regulatory function, might also be the beginning of the structural gene for z. However, O^c mutations have been found to cause no detectable change in the nature of the β-galactosidase produced. Moreover, the initiating function of the p region, which separates O from z, provides further evidence that they are not part of the same structural gene.

Extreme polarity mutations were initially considered operator-negative (O^o) mutations: the first ones appeared to map in the O region, and they seemed formally to be alleles of the operator locus, opposite in effect from O^c mutations. However, more careful mapping has located them in the z gene, and not in the O region (defined by O^c mutations): they can be eliminated by deletions confined to the z gene, which restore normal operator control over the rest of the operon. This absence of true O^o mutations is in harmony with the further recent finding that all O^c mutations are deletions (p. 271). Hence the O region has only the function of providing an anchor point for a repressor: a change of a single nucleotide in its sequence does not destroy its affinity for the repressor, but a deletion (O^c) can; and no mutation has been found to allow the operator to block initiation in the absence of an effective repressor.

According to the prevailing model the repressor recognizes the DNA sequence of the O region, and by combining with it blocks initiation of transcription. However, the possibility has not been excluded that the repressor combines with an RNA transcript of the O region, whose specificity would be more readily accessible than that of the double-stranded DNA.

Application to More Complex Regulatory Systems

Bacterial Systems. To provide efficient regulation of **branched** pathways the pattern of regulator genes and operons is appropriately modified. In some cases the pathway preceding a branch has **parallel** enzymes, catalyzing the same reaction but subject to different regulatory influences. For example, carbamyl phosphate, a precursor of both arginine and pyrimidines (Ch. 4), is formed in *E. coli* by two kinds of carbamyl phosphokinase, each repressible by one of the endproducts. In other branched pathways, such as that to isoleucine, leucine, and valine, the mechanism invoked is **multivalent repression,** in which the several endproducts act in concert in repressing an enzyme. Either mechanism prevents one product of a branched pathway from interfering with the synthesis of another (see below, Regulation of enzyme function).

The *R* gene-operon regulatory mechanism also applies to more complex processes in bacteria. Thus in **lysogeny** (Ch. 24) the phage has an immunity system, involving a repressor, which prevents expression of the rest of its genome. A similar system of regulation is probably involved in the triggering of **sporulation** and **germination,** which involve major shifts in the chemical nature as well as in the amounts of the various cell components (Ch. 5). Mutants altered in ability to sporulate are now being studied from this point of view.

Differentiation in Higher Forms. The recognition of a well defined system of gene regulation in bacteria has stimulated the study of developmental biology, in higher organisms, at the level of gene function. It now appears quite certain that in general the various differentiated cells of an animal contain the same complete set of genes, of which only a small fraction are ever active in any one type of cell. The mechanisms responsible for triggering and maintaining this selective gene activation constitute a new area of investigation, intimately linked with genetics; it has been called **epigenetics.** The re-

mainder of developmental biology may profitably all be grouped as **morphogenesis,** since at all levels of organization, from the polypeptide leaving the ribosome to the aggregation of cells into an organ, a single kind of process—the complexing of complementary surfaces through weak chemical forces—shapes the direct gene products (proteins), and the products of their catalytic activity, into an organism. These two aspects of development are seen even in the multiplication of viruses, in which 1) different groups of genes are activated at different times (epigenetics), and 2) the resulting products then spontaneously aggregate to form a mature virus (morphogenesis; Ch. 23).

The bacterial system, however, does not provide any adequate model for one striking characteristic of the epigenetic changes in the cells of higher organisms: their self-perpetuating nature, inherited from one generation of cells to the next within the differentiated tissue. Thus the changes seen in bacteria tend to be homeostatic: they promote the ability of the cell to produce more of the **same** cell despite differences in the environment. Hence the endproducts in bacteria participate in **negative feedback loops,**[*] in which a rise in concentration of an endproduct represses formation of its biosynthetic enzymes. In contrast, various differentiated cells, by definition, maintain their **differences** in an identical environment; this process suggests the presence of **positive feedback loops,** in which a group of genes, once activated, produce something that ensures their continued activity. In this connection histones, which are prominent in the chromosomes of eucaryotic organisms and absent from bacteria, are under active investigation.

---

[*] The analysis of biological regulation has profited from application of the cybernetic concept of feedback. There is obviously close analogy between the regulatory processes described in this chapter and the negative feedback loops of electronic circuits and other engineering devices, in which a rise in a potential or pressure feeds back information to a valve, whose response prevents a further rise.

REGULATION OF ENZYME FUNCTION

Endproduct Inhibition

Regulation of the rate of formation of an enzyme would be expected to influence in turn the rate of synthesis of its product. However, this effect is sluggish, since it does not influence the enzyme molecules already present in the cell. Yet the activity of a biosynthetic pathway responds exceedingly rapidly to a supply of the endproduct, as was shown by two early observations. 1) A labeled amino acid, added to a culture of *E. coli* growing in minimal medium, begins at once to supply practically all the molecules of that species incorporated into protein; hence the endogenous synthesis of that amino acid must be immediately inhibited.* 2) Auxotrophic mutants accumulate biosynthetic intermediates (Ch. 4) only when growth ceases from exhaustion of the required endproduct. Indeed, in the accumulation of a metabolite whose concentration can be followed instantaneously, by optical measurements, the inhibitory effect of added endproduct can be seen within a few seconds (Fig. 9-13).

These findings suggested that the endproduct of a pathway directly and immediately inhibits the **action** of an enzyme of that pathway; and since the endproduct affects the accumulation of **all** the intermediates of the pathway, it would have to inhibit the initial enzyme. Such an interaction was established with extracted enzymes in 1957, by Umbarger for the pathway to isoleucine, and by Pardee for the pathway to pyrimidine nucleotides. Thus threonine deaminase, the first enzyme on the specific pathway to isoleucine, is inhibited by even a very low concentration of isoleucine, but not by earlier intermediates in its pathway or by other amino acids. Such **endproduct inhibition** (also called **feedback inhibition** or **retroinhibition**) has now been

demonstrated for a large fraction of the known biosynthetic pathways.

Inhibition and repression differ in several respects. 1) **Endproduct inhibition affects only the initial enzyme of a sequence** (except for branched sequences, discussed below), **while repression affects all the enzymes of the sequence.** 2) The two mechanisms are influenced by different mutations, situated in different loci. 3) While amino acids are apparently only **indirect repressors,** requiring conversion to aminoacyl-tRNA (p. 266), they are **direct inhibitors,** since they instantly inhibit even the purified sensitive enzymes.

Isozymes. The importance of endproduct inhibition is illustrated by a special pattern of regulation of those enzymatic reactions that are used in a cell for more than one purpose: examples are 1) **reactions involved in both an anabolic and a catabolic pathway,** and 2) **reactions in a biosynthetic path-**

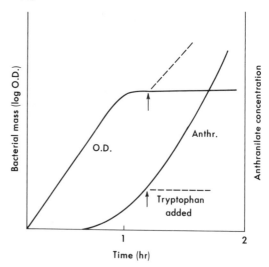

Fig. 9-13 Feedback inhibition by end product. Effect of tryptophan on accumulation of anthranilate by a tryptophan auxotroph blocked immediately after anthranilate (Ch. 4, Aromatic biosynthesis). Growing culture starts accumulating anthranilate in the medium as growth ceases for lack of tryptophan (solid lines). Dotted lines depict the behavior of a sample of the culture to which a small amount of tryptophan (1 μg/ml) is added.

---

* Because of active transport (Ch. 5) the effect persists until the added compound reaches a very low concentration in the medium (ca. 1 μg/ml); the sparing effect of added nutrients is thus very efficient.

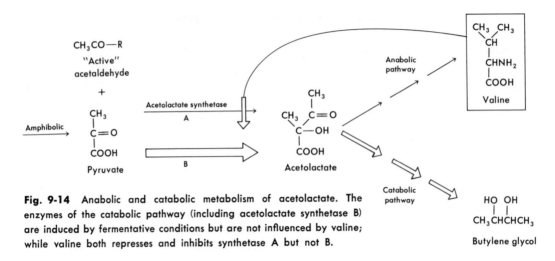

Fig. 9-14 Anabolic and catabolic metabolism of acetolactate. The enzymes of the catabolic pathway (including acetolactate synthetase B) are induced by fermentative conditions but are not influenced by valine; while valine both represses and inhibits synthetase A but not B.

way that subsequently branches. The cell then often uses a double investment of genetic material and makes **two different enzymes,** for the same reaction, which differ in regulatory response.

An example of an anabolic-catabolic pair is provided by acetolactate synthetase, whose reaction is the first step in the specific biosynthesis of valine (Fig. 9-14), and is also a step in the formation of butylene glycol during fermentation (in *Aerobacter*) at low pH (Ch. 3). A shift from aerobiosis to such fermentative conditions induces a large increase in the level of enzyme activity. However, the additional, induced enzyme (catabolic) differs from the initial enzyme

(anabolic) in many respects: in particular, valine inhibits the anabolic enzyme but not the catabolic enzyme. By thus separately regulating two enzymes for the same reaction the cell can adjust its synthesis of the product, under a variety of conditions, to the required rate. Hence the formation of valine, and the characteristic *Aerobacter* fermentation, can proceed separately or together, according to circumstances, without mutual interference.

Regulation has also been studied in the branched biosynthetic pathway that leads from aspartate to threonine and isoleucine, to diaminopimelate and lysine, and to methionine (Fig. 9-15). *E. coli* makes at least two species of the first enzyme of this pathway (asparto-

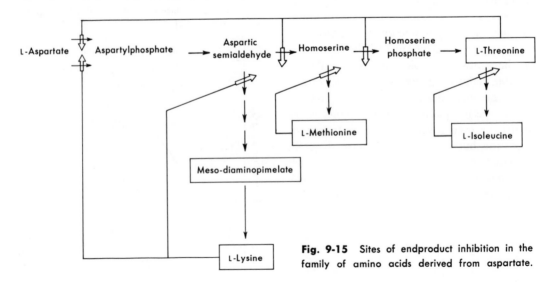

Fig. 9-15 Sites of endproduct inhibition in the family of amino acids derived from aspartate.

kinase), which are subject to repression and inhibition by different endproducts. Moreover, at each fork in the pathway the initial enzyme of each branch is subject to inhibition by the appropriate endproduct. The flow of material in the cell thus resembles that of a piped irrigation system: complete control requires a valve only at each branch point.

The presence of **multiple enzymes for the same reaction,** differing in electrophoretic mobility, has also been observed in mammalian cells, e.g., with alkaline phosphatase and lactic dehydrogenase. These **isozymes** are presumably adapted to even more intricate regulatory mechanisms than those analyzed thus far in bacteria.

In some systems another pattern of regulation of a branched pathway has been evolved, consisting of **concerted feedback inhibition** of a single enzyme by several endproducts, analogous to the multivalent repression noted above.

The Molecular Mechanism: Allosteric Inhibition

Well before the discovery of endproduct inhibition the inhibition of enzymes by metabolite analogs had been extensively studied in connection with chemotherapy (Ch. 10). The results indicated that a competitive inhibitor must bear a close structural resemblance to the normal substrate, and thus presumably competes with it for the active site of the enzyme. It was therefore a surprise when endproduct inhibitors of enzymes were also found to be competitively antagonized by the substrate, despite their structural dissimilarity. Enzymes with this property evidently have two kinds of interacting specific sites, one acting on the substrate and one responsive to the inhibitor. The next question is how the inhibitory site, by complexing with its effector, competitively influences the function of the catalytic site. The analysis of this problem, though only recently begun, has revealed new features of enzymes that have deep significance for biology and for protein chemistry.

In the simplest model the two sites would overlap, and complexing of the enzyme with either ligand would sterically block it from complexing with the other. However, this model does not fit various anomalous kinetics of the enzymes, described below. Pardee, and Monod and Changeux, therefore proposed an alternative model, which has been summarized by designating this special class of enzymes as **allosteric** (Gr., "other shape"). Such enzymes would be able to shift reversibly between an active and an inactive configuration. An **allosteric inhibitor** (allosteric effector), complexing with an inhibitory site, would favor an inactive configuration; while the substrate, complexing with a catalytic site, would have an opposing effect. In this model the sites of inhibition and of catalysis need not be close together on the enzyme.

The anomalies that gave rise to the allosteric model are the following:

1) **The effect of the inhibitor** is often not proportional to its concentration (first-order kinetics), as in the usual competitive inhibition (Ch. 10), but is proportional to the square of its concentration (**second-order kinetics).** This finding implies that two molecules of the inhibitor complex cooperatively with the enzyme to influence a catalytic site; and this pattern would be difficult to reconcile with overlapping sites on a rigid protein molecule.

2) **The interaction with a substrate** similarly exhibits **second-order** kinetics (Fig. 9-16A), which implies that complexing of one catalytic site with substrate promotes a configuration that favors the complexing of a second such site on the same enzyme.

3) **Analogs of the inhibitor can reverse its effect.** For example, valine antagonizes the inhibitory effect of isoleucine on threonine deaminase; and ATP antagonizes the inhibitory effect of CTP on aspartate transcarbamylase. Such **allosteric stimulators** might occupy the same site as the inhibitor but not fill it in quite the same way, and hence not produce the same configurational modification.

4) **The effect of denaturation** provides the strongest evidence for the allosteric model. Denaturation is known to alter protein con-

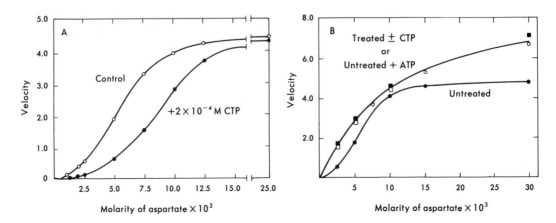

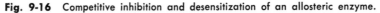

Fig. 9-16 Competitive inhibition and desensitization of an allosteric enzyme.

A. Aspartic transcarbamylase purified from *E. coli*, showing inhibition of activity by the endproduct of its pathway, cytidine triphosphate (CTP), and reversal of the inhibition by increased concentration of the substrate, aspartate. Note **sigmoid** shape of curve, signifying cooperative interaction of multiple substrate molecules with enzyme.

B. Desensitized (treated) enzyme: some points obtained with enzyme heated for 4 minutes at 60°, and others with unheated enzyme in presence of 10^{-6} M Hg^{++}. Note the **higher** level of activity of the treated enzyme and the **hyperbolic** shape of the curve (first-order kinetics). The association of these two changes suggests that 1) the native enzyme is subject to an internal inhibition, which lowers its activity; and 2) the cooperative substrate effect in this enzyme (second-order kinetics) is concerned with overcoming that inhibition.

Results identical to those of the "treated" curve were obtained 1) with treated enzyme plus CTP, showing that the desensitized enzyme is no longer responsive to an inhibitory effector; and 2) with untreated enzyme plus 2×10^{-3} M ATP, showing that a stimulatory effector can have the same effect as mild denaturation. (From J. C. Gerhart and A. B. Pardee. *J. Biol. Chem.* 237:891, 1962.)

figuration by destroying weak bonds responsible for secondary and tertiary structure. **Mild denaturation was found to destroy the allosteric property of an enzyme without destroying its catalytic activity.** This effect has been achieved with both physical agents (mild heating) and chemicals (e.g., Hg^{++}, high pH). The **desensitized** enzyme shows no loss of ability to **bind** its previous inhibitor (as measured with purified enzyme and radioactive inhibitor); hence it appears that the damage to the protein has destroyed the functional **connection** between two kinds of sites.

This interpretation is supported by further observations that would be quite paradoxical from the point of view of classic enzymology. Mild damage to aspartate transcarbamylase **increases its activity** (Fig. 9-16B). Moreover, such damage converts the anomalous sigmoid-

shaped enzyme kinetics to classic first-order kinetics with respect to substrate concentration: each site now has the same Michaelis constant, and its activity does not influence that of a neighboring site. It follows that the catalytic sites have been released from the configurational effect of the inhibitory sites, and the configurational interactions between one catalytic site and another have also been destroyed.

These findings support a model (Fig. 9-17) in which the flexible native allosteric enzyme has multiple catalytic and multiple regulatory sites. Complexing of a catalytic site with substrate not only results in catalytic action but stabilizes the active configuration at one or more additional catalytic sites. In contrast, complexing with inhibitor favors a less active configuration, and the multiple inhibitory

Monomer

Polymer
(relaxed state)

Polymer
(constrained state)

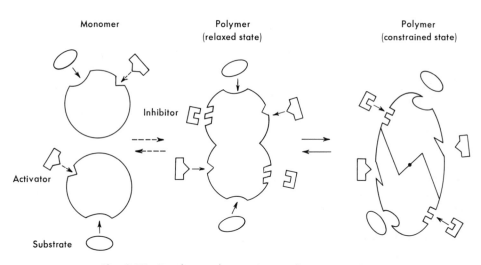

Inhibitor

Activator

Substrate

Fig. 9-17 Regulatory changes in an allosteric model. (From J. P. Changeux. *Scient. Am.* April, 1965, p. 36.)

sites interact cooperatively to stabilize this configuration.

Further kinetic studies have led to the conclusion that allosteric enzymes do not have a variety of intermediate configurations, but snap back and forth between two "normal," stable configurations, one fully active and the other inactive. The activity of the enzyme in a given solution therefore depends on the fraction of the molecules in the active configuration, and this value is a complex function of substrate and inhibitor concentrations. Mild denaturation apparently irreversibly destroys the ability of the enzyme to shift to the inactive normal configuration, thereby yielding a stable (i.e., relatively rigid), active molecule with classic kinetics.

Separation of Subunits. An important recent advance has been the discovery that **the catalytic and the inhibitory sites of an enzyme are located on different subunits.** Thus when aspartate transcarbamylase is treated with a sulfhydryl reagent (e.g., *p*-mercuribenzoate) it yields two fractions, which can be separated by ultracentrifugation. Only one of these subunits is enzymatically active, while the other carries the sites that bind the inhibitor (CTP). The isolated active subunit not only has lost its response to the inhibitor, but it no longer has mutually interacting sites: like the original Hg^{++}-treated enzyme,

it exhibits classic (first-order) enzyme kinetics with respect to substrate. However, when the mercurial is removed and the two isolated fractions are mixed they spontaneously re-aggregate to restore the native enzyme, with its characteristic kinetics and allosteric response.

The physical separation of the regulatory and the catalytic moieties unequivocally establishes, for this enzyme, the model in which the sites interact through effects on configuration. This analysis also confirms the multiplicity of sites, inferred from the kinetics discussed above: the intact enzyme molecule was found to consist of two catalytic subunits and four smaller regulatory subunits (Fig. 9-18). There appears to be no theoretical chemical reason to believe that the catalytic and the inhibitory sites of an allosteric enzyme must always be provided by separate polypeptides, but it may be easier for such sites to be evolved in this manner.

The Analogy with Hemoglobin. In both physiological function and kinetics allosteric enzymes closely resemble hemoglobin, whose special properties have long been recognized. The allosteric curve of Figure 9-16 is essentially identical with the well known S-shaped oxygen dissociation curve of hemoglobin. Because of this peculiar binding curve of hemoglobin a moderate drop in oxygen tension, in the range encountered as the blood passes

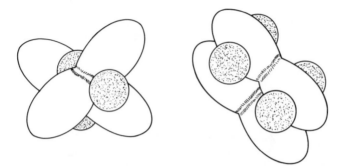

Fig. 9-18 Two possible arrangements of the catalytic and regulatory subunits in aspartate transcarbamylase. The two catalytic subunits (white; M.W. 90,000) are portrayed as being elongated and constricted at the equator because they probably consist of smaller subunits. The four regulatory subunits (black; M.W. 30,000) are known to bind two molecules of inhibitor each. (After J. C. Gerhart. *Brookhaven Symp. Biol.,* No. 17, p. 222, 1964.)

through the tissues, permits a much larger fraction of the bound ligand to be dissociated than would occur if hemoglobin had a first-order dissociation curve. In allosteric enzymes, similarly, the second-order kinetics, observed with both substrate and endproduct, intensify the response of enzyme activity to small changes (in the proper range) in the concentration of either compound. These enzymes are thus designed, like hemoglobin, for efficient homeostasis, i.e., for maintaining the steady-state concentration of their ligands in the organism within a narrow range.

These parallel effects are apparently achieved through a similar chemical mechanism, requiring a rather elaborate protein. Thus, the anomalous binding curve of hemoglobin depends on the allosteric interaction of multiple binding sites on the molecule: dissociated monomers exhibit a first-order dissociation curve, just as the separated catalytic subunit of aspartate transcarbamylase exhibits first-order kinetics; and the configurational shift postulated for allosteric enzymes has actually been demonstrated for hemoglobin by X-ray crystallography, which reveals a marked difference in configuration between the oxygenated and the reduced molecule.

Allosteric Stimulation

We have already seen, in the first section of this chapter, that in induction of enzyme formation a presumably allosteric repressor is **inactivated** by complexing with the corresponding inducer, while in repression, conversely, it is **activated** by complexing with its corepressor. Similar symmetrical responses have been found among allosteric enzymes. For example, with aspartate transcarbamylase, which can be inhibited by its pyrimidine nucleotide endproducts, purine nucleotides (e.g., ATP) not only overcome the inhibition but even stimulate activity in the absence of the inhibitor (Fig. 9-16B). Thus the purine and pyrimidine pathways, which should ordinarily remain parallel in activity, exhibit a cross-linking positive feedback as well as the usual direct negative feedback.

The concept of allosteric stimulation leads to a fuller interpretation of various organic cofactor requirements that have been observed, over many years, with various enzymes, especially from animal tissues. For example, in extracts of liver AMP stimulates the action of phosphorylase. Since phosphorylase provides a source of energy by initiating the catabolism of glycogen, and since an increased energy supply should decrease the level of AMP by converting it to ATP, this allosteric effect of AMP appears to regulate a supply of energy.

Though allosteric stimulation has not thus far been emphasized as much as allosteric inhibition in studies on bacterial metabolism, it seems likely also to have widespread importance.

REGULATION OF THE SYNTHESIS OF MACROMOLECULES

Effects of Growth Rate on Cell Size and Composition

Studies of regulation have focused for many years on the formation of individual enzymes, and only recently on the equally fundamental mechanisms that control the flow of material into the various major classes of macromolecules. Some variation in this flow could be inferred from the early observation that cells are smaller in the stationary than in the exponential phase (Ch. 5). To analyze more closely the factors involved in this shift, Maaløe in Denmark determined the size and composition of *Salmonella typhimurium* cells in **balanced** growth (i.e., growth with unchanging composition) at various rates.

As Table 9-2 shows, an increase in growth rate, due to a change in the medium, is accompanied by a striking increase in cell size (fourfold over the range studied). This enlargement is due primarily to a delay between nuclear and cell division, since the number of nuclei per cell (determined by staining and by DNA analyses) increases. There is also an increase in the amount of cytoplasmic material (especially RNA) per nucleus. It is evident that the over-all macromolecular composition of the cell is determined by intricate mechanisms that respond to environmental changes.

Control of Rate of Protein Synthesis

When the RNA in *Salmonella* is further analyzed in terms of its ribosomal (rRNA) and transfer (tRNA) components a striking relation to protein synthesis is seen (Table 9-3). The amount of protein and of tRNA per unit of DNA remains essentially constant over a 10-fold range of growth rate; but the rRNA concentration varies widely. Indeed, over the whole range observed **the rate of protein synthesis in balanced growth is proportional to the number of ribosomes present.** Each ribosome thus functions at a constant average rate, suggesting that the rate of protein synthesis on an active ribosome is independent of growth rate. Such constancy of activity per ribosome is consistent with the observation that **the tRNA concentration is constant over the whole range of growth rates,** which means that the individual ribosome has the same rate of contact with tRNA molecules whether the ribosomal population is sparse or crowded.

It can be calculated that in balanced growth at any rate protein synthesis proceeds at about

TABLE 9-2. COMPOSITION AND SIZE OF S. TYPHIMURIUM AT VARIOUS GROWTH RATES

Medium	Doubling time at 37° (min)	Dry wt/10⁹ cells (µg)	Nuclei/cell	RNA/10⁹ nuclei (µg)
Lysine salts	96	240	1.1	22
Glucose salts	50	360	1.5	31
Broth	25	840	2.4	64
Heart infusion	21	1090	2.9	84

The growth rate was controlled by providing different carbon and nitrogen sources, which could be used at different maximal rates. To avoid changes in the medium that would result in unbalanced growth, the cells were harvested at densities below 0.15 mg dry wt per milliliter (1 to 5 × 10⁸ bacteria per milliliter, depending on medium); above this value the composition and the size of the cells began to shift. (Considering that in the conventional plot growth remains apparently exponential until much closer to the saturation level of ca. 1 to 2 mg/ml, it is evident that much of the literature on exponential cells, generally harvested close to the maximal exponential yield, is not dealing with cells in truly balanced growth.)

From M. Schaechter, O. Maaløe, and N. O. Kjeldgaard, J. Gen. Microbiol. 19:595 (1958).

TABLE 9-3. RNA DISTRIBUTION AND PROTEIN SYNTHESIS IN *S. TYPHIMURIUM* AT VARIOUS GROWTH RATES

Carbon source	Growth rate, μ (generations/ hr)	DNA (μg/mg bact. dry wt.)	rRNA/ DNA	tRNA/ DNA	Protein/ DNA	Protein synthesis per hr*	
						Per unit RNA	Per unit rRNA
Broth	2.4	30	8.3	2.0	22	3.7	4.5
Glucose	1.2	35	3.9	2.4	21	2.8	4.6
Glycerol	0.6	37	2.4	2.4	21	1.8	3.6
Glutamate	0.2	40	0.9	2.1	21	1.0	3.3

The rate of protein synthesis was calculated as protein $\times \mu \times 0.69$; the factor 0.69 converts the exponential growth rate μ (1/doubling time) into the instantaneous growth rate α (Ch. 5).
From N. O. Kjeldgaard. "Dynamics of Bacterial Growth." Thesis, Univ. of Copenhagen, 1963.

15 amino acids per ribosome per second at 37°, if all ribosomes are active. The maximal growth rate of bacteria (doubling time 20 minutes) appears to be limited by the crowding of ribosomes, for in cells growing at this rate the average distance between ribosomes approximately equals the diameter of a ribosome.

Shifts of RNA Synthesis with Growth Rate. These observations suggest that the various participants in protein synthesis are formed in a closely regulated manner, yielding at each growth rate the proportions that ensure efficient function of each component. This inference is strongly supported by the extremely sensitive ("irritable") response of RNA synthesis when cells in balanced growth are put into imbalance by an abrupt shift in composition of the medium.

Thus when cells are transferred to a medium with a carbon source that can support faster growth (**shift up**) the growth rate actually remains unchanged for some time, and then only gradually changes to the new rate characteristic of balanced growth under the new conditions. **The rate of RNA synthesis,** however, rises abruptly following the shift of medium (Fig. 9-19A), the change reflecting largely an increased synthesis of rRNA. Thus the number of ribosomes per cell changes first, and then the rate of protein synthesis adjusts to the new number of ribosomes.

Similarly, in a **shift down** from a good carbon source to a poorer one the supply of energy and material is curtailed; hence the growth rate decreases abruptly, and protein synthesis is reduced to approximately the rate characteristic of the new medium. The ribosomes, however, are present in excess of the amount needed for the new growth rate; and in an exquisite response the cell immediately ceases all **net** synthesis of RNA, though mRNA turnover, and the synthesis of protein and DNA, continue (Fig. 9-19B). When this unbalanced synthesis has sufficiently reduced the ribosome concentration (by dilution) balanced growth is resumed.

Control of RNA Synthesis

A possible key to the connection between net RNA synthesis and growth rate was provided by studying the effects of blocking protein synthesis at different stages. When this block is achieved, with various auxotrophs, by **deprival of the required amino acid,** net RNA synthesis **ceases.** In contrast, when the block is produced by adding **chloramphenicol** RNA synthesis not only continues but is **stimulated.** Since deprival of an amino acid prevents the charging of the corresponding tRNA, whereas chloramphenicol, by blocking protein synthesis at a later step (Ch. 10), should cause the pool of tRNA to become more completely charged, Kurland and Maaløe have suggested that the regulation of RNA synthesis depends on **the ratio**

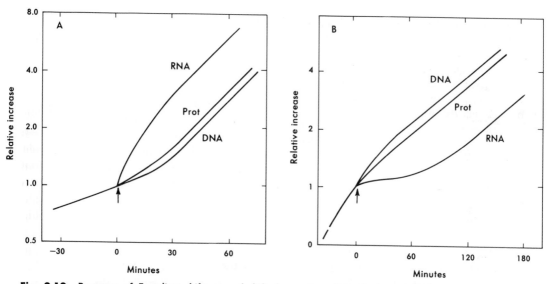

Fig. 9-19 Response of *E. coli* to shift up and shift down of medium. **A.** Net synthesis of total protein, RNA, and DNA in a culture shifted to a richer medium at zero time. The curves are idealized and the value of each component per milliliter of culture is normalized to 1.0 at zero time. **B.** Similar measurements in a culture shifted to a poorer medium at zero time. The behavior shown is that seen when no diauxic lag is produced by the shift; diauxie produces an additional lag in all syntheses.

of the concentration of uncharged to charged tRNA in the cell.

This hypothesis is consistent with the observations noted above. Thus, in a shift up the increased supply of energy and material increases the rate of charging of tRNA, while the rate of uncharging is limited by the supply of ribosomes (which, as we have seen, limits the rate of protein synthesis): hence charged tRNA should accumulate. In a shift down, in contrast, the large supply of ribosomes, relative to the limited supply of amino acids, uncharges the tRNA excessively. Recently more direct evidence for the role of uncharged tRNA has been obtained with a mutant possessing a **temperature-sensitive** valine-activating enzyme. In this organism an elevation of temperature, which prevents the charging of valine tRNA, halts RNA synthesis, although the supply of valine (and all other amino acids) is unimpaired.

The control of RNA synthesis is altered in certain bacterial mutants, designated as **relaxed control (RC^{rel}),** which continue to synthesize RNA after deprival of a required amino acid. The contrast with the wild type, which is designated as a stringent control (RC^{str}) strain, shows that control of RNA synthesis depends on a **single** protein able to respond (in its wild-type form) to **any** uncharged tRNA. RNA polymerase seemed to be a candidate for this job, but efforts to demonstrate a direct effect of uncharged tRNA on the action of this enzyme in vitro have not yielded impressive results. Moreover, since the relative rates of synthesis of mRNA, rRNA, and the tRNA can vary widely under different conditions, as we have seen, it is difficult to assign the control of all three classes to direct regulation of a single enzyme.

The original hypothesis presents another difficulty. Complete uncharging of the tRNA for 1 of the 20 amino acids would increase the level of total uncharged tRNA by only about 5% of the total tRNA of the cell. At the same time, the tRNAs for the other 19 amino acids would shift from their normal steady-state levels to presumably full charging; and it seems probable that this increase in charging would largely balance, and even exceed, the decrease contributed by the specific deprival. Hence, though the charging of tRNA surely has an important role in the regulation of RNA synthesis, the mechanism is still obscure. One possibility is that all RNA species are controlled by operon regulation, and that an rRNA operon is responsive to the level of its "endproduct": i.e., free ribosomes not engaged in polysomes. Thus the ratio of free ribosomes to polysomes is increased by amino acid starvation in an RC^{str} strain and not in an RC^{rel} strain.

Control of DNA Synthesis

The Key Role of Initiation. The synthesis of DNA is unique in more than one respect. Not only does DNA provide the information for its own replication, but it has a special mechanism of synthesis, and of regulation of that synthesis, designed to ensure precise replication of the entire chromosome. As we have seen in Chapter 8, a round of replication of a chromosome is a single event per cell division, unlike the statistically regulated synthesis of numerous identical units of RNA or protein; and **synthesis ordinarily occurs at only one growing point on a bacterial chromosome,** proceeding continuously from a point of initiation to the completion of the circle.

In an *E. coli* cell growing on glucose the cycle of DNA replication occupies more than 90% of a cycle of cell division. This conclusion is based on 1) the proportion of the cells in a nonsynchronized culture that take up tritiated thymidine from a brief pulse, and 2) the fraction of the length of a chromosome that is labeled, in radioautographic studies, in such a pulse. In slower growth, on a poor carbon source, the resting interval, between completion of one round of DNA replication and initiation of the next, becomes greater.

In fast growth on a rich medium an additional mechanism appears: formation of additional growing points, on the already replicated portions of the chromosome, before completion of the first round of replication (Fig. 9-20). This increased branching is indicated by a change in the relative transforming activity of the DNA for two genes, one near the site of initiation of replication and one near the distal termination of the chromosome. During slow growth the ratio of the two activities is nearly 2:1, but in fast growth it approaches 4:1. **The regulation of DNA synthesis thus depends on controlling the initiation of replication,** rather than on controlling its rate of progress once initiated. This rate of progress is about 1000 nucleotides (per two strands) per second per growing point at 37°.

The Control of Initiation. The mechanism of initiation of DNA replication was opened to biochemical exploration by the brilliant investigation of a curious phenomenon called **thymineless death.** When a thymine auxotroph (T$^-$) of *E. coli* is deprived of T (a specific DNA precursor), in an otherwise

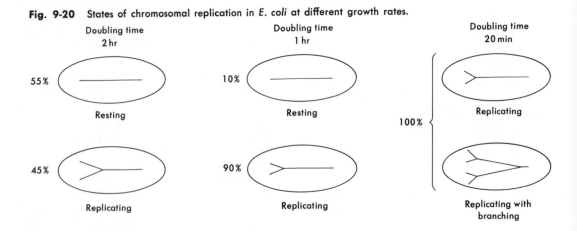

Fig. 9-20   States of chromosomal replication in *E. coli* at different growth rates.

adequate medium, the viable number exhibits a rapid exponential decline after about a 30-minute lag. (No such lethal effect is seen on deprival of an amino acid or of an RNA precursor.) This effect appears to involve the abortive formation of abnormal DNA, since the mutation rate is increased among the survivors.

Maaløe found that when a glucose-grown culture of T^- cells is deprived of thymine and simultaneously blocked in protein synthesis (by chloramphenicol or by deprival of a required amino acid), thymineless death fails to occur in about 5% of the cells (Fig.

Fig. 9-21 Thymineless death in presence (+AU) and absence (−AU) of protein synthesis. **A.** Fast growth. A mutant of *E. coli* auxotrophic for thymine (T), arginine (A), and uracil (U) was grown in glucose plus TAU and transferred at zero time to media containing glucose plus indicated supplements. Note that in the absence of protein synthesis (−AU) thymine deprival fails to cause death of an immune fraction of the population, amounting to about 5% of the cells. There is a variety of evidence that these cells are resting between rounds of DNA replication and are unable to initiate a new round. Resumption of protein synthesis (+AU) restores their sensitivity to T^- killing, and can be shown to restore the synthesis of DNA when T is present.

B. Slow growth. Similar experiment with the glucose replaced by succinate, which supports slower growth. Note the larger fraction (ca. 30%) of cells immune to T^- death without protein synthesis. (From O. Maaløe. *Cold Spring Harbor Symp. Quant. Biol.* 26:45, 1961.)

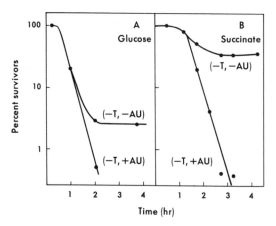

9-21). Moreover, if T is provided and protein synthesis is simultaneously blocked, DNA synthesis continues but levels off after about a 50% increment. These results could both be accounted for by the hypothesis that **some protein synthesis is required for the initiation of each new round of DNA replication, but not for the completion of a round.** In the experiments just described the block in protein synthesis would fix the cells in two classes: 1) those actively engaged in DNA replication, which can synthesize the fraction of a chromosome (averaging about 50%) necessary to complete their current round of replication; and 2) a small number of cells, in the resting interval between periods of DNA replication, which evidently cannot initiate a new round and hence are **immune** to thymineless death.

Further evidence for this inference was provided by allowing such completion of DNA replication, in cells deprived of protein synthesis, to be followed by a brief resumption of protein synthesis. Even when this resumption was limited to as little as 5 minutes the cells initiated a new round of DNA replication: when T was provided the DNA content doubled, and when T was withheld essentially no cells were immune to thymineless death.

The nature of the unstable "replication protein" is not known. It cannot be the DNA polymerase that is recognized in extracts: this enzyme is much too stable, and the amount present per cell does not oscillate during stepwise DNA synthesis in synchronized cultures.

The Replicon. The unstable replication protein probably participates in a regulatory mechanism whose general features have been revealed through the behavior of certain temperature-sensitive bacterial mutants, which can synthesize DNA at 30° but not at 40°. The mutant protein is apparently specific for bacterial DNA, since bacteriophage DNA is synthesized normally in these cells even at 40°. Similarly, some temperature-sensitive mutations of the F episome can prevent its replication at 40°, without affecting the replication of cellular DNA in the same cell. On the basis of these findings Jacob and Brenner have proposed the existence of a functional unit of DNA replication, called the **replicon.** Like the regulator-operon complex, the replicon consists of two genetic elements: an **initiator** locus, which produces a cytoplasmic initiator, and a **replicator** locus, which responds to that product by starting a round of replication. The same cell can contain different replicators (e.g., on bacterial chromosome, phage genome, or F episome), which respond to different initiators. This model also explains the observation that in the bacterial chromosome the site of initiation of replication can shift when an F-factor becomes integrated and engages in conjugation (Ch. 7).

Control of Other Components

How the cell regulates formation of the components of its **wall** and **membrane** is quite unknown. As we have seen in Chapter 4, a block in basal wall synthesis (e.g., by penicillin) leads to extensive accumulation of mucopeptide and teichoic acid precursors in cells of some species, which implies a striking lack of feedback inhibition.

Selective starvation for nitrogen, phosphorus, or sulfur, in the presence of a carbon source, often leads to extensive accumulation of **storage materials,** such as poly-β-hydroxybutyrate in *Bacilli* and a glycogen-like polysaccharide in *E. coli*; the concentration can reach 25% of the dry weight. Nitrogen starvation also leads to polymetaphosphate accumulation in many organisms, up to 1 to 2% of cell weight. The mechanisms that regulate flow of material in and out of these reserves have not been thoroughly analyzed, but the enzymes involved in forming and those involved in depolymerizing polymetaphosphate are known to be induced by appropriate cultural conditions.

Macromolecule Synthesis During Starvation

DNA and Wall Synthesis in a Nongrowing Cell. Recent studies have indicated that in the transition from exponential to stationary phase changes in cell size and composition may occur not only during slowing of growth, but even after growth (in terms of mass)

has ceased. Specifically, when cells are abruptly transferred from growth medium to a nitrogen-free or a carbon-free medium, or to one lacking a required amino acid or pyrimidine (Fig. 9-22), **the DNA and the cell number increase** by 40 to 75%, while the optical density and the protein content remain constant and the RNA drops a bit. **Cell wall** also continues to be synthesized under conditions that prevent protein synthesis.

Such large percentage increases of DNA and wall are economically possible without over-all growth because these components constitute rather small fractions of the cell mass (ca. 5 and 10%, respectively). The continued synthesis of DNA in starved cells, which contrasts strikingly with the response of RNA and protein, reflects the peculiar cyclical control of DNA synthesis, and suggests that completion of a round of DNA replication has priority in a starved cell. This completion is also implied by the observation that stationary phase cells, inoculated into fresh medium, can initiate synchronized growth (Ch. 5).

It is evident that the stationary period is not altogether stationary. As a practical matter, in doing viability counts it is not safe to delay plating on the assumption that dilution in an inadequate medium will prevent further division.

Turnover. Studies with labeled amino acids have shown that in a **growing** bacterial culture there is no detectable protein turnover. When formation of a specific enzyme is repressed the molecules already present are diluted out during further growth, but they are not used as sources of other proteins; and when a new enzyme is induced in a growing culture it is formed entirely, as noted earlier, from the amino acid pool. In **nongrowing** cultures, however, turnover may occur. Thus in an auxotroph of *E. coli* deprived of required amino acid A, but in an otherwise adequate medium, labeled amino acid B is incorporated into protein at a rate corresponding to 5% turnover per hour; moreover, preexisting labeled protein can be shown to be broken down at the same rate.

Protein turnover has evident value for cells

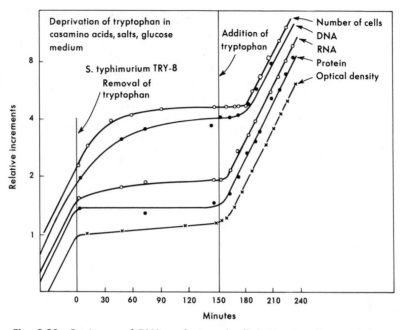

Fig. 9-22 Persistence of DNA synthesis and cell division in cells starved for an amino acid. A tryptophan auxotroph of *S. typhimurium* was deprived of the required amino acid in an otherwise rich medium, and was supplied with it again after 150 minutes. Note the "overshoot" of DNA synthesis and cell division after the deprival, and the subsequent delayed response after the restoration. (From M. Schaechter. *Cold Spring Harbor Symp. Quant. Biol.* **26**:53, 1961.)

adapting to transfer from a rich to a poor medium. Such cells are initially starved for amino acids, since the biosynthetic enzymes for these metabolites have been repressed in the rich medium; and if this repression for any of the enzymes were complete, cells without turnover could not achieve the initial enzyme synthesis required to make the building blocks that would permit more enzyme synthesis. Turnover thus primes the pump.

FUNCTIONS OF THE VARIOUS REGULATORY MECHANISMS

Responses to Exogenous and Endogenous Stimuli

Though feedback **inhibition** and **repression** were discovered by observing the sparing effects of added metabolites on various biosyntheses, these responses to **foreign imports** represent only part of the economic gain provided by these mechanisms. At least equally important is their role in the **domestic economy** of the cell. Thus enzymes differ in their pH optima and their temperature coefficients; yet with wide variations in pH and tempera-

ture normal bacterial cells form their building blocks in the correct proportions, without any wasteful loss. Moreover, a strain blocked in the biosynthesis of one amino acid does not excrete the other amino acids, though the necessary biosynthetic enzymes and fuels for their synthesis are available. Such efficient patterns suggest that feedback mechanisms respond not only to exogenous but also to endogenous supplies of the endproduct.

This internal regulatory function has been unequivocally established by observing the consequences of removing the responsive element in a control system. Thus when the regulatory enzyme of a pathway is altered, by mutation, to a **feedback-resistant** form, the endogenous endproduct, unable to regulate its own synthesis, rises in level in the cell and is excreted. Similarly, in mutants that are no longer repressible by an added amino acid the levels of the enzymes of the pathway, in cells growing in minimal medium, are often elevated. The defective regulatory mechanisms evidently fail to respond to endogenous as well as to exogenous stimuli. Similar results may be obtained with an intact regulatory system deprived of its normal stimulus. Thus when an auxotrophic mutant is deprived of its required endproduct the substrate of the blocked reaction increases in concentration and is excreted (Fig. 9-13), and the enzymes of the pathway also rise in level; but these effects do not occur when the pathway is blocked **after** the endproduct (e.g., by preventing protein synthesis in various ways). It is thus evident that normal endogenous regulation involves constant partial inhibition and repression of biosynthetic pathways by the intracellular levels of their endproducts.

The regulation of the synthesis of various **classes of macromolecules** also responds both to internal and, indirectly, to external influences. We have seen that in steady-state growth the proportions of the various components of the protein-synthesizing machinery, for example, are maintained at levels adapted to the growth rate. When an external change is imposed on this internal regulation, as in a shift down, the cell acts as though it "knows" that it possesses more rRNA than will be useful at the new growth rate, and it shifts its syntheses accordingly in an intricate pattern. Moreover, the specificity of these adjustments excludes any "naive" responses to building blocks available in the environment: addition of amino acids or of nucleosides does not stimulate the synthesis of protein or of nucleic acids, respectively, except in the harmonious proportions governed by the cell's regulatory mechanisms.

Repression vs. Inhibition

It has often been suggested that repression represents a "coarse" and sluggish control, and inhibition a "fine" and immediate control, over the synthesis of an endproduct. However, it seems more likely that repression is concerned primarily with economy in mRNA and protein synthesis, while metabolite synthesis is regulated largely by endproduct inhibition. Thus in mutants that have lost the inhibitory mechanism for a pathway the endproduct is heavily excreted, as noted above, even though the repressive mechanism is still present. Conversely, in mutants with a considerable derepression of the biosynthetic enzymes the endproduct is not excreted, so long as endproduct inhibition is normal.

Up to this point we have stressed, for purposes of clarification, the differences between repression and inhibition, both in mechanism and in function. At a molecular level, however, the endproduct undoubtedly acts on the two kinds of regulatory macromolecules—the postulated repressor and the demonstrated feedback-sensitive enzyme—through essentially the same allosteric mechanism.

Pseudo-feedback Inhibition

The regulatory mechanisms present in a cell must be selected for great specificity with respect to normal metabolites, in order to minimize the inefficiency that would arise if the endogenous chemical signals acted on the wrong receptors. However, the specificity is not so great with respect to **compounds that have not been exerting evolutionary selective pressure;** hence it is possible to deceive regulatory mechanisms, just as it is possible to deceive enzymes (Ch. 10), with **metabolite analogs.** For example, 5-methyltryptophan inhibits growth by mimicking the feedback-inhibitory effect of tryptophan, thus causing the cell to cease making the tryptophan that it needs. Such pseudo-feedback inhibition can be eliminated by a mutation that alters the sensitive enzyme. Altered enzymes of this type are often resistant to the normal as well as to the false stimulus, resulting in increased intracellular levels and therefore in excretion of the endproduct. Such mutants therefore sometimes have commercial as well as scientific value.

Reserve Capacity for Enzyme Formation

Endogenous regulation, as noted above, includes continuous partial repression of enzyme **formation,** as shown by the effects of mutations altering this regulation. This effect is also seen in the kinetics of restoration of a repressed enzyme. For example, cells of *E. coli* growing in minimal medium form the enzymes of the arginine biosynthetic pathway at a constant rate per unit of protein synthesized, thus maintaining a constant "normal" level of enzyme. When arginine is added these enzymes are no longer formed, and their levels fall exponentially and become negligible after several generations. If the arginine is then exhausted growth temporarily ceases, but within 10 minutes the normal rate is restored. During that interval there is strikingly **preferential synthesis** of the required enzymes. Indeed, measurements at short intervals of one of the enzymes of this pathway, ornithine transcarbamylase, revealed that when cells are **derepressed,** i.e., transferred from a repressing (arginine-containing) to a nonrepressing medium, they initially synthesize their enzyme at 25 to 50 times the normal rate (relative to total protein synthesis) in response to a lowering of the intracellular arginine concentration. After the enzyme attains the normal level its rate of synthesis is reduced to normal, presumably in response to the achievement of the intracellular arginine concentration for which the regulatory system is set (Fig. 9-23). It is evident that in normal growth the cell uses only a small fraction of its capacity for the formation of this enzyme.

Indeed, when the absence of repression is caused to persist the derepressed enzymes continue to be synthesized at a high rate, and they reach a steady-state level far above normal (Fig.

9-23). Such continuous derepression can be achieved by inactivating the regulatory gene (derepressed mutant), or by maintaining an abnormally low intracellular level of corepressor. The latter effect can be produced in several ways: 1) growth of an auxotroph in the chemostat (Ch. 5) with limiting endproduct; 2) growth of an auxotroph on a slowly utilizable source of the endproduct (e.g., formylhistidine, which is slowly hydrolyzed in the cell to histidine); and 3) growth of an incompletely blocked mutant in minimal medium.

Various fully derepressed enzymes have each been shown to constitute, like fully induced β-galactosidase, 5% or more of the cell protein. Since the cell contains many hundreds of enzymes they must all, or nearly all, be under partial repression. The reserve capacity for their more rapid synthesis, however, is not wasted: it obviously speeds adjustment to changes in the medium—and change is undoubtedly the rule in the natural habitat of bacteria. Thus when cells are suddenly deprived of a specific nutrient the resulting derepression is associated with preferential synthesis of the required enzymes; hence even the slow rate of protein turnover, noted above, leads to rapid restoration of these enzymes and thus to rapid resumption of growth.

Regulator genes may well lack this reserve capacity. Thus when a *lac* R^+ gene is introduced into an R^- cell the effect of the R^+ gene, though dominant, is not phenotypically expressed (i.e., the cell is not converted from constitutive to inducible) until after 60 to 90 minutes. This slow development of the steady-state level of the R-gene product probably reflects absence of reserve biosynthetic capacity. Indeed, since the products of the many R genes in a cell obviously cannot each constitute 5% of the cell protein, some process must restrict the rate of expression of these genes; and these kinetics suggest that the regulator gene is not controlled by another regulator, but rather is restricted by some other, unknown process.

Evolution of Regulatory Mechanisms

The developments described in this chapter have made it increasingly profitable to view the cell as a machine that is self-regulated through an intricate set of feedback circuits. In the "primitive" bacterial cell these devices

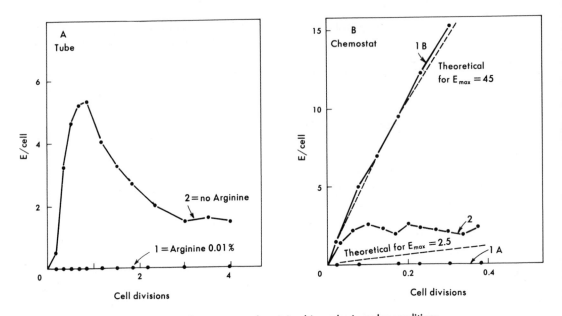

Fig. 9-23 Accelerated formation of an enzyme of arginine biosynthesis under conditions of arginine derepression. **A.** Transient derepression in the wild type. Cells of wild-type *E. coli,* grown in minimal medium plus excess arginine, were washed and incubated in minimal medium with and without arginine. Samples were taken at intervals for determination of optical density and the concentration of ornithine transcarbamylase, an enzyme of the arginine pathway. It is seen that the enzyme content per cell rose above the normal level within a fraction of a generation and then, through the diluting effect of further growth, decreased exponentially to the normal level (1.5 arbitrary units), which was then maintained indefinitely. (The overshoot presumably reflects a lag in attaining the normal intracellular level of arginine, which may be due to a less explosive response of some other essential enzyme of the pathway to these derepressive conditions.)

B. Prolonged derepression with an arginine auxotroph in the chemostat. Cells grown with excess arginine were washed and transferred to a chemostat with a flow rate that prolonged the division time to 460 minutes.

1B. Arg⁻ hist⁻ mutant in medium with limiting arginine and excess histidine. The curve seen is only the early part of a curve of exponential increase in ornithine transcarbamylase concentration, which gives 50% of the final value after one generation, 75% after two, etc.

1A. The same mutant with excess of arginine and limiting histidine.

2. His⁻ mutant in medium with limiting histidine and synthesizing its own arginine. Under these conditions no overshoot in formation of the enzyme is seen, and the normal level is reached in about 0.1 generation. (From L. Gorini and W. K. Maas. *Biochim. et biophys. acta* 25:208, 1957.)

have evidently developed in response to constant evolutionary pressure for faster growth and for faster adaptation. Feedback responses meet this pressure in several ways:

1) It is only through a large number of feedback responses that a bacterial culture

adapts to enrichment, and grows three times as fast in broth as in minimal medium. The limitation is not that the cell cannot make a given amino acid as rapidly as it can take it in from the outside; rather, the sparing of the machinery for making amino acids permits more rapid manufacture of other, growth-rate-limiting machinery, such as ribosomes.

2) The same feedback responses also promote **efficiency of growth** in a constant medium, for it is obvious that growth would be slower if biosynthesis were not harmonized, i.e., if part of the flow of foodstuff were wasted on the synthesis of excessive amounts of various metabolites and macromolecules.

3) Finally, the possession of a large reserve capacity for the formation of various enzymes, as noted above, has obvious value in allowing rapid **adaptation to exhaustion** of a nutrient in the environment.

The regulatory devices that have recently been discovered reveal three fundamental principles that are among microbiology's most profound contributions to biology. 1) The first is the widespread evolution of exquisite **allosteric proteins**—regulatory enzymes and probably also regulators of gene expression—whose conformation, and therefore activity, can alter in response to a chemical signal. 2) The second principle is the regulation of the biosynthesis of macromolecules, on a template, by controlling the **frequency of initiation** of a chain, rather than by controlling the velocity of extension of the chain. Such regulation has been firmly established for DNA replication; for protein synthesis it is implied by the dependence of rate on concentration of ribosomes; and for RNA synthesis this mechanism would fit the decisive control of the operator over the initiation of transcription of an operon. 3) Finally, the **linking of genes** in chromosomes has long been recognized as a device that insures equipartition of the genetic material at cell division. We can now see another consequence of gene linkage, perhaps equally fundamental: the function of the operon as a unit of regulation.

SELECTED REFERENCES

Books and Review Articles

AMES, B. N., and MARTIN, R. G. Biochemical aspects of genetics: The operon. *Ann. Rev. Biochem. 33*:235 (1964).

Cellular regulatory mechanisms. *Cold Spring Harbor Symp. Quant. Biol. 26*:1 (1961).

JACOB, F., and MONOD, J. Genetic regulatory mechanisms in the synthesis of protein. *J. Molec. Biol. 3*:318 (1961).

JACOB, F., and MONOD, J. Genetic Repression, Allosteric Inhibition, and Cellular Differentiation. In *Cytodifferentiation and Macromolecular Synthesis* (21st Growth Symposium; M. Locke, ed.) Academic Press, New York, 1963.

MAALØE, O., and KJELDGAARD, N. O. *Control of Macromolecular Synthesis.* Benjamin, New York, 1965.

MAAS, W. K., and MCFALL, E. Genetic aspects of metabolic control. *Ann. Rev. Microbiol. 18*:95 (1964).

MANDELSTAM, J. The intracellular turnover of protein and nucleic acids and its role in biochemical differentiation. *Bact. Rev. 24*:289 (1960).

MARKERT, C. L. Developmental genetics. *Harvey Lect. 59*:187 (1963–64).

MONOD, J. La biosynthèse induite des enzymes (adaptation enzymatique). *Advances Enzymol. 13*:67 (1952).

MONOD, J., CHANGEUX, J.-P., and JACOB, F. Allosteric proteins and cellular control systems. *J. Molec. Biol. 6*:306 (1963).

NEIDHARDT, F. C. Effects of environment on the composition of bacterial cells. *Ann. Rev. Microbiol. 17*:61 (1963).

NEIDHARDT, F. C., The regulation of RNA synthesis in bacteria. *Progr. in Nucleic Acid Res. and Molec. Biol. 3:145* (1964).

RILEY, M., and PARDEE, A. B. Gene expression: Its specificity and regulation. *Ann. Rev. Microbiol. 16*:1 (1962).

Synthesis and structure of macromolecules. *Cold Spring Harbor Symp. Quant. Biol.* 28:1 (1963). Especially relevant are the sections on messenger RNA (p. 161), regulation of synthesis of macromolecules (p. 329), and allosteric interactions (p. 461).

WATSON, J. D. Involvement of RNA in the synthesis of protein. (Nobel lecture.) *Science 140*:17 (1963).

WILSON, A. C., and PARDEE, A. B. Comparative Aspects of Metabolic Control. In *Comparative Biochemistry*, vol. VI. (M. Florkin and H. S. Mason, eds.) Academic Press, New York, 1964.

Specific Articles

GERHART, J. C., and SCHACHMAN, H. K. Distinct subunits for the regulation and catalytic activity of aspartate transcarbamylase. *Biochemistry 4*:1054 (1965).

HALL, B. D., and SPIEGELMAN, S. Sequence complementarity of T2-DNA and T2-specific RNA. *Proc. Nat. Acad. Sc. 47*:137 (1961).

KJELDGAARD, N. O., MAALØE, O., and SCHAECHTER, M. The transition between different physiological states during balanced growth of *Salmonella typhimurium. J. Gen. Microbiol. 19*:607 (1958).

MOYED, H. S. False feedback inhibition: Inhibition of tryptophan biosynthesis by 5-methyltryptophan. *J. Biol. Chem. 235*:1098 (1960).

PARDEE, A. B., JACOB, F., and MONOD, J. The genetic control and cytoplasmic expression of "inducibility" in the synthesis of β-galactosidase by *E. coli. J. Molec. Biol. 1*:165 (1959).

STADTMAN, E. R., COHEN, G. N., LEGRAS, G., and DE ROBICHON-SZULMAJSTER, H. Feedback inhibition and repression of aspartokinase activity in *Escherichia coli* and *Saccharomyces cerevisiae. J. Biol. Chem. 236*:2033 (1961).

STENT, G., and BRENNER, S. A genetic locus for the regulation of RNA synthesis. *Proc. Nat. Acad. Sc. 47*: 2005 (1961).

UMBARGER, H. E., and BROWN, B. Evidence for two L-threonine deaminases. *J. Bact. 73*:105 (1957).

VOGEL, H. J. Repression and Induction as Control Mechanisms of Enzyme Biogenesis. In *The Chemical Basis of Heredity,* p. 276. (W. D. McElroy and B. Glass, eds.) Johns Hopkins Univ. Press, Baltimore, 1957.

YATES, R. A., and PARDEE, A. B. Control of pyrimidine biosynthesis in *Escherichia coli* by a feedback mechanism. *J. Biol. Chem. 221*:757 (1956).

Poisons are veritable reagents of life, extremely delicate instruments which dissect vital units.

CLAUDE BERNARD, 1857

10 CHEMOTHERAPEUTIC ACTIONS ON BACTERIA

Chemotherapeutic agents are defined as **chemicals that can directly interfere with the proliferation of microorganisms, at concentrations that are tolerated by the host.** Accordingly, their essential feature is **selective toxicity.** Some of these drugs are **bacteristatic,** the inhibition of growth being **reversed** when the drugs are removed. Others are **bactericidal,** exerting an **irreversible,** lethal effect.*

This chapter will consider the effects of various chemotherapeutic agents on bacteria in the relatively well defined environment of a culture, and also on biochemical systems extracted from bacteria.

The Development of Chemotherapy

Origins. The Peruvian Indians used cinchona bark (containing quinine) centuries ago to treat malaria, without knowing that it acted directly on a parasite. The idea of such direct action was forcefully advanced by Paul Ehrlich, a physician working at a time when organic chemistry was blossoming in Germany. Ehrlich was fascinated by the possibility of using the specific affinities of organic compounds to solve medical problems, and while a medical student in 1870 he introduced dyes that are still used in histology for the selective staining of basophilic and acidophilic cell components. Becoming involved later in the exciting development of antitoxins, he formulated the essentially correct "side chain" theory to account for the extraordinarily specific interactions of antibodies with antigens. In 1904, drawing on these experiences, he began to seek synthetic chemicals that would exhibit a greater affinity for parasites than for host cells (*nihil agit nisi fixatur*); and for this selective action he coined the word "chemotherapy." But though Ehrlich did discover dyes that were useful against trypanosomes, and arsenicals that were useful against spirochetes, he was disappointed at not finding any "magic bullets" against bacteria (other than spirochetes).

Following Ehrlich's death in 1915 the medical world returned to the conviction that chemotherapy was an impractical dream. According to the prevailing view, the struggle between host

---

* Though the traditional words are "bacteriostatic" and "bactericidal," the continued use of different stems in these parallel words hardly seems desirable.

and parasite was too complex to permit such a direct attack, and one could better seek to stimulate host defenses. This vitalistic attitude hindered further progress for 20 years, but it did have an experimental basis, since the drugs then known to exhibit antimicrobial activity in vivo were inactive in vitro. We now know why: these drugs were precursors that became active only after metabolic conversion by the host. For example, Ehrlich's antisyphilitic arsphenamine was active only in vivo; but many years later this arseno compound $(RC_6H_4As{=}AsC_6H_4R)$ was found to be oxidized in the body to the corresponding arsenoxide $(RC_6H_4As{=}O)$, which was active in vitro as well as in vivo.

Sulfonamides. Modern antibacterial chemotherapy was launched in 1935 at the I. G. Farben industry in Germany, where Domagk developed a dye, Prontosil, that dramatically cured streptococcal infections. But despite the theoretical foundations furnished by Ehrlich, the affinity of the dye proved irrelevant. It was inactive in vitro; a year later Tréfouel, in France, showed that patients given the dye excreted a simpler, colorless product, **sulfanilamide,** which was active in vitro. This compound was then used directly as a drug, and was soon succeeded by more potent derivatives; the class is known in medicine as the **sulfonamides.**

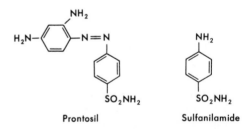

Prontosil   Sulfanilamide

Sulfanilamide unequivocally reestablished Ehrlich's principle of direct chemotherapeutic action on the parasite. Since then thousands of antimicrobial compounds have been discovered by screening for activity in vitro. Of these, however, only a few dozen have been sufficiently selective to be useful.

Antibiotics. The success of sulfonamides stimulated a search for other kinds of chemotherapeutic agents. The next triumph was achieved with **antibiotics,** which are defined as **antimicrobial agents of microbial origin.*** Fleming had reported in 1929 the antibiotic action of a colony of the mold *Penicillium notatum* contaminating a culture of staphylococci (Fig. 10-1). The inhibitory material, which he named penicillin, seemed too unstable to isolate, and so the problem was dropped. Some years later Chain and colleagues, in Florey's laboratory at Oxford, undertook the purification of penicillin, and they showed in 1940 that it was reasonably stable, once purified and dried. More important, it was remarkably nontoxic to man and was even more effective than sulfonamides against susceptible organisms.

The success of penicillin led to a search for new antibiotics on an enormous scale, initially in medical research centers and laboratories of soil microbiology, and then in the pharmaceutical industry. This massive effort has yielded many valuable products. At the same time a new, high-pressure pattern of drug promotion has emerged. One factor has been the large financial consequences of having one antimicrobial drug displaced in the market by another: in 1964 the sale of antibiotics in the United States amounted to 320 million dollars wholesale.

Terminology. Though the term "antibiotic" is useful, the distinction that it makes, between naturally occurring and synthetic antimicrobials, is not of fundamental consequence. Thus chloramphenicol was discovered as an antibiotic but is now produced commercially by chemical synthesis. It is more important to distinguish those few antimicrobial agents, whether antibiotic or synthetic in origin, that have proved selective enough to be used for chemotherapy.

Since the term "chemotherapy" has become popularly identified with "miracle drugs," it is now often extended, for promotional purposes,

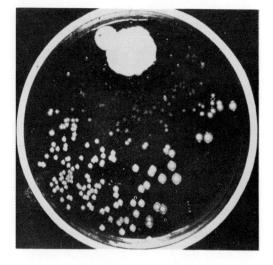

Fig. 10-1 The discovery of penicillin. Note lysis of colonies of *Staphylococcus aureus* surrounding a contaminating colony of *Penicillium notatum*. (From A. Fleming. *Brit. J. Exp. Path.* 10:226, 1929.)

to other novel pharmaceutical developments. Ehrlich's useful distinction, of drugs that act directly on the parasite rather than on the host, therefore seemed in danger of being lost. However, this distinction has been rescued by the term "antimicrobial drugs."

Effects of Drugs on Growth and Viability

Simple studies of the effect of an antimicrobial agent on bacterial growth in cultures can yield several kinds of information that are of value in guiding and understanding therapeutic use. These include the sensitivity of an organism, the kinetics of inhibition, and the presence or absence of lysis and bactericidal action.

1) **The sensitivity** of an organism is most precisely determined by the **tube dilution** method, in which identical inocula are incubated in tubes containing different concentrations of the drug. The endpoint is the lowest concentration that prevents the development of turbidity after a fixed period of incubation.

In the more convenient **agar diffusion** method solid medium is heavily seeded with bacteria and a sample of drug is deposited on it (e.g., in a disc of thick filter paper, a small cylinder,

---

* Inhibition of some microbes by others (i.e., **antibiosis,** an ecological relation opposite to symbiosis) was first recorded in 1877 by Pasteur, who observed sterilization of anthrax bacilli in a contaminated culture. In the next half-century a number of similar accidental observations were reported, together with a few abortive attempts at putting the inhibitory substances to therapeutic use.

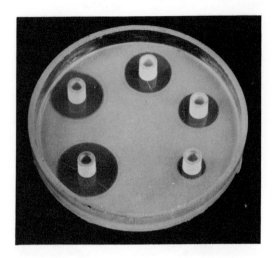

Fig. 10-2 Plate assay for an antibiotic. Plate seeded on the surface with the standard test strain of *S. aureus* (Oxford strain). To the open cylinders were added equal amounts of penicillin solutions containing 4, 2, 1, 0.5, and 0.25 U/ml, and the plates were incubated overnight. Today filter paper discs are generally used instead of cylinders. (From E. Chain and H. Florey. *Endeavour*, Jan. 1944, p. 3.)

or a hole cut in the agar). After the bacterial lawn has grown out the deposit may be surrounded by a clear zone. For a given drug sample the diameter of this zone provides an index of the level of sensitivity of the organism; or the test may be used with a known organism to assay the drug (Fig. 10-2). The diameter is also influenced by the growth rate of the organism and the density of the inoculum, since it reflects a race between multiplication of the organism and diffusion of the drug.

The disc method is widely used for determining the **sensitivity spectrum** of strains freshly isolated from patients. Reasonably stable test discs, impregnated with a solution of a drug and then dried, are now commercially available. If the test dose is properly chosen, a zone of inhibition will indicate that the drug is active against the organism at levels attainable in the patient. From these active drugs the one to be used is then selected on the basis of a variety of pharmacological considerations, and should **not** be simply the drug yielding the widest zone of inhibition.

2) **The kinetics of inhibition, and the presence of lysis,** may be observed by **turbidimetric** measurements following addition of drug to a growing culture. Several patterns are illustrated in Figure 10-3A: thus sulfona-

Fig. 10-3 Kinetics of antimicrobial action of representative drugs. Drug added at arrow to exponentially growing culture.

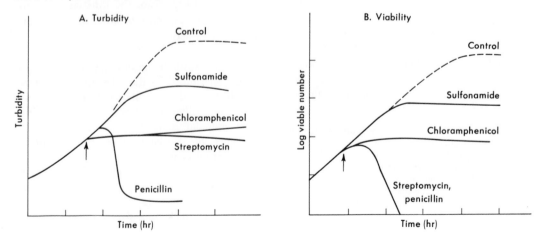

mide inhibition of growth is delayed for several generations; chloramphenicol and streptomycin cause an almost immediate leveling off of turbidity; and penicillin causes lysis, indicated by a sharp fall in turbidity.

3) **Bactericidal action** is, of course, evident when there is gross lysis (e.g., with penicillin). To quantitate the rate of killing, however, and also to recognize killing when the cells remain morphologically intact, **viability counts** are required (Fig. 10-3B). For this purpose samples are taken at intervals, diluted appropriately, and plated on an adequate medium. The dilutions must be great enough to eliminate further action of the drug. Indirect indices of cell death, such as inhibition of respiration, inhibition of dye reduction, or intracellular staining, are less reliable than viability counts.

The distinction between bactericidal and bacteristatic action is not rigorous. At borderline concentrations some ordinarily cidal agents appear to be static or exhibit long bacteristatic lags before their cidal action; conversely, bacteristasis from any cause is eventually followed by a decrease in viable number. Nevertheless, it is important, from the points of view of both mechanism and clinical use, to distinguish those agents that cause the viable count to remain essentially constant for several hours and those that cause it to decline by decimal orders of magnitude.

In contrast to the disinfectants, most of the chemotherapeutic agents that are bactericidal exert this effect only under conditions that allow cell growth. This property has allowed penicillin to be useful in the selection of auxotrophic mutants (Ch. 4).

THE ACTIONS OF METABOLITE ANALOGS

Competitive Inhibition

Certain inhibitors of biochemical reactions were shown early to act by competing with a structurally related metabolite for attachment to a specific site on a protein. For example, carbon monoxide ($C{=}O$) competes with oxygen ($O{=}O$) for binding sites of hemoglobin, and malonic acid ($HOOC{-}CH_2{-}COOH$) interferes with the action of succinic dehydrogenase on succinic acid ($HOOC{-}CH_2{-}CH_2{-}COOH$). However, the principle of competitive inhibition became prominent in biochemistry and pharmacology only after it furnished the explanation for the action of a useful chemotherapeutic agent, sulfanilamide (see below).

Kinetics. The characteristics of competitive inhibition follow from the Michaelis-Menten application of the mass law to enzyme kinetics. If a substrate (S) and its analog (A) can each form a reversible complex with an enzyme (E), the extent of formation of each complex will be proportional to both the concentration of the corresponding unbound ligand and its affinity for the enzyme (i.e., the inverse of the dissociation constant, K, of the complex).

$$\frac{(ES)}{(E)} = \frac{1}{K_S}(S)$$

$$\frac{(EA)}{(E)} = \frac{1}{K_A}(A) \qquad (2)$$

By combining equations (1) and (2) one sees that in a mixture of E with both S and A the ratio of the two complexes will be proportional to the ratio of the concentration of the two ligands.

$$\frac{(ES)}{(EA)} = \frac{K_A}{K_S} \cdot \frac{(S)}{(A)} \qquad (3)$$

Since the rate of the enzyme reaction is proportional to the concentration of the ES complex, the analog slows the reaction to the extent that it replaces ES by the inactive EA. We thus see from equation (3) the criterion for competitive inhibition: at the usual concentration of substrate, at which the amount of enzyme is limiting, **the rate of the reaction is constant for a particular analog/substrate ratio.** In other words, if one doubles the concentration of the analog one can maintain the same enzyme activity by also doubling the concentration of substrate.

Sulfonamides and PAB. Yeast extract was observed to antagonize the inhibition of bacterial growth by sulfanilamide, and D. D. Woods in 1940, in England, identified the most important antagonist in the extract as *p*-aminobenzoate (PAB). He further showed that PAB and sulfanilamide acted competitively, and he stressed their close structural resemblance (Fig. 10-4). These findings led to the suggestion that 1) PAB must be an **essential metabolite,** i.e., the substrate of an essential (though then unknown) metabolic reaction, and 2) sulfanilamide competitively inhibits this postulated reaction. This interpretation was soon confirmed by identifying PAB as a component of folic acid. (Fig. 10-4), and the postulated inhibition of a PAB-incorporating enzyme on the pathway to folate has recently been directly demonstrated with extracts. These enzymatic studies have further shown, however, that the story is not so simple: as with many other analogs (see below), sulfonamides not only inhibit an enzyme but also serve as a competitive substrate for it, and are thus converted to products that then jam later reactions.

The function of PAB as a precursor of a coenzyme explains the delay in the bacteristatic effect of sulfonamides: the folate in the cell must be depleted before growth is slowed. As we have seen (Fig. 5-5), deprival of a required building block (amino acid, nucleotide) inhibits growth rapidly, whereas deprival of a coenzyme has only a gradual effect.

The concept of **essential metabolite** should be distinguished from that of **essential nutrient:** sulfonamides are equally effective against organisms that can synthesize PAB and against those few that require it for growth.

The Antimetabolite Program

The explanation of sulfonamide action confirmed Ehrlich's earlier, intuitive notion that chemotherapeutic agents acted by combining with specific cellular receptors. The hope then arose that the development of new agents, hitherto entirely empirical, could now be rationally based on the synthesis of **antimetabolites,** i.e., analogs of known essential metabolites. Accordingly, thousands of analogs of vitamins, purines, pyrimidines, and amino acids have been synthesized, and many proved to be effective inhibitors of bacterial growth in vitro. Unfortu-

Fig. 10-4 Metabolism interfered with by sulfonamides.

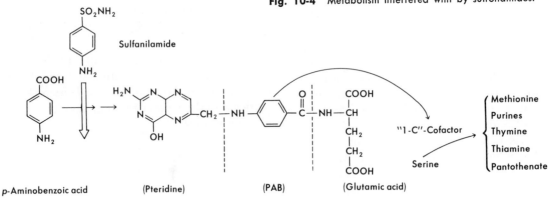

p-Aminobenzoic acid   (Pteridine)   (PAB)   (Glutamic acid)

Folic acid
(pteroylglutamic acid)

nately, these analogs have failed to exhibit the required selectivity, in part because they were modeled on metabolites that are also essential for the host. PAB, in contrast, is not an essential metabolite in man, who must obtain folic acid in his diet.

The antimetabolite program has had some success, however, in cancer chemotherapy, where one cannot afford to insist on so broad a margin of selectivity as with bacterial infections. Useful analogs have been modeled on folic acid (e.g., aminopterin, amethopterin), purines (6-mercaptopurine, 8-azaguanine), and pyrimidines (5-fluorouracil and its deoxyriboside).* Antimetabolites have also been valuable in studies in cell physiology. In addition, the principle of competitive inhibition has contributed immensely to pharmacology, since it has explained the action of many drugs that were not synthesized on this basis.

Noncompetitive Reversal of Growth Inhibition

Inhibition of growth can be reversed not only by the substrate of the blocked enzyme but also by a later product in the same sequence, if it can enter the cell. Furthermore, reversal by a product is noncompetitive, i.e., an adequate quantity restores growth, regardless of how tightly the preceding reaction is shut off.

Sulfonamides, Folic Acid, and 1-Carbon Metabolism. Table 10-1 illustrates the noncompetitive reversal of sulfonamide inhibition by folic acid in *Streptococcus faecalis*, an organism that occasionally causes endocarditis.

Since folic acid is an essential nutrient in man, and therefore is present in body fluids, it is hardly surprising that in the body this species, which can utilize exogenous folic acid, does not respond to sulfonamide therapy. Most bacterial species, however, cannot use exogenous folic acid, presumably because of impermeability; and the chemotherapeutic value of sulfonamides depends on this fortunate fact.

Even bacteria responsive to sulfonamide chemotherapy are influenced by another source of noncompetitive reversal. In a medium containing meat digest (which includes hydrolysis products of proteins and nucleic acids, but no free PAB) the sulfonamide concentration required for inhibition is roughly 10 times that in a minimal medium. The principal reversing agents are methionine, serine, purines, and the pyrimidine thymine (Fig. 10-4). These effects became understandable when folic acid was found to be a coenzyme in the transfer and reduction of 1-carbon fragments: serine is the donor, and the other compounds noted are recipients, in these reactions.† Such a partial set of 1-carbon products can therefore spare part of the folate requirement, and so their presence raises the level of sulfonamide required for inhibition. (In fact, bacteria become essentially indifferent to sulfonamides with the further addition of pantothenate and thiamine, more recently

---

† Indeed, the metabolic relation of folic acid to purines was first indicated by the finding that sulfonamide-inhibited bacteria accumulate 4-amino-5-imidazole carboxamide, which was later discovered to be an intermediate (as the ribonucleotide) in purine biosynthesis (Ch. 4).

---

* For structures, see Chapter 8.

TABLE 10-1. COMPETITIVE AND NONCOMPETITIVE REVERSAL OF INHIBITION OF *S. FAECALIS*

Antagonist	Sulfadiazine (μg/ml)			
	1	10	100	1000
	Concentration restoring 50% growth (μg/ml)			
PAB	0.003	0.03	0.3	3.0
Folic acid	0.0003	0.0003	—	0.0003

From J. Lampen and M. J. Jones. J. Biol. Chem. 116:435 (1946).

discovered also to be biosynthetic products of 1-carbon metabolism.)

Sulfonamide chemotherapy thus depends on some fortunate features of mammalian metabolism. Our body fluids do contain detectable quantities of the amino acids, and so the inhibitory drug level in vivo is somewhat higher than that required in a simple medium. Purines and pyrimidines, however, are synthesized in all cells and are not present in our body fluids, at least in forms (free bases or nucleosides) that can be utilized by bacteria.* This analysis clarifies a major limitation on the value of these drugs: **sulfonamides are ineffective in sites of extensive tissue destruction,** such as purulent exudates, burns, and wounds, since autolysis releases the noncompetitive antagonists, including those that are not present in normal body fluids.

Biosynthetic Incorporation of Antimetabolites

The classic interpretation of competitive inhibition was based on the assumption that biosynthetic enzymes possess essentially absolute specificity. To be sure, poisoning of animals by fluoroacetate was shown to involve its conversion to fluorocitrate, and in selenium poisoning selenium was found to replace part of the sulfur of proteins; but these stood for some years as exceptional cases of "lethal synthesis." However, following the synthesis of radioactively labeled analogs and the development of chromatographic methods for identifying radioactive compounds recovered from the organism, this assumption of specificity was shattered. In 1953, 5-bromouracil and 8-azaguanine were found to be incorporated into nucleic acids, and soon many other antimetabolites were shown to deceive as well as to inhibit an enzyme, i.e., to serve as **competitive substrates.** The instances observed have included incorporation into coenzymes and proteins as well as into RNA and DNA.

Some amino acid analogs (e.g., 7-azatryptophan) can replace as much as 50% of the corresponding amino acid in the protein being formed, whereas others (e.g., 5-methyltryptophan) inhibit growth without being substantially incorporated. The incorporation of an analog is associated in some cases with the formation of a functional protein but in others with loss of function. Thus, when p-fluorophenylalanine replaced 20 to 45% of the phenylalanine and tyrosine in protein in *Escherichia coli* the cell formed altered but still functional β-galactosidase, whereas no active β-galactoside transport system could be formed. This formation of inactive protein is associated with linear bacterial growth, discussed in Chapter 5.

Extensive incorporation of amino acid analogs into bacteria is not necessarily lethal, since the cells have both the genetic information and the residual enzymatic capacity required to replenish those enzymes that have become diluted with inactive, analog-containing protein.

Base analog incorporation has been extensively studied, especially in relation to cancer and to inhibition of viral synthesis; a few key findings will be summarized here.

Before these compounds can affect growth they must be converted to the corresponding nucleotide analogs. The enzymes involved (one set for purines and one for pyrimidines) are the same ones that convert normal bases and nucleosides to nucleotides. However, these enzymes are not essential for growth, since purines and pyrimidines do not appear in normal biosynthesis as free bases or as nucleosides, but rather are synthesized de novo from intermediates at the level of nucleotides (Ch. 4). Hence a cell readily tolerates loss of these "salvage" pathways for the utilization of free bases, and such mutants are readily selected since they are completely resistant to purine or to pyrimidine analogs.

Some base analogs are incorporated primarily into DNA and others into RNA. The size of the bromine atom is close to that of the CH_3 group, and **5-bromouracil** substitutes well for thymine; indeed, it can replace the bulk of the thymine in bacteria or bacteriophage with little loss of viability. The mutagenic consequence of this substitution has been discussed in Chapter 8.

In contrast **5-fluorouracil,** which resembles uracil more than thymine, is rapidly bactericidal. It is incorporated into RNA but not detectably

---

* In support of this interpretation we may note that mutations of *Salmonella* to various amino acid requirements do not affect virulence in mice; but a requirement for PAB or for purines eliminates virulence unless the required factor is injected along with the organisms.

into DNA; it also becomes converted, like uracil, to a deoxyribonucleotide. This compound, 5-fluorodeoxyuridylate, then inhibits the conversion of deoxyuridylate, by thymidylate synthetase, to deoxythymidylate, a normal precursor of DNA. The resulting special kind of block in DNA synthesis causes the cell to undergo "thymineless death" (Ch. 9).

In the presence of thymine 5-fluorouracil is no longer lethal, and its incorporation into RNA can then be studied more cleanly. Such incorporation into mRNA is found to produce errors in the translation of information from DNA into protein, resulting both in loss of the ability to produce normal enzyme (resulting in linear growth) and in phenotypic suppression of many mutations (Ch. 8).

Additional Actions of Antimetabolites

Membrane transport is an additional site of competition between synthetic analogs and the corresponding normal metabolites. Accordingly, metabolites can restore growth not only by the mechanisms discussed earlier, but also by blocking the entry of the analog; analogs, on the other hand, can inhibit growth by inhibiting entry of an essential nutrient.

For example, D-serine is an antimetabolite of β-alanine: it inhibits completely the enzyme that converts β-alanine to pantothenate, and its growth inhibition is reversed competitively by β-alanine and noncompetitively by pantothenate.

However, the growth inhibition is also reversed by several metabolically distant compounds, including glycine and some other amino acids. This finding was puzzling until these compounds were shown to block the entry of D-serine. It is thus evident that though several metabolites may be able to reverse the action of the same inhibitor they are not necessarily members of the same biosynthetic family: they may be strangers riding on the same ferry.

Since inhibitors must be transported across the cell membrane before they can act on intracellular enzymes, the properties of the transport system can influence the potency of an inhibitor. Thus sulfanilic acid (p-$NH_2 \cdot C_6H_5 \cdot SO_3H$) is less potent than sulfanilamide in inhibiting growth, but much more potent in inhibiting the extracted enzyme that converts PAB. Furthermore, the competitive ratio of sulfonamide to PAB is much lower with intact cells than with extracts. Hence even in this classic example the quantitative relations observed with intact cells probably reflect competition at a transport system rather than the competition that also exists at an enzyme.

Pseudo-feedback inhibition (allosteric inhibition) presents a novel mechanism of antimetabolite action, in which the analog mimics the feedback inhibitory action of a biosynthetic end-product on the initial (i.e., branchpoint) enzyme of its pathway. The result is interference with the **formation** rather than with the function of the metabolite. This mechanism has been observed with compounds of theoretical interest (Ch. 9), but not with any useful chemotherapeutic agents.

MECHANISMS OF BACTERICIDAL ACTION

The best understood mechanism of antimicrobial action is inhibition of a specific enzyme, but this effect will in general stop growth only reversibly. Hence the mechanisms responsible for the irreversible effect of bactericidal (or, more generally, cytocidal) agents constitute a special problem which is important not only for antimicrobial chemotherapy but also for understanding cytotoxic processes in mammalian pathology and phar-

macology. Indeed, cytocidal action is desirable but not essential in antimicrobial chemotherapy, since host defenses can eliminate such foreign cells during a period of stasis; but cytocidal action seems much more important in chemotherapy directed against cancer cells, which are less foreign to the host. It is therefore of interest to try to define those kinds of damage to a cell that are irreparable.

In seeking general principles in this area it is useful to emphasize the distinction between those elements of the cell that are unique and those that are present in replaceable units. The class of unique units obviously includes **the DNA chain:** while damage at certain sites causes a recognizable mutation compatible with survival, most damage to DNA yields the undifferentiated class of lethal mutations. Similarly, a hole anywhere in **the cell membrane** cannot be compensated for by the integrity of the rest of the membrane; and unless the break can be repaired, the damage will be lethal. Finally, if all the molecules of any enzyme required for protein synthesis are inactivated the cell cannot regenerate that enzyme. With most other enzymes, in contrast, inactivation of all the molecules of a given species will still permit at least a trace of protein synthesis; hence the depleted species can be regenerated.

While inhibition of an enzyme will thus in general not be lethal, there are exceptions in which the originally reversible inhibition has irreversible secondary consequences. Familiar examples include the effect of 5-fluorouracil on **DNA synthesis** and that of penicillin on **wall synthesis** (Ch. 2). Inhibition of an enzyme required for **membrane formation** would presumably also be lethal.

THE INDIVIDUAL CHEMOTHERAPEUTIC AGENTS

PAB Analogs

We have already noted (pp. 302, 306) the discovery of sulfanilamide (*p*-aminobenzene sulfonamide) and the finding that it acts by competing with PAB. Several thousand congeners, known as the sulfonamides, have been synthesized. Some of those in current use are shown in Figure 10-5.

Structure-Activity Relations Among the Sulfonamides

A variety of substitutions on the sulfonamide group (N^1) of sulfanilamide were found to increase its activity, while any substitution on the amino group (N^4) inactivated it. The latter substitution, however, is used in one special class of drugs, such as sulfasuxidine (Fig. 10-5). This drug is inactive in vitro, but it is poorly absorbed and is slowly hydrolyzed in the gut to yield an active compound, sulfathiazole.

In a series of sulfonamides potency was found to correlate closely with pK. Sulfanilamide is a weak acid (pK ca. 10), and the most active derivatives (sulfadiazine, sulfathiazole) turned out to be stronger acids (pK ca. 7). However, even more electrophilic substituents, which still further increased the acidity of the sulfonamide group, weakened the drug. The most potent sulfonamides are found to be those that are 50% dissociated (pK = pH of test medium).* A theoretical explanation for this maximum of potency has been provided by Bell and Roblin, who recognized that the pK influences the electronegativity of the sulfone ($-SO_2-$) groups: increasingly electrophilic substituents on this group increase and then decrease the negativity of its sulfone component. The more negative the sulfone group the closer its resemblance to the carboxyl of PAB (pK 4.8), which is essentially fully ionized at the usual cultural pH.

Antimicrobial Spectrum

Sulfonamides are active in vitro against all bacteria (except the few that require exogenous folic acid), but the level of sensitivity varies widely from one species to another. Sulfanilamide was useful in vivo only against streptococci and a few other organisms. The newer derivatives do not show any specific

---

* For this reason the sulfonamides selected for maximal activity at pH 7.4 are ordinarily less potent in the urine (pH ca. 5 to 6) than those with a lower pK, such as sulfacetamide.

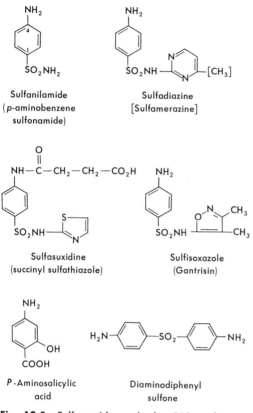

Fig. 10-5 Sulfonamides and other PAB analogs.

Diaminodiphenyl Sulfone

This drug (Fig. 10-5) was synthesized as a congener of sulfanilamide. It does not have a sulfonamide group, however, and unlike the sulfonamides it exhibits marked specificity: it is valuable in the treatment of only one bacterial infection, **leprosy.** Its effect is not dramatically curative, but it is the best agent presently available against this disease. Its mechanism of action may well involve competition with PAB, but the failure of the leprosy bacillus to grow in vitro has made it impossible to test this inference.

p-Aminosalicylic Acid (PAS)

Substitutions for ring hydrogens of the PAB molecule can also be used to create analogs. One of these, *p*-aminosalicylate (PAS; Fig. 10-5), is useful in treating tuberculosis. Though it was synthesized as an analog of salicylate (*o*-hydroxybenzoate) because that compound can be metabolized by mycobacteria, it was later shown to act as a PAB analog: 1) it is antagonized competitively by PAB and noncompetitively by the products of 1-carbon metabolism, and 2) bacteria can incorporate it into an analog of folic acid.

The effect of PAS in tuberculosis is not as dramatic as that of isoniazid or streptomycin, but it is useful in combination with either of these agents (see below). Like sulfonamides, it penetrates mammalian cells, and it is bacteristatic.

Though PAS is effective against the tubercle bacillus, against other bacteria it shows low potency in vitro and no value in vivo. This spectrum contrasts strikingly with that of the sulfonamides, in which various substituents influence effectiveness against different bacterial species in a parallel manner. Since PAS and sulfonamides are analogs substituted on different parts of the PAB molecule, their differences in antimicrobial spectrum imply that bacterial species can differ in the structure of the active site in this enzyme. Presumably in the tubercle bacillus this active site has a shape particularly

changes in antimicrobial spectrum, but their marked increase in potency permits them to be useful against many additional species. In drug sensitivity tests a single sulfonamide will suffice, since resistant mutants exhibit a comparable increase in resistance to all members of the group.

Research on sulfonamides in recent years has sought improvements in pharmacological rather than in antimicrobial properties. One form of toxicity, due to crystallization in the urine, can be avoided with a highly soluble derivative (sulfisoxazole: Gantrisin). In addition, slower excretion and therefore longer action has been achieved (sulfamethoxypyridazine: Kynex). We might note that whereas drugs of this class were formerly given trade names that identified them by the prefix "sulfa," the more recent additions, in this age of antibiotics, have been given names that do not emphasize their old-fashioned family connections.

well fitted to PAS, while in other bacteria it is better fitted to sulfonamides.

Penicillins and Other Drugs That Inhibit Wall Synthesis

Production

We have already noted (p. 302) that the chemotherapeutic value of penicillin was discovered in England in 1940. Because of the pressures of the war on British laboratories, the development of this drug took place chiefly in the United States as one of the first large government-supported medical research projects. The problems involved in making the pure drug on a large scale were thus rapidly solved. The procedures devised have provided a model for the development of all subsequent antibiotics.

Major improvements in production have been achieved by successive selections of higher-yield strains, usually obtained by empirically testing large numbers of clones after mutagenic irradiation. Modifications of the culture medium have

also made large contributions. Finally, since molds are obligate aerobes they are conventionally cultivated as a surface mycelial growth on shallow layers of medium; but it proved more economical to produce penicillin in aerated submerged culture. Fermenters have therefore been developed that can maintain good aerobiosis in 50,000-gallon cultures. These advances in fermentation technology, together with genetic changes in the organism, have increased the broth potency no less than 5000-fold, compared with the original laboratory cultures.

Chemistry and Biosynthesis

The substance originally designated as penicillin was found to be a mixture of several active compounds; they have in common a binucleate structure, 6-aminopenicillanic acid, but differ in the acyl side chain that is condensed with the 6-amino group (Fig. 10-6).

The four-membered (β-lactam) ring of penicillin has a strained configuration, and its CO–N bond is therefore readily hydrolyzed, yielding an inactive product, penicilloic acid (Fig. 10-6). Hence penicillin is

Fig. 10-6 Structure of some natural penicillins and derivatives.

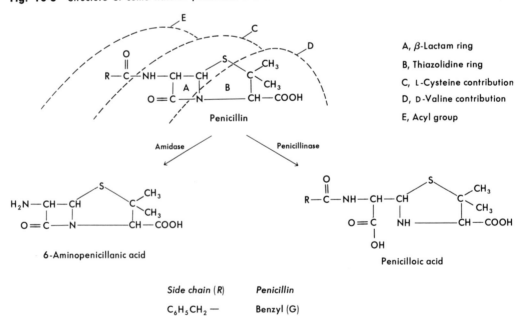

A, β-Lactam ring
B, Thiazolidine ring
C, L-Cysteine contribution
D, D-Valine contribution
E, Acyl group

unstable in solution and is relatively rapidly destroyed by the acid of the stomach. The lability to acid varies with different penicillins; with penicillin G it permits roughly 1/5 of an orally administered dose to be absorbed. The same bond is also hydrolyzed by penicillinase (penicillin lactamase), an enzyme formed by certain bacteria (see below).

The penicillin nucleus can be visualized as a peculiarly condensed peptide of two familiar amino acids, cysteine and valine, as outlined in Figure 10-6. Indeed, isotopic studies have provided evidence for biosynthesis of the nucleus from L-cysteine and D-valine (whose configurations correspond to those found in the product).

Modified Biosynthesis. The variety of side chains found in the original penicillin showed that the enzyme responsible for incorporating the acyl group is relatively nonspecific. Indeed, the nature of this group in the product could be controlled by varying the acids present in the medium. Thus when benzylpenicillin (penicillin G) proved to be the most satisfactory of the original penicillins, it was found that an almost pure yield of this product could be obtained by providing an excess of the corresponding acyl donor (phenylacetic acid). It is still the most widely used and inexpensive penicillin.

By adding various other acyl donors to the medium a number of novel penicillins were obtained. Among these, penicillin V (phenoxymethyl penicillin, Fig. 10-6) proved unusually resistant to gastric acidity.

Penicillin G is still marketed in Oxford units, originally defined in terms of the inhibition of a standard strain of *S. aureus*; one unit equals 0.6 μg. The penicillins developed later, as well as all other antibiotics, are prescribed on a weight basis.

Semisynthetic Penicillins

While penicillin G is an extremely effective and nontoxic drug, it has several limitations: a relatively narrow antimicrobial spectrum (see below), destruction by acid, destruction by penicillinase, and elicitation of allergic responses. Efforts at improvement have therefore continued; a major advance was the discovery in a British drug firm, in 1960, that if the medium lacks any acyl side chain donor the mold produces mostly a precursor, 6-aminopenicillanic acid, rather than penicillin itself.* Since 6-aminopenicillanic acid can be condensed chemically with many acids that cannot be incorporated by biosynthesis, the number of possible penicillins is now almost unlimited; several are illustrated in Figure 10-7.

Resistance to Penicillinase. One of the early semisynthetic penicillins, **methicillin**, provided an effective solution to the problem of penicillinase-producing staphylococci, for it is essentially inert to penicillinase. This resistance is probably promoted by the steric effect of the bulky *o*-methoxy groups near the site of enzymatic attack. Methicillin is very labile to acid and is only 1/30 as potent as penicillin G (against nonproducers of penicillinase); hence it must be given parenterally and in large doses. However, a later penicillinase-resistant product, **oxacillin**, is more resistant to acid and hence can be given orally; it is also more potent, but still only about 1/10 as potent as penicillin G. Commercial competition has led to the recent introduction of additional semisynthetic penicillins (cloxacillin, nafcillin, diphenicillin) with biological properties much like those of oxacillin; cloxacillin is better absorbed.

These penicillins not only resist the action of penicillinase but they cause it to shift to a stable, inactive configuration, as tested by **subsequent** addition of a sensitive penicillin. However, the enzyme has much greater affinity for the sensitive than for the resistant drug; hence on **simultaneous** addition of the two drugs to the enzyme, the resistant drug fails to protect the sensitive one from destruction.

---

* This discovery was based on the accidental observation of discrepancies, in certain cultures, between chemical determinations of penicillin, which are based on reactivity of the β-lactam ring, and microbiological assays, which require the whole molecule.

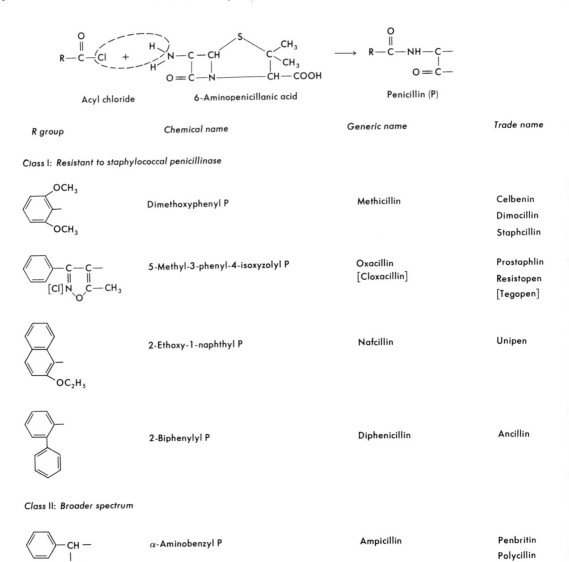

Fig. 10-7 Some semisynthetic penicillins.

Broadening of Antimicrobial Spectrum. Research on semisynthetic penicillins has also led to an even more important improvement: products with a broadened antimicrobial spectrum. Thus the presence of the amino group on the side chain makes **ampicillin** (α-aminobenzyl penicillin; Fig. 10-7) much more active than penicillin G against many gram-negative bacilli. It is also half as active against gram-positive organisms, and it can be given orally. As might be expected from the lack of a bulky group near the β-lactam ring, ampicillin is sensitive to penicillinase.

Cephalosporins

Cephalosporin C, an antibiotic similar to the penicillins but much less potent, was isolated in 1952 from a mold of the genus *Cephalosporium*. Ten years later the nucleus was isolated and used as the basis for making a series of semisynthetic derivatives, analogous to the newer penicillins. One of these

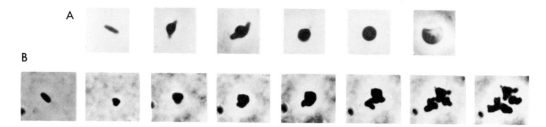

Fig. 10-8 Formation of spheroplasts during growth in the presence of penicillin. **A.** Phase contrast photomicrograph of *E. coli* cells growing in liquid medium in presence of penicillin (1000 U/ml) and sucrose (10%). After formation of spheroplasts further growth leads to formation of crescentic peripheral vacuole. **B.** In solid medium with same additions irregular division occurs, leading to microcolonies of L forms. (From J. Lederberg and J. St. Clair. *J. Bact. 75:*143, 1958.)

derivatives, **cephalothin,** has proved useful. While it is not, strictly speaking, a penicillin, its similarity in structure and action justifies grouping with the penicillins.

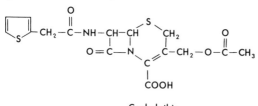

Cephalothin

Cephalothin has a broad enough spectrum to be useful against some gram-negative bacilli as well as against staphylococci, and it is resistant to staphylococcal penicillinase. Its altered ring structure gives it the particular advantage of **not causing allergic reactions** in many patients who are allergic to penicillin. This antibiotic thus promises to open up a new range of drugs, similar in action to the penicillins but not cross reacting immunologically with them. However, it is less potent than the classic penicillins against most organisms, and it must be administered by injection.

Mechanism of Action of Penicillins

Penicillin lyses growing cells and is therefore bactericidal (Fig. 10-3); it has no effect on the viability of resting cells. In 1957 Lederberg showed that this drug, like the enzyme lysozyme (Ch. 2), leads to protoplast forma-

tion in a hypertonic medium.* In contrast to lysozyme, however, which directly attacks the wall, penicillin only interferes with its formation, while permitting the rest of the cell to grow. In fact, it is the **growth** of the cell out of its protective wall, followed by osmotic lysis, that accounts for penicillin's bactericidal effect. Transitional "rabbit-ear" forms, in which bacilli have expanded in the center while the original walls remain attached on either end, are shown in Figure 10-8. Borderline concentrations of penicillin lead to the appearance of long filaments, suggesting that septum formation is especially sensitive to the drug.

While the osmotically sensitive spherical cells formed in the presence of penicillin in a hypertonic medium look like those formed by lysozyme, they differ in retaining wall components other than the mucopeptide layer; hence they are not true protoplasts (wall-less cells), and they are called **spheroplasts.** Unlike protoplasts, the cells can usually resume growth and division on subculture into penicillin-free hypertonic medium. With most strains such growth usually restores the

---

* Two earlier observations had already pointed to damage to the cell integument: Duguid observed under the microscope that penicillin causes the growing cell to burst out of its wall; Gale, studying the biochemical effects of the drug, observed impairment of the active transport of amino acids. These observations, however, had little impact on a scientific community not yet widely interested in cell organization.

normal bacterial form rapidly, but with some, the cells continue to grow slowly as stable (i.e., hereditary) L forms (Ch. 2), presumably lacking the primer for reinitiating organization of a normal wall.

In an independent approach to penicillin action, long before these morphological observations, J. T. Park discovered in 1949 that this drug causes *S. aureus* to accumulate a novel compound containing a nucleotide, a novel hexosamine, and a peptide. The interpretation of this finding was obscure until the study of staphylococcal cell walls, elsewhere, led to identification of the constituents of the basal wall (Ch. 2). Park and Strominger then showed, in 1957, that the accumulated "penicillin nucleotide" contains the same amino acids and the same novel hexosamine (N-acetylmuramic acid) as the wall. This discovery, made at the same time as the discovery of spheroplasts, led to the conclusion that 1) the uridine nucleotide (which is not found in the wall) must be a carrier for a prefabricated set of building blocks that is incorporated into the growing wall as a glycopeptide unit; and 2) penicillin somehow inhibits this incorporation. This discovery explains the remarkable lack of toxicity of this drug for mammalian cells, for these lack the mucopeptide wall layer characteristic of bacteria.

However, Martin subsequently found that penicillin-treated cells continued to synthesize the wall glycopeptide polymer (mucopolymer), but in a more soluble, presumably less-crosslinked form. The specific metabolic effect of penicillin was then defined through in vitro studies, by Strominger and by Park, on the enzymatic reactions of mucopeptide synthesis (Ch. 4). These reactions, as observed in *S. aureus* extracts, are reviewed in Figure 10-9. First the muramic pentapeptide is transferred from its nucleotide carrier to a lipid carrier, on which an acetylglucosamine residue is added to the muramate and a pentaglycine branch to the pentapeptide. This enlarged building block is then transferred across the membrane and polymerized, to yield the alternating glucosamine-muramate backbone of the wall. In the final step a transpeptidation reaction forms cross-links between polypeptide side chains by substituting the free end of the glycine chain of one polypeptide for the terminal D-alanine of a nearby polypeptide.

Penicillin specifically inhibits the final bridge-closing reaction. As a result the cell synthesizes disorganized glycopeptide, which can be recognized chemically through the excess of free (non-cross-linked) terminal glycine and D-alanine; this accumulation is also recognized in the electron microscope as fibrous material in localized masses between membrane and wall (Fig. 10-10). The accumulation of precursor nucleotide, discovered much earlier, evidently represents a backing-up far behind the actual metabolic lesion.

The inhibitory action of penicillin may well depend on its structural resemblance, demonstrable with atomic models, to a model substrate of the reaction, D-alanyl-D-alanine; the highly reactive amide of the β-lactam of penicillin, which would correspond to the peptide bond of the substrate, presumably reacts irreversibly with the enzyme, causing the formation of an inactive penicilloyl-enzyme. This reaction would account for the observation that bacterial cell membranes contain a small amount of a component that irreversibly binds radioactive penicillin. And the site of action of penicillin at the interface between membrane and mucopeptide layer may well explain the fact that penicillin is active only at high concentrations with most gram-negative bacteria, which have unusually extensive wall layers surrounding the basal mucopeptide layer.

Penicillinase and Drug Resistance

Penicillinase, an enzyme that splits the lactam bond of penicillin (Fig. 10-6), is produced by many bacteria, including many enteric organisms (e.g., *E. coli*), *Bacilli*, and some strains of *Staphylococcus*. In some of these the enzyme is inducible; in others it is constitutive. Some organisms release peni-

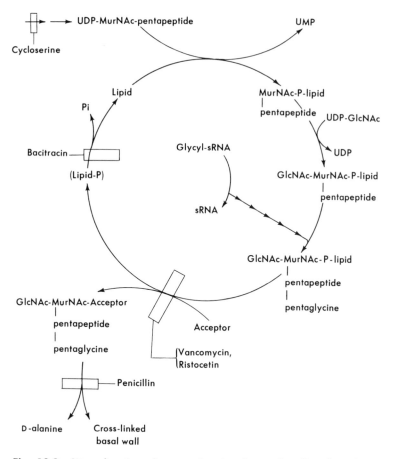

Fig. 10-9 Sites of action of agents that interfere with cell wall synthesis. (After M. Matsuhashi, C. P. Dietrich, and J. L. Strominger. *Proc. Nat. Acad. Sc. 54:587, 1965.*)

Fig. 10-10 Disorganized cell wall formation in *Bacillus megaterium* grown in the presence of penicillin. Note the pocket of fibrous material between cell membrane and cell wall. Such accumulations are usually seen earliest in the region of the growing septum. (From P. Fitz-James and R. Hancock, *J. Cell. Biol. 26: 657, 1965.*)

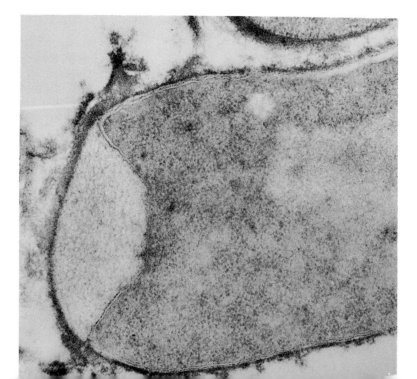

cillinase into the medium while others retain it largely in or on the cell. The evolutionary survival value of penicillinase, before the era of antibiotics, was for some time a mystery; but recently the enzyme has been shown to be a peptidase, able to act on a variety of peptides that are more likely to be encountered in Nature than penicillin. It has also been suggested that penicillinase may be a variant of the transpeptidase that ordinarily is irreversibly inhibited by penicillin.

When penicillinase-producing organisms are inoculated into a medium containing penicillin the result, whether sterilization or outgrowth, is determined by a race between killing of bacteria by penicillin and destruction of penicillin by bacteria. Hence the apparent sensitivity of a strain can vary enormously with bacterial population density (even with those strains whose enzyme remains cell-bound). Individual cells, widely separated on solid medium, show only a moderate increase (ca. 10-fold) in resistance compared with non-penicillinase-producing mutants, whereas a dense lawn of the same cells can show a 1000-fold increase. Quantitation of the level of resistance is thus almost meaningless when resistance depends on a drug-destroying enzyme.

Since staphylococci characteristically produce localized infections, with a high bacterial density, it is easy to understand why penicillinase-producing staphylococci are clinically completely resistant to penicillin G. There is also evidence that in mixed infections such penicillinase producers may protect neighboring sensitive organisms, such as streptococci and gonococci, by destroying the drug.

Since many staphylococcal strains produce penicillinase, drug sensitivity tests are especially important for this species. The usual disc assay involves a heavy inoculum, and so it records penicillinase producers as resistant.

Sensitive staphylococcal strains fail to yield penicillinase-producing mutants in vitro, presumably because these strains lack an inactive gene for this enzyme and hence do not have the genetic background necessary for producing an active gene by mutation. Indeed, penicillinase

producers spontaneously lose the gene for this enzyme with high frequency, and its loss is accelerated by acridines, which are known to "cure" episomes such as the F (fertility) agent of *E. coli* (Ch. 7). This finding suggests that the penicillinase gene in staphylococci resides in a cytoplasmic particle (plasmid); but because of the absence of conjugation in this species it is not possible to determine whether or not this gene is part of an episome (i.e., a unit that can shift between a chromosomal and a cytoplasmic state), like the genes for resistance on the resistance transfer factor (RTF) of *E. coli* (Ch. 7).

Because of these in vitro observations it seems highly probable that penicillinase-producing staphylococci, seen so frequently in hospitals, reach the patient by contamination from the environment, rather than by mutation of sensitive organisms already present.

Other Types of Resistance. A variety of organisms have yielded mutants with moderate increases in resistance to penicillin which are due to unknown mechanisms, not involving penicillinase. It is particularly significant that a few strains of staphylococci isolated from patients have exhibited resistance to penicillinase-resistant penicillins (e.g., oxacillin) and to cephalothin.

Cycloserine (Oxamycin)

This antibiotic is produced, in contrast to penicillin, by an actinomycete. It has an unusually simple structure for an antibiotic, and has been synthesized; it is the product of cyclization of the amide of D-serine. The antimicrobial spectrum of cycloserine is quite different from that of penicillin, and it is too toxic for general clinical use, but it is sometimes used in treating resistant tuberculosis.

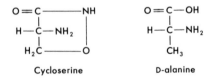

Cycloserine has much the same effects as penicillin on growing cells (lysis, spheroplast formation, muramic nucleotide accumulation). It apparently acts as an antimetabolite of D-alanine, which can reverse its effect on growing cells. Furthermore, as shown by Strominger, in bacterial extracts cycloserine inhibits directly the enzyme that racemizes L-alanine to yield D-alanine, and also the enzyme that converts the latter to the dipeptide D-ala-D-ala (Ch. 4). Cycloserine thus interferes as an antimetabolite with two early reactions in the formation of wall glycopeptide (Fig. 10-9).

Antibiotics Resembling Penicillin in Antimicrobial Spectrum

The drugs listed in this section have been of value especially against penicillinase-producing staphylococci. However, they are all either more toxic or less effective than the recently introduced penicillinase-resistant ampicillin, which is now the drug of choice for this purpose.

Bacitracin is produced by a strain of *Bacillus subtilis* (isolated from an infection in a patient named Tracy). It consists of a family of cyclic polypeptides, whose main component, bacitracin A, is depicted in Figure 10-11.

Bacitracin is seen to contain D as well as L-amino acids. Like penicillin it causes accumulation of wall precursor nucleotides, and it interferes with the binding of radioactive penicillin by bacteria. However, its bactericidal action may have a different origin, for in contrast to penicillin it inhibits the growth of protoplasts formed by lysozyme.

Like other polypeptide antibiotics (gramicidin, polymyxin) bacitracin is quite toxic;

hence it is used systemically only in grave illnesses resistant to other agents. For this purpose it must be given parenterally. Bacitracin is used widely in topical therapy (eye, skin) and in abscess cavities or infected body cavities.

Novobiocin, produced by the actinomycete *Streptomyces niveus,* has the structure shown below. The presence of an aromatic lactone (cyclic ester) causes it to be classed chemically as a coumarin; it also contains a novel sugar and a substituted phenol.

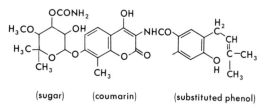

(sugar)   (coumarin)   (substituted phenol)

The antibacterial spectrum of novobiocin resembles that of penicillin, but in addition includes penicillin-resistant staphylococci and some strains of *Proteus* and other gram-negative organisms. This drug is bacteristatic against most sensitive organisms; it inhibits DNA and RNA synthesis in cells and also in extracts, apparently by directly inhibiting the polymerases since it does not complex with DNA. Novobiocin also causes wall precursors to accumulate, and with some strains the cell membrane becomes leaky, after a lag, and a slow bactericidal action is seen. The relation between these effects is not understood.

Vancomycin and the very similar **ristocetin** are large molecules (M.W. ca. 3500) which contain sugars and amino acids, but their structures have not yet been established. They are poorly absorbed by mouth, and are quite toxic. Both drugs are bactericidal; and like penicillin, they interfere with wall formation and cause accumulation of wall precursor nucleotides. They have been shown in extracts to interfere with glycopeptide polymerization, specifically with the transfer of disaccharide-pentapeptide from a lipid carrier (normally in the membrane) to an acceptor (normally in the wall; Fig. 10-9). Since these drugs are glycopeptides, this action may

Fig. 10-11 Bacitracin A. The portion presented in detail consists of an isoleucine and a cysteine residue, condensed to form a thiazoline ring rather than the usual peptide linkage of a polypeptide.

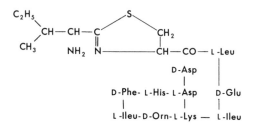

well depend on structural analogy with the substrate. However, vancomycin does interfere, unlike penicillin, with the growth of protoplasts, which suggests that interference with the function of the lipid carrier may damage the membrane as well as block synthesis of the wall.

The Macrolides. Erythromycin is produced by a red actinomycete, *Streptomyces erythreus*. Several erythromycins, identical in action, have been separated; their structures are indicated in Figure 10-12.

Erythromycin has an antibacterial spectrum essentially identical with that of penicillin, but including penicillinase producers. Its mechanism of action, however, is quite different: like chloramphenicol (see below), it is bacteristatic and causes immediate cessation of protein synthesis. Erythromycin-resistant mutants arise frequently with some organisms, and the drug is fairly toxic.

The erythromycins are members of a group of antibiotics with a similar structure, action, and antimicrobial spectrum. These are called the **macrolides** because they contain a large ring, formed from a chain of 14 to 20 carbon atoms by lactone condensation of a carboxyl with a distant hydroxyl group (Fig. 10-12). Various unusual sugars, often containing amino groups, are attached.

A variety of macrolides have been promoted commercially, but they have the same antibacterial spectrum as erythromycin and are less potent.

Lincomycin, a recently introduced antibiotic, resembles the macrolides in its spectrum; it is also bacteristatic and blocks protein synthesis by action on the ribosome. It differs markedly in structure, however, from the macrolides, and there is no cross-resistance. Lincomycin appears to be less toxic than the macrolides and therefore more valuable for treating gram-positive infections when penicillin is contraindicated.

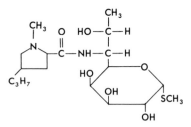

Aminoglycosides: Streptomycin, Kanamycin, Neomycin

The discovery of **streptomycin** by Schatz, Bugie, and Waksman in 1944 was the next major advance in chemotherapy following the introduction of penicillin in 1939. It extended the range of chemotherapy to the tubercle bacillus and to many gram-negative organisms. This antibiotic is produced by the actinomycete *Streptomyces griseus*.

Structure

Streptomycin is a highly polar, polycationic compound, with basic groups attached to three of its carbon atoms and an oxygen on each of the others (Fig. 10-13). It can be split into streptidine (an inositol substituted with two strongly basic guanidino groups) and streptobiosamine (a novel disaccharide). Chemical reduction of the aldehyde side chain on one of the sugars yields dihydrostreptomycin, which was used as a drug for some time but proved more toxic than the parent compound.

Two other useful antibiotics resemble streptomycin in structure and action: **kanamycin,**

Fig. 10-12 Erythromycin A. Other erythromycins differ in methyl and hydroxyl groups; other macrolides differ in the macrolide ring and in the attached sugars.

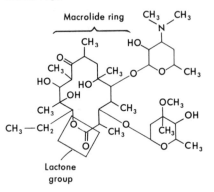

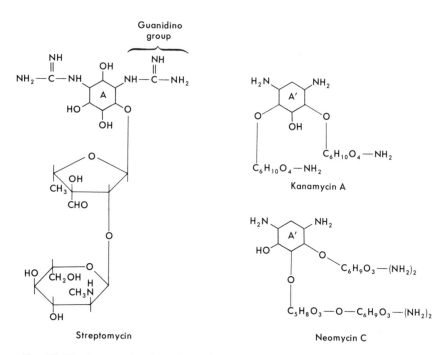

Fig. 10-13 Some aminoglycoside antibiotics. All three have a similar inositol residue with two amino substituents (streptamine, ring A; deoxystreptamine, ring A'); they differ in the attached sugar residues and in the guanidino groups of streptomycin.

which has four basic groups, and **neomycin,** which has six (Fig. 10-13). Both include novel sugars and an inositol. These **aminoglycosides** differ somewhat from each other, however, in antimicrobial spectrum, and mutants generally exhibit rather specific resistance, though cross-resistance is seen (especially between neomycin and kanamycin). Several other aminoglycosides are known that have a similar action but are more toxic; these include **paromomycin** and **gentamicin.**

Resistance and Dependence

Single-step mutations can cause only a moderate increase in resistance to most chemotherapeutic agents. With streptomycin, however, various bacteria readily yield mutants with high-level resistance, increased in one step by a factor of hundreds; and many of these strains also show **dependence** on the presence of the drug for growth (Fig. 10-14). The mechanisms will be discussed below. Mutations to high-level resistance and to de-

Fig. 10-14 Mutations to altered response to streptomycin. Three strains of *Escherichia coli* have been streaked in parallel, for equal distances, at right angles to a strip of filter paper containing streptomycin. **Top,** a resistant mutant; **middle,** the sensitive wild type; **bottom,** a dependent mutant. (B. D. Davis.)

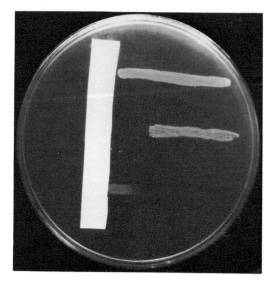

pendence have not been seen in *E. coli* with kanamycin and neomycin.

Mechanism of Action

Factors Affecting Activity in Vitro. Streptomycin is rapidly bactericidal, after a lag of a few minutes, but in contrast to penicillin it is not grossly lytic (Fig. 10-3). A small amount of **growth** is required; hence its bactericidal action is prevented if protein synthesis is inhibited by chloramphenicol or by starvation. Streptomycin is also sensitive to **anaerobiosis**: with facultative organisms it is only about 1/10 as potent under anaerobic as under aerobic conditions, and it is not useful against any obligate anaerobes. The reasons for this sensitivity to anaerobiosis are not clear.

The concentrations required for killing increase strikingly with increasing **acidity** and also with increasing concentrations of **salts** (especially of polyvalent ions such as Mg^{++} and HPO_4^{--}). These effects suggest that ionic bonds are important in the binding of streptomycin to its site of lethal action.

Factors Affecting Activity in Vivo. Since urine differs markedly in composition from body fluids, the antagonistic effects of salts and acidity on streptomycin action, noted above, are of practical importance in the treatment of urinary tract infections. Similarly, purulent or caseous foci in tissues are acidic, ischemic, and poorly nourished, and all these properties antagonize the action of the drug. In contrast to sulfonamides, however, streptomycin is not specifically antagonized by any metabolic products of tissue autolysis.

Considerably higher concentrations of streptomycin are required to kill **intracellular** (i.e., phagocytized) compared with extracellular bacteria. This effect has been considered to imply poor penetration of the drug into mammalian cells. However, since Mg^{++} and HPO_4^{--} ions strongly reduce streptomycin activity, it is also possible that the high concentration of these ions in the host cell may be responsible for the insensitivity of intracellular bacteria.

Effects on Cell Metabolism. Streptomycin exerts a confusing variety of effects on growing bacteria. When added to a culture it first inhibits protein synthesis, after a lag, at about the time that killing starts (as determined by plating on drug-free medium). Later it inhibits respiration and RNA and DNA synthesis, and it causes progressive impairment of the integrity of the cell membrane, but without gross lysis. The membrane damage is revealed by leakiness in both directions: loss of intracellular metabolites, such as nucleotides and amino acids, and increased hydrolysis of substrates for which the cell is cryptic (e.g., hydrolysis of *o*-nitrophenyl-β-galactoside by a mutant that contains β-galactosidase but lacks the transport system).

The key to the action of streptomycin was found in the course of studying streptomycin dependence. Sensitivity, resistance, and dependence are known to be due to allelic forms of the same gene (the *Sm* locus); and Spotts and Stanier observed that protein synthesis was impaired early in dependent cells starved of the drug, just as in sensitive cells treated with it. They therefore proposed that streptomycin acts directly on ribosomes: those of dependent mutants would be effective only when complexed with the drug, those of sensitive alleles would be inactivated by it, and those of resistant alleles would be indifferent.

This bold hypothesis was substantiated in several laboratories by studies on protein synthesis in extracts. With ribosomes from sensitive cells streptomycin inhibited protein synthesis, irreversibly, at concentrations as low as one molecule per ribosome, whereas ribosomes from dependent cells could be stimulated, and those from resistant cells were resistant. Since mutation to resistance presumably affects only one component of the cell, and since it has clearly affected the ribosomes, it presumably has not altered the membrane; hence the damage to the membrane, which occurs in sensitive but not in resistant cells, is apparently secondary (by an unknown mechanism) to the effect of the drug on the ribosomes.

The interaction of streptomycin with ribosomes has provided several powerful tools for studying ribosome function. Gorini discovered a class of **conditionally streptomycin-dependent** mutants, which require either streptomycin or a given amino acid, and showed that streptomycin partially restores the ability of these mutants to make the missing biosynthetic enzyme. Apparently streptomycin, in its interaction with ribosomes, causes occasional mistakes in the reading of the genetic code; and some of these mistakes cancel the mutant's genetic error, thus restoring a low level of functional enzyme (phenotypic suppression, Ch. 8). This development focused attention on the previously unsuspected role of the ribosome in determining the precision of the translation mechanism, and also showed that this precision was susceptible to environmental influence. In addition, the *Sm* locus is the first locus known to determine the structure of a ribosomal component; and mutations in this locus provide a variety of genetically altered ribosomes, which offer great promise in unraveling the physiology of the ribosome.

The inferred misreading was readily confirmed in cell extracts. For example, in a system employing sensitive ribosomes and the synthetic messenger poly U, which codes for phenylalanine, the addition of streptomycin not only inhibits the incorporation of phenylalanine into polypeptide, as noted earlier, but markedly stimulates the incorporation of isoleucine and serine (Table 10-2). The drug apparently causes an mRNA codon (on the ribosome) occasionally to bind a species of aminoacyl tRNA that normally would bind to a different codon. This misreading, however, is not random: with a given synthetic messenger only a few additional species of amino acid are incorporated. Most of these additions can be accounted for in terms of misreading one nucleotide of a triplet codon (Table 10-2).

This misreading, diagrammatically represented in Figure 10-15, probably involves distortion of the 30S subunit of the ribosome (which binds mRNA), since this component can be shown (by dissociation and reconstitution of ribosomes) to carry the alteration in streptomycin-resistant ribosomes. The interaction of ribosome and drug is subtle: neomycin (Table 10-2) and kanamycin each cause misreading in a characteristic pattern, not identical with that caused by streptomycin; and ribosomes resistant to streptomycin still respond normally to neomycin.

While this exciting development has cast much light on the action of aminoglycoside antibiotics, it is not certain that the effects of misreading will explain the early cessation of protein synthesis, the damage to the cell membrane, and the lethal action of these drugs. One can only speculate, however, about alternative possibilities, such as a further damaging effect of the drug on ribosomes and subsequent damage to membrane to which they may be attached.

In a partially diploid cell, heterozygous for the streptomycin locus, sensitivity is dominant over resistance; the mechanism is not understood.

TABLE 10-2. MISREADING OF GENETIC CODE IN PRESENCE OF STREPTOMYCIN. A protein-synthesizing extract from a sensitive strain of *E. coli* was incubated with a ^{14}C-labeled amino acid plus poly U and the 19 other unlabeled amino acids, until polypeptide synthesis ceased (30 min). The polypeptide was precipitated with trichloroacetic acid and washed, and the radioactivity was counted. The amount of phenylalanine (in moles) incorporated without drug was considered 100%; the other results are given relative to that value.

Labeled amino acid	Antibiotic (4 μg/ml)			Possible codon readings
	None	Streptomycin	Neomycin	
	Relative incorporation			
Phenylalanine	100	60	40	UUU, UUC
Isoleucine	8	30	37	AUU, AUC
Serine	4	20	48	UCU, UCC, UCA, UCG, AGU, AGC
Tyrosine	26	38	290	UAU, UAC
Leucine	5	10	6	CUU, CUC, CUA, CUG, UUA, UUG
Others	<1	<1	<1	

Adapted from J. Davies, L. Gorini, and B. D. Davis. Molec. Pharmacol. 1:93 *(1965).*

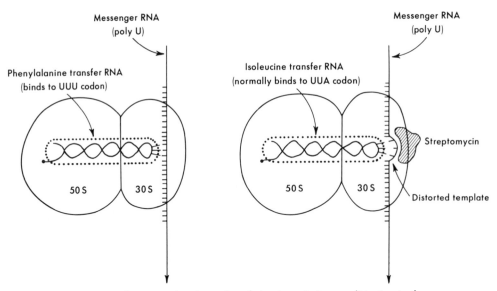

Fig. 10-15 One way of representing the action of streptomycin is as a distortion in the relation of the messenger RNA template to the tRNA. If this change is of the right kind it may correct the effect of a mutation producing an error in the genetic message.

Isoniazid

Isoniazid (Fig. 10-16) a compound long known to organic chemists, was discovered in 1951 to have chemotherapeutic value against tuberculosis. In the postsulfonamide, antibiotic era it represents the only major advance in chemotherapy based on screening of synthetic compounds.

Isoniazid is bactericidal to growing *Mycobacterium tuberculosis* at a remarkably low concentration (<1 μg/ml). Its useful action is curiously restricted to tuberculosis, on which it has a dramatic effect.

Isoniazid is bactericidal (in contrast to PAS), and is effective against intracellular bacteria (in contrast to streptomycin). These properties no doubt contribute to its value in tuberculosis. Resistant mutants are not as

serious a problem as with streptomycin: they exhibit only small-step increments of resistance, and they are often less virulent (at least in guinea pigs) than the sensitive parent strains.

Isoniazid resembles nicotinamide structurally (Fig. 10-16), and the extracted enzymes that convert nicotinamide to diphosphopyridine nucleotide (DPN = NAD) can also incorporate isoniazid instead. Isoniazid also resembles pyridoxamine, and it can inhibit a number of enzymes (e.g., transaminases) that require pyridoxal (or pyridoxamine) phosphate as cofactor. It is not certain whether either of these competitions is responsible for the antimicrobial action of the drug. The clinical toxicity of isoniazid, however, resembles pyridoxine (B_6) deficiency, and this toxicity is reported to be antagonized by large doses of this vitamin.

Broad-Spectrum Antibiotics: Inhibition of Protein Synthesis

The definition of a broad spectrum is relative; the term is conventionally applied to **chloramphenicol and the tetracyclines,** which are essentially identical in antimicrobial spectrum. Though differing markedly in struc-

Fig. 10-16 Isoniazid (isonicotinic hydrazide; pyridine-4-hydrazoic acid) and two metabolites that it resembles.

Isoniazid   Nicotinamide   Pyridoxamine

ture, these drugs are also identical in their over-all mechanism of action: they are bacteristatic (Fig. 10-3), and they cause an immediate and reversible inhibition of protein synthesis, while nucleic acid synthesis continues for some time (Fig. 10-17).

Chloramphenicol (Chloromycetin) is produced by *Streptomyces venezuelae.* It contains a nitro and a dichloroacetyl group, both unusual in a natural product. Though discovered as an antibiotic, it is now produced commercially by chemical synthesis.

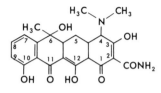

Fig. 10-18 Tetracycline. Chlortetracycline (Aureomycin) is 7-chlorotetracycline; oxytetracycline (Terramycin) is 5-hydroxytetracycline; demethylchlortetracycline (Declomycin) is chlortetracycline without the 6-methyl group.

$$NO_2 - \langle \rangle - CH - CH - CH_2 - OH$$
$$\quad\quad\quad\quad OH\quad NH-CO-CHCl_2$$

The tetracyclines have a structure with four fused rings; hence their generic name. **Chlortetracycline** (Aureomycin), the first major success in industrial research on antibiotics, is produced by *Streptomyces aureofaciens,* presumably named for the golden color of its colony. Several closely related compounds, shown in Figure 10-18, were discovered in various drug firms as products of other streptomycetes. Formation of the chlorine-free compound tetracycline is favored by a low-chloride fermentation medium, or by mutations that block chlorination.

The several tetracyclines have identical antimicrobial spectra, and cross-resistance among them is complete; hence in a drug sensitivity test one representative suffices. Chlortetracycline is unstable in solution, and so disc assays for sensitivity underestimate its potency. Stability, and therefore intestinal absorption, appear to increase in the order chlor-, oxy-, and tetracycline; the position of demethylchlortetracycline is disputed, but it is clearly more stable than chlortetracycline.

All four drugs are being vigorously promoted on the basis of our patent laws, which regard naturally occurring compounds possessing any chemical difference, however trivial, as independently patentable "compositions of matter." The physician is therefore barraged with claims of superiority based on small differences and selected literature references.

Mechanism of Action

Chloramphenicol and tetracycline apparently inhibit different steps in the ribosomal cycle (Ch. 4) that transfers amino acids from aminoacyl tRNA to a growing polypeptide. In extracts tetracycline interferes with the binding of charged tRNA by ribosomes, but chloramphenicol does not have this effect (though it does inhibit amino acid incorporation). Moreover, chloramphenicol can be shown to be bound by ribosomes or by their 50S subunits, but tetracycline does not block this binding.

Inhibition of protein synthesis on the ribosome is also responsible for the action of **macrolides** and **lincomycin,** which were discussed earlier because of their penicillin-like spectrum.

The chemotherapeutic selectivity of chlor-

Fig. 10-17 The effect of chloramphenicol or tetracycline on macromolecule synthesis.

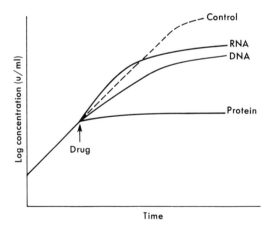

amphenicol and tetracycline can be explained by the observation that they exert little influence on protein synthesis in vitro by systems employing mammalian ribosomes. However, in cells chloramphenicol does inhibit certain mammalian protein-synthesizing systems, including initiation of antibody formation in cultured lymphoid cells and in the intact animal, and in extracts it interferes with protein synthesis by mitochondria from mammalian cells. The toxicity of this drug may well be related to its inhibition in the host of the mitochondrial protein synthesis required for extensive cell division.

Metabolic Applications. Chloramphenicol has been valuable in studying the relation of protein synthesis to a variety of processes such as mutagenic action, DNA replication, and the kinetics of phage growth. Furthermore, since it allows RNA synthesis to proceed without protein synthesis it has provided important evidence on the regulation of RNA synthesis (Ch. 9). Finally, the RNA that accumulates in the presence of chloramphenicol (or tetracycline) appears to be in the form of precursors of the ribosomal subunits. This accumulation is proving useful in studying the morphogenesis of ribosomes, much as intermediates accumulated by auxotrophic mutants have been useful in the analysis of biosynthetic pathways.

Polymyxins

The polymyxins (Aerosporins, Brit.) are a group of closely related cyclic polypeptides produced by *Bacillus polymyxa* and related bacilli. They contain D- as well as L-amino acids, and the novel amino acid α, γ-diaminobutyric acid (Fig. 10-19). The cationic γ-amino groups of the diaminobutyrate residues, together with the hydrophobic side chain of a C9 fatty acid, give these antibiotics the surface-active properties of a cationic detergent. The least toxic polymyxins are B and E. **Colistin** (Colimycin), introduced as a separate and allegedly less toxic antibiotic, was eventually found to be identical with polymyxin E.

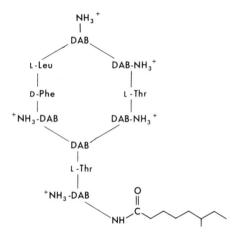

Fig. 10-19 Polymyxin B. DAB is α, γ-diaminobutyrate [$NH_2CH_2CH_2CH(NH_2)$ COOH]. Aliphatic residue is 6-methyloctanoic acid.

Polymyxin damages the bacterial membrane, much like cationic detergents. This effect is readily recognized in several ways: decrease of turbidity, leakage of soluble constituents (including nucleotides and inorganic ions), penetration of normally excluded substrates into the cell, and fluorescent staining of the cell by a dye that fluoresces when bound to proteins. Furthermore, a fluorescent derivative of polymyxin can be shown to become concentrated at the cell membrane (Fig. 10-20). The cell lysis caused by polymyxin leaves the intact wall as a relatively nonrefractile ghost, and is not prevented by hypertonic media; it thus differs from the disruption of the wall caused by growth in the presence of penicillin, and from dissolution of the wall by lysozyme.

Polymyxin is unique among antibacterial chemotherapeutic agents in having a disinfectant-like action, i.e., in being bactericidal in the absence of cell growth. For systemic use it must be injected, like other polypeptide antibiotics. Its major toxicity is renal and neurological, perhaps reflecting a detergent-like damage to host cell membranes.

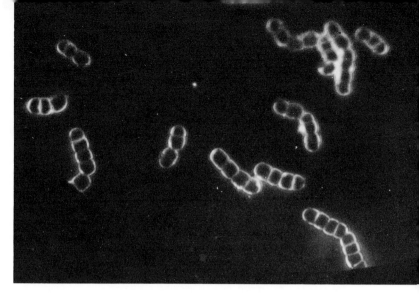

Fig. 10-20 Fluorescence photomicrograph of *B. megaterium* treated with a fluorescent derivative of polymyxin. (From B. A. Newton. *J. Gen. Microbiol.* 12:226, 1955.)

Compounds Used for Urinary Antibacterial Therapy

The nitrofurans, a group of synthetic compounds, are bactericidal against a variety of gram-positive and gram-negative bacteria. One of these drugs, **nitrofurantoin** (Furadantin), is widely used against low-grade, chronic urinary tract infections. It is excreted in the urine in high concentrations, but the concentrations attained in the body fluids are too low to provide any systemic chemotherapy.

Nalidixic acid, a recently introduced synthetic compound, has a similar use in urinary tract infections caused by gram-negative bacilli. It has the interesting property of inhibiting DNA synthesis without impairing RNA and protein synthesis; hence the mechanism of its bactericidal action may be related to that of thymineless death (Ch. 9).

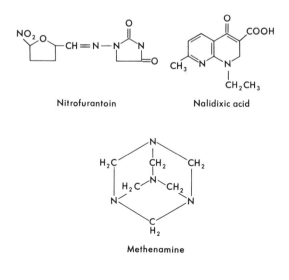

Nitrofurantoin   Nalidixic acid

Methenamine

Methenamine, like nitrofurantoin, is a urinary antiseptic. It is not active in vitro, but on reaching the urine after oral administration, it is split, if the urine is acidic, into ammonia and the bactericidal compound formaldehyde; a mixture with mandelic acid (Mandelamine) is often used to promote acidity of the urine. *Proteus* is resistant because it forms urease, which splits urea to carbon dioxide and ammonia and hence makes the urine alkaline.

Antifungal chemotherapy (with polyenes and griseofulvin), and **antiviral chemotherapy,** will be discussed in Chapters 21 and 24.

Reagents for Studying Cell Physiology

Antibiotics that are not selective enough to be useful against infections may nevertheless be of interest to microbiologists; studies on both their production and their action have contributed to cell physiology. In addition, some show promise in the chemotherapy of cancer. Some especially valuable investigative reagents, derived from streptomycetes, are discussed below.

Puromycin reversibly blocks protein synthesis in both mammalian and microbial cells and in extracts. It apparently acts as an analog of the terminal group of phenylalanyl tRNA (Fig. 10-21), displacing charged tRNA on the ribosome and then condensing with the growing peptide. Since the analog does not have enough affinity to provide stable anchorage to the ribosome, short peptide chains are released, each terminating in a puromycin residue. The result

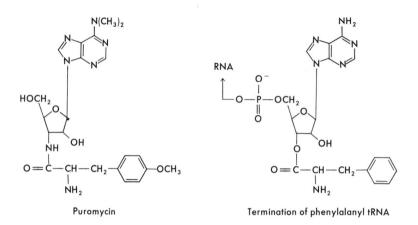

Puromycin   Termination of phenylalanyl tRNA

Fig. 10-21 Puromycin and its metabolic analog, the aminoacyl end of tRNA. (After M. B. Yarmolinsky and G. L. de la Haba. *Proc. Nat. Acad. Sc.* 45:1721, 1959.)

is thus abortive protein synthesis rather than pure inhibition.

Actinomycin D consists of an aromatic chromatophore attached to a peptide (Fig. 10-22). It rapidly and completely blocks the synthesis of RNA on a DNA template, both in the cell and in extracts; and at considerably higher concentrations it also blocks DNA replication. Actinomycin complexes reversibly in vitro with double-stranded but not with single-stranded DNA, and the amount bound increases with guanine content. Steric models suggest that the cyclic chromatophore of the drug can form hydrogen bonds with a guanylic residue, while the peptides are packed in the minor groove in the double helix. The sharp cutoff of RNA synthesis by actinomycin has made it a valuable tool in studying such problems as the kinetics of mRNA breakdown (Ch. 9).*

Phleomycin also binds to DNA, but probably in a different manner, for it inhibits the replica-

tion of DNA more than its transcription into RNA.

The mitomycins, and the closely related **porfiromycins,** are converted enzymatically in the cell to chemically reactive compounds that cross link complementary strands of DNA; they consequently also block DNA synthesis and in addition exert a mutagenic and lethal action.

Other valuable selective effects include those of novobiocin and nalidixic acid on nucleic acid synthesis, and the reversible inhibition of protein synthesis by chloramphenicol and several other antibiotics (see above).

Fig. 10-22 Actinomycin D. Sar, sarcosine (N-methyl glycine); Me-Val, N-methyl L-valine.

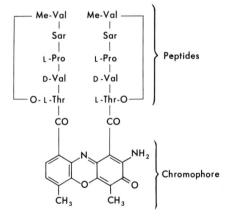

* Actinomycin A, a very closely related compound, was the first antibiotic to be isolated after penicillin, and the first of a long series obtained from streptomycetes. It was soon discarded because of its toxicity for mammals, and its remarkable mechanism of action was not discovered until the actinomycin group was reevaluated in a cancer chemotherapy screening program nearly 2 decades later. In this field, in contrast to antimicrobial chemotherapy, some toxicity to normal mammalian cells can hardly be avoided, since the neoplastic target cell is itself a mammalian cell.

PHYSIOLOGY AND ECOLOGY OF ANTIBIOTIC PRODUCTION

The "pure" polypeptide antibiotics are produced by sporulating bacteria, and the penicillins by sporulating fungi (which also produce griseofulvin). All the other major useful groups of antibiotics, including macrolides, aminoglycosides, novobiocin, chloramphenicol, tetracyclines, and polyenes, are produced by streptomycetes, a sporulating group of actinomycetes. The prominent role of the streptomycetes is curious. In addition to the dozen-odd useful antibiotics noted, these organisms have yielded about 500 other distinct antibiotics that have proved too toxic for clinical use; few such products have been isolated from other microbial groups. Yet the streptomycetes otherwise show only a narrow range of properties. The reason for this predilection of the streptomycetes is entirely unknown.

Biosynthesis. Isotopic studies, as well as structural relations, support the conclusion that all the major biosynthetic pathways contribute precursors to the various antibiotics. The polypeptides, including penicillins and actinomycins, are derived from amino acids; the extraordinarily varied sugar residues of many antibiotics from the carbon chain of glucose; and the long chains and rings of macrolides, polyenes, and tetracycline from lipid precursors (acetate and propionate). Puromycin is unusual in containing a modified nucleoside.

None of these biosyntheses have been worked out in detail, but the fragmentary evidence available suggests a close relation to cell wall biosynthesis. Thus many antibiotics are produced only when the cultures enter the stationary phase and begin sporulating, a process that is accompanied by degradation of the wall of the vegetative cell; in a *Bacillus* the ability to produce an antibiotic has been eliminated by mutations that block an early stage in sporulation. Furthermore, the polypeptide antibiotics all contain D-amino acids, which are also found in wall and in capsular polypeptides but not in intracellular proteins; and the specific amino acids present in bacitracin have also been found in the wall of the organism that produces it. The nucleus of penicillin also contains a D-amino acid, as noted earlier. Since the walls of streptomycetes have not been studied there is no direct evidence for their biosynthetic relation to the many antibiotics that these organisms produce; but we may note that these antibiotics include a variety of novel sugar residues, just as do many surface antigens of bacteria.

Ecological Role. These findings suggest that at least some antibiotics may arise as byproducts of pathways concerned with wall formation or with the wall degradation associated with sporulation, rather than from long pathways evolved specifically for purposes of aggressive competition. While the excretion of such byproducts could have evolutionary survival value, they could also be fortuitous, like the excretion of biosynthetic intermediates by mutants with blocked pathways or with defective control mechanisms. Hence, though the production of antibiotics was initially thought to reflect a fundamental ecological relation (antibiosis) between competing microbes in Nature, we must consider the alternative possibility that it simply reflects a mutation in biosynthesis that may not be beneficial to the organism, and may even be deleterious. This view is supported by several findings: 1) antibiotic-producing organisms constitute only a tiny fraction of the microbial population in soil samples, and thus do not appear to have a striking advantage; 2) the strains found in Nature excrete only small amounts of antibiotics; and 3) the late appearance of the antibiotic in the growth cycle does not seem adapted to help in the competition for growth in Nature.

DRUG RESISTANCE

Ehrlich discovered that during treatment protozoa can become resistant ("drug-fast") to an antimicrobial agent. This phenomenon, rediscovered with antibacterial drugs, led to the fear that in our race with the adapting microbial population we would be required, like the Red Queen, to keep running faster and faster merely to stand still. This dire prophecy, fortunately, has not been fulfilled, and the emergence of resistance has turned out to be a serious problem with only a few combinations of drug and microbial species. The clinical importance of drug resistance, however, is real. Furthermore, it extends even beyond infectious disease, for in the treatment of leukemia with analogs of folic acid the emergence of drug-resistant leukemic cells usually limits the duration of effective therapy.

The term drug resistance ordinarily refers to **genotypic** changes, which persist during further cultivation in the absence of the drug. We discussed in Chapter 6 the evidence, from fluctuation analysis, that such drug-resistant clones emerge by mutation and selection, the drug playing a purely selective role.* We shall now consider the various phenotypic changes that are responsible for the expression of genotypic drug resistance, bearing in mind that resistance to the same drug may depend on different mechanisms in different strains.

Physiological (Phenotypic) Changes Responsible for Drug Resistance

1) **Increased destruction of the drug** is exemplified by penicillinase. The level of resistance observed with this mechanism, as noted above, depends strongly on the density of the bacterial population.

Various enzymes have been encountered that destroy the activity of cephalosporins, tetracyclines, chloramphenicol, streptomycin, and sulfonamides.

2) **Decreased activation of the drug** is seen in mutants resistant to purine or pyrimidine analogs (used in cancer chemotherapy), which must be converted to nucleotides be-

---

*In a special case penicillin directs the emergence of resistant L forms through an inheritable but nongenotypic change, since it eliminates a wall component that is apparently necessary as a primer for further normal wall synthesis.

fore they can interfere with essential reactions. With the antimicrobial agents in current use, however, this mechanism does not apply, since these drugs are all active without further chemical alteration.

3) **Formation of an altered receptor** is an important mechanism. Altered, resistant enzymes have been found in mutants resistant to a substrate analog (e.g., sulfonamides), and also in mutants resistant to analogs of an allosteric feedback inhibitor. Similarly, a more selective phenylalanine-activating enzyme is present in a mutant that can no longer incorporate p-fluorophenylalanine into protein.

As Hotchkiss has shown with analogs of PAB substituted in different parts of the metabolite molecule, resistance to these different compounds arises from mutations in different regions of the same gene. Presumably each region shapes a different part of the active site of the enzyme that metabolizes PAB.

A striking example of an altered receptor is seen in high-level resistance to aminoglycosides, in which an altered configuration of the ribosome can cause essentially complete resistance to streptomycin, while other configurations cause drug dependence (p. 322). The resistant and the dependent ribosomes can still bind streptomycin, since they respond to it with a low level of misreading of the genetic code. Hence, though the characteristic lethal action of the drug has been eliminated, one cannot say that the altered receptor has a lower affinity for the drug; rather, their interaction has different consequences.

4) **Decreased permeability** to the inhibitor has been demonstrated in mutants resistant to amino acid analogs: these mutants have often lost the system that actively transports the normal amino acid as well as its analog. Permeability barriers are probably also responsible for a good deal of the "natural resistance" that limits the antimicrobial spectrum of various agents.

Thus actinomycin inhibits RNA synthesis in many gram-positive bacilli and cocci, but not in gram-negative bacilli; yet the extracts of both groups are equally sensitive. Furthermore, such unresponsive cells become sensitive following a treatment that increases nonspecific permeability, such as conversion to spheroplasts or exposure to a chelating agent (ethylenediamine tetraacetic acid: EDTA).

Decreased uptake of the drug by intact cells has been used as an index of decreased permeability, but it is unreliable: it could also be due to a reduction in number or in affinity of the binding sites. Moreover, much of the binding may involve receptors that are irrelevant to drug action. Studies on binding to isolated cell components, however, have yielded significant results (e.g., polyene antifungal agents, which bind to fungal but not to bacterial membranes; Ch. 21).

Other theoretically possible mechanisms include an increased synthesis of the reversing metabolite, and an increased formation of the sensitive enzyme. These have not been observed, however, to give rise to significant resistance.

Genetic Dominance of Sensitivity and Resistance

Analysis of the phenotypic mechanisms of resistance has made it possible to understand why some genes for resistance are dominant and others recessive, when present in a heterozygote along with the sensitive allele. Thus the production of an altered, resistant enzyme would be expected to be dominant, since the drug would inhibit only part of the activity of a mixture of sensitive and resistant enzyme molecules. The production of a drug-destroying enzyme is also dominant. This mechanism had been observed for the multiple resistance induced by the episomal resistance transfer factor (RTF; Ch. 7), which produces several enzymes that acylate or otherwise alter sulfonamides, chloramphenicol, tetracycline, and streptomycin. Indeed, only a dominant mechanism of resistance could be readily detected on an episome, since its injection into a sensitive cell does not displace the genes for sensitivity. High-level resistance to streptomycin, in contrast, is recessive, although it is based on altered, resistant ribosomes. Apparently in a mixture the sensitive ribosomes, interacting with the drug, either trap the resistant ribosomes in inactive polysomes or produce some other irreversible damage to the cell.

Induced Phenotypic Resistance

When some antimicrobial agents are added to a growing culture at borderline concentrations they are seen to cause only a **transient bacteristasis**. Two mechanisms have been recognized.

In the first mechanism the resumption of growth is due to a compensatory metabolic response within the cells. This response is observed with those unusual antimetabolites that inhibit the **synthesis** of a building block. For example, 2-thiazole-alanine exerts pseudo-feedback inhibition of histidine synthesis, but it does not repress formation of the histidine biosynthetic enzymes. Since the inhibition lowers the intracellular histidine level, it causes immediate bacteristasis; but since this starvation for histidine in turn de-represses the enzymes of the histidine pathway the level of the partly inhibited enzyme rises, and in a few minutes growth is restored.

In the second mechanism growth is resumed because of destruction of the drug, e.g., through the action of an induced penicillinase.

In contrast to the genotypic resistance discussed in previous sections, which persists in the absence of the drug, induced phenotypic resistance is lost after several generations of growth without the inhibitor; for without the continued stimulus to increased production of the enzyme the excess is diluted out. Accordingly, transient "induced phenotypic resistance" does not represent increased resistance in the usual (i.e., genotypic) sense. Rather, it is part of what determines the observed level of resistance of a strain, which is defined in terms of ultimately yielding growth or not, at a given drug concentration.

Combined Therapy and Drug Resistance

Therapeutic "escape" for bacteria can occur through the development of successive small increments of resistance; in addition, as noted above, with streptomycin one-step mutations can cause a high level of resistance. The former process, but not the latter, can be blocked by continuously maintaining drug concentrations high enough to inhibit the first-step mutant.

Since no method is available for effectively decreasing spontaneous mutation rates it is not possible to prevent the **formation** of resistant mutants in growing populations. It is possible, however, to prevent their **selection** by having present a second, non-cross-resistant drug. This solution of the problem by combined therapy, originally suggested by Ehrlich, has a simple genetic rationale: if 1 cell in 10^6 mutates to resistance to drug A and 1 in 10^7 to drug B, only 1 in 10^{13} will develop both mutations. This approach has been especially successful in the treatment of tuberculosis.

Synergism and Antagonism

Since combined therapy is widely used to prevent drug resistance, its additional consequences deserve attention. Some combinations of antimicrobial agents are synergistic and others are antagonistic. These interactions are readily seen in vitro, and they have also been demonstrated under certain circumstances in experimental animals. They are difficult to establish with certainty in patients, but the extrapolation seems reasonable.

Antagonism occurs when a drug that requires growth for its bactericidal action (penicillin, streptomycin) is combined with a bacteristatic agent (a sulfonamide, tetracycline, or chloramphenicol) (Fig. 10-23). **Synergism of bactericidal action** can be seen with certain mixtures of two bactericidal drugs, such as penicillin and streptomycin: a low concentration of one drug can accelerate the lethal

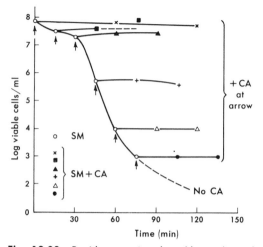

Fig. 10-23 Rapid protection by chloramphenicol against killing by streptomycin in growth medium. Streptomycin (30µg/ml) was added to exponentially growing *E. coli* at 0 time. At intervals the viable count was determined, and samples were transferred (arrows) to flasks containing sufficient chloramphenicol to yield a final concentration of 20 µg/ml. These flasks were similarly incubated, and samples were removed for viable counts after 30 and 60 minutes. (From P. Plotz and B. D. Davis. *J. Bact. 83*:802, 1962.)

action of the other, and can also markedly lower its minimal effective concentration.

When this synergism was analyzed kinetically sublethal pretreatment with penicillin was found to increase sensitivity to streptomycin and to accelerate its uptake, whereas pretreatment with streptomycin did not influence the subsequent interaction with penicillin. Presumably damage to the wall by penicillin facilitates subsequent entry of streptomycin and loss of antagonistic ions.

CODA

It would be difficult to exaggerate the impact of antibacterial chemotherapy on the practice of medicine. For nearly 2 decades, however, the continuing practical advances in this field were not paralleled by comparable progress in our understanding of the mechanisms involved. It is only within the past 10 years that our increasing knowledge of

bacterial organization and macromolecular synthesis has made possible real insight into the mechanism of action of most antimicrobial drugs, so we can now confidently classify them in terms of mechanism of action, rather than in terms of more trivial properties.

Chemotherapy has in turn contributed to cell physiology, in a true dialogue.

We have seen how penicillin has contributed to the study of the cell wall; chloramphenicol, actinomycin, and puromycin to the understanding of protein and RNA synthesis; and aminoglycosides to the recognition of the influence of ribosomes on the fidelity of translation. The value of cytotoxic drugs as reagents in cell physiology in thus firmly established. Nevertheless, the defect produced is not always as sharply circumscribed as that resulting from a mutation, since drugs often influence (especially at increasing concentrations) more than one cell component.

In this chapter we have summarized current knowledge of the mechanism of action of various chemotherapeutic agents, derived from biochemical studies on both intact bacteria and their extracts. In addition, we have considered certain problems that bear on the clinical use of these drugs: their effects on bacterial growth and viability, and the influence of both environmental factors and mutations on the sensitivity of the bacteria. The phenomena described provide the fundamental elements for approaching the more complicated problems that arise during chemotherapy of the infected patient.

SELECTED REFERENCES

Books and Review Articles

ALBERT, A. *Selective Toxicity,* 3rd ed. Wiley, New York, 1965. (Chemotherapy considered as part of a broader problem, with emphasis on physicochemical factors. Chapter III provides an excellent historical account.)

BARBER, M., and CHAIN, E. B. Antibacterial chemotherapy. *Ann. Rev. Pharmacol.* 4:115 (1964).

Biochemical Studies of Antimicrobial Drugs. 16th Symposium, Society of General Microbiologists, Cambridge Univ. Press, London, 1966.

Biochemistry of Antibiotics. Proceedings, Fourth International Congress on Biochemistry, Vienna, 1958. Vol. V, Symp. V. Pergamon Press, New York, 1958.

BROCK, T. D. Chloramphenicol. *Bact. Rev.* 25:32 (1961).

The Chemistry of Penicillin. (H. T. Clarke, J. R. Johnson, and R. Robinson, eds.). Princeton Univ. Press, Princeton, N.J., 1949. (Few small molecules have presented such a challenge to chemists and have been subject to such intensive investigation, summarized in this thousand-page book.)

DATTA, N. Infectious drug resistance. *Brit. M. Bull.* 21:255 (1965).

DAVIS, B. D., and FEINGOLD, D. S. Antimicrobial Agents: Mechanism of Action and Use in Metabolic Studies. In *The Bacteria,* Vol. IV, p. 343. (I. C. Gunsalus and R. Y. Stanier, eds.), Academic Press, New York, 1962.

Drug Resistance in Microorganisms. (G. E. W. Wolstenholme and C. M. O'Connor, eds.). Ciba Symposium. Little, Brown, Boston, 1962.

EHRLICH, P. *Collected Papers,* Vol. III; *Chemotherapy.* Pergamon Press, New York, 1960.

FINLAND, M. Emergence of antibiotic-resistant bacteria. *New England J. Med.* 253:909, 969, 1019 (1955).

FLOREY, H. W., CHAIN, E., HEATLEY, N. G., JENNINGS, M. A., SANDERS, A. G., ABRAHAM, E. P., and FLOREY, M. E. *Antibiotics.* Oxford Univ. Press, London, 1949. (An exhaustive and fascinating account of early work.)

GOLDBERG, I. H. Mode of action of antibiotics. II. Drugs affecting nucleic acid and protein synthesis. *Am. J. Med.* 39:722 (1965).

HITCHINGS, G. H., and BURCHALL, J. J. Inhibition of folate biosynthesis as a basis for chemotherapy. *Advances Enzymol.* 27:417 (1965).

KLEIN, J. O., and FINLAND, M. The new penicillins. *New England J. Med.* 269:1019, 1074, 1129 (1963).

MOYED, H. S. Biochemical mechanisms of drug resistance. *Ann. Rev. Microbiol.* 18:347, (1964).

NEWTON, B. A. The properties and mode of action of the polymyxins. *Bact. Rev.* 20:14 (1956).

PETERSDORF, R. D., and PLORDE, J. J. The usefulness of *in vitro* sensitivity tests in antibiotic therapy. *Ann. Rev. Med.* 14:41 (1963).

Resistance of Bacteria to the Penicillins. (A. V. S. de Reuck and M. P. Cameron, eds.) Little, Brown, Boston, 1962.

RICHMOND, M. H. The effect of amino acid analogues on growth and protein synthesis in microorganisms. *Bact. Rev. 26:*398 (1962).

STOKSTAD, E. L. R. Antibiotics in animal nutrition. *Physiol. Rev. 34:*25 (1954).

STROMINGER, J. L., and TIPPER, D. J. Bacterial cell wall synthesis and structure in relation to the mechanism of action of penicillins and other antibacterial agents. *Am. J. Med. 39:*708 (1965).

WAKSMAN, S. A., and LECHEVALIER, H. A. *The Actinomycetes,* Vol. III, *Antibiotics of Actinomycetes.* Williams & Wilkins, Baltimore, 1962. (Useful as a reference on the isolation and the chemistry of several hundred antibiotics.)

Specific Articles

BELL, P. H., and ROBLIN, R. O., JR. A theory of the relation of structure to activity of sulfanilamide compounds. *J. Am. Chem. Soc. 64:*2905 (1942).

BROWN, G. M. Biosynthesis of folic acid. II. Inhibition by sulfonamides. *J. Biol. Chem. 237:*536 (1962).

DUGUID, J. P. The sensitivity of bacteria to the action of penicillin. *Edinburgh M. J. 53:*407 (1945).

GOLDBERG, I. H., and REICH, E. Actinomycin inhibition of RNA synthesis directed by DNA. *Fed. Proc. 23:*958 (1964).

GORINI, L., and KATAJA, E. Phenotypic repair by streptomycin of defective genotypes in *E. coli. Proc. Nat. Acad. Sc. 51:*487 (1964).

NATHANS, D. Inhibition of protein synthesis by puromycin. *Fed. Proc. 23:*984 (1964).

PARK, J. T., and STROMINGER, J. L. Mode of action of penicillin. *Science 125:*99 (1957).

SPOTTS, C. R., and STANIER, R. Y. Mechanism of streptomycin action on bacteria: A unitary hypothesis. *Nature 192:*633 (1961).

WISE, E. M., JR., and PARK, J. T. Penicillin: Its basic site of action as an inhibitor of a peptide cross-linking reaction in cell wall mucopeptide synthesis. *Proc. Nat. Acad. Sc. 54:*75 (1965).

11 STERILIZATION AND DISINFECTION

The development of technics for eliminating viable microbes from various materials was indispensable for the advance of microbiology, and for its application to medical and surgical practice (Ch. 1). The present chapter will consider the agents used for this purpose, with emphasis on their mechanisms of action.

History. The early arts of civilization included practical means of preventing putrefaction and decay, discovered long before the role of microorganisms in these processes was appreciated. Thus perishable foods were preserved by drying (Ch. 5), by salting, and by acid-producing fermentations (Ch. 3). Embalming was practiced in ancient Egypt, but the essential oils used were probably less important than the dry climate. As was noted in Chapter 1, the canning of food was introduced 50 years before Pasteur's researches gave it a rational basis. Finally, chlorinated lime (calcium hypochlorite) and carbolic acid (phenol) were introduced in the early nineteenth century as deodorants, to treat sewage and garbage (and subsequently wounds), even before the microbial basis of putrefaction, and the germicidal action of these substances, were recognized.

Disinfection of pure cultures of bacteria was first studied in 1871 by Koch, employing mercuric chloride; and in 1897 Krönig and Paul showed, in the first quantitative studies, that disinfectants reduce the viable number of a culture gradually rather than abruptly.

Definitions

Sterilization denotes the use of either physical or chemical agents to eliminate all viable microbes from a material, while **disinfection** generally refers to the use of germicidal chemical agents to destroy the potential infectivity of a material (which need not imply elimination of all viable microbes). **Sanitizing** refers to procedures used to lower the bacterial content of utensils used for food, without necessarily sterilizing them. Agents used for these purposes must be effective against all kinds of microbes and must be relatively insensitive to their metabolic state; and such agents, in contrast to chemotherapeutic agents

(Ch. 10), need not differentiate in their cytotoxicity between microbes and host cells.

Antisepsis usually refers to the topical application of chemicals to a body surface to kill or inhibit pathogenic microbes. For skin antisepsis in preparation for surgery many different disinfectants are widely used. For prophylactic application to open wounds, however, or for topical application to superficial infections, disinfectants have been largely replaced by various antibiotics, which are painless and less damaging to the tissues.

The search for improved antisepsis, before the era of chemotherapy, was responsible for the discovery of the antibacterial action of a variety of simple compounds. Interest in this field has recently been stimulated again by several developments: the need to protect military equipment against mildew (fungal growth) in the tropics, the increased emphasis on prolonging the shelf-life of foods, the desire to sterilize spacecraft in order not to interfere with the search for extraterrestrial life, and the danger of biological warfare.

Criteria of Viability

We have noted that some chemotherapeutic agents are bactericidal while others are only bacteristatic (Ch. 10). Both kinds of compounds may be useful as antiseptics. An effective disinfectant, however, must be bactericidal. For precise quantitation of bactericidal action an operational definition of viability is necessary. The fundamental criterion is the **ability of the organism to propagate indefinitely** when placed in a suitable environment. Depending on the bactericidal agent used, nonviable or "killed" cells may or may not exhibit changes in such properties as morphology (e.g., lysis), staining (e.g., penetration of normally excluded dyes), motility, and enzymatic activities.

For example, a boiled suspension of vegetative cells will not respire, whereas a suspension treated lethally with ultraviolet or X-rays will retain this and other metabolic activities, and many of the nonviable cells can even undergo several divisions before proliferation ceases. Similarly, spores can often germinate after irradiation but may then exhibit little or no division. It follows that indirect biochemical or microscopic criteria for measuring bactericidal action cannot be considered definitive unless checked by direct tests for viability.

Effect of the Test Medium. Even direct tests for viability may give ambiguous results: two different media, which give identical viable counts with ordinary cells of a given species, may give quite different counts with damaged cells. The repair of certain kinds of damage is evidently influenced by several factors, including osmotic tonicity and nutritional richness. A striking example involves mercuric ion, whose antibacterial action depends on combination with sulfhydryl groups in the cell. As early as 1889 it was found that Koch had grossly overestimated the disinfectant action of this agent, since anthrax spores that it had "sterilized" could be "resurrected" by washing with a solution of H_2S, which forms an essentially nondissociable compound with Hg^{++} and hence reverses its combinations in the cell.

The considerations introduced here assume practical importance in the preparation of vaccines, which are often sterilized as gently as possible in order to retain maximal immunogenicity. To test their sterility artificial culture media do not have the final word: pathogenic microbes have been adequately sterilized only if they are unable to initiate infection in the animal body. This problem has proved especially important in the preparation of viral vaccines (Ch. 26).

It should be emphasized that **sterilization** is not identical with **destruction** of bacteria or their products, though the terms are often loosely interchanged. For example, in preparing solutions for intravenous administration it is not sufficient to take pains to ensure sterility; it is also necessary to minimize previous bacterial contamination, since pyrogenic bacterial products (endotoxins; Ch. 20) may survive autoclaving or filtration and subsequently produce a febrile, toxic response. Hence, in the preparation of biologicals and parenteral fluids the water and the reagents used must satisfy criteria of purity quite different from those required for analytical chemical work.

Differential Susceptibility. The susceptibility of the cells of a given species to disinfectants or to heat varies with their physiological state: the cells in a young culture are generally somewhat more susceptible to various physical and chemical agents than those in an old culture approaching nutritive exhaustion. Differences in the sensitivity of different species will be noted below. From a practical point of view the most important difference is the increased resistance of the **spores** formed by certain species (Ch. 5).

PHYSICAL AGENTS

Temperature

Heat

Moist Heat. This procedure is generally preferred for sterilizing all materials except those that it would damage. The process is rapid, all organisms are susceptible, and the agent penetrates clumps and reaches surfaces that might be protected from a chemical disinfectant. Fungi, most viruses, and the vegetative cells of various pathogenic bacteria are sterilized within a few minutes at 50 to 70°;

and even the much more resistant spores of clostridia and other spore-forming pathogens are sterilized within a few minutes at 100°. Consequently, it has been a common practice to sterilize syringes, needles, and instruments for minor surgery by heating for 10 to 15 minutes in boiling water, or even better in a boiling dilute solution of alkali (e.g., washing soda).

The spores of some saprophytes can survive boiling for hours, as Tyndall observed in the 1880s (Ch. 1). Since absolute sterility is essential for culture media, and for the instruments used in major surgical procedures, it has become standard practice to sterilize such materials in an autoclave with steam at a temperature of 121° C (250° F) for 15 to 20 minutes. This temperature is attained by steam at a pressure of 15 lb per square inch (psi) in excess of atmospheric pressure, at altitudes near sea level; at high altitudes slightly higher pressures are necessary (e.g., 3 lb psi higher in Denver, at an altitude of 5000 ft). The rapid action of steam depends in part on the large latent heat of water (540 cal/gm): cold objects are thus rapidly heated by condensation on their surface.

In using an autoclave it is important that flowing steam be allowed to displace the air before building up pressure, for in steam mixed with air the temperature is determined by the partial pressure of water vapor. Thus saturated steam (i.e., free of air) at 15 lb (1 atmosphere) gauge pressure has a temperature of 121°; but if no air is evacuated from the chamber, and if steam is added to produce the same gauge pressure, the total pressure of 2 atmospheres will be contributed by 1 atmosphere of air and 1 atmosphere of steam, and the average temperature will be only 100°. (In fact, the effect of the air is even worse, for it will tend to remain unheated at the bottom of the chamber.)

It is also important that vessels be loosely plugged or capped and not completely filled with liquid, in order to permit free ebullition of the dissolved air during heating, and free boiling of the superheated liquid when the steam pressure is lowered. With bulky porous objects (e.g., bundles of surgical dressings), or with large volumes of liquid, increased time must be allowed for heating throughout. Modern autoclaves are provided with an outer jacket in which the steam pressure may be maintained while it is lowered in the central chamber; in this way objects wet by condensation may be rapidly dried.

Pasteurization, introduced to sterilize wine, is now used primarily to prevent milkborne infection and to delay the decomposition of milk. It consists of heating at 62° for 30 minutes, or in "flash" pasteurization, at a higher temperature for a fraction of a minute. Pasteurization is effective because the common milkborne pathogens (tubercle bacillus, salmonella, streptococcus, and brucella) do not form spores and are reliably sterilized by this procedure; in addition, the total bacterial count is generally reduced by 97 to 99%.

Kinetics. The sensitivity of an organism to heat is often expressed in practical work as the **thermal death point:** the lowest temperature at which 10 minutes' exposure of a given volume of a broth culture or a turbid suspension of cells results in sterilization. The value is about 55° for *Escherichia coli,* 60° for the tubercle bacillus, and 120° for the most resistant spores.

For precise studies this qualitative endpoint has been replaced by quantitative determination of the numbers of survivors at different times; and since killing by heat turns out to have simple exponential kinetics (see final section of this chapter), the rate of killing can be expressed in terms of the constant, k, in the exponential decay curve (Fig. 11-1), log $n/n_o = -kt$ (where n = number of surviving cells and n_o = initial number). Another convenient index is the "decimal reduction time," D (the time required for a 10-fold reduction of viability), which is inversely proportional to the rate of killing. The logarithm of D varies linearly with temperature (Fig. 11-2); and from the slope of the curve it can be seen that the rate of killing (of the spores studied in this figure) increased about 10-fold with a rise of 10°. From D it is easy to calculate the time required to sterilize (within statistical variation) a sample of a given size: for example, a suspension containing 10^5 cells would require about $5 \times D$ minutes (which would reduce the viable number to 10^{-5} times its initial value; i.e., to 1 cell).

The **mechanism** of sterilization by heat evidently involves **protein denaturation** (though the "melting" of membrane lipids may also be important). Thus the temperature range is one in which many proteins are denatured (whereas carbohydrates are stable and nucleic acid denaturation is readily reversible). Moreover, both sterilization (Fig. 11-2) and protein denaturation have a high temperature coefficient. Finally, both processes require a

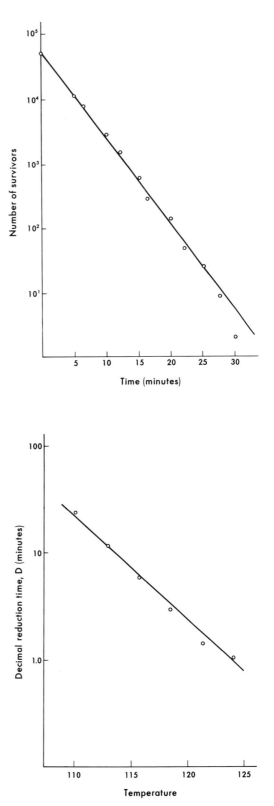

Fig. 11-1 Exponential killing by heat of spores of a thermophilic bacillus. Number of survivors plotted on a logarithmic scale against time of exposure to 120°. (After C. C. Williams, C. M. Merrill, and E. J. Cameron. *Food Res.* 2:369, 1937.)

higher temperature when the material is thoroughly dried, or when the water activity of the medium is reduced by the presence of a high concentration of a neutral substance such as glycerol or glucose.

The role of water in promoting an alteration of protein conformation by heat is illustrated by the usefulness of steam in pressing woolen fabrics (i.e., in shifting the multiple weak bonds between fibrous molecules of keratin). The explanation is that the native conformation of a protein is stabilized in part by hydrogen bonds (especially between the $> C=O$ and the $HN <$ of different peptide groups in helical regions of the polypeptide), and such bonds are more readily broken if they can be replaced with hydrogen bonds to water molecules (Fig. 11-3).

Dry Heat. Accordingly, when bacteria and viruses are dry they require, like isolated enzymes, a higher temperature for irreversible damage: reliable sterilization by dry heat requires 160° for 1 to 2 hr. Dry heat has the further disadvantage that hot air penetrates porous materials much more slowly than does condensing steam, so that after an hour in an oven at 160° the center of a large package of surgical dressings may not even have reached 100°. Sterilization by dry heat is ordinarily used only for glassware and metal objects. Intense dry heat is used in flaming contaminated surfaces in the process of aseptic trans-

Fig. 11-2 Rate of killing of spores of a thermophilic bacillus at various temperatures, indicated in terms of the time required for a 10-fold reduction in viability. (From C. F. Schmidt. In C. F. Reddish (ed.). *Antiseptics, Disinfectants, Fungicides, and Sterilization.* Lea & Febiger, Philadelphia, 1957, p. 831.)

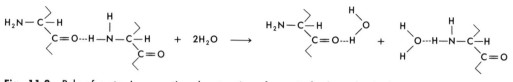

Fig. 11-3 Role of water in promoting denaturation of protein by heat, by facilitating disruption of intramolecular hydrogen bonds between peptide groups.

fer,* and in disposing of infectious material by incineration.

Freezing

When a suspension of bacteria is frozen the crystallization of the water results in the formation of tiny pockets of concentrated solutions of salts, which do not themselves crystallize unless the temperature is lowered below the eutectic point (ca. $-20°$ for NaCl); at this temperature the solution becomes saturated and the salt also crystallizes. The localized high concentrations of salt, and possibly the ice crystals, damage the bacteria, as shown by increased sensitivity to lysozyme. Only some of the cells, however, are killed, but repeated cycles of freezing and thawing result in progressive decrease in the viable count.

Once frozen, the surviving cells retain their viability indefinitely if the temperature is kept below the eutectic points of the various salts present; a household freezing unit ($\sim -10°$) is not cold enough, but a satisfactory temperature is provided by solid CO_2 ($-78°$) or liquid N_2 ($-180°$). Freezing is therefore a useful means of preserving viable cultures.

In preserving bacteria, viruses, or animal cells by freezing it is helpful to add a relatively high concentration of glycerol, dimethylsulfoxide, or various proteins. By increasing the chemical heterogeneity of the system these agents promote amorphous, vitreous solidification on cooling, rather than crystallization; local high concentrations of salt are thus avoided. To achieve a similar protective effect in preserving bacteria by **lyophilization** (desiccation from the frozen state) protein-rich materials (milk, serum) are sometimes added.

---

* In the early days of developing a satisfactory ritual for aseptic transfer Pasteur recommended quick flaming of the bacteriologist's hands!

Radiation

Ultraviolet Radiation

Distribution. The well known sterilizing effect of sunlight on bacteria is due mainly to its content of ultraviolet (UV) light. By far the greatest proportion of this light reaching the earth's atmosphere from the sun is screened out by the ozone present in the outer regions of the atmosphere; otherwise most kinds of organisms present on the earth's surface could not survive.

With decreasing wave length sterilization of bacteria first becomes appreciable at 3300 A and then increases rapidly (Fig. 11-4). The lowest wave length of sunlight reaching the earth's surface in quantity is approximately 2900 A. Intense UV light of predominantly shorter wave lengths can be produced by low-pressure mercury vapor lamps ("germicidal" lamps) whose emission is 90% at 2537 A. Since glass effectively absorbs UV light bacteria should be exposed either in an uncovered vessel or in one made of a material (e.g., fused silica) that transmits these wave lengths.

Photochemistry. The amount of light absorbed by a material is proportional to its absorbancy and thickness, and to the product of the intensity and duration of the irradiation. The energy of UV light is absorbed in quanta by molecules of an appropriate structure. The absorbing molecule is thereby activated, resulting either in increased interatomic vibration or in excitation of an electron to a higher energy level. This extra energy may then follow a variety of paths: the activated molecule may undergo rupture of a chemical bond, leading to the formation of new bonds; or it may transfer most of its extra energy by collision to an adjacent molecule, which then undergoes chemical reaction; or the energy may be entirely dissipated by collision as increased translational energy (heat), without any chemical change.

UV absorption by bacteria is due chiefly to nucleic acids (in which the purines and the pyrimidines absorb heavily with an average maximum at 2600 A) and less to proteins (in which the aromatic rings of tryptophan, tyrosine, and phenylalanine absorb more moderately with an average maximum at 2800 A). The sterilization action spectrum (i.e., the efficiency of sterilization by radiation of various wave lengths) (Fig. 11-4) parallels the absorption spectrum of the bacteria, suggesting that absorption by either nucleic acid or protein can have a lethal effect.

Mechanism of Killing by UV. The major molecular mechanism of UV killing is probably irreversible damage to the DNA, of two kinds: 1) lethal mutations, and 2) chemical modifications that interfere with subsequent DNA replication (e.g., cross-linking between bases). The number of survivors observed on testing an irradiated cell suspension, like the number of mutants, varies with the speed of resumption of growth following irradiation, and with exposure to visible light shortly after UV irradiation (photoreactivation). These effects are explained by the processes of dark repair and light repair of damage to DNA (Ch. 8, Error correction): mutants blocked in one of these processes show unusually marked sensitivity to UV irradiation.

These effects of UV on DNA may be in part indirect. Thus UV irradiation (especially of lower wave lengths) causes formation of ozone (O_3) in air, of hydrogen peroxide (H_2O_2) in water containing dissolved oxygen, and of organic peroxides in the presence of oxygen and various organic compounds; hence after intense irradiation media are toxic for some time to subsequently inoculated bacteria.

The quantum yield of UV sterilization is small; the average *E. coli* cell has absorbed over 10^6 quanta by the time it is sterilized, and even the smallest viruses require many quanta. Hence the vast majority of the absorbed quanta must be dissipated either without producing a chemical reaction, or through a reaction in a molecule that is not essential for survival, or through a reversible reaction.

Practical Uses. Inexpensive mercury vapor lamps are widely used as sources of UV radiation to decrease airborne infection, e.g., in places of public crowding, barracks, hospital wards, surgical operating rooms, and rooms

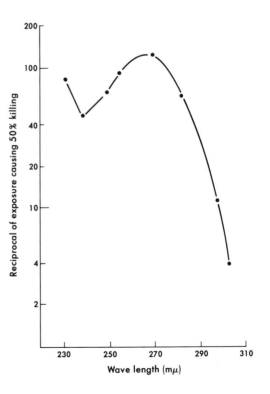

Fig. 11-4 Action spectrum of UV killing of *E. coli.* (Ordinate: reciprocal of the incident energy required for 50% killing.) (After F. L. Gates. *J. Gen. Physiol.* 14:31, 1930.)

containing experimental animals. However, air sanitation is still in a primitive state of development compared with water sanitation. The effectiveness of UV treatment of air in public places seems uncertain, but it has been convincingly demonstrated in hospital wards and in animal houses, where the infected individuals cannot make close contact with other individuals.

Thus tuberculous cross-infection in rabbits, caused by dust from bedding contaminated by urine, can be completely prevented by UV lamps. It is not necessary that a wall of UV light be formed between the cages ("UV barrier"); the air need only be exposed to enough radiation in the course of circulating through the room. In contrast, contaminated surfaces (e.g., toilet seats) are sterilized only by direct exposure.

In laboratory areas used for bacterial transfers UV lamps are similarly useful to decrease contamination of cultures and infection of workers. It is important to protect the eyes by eyeglasses, since excessive exposure of the cornea to UV causes severe irritation, with a latent period of about 12 hours.

In preparing killed bacterial and viral vaccines UV irradiation has a theoretical advantage, since the genome is much more sensitive to UV damage than are the immunologically important surface antigens. Nevertheless, this approach has not been particularly successful. One problem is the difficulty of avoiding clumps, in whose centers virulent organisms remain unexposed. It should also be noted that tissue extracts, even when considerably diluted, make the medium opaque to UV light.

Photodynamic Sensitization

In strong visible light certain dyes (e.g., methylene blue, rose bengal, eosin), at low concentrations, sterilize bacteria and viruses (and also lyse red blood cells and denature proteins). This photodynamic sensitization is seen with a comparatively small number of dyes, which have in common the property of fluorescing, i.e., of retaining an absorbed quantum for a comparatively long time (10^{-6} to 10^{-8} seconds) and then releasing much of its energy in a single unit, usually by light emission of longer wave length. Sometimes the energy is transferred instead by collision with another molecule, which may then undergo chemical change.

Photosensitization has not been of much practical value in microbiology. It must be borne in mind, however, when working with potentially photosensitizing dyes. Indeed, even in the absence of added dyes intense visible light is capable of killing bacteria, presumably via physiologically occurring photosensitizing substances, such as riboflavin and porphyrins. This effect makes it inadvisable to expose bacterial cultures to direct sunlight, even when protected by glass. For example, BCG vaccine in glass (i.e., UV-absorbing) ampules has been observed to lose all viability and effectiveness on exposure to bright sunlight, as may easily occur in outdoor field stations.

X-rays and Other Ionizing Radiations

Distribution. X-rays, and γ-rays of radioactive chemical elements, are electromagnetic radiations of wave length 0.01 to 10 A. Other ionizing irradiations include beams of high-speed electrons (cathode rays and the β-rays emitted by radioactive substances), and high-energy protons, neutrons, or other particles produced by various accelerating devices. These radiations are lethal, in sufficient dosage, to all cells, including bacteria.

Though bacteria are widely used for studying the lethal and the mutagenic actions of ionizing radiations, these radiations have not been of much practical use in microbiology. Intense sources of radiation can be used to sterilize hospital goods, foods, etc., without much rise in temperature. With foods, however, since very large doses are required (millions of rads), undesirable effects on flavor are often induced.

Mechanism. The quantum energy values of ionizing radiations are hundreds to thousands of time as great as those of UV light, and their mode of action is entirely different. An ionizing quantum is absorbed, not by a molecule of appropriate configuration, but by an **atom,** which is caused to eject a very high-energy electron (i.e., to become ionized). This electron in turn ionizes each of several hundred atoms of any kind that lie in its path, regardless of the chemical structures in which those atoms are located. The molecules containing the ionized atoms then undergo chemical changes, involving the rupture of old bonds and the formation of new ones. The ultimate results are thus chemically more varied than those obtained with UV radiation; moreover, the energies involved are so high that a single quantum alters many molecules, and thus may inactivate more than one bacterium.

Since ionizing quanta act on all atoms in their path much of their absorption is due to the bulk constituent of biological material: water. The following reactions result:

$$H_2O \rightsquigarrow H_2O^+ + e^- \text{ (primary event)}$$

$$H_2O^+ \longrightarrow H^+ + OH \text{ (free radical)}$$

$$e^- + H^+ \longrightarrow H \text{ (free atom)}$$

The hydroxyl radical is a powerful oxidant and the hydrogen atom a powerful reductant; both undergo rapid chemical reactions with nearby organic molecules. Sulfhydryl groups are effective in capturing hydroxyl radicals before they have interacted with macromolecules; hence the cytotoxic effects of ionizing radiations can be substantially mitigated by the addition of various sulfhydryl compounds. Absence of oxygen also decreases the effect of ionizing radiations.

The damaging effect of the radiolytic products of water on essential molecules in the cell constitutes an **indirect** mode of action of radiation. In dry materials, however, the action is predominantly a **direct** one on these molecules. Under these circumstances the kinetics of lethal action of ionizing radiations on cells and viruses are reasonably well approached on the basis of **target theory.** This theory postulates that a cell will be killed, or an enzyme molecule inactivated, whenever a chain of ionizations passes through any part of its **"sensitive volume"** (Ch. 8, Appendix). If radiation-induced cell death is primarily the result of damage to the genome, target theory predicts that the relative sensitivity of viruses, bacteria, and cells of higher organisms will follow the inverse order of their genome

or DNA volumes. Experiment has confirmed this prediction.

Mechanical Agents

Ultrasonic and Sonic Waves

Sound waves, which are longitudinal mechanical vibrations, have quite different effects from the transverse electromagnetic vibrations of light. In the supersonic (ultrasonic) range, with a frequency of 15,000 to several hundred thousand per second, these vibrations denature proteins, disperse a variety of materials, and sterilize and disintegrate bacteria. Audible sonic waves of sufficient intensity are also bactericidal. The effect has not been of practical value as a means of sterilization but it is useful for disrupting cells and extracting enzymes and antigens ("sonication").

Filtration

Bacteria-free filtrates may be obtained by the use of filters with a maximum pore size not exceeding 1 μ.

The Seitz filter, of asbestos, and the Berkefeld filter, of diatomaceous earth, are still widely used but are quite adsorptive; in addition, the Seitz filter contributes Ca ions (which would cause clotting of citrated plasma), and also Fe ions. The early Chamberland unglazed porcelain filter has been modified, with more accurate control of pore size, by the modern porcelain industry (e.g., Selas filters); and effective sterilizing filters of sintered (fritted) glass (e.g., Corning UF) are also available. These two types of filters adsorb very little and are ideal for the sterilization of solutions that cannot tolerate sterilization by heat (e.g., sera, and media containing proteins or labile metabolites).

These advantages of porcelain and glass filters also apply to modified cellulose films of accurately graded porosity (e.g., Millipore filters), which in addition filter considerably faster. Such membrane filters permit quantitative recovery of bacteria for chemical analysis, for rapid transfer to new media, etc. Large filters of this type have been used by armed forces for rapid sterilization of drinking water in the field.

CHEMICAL AGENTS

General

Disinfectants are lethal to all sorts of cells. Because of this nonspecificity it is not surprising that bacteria develop little resistance to these agents (in contrast to the much more selectively acting chemotherapeutic agents). Classification as a disinfectant, however, is somewhat arbitrary, for at a high enough concentration a great variety of compounds will inhibit bacterial growth. Indeed, whether a given substance is a meat or a poison to bacteria is often simply a matter of concentration. Thus oxygen, various salts, fatty acids, some amino acids, and glycerol, in high enough concentrations, may be bacteristatic or even actively bactericidal to bacteria that also can utilize or even may require them for growth.

In contrast to most bactericidal chemotherapeutic agents, disinfectants act directly on cell structures, and thus do not require specific metabolic activities on the part of the microbe. Two major mechanisms can be distinguished: solution of lipids from the cell membrane (by detergents and lipid solvents), and irreversible alteration of proteins (e.g., by denaturants, oxidants, alkylating agents, and sulfhydryl reagents).

Effect of the Environment. The rate of killing by disinfectants increases with concentration of the compound and with temperature, as is true of chemical reactions in general. Those antibacterial agents that are capable of ionizing as acids (phenols, some dyes, and short-chain organic acids) are more active with increasing acidity of the solution, while the opposite is true of cationic reagents. This effect of pH has at least two sources: greater penetration of dissociable compounds in their nonionized form; and increased ionization of cellular constituents in the opposite direction, leading to greater affinity.

Determination of Disinfectant Potency

Phenol Coefficient. Ever since Lister began spraying surgical operating rooms with phenol this compound has been considered the standard disinfectant, though it is required in a higher concentration than almost any other: 0.9% will sterilize a suspension of *Salmonella typhosa* under ordinary conditions in 10 minutes, and to provide a margin of safety a concentration of 5% is ordinarily used for general disinfection.

The **phenol coefficient** of a compound is the ratio of the minimal sterilizing concentration of phenol (under standard conditions) to that of the compound. In the official test, used by regulatory agencies of the U.S. government, a broth culture is diluted 1:10 with various concentrations of the test compound. The endpoint is the lowest concentration that yields, after incubation for 10 minutes at 20°, sterile loopful samples; and the germicide is generally recommended for use at 5 times this concentration. Two organisms are ordinarily used: *S. typhosa*, as a representative enteric pathogen, and *Staphylococcus aureus*, as the major environmental source of wound infection.

The phenol coefficient provides a reasonable index for comparing various phenol derivatives, which exhibit similar kinetics and mode of action; but it is less satisfactory for other agents, which may differ in their concentration-action curves and in their susceptibility to neutralization by the environment. Thus the concentrations of a disinfectant, c, required to sterilize a bacterial population in varying time, t, generally correspond to a curve which may be fitted by the equation ($c^n t = k$); and while phenol has the remarkably high concentration coefficient (n) of 5 to 6, oxidants such as hypochlorite have a value of about 1. Hence the 5-fold increase above the endpoint concentration provides a much wider margin of safety for phenols than for oxidants.

Problems in Evaluating Disinfectants. Some agents (e.g., mercurials, detergents) may adhere to the bacteria and thus exert a bacteristatic action, in the subinoculated samples, that mimics bactericidal action. To test such materials for bactericidal action it is important to include a neutralizing compound in the test medium.

In addition, the effectiveness of a disinfecting procedure often depends strongly on the "cleanness" of the material. For example, both gases and organic liquids may not reach bacteria encased in crystals deposited by the drying of an aqueous solution: hence porous surfaces (fibers), which take up the drying solution, may be easier to sterilize than non-porous surfaces (metal, glass). Moreover, the presence of a large amount of organic matter (e.g., in excreta or discarded cultures) rapidly neutralizes the action of many types of agents: reactive chemicals (such as oxidants) are chemically altered, and many compounds are adsorbed (especially by serum albumin in samples containing blood).

Because of these considerations, different kinds of disinfectants are used for different purposes. The long-term action of a skin antiseptic, for example, poses requirements quite different from those of a disinfectant used for rinsing dishes, or one used for discarded cultures. Efficacy must therefore finally be tested under the conditions of use.

We have noted above that because killing by heat is exponential, the sensitivity of an organism can be expressed more precisely as the slope of the semilogarithmic curve for killing as a function of time, rather than as an endpoint for the time and temperature yielding complete sterilization. The same consideration applies to certain disinfectants that also exhibit exponential kinetics (see final section of this chapter). However, the curves for chemical disinfection are often imperfectly exponential, with the physiologically more resistant members of the population surviving longer than would be predicted by extrapolation. Hence the endpoint of complete sterilization remains of practical value. The kinetics of chemical disinfection, and the statistical problem of defining complete sterilization, will be further considered in connection with the preparation of viral vaccines (Ch. 26).

Specific Chemical Agents

Acids and Alkalis. Strongly acid or alkaline solutions are actively bactericidal. For example, 0.01 N HCl or H_2SO_4 sterilizes a suspension of *E. coli* in 40 minutes. However, mycobacteria are somewhat more resistant, it being common

practice to liquefy sputum by exposure for 30 minutes to approximately 1 N NaOH or H_2SO_4. The success of this procedure depends on the survival of a fraction of the population, rather than on complete resistance of the bacteria. Gram-positive staphylococci and streptococci also frequently survive.

Weak organic acids exert a greater effect than can be accounted for by the pH: the presence of highly permeable undissociated molecules promotes penetration of the acid into the cells, and the increasing activity with chain length suggests a direct action of the organic compound itself. (Long-chain fatty acids will be considered below under Detergents.) Lactic acid is the natural preservative of many fermentation products; and salts of propionic acid (CH_3CH_2COOH) are now frequently added to bread and other foods to retard mold growth. (Higher homologs would be more potent, but would affect the flavor adversely.)

Salts. Pickling in brine, or treatment with solid NaCl, has been used for many centuries as a means of preserving perishable meats and fish. There is considerable variation in bacterial susceptibility; NaCl prevents the growth of tubercle bacilli at a concentration of 2%, *E. coli* at around 6%, and *Bacillus subtilis* only at over 9%. In contrast, as was noted in Chapter 5, certain halophilic organisms require 10 to 12% NaCl for growth, and can withstand much higher concentrations.

Physiological saline is widely used as a diluent for bacteria, because of its presence in laboratories where serological tests are performed, but it is not very suitable; a balanced salt solution, containing Mg^{++} and phosphate buffer, permits much better survival of many kinds of bacteria. Strains vary widely in their ability to survive in distilled water. Some of the lethal action, however, is due not to the water itself but to contaminating traces of heavy metal ions, which are more bactericidal in the absence of competitive ions.

Heavy Metals. The various metallic ions can be arranged in a series of decreasing antibacterial activity; Hg^{++} and Ag^+, at the head of the list, are effective in concentrations less than 1 part per million (ppm). This potency, however, does not reflect any remarkable effect of comparatively few ions on the cell, for it has been shown that cells take up relatively large numbers of these ions from very dilute solutions. Thus bacteria, trypanosomes, or yeast killed by Ag^+ contain 10^5 to 10^7 Ag^+ ions per cell. Because of this relation the concentration required for killing is markedly affected by the inoculum size.

As was noted above, the initial antibacterial action of Hg^{++} can be readily reversed by sulfhydryl compounds (whose affinity for Hg^{++} gave rise to the term "mercaptan"). This reversibility is readily understandable, since the inactivation of various enzymes in solution, by combination of their sulfhydryl groups with Hg^{++}, has similarly been shown to be reversible by sulfhydryl compounds. The antibacterial effect of Hg^{++}, as well as that of arsenicals, presumably depends upon combination with protein sulfhydryl groups within the cell.

Mercuric chloride, once popular as a disinfectant, is now obsolete. However, various organic mercury compounds (e.g., Merthiolate, Mercurochrome, Metaphen), in which one of the valences of Hg is covalently combined, are used as relatively nonirritating antiseptics, and also as preservatives for sera and vaccines.

Silver has long been used as a mild antiseptic in the form of a proteinate (e.g., Argyrol), which slowly releases silver ions; and colloidal silver metal is also a potent antibacterial agent, of unknown mechanism. Before penicillin became available silver nitrate was used topically for the prophylaxis of neonatal gonococcal ophthalmitis. Organic compounds of arsenic, bismuth, and antimony have been used in the chemotherapy of syphilis and of certain protozoal diseases. Gold has also been used chemotherapeutically but with questionable value. Copper salts have great importance as fungicides in agriculture but not in medicine.

Inorganic Anions. Inorganic anions are much less toxic than some of the cations. Boric acid has found wide use as a very mild antiseptic. Fluoride, which inhibits several enzymes, is toxic to many bacteria but only in relatively high concentrations. Tellurite is particularly inhibitory to gram-negative organisms and least to corynebacteria, and it is therefore used in the selective cultivation of diphtheria bacilli.

Halogens.   Tincture of iodine (a 2 to 7% solution of I_2 in aqueous alcohol containing KI) is one of the most rapidly acting bactericides. It is a reliable antiseptic for skin and for minor wounds, but its painful and destructive effect on exposed tissue has led it to be discarded in the treatment of large wounds. Iodine combines irreversibly with proteins (e.g., by iodinating tyrosine residues), and it is an oxidant.

Chlorine was the antiseptic introduced (as chlorinated lime) by O. W. Holmes in Boston in 1835, and by Semmelweis in Vienna in 1847, to prevent transmission of puerperal sepsis by the physician's hands. Chlorine combines with water to form hypochlorous acid (HOCl), a strong oxidizing agent:

$$Cl_2 + H_2O \rightleftharpoons HCl + HOCl$$

$$or$$

$$Cl_2 + 2NaOH \rightleftharpoons NaCl + NaOCl + H_2O$$

Hypochlorite solutions (200 ppm Cl_2) are widely used to sanitize clean surfaces in the food and the dairy industries and in restaurants; and Cl_2 gas, added at 1 to 3 ppm, is widely used to disinfect water supplies and swimming pools. Although chlorine is a reliable, rapidly acting disinfectant for such "clean" materials, it is less satisfactory for treating materials rich in organic matter, because it is rapidly destroyed by reacting with many compounds; the "chlorine demand" of a water supply increases with its content of organic matter, and chlorination must be titrated to a definite level of free Cl_2. This reactivity of hypochlorite is a virtue in the sanitizing of food utensils: residual traces of chlorine will be rapidly destroyed on subsequent contact with food, leaving no flavor or odor.

Hypochlorite was also widely used in World War I to irrigate wounds, and was largely replaced by chloramines: organic compounds with a labile Cl atom attached to N, which release free chlorine in solution and are less irritating to tissues. These compounds have now been replaced by chemotherapeutic agents in the prophylaxis and the treatment of wound infection, but tablets of chloramino compounds are useful in rendering drinking water safe on a small scale.

Other Oxidizants. **Hydrogen peroxide** (H_2O_2), in a 3% solution, was once widely used as an antiseptic, but it cannot be strongly recommended. Bacteria vary widely in their susceptibility, since some species possess catalase. Potassium **permanganate** ($KMnO_4$) is of value as a urethral antiseptic in concentrations around 1/1000. **Peracetic acid** (CH_3CO-O-OH), a strong oxidizing agent, is used as a vapor for the sterilization of chambers for germ-free animals; its reliable disinfection compensates for the inconveniently long flushing required because of its toxicity for animals. These compounds, as well as the halogens, presumably act by oxidizing SH and S-S groups of enzymes and membrane components.

Alkylating Agents. Formaldehyde and ethylene oxide replace the labile H atoms on -NH₂ and -OH groups, which are abundant in proteins and nucleic acids, and also on -COOH and -SH groups of proteins. By reacting one molecule with two groups these reagents also form cross-linking methylene or ethylene bridges, respectively (Fig. 11-5). The reactions of formaldehyde are in part reversible; but the high-energy epoxide bridge of ethylene oxide leads to irreversible reactions. These alkylating agents, in contrast to other

disinfectants, are reported to be nearly as active against spores as against vegetative bacterial cells; the reason is not clear.

Formaldehyde is a gas that is marketed as a 37% aqueous solution (formalin). It has long been used in preparing vaccines: i.e., sterilizing bacteria, or inactivating toxins or viruses, without destroying their antigenicity. For this purpose addition to a concentration of 0.1% is usual.

Formaldehyde may be used as a gas for sterilizing dry surfaces: e.g., in the formerly popular practice of "terminal fumigation" of rooms of patients with serious infections, and more recently in the preparation of disposable plasticware for bacteriological laboratories. However, it is extensively adsorbed on surfaces as a reversible polymer (paraformaldehyde), and this adsorption has several undesirable consequences: formaldehyde does not penetrate well through porous substances; an irritating residue persists and is not readily flushed out because of the slow depolymerization of the deposits of paraformaldehyde; and a high humidity is essential to provide a layer of active, dissolved formaldehyde, rather than the polymer, on the bacterial surface.

Ethylene oxide, a highly water-soluble gas, was introduced more recently (1940), and has proved to be the most reliable substance available for gaseous disinfection of dry surfaces, with none of the disadvantages listed above for formaldehyde. However, its action is much slower than that of steam, and it is

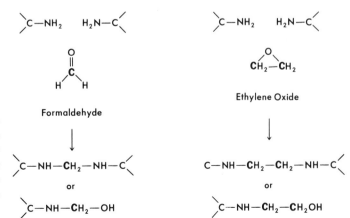

Fig. 11-5 Reactions of formaldehyde and ethylene oxide with amino groups. Similar condensations may take place with other nucleophilic groups. Bridges may be formed between groups on the same molecule or on different molecules.

more expensive to use and presents some hazard of residual toxicity (vesicant action). Indeed, the potential hazards of mutagenicity and carcinogenicity for man deserve careful investigation, since formaldehyde and ethylene oxide, like other alkylating agents (Ch. 8), have been shown to be mutagenic to bacteria, plant seeds, and *Drosophila*.

The main medical use of ethylene oxide is in the sterilization of heat-sensitive objects: plasticware; surgical equipment; hospital bedding; and books, leather, etc. handled by patients. Ethylene oxide is explosive, but this hazard is eliminated by using a mixture with 90% CO_2 or a fluorocarbon.

Surface-Active Agents. In recent years the chemical industry has developed a variety of surface-active compounds (surfactants), which are generally called synthetic detergents though other of their surface-active properties (wetting, emulsifying, foaming) are often more prominent than their detergent (cleansing) action. Such surface-active compounds accumulate in an oriented layer at aqueous interfaces because they contain both a hydrophobic portion (which tends to aggregate in water) and a hydrophilic portion (which tends to remain in contact with water). The hydrophobic portion of the molecule is predominantly or solely hydrocarbon; the hydrophilic portion may be either an ionizable group or a nonionic but highly polar structure (e.g., a polyhydric alcohol such as sorbitol).

The anionic compounds generally have as their hydrophilic portion a sulfate (RSO_4H) or a sulfonate (RSO_3H) group (e.g., Duponol), while the cationic compounds have a substituted amine or a heterocyclic nitrogenous group (e.g., pyridine). When the nitrogen has one to three organic substituents it will ionize only in acid solution, whereas quaternary ammonium compounds (R_4N^+) are ionized at any pH.

The nonionic detergents are not particularly inhibitory to bacteria, and some are even good nutrients. The synthetic anionic detergents, like the very similar soaps (salts of long-chain fatty acids), are moderately bactericidal to gram-positive but less to gram-negative bacteria; hence they are not reliable disinfectants. (Phenols, a special class of weakly anionic detergents, will be discussed below.)

Cationic detergents, in contrast, are active against all kinds of bacteria (perhaps because, unlike anionic detergents, they are not repelled by the ordinarily negative net charge of the bacterial surface). The most effective types are the **quaternary** compounds, containing three short-chain alkyl groups as well as a long-chain alkyl group (e.g., benzalkonium chloride, Fig. 11-6). These compounds are widely used for skin antisepsis and for sanitizing food utensils. Their detergent action provides the advantage of dissolving lipid films that may protect bacteria, and they have the further advantage of leaving a tenacious bactericidal surface film. A variety of cationic germicides are on the market because of patent rights, but their differences do not seem fundamental. In the absence of adsorbing macromolecules or lipids they may be rapidly bactericidal at concentrations as low as 1 ppm; and unlike many other disinfectants, they are not poisonous to man. Their activity is neutralized by soaps and phospholipids, since oppositely charged surfactants precipitate each other.

Homologous series of detergents show an increase, with increasing chain length, in bactericidal potency as well as in surface tension depression, but both effects decrease at high chain lengths: above 8 to 10 carbon atoms for the alcohols and substituted phenols (see below), or 12 to 18 for the more soluble ionic detergents.

Fig. 11-6 Benzalkonium chloride (benzyldimethyl alkonium chloride; Zephiran). A typical quaternary ammonium detergent; the long-chain alkyl group is a mixture obtained by the reduction and amination of the fatty acids of vegetable or animal fat.

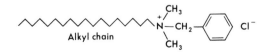

The presence of an optimal length is readily explained. The increasing size of the hydrophobic portion of the molecule tends to drive it out of aqueous solution, whether to form an oriented layer at any air-water interface (surface tension effect) or to be adsorbed on a bacterial surface (a prerequisite for bactericidal action). At excessive chain lengths, however, these effects decrease because of the insufficient solubility of the compound in water. This relative insolubility is reflected in an increased tendency to aggregate in large micelles, in which the hydrophilic regions face outward and the hydrophobic regions inward.

Mechanism of Action. Detergents dissolve lipids, and they denature proteins in solution. The same high dilutions that sterilize bacteria cause their lysis, as evidenced by the extraction of metabolites from the cells, whereas sterilization by various other agents (metal ions, chlorine, formaldehyde) does not cause such extraction. It therefore appears that detergents sterilize by disrupting the cell membrane, presumably through combining primarily with its lipids. This mechanism explains why detergents are less active against those viruses that lack a lipoprotein surface membrane than against those possessing such a membrane.

Phenols. Phenol (C_6H_5OH) is an effective denaturant of proteins (a property widely used in the purification of nucleic acids), and it exerts a detergent effect on lipids. By either mechanism its bactericidal action apparently depends, like that of detergents, on membrane damage and cell lysis, for the killing is accompanied by discharge of cytoplasmic material into the medium.

The antibacterial activity of phenol is increased by halogen or alkyl substituents on the ring, which increase the polarity of the phenolic OH group and decrease solubility in water. Since one end of the molecule thus becomes increasingly hydrophilic and the other increasingly hydrophobic, the molecule as a whole becomes more surface-active and the antibacterial potency may be increased a hundredfold or more.

The activity of these substituted phenols may be increased by mixing with soaps, which increase their solubility and promote penetration, thereby exerting a synergistic effect. However, if the proportion of soap is too high the activity is impaired, presumably because the high solubility of the disinfectant molecules in the soap micelles decreases their adsorption to the bacteria. For similar reasons phenols are sometimes less effective in organic solvents than in water.

While short-chain substituents on phenols increase their potency to more or less the same extent for a variety of microbes, with gram-negative bacteria activity becomes maximal, and then rapidly falls off, at increasing chain lengths that still exhibit increasing activity against other organisms (Fig. 11-7). This effect suggests that

Fig. 11-7 Germicidal activity of homologous series of o-alkyl-p-chlorophenol derivatives against four organisms. The parent compound (p-chlorophenol) had a phenol coefficient (see p. 344) of 4 against all the organisms. Note the strikingly increased activity of the longer-chain (C-6 and C-7) derivatives against the gram-positive staphylococcus, and the opposite response of the gram-negative salmonella. A similar divergence in response at greater chain lengths has also been observed with other homologous series of phenol derivatives. (From E. G. Klarmann and E. S. Wright. In G. F. Reddish (ed.). *Antiseptics, Disinfectants, Fungicides, and Sterilization.* Lea & Febiger, Philadelphia, 1957, p. 506.)

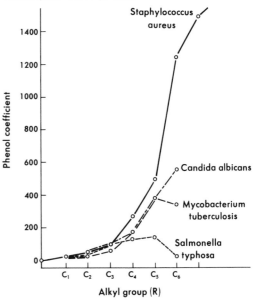

the outer layers of the gram-negative wall, which apparently exclude various drugs and enzymes (Ch. 2), also tend to exclude bulky substituted phenols (or their micelles). With substituents of still higher chain length action against all bacteria decreases, presumably because of low solubility.

Uses of Phenols. A mixture of **tricresol** (mixed *ortho, meta,* and *para*-methylphenol) and soap is probably the most widely used disinfectant for discarded bacteriological materials. Its action is not impaired by the presence of organic matter, because it must be used in a relatively high concentration and it is not extensively destroyed or bound by organic molecules.

The essential oils of plants have been used since antiquity as preservatives and antiseptics, and from these materials a variety of phenolic compounds have been isolated. One example is thymol (5-methyl-2-isopropylphenol), of which a crystal or two, saturating the solution, is a useful preservative of urine, enzymatic digests, etc. Another example, eugenol (4-allyl-2-methoxyphenol), is used in dentistry as an antiseptic in cavities.

Halogenated bis-phenols, such as **hexachlorophene,** are bacteristatic in very high dilutions,

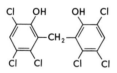

and appear to be less inactivated by soaps or other anionic (or nonionic) detergents than are ordinary phenols. This compound is also not very volatile, and lacks the unpleasant odor of many phenols. Hexochlorophene is widely used as a skin antiseptic, especially mixed with a detergent (pHisoHex); it is also used in deodorant soaps designed to hinder bacterial decomposition of sweat. The bactericidal action of this group may easily be overestimated because their persistent bacteristatic action is not readily neutralized.

Hexylresorcinol   (4-hexyl-1,3-dihydroxybenzene) is used as a skin antiseptic. One of the

two hydroxyl groups can be esterified or alkylated with little effect, but activity disappears if both are substituted. Alkyl esters of **p-hydroxybenzoate** are used as preservatives of foods and pharmaceuticals: such an ester-substituted phenol acts on bacteria much like an alkyl-substituted phenol; but its rapid hydrolysis in the gut yields free *p*-hydroxybenzoate, which, unlike most phenols, is nontoxic to mammals (or bacteria) even in high concentrations. **Benzoic acid** itself is widely used as a nontoxic food preservative, but it is useful only in acid foods (pH < 4.5), where there would be an appreciable concentration of the undissociated acid; this compound somewhat resembles phenol in structure, and may have a similar action.

Alcohols and Other Organic Solvents. The disinfectant action of the aliphatic alcohols increases with chain length up to 8 to 10 carbon atoms, above which the water solubility becomes too low. Although **ethanol** (CH_3-CH_2OH) has received widest use, **isopropyl alcohol** ($CH_3CHOHCH_3$) has the advantage of being less volatile, slightly more potent, and not subject to legal restrictions as a potential beverage.

The disinfectant action of alcohols, like their denaturing effect on proteins, involves the participation of water. Ethanol is most effective in 50 to 70% aqueous solution: at 100% it is a poor disinfectant, in which anthrax spores have been reported to survive for as much as 50 days; and its bactericidal action is negligible at concentrations below 10 to 20%. Some organic disinfectants, such as formaldehyde or phenol, are less effective in alcohol than in water, because of the lowered affinity of the disinfectant for the bacteria relative to the solvent. On the other hand, alcohol removes lipid layers that may protect skin organisms from some other disinfectants. Alcohols do not act rapidly enough to be reliable for skin disinfection for surgery, but they are widely used in preparation for cutaneous injections, in which the tissue trauma is so minimal that a few contaminating organisms are readily eliminated by host defences. Alcohols are also satisfactory for prolonged disinfection (e.g., of thermometers), though hepatitis virus is highly resistant.

Organic solvents, such as ether, benzene, acetone, or chloroform, also kill bacteria but are not reliable as rapid disinfectants. However, the addition of a few drops of toluene or chloroform, to saturate aqueous solutions, will prevent growth of fungi or bacteria. Glycerol, a polyhydric alcohol, is bacteristatic in concentrations exceeding 50%; it is used at these high concentrations as a preservative for vaccines and other biologicals, since it is also not irritating to tissues.

Dyes. There is wide variation in the extent to which staining by various dyes is lethal. In general, as with detergents, basic (cationic) compounds are more effective than acidic ones, and some are bactericidal at concentrations as low as 0.1 ppm. The use of antibacterial dyes is largely restricted to selective culture media (e.g.,

malachite green in media for the tubercle bacillus). Dyes have been disappointing as antiseptics, probably because of their binding by tissue constituents.

Aerosols. To prevent airborne infection chemical disinfection of air has been attempted, but so far without practical success. Certain glycols, such as propylene glycol (CH_3CHOH-CH_2OH) and diethylene glycol ($HOCH_2CH_2$-OCH_2CH_2OH), reduce the bacterial count in air when dispersed in fine droplets, and at the required concentrations they are nontoxic to man. However, their use is limited because their action involves condensation of the glycol onto the bacteria, which occurs in only a narrow range of humidity: at high humidities the hygroscopic glycols are excessively diluted by water taken up by their droplets, while at low humidities the desiccated bacteria no longer attract glycols. Moreover, the glycols do not disinfect surfaces (e.g., bedding, floor dust), from which aerial contamination is renewed.

EXPONENTIAL KINETICS OF STERILIZATION

When bacteria are exposed to any ionizing radiations, or to UV radiation, the rate of sterilization follows the exponential curve characteristic of a first-order reaction:

$$-dn/dt = kn; \text{ therefore}$$
$$n/n_0 = e^{-kt}, \text{ or}$$
$$\ln n = \ln n_0 - kt,$$

where n_0 is the initial number of viable bacteria, n is the number after exposure for time t, and k is a coefficient which depends upon the intensity of exposure and the sensitivity of the organism. Hence when the logarithm of the number of surviving bacteria is plotted against time the data fall on a straight line: i.e., a constant proportion of the surviving bacteria are sterilized per unit time (Fig. 11-8). These kinetics mean that the chance of killing a given cell during a given interval of exposure is independent of the duration of preceding exposure. This absence of a cumulative effect ("one-hit" kinetics) implies that death is caused by the irreversible effect of the random absorption of a **single** ionizing electron or UV photon in an appropriate loca-

tion in the cell (the "sensitive" volume; see above, p. 343, and Ch. 8, Appendix).

These first-order kinetics are readily understood, since these radiations damage the genome, in which a single mutation in certain regions, or a single cross-link that blocks replication, will be lethal. Radiation damages enzyme molecules as well, but this effect is not likely to be a significant source of killing, since each enzyme is represented by a large number of interchangeable individual molecules. Indeed, any lethal action that depended on inactivation of enzymes alone would have to involve either a large proportion of all the enzyme molecules in a cell, or else in particular an enzyme of protein synthesis; for as long as the apparatus for making proteins remains active even a trickle of building blocks and energy should lead to restoration of the deficient enzymes (as in the derepression of a repressed enzyme; Ch. 9).

Similar exponential curves are also obtained with agents other than radiation. Thus an exponential curve was observed as early as 1907 by Madsen and Nyman, and by Chick, for the

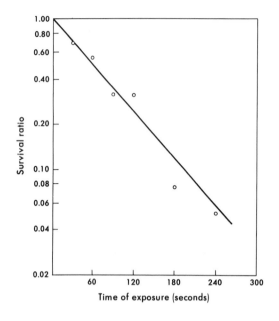

Y-axis: Survival ratio
X-axis: Time of exposure (seconds)

Fig. 11-8 Exponential killing of spores of *Bacillus megaterium* by UV irradiation. (Adapted from F. Hercik. *J. Gen. Physiol.* 20:589, 1936–37.)

The simplest chemical model for such a phenomenon would involve the reaction of a disinfectant molecule (or heat) with a single **indispensable** bacterial molecule, e.g., part of the genetic apparatus of the cell, or part of a structural element (such as the cell membrane) whose integrity is essential for viability. Thus once a critical reaction occurs in a membrane the resulting increase of permeability to the disinfectant may cause a greatly increased rate of subsequent reactions. The lethal effect could then be represented as the single chemical "hit" that resulted in the altered threshold. Before this reaction there might have been a great number of "hits" with other molecules in the cell, whose integrity is not important for viability.

A single-hit inactivation curve implies that the individual cells in a bacterial population are uniformly susceptible to the action of heat or of the disinfectant, and hence can be considered statistically equivalent to a reagent in a chemical reaction. This interpretation is supported by the observation that the best exponential killing curves have been obtained with spores (e.g., Figs. 11-1 and 11-8), which are more uniform in structure than vegetative cells. With vegetative cells the initially exponential killing tends to slow up later, as would be expected from a population that is somewhat heterogeneous with respect to susceptibility (Ch. 8, Appendix).

Exponential curves are not obtained with all chemical disinfectants. Chlorine, for example, gives a sigmoid curve with an initial plateau, which would be explained by the requirement for damage to many molecules (? of a given species of enzyme) within the same cell.

sterilization of bacteria by heat (Fig. 11-1) or by phenol or certain other disinfectants (Fig. 11-9). The significance of these kinetics is not entirely certain, since the events appear to be stoichiometric rather than quantal. However, these first-order kinetics do not mean that in a cell just killed only one disinfectant molecule has reacted with the cell, or only one molecule of protein has been denatured by heat; they do mean that the chance of undergoing a **lethal** reaction is independent of the previous effects of the disinfectant or heat on the cell.

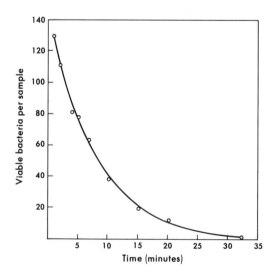

Y-axis: Viable bacteria per sample
X-axis: Time (minutes)

Fig. 11-9 Exponential killing of *Salmonella paratyphosa* by 0.6% phenol at 20°. The solid line, which fits the experimental points well, was drawn from the theoretical first-order reaction equation, $-dn/dt = kn$; on a semilogarithmic plot (e.g., Fig. 11-8) the curve would be linear. (From H. Chick. *J. Hyg.* 8:92, 1908.)

SELECTED REFERENCES

Books and Review Articles

ALBERT, A. *Selective Toxicity,* 3d ed. Wiley, New York, 1965.

BRUCH, C. W. Gaseous sterilization. *Ann. Rev. Microbiol. 15:*245 (1961).

CHICK, H., and BROWNING, C. H. The theory of disinfection. Med. Res. Council Syst. Bact., London *1:*179 (1930).

LEA, D. E. *Actions of Radiations on Living Cells,* 2nd ed. Cambridge Univ. Press, London, 1955.

PHILLIPS, C. R., and WARSHOWSKY, B. Chemical disinfectants. Ann. Rev. Microbiol. *12:*525 (1958).

REDDISH, G. F. (ed.). *Antiseptics, Disinfectants, Fungicides, and Sterilization.* Lea & Febiger, Philadelphia, 1957.

WELLS, W. F. Air-borne Contagion and Air Hygiene. Harvard Univ. Press, Cambridge, Mass., 1955.

ZELLE, M. R., and HOLLAENDER, A. Effects of Radiation on Bacteria. In *Radiation Biology,* vol. II, p. 365. (A. Hollaender, ed.) McGraw-Hill, New York, 1955.

Specific Articles

HOTCHKISS, R. D. The nature of the bactericidal action of surface active agents. *Ann. New York Acad. Sc. 46:*479 (1946).

IMMUNOLOGY

12 INTRODUCTION TO THE IMMUNE RESPONSE

The capacity to adapt to changes in the environment appears to be a universal attribute of living things. As we have already seen in Chapter 9, the adaptive regulation of specific enzyme synthesis in bacteria is now understood in considerable detail at a molecular level. In the next few chapters we shall be concerned with another kind of adaptive change involving specific protein synthesis, the immune response. This response seems to have been acquired relatively late in evolution, since it has been encountered only in vertebrates; but it is of vast importance for their survival, constituting their principal means of defense against pathogenic microorganisms.

The Origins of Immunology

For almost as long as there are written records of man's observations of mankind it seems to have been suspected that persons who recover from certain diseases become incapable of suffering the same disease again: they become immune. Thucydides, for example, pointed out 2500 years ago, in a remarkable description of an epidemic in Athens (of typhus fever or plague), that fear of contagion led to neglect of the sick and dying, but whatever attention they received was "tended by the pitying care of those who had recovered, because they . . . were themselves free of apprehension. For no one was ever attacked a second time, or with a fatal result." This awareness led to deliberate attempts, beginning in about the fifteenth century, to induce immunity by inoculating well persons with material scraped from skin lesions of persons suffering from smallpox. The procedure was hazardous; and its protective value was disputed up until the late eighteenth century, when it was validated, in principle, by the work of the English physician Jenner.

Jenner shared the impression, widely held by laymen and physicians at the time, that those individuals who had had cowpox (a benign disease acquired from cows infected with what seemed to be a mild form of smallpox) were spared when smallpox epidemics subsequently raged in their neighborhood. To test this belief he inoculated a boy with pus from a lesion of a dairy maid who had cowpox. Some weeks later the boy was inoculated deliberately with infectious pus from a patient in the active stage of smallpox, but the child failed to become ill. Repetition of the experiment many times led to Jenner's classic report, followed by widespread adoption of his procedure and confirmation of his conclusion that **vaccination** (L. vacca, "cow") leads to immunity against smallpox.

In view of the speed with which new discoveries are extended in contemporary science, it seems remarkable in retrospect that Jenner's work was not extended until nearly 100 years later. And even then it was a fortuitous observation that led Pasteur to recognize and exploit some of the principles underlying vaccination against smallpox. In the course of studying chicken cholera Pasteur happened to inoculate some animals with an old culture of the causative agent (*Pasteurella aviseptica*), and, in contrast to his previous results, the chickens failed to become ill. When the same animals were reinoculated with a fresh culture, which was known to be virulent, they again failed to become ill. Pasteur then proceeded to demonstrate that aged cultures lose virulence but retain the capacity to induce immunity against cholera, a striking illustration of his later epigram that "chance favors only the prepared mind." Pasteur's observations were soon extended to many other infectious diseases.

A variety of procedures have been used to attenuate the virulence of pathogenic organisms for purposes of vaccination; examples are aging of cultures or passing the microorganisms through "unnatural hosts" (e.g., the agent of rabies through the rabbit). The latter effect provides a plausible explanation for Jenner's earlier success: the virus causing human smallpox was apparently so altered, by multiple passages in the cow, that it lost the capacity to produce serious disease in man; but it retained the capacity to induce immunity in man against virulent forms of the virus.

Induction of immunity to infectious diseases does not always require inoculation of the causative microorganism. Following the demonstration of a powerful **toxin** in culture filtrates of diphtheria bacilli (by Roux and Yersin in 1888), von Behring showed that injection of nonlethal doses of these bacteria-free filtrates could induce immunity to diphtheria; and Kitasato made similar observations with cultures of the tetanus bacillus. These results were then generalized by Ehrlich and Calmette, who similarly established immunity to toxins of **nonmicrobial** origin, e.g., to snake venoms and to ricin from castor beans.

The basis for these immune responses was revealed in the classic report in 1890 of von Behring and Kitasato, who demonstrated that induced immunity to tetanus was due to the appearance in the immune animal's serum of a capacity to neutralize the toxin. The neutralizing activities of immune sera were, in fact, so stable and potent that they could be transferred to animals by infusions of blood or serum from immune individuals. Moreover, Ehrlich's observations on the toxic effects of ricin on red cells in vitro established that immune sera exerted their protective action through the combination of specifically reactive components of the sera with the corresponding toxin; and it seemed reasonable to suppose that a similar combination accounted for the effects of immune sera on infectious agents. These observations served dramatically to open the way to analyses of the substances responsible for immunity and to the practical treatment of many infectious diseases by infusions of serum from immune animals.

Within the ensuing 10 years (1890 to 1900) the study of immune sera led to the discovery of most of the now known serological* reactions. In vitro mixtures of immune sera and the substances used for induction of immunity led to a variety of readily observable responses. For example:

1) **Bacteriolysis:** Cholera vibrio disintegrated when incubated with serum from animals that had previously been inoculated with this organism (Pfeiffer and Issaeff, 1894).

2) **Precipitation:** Cell-free culture filtrates of plague bacilli formed a precipitate on being added to serum from animals previously inoculated with cultures of plague bacilli (Kraus, 1897).

3) **Agglutination:** Bacterial cells suspended in serum from an animal previously injected with these bacteria underwent clumping (Gruber and Durham, 1898).

These reactions were all specific, i.e., the immune serum reacted only with the substance inoculated for induction of the immune response, or, as we shall see later, with substances of similar chemical structure.

It was further realized by about 1900 that an immune response can be elicited even by nontoxic agents. For example, when proteins of milk or egg white are injected into rabbits their sera acquire the capacity to react selectively with these proteins.

Definitions

The inoculated agents, and the substances whose appearance in serum they evoked, were designated antigens and antibodies, respectively.

An **antigen** is any substance which is capable, under appropriate conditions, of inducing the formation of antibodies and of reacting specifically in some detectable manner with the antibodies so induced. Two properties are specified for complete antigen: **immunogenicity†**, i.e., the capacity to stimulate the formation of antibodies; and the **ability to react** specifically with these antibodies. The distinction is important, because substances known as **haptens** (which are described more fully below) are not immunogenic but do react specifically with the appropriate antibodies. "Specific" means here that the antigen will react in a highly selective fashion with

---

* The specific reactions of immune sera are generally referred to as serological reactions.

† The term **immunogen** is often used in referring to the substance that stimulates the formation of the corresponding antibodies.

the corresponding antibody and not with a multitude of other antibodies evoked by other antigens.

The term **antibody** refers to substances, now known to be proteins, which are formed in response to administration of an antigen and which react specifically with that antigen and, to a variable extent, with substances of similar structure. Antibodies fall within a group of closely related, relatively large serum proteins, the immunoglobulins, whose chemical properties will be considered later (Ch. 14).

Though the definition of antibodies states that they are formed in response to antigens, there are some "normal" serum proteins, with the structural properties of the immunoglobulins, that react specifically with certain antigens even though the individuals in which they are found have not had any known exposure to those antigens. These immunoglobulins are referred to as **natural antibodies**. When present in serum they are in low titer, but they may exercise a significant role in conferring resistance to certain infections. It is not clear whether natural antibodies are formed without an immunogenic stimulus or in response to unknown exposure to naturally occurring antigens, e.g., in inapparent infections or in food.

In contrast to the restricted group of proteins that possess antibody activity, an enormous variety of macromolecules can behave as antigens—virtually all proteins, many polysaccharides, nucleoproteins, lipoproteins, numerous synthetic polypeptides, and even, under appropriate conditions, small molecules if they are suitably linked to proteins or to synthetic polypeptides.

It is important to recognize the operational nature of the foregoing definition of antigen. For example, when rabbit serum albumin (RSA) is isolated from a rabbit and then injected back into the same animal, antibodies specific for RSA are **not** formed. Yet the same preparation of RSA injected into virtually any other species of vertebrate may evoke copious amounts of anti-RSA anti-

bodies. Moreover, the formation of these antibodies depends not only on the injection of RSA into an appropriate species, but also on the other conditions employed: viz., the quantity of RSA injected and the route and frequency of injection. It is clear, therefore, that **immunogenicity is not an inherent property of a macromolecule**, as is, for example, its molecular weight or absorption spectrum; immunogenicity is operationally dependent on the biological system and conditions employed. As we shall see later, one cardinal condition is that the putative immunogen be recognized as alien (i.e., not self) by the responding organism.

Antigenic Determinants

The reaction between an antigen and the corresponding antibody in an immune serum was shown by Ehrlich to involve an actual combination of the two. We shall consider in Chapter 13 the nature of this combination, which is the fundamental reaction common to nearly all immunological phenomena. For the present, however, it is useful to distinguish between the antigen molecule as a whole and its **antigenic determinants**, i.e., those restricted portions of the antigen molecule that determine the specificity of antibody-antigen reactions. Attempts to evaluate the size and conformation of an antigenic determinant involve indirect and sophisticated procedures, and at best lead to approximations (Ch. 14, Size of active sites of antibodies). Nevertheless, considerable evidence indicates that these determinants are very limited in size as compared with a typical macromolecule, being equivalent in volume to, perhaps, 4 or 5 amino acid residues.

That antibodies can be formed against a range of noninfectious and nontoxic antigens was first emphasized by Obermayer and Pick (1903), who attached NO_2 groups to rabbit serum proteins. They found that the serum obtained after injecting these nitrated rabbit proteins into rabbits reacted with the nitrated proteins of rabbit, horse, or chicken sera, but not with the corresponding unmodified proteins. They inferred, therefore, that the antibodies formed were capable of specifically recognizing the nitro groups or some other uniquely altered structures in the nitrated proteins used as immunogens.

The suggestion that the immune response could be directed to chemically defined substituents of modified proteins was developed with vigor and ingenuity by Karl Landsteiner and his associates to explore the chemical basis of antigenic specificity. They exploited the reactivity of diazonium salts to couple a wide variety of aromatic amines to proteins, as indicated by the representative reactions shown below.

Rabbits injected with p-azobenzenearsonate-globulin form antibodies that react with this protein and with other proteins containing p-azobenzenearsonate substituents, but not with the latter proteins in unsubstituted form. This indication that antibodies react specifically with the p-azobenzenearsonate group was further substantiated by the discovery (Landsteiner and Lampl, 1920) that p-aminobenzenearsonate alone can competitively inhibit the reaction with p-azobenzenearsonate proteins, whereas other aromatic amines (with a few important exceptions) do not. Additional evidence of this and other kinds will be described later (Ch. 13) to show that the benzenearsonate combines in a highly selective manner with the antibodies formed in response to injection of the corresponding azoprotein.

Injections of benzenearsonate itself do not,

however, evoke the formation of antibodies. Substances of this type are defined as **haptens: they are not immunogenic but they react selectively with antibodies of the appropriate specificity.** In the example cited the hapten is a small molecule; but it should be noted that the definition does not say anything about molecular weight, and even some macromolecules are haptens. While the formal difference between antigen and hapten is clear, in actual practice it is not always easy to make the distinction because it may be difficult to decide whether a substance is weakly immunogenic or completely nonimmunogenic. Generally, however, small molecules (M.W. <1000) are not immunogenic, unless covalently linked to proteins in vitro or in vivo (see, for example, Ch. 17, Contact skin-sensitivity).

The diazo reaction introduces azo groups as substituents in tyrosine, tryptophan, histidine, and lysine residues (Fig. 12-1). There are many other methods for coupling haptens to proteins, and some are even more satisfactory because they provide a more stable linkage and substitute fewer kinds of amino acid residues. Some of these other methods will be referred to in subsequent chapters.

Proteins bearing substituents that are covalently linked to their amino acid side chains are usually referred to as **conjugated proteins**; and the substituents, sometimes including the amino acid residues to which they are linked (when these are known), are designated the **haptenic groups.** These distinctions are shown in Figure 12-2. While a haptenic group is thus part of an antigenic determinant, it is

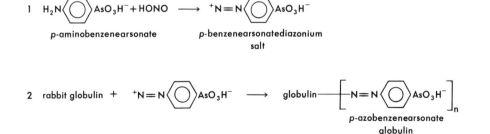

1 H_2N⟨◯⟩AsO_3H^- + HONO ⟶ $^+N{=}N$⟨◯⟩AsO_3H^-

      p-aminobenzenearsonate   *p*-benzenearsonatediazonium
                                            salt

2 rabbit globulin + $^+N{=}N$⟨◯⟩AsO_3H^- ⟶ globulin—[—$N{=}N$⟨◯⟩AsO_3H^-]$_n$

                                                       p-azobenzenearsonate
                                                       globulin

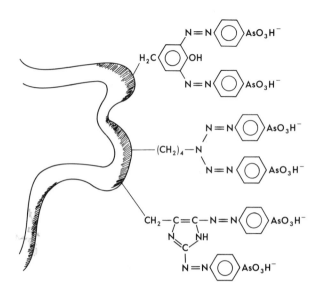

Fig. 12-1 Some azo substituents on tyrosine, lysine, and histidine residues of a representative azoprotein.

Fig. 12-2 Schematic representation of the distinctions between conjugated proteins, antigenic determinants, haptenic groups, and haptens.

A. Conjugated protein with substituents represented as solid hexagons.

B. A representative **haptenic group:** a 2,4-dinitrophenyl (DNP) group substituted in the ε-NH$_2$ group of a lysine residue. The haptenic group is outlined by solid line, whereas the **antigenic determinant** might be visualized as the area outlined by the broken line. Amino acid residues contributing to the antigenic determinant need not be the nearest covalently linked neighbors of the ε-DNP-lysine residue, as shown; they could be parts of distant segments of the polypeptide chain looped back to come into contiguity with the DNP-lysyl residue.

C. Some **haptens** that correspond to the haptenic group in **B.** (1) m-dinitrobenzene; (2) 2,4-dinitroaniline; (3) ε-DNP-lysine; (4) α, ε-bis-DNP-lysine. With respect to antibodies specific for the DNP group, haptens 1, 2, and 3 are univalent haptens (one combining group per molecule), and hapten 4 is bivalent.

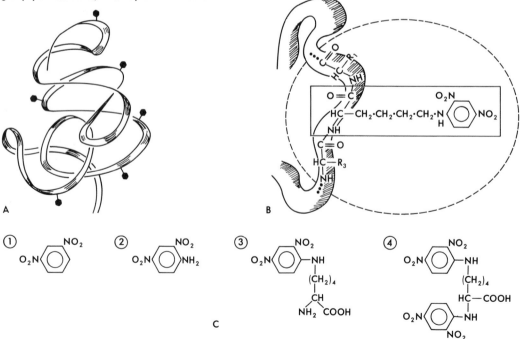

not yet clear just how much of the complete antigenic determinant it represents.

Immunology and Immunity

As indicated above, immunology—the study of the immune response—originated from interest in the protection afforded man by antibodies to virulent microbes. Within the past few decades interest in the immune response has broadened considerably—to the extent that some immunologists are no longer preoccupied with antibodies, and many others are no longer concerned with infectious diseases.

There are several reasons for these changes. First, some of the specific responses elicited by immunogens do not appear to involve antibody molecules, at least of the type found easily in serum, but involve the appearance of specifically altered lymphoid cells, e.g., lymphocytes and macrophages (see, for example, Ch. 19, Host-parasite relations, and Ch. 17, Delayed type hypersensitivity). Second, it has become increasingly clear that antibody formation and other manifestations of the immune response are general phenomena: they are capable of being directed against an almost limitless number and variety of substances; and of this vast population of immunogenic molecules microbial antigens constitute only a small minority. Hence immunity against infectious agents represents only a special facet of the immune response.

Coincident with this expanded view of the immune response, interest has grown in 1) the antibody-antigen reaction as a model for specific noncovalent interactions in general (e.g., those between viruses and their host cell membranes, or those causing cell aggregation in such phenomena as fertilization and morphogenesis; 2) antibody formation as a model for cellular differentiation; 3) the use of antibody molecules as highly specific analytical reagents for exploring the structure of complex macromolecules (e.g., blood group mucopeptides), comparing wild-

type and mutant bacterial enzymes, etc.; and 4) the pathogenetic effects of immune responses to nontoxic immunogens (e.g., allergic responses to tissue grafts, pollens, and drugs). Parallel with this evolving view of the immune response, the study of immunity —i.e., of resistance to infectious microbes— has also expanded to encompass diverse biochemical and physiological aspects of pathogenic microbes and their hosts, unrelated to the immune response.

It has thus become increasingly evident that there is much more to immunology than immunity, and much more to immunity than immunology. Nevertheless, the cardinal role of infectious diseases in stimulating awareness of the immune response has left an indelible imprint. While immunology, by its name, acknowledges this heritage, it does so at considerable cost, for its nomenclature easily becomes confusing. Thus, despite the fact that the vast majority of antigens are neither infectious nor particularly toxic, it is still conventional to refer to the stimulation of antibody formation (by injections of immunogen) as **immunization**. (**Vaccination** is a special term reserved for immunization procedures in which the antigen, in this case referred to as a **vaccine**, is a suspension of infectious agents, or some part of them, given for the purpose of establishing resistance to an infectious disease; i.e., immunity in the literal sense.)

In the chapters that immediately follow it would be logical to consider first the structure of antibody molecules, and then, perhaps, how they are made and how they function. The present view of the structure of antibodies, however, is extensively based on the use of antibody molecules themselves as analytical reagents, and so it is necessary to begin with a consideration of specific antibody-antigen reactions. For a preview of some of the properties of antibody molecules that will be emphasized, the reader should consult Table 12-1, in which antibodies are compared with enzymes, a more familiar group of protein molecules.

TABLE 12-1.   PROPERTIES OF ENZYMES AND ANTIBODIES

Property	Enzymes	Antibodies
Phylogenetic distribution	Ubiquitous; in all cells	A late evolutionary acquisition; only in vertebrates
Structure	Widely variable in chemical and physical properties but molecules of a given specificity and from any particular organism are homogeneous; many have been crystallized	A group of closely related proteins having a common multichain structure with the chains held together by —SS— bonds. Even molecules of a given specificity are heterogeneous in structure and function
Constitutive	Yes	"Natural" antibodies?
Inducible	Often	Yes
Function	Specific reversible binding of ligands* with breaking and forming covalent bonds	Specific reversible binding of ligands* without breaking or forming covalent bonds
Reaction with ligands*	Wide range of affinities; populations of enzyme molecules of a given specificity are uniform in affinity for their ligand	Wide range of affinities; but populations of antibody molecules of the same specificity are heterogeneous in affinity for their ligand
Affinity	Usually measured kinetically	Usually measured with reactants at equilibrium
Number of specific ligand-binding sites per molecule	Different in different enzymes	2 per molecule for the most prevalent antibodies (M.W. ⌣ 160,000)
Inducers	Primarily small molecules	Macromolecules, especially proteins and conjugated proteins

Ligand = substrate or coenzyme in case of enzymes, and antigen or hapten in case of antibodies.

SELECTED REFERENCES

Books and Review Articles

ARRHENIUS, S. *Immunochemistry.* Macmillan, New York, 1907.

The Collected Papers of Paul Ehrlich, vol. II (F. Himmelweit, ed.) Pergamon Press, New York, 1957.

TOPLEY, W. W. C., and WILSON, G. S. *The Principles of Bacteriology and Immunity,* 2nd ed. Wood, Baltimore, 1936.

ZINSSER, H., ENDERS, J. F., and FOTHERGILL, L. D. *Immunity: Principles and Applications in Medicine and Public Health,* 5th ed. Macmillan, New York, 1939.

13 ANTIBODY-ANTIGEN REACTIONS

The combination of antibody with antigen constitutes the fundamental molecular process that underlies most immunological phenomena. Our understanding of this reaction has arisen largely from the use of model systems in which simple haptens, with well delineated structures, have been used as substitutes for antigens. This expedient has been resorted to because most antigens in wide use are proteins; and even when the covalent structure of a protein is completely established, as has now been accomplished in several instances, the antigenic structure is still obscure with respect to the identity and conformation of the functional groups and even the number and variety of these groups per molecule. In the following pages we shall, therefore, consider first specific antibody reactions with simple haptens, and subsequently the more complicated reactions with macromolecular antigens. Since the distinction between haptens and antigens, based on immunogenicity, is largely irrelevant for the present discussion (Ch. 12, Definitions), we shall frequently use the generic term **ligand** to include both groups.

REACTIONS WITH SIMPLE HAPTENS

Two methods are frequently used to obtain antibodies specific for simple haptens. One involves immunization with bacterial cells whose walls or capsular polysaccharides contain well defined immunogenic groups, e.g., the cellobiuronic acid residues of type 3 pneumococcus capsule (Fig. 13-17); in some instances immunization even with a purified polysaccharide itself may be effective. The second method involves the injection of conjugated proteins with defined immunogenic substituents, e.g., the 2,4-dinitrophenyl (DNP) groups of DNP-proteins (Ch. 12, Fig. 12-2). In both cases simple haptens, corresponding to the haptenic groups of the immunogens, are available. Moreover, it is relatively easy to isolate in purified form those antibodies that react selectively with the haptenic groups (Appendix, this chapter). It thus becomes possible to examine in detail the reactions by which simple ligands and antibody molecules combine to form specific antibody-ligand complexes.

Valence and Affinity of Antibodies

If we consider ligands with one combining group per molecule, **univalent ligands** (L), the reactions we are interested in can be represented as:

$$Ab + L \underset{k'_1}{\overset{k_1}{\rightleftharpoons}} AbL,$$

$$AbL + L \underset{k'_2}{\overset{k_2}{\rightleftharpoons}} AbL_2, \qquad (1)$$

$$\cdots$$

$$AbL_{n-1} + L \underset{k'_n}{\overset{k_n}{\rightleftharpoons}} AbL_n,$$

where n represents the number of ligand-binding sites per antibody (Ab) molecule, or **antibody valence**, and each rate constant (k) refers to the reaction whereby a site on the antibody becomes reversibly occupied by a ligand molecule. If we assume that the binding sites on Ab act independently, that the forward rate constants are the same ($k_1 = k_2 \ldots = k_n$), and that the backward rate constants are also the same ($k'_1 = k'_2 \ldots = k'_n$), the **intrinsic binding reaction** can be represented as:

$$S + L \underset{k'}{\overset{k}{\rightleftharpoons}} SL, \qquad (2)$$

where S is a specific binding site on antibody, and k and k' are the rate constants for association and dissociation, respectively. If it were possible to follow the concentrations of the reactants and products as a function of time, one could determine the rate constants k and k' and the equilibrium (association) constant K, which is their ratio k/k'. The rates are very rapid, however, and difficult to measure. It is far easier to determine the **intrinsic association constant** (K), from the concentrations of all participants when the reaction has gone to equilibrium. Thus,

$$K = \frac{k}{k'} = \frac{[SL]}{[S][L]}, \tag{3}$$

the terms in brackets referring to concentrations, at equilibrium, of the occupied antibody sites (SL), vacant antibody sites (S), and free (unbound) ligand molecules (L).

Equilibrium Dialysis

The most general method for acquiring the information necessary to measure an association constant is equilibrium dialysis, the principles of which are shown in Figure 13-1.* A solution containing antibody molecules specific for a simple haptenic group, such as 2,4-dinitrophenyl, is placed in a compartment (A), and this is separated by a membrane from another compartment (B), which contains a solution of an appropriate ligand (e.g., dinitroaniline; Ch. 12, Fig. 12-2). The membranes used are impermeable to

---

* Hapten inhibition of precipitation, described later in this chapter, is widely used to obtain relative values of association constants for a series of homologous haptens, in relation to a reference hapten and a reference antigen. Other methods are also useful with special systems, e.g. ultracentrifugation, fluorescence quenching (see below).

Fig. 13-1 Equilibrium dialysis. **A.** Compartments A and B are separated by a membrane (m), which is permeable to small molecules but not to large ones: hence small, univalent haptens (shaded area) can diffuse freely between the compartments, but antibody molecules (large dots) cannot. At equilibrium the greater concentration of dialyzable hapten in A is due to antibody binding. **B.** Change in hapten concentration with time; equilibrium is reached in about 4 hours in the diagram. In practice the time required for equilibration varies with several parameters, e.g., temperature, volumes of the compartments, and surface area of the membrane. Δ is the concentration of antibody-bound ligand in compartment A.

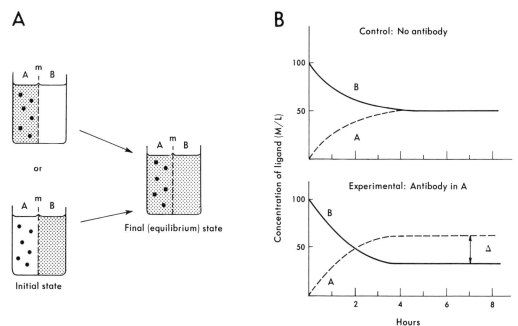

antibodies, but freely permeable to small molecules (M.W. <1000). If the concentration of ligand were measured periodically it would be observed to decline in B and to rise in A until equilibrium was reached; thereafter the concentrations in the two compartments would remain unchanged. If compartment A had simply contained the solvent, or a protein which was incapable of binding dinitroaniline, the concentration of the ligand would ultimately become the same in both compartments. On the other hand, we specified that compartment A contained antibody molecules capable of combining with dinitroaniline, and so the final (equilibrium) concentration of the ligand in A will exceed its concentration in B.* The difference represents ligand molecules bound to antibody molecules.

It is important to note that the final concentration of ligand in either compartment at equilibrium is independent of whether the antibody and ligand are initially placed in the same or in separate compartments. Hence the amount of bound ligand depends not on the initial but on the final (equilibrium) concentration of unbound, or free, ligand. And since the rate of reaction is almost instantaneous (at the concentrations generally used; see Reaction rates, below) **the com-**

---

* Even without specific binding by antibody, charged ligands could be unevenly distributed across the membrane at equilibrium because of the net charge on the protein. This inequality, or Donnan effect, is avoided by carrying out the dialysis in the presence of a relatively high salt concentration, e.g., 0.15 M sodium chloride. Donnan effects are irrelevant with uncharged ligands.

bination of antibody and univalent ligand to form a specific complex must be fully and readily reversible.

Equation (3) may be rewritten as:

$$K = \frac{r}{(n-r)c}, \qquad (4)$$

or, more conveniently, as:

$$\frac{r}{c} = Kn - Kr, \qquad (5)$$

where, at equilibrium, r represents the number of ligand molecules bound per antibody molecule at c free concentration of ligand, and n is the maximum number of ligand molecules that can be bound per antibody molecule (i.e., the antibody valence). By examining a series of dialysis chambers at equilibrium, each of which contains the same amount of antibody but a different total amount of ligand, a set of values for r and c is obtained.

Two features of equation (5) are notable. 1) A plot of r/c vs. r should give a straight line of slope $-K$, provided the original assumption was correct that all forward and all backward rate constants in equation (1) were identical; hence linearity or nonlinearity of this plot provides information with respect to the homogeneity of association constants. 2) When the concentration of unbound ligand (c), becomes very large, r approaches n; i.e., the number of ligand molecules bound per antibody molecule approaches the number of ligand-binding sites, or antibody valence.

Antibody Valence. Representative data are shown in Figure 13-2 for the binding of univalent ligands by antibodies of the most

Fig. 13-2 Specific binding of ligands by some antibodies and an enzyme, plotted according to equation (5). For all antibody-ligand systems (**A** to **D**) the extrapolation indicates two ligand-binding sites per antibody molecule of M.W. 160,000; and nonlinearity indicates heterogeneity with respect to affinity. For the systems in **B** and **C** affinity is higher at 7.1° than at 25°. For the system in **D** two purified antibody preparations of the same specificity differ about 30-fold in affinity for the homologous hapten, and even larger variations occur (Table 13-1 and Ch. 15, Variations in affinity with time of immunization). In contrast to the antibodies, muscle phosphorylase a has four ligand-binding sites per molecule (M.W. 495,000), and is uniform in affinity (**E**).

(Data based on: (**A**) H. N. Eisen and F. Karush, J. Am. Chem. Soc. 71:363; 1949; (**B** and **C**) F. Karush, J. Am. Chem. Soc. 78:5519, 1956, and 79:3380, 1957); (**D**) H. N. Eisen and G. Siskind, Biochemistry 3:996, 1964; (**E**) N. B. Madsen and C. F. Cori, J. Biol. Chem. 224:899, 1957.)

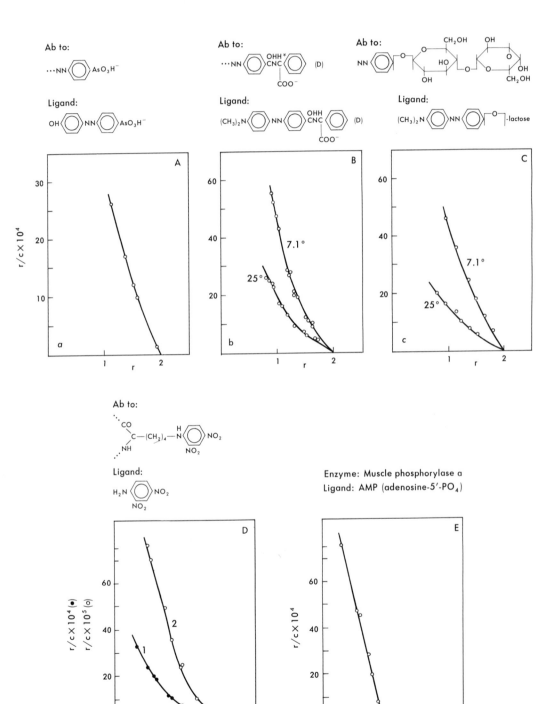

Fig. 13-2 *(See legend on facing page)*

common type (M.W. ca. 160,000; see Ch. 14, γG-immunoglobulins). The limiting value for r is 2 as c approaches infinity. That is, there are two binding sites per antibody molecule. Bivalence of antibodies has been repeatedly observed with many systems in which the ligands are small dialyzable molecules. Even in the more complex reactions with macromolecular antigens the same stoichiometry has been observed; at saturation two antigen molecules are bound by one antibody molecule (Fig. 13-11).

Heterogeneity with Respect to Affinity. As is shown in Figure 13-2, the relation between r/c and r is **not** linear. This result is typical of antibody-ligand systems. According to the assumptions made above, nonlinearity means that the association constants are not uniform. Moreover, bivalent antibody molecules can be cleaved by proteolytic enzymes into univalent fragments (Ch. 14), and these exhibit similar nonlinearity in the reaction with their ligands. Hence the nonuniformity of association constants is not due to the modification of a vacant binding site by occupancy of the other site on the same antibody molecule. As we shall see later there are several independent lines of evidence that antibody molecules of any particular specificity are indeed variable with respect to their affinity for the corresponding ligand. This heterogeneity stands in contrast to the uniformity of enzyme molecules of a given specificity, with respect to affinity for ligand (substrate or coenzyme). For example, in Figure 13-2 we see that the plot of r/c vs. r is linear for the binding of adenosine-5'PO$_4$ (AMP) by muscle phosphorylase a.

Because of the nonuniformity of antibody-ligand association constants it is convenient to define for each system an **average** constant: that K which obtains when 1/2 the antibody sites are occupied. Thus, substitution of $r = n/2$ in equation (5) leads to

$$K_0 = \frac{1}{c}. \qquad (6)$$

K_0 is designated the **average intrinsic associa-**

tion constant; it is also frequently referred to as **average affinity** or as **affinity.** The higher the affinity of a given population of antibody molecules for their ligand, the lower the concentration of free ligand need be for their binding sites to become occupied. (The analogy to the equilibrium constant for ionization reactions should be evident; by convention, however, the ionization constant is expressed as the dissociation constant [reciprocal of the association constant], which for the reaction $HA \rightleftharpoons H^+ + A^-$ is the H^+ concentration at which 1/2 of total A is ionized.)

The heterogeneity of antibodies with respect to affinity is conveniently evaluated by the Sips distribution function, which is similar to the normal distribution function commonly used in statistics. The Sips function leads to the explicit statement:

$$\frac{r}{n} = \frac{(Kc)^a}{1 + (Kc)^a}, \qquad (7)$$

or,

$$\log \frac{r}{n-r} = a \log K + a \log c, \qquad (8)$$

where r, n, K, and c have the same meanings as before, and a is an index of the dispersion of equilibrium constants about the average constant, K_0. The term a is thus similar to the standard deviation in the more familiar normal distribution.

As is shown in Figure 13-3, a plot of $\log r/n-r$ vs. $\log c$ is indeed a straight line, and a, the index of heterogeneity with respect to affinity, is obtained as its slope. Values for a range in theory from 1 to 0. When $a = 1.0$, all sites are identical with respect to K, and equation (7) is then equivalent to equations (4) and (5); the smaller the a value, the greater the degree of heterogeneity. In Figure 13-3 we see that a representative antibody-ligand reaction is typically heterogeneous with respect to association constant ($a < 1.0$), whereas an enzyme-ligand reaction is homogeneous ($a = 1.0$). A heterogeneity index (a) of 0.5, which is commonly observed, means that 20% of the sites in the sample of antibody molecules have

Fig. 13-3 Contrast between the uniformity of an enzyme and the heterogeneity of an antibody with respect to affinity for their respective ligands. Antibody: anti-2,4-dinitrophenyl binding 2,-4-dinitroaniline. Enzyme: muscle phosphorylase a binding adenosine-5′-PO$_4$. Data are plotted according to equation (8); the slope, corresponding to the heterogeneity index (a) is 0.5 for the antibody (heterogeneous) and 1.0 for the enzyme (homogeneous). (Data for the phosphorylase-AMP system from N. B. Madsen and C. F. Cori. J. Biol. Chem. 224:899, 1957.)

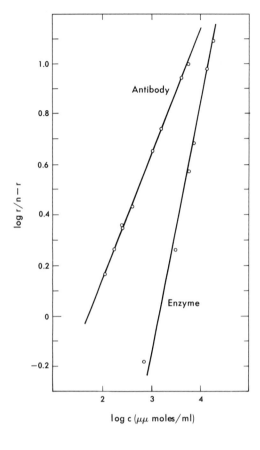

K values that fall outside the range between K$_0$/40 and 40 K$_0$.

Some average association constants are shown in Table 13-1. It should not be concluded, however, that each antibody-ligand system is characterized by a fixed average association constant: Table 13-1 is intended only to convey a sense of the range of values that have been observed. With different conditions of immunization substantial differences are observed among antibody molecules of a given specificity (Ch. 15). As perhaps an extreme example, it may be noted that different populations of antibodies specific for the dinitrophenyl (DNP) group differ as

TABLE 13-1. AVERAGE ASSOCIATION CONSTANTS FOR SOME REPRESENTATIVE ANTIBODY-LIGAND INTERACTIONS

Antibody specific for	Ligand	Average association constants (K$_0$) in liters mole^{-1}
p-Azobenzenearsonate	OH⟨○⟩NN⟨○⟩AsO$_3$H$^-$	3.5×10^5
p-Azobenzoate	I⟨○⟩COO$^-$	3.8×10^4
2,4-Dinitrophenyl-lysyl	$^-$OOC(NH$_2$)CH—(CH$_2$)$_4$NH⟨○⟩—NO$_2$ (NO$_2$)	1×10^4 to 1×10^9
p-Azophenyl-β-lactoside	(CH$_3$)$_2$N⟨○⟩NN⟨○⟩—O-lactose	1.6×10^5
Bovine serum albumin	Bovine serum albumin	8×10^3
Ovalbumin	Ovalbumin	1.2×10^4
Ribonuclease	Ribonuclease	4×10^3
Beef insulin	Beef insulin	1×10^9
Mono-DNP-ribonuclease	Mono-DNP-ribonuclease	1×10^6

Based on references given in F. Karush, Advances Immunol. 2:1 (1962); S. J. Singer, in The Proteins, vol. 3, p. 269, 1965; H. N. Eisen and J. H. Pearce, Ann. Rev. Microbiol. 16:101 (1962).

much as 10,000-fold in affinity for ε-DNP-lysine.

Thus the term antibody, which is used in the singular, is really a collective noun and refers to a population or set of molecules, the set being defined by the capacity, common to all its members, to bind a given functional group. With simple ligands it is relatively easy to specify the functional group and thereby the corresponding set of antibody molecules. For example, the set that binds benzoic acid may be unambiguously designated as "antibenzoate antibody;" similarly, the antibodies that bind lactose constitute the "antilactose antibody." With protein antigens, however, the functional groups (antigenic determinants) cannot be identified experimentally; but it is reasonable to assume that each of these groups also specifies a set of heterogeneous antibody molecules.

Reaction Rates. Antibodies and their ligands combine so rapidly the rate of association cannot be measured by conventional methods, unless the reactants are at very low concentrations (e.g. 10^{-8} to 10^{-11} M). At these levels some biologically active antigens, such as viruses, can be measured, but because of the complexity of their determinant groups it is difficult to interpret the kinetic data in molecular terms. In contrast, simple, univalent haptens cannot be readily measured in extremely dilute solutions, and at higher concentrations it has been possible to measure their rate of combination with antibody only with highly sophisticated instruments.

The forward (association) reaction has turned out to be one of the fastest biochemical reactions known: its bimolecular rate constant is about 10^8 liters mole^{-1} sec^{-1}. This value, which is close to the theoretical limit of 10^9 liters mole^{-1} sec^{-1} for diffusion-limited reactions, is thus determined essentially by the frequency with which antibody molecules and ligand molecules collide. Two different antibody-ligand pairs, whose equilibrium constants differed about 100-fold, have surprisingly exhibited about the same forward rate constant. Presumably therefore the system with the higher affinity has a 100-fold lower dissociation rate constant than the low affinity system. If these initial observations should turn out to be generally valid, then differences in the

stabilities of various antibody-ligand complexes will reflect differences in their dissociation rate constants, rather than differences in their rates of combination.

Effects of Temperature, pH, and Ionic Strength

Antibodies are unusually stable proteins. While their reactions with ligands are usually carried out at 4 to 40° in dilute salt solutions at neutral pH (7 to 8), they can tolerate, at least for short periods, extremes of pH (1 to 11) and temperatures as high as 70 or 80°. Nevertheless, antibody-ligand interactions are influenced by variations in pH, temperature, and ionic strength, in some systems to a pronounced degree. In fact, the dependence of association constants on these parameters provides information as to the nature of the forces that stabilize the antibody-ligand complex, and indirectly furnishes clues as to the chemical nature of the specific binding sites. For example, a system in which the equilibrium constant varies markedly with change in pH from 6 to 8 may be inferred to have a critical ionizable group (of antibody or ligand) whose pK_a lies within this pH region.

The binding of ionized ligands generally decreases as pH departs from neutrality and also as the ionic strength is raised to high levels (as in 1 M sodium chloride). Both effects suggest that the specific binding involves ionic interactions between oppositely charged groups of these ligands and the antibody's active site.

Temperature variations have, broadly speaking, two kinds of effects. With some systems **increasing** temperature **decreases** the association constant; i.e., binding is exothermal. In others, association constants are unaltered between 4 and 40°. But no antibody–simple ligand systems have displayed increasing affinity with increasing temperature. Nevertheless, the general practice of incubating mixtures of antisera and antigens at 37° is often helpful in speeding up some of the secondary reactions of antibody-antigen complexes, e.g., precipitation, agglutination, and complement fixation (see below and also Ch. 16).

Thermodynamics. The formation of the antibody-ligand complex results in a change in free energy, ΔF, which is exponentially related to the average association constant by the equation

$$\Delta F = -RT \ln K_0, \qquad (9)$$

where R is the gas constant (1.987 cal/mole-deg), T the absolute temperature, and $\ln K_0$ the natural logarithm of the average intrinsic association constant. $\Delta F°$, the standard free energy change, is the gain or loss of free energy in calories, as 1 mole of antibody sites and 1 mole of free ligand combine to form 1 mole of bound ligand; when the concentrations of antibody, ligand, and complexes are expressed in moles per liter, ΔF in equation (9) is $\Delta F°$.

The observed $\Delta F°$ values for various antibody-hapten pairs range from about -6000 to $-11,000$ calories (per mole hapten bound); these values correspond to association constants of 1×10^5 liters mole^{-1} and 1×10^9 liters mole^{-1}, respectively, at 30° (Table 13-1).

In evaluating the forces involved in the specific binding of a ligand by antibody it is often useful to determine whether the free energy change comes about from a change in heat content (enthalpy) or in the entropy of the system. This determination is based on the equation

$$\Delta F° = \Delta H° - T\Delta S°, \qquad (10)$$

where $\Delta H°$ refers to the change in enthalpy, measured in calories; T is absolute temperature; and $\Delta S°$ is the entropy change. $\Delta H°$ is determined experimentally by measuring the average intrinsic association constant (K_0) at two or more temperatures:

$$\Delta H° = \frac{R \ln \dfrac{K_2}{K_1}}{\dfrac{1}{T_1} - \dfrac{1}{T_2}}, \qquad (11)$$

where K_1 and K_2 are average association constants (K_0) at temperatures T_1 and T_2. The observed $\Delta H°$ values for the formation of diverse antibody-ligand complexes cover a wide range—from 0 (no change in affinity with temperature), in which case the driving force for complex formation is the $T\Delta S$ term of equation (10), to $-20,000$ calories per mole ligand bound, in which case the decrease in heat content drives the reaction. The formation of apolar or hydrophobic bonds is essentially athermal ($\Delta H° \cong 0$), whereas the formation of hydrogen bonds is exothermal ($\Delta H° \cong -1000$ calories per hydrogen bond).

Specificity

Immune reactions are justifiably reputed to be highly specific. By specific we mean that a given population of antibody molecules may bind one ligand strongly but bind weakly a second ligand of very similar structure. In considering the basis for the specificity of antibody reactions one is really considering the forces that determine the stability of antibody-ligand complexes. Considerable insight into this question has been obtained by comparing the extent to which structurally related ligands are bound by the corresponding antibodies.

The earliest studies of this kind, by Landsteiner, were classics—elegant in their simplicity and extremely illuminating. These experiments took advantage of the fact that antisera to a conjugated protein, such as sulfanilate-azoglobulin, form specific, insoluble complexes (precipitates) with other proteins conjugated with the same azo substituent, e.g., sulfanilate-azoalbumin, but not with the albumin itself. Thus the reaction is specific for the sulfanilate azo group. By comparing the precipitating effectiveness of various conjugates, each substituted with a different azo group, the antibody's reactivity with diverse groups could be evaluated. Some representative results are shown in Figures 13-4 and 13-5.

Some more recent examples of the dependence of affinity on the structure of ligands are given in Figures 13-6 and 13-7. From these and many other examples the generalizations discussed below have been drawn.

1) The ligands bound most strongly by a given set of antibody molecules are those which most closely simulate the structure of the determinant groups of the immunogen. This generalization is part of the broader

	ortho	meta	para
$R=SO_3^-$	+±	++	±
$R=AsO_3H^-$	0	+	0
$R=COO^-$	0	±	0

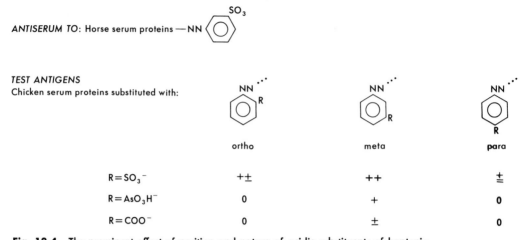

Fig. 13-4 The prominent effect of position and nature of acidic substituents of haptenic groups on the reaction between antibodies to *m*-azobenzenesulfonate and various test antigens. R in the test antigen refers to the acidic substituents SO_3^-, AsO_3H^-, and COO^-. The homologous reaction is most intense (largest amount of precipitation), and is shown in heavy type. (From K. Landsteiner and J. van der Scheer. J. Exp. Med. 63:325, 1936.)

rule that antibodies react more effectively with the antigen that stimulated their formation than with other antigens; within this context the former is generally designated **homologous antigen**, and the latter **heterologous antigens**. Similarly, the available haptens that resemble most closely the haptenic groups of the immunogen are the **homologous haptens** (Ch. 12, Fig. 12-2).

2) Those structural elements of the determinant group that project distally from the central mass of the immunizing antigen seem to play a dominant role in determining the antibody's specificity. Thus, as in the examples shown in Figures 13-6 and 13-7, antibodies to *p*-azophenyl-β-lactoside and to 2,4-dinitrophenyl bind the **terminal residues** almost as well as the larger haptenic structures of which

Fig. 13-5 The effect of nature and position of uncharged substituents of haptenic groups on the reactions between antibodies to the *p*-azotoluidine group and various test antigens. The homologous reaction is shown in heavy type. (From K. Landsteiner and J. van der Scheer. J. Exp. Med. 45:1045, 1927.)

	ortho	meta	para
$R=CH_3$	+±	+±	++
$R=Cl$	+	+±	++
$R=NO_2$	±	+	+±

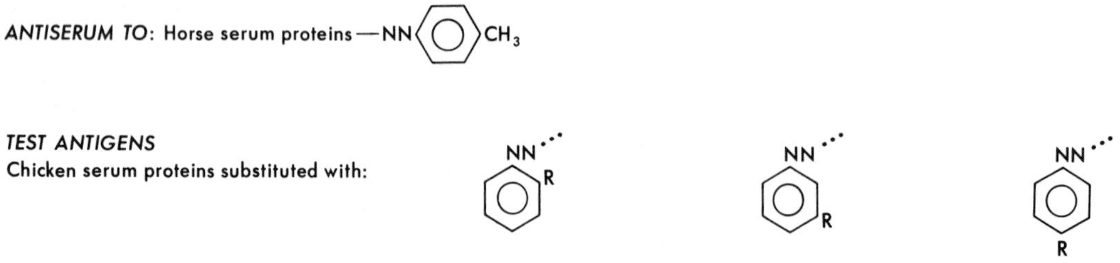

HAPTENIC GROUP OF IMMUNOGEN	TEST HAPTEN	AVERAGE AFFINITY K_0, liters mole^{-1} $\times 10^4$

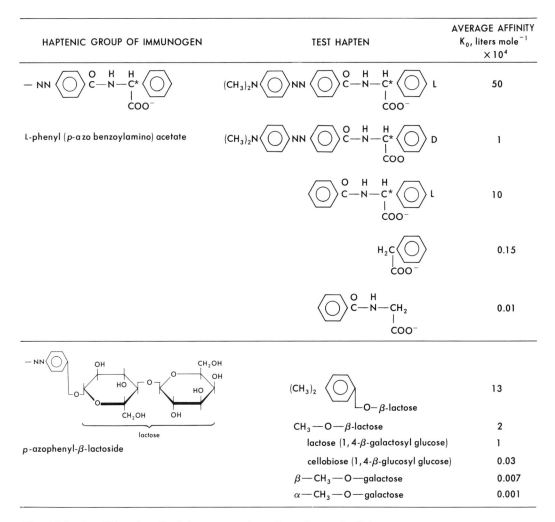

Fig. 13-6 Specificity of antibody-hapten reactions: Dependence of affinity on structure of the hapten. (From F. Karush. J. Am. Chem. Soc. 78:5519, 1956, and 79:3380, 1957.)

these residues constitute the end groups: for example, compare lactose with a phenyl-β-lactoside, and dinitroaniline with ε-DNP-lysine. A particularly striking example of this principle is provided by antibodies to the human blood group substances: specificity is dictated by the terminal hexose residues of the polysaccharide branches of these large mucopeptides—anti-A antibody is specific for terminal N-acetylgalactosamine residues, and anti-B is specific for terminal galactose residues (Ch. 18, ABO system).

However, nonterminal residues also con-

tribute to specific binding, sometimes decisively. For example, in the cell wall lipopolysaccharide that determines the serological specificity of various groups of salmonella the sugars that react specifically with antibodies to group E organisms are nonterminal mannosyl-galactose residues (Fig. 13-19).

3) The **resolving powers** of antibodies are, in general, comparable to those of enzymes. Some antibodies readily distinguish between two molecules that differ only in the spatial orientation of hydrogen and hydroxyl about one carbon, e.g., between glucose and galac-

HAPTENIC GROUP OF IMMUNOGEN	TEST HAPTEN	AVERAGE AFFINITY K_0, liters mole^{-1} $\times 10^5$
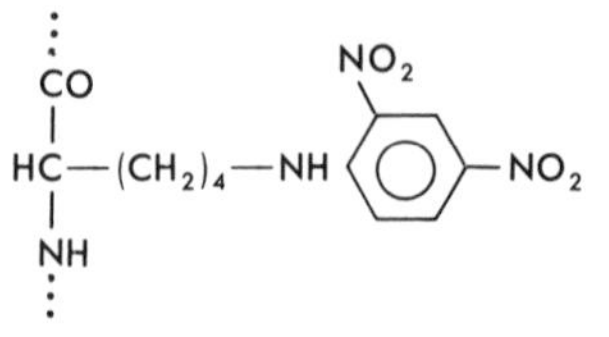 2,4-dinitrophenyl-L-lysyl group	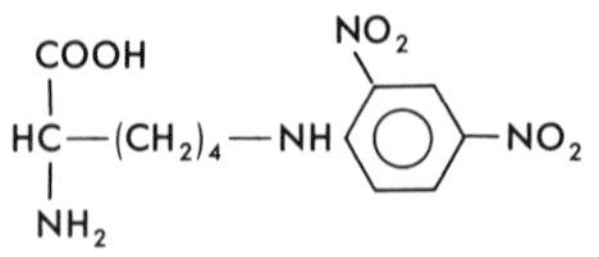 ϵ DNP-L-lysine	200
	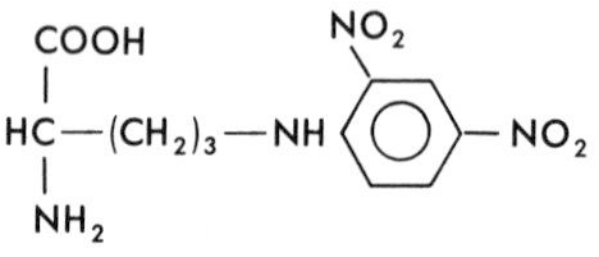 δ-DNP L-ornithine	80
	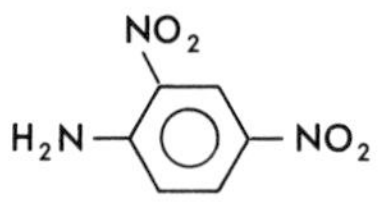 2,4-dinitroaniline	20
	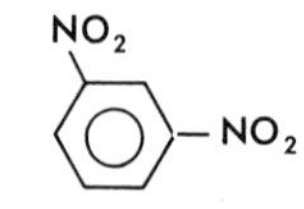 m-dinitrobenzene	8
	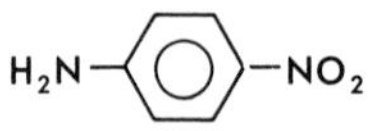 p-mononitroaniline	0.5

Fig. 13-7 Specificity of antibody-hapten reactions: Dependence of affinity on structure of the hapten. The haptens that approximate more closely the haptenic group of the immunogen are bound more strongly. (From H. N. Eisen and G. W. Siskind. Biochemistry 3:996, 1964.)

tose. Optical enantiomorphs, such as D- and L-tartrate, are also readily distinguished (see also Fig. 13-6).

4) The specific binding of a ligand by an antibody molecule may be looked upon as a competitive **partition** of ligand between water and antibody-binding sites; the latter are relatively hydrophobic owing to apolar residues in amino acid side chains. Hence **ligands that are sparingly soluble in water,** such as those containing picryl and dinitrophenyl groups, tend to form **stable complexes** with antibody, whereas ligands that are highly soluble in water, such as sugars and organic ions (e.g., benzoate), tend to form more dissociable complexes.

From a vast number of observations on the interactions between antibodies and their ligands there has emerged a consistent view of the processes by which specific immune complexes are formed. According to this view the strength of the over-all bond between an antibody molecule and a ligand molecule reflects the sum of many constituent interactions; in each interaction atomic groups of the ligand form **noncovalent bonds** with side chains of amino acid residues that constitute the binding site of antibody. The greater the number of constituent interactions, and the greater their individual strength, the more stable is the antibody-ligand complex. It is easy to visualize intuitively that the number of bonds formed is greater the more closely the three-dimensional surface of the ligand matches, in a complementary sense, the three-dimensional contour of the antibody site. It should be realized, however, that **complementarity has chemical as well as spatial features.** Thus, even with ideal geometrical interdigitation of the reactants, binding is favored if, for example, an anionic group of the ligand is contiguous to a cationic group of the antibody, or a hydrogen-bond acceptor of the ligand is adjacent to a hydrogen-bond donor of the antibody.

Virtually all the known noncovalent bonds appear to participate in various antibody-ligand interactions: e.g., ionic bonds, hydrogen bonds, apolar (hydrophobic) bonds, charge-transfer bonds (Effects of temperature, pH, and ionic strength). The formation of these bonds is usually exquisitely dependent on distance between the interacting groups; some bond strengths are inversely proportional to distance to the sixth or seventh power. Hence the stability of immune complexes is critically dependent on the closeness of approach of ligand groups to antibody groups. Unfavorably situated bulky substituents on ligands hinder close approach and thereby diminish the strength of binding (**steric hindrance**; for example, see Fig. 13-16).

The binding sites of antibody molecules are, by definition, those areas that make contact with specifically bound ligand molecules. Since these sites must be accessible to determinant groups of macromolecules, including those on cell surfaces, these sites must exist on the surface of antibody molecules, probably as invaginations or as shallow depressions.

Specificity and Affinity

As noted above, the specificity of an antibody population refers to its capacity to discriminate between ligands of similar structure by combining with them to detectably different extents: the greater the difference in affinity for two closely related structures, the more specific the antibody. Long before affinity was measurable this viewpoint was recognized by Landsteiner, who defined specificity as "the disproportional action of a number of related agents on a variety of related substrates;" by "related agents" he meant antibodies, and by "related substrates" he meant haptens and antigens.

Failure to distinguish between specificity and affinity has led to confusion. For example, antiserum to the *m*-azobenzenesulfonate group distinguishes sharply among *p*-, *o*-, and *m*-azobenzenesulfonates, but antiserum to *p*-azotoluidine does not differentiate methyl, chloro, or nitro groups in the para position (Figs. 13-4 and 13-5). Thus the antisulfonate serum is highly specific and antitoluidine is much less specific. From observations of this kind it has been incorrectly inferred that in general antibodies have higher affinity for organic ions than for uncharged groups. As was seen in Table 13-1, however, there is no simple correlation between a ligand's charge and the strength with which it is bound: uncharged sugars and organic anions are bound about equally well, but both are bound much less strongly than the uncharged and relatively hydrophobic dinitrophenyl group.

Antibodies with relatively high affinity for the homologous ligand often give easily detectable reactions with related ligands, for which their affinity may be very much lower. However, antibodies whose affinity for the homologous ligand is so low as just to permit a detectable reaction are not likely to react perceptibly with any other ligand. Thus, **high-affinity antibodies tend to have broader specificity than low-affinity antibodies.** Since antibodies to apolar groups tend to have high affinity (see item 4 under Specificity, above) they generally appear to be less specific than antibodies to polar groups, such as organic anions and sugars (cf. Figs. 13-4 and 13-5).

REACTIONS WITH SOLUBLE MACROMOLECULES

Up to this point we have been considering the reaction by which antibodies and small univalent ligands combine to form soluble complexes. Frequently, however, when an antigen is added to the corresponding antiserum the complexes that form become insoluble and precipitate from solution. This is called the **precipitin reaction**, because for several decades after it was described the antibodies that form precipitates were regarded as members of a unique class, called "precipitins." It is now clear, however, that most antibodies, though not all, are capable of precipitating with their antigens (see Nonprecipitating antibodies, Blocking antibodies, and The unitarian hypothesis, this chapter).

Precipitin Reaction in Liquid Media

From the time of its discovery in 1897 the precipitin reaction was used extensively as a qualitative or semiquantitative assay for estimating antibody titers in sera. But though a number of attempts were made to measure precipitates quantitatively, they were of limited value until Heidelberger and Avery discovered, in 1923, that an important antigen of the pneumococcus, the capsule, was a polysaccharide. This discovery had several important consequences. 1) It established that some macromolecules besides proteins could be immunogenic. 2) The structural basis for the specificity of natural antigens could be explored because the antigenic determinants of polysaccharides, unlike those of proteins, are not markedly influenced by the macromolecule's conformation; hence small oligosaccharides, isolated from polysaccharides, could be used as simple haptens. 3) The antibodies precipitated from serum could be identified as proteins. And, finally, 4) quantitative procedures for measuring proteins in general could be applied to the analysis of the precipitin reaction.

The Quantitative Precipitin Reaction

For purposes of illustration consider an antiserum prepared by immunizing a rabbit with type 3 pneumococcus, the capsule of which is made up of a well characterized polysaccharide (Fig. 13-17). When the purified polysaccharide is added to the antiserum a precipitate appears, increases in amount with time, and becomes maximal after some days. (The reaction can easily be shown to be specific: if the polysaccharide were added to serum obtained before immunization, or to serum from rabbits immunized with other antigens, no precipitate would appear.) After thorough washing of the precipitate, analysis reveals that it contains only protein and the type 3 polysaccharide. And when the precipitated protein is recovered, free of polysaccharide (Appendix, this chapter), it can be shown to be precipitated completely and specifically by the type 3 polysaccharide. Thus, we may consider that all the precipitated protein is antibody, which can be measured with precision by a variety of quantitative procedures, e.g., by Kjeldahl analysis for nitrogen. (Trace amounts of some other proteins, called complement, are also precipitated; these are considered in Chapter 16.)

As is shown in Figure 13-8 and in Table 13-2, the amount of protein precipitated in a series of tubes, each with the same volume of antiserum, increases with the amount of polysaccharide added up to a maximum, beyond which larger amounts of antigen lead to progressively less precipitation. The precipitation of a **maximum** amount of antibody by an **optimal** amount of antigen may appear inconsistent with the binding reaction discussed earlier, in which the number of antibody sites occupied by ligand increased to saturation as increasing amounts of ligand were added, without going through a maximum. This apparent discrepancy is due to special features of precipitation, which are discussed below, under Lattice theory.

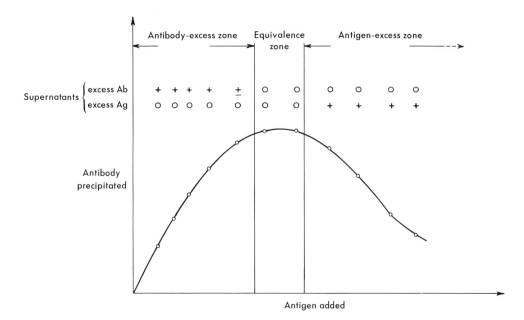

Fig. 13-8 Precipitin curve for a monospecific system: One antigen and the corresponding antibodies.

When the antigen used for the precipitin reaction is a protein instead of a polysaccharide, the measurement of precipitated antibody must be modified (Table 13-3). In this case the amount of antibody is determined by deducting precipitated antigen protein from the total amount of precipitated protein. This calculation requires, of course, that one know the antigen content of the precipitate. It turns out, fortunately, that in certain regions of the precipitin curve (marked antibody-excess and equivalence zones in Figure

TABLE 13-2. PRECIPITIN REACTION WITH A POLYSACCHARIDE AS ANTIGEN

Tube no.	S 3 added (mg)	Total protein (or antibody) precipitated (mg)	Supernatant test
1	0.02	1.82	Excess Ab
2	0.06	4.79	Excess Ab
3	0.08	5.41	Excess Ab
4	0.10	5.79	Excess Ab
5	0.15	6.13	No Ab, no S 3
6	0.20	6.23	Excess S 3
7	0.50	5.87	Excess S 3
8	1.00	3.76	Excess S 3
9	2.00	2.10	Excess S 3

The antigen (S 3) is purified capsular polysaccharide of type 3 pneumococcus. Each tube contained 0.7 ml of antiserum obtained by injecting rabbits repeatedly with formalin-killed, encapsulated type 3 pneumococci. The supernatant of tube 6, which had the maximum amount of precipitated antibody, contained a slight excess of antigen; this is often observed and reflects the presence of some nonprecipitable or poorly precipitable antibody (see text). Based on M. Heidelberger and F. E. Kendall. J. Exp. Med. 65:647 (1937).

TABLE 13-3. PRECIPITIN REACTION WITH A PROTEIN AS ANTIGEN

Tube No.	EAc added (mg)	Total protein precipitated (mg)	Antibody precipitated, by difference (mg)	Supernatant test	Ab/Ag in precipitates	
					Weight ratio	Mole ratio
1	0.057	0.975	0.918	Excess Ab	16.1	4.0
2	0.250	3.29	3.04	Excess Ab	12.1	3.0
3	0.312	3.95	3.64	Excess Ab	11.7	2.9
4	0.463	4.96	4.50	No Ab, no EAc	9.7	2.4
5	0.513	5.19	4.68	No Ab, trace EAc	9.1	2.3
6	0.562	5.16	(4.60)	Excess EAc	(8.2)	(2.1)
7	0.775	4.56	(3.79)	Excess EAc	(4.9)	(1.2)
8	1.22	2.58	—	Excess EAc	—	—
9	3.06	0.262	—	Excess EAc	—	—

Each tube contained 1.0 ml of antiserum obtained by injecting rabbits repeatedly with alum-precipitated crystallized chicken ovalbumin (EAc).

Antibody content of precipitates in tubes 6-9 could not be determined by difference, because too much EAc remained in the supernatants. The latter was measured independently in the supernatants of tubes 6 and 7, allowing an estimate to be made of EAc and antibody in the corresponding precipitates (values in parentheses).

Mole ratio Ab/Ag was estimated by assuming molecular weights for EAc and antibody (Ab) of 40,000 and 160,000, respectively.

Based on M. Heidelberger and F. E. Kendall. J. Exp. Med. 62:697 (1935).

13-8) the precipitated antigen is essentially equivalent to the amount of antigen added. This fact had been inferred many years ago from the failure to detect the antigen (by qualitative precipitin tests) in the corresponding supernatants; and subsequently, a direct demonstration was provided by the use of antigens labeled with radioactive iodine (^{131}I) or with intensely colored substituents. The traces of antigen not precipitated in this part of the curve are negligible and, in fact, usually not even detectable.

Zones of the Precipitin Curve. Useful information emerges from an examination of the supernatants by qualitative tests to detect unreacted antibody and unreacted antigen. For this purpose each supernatant is divided into aliquots, to one of which is added a small amount of fresh antigen, and to the second a small amount of fresh antiserum. If a supernatant contains sufficient unreacted antibody, precipitation is observed with the former; sufficient unreacted antigen yields precipitation in the latter. It has been found that if the antigen is homogeneous (i.e., consists of a single uniform group of molecules),

or if the antigen is really a mixture of several different antigens but the antiserum is capable of reacting with only one of them, then **none** of the supernatants contains **both** unreacted antibodies and unreacted antigen in detectable amounts. Instead, the residual soluble reactants are distributed as shown in the precipitin curve of Figure 13-8: on the ascending limb, or **antibody-excess zone**, the supernatants contain free antibody; on the descending limb, or **antigen-excess zone**, the supernatants contain free antigen. In the region of maximum precipitation, the **equivalence zone** or **equivalence point**, the supernatants are usually devoid of both detectable antibody and detectable antigen; and the amount of antibody in the corresponding precipitate is taken to represent the weight of antibody in the volume of serum tested. (In Tables 13-2 and 13-3 it should be noted that the maximum amount of antibody is precipitated when there is a slight excess of free antigen in the supernatant; this is commented on below, under Nonprecipitating antibodies.)

Up to this point we have been considering

a **monospecific** system, i.e., one in which only one antigen and the corresponding antibodies form the precipitates. In many precipitin reactions, however, the situation is more complex. Most antigens, including those that satisfy existing physical and chemical criteria of purity, are contaminated by small amounts of immunologically unrelated antigens; and in the immunized animal the contaminants are often capable of provoking an independent immune response. The precipitin reaction between such a contaminated antigen and its antiserum is thus usually the sum of two or more independent precipitin reactions, each monospecific.

This complex (but commonplace) situation is shown schematically in Figure 13-9. Contrary to what was observed with a truly monospecific system (Fig. 13-8), we see here that some supernatants contain **both** unreacted antibodies and unreacted antigen. This result is expected, of course, because the antigen-excess zone of one system overlaps the antibody-excess zone of another. Thus qualitative

testing of supernatants in the precipitin reaction provides a simple means for detecting the existence of multiple systems. As we shall see subsequently, however, the precipitin reaction in agar gel provides a simpler method, which can, in addition, indicate how many monospecific systems are present in a given pair of reactants.

Antibody/Antigen Ratios in the Precipitin Reaction. With most monospecific systems the Ab/Ag ratio in precipitates varies nearly linearly over the antibody-excess zone with the amount of antigen added (Fig. 13-10). With antibody in large excess the mole ratio greatly exceeds 1.0, showing that many antibody molecules can combine simultaneously with one molecule of antigen; i.e., antigen is multivalent. In the antigen-excess zone the mole ratio tends to plateau with a limiting value of slightly over 1.0 (Table 13-3, Fig. 13-10). These variations in Ab/Ag ratio are explicable in terms of the lattice theory, described below.

Fig. 13-9 Precipitin curve for a multispecific system. The precipitation observed (—•—) may be visualized as the summation of two or more component curves (- - -). The significant difference from the monospecific system shown in Figure 13-8 is that some supernatants have **both** excess antigen(s) and excess antibodies (indicated by pluses in heavy type.)

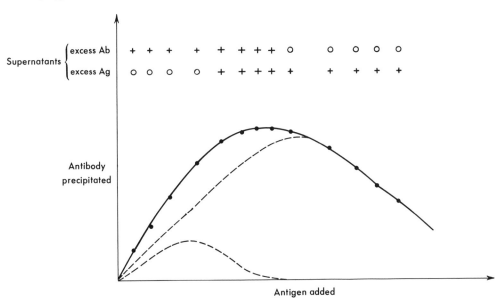

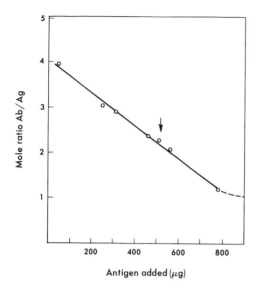

Fig. 13-10 Continuous decline in Ab/Ag ratio of precipitates with increasing amount of antigen added to a fixed volume of antiserum. Chicken ovalbumin (EAc) is the antigen and the serum is rabbit anti-EAc. The limiting mole ratio and slope vary about ±30% in different sera. The arrow marks the equivalence zone. (Data are those of Table 13-3.)

Lattice Theory

Multivalency of antigens suggested to Marrack, and to Heidelberger and Kendall, that the precipitin reaction could be a consequence of the growth of antibody-antigen aggregates in such a way that, broadly speaking, each antigen molecule is linked to more than one antibody molecule and, in turn, each antibody molecule is linked to more than one antigen molecule. When the aggregates grow beyond some critical volume they settle out of solution spontaneously, since sedimentation rate is proportional to $V(\rho - \rho_0)g$, where V is the volume of a particle, ρ and ρ_0 are the densities of the particle and solvent, respectively, and g is the gravitational field. When the lattice theory was proposed it had to be assumed that antibodies are also multivalent, and this assumption was subsequently validated by equilibrium dialysis with univalent haptens (Fig. 13-2).

As is shown in Figure 13-11, the lattice theory makes it easy to visualize how the Ab/Ag ratio can vary so widely and continuously. With systems in which the antigen is distinctively labeled, and thus can be measured directly, it could be shown that precipitates formed in the presence of excessive amounts of antigen have Ab/Ag ratios that approach 1.0 as a limiting value. This result

suggests that the least complicated precipitating complex is a large linear aggregate with alternating antibody and antigen molecules (. . . Ab.Ag.Ab.Ag.Ab.Ag . . .).

In the region of antigen excess the supernatants contain complexes, which are not easily sedimentable because they are so small (Fig. 13-11). Ultracentrifugal and electrophoretic analyses have shown that these soluble complexes vary in composition with the degree of antigen excess; for example, the molar ratio varies from about 0.75 (Ab_3Ag_4) near the equivalence zone to about 0.67 (Ab_2Ag_3) where antigen is in considerable excess. In extreme excess the limiting complex is $AbAg_2$, as expected from the bivalence of antibody molecules.

Valence and Complexity of Protein Antigens

The limiting mole ratio of Ab/Ag in extreme antibody excess is often taken as a measure of the antigen molecule's valence. Since antibody molecules are bivalent, however, the actual number of binding sites on the antigen can be almost twice the limiting mole ratio. And the limiting ratio provides only a **minimal** estimate of the antigen valence: a larger number of reactive sites could exist but fail to be expressed, either because limitations at the surface preclude the pack-

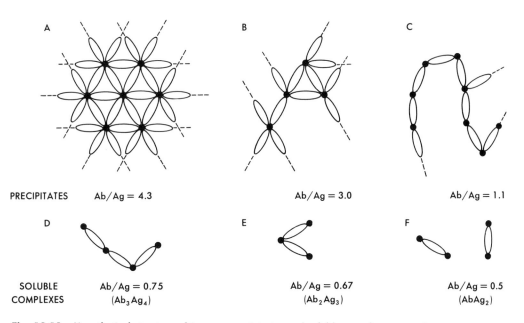

PRECIPITATES   Ab/Ag = 4.3   Ab/Ag = 3.0   Ab/Ag = 1.1

SOLUBLE   Ab/Ag = 0.75   Ab/Ag = 0.67   Ab/Ag = 0.5
COMPLEXES   (Ab$_3$Ag$_4$)   (Ab$_2$Ag$_3$)   (AbAg$_2$)

Fig. 13-11 Hypothetical structure of immune precipitates and soluble complexes according to the lattice theory. The numbers refer to mole ratios of antibody (Ab) to antigen (Ag). Dotted lines with precipitates are intended to indicate that the complexes continue to extend as shown. The precipitates may be visualized as those found in the antibody-excess zone (**A**), the equivalence zone (**B**), and the antigen-excess zone (**C**). The soluble complexes correspond to those in supernatants in moderate (**D**), far (**E**), or extreme (**F**) antigen excess. Black circles, antigen molecules; open elipses, antibody molecules.

ing of more antibody molecules about one antigen molecule, or because in the particular antiserum used the antibodies specific for some potentially functional groups are at too low a concentration or of too low affinity.

An antigen molecule of high molecular weight should be able to bind more antibody molecules simultaneously than an antigen of low molecular weight; and, as is shown in Table 13-4, this relation between molecular

TABLE 13-4.   CORRELATION BETWEEN MOLECULAR WEIGHT AND VALENCE OF ANTIGENS

Antigen	Molecular weight	Approximate mole ratio Ab/Ag of precipitates in extreme antibody excess*
Bovine pancreatic ribonuclease	13,600	3
Chicken ovalbumin	42,000	5
Horse serum albumin	69,000	6
Human γ-globulin	160,000	7
Horse apoferritin	465,000	26
Thyroglobulin	700,000	40
Tomato bushy stunt virus	8,000,000	90
Tobacco mosaic virus	40,000,000	650

The values given are representative, but vary about ± 30% with different antisera, tending to be higher with those obtained late in the course of immunization. Since the antibody molecules involved are bivalent, the antigen valences are probably about twice the mole ratios listed.

Based on E. A. Kabat. In Kabat and Mayer's Experimental Immunochemistry, 2nd ed. Thomas, Springfield, Ill., 1961.

weight and valence of antigens is, in general, found. It should be especially noticed that all antigens capable of giving a precipitin reaction have a valence of at least two. Even some small bivalent haptens form specific precipitates; for example some antibodies to the 2,4-dinitrophenyl (DNP) group are specifically precipitated by *a*,*ε*-bis-DNP-lysine (Ch. 12, Fig. 12-2; Fig. 13-13).

The multivalency of many **polysaccharides** is readily understandable, since they are made up of repeating residues (e.g., dextran, composed exclusively of glucose residues, and the pneumococcal capsular polysaccharides shown in Figure 13-17). With **proteins**, however, the chemical basis for their multivalency is vastly more complex and is still only dimly perceived. Thus, from the recently established covalent structures of several proteins (e.g., ribonuclease, myoglobin) it appears that groups of amino acid residues do **not** recur as repetitive sequences in a given polypeptide chain. Hence, each antigenic determinant in a single-chain protein usually occurs only once per molecule. This appears to be sufficient to stimulate the formation of the corresponding antibodies.

For example, bovine pancreatic ribonuclease (RNase) carrying a single 2,4-dinitrophenyl (DNP) group per molecule (mono-DNP-RNase) evokes the formation of antibodies specific for the DNP group. As predicted by the lattice theory, when these anti-DNP molecules are isolated and mixed with the mono-DNP-RNase only soluble complexes are formed, since this antigen is univalent with respect to these antibody molecules (Fig. 13-12). But with antisera to RNase this antigen is multivalent, giving a classic preciptin reaction. These observations emphasize the operational nature of the definition of valence: **a given molecule of antigen can be univalent with respect to some antibody molecules and multivalent with respect to others.**

These observations also reenforce the view that a typical globular protein is a composite within one molecule of many determinants, each of them occurring once, or perhaps more than once in those proteins with more than

Fig. 13-12 The operational nature of antigen valence illustrated with mono-DPN-RNase (bovine pancreatic ribonuclease with one 2,4-dinitrophenyl group per molecule) which induces the formation of anti-DNP and other antibodies, arbitrarily called anti-X, anti-Y, and anti-Z. The immunogen is **univalent** with respect to the anti-DNP antibodies, with which it forms soluble complexes. The same immunogen, however, is **multivalent** with respect to the mixture of diverse sets of antibodies (anti-X, anti-Y, etc.) that are formed against its various non-DNP determinants; the number and composition of the latter are unknown and they are arbitrarily designated X, Y, Z. (Based on H. N. Eisen, E. S. Simms, J. R. Little, and L. A. Steiner. Fed. Proc. 23:559, 1964.)

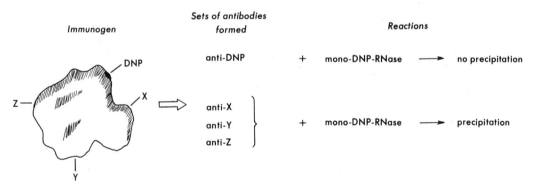

one copy of a given chain per molecule. **An antiserum prepared against a protein must, correspondingly, consist of many populations or sets of antibody molecules, each set being defined by the capacity of all its members to react with a single functional group.** This generalization is supported by observations on the proteolytic cleavage of bovine serum albumin (BSA, M.W. 70,000) into several large fragments, each of which gives a precipitin reaction with a different antibody population in antiserum prepared against the whole BSA molecule.

The minimum number of sets of antibodies in an antiserum to a globular protein is probably given by the limiting mole ratio of Ab/Ag in the far antibody-excess region of its precipitin curve. When we consider that each set is, in turn, probably made up of antibody molecules of different affinities, we see how truly remarkable is the molecular and functional complexity encompassed by such deceptively simple terms as anti-BSA antibody or tetanus antitoxin.

From the argument that a protein antigen is a constellation or mosaic of determinants, it follows that the precipitin reaction involves the **cooperation** between different sets of antibody molecules, each specific for a different ligand group. This conclusion is supported by the observations summarized in Figure 13-13: the small ligand R-X, in which the functional group R and the functional group X each occurs once per molecule, does not precipitate when mixed with an anti-R serum or with an anti-X serum, but it does precipitate with a mixture of the two antisera.

All the foregoing considerations lead to the general view of the precipitin reaction shown schematically in Figure 13-14.

Homospecificity of Antibodies. Since there is a diversity of functional groups in any particular antigen, it may be asked whether a given bivalent antibody molecule can have binding sites that are specific for two different ligand groups. Existing evidence indicates that this does not occur: **bivalent antibodies are homospecific.** For example, in antisera prepared against dinitrophenylated bovine γ-globulin (DNP-BγG) one could imagine antibody molecules with one binding site specific for DNP and one binding site specific for a nonhaptenic group of BγG. However, it has been found that removal of all the antibodies that can react with BγG does not reduce the capacity of the antiserum to bind DNP ligands.

Fig. 13-13 Cooperation between antibodies of different specificities (anti-R and anti-X) in the precipitin reaction with a synthetic ligand, R-X. (The small amount of precipitate ($\pm$) formed by R-X with anti-R alone or with anti-X alone is probably due to some aggregation of R-X.) The insert shows a hypothetical segment of the precipitate with alternation of anti-R and anti-X molecules in a linear aggregate. (Based on L. Pauling, D. Pressman, and D. H. Campbell. J. Am. Chem. Soc. 66:330, 1944.)

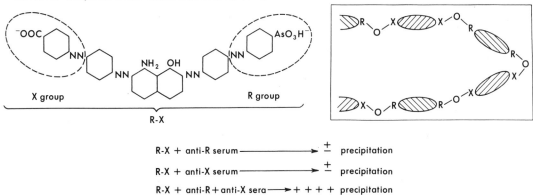

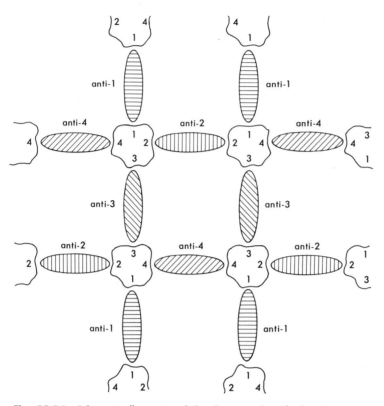

Fig. 13-14 Schematic illustration of the diversity of antibodies formed against a pure antigen and their cooperative effects in the precipitin reaction with that antigen. Further complexities arise because each set of antibodies (anti-1, anti-2, etc.) is probably heterogeneous with respect to affinity for the corresponding antigenic determinant; in addition antibodies of the same specificity may differ considerably in structure (Ch. 14). Antigenic determinants are arbitrarily labeled 1, 2, 3, 4.

Nonspecific Factors in the Precipitin Reaction

Though specific interactions between ligand-binding sites of antibodies and functional groups of antigen molecules are **necessary** for the precipitin reaction, considerable evidence indicates that they are not **sufficient.** For example, by measuring free antigen concentrations in various ways it has been found that the specific interactions occur very rapidly, being completed within a few minutes; yet precipitate formation usually requires 1 to 2 days and sometimes even longer to reach completion. Furthermore, antibodies can be modified chemically so that they lose their ability to precipitate with antigen without impairing their ability to form specific

soluble complexes with that antigen. Such a change is produced, for example, when the negative charge on antibodies is increased by acetylation of their free amino groups. These, and similar observations, have led to the conclusion that **the precipitin reaction actually involves two distinct stages:** the **rapid** formation of soluble antibody-antigen complexes, and then the **slow** aggregation of these complexes to form visible precipitates. Certain bivalent antibodies of the $\gamma G(T)$ class (Ch. 14) provide striking examples of defective ability to participate in the aggregation stage: they do not form precipitates, but they combine effectively with antigen.

While the lattice theory is clearly relevant for the first stage of the precipitin reaction, an older view, that of Bordet, contains elements of interest for the second stage. This view suggests that the close packing of antibody molecules when bound to an antigen molecule provides opportunities for neighboring antibody molecules to react with each other, mostly by way of ionic bonds between oppositely charged groups (Fig. 13-11). As a consequence the complexes, which are usually predominantly made up of antibody molecules, become relatively hydrophobic, and so tend progressively to associate with each other and to become increasingly insoluble. This view is supported by the effects of ionic strength on precipitation (less precipitation at low salt concentrations), and by observations, such as those cited above, that the net charge on antibody molecules influences the rate and extent of the slow aggregation stage of the precipitin reaction.

Nonprecipitating Antibodies

It is generally expected that the amount of antibody precipitated from a given volume of antiserum is maximal when the "equivalent" amount of antigen is added, i.e., that amount which, after removal of the precipitate, leaves the supernatant free of detectable antibody and antigen. In actual practice, however, the maximal amount of antibody is often brought down when slightly more than the equivalent amount of antigen has been added, and there is, correspondingly, a trace of free antigen detectable in the supernatant (Tables 13-2 and 13-3). This trace is usually so small that neglecting it introduces no significant error in calculating the amount of antibody in the corresponding precipitate. This observation must mean that in the supernatant at the equivalence point of certain precipitin reactions there exist some antibody molecules that are particularly refractory to precipitation; these are called **nonprecipitating** antibodies.

The existence of nonprecipitating antibodies can be demonstrated by comparing the amounts of antibody precipitated after the addition of antigen by two different procedures.

In **procedure A** each of a series of tubes, containing the same amount of antiserum, receives a different amount of antigen, systematically increasing as in Figure 13-8 and Tables 13-2 and 13-3. By analysis of the precipitates the quantity of antigen necessary to precipitate the maximal amount of antibody is established.

In **procedure B** a single volume of serum has added to it about 1/10 the equivalent amount of antigen, as defined by procedure A. After the precipitate that forms is removed, the supernatant has added to it a second, equally small, amount of antigen. The second precipitate is likewise removed and to the residual supernatant a third small amount of antigen is added, and so on, until no more precipitation is observed.

It usually is found that the sum of all the antibody precipitated by the successive reactions of procedure B is considerably less than that precipitated at the equivalence point in procedure A. The difference represents **nonprecipitating antibody**, i.e., those molecules which are incapable by themselves of precipitating with antigen, but which can become incorporated in antigen-antibody precipitates of the same specificity, especially those with a relative abundance of antigen (low Ab/Ag ratio).

Under the influence of the lattice theory, nonprecipitating antibody has been widely assumed to be univalent (Blocking or incomplete antibodies, below). This assumption is unwarranted, however, because some nonprecipitating antibodies will precipitate with antigen if certain ancillary proteins, known as complement (Ch. 16), are added. Furthermore, some nonprecipitating antibodies have unusually low affinities for their ligands, and this property could explain why the antigen level must be unusually high in order for these molecules to be included in precipitates. Finally, some purified nonprecipitating antibodies, of the $\gamma G(T)$ class (Ch. 14), have been shown by equilibrium dialysis to be bivalent and of high affintiy. Perhaps these antibody molecules resist the close packing required for precipitation because they carry an excessive amount or anomalous distribution of charged groups; alternatively, their two bindings sites may be too close together for simultaneous occupancy by large antigen molecules (i.e., they are excessively sensitive to steric hindrance).

Antisera vary a good deal with respect to the proportion of their total antibody that is nonprecipitable. In general, the proportion seems to be greatest in serum obtained soon after immunization is begun (Ch. 15).

Reversibility of Precipitation

Antibody-antigen precipitates will often dissolve when suspended in a concentrated solution of the antigen. This means that even after a precipitate has formed its complexes can dissociate and reequilibrate with a fresh charge of antigen. When the latter is in sufficient excess the antibody behaves as it would have done before the initial precipitation: small soluble complexes are formed. It is thus clear that the combination of antibody and antigen to form specific precipitates is reversible. This reversibility, in fact, provides the basis for most of the procedures used to isolate purified antibodies (see Appendix, this chapter).

In practice, however, it is often so difficult to observe dissociation that up until about 1930 the formation of antibody-antigen aggregates was widely held to be an irreversible process. A particularly striking example of the refractoriness of some aggregates to dissociation was described by Danysz in 1902, and the phenomenon is still associated with his name.

The **Danysz phenomenon** is well illustrated with the diphtheria toxin-antitoxin system. When an equivalent amount of diphtheria toxin is added to an antitoxic serum the residual toxicity depends upon the manner in which the reagents are mixed. If the toxin is added to the antiserum all at once the mixture is nontoxic; but if the same quantity of toxin is added in two or more portions, at intervals of about 30 minutes, the mixture is toxic. Originally observed with a toxic plant protein (ricin), this phenomenon was interpreted by Danysz to mean that the first addition of toxin led to the formation of complexes with a high Ab/Ag ratio, and that these complexes were hardly, if at all, dissociable. Accordingly, insufficient free antibody remained available to neutralize all the toxin molecules that were subsequently added.

All antibody-antigen reactions are reversible in principle; those that appear irreversible probably have unusually slow dissociation rates, requiring days, or perhaps even months, rather than minutes for equilibrium to become reestablished when the system is perturbed. **Apparent irreversibility** is especially striking with many antibody-virus complexes: some are so stable that they do not perceptibly dissociate even, for example, when a given mixture of virus and antiserum is diluted many thousandfold, with a corresponding reduction in the concentrations of free virus and free antibody (Ch. 27).

It is not known whether the apparent irreversibility of some aggregates is due to some unusual property of the interaction between specific sites of antigen and antibody, or to intermolecular bonds other than those involved in specific site reactions, or perhaps even to conformational changes in the aggregated antibody (or antigen).

Applications of the Precipitin Reaction

Measurement of Antibody Concentration. The quantitative precipitin reaction is the most reliable method available for determining the concentration of antibodies (in weight units) in an antiserum. The assay is performed as described above: various amounts of antigen are added to a constant volume of antiserum, and the resulting specific precipitates are washed and analyzed for total protein. From the results, plotted as shown in Figure 13-8, the maximum amount of precipitable antibody is estimated.

Attempts have been made to simplify the procedure by exploiting the linear relation in the region of antibody excess between Ab/Ag ratios in the precipitates and the amount of antigen added. This relation can be expressed empirically as:

$$\frac{Ab}{Ag} = a - bAg', \qquad (12)$$

where Ab and Ag are amounts of antibody and antigen precipitated, Ag' is amount of antigen added, and a and b are the intercept and the slope of the straight line (Fig. 13-10). In the region of the precipitin curve under discussion essentially all the antigen added is precipitated, and equation (12) may therefore be written as:

$$Ab = aAg - b(Ag)^2. \qquad (13)$$

An expression of similar form was derived by Heidelberger and Kendall for the precipitin reaction in the antibody excess region, over a twofold range in Ab/Ag ratio: if 2R is the limiting value for Ab/Ag in extreme antibody excess (intercept), they considered the equivalence point to be reached when this ratio equaled R. The expression they derived is:

$$Ab = 2RAg - \frac{R^2}{Ab_{max}} (Ag)^2, \qquad (14)$$

where Ab_{max} is the maximum amount of antibody precipitated, presumed to be at the equivalence point, and the slope and intercept of equation (13) are $-R^2/Ab_{max}$ and $2R$, respectively.

Thus, in principle, the concentration of precipitable antibody in an antiserum could be determined from analysis of a single precipitate, prepared by adding to an aliquot of serum less than an equivalent amount of antigen, provided Ab/Ag at the equivalence point (R) and the slope were known for the system being analyzed. Unfortunately, the slope is by no means the same in all antisera of a given specificity, and even R is not invariant. Moreover, in some systems the range in Ab/Ag is as much as threefold from the intercept in extreme antibody excess to the equivalence point, and this necessitates a far more complex equation than (14). Finally, some systems, ostensibly monospecific, deviate somewhat from the linear relation of equation (12) and Figure 13-10.

Accordingly, the measurement of antibody content of an antiserum requires the analysis of many precipitates. Even with the aid of some technical tricks it is necessary, in effect, to construct a precipitin curve in order to define the maximum amount of precipitable antibody in a given volume of antiserum.

As an assay, the precipitin reaction can, with care, be highly **reproducible**; and its precision is virtually as good as the most precise methods for measuring proteins (i.e., by Kjeldahl analysis of nitrogen, ultraviolet absorbance, etc.). There must, however, remain some reservations as to its **accuracy**, i.e., the extent to which the values obtained correspond to "true" values. Uncertainty arises because a variable fraction of antibody (e.g., molecules of low affinity) may not bind to the antigen under the conditions of assay. While it could, of course, be argued that molecules of such low affinity should not be classified as antibodies, we have seen before that the specific binding reaction is a function of antibody **activity**, i.e., **both** antibody concentration and affinity. Thus, at low concentration low-affinity antibody molecules may not react with antigen, but at a higher concentration the same antibody molecules might react very well. Despite this caveat, and the laboriousness of the procedure, the precipitin reaction remains the most reliable method for measuring antibody concentrations.

Measurement of Antigen Concentration. Once a precipitin curve has been constructed for a given antiserum and the corresponding antigen, the antiserum can be used to measure the concentration of that antigen in unknown solutions. The precipitin assay is carried out in the antibody-excess region; and it is only necessary to establish that the antiserum is free of extraneous antibodies that could precipitate other antigens in the test solution. Antisera have the advantage of being stable on prolonged storage; and the precipitin reaction is sensitive enough to measure accurately and precisely small quantities (μg range) of antigens in complex solutions. For example, rabbit antisera to human immunoglobulins (HIG) have been used effectively to measure concentrations of HIG in spinal fluid.

Another application of the precipitin reaction is based on its susceptibility to specific inhibition by univalent haptens. This application, discussed below, has contributed to analysis of the structure of antigenic determinants in complex polysaccharides, such as those in blood group substances (Ch. 18), and, conversely, to probing of the nature of binding sites in antibodies (Ch. 14).

Hapten Inhibition of Precipitation

Qualitative Hapten Inhibition. Long before its quantitative features had been characterized by Heidelberger and his associates the precipitin reaction had been widely used as a visual, qualitative, test to detect antibody-antigen reactions. It was, in fact, in just this simple fashion that Landsteiner had exploited it, by means of hapten inhibition, in his classic investigations of immunological specificity. In general terms, in the precipitin system that he used the antiserum was prepared against one conjugated protein, which may be designated X-azoprotein *A,* and the precipitating agent was another conjugate with the same azo substituent attached to a different protein, X-azoprotein *B. A* and *B* were chosen to be quite unrelated, e.g., horse and chicken serum proteins (Figs. 13-4 and 13-5). Hence it was improbable that antibodies formed to nonhaptenic determinants of *A* would react with protein *B,* and so the reactions observed could be ascribed with confidence to anti-X antibodies. X-azoprotein *B* was prepared so that there were several X-azo groups per molecule, and this multivalent conjugated protein formed precipitating complexes with anti-X antibodies. In contrast, simple haptens, in which the X group occurred once per molecule, formed soluble complexes with anti-X, and hence could competitively inhibit this precipitin reaction (Fig. 13-15). The greater the antibody's affinity for the hapten, relative to its affinity for the precipitating azoprotein, the more effectively is its precipitation inhibited.

Quantitative Hapten Inhibition. By combining hapten inhibition with quantitative measurements of precipitates, Pauling and Pressman were able to obtain more insight into the specificity of antibody reactions than

had been possible with the qualitative method. In the quantitative assay analyses are carried out by adding equal volumes of an anti-X serum to a series of tubes with varying amounts of univalent X haptens. After brief incubation a multivalent precipitating agent (e.g., an X-azoprotein) is added in that amount which, in the absence of hapten, would give roughly maximal precipitation of anti-X antibodies. When the precipitates are analyzed it is observed that the amount of antibody precipitated decreases as the concentration of added hapten increases (Fig. 13-16).

If all the anti-X molecules had the same tendency to discriminate between the univalent and the multivalent ligand a linear competitive relation would be expected. Usually, however, the decrease in amount of anti-X precipitated is not linear with the quantity of hapten added, suggesting heterogeneity in the antibody population. The relative effectiveness of univalent haptens is characterized, therefore, by specifying the concentration required to inhibit precipitation by 50%. This value permits comparisons to be made between diverse haptens, referring each of their inhibitory activities to that of one of them, the reference hapten. Thus the concentration required of the reference hapten for 50% inhibition, divided by the concentration required of a second hapten, provides an index of the antibody's affinity for the second hapten, relative to the antigen used for precipitation. Some representative results are shown in Figure 13-16.

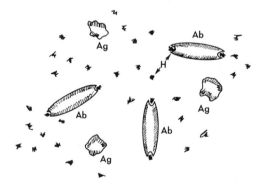

Fig. 13-15 Diagram of competitive inhibition of the precipitin reaction by a univalent ligand. Ag, multivalent ligand; Ab, antibody; H, univalent ligand.

Fig. 13-16 Hapten inhibition of the precipitin reaction: Decline in precipitation of antibody with increasing concentration of several univalent benzenearsonates. The antiserum was prepared against p-azobenzenearsonate; hence the hapten with -CH$_3$ in the para position is bound best, i.e., is most inhibitory (K' = 1.9). With the methyl group in the meta or ortho position steric hindrance reduces affinity for antibody and the extent of inhibition. (From D. Pressman. Adv. in Biol. and Med. Physics, 3:99, 1953.)

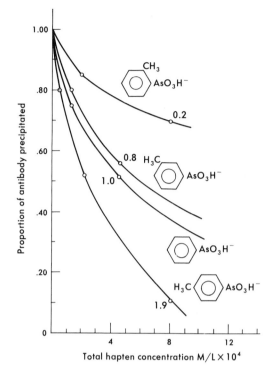

The heterogeneity noted in Figure 13-16 resembles that discussed above in connection with measurements of affinity by equilibrium dialysis (Figs. 13-2 and 13-3). But while both kinds of heterogeneity undoubtedly reflect structural variations in the ligand-binding sites of antibodies, they are not formally equivalent. In the reaction that involves only one ligand, as in equilibrium dialysis, the heterogeneity concerns the antibody's affinity for that ligand. But where the reaction involves competition between a univalent ligand and a multivalent ligand one cannot tell whether the antibody molecules are all uniform in affinity for the former but heterogeneous for the latter, or vice versa, or heterogeneous for both.

Cross-Reactions

Besides reacting with its immunogen, an antiserum will usually react with other antigens (called heterologous antigens) if sufficiently similar to the immunogen. The reactions with heterologous antigens are called cross-reactions; some examples are illustrated in Figures 13-17 and 13-18. In the following discussion cross-reactions are considered in

three general categories, two arising from the properties of antigens, and the third from the properties of antibodies.

Cross-Reactions Due to Impurities in Antigens. Most substances used as immunogens are actually complex mixtures of many different kinds of antigenic molecules. This is obviously true when the immunogen is a bacterial or an animal cell. It is also usually true, though less obvious, with purified soluble proteins as antigens, since these are nearly always contaminated with other immunogenic proteins. Even when the contaminants are present at trace levels (e.g., 1%) they can often provoke the formation of detectable amounts of antibody. Hence, antisera prepared against these impure mixtures consist of several antibody populations, each reactive with one antigen.

If, for example, crystallized chicken ovalbumin (EAc) contaminated with trace amounts of chicken serum proteins were used as immunogen the anti-EAc serum would probably contain low levels of antibodies to the contaminants; hence anti-EAc

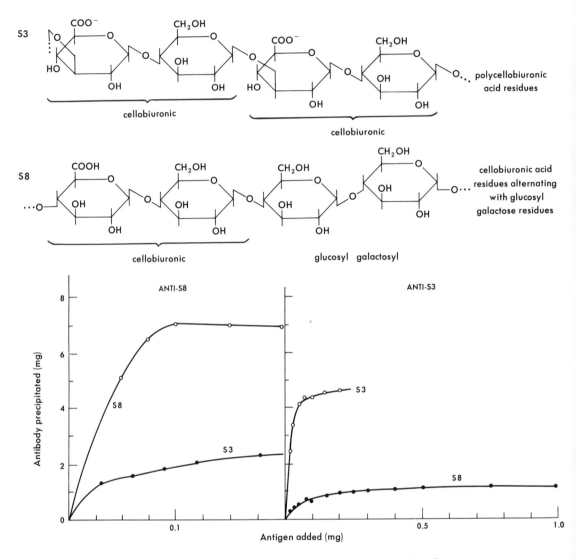

Fig. 13-17 Cross-reactions between type 3 and type 8 capsular polysaccharides of pneumococci. **Left:** Horse antiserum to type 8 pneumococcus, reacted with purified S 8 and S 3 polysaccharide. **Right:** Horse antiserum to type 3 pneumococcus, reacted with S 3 and S 8 polysaccharide. (Based on M. Heidelberger, E. A. Kabat, and D. L. Shrivastava, J. Exp. Med. 65:487, 1937, and M. Heidelberger, E. A. Kabat, and M. Mayer, J. Exp. Med. 75:35, 1942.)

would probably form precipitates (i.e., cross-react) with some chicken serum proteins. In this example, of course, supernatant tests would probably reveal that the homologous precipitin reaction (i.e., EAc with anti-EAc) was not monospecific; and this would be even easier to establish by precipitin reactions in agar gel (Fig. 13-26).

Cross-Reactions Due to Common Functional Groups in Different Antigens. We have already discussed some of the evidence that even in a single protein there are many different antigenic determinants per molecule, each of which can potentially evoke the formation of a corresponding set of antibody molecules. And the same is true of most

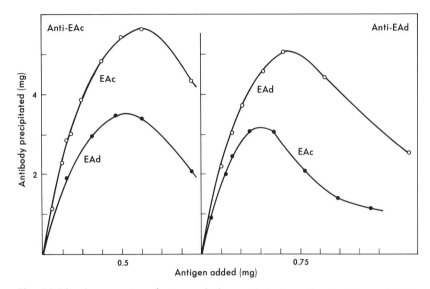

Fig. 13-18 Cross-reactions between chicken and duck ovalbumin, EAc and EAd, respectively. **Left:** Rabbit antiserum to EAc, reacted with EAc and EAd. **Right:** Rabbit antiserum to EAd, reacted with EAd and EAc. (Based on A. G. Osler and M. Heidelberger. J. Immunol. **60:327**, 1948.)

polysaccharides and conjugated proteins. If two different antigen molecules happen to have one or more groups in common a cross-reacting relation between them is usually encountered.

This type of cross-reaction is frequently observed with bacterial cell wall and capsular polysaccharides, and provides the basis for classifying many groups of closely related bacteria. The 500 or more varieties of salmonella, for example, have been arranged into several serological groups, each identified by mutual cross-reactions: an antiserum to any strain of a particular group reacts with the other strains of that group. The common antigenic determinants responsible for the group-specific cross-reactions have been shown to be particular sugar residues. For example, the determinant that defines group O salmonella has as its principal residue colitose (3,6-dideoxy-L-galactose), attached as a terminal residue on a branch of the cell wall lipopolysaccharide. Other terminally attached dideoxyhexoses are responsible for the cross-reactions that characterize other groups of salmonella, e.g., paratose in group A, abe-

quose in group B, and tyvelose in group D (Ch. 20).

The determinants responsible for cross-reactions need not, however, be terminal residues. The strains of salmonella that constitute group E, for example, cross-react because they all possess nonterminal mannosyl-rhamnose residues as repeating units in their cell wall lipopolysaccharides (Fig. 13-19).

Another example, of considerable historical importance in illuminating the structural basis for cross-reactions in natural antigens, is provided by the pneumococcus. The capsular polysaccharide of type 3 pneumococcus is a linear polymer made up of repeating cellobiuronic acid residues (β-1,4-glucuronidoglucose), while in the capsular polysaccharide of type 8 cellobiuronic acid residues alternate with glucosyl-galactose residues. It is readily understandable, therefore, that anti-3 sera cross-react extensively with type 8 polysaccharide, and vice versa (Fig. 13-17).

A similar principle accounts for the cross-reactions that are commonplace with conjugated proteins; for example, antisera to 2,4-dinitrophenyl (DNP) bovine γ-globulin react with

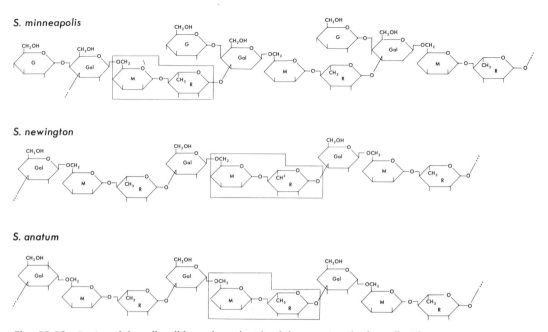

Fig. 13-19   Portion of the cell wall lipopolysaccharide of three strains of salmonella. The strains are assigned to the same group (O) because of their serological cross-reaction, due to their common mannosyl-rhamnose residues (circled). They are also distinguishable serologically because each has some unique structural feature, e.g., the terminal glucose residue in *S. minneapolis,* and the α or β glycosidic bond linking galactose (Gal) to mannose (M). (Based on P. W. Robbins and T. Uchida. Fed. Proc. 21:702, 1962.)

DNP human serum albumin because DNP groups are present in both conjugates.

Cross-Reactions Due to the Imperfect Specificity of Antibodies. Cross-reactivity does not require that a functional group of the heterologous ligand be **identical** with the corresponding group of the immunogen; it need only be sufficiently similar. For example, antibodies to *m*-azobenzenesulfonate cross-react with *m*-azobenzenenearsonate (Fig. 13-4), and antibodies to the 2,4-dinitrophenyl-lysyl group cross-react with 2,4,6-trinitrobenzene. On this basis, some cross-reactions should be exhibited by all antisera and purified antibodies, including hypothetically those to an immunogen whose determinant groups are not precisely duplicated in any other antigen.

General Characteristics of Cross-Reactions. The following generalizations are drawn from the study of many cross-reactions.

1) An antiserum precipitates more copiously with its immunogen than with cross-reacting antigens (Figs. 13-17 and 13-18). Important in the practical diagnostic applications of serological methods (see below), this rule is understandable because any heterologous ligand reacts only with some proportion of the total antibody to the immunogen. In addition, purified antibodies of a given specificity will virtually always have greater affinity for the homologous ligand than for cross-reacting ligands (Figs. 13-6 and 13-7).

2) The mutual cross-reactions between a pair of antigens are usually not quantitatively equivalent; antibodies to the first antigen may react more extensively with the second antigen than antibodies to the second react with the first (Fig. 13-17).

3) Different antisera to a given immunogen are likely to vary in the extent of their cross-reactions with diverse heterologous antigens.

4) Cross-reacting ligands tend to be bound more strongly by antibodies with high affinity

than by those with low affinity for the homologous ligand. Thus, fewer cross-reactions are exhibited by low- than by high-affinity antibodies (Specificity and affinity, above). Since polysaccharide/antipolysaccharide systems are, in general, characterized by low affinities (see above), this generalization may account for the extraordinary specificity of many antipolysaccharide sera, such as those used in the serological typing of bacteria and red blood cells (Ch. 18).

Comparison of Various Types of Cross-Reactions. The three types of cross-reactions discussed above may be contrasted as follows. 1) The presence of antigenic impurities is trivial conceptually but of considerable importance technically in the practical applications of serological reactions for diagnostic and investigative purposes. 2) The presence of identical functional groups in different antigens is particularly relevant for those groups that are relatively insensitive to the fine structure of the macromolecule, such as lactose, 2,4-dinitrophenyl, etc. Groups of this type are usually found in polysaccharides, nucleic acids, and conjugated proteins. 3) Cross-reactions based on similarity rather than identity of determinants are probably of particular importance among proteins, for the determinant groups in these antigens may be only dimly perceived as clusters of amino acid residues, whose three-dimensional conformation and charge density are exquisitely sensitive to the entire macromolecule's tertiary structure. While the second and third types of cross-reactions may be distinguished formally, it is not usually possible to differentiate between them experimentally.

Removal of Cross-Reacting Antibodies (Adsorption and Absorption). It is usually necessary to remove certain cross-reacting antibodies before an antiserum is sufficiently **monospecific** for use as an analytical reagent, e.g., in typing bacteria, measuring enzyme levels in bacterial extracts, etc. Removal is accomplished simply by allowing the antiserum to react with the appropriate cross-reacting antigens. If the complexes formed are large (e.g., precipitates, or antibodies bound to cells) they are easily removed along with the cross-reacting antibodies. When, however, the complexes are soluble and difficult to remove, cross-reacting ligand may be added in large excess to saturate the cross-reacting antibodies, eliminating them functionally from the system without excluding them physically.

Antisera treated by the foregoing procedures are generally called adsorbed or absorbed sera. In this volume we shall use the terms **adsorption** and adsorbed serum when antibodies are removed by specific binding on the surface of particulate antigens (e.g., red cells or bacteria), and **absorption** and absorbed serum when antibodies are removed or neutralized by reaction with soluble antigens.

Avidity

The individual antisera prepared against a given antigen, particularly a protein antigen, often differ in **avidity**, i.e., in the tendency to combine and form stable complexes with the antigen. Such differences may be demonstrated by **dilution** of antiserum-antigen mixtures. The concentrations of free antibody and free antigen are thereby reduced, causing dissociation of the immune complexes: dissociation is less evident with more avid antisera. This procedure is particularly applicable when the unbound antigen can be measured with high sensitivity, e.g., as toxin or infectious virus, and when neutralization involves soluble antibody-antigen complexes. Variations in the **shape of precipitin curves** also reveal differences in avidity. For example, in Figure 13-20 antiserum A is more avid than B, which is more avid than C, etc.

Differences in avidity have been noted with such antigens as diphtheria toxin, diverse viruses (Ch. 27), and some isotopically labeled proteins. Since a protein antigen contains many kinds of functional groups per molecule, the basis for a difference in avidity is usually not clear.

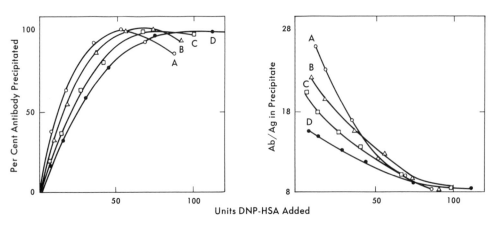

Fig. 13-20 Precipitin curves showing differences in avidity (combining power) of four antisera for the same antigen. The sera were prepared against 2,4-dinitrophenyl (DNP) bovine γ-globulin and tested with human serum albumin substituted with about 30 DNP groups per protein molecule (DNP-HSA). The order of avidity of the sera is A>B>C>D. A similar order in affinity for ε-DNP-lysine was found for anti-DNP molecules isolated from each of the sera: K_0 in liters mole^{-1} were: (A) $> 10^8$, (B) 1×10^7, (C) 5×10^6, and (D) 1×10^6. (From L. A. Steiner and H. N. Eisen. In Immunological Diseases. M. Samter, ed. Little, Brown, Boston, 1965.)

If, for example, the precipitating antigen in Figure 13-20 were diphtheria toxin, one could not decide whether to ascribe the difference between serum A and serum C to 1) more sets of antibodies in A than in C, each set being specifically reactive with a different functional group in the toxin (Fig. 13-14); 2) greater affinities of some or all of the sets of antibodies in A than in C; or 3) differences in the nonspecific interactions of the antibodies, i.e., those differences that arise from structural properties of antibody molecules other than at their specific binding sites (Nonspecific factors in the precipitin reaction and Mechanisms of agglutination; this chapter).

Actually, in the example illustrated in Figure 13-20 the sera were prepared against 2,4-dinitrophenyl (DNP) bovine γ-globulin; the precipitating ligand was DNP human serum albumin; and anti-DNP molecules subsequently isolated from sera A, B, C, and D, respectively, turned out to have progressively decreasing **affinity** for ϵ-DNP-lysine, the common haptenic group of both the immunogen and the precipitating antigen. Hence in this example increasing avidity for antigen correlates well with increasing affinity for the homologous univalent hapten. However, this explanation may not apply to

all examples of variations in avidity of antisera.

Antibodies of very high molecular weight (about 900,000; see γM immunoglobulins, Ch. 14) have recently been shown to have at least 5 binding sites per molecule. Such a pentavalent antibody would be expected to form less dissociable complexes with multivalent antigen than would the corresponding bivalent antibody, even if the 2 antibodies had the same intrinsic association constant for univalent ligand. Thus, despite their having the same affinity (per site) the pentavalent antibody would very likely appear to be more avid than the bivalent one.

The Flocculation Reaction

The precipitin reactions of certain antisera differ from the classic precipitin reaction in that insoluble aggregates are not observed until the amount of antigen added exceeds some relatively large value. Thus, for these systems a plot of antibody (or total protein) precipitated vs. antigen added does not extrapolate to the origin (compare Figs. 13-17, 13-18, and 13-21). In these anomalous reactions, which are referred to as **flocculation** reactions, precipitation is inhibited by extreme antibody excess as well as

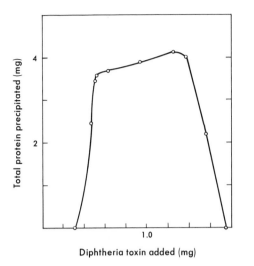

Fig. 13-21 Precipitin reaction of the flocculation type. Each value represents the precipitate formed by 1.0 ml of horse antiserum to diphtheria toxin and the indicated amount of toxin. (Based on A. M. Pappenheimer, Jr., and E. S. Robinson, J. Immunol. 32:291, 1937.)

by antigen excess; precipitation is thus observed only over a narrow range of Ab/Ag ratios.

Flocculation reactions are regularly given by certain horse antisera, particularly those prepared against diphtheria toxin and some streptococcal toxins. The explanation for the special features of the flocculation reaction must lie in the properties of the antibodies involved, rather than the antigens, because the same antigens give typical precipitin reactions with rabbit antisera. Aside from the exceptions just mentioned, horse antisera to most other proteins, and to polysaccharides, give the usual precipitin reaction; and no rabbit sera have so far been observed to give flocculation reactions. The precipitation of some human antisera with thyroglobulin has been of the flocculation type.

The basis for the difference between the flocculation and the usual precipitin reaction is not understood.

Precipitin Reaction in Gels

The precipitin reaction can be carried out in gels as well as in liquid systems. When antibodies and antigen are introduced into different regions of an agar gel they diffuse freely toward each other. If their reaction in aqueous solution can lead to precipitation readily visible opaque bands of precipitate appear at the junction of their diffusion fronts. A number of simple and ingenious applications of this principle provide powerful methods for analyzing the multiplicity of antibody-antigen reactions within a system. The most widely used of these methods are illustrated in Fig. 13-22 and described below.

Fig. 13-22 Some widely used arrangements for gel diffusion precipitin reactions. **A.** Single diffusion in one dimension. **B.** Double diffusion in one dimension. **C.** Double diffusion in two dimensions. Arrows show direction of diffusion. Stippled areas are opaque precipitation bands.

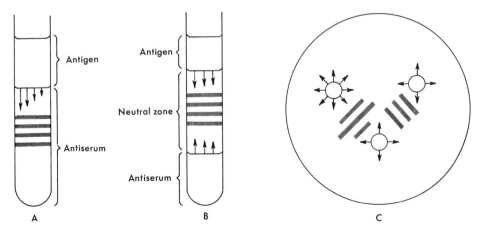

Single Diffusion in One Dimension. This procedure, developed by Oudin in France, is generally performed by placing a solution of antigen over an antiserum which has been incorporated in a column of agar gel. By diffusion, a concentration gradient of antigen advances down the agar column (provided the concentration of antigen in the upper reservoir is high relative to the concentration of antibody in the agar phase), and a precipitate forms in the agar at the advancing diffusion front. This precipitate extends upward to that level in the gradient at which antigen excess is sufficient to prevent precipitation. With continuing diffusion of antigen from the liquid reservoir, the leading edge of the precipitate advances downward. The trailing edge of the precipitate likewise advances, since the additional antigen migrating into the region of the specific precipitate serves to dissolve it by forming soluble complexes, as expected from the precipitin reaction in liquid. Thus, a band of precipitate migrates down the column of agar, the distance moved being proportional to the square root of time, in accord with the laws of diffusion.

The rate of migration depends on the diffusion coefficient of the antigen and on its concentration in the upper reservoir. Accordingly, when several antigens diffuse into an antiserum that can react with them, several distinct bands of precipitation are observed, and each migrates at a distinctive rate. It is improbable, though not impossible, that two different antibody-antigen systems will form completely overlapping bands that migrate at indistinguishable rates; hence the number of bands observed represents the **minimum** number of antibody-antigen systems in the substances being analyzed.

The rate of band migration varies with the concentration of antigen introduced, and the optical density of a precipitate (which can be measured by suitable photometers) depends on the concentration of antibody in the antiserum. On this basis it is possible, with the use of appropriate standards (solutions of known antigen concentration and antisera of known anti-

body concentration), to measure the concentration of antigen in unknown solutions and the concentration of precipitating antibodies in antisera.

The arrangement shown in Figure 13-22A can be reversed by incorporating antigen in the agar column below and overlaying it with antiserum. If the concentration of antibodies greatly exceeds the concentration of relevant antigens, precipitation takes place at the interface and migrates into the lower gel phase. By means of this arrangement precipitin and flocculation reactions can be distinguished. In a flocculating system inhibition of precipitation by antibody excess produces an advancing band with a clear zone, free of precipitation, extending from the trailing edge of the precipitate to the antiserum-agar interface. In a system that gives a precipitin reaction, on the other hand, precipitation extends all the way from the antigen-antibody interface to the advancing front of the precipitation band (Fig. 13-23).

Double Diffusion in One Dimension. In this procedure the antiserum in agar is overlaid by a column of clear agar which in turn is overlaid by antigen, added either as liquid or incorporated into agar. Antigen and antibody molecules diffuse across the respective interfaces into the clear neutral zone and advance toward each other. At that junction of their diffusion fronts where antibody and antigen are in equivalent proportions a precipitation band forms, and it increases in density with time as more antibody and antigen molecules continue to enter this zone in optimal (i.e., equivalent) proportions (Fig. 13-22B). If the antigen and antibody are added to their respective reservoirs in proportions that correspond to the equivalence zone in solution, the precipitation band has maximal sharpness and is stationary. If, however, either antigen or antibody is added in relative excess, the band migrates slowly away from the excess.

This method, which is extremely sensitive (detecting as little as 10 μg antibody per milliliter) is particularly valuable for determining the number of antibody-antigen systems in complex reagents. For example, with

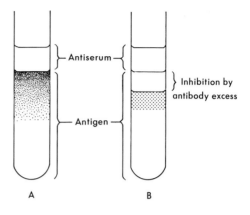

Fig. 13-23 Gel diffusion illustrating differences between the usual type of precipitin reaction (**A**) and the flocculation reaction (**B**). Compare antibody-excess zones of Figures 13-17, 13-18, and 13-21.

highly purified diphtheria toxin as antigen and a human antiserum to diphtheria toxin as many as six bands of precipitation have been observed. These same reactants in liquid solution would very likely have displayed a precipitin curve with a single zone of maximum precipitation; with careful supernatant analysis it might have been possible to recognize that more than one antibody-antigen system was involved, but not how many.

Double Diffusion in Two Dimensions. Additional insight into the complex relations between antibodies and antigens can be obtained by the simple but elegant procedure, developed mainly by Ouchterlony in Sweden, of placing antigen and antibody solutions in separate wells cut in an agar plate (Fig. 13-22C). A large number of geometric arrangements are possible; some of the more simple ones are shown in Figures 13-24 and 13-26. The reactants diffuse from the wells, and precipitation bands form where they meet at equivalent proportions. The bands form first where the distance between the antibody and antigen reservoirs is at a minimum, and then they spread laterally. If the concentration of antibody introduced is in relative excess over antigen, the band first forms closer to the antigen well; and the converse occurs if the antigen is introduced in relative excess. The curvature of the precipitin band also provides a clue to the molecular weight of the antigen, provided antigen and antibody are present in roughly equivalent amounts.

If the antigen and antibody have about the same molecular weight the precipitation band appears as a straight line; if the antigen has a higher molecular weight the band is concave toward the antigen source; and if the antigen is of lower molecular weight the band is concave toward the antibody reservoir. These relations follow from the fact that the rate of diffusion of a substance increases with its concentration and decreases with its molecular weight.

The arrangements shown in Figures 13-24 to 13-26 are particularly useful for comparing antigens or antisera for the presence of identical or cross-reacting components. If a solution of a pure antigen is placed in two adjacent wells and the homologous antibody is placed in the center well, the two precipitin bands eventually join at their contiguous ends and fuse (Fig. 13-24A). This pattern, known as the **reaction of identity**, is seen whenever indistinguishable antibody-antigen systems react in adjacent fields. If, on the other hand, unrelated antigens are placed in adjacent wells and diffuse toward a central well that contains antibodies for each, the two precipitin bands form independently of each other and cross (**reaction of nonidentity**, Fig. 13-24B). If, however, the antigen in one of the wells and the antiserum in the central well constitute a homologous pair, and the antigen in an adjoining well is a cross-reacting antigen, the precipitation bands fuse, but in addition form a spurlike projection that extends

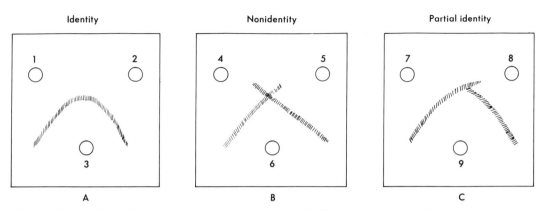

Fig. 13-24 Double diffusion precipitin reactions in agar gel illustrating reactions of identity, nonidentity, and partial identity. In **A** the same antigen was placed in wells 1 and 2, and the antiserum was in well 3. In **B** different antigens were placed in wells 4 and 5, and antisera to both were placed in well 6. In **C** an antigen and its antiserum were placed in wells 7 and 9, respectively, and a cross-reacting antigen was placed in well 8.

toward the cross-reacting antigen (**reaction of partial identity** or **cross-reaction**, Fig. 13-24C). From what is known of precipitin reactions in liquid the spur can be readily interpreted: it represents the reaction between homologous antigen and those antibody molecules that do **not** combine with the cross-reacting antigen and hence diffuse past its precipitation band. Since these noncross-reacting antibodies represent only a fraction of the total antibody involved in the homologous precipitin reaction (see Figs. 13-17 and 13-18, for example), the spur is usually less dense than the band from which it projects and tends to have increased curvature toward the antiserum well (Fig. 13-24C).

In the event that neither of the antigens is homologous with respect to the antiserum (i.e., neither is the immunogen) a pattern of partial identity might be observed, with the spur projecting toward the less reactive antigen; or there might be partial fusion with two crossing spurs, indicating that some antibodies react with one of the cross-reacting antigens but not the other, and vice versa. Unless inspected carefully for attenuation and curvature of the spurs, double spur formation can be mistakenly interpreted to mean that the adjacent systems are unrelated.

As in diffusion in one dimension, if one well contains a mixture of different antigens and the facing well contains antibodies to several of them, the number of bands forming between the wells represents the minimum number of antibody-antigen systems involved. These bands may be identified if the appropriate pure antigens are placed in adjacent wells. For example, if whole human serum in one well is flanked by purified human serum albumin on one side and by a purified human immunoglobulin on the other, and the three wells form an arc about a central well that contains a rabbit antiserum against whole human serum, the band patterns will reveal two reactions of identity with the known antigens; these identify the corresponding precipitin lines in the series of bands between the homologous reactants (Fig. 13-25).

Double diffusion in two dimensions provides a simple means for evaluating, to a limited extent, the basis for cross-reactions observed in liquid media. Thus, of the several classes of cross-reactions discussed earlier, that which arises from a common impurity can usually be recognized unambiguously, as is shown in Figure 13-26. On the other hand, when two purified antigens, such as chicken and duck ovalbumins (Fig. 13-18), give rise to a cross-reaction it is not possible by gel

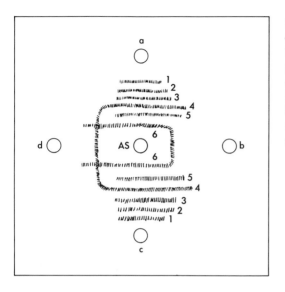

Fig. 13-25 The use of purified antigens to identify components of a complex series of precipitin bands. The center well (AS) contains rabbit antiserum prepared against unfractionated human serum. Wells a and c contain human serum; well b has purified human serum albumin; and well d has a purified human immunoglobulin. Thus, bands 4 and 6 correspond to immunoglobulin and serum albumin, respectively.

diffusion analysis to decide whether their common determinant groups are identical or only similar; in both cases partial fusion would be observed, with projection of the spur toward the cross-reacting antigen (Fig. 13-26).

Immunoelectrophoresis

By combining electrophoresis with precipitation in agar gel, Grabar and Williams developed a simple but extraordinarily powerful method for identifying antigens in complex mixtures (Fig. 13-27). The complex mixture of antigens is introduced into a small well in agar that has been cast on a plate, say an ordinary microscope slide. By applying an electric field across the plate for 1 to 2 hours the proteins are made to migrate, each according to its own electrophoretic mobility. After the proteins are separated the electric gradient is discontinued, and antiserum is introduced into a trough whose long axis parallels the axis of electrophoretic migration. The antibodies and antigens now diffuse toward each other, and precipitin bands form at the

Fig. 13-26 An example of the use of gel diffusion to discriminate between two types of cross-reactions. In liquid medium an antiserum (AS) prepared against crystallized chicken ovalbumin (EAc) precipitates copiously with EAc and less well with crystallized duck ovalbumin (EAd; see Fig. 13-18); it also precipitates slightly with crystallized chicken serum albumin (CSA). From the gel precipitin pattern shown it is concluded that 1) EAc is contaminated with CSA, hence the antiserum contains some antibodies to CSA; 2) CSA and the main component of EAc are unrelated antigenically (reaction of nonidentity); and 3) some antigenic determinants of EAd are similar to or identical with some determinants of EAc (reaction of partial identity). The antibodies that cause the spur (arrow) are those that in the quantitative precipitin reaction of Figure 13-18 precipitate with EAc but not with EAd.

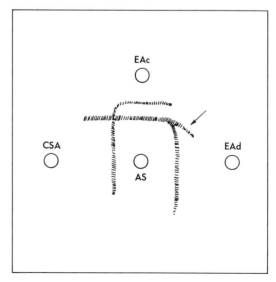

A

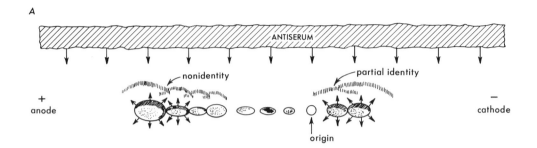

B

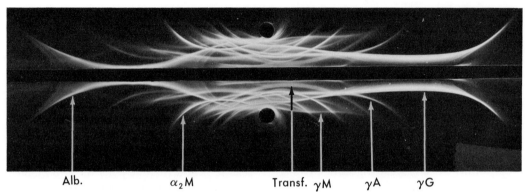

Alb. α_2M   Transf. γM γA γG

Fig. 13-27   Immunoelectrophoresis. A. A thin layer of agar gel (ca. 1 to 2 mm) covers a glass slide, and a small well near the center (marked origin) receives a solution containing various antigens. After electrophoresis of the antigens the current is discontinued and antiserum is added to the trough. Precipitation bands form as in double diffusion in two dimensions. The apex of each precipitin band corresponds to the center of the corresponding antigen.

B. Human serum, placed at the origin, was analyzed with an antiserum prepared against unfractionated human serum. (Courtesy of Dr. Curtis Williams.)

intersection of their diffusion fronts. The principles involved in the precipitation stage are those already described above, and the familiar reactions of identity, nonidentity, and partial identity may be seen.

By means of immunoelectrophoresis it is possible to detect as many as 30 different antigens in human serum, and to identify otherwise indistinguishable proteins (see, for example, various immunoglobulins, Ch. 14). Many important applications of this method will be encountered in subsequent chapters.

REACTIONS WITH PARTICULATE ANTIGENS

The Agglutination Reaction

Bacterial and other cells in suspension are usually clumped (agglutinated) when mixed with antisera prepared against them. The principles involved are fundamentally the same as those described above for reactions with soluble antigens. Nevertheless, agglutination requires special consideration, for it is widely used as a simple and rapid method for identifying various bacteria, fungi, and types of erythrocytes; and, conversely, with the use of known cells it provides a simple test to detect and roughly quantitate antibodies in sera.

Mechanisms of Agglutination. Agglutination is carried out in neutral dilute salt solutions, e.g., 0.15 M sodium chloride. The ionic strength is important, for at neutral pH bacteria ordinarily bear a net negative surface charge, and the addition of sufficient salt can, by damping these charges, lead to agglutination in the absence of antibodies. Moreover, even with antibodies bound specifically to bacterial surfaces agglutination may not occur if the salt concentration of the medium is too low, e.g., less than 10^{-3} M sodium chloride. The requirement for a suitable ionic environment probably means that a cell's highly negative surface charge must be adequately damped by counter-ions before it can approach other cells closely enough for bivalent antibody molecules to form specific bridges between them.

The influence of ionic strength led Bordet to suggest that agglutination of bacteria by antibodies is due primarily to the nonspecific effect of salt, cells with antibodies specifically bound on their surface being excessively sensitive to the ionic environment. However, when a mixture of readily distinguishable particles, such as nucleated avian erythrocytes and nonnucleated mammalian erythrocytes, is added to a mixture of their respective antisera, each clump that forms consists of cells of one or the other type (Ch. 14, Fig. 14-12Bc). Thus, as expected from the lattice theory (above), each cell-antibody system agglutinates independently of the others in the same medium.

Quantitative Agglutination Reaction. The basic similarity between agglutination and precipitation is also brought out by the agreement between them when used quantitatively to measure antibody concentrations. In the quantitative agglutination procedure the amount of antibody specifically adsorbed from an antiserum by bacterial cells is measured. The amount of antibody bound is taken as the difference between the total protein or N of 1) the specifically agglutinated bacteria, and 2) nonagglutinated bacteria exposed to a control serum. The agglutination method has the advantage that

adsorption is not inhibited by an excess of the antigen. However, its precision is low, since the amount of antibody bound is small relative to the total protein of the bacterial mass used for adsorption. Hence the method is not used routinely; it did, however, serve a useful purpose in demonstrating the essential identity of the antibodies that precipitate soluble pneumococcal capsular polysaccharide and those that agglutinate encapsulated pneumococci (The unitarian hypothesis, below).

Titration of Sera. The agglutination reaction is widely employed as a semiquantitative assay. A given volume of a cell suspension is added to a series of tubes, each containing a fixed volume of antiserum at a different dilution, usually increasing in twofold steps. The reaction is speeded up by shaking and warming to 37° (sometimes to 56°); then, after the cells have been allowed to settle, or have been centrifuged lightly, the clumping is detected by direct inspection. When the dilution of antiserum becomes too great agglutination no longer occurs. The relative strength of an antiserum is expressed as the reciprocal of the highest dilution that causes agglutination. If, for example, a 1:512 dilution gives perceptible agglutination but a 1:1024 dilution does not, the titer is 512.

Agglutination titers are not precise ($\pm$ 100%), but they are easily obtained and provide valid indications of the relative antibody concentrations of various sera, with respect to a particular strain of bacteria. Hence agglutination titrations are of immense practical value in following changes in antibody titer with time during acute bacterial infections (Application of serological tests in diagnosis, below).

Agglutination titers obtained with **different** bacteria are, however, not necessarily at all comparable. In one set of observations, for example, an antiserum to type 1 pneumococcus agglutinated these organisms at a dilution of 1:800 and was found to have about 1.5 mg of antibody per milliliter by the quantitative agglutination reaction. But an antiserum to type 1R pneumococcus with 9.6 mg of antibody per milliliter agglutinated these organisms to a titer of only 1:80. Apparently the number and distribution of determinant groups and of charged groups on the bacterial cell surface can influence titer to a marked degree.

Though agglutination reactions are, in principle, neither more nor less specific than other serological reactions, they present a number of difficulties in actual practice. These arise because a cell surface possesses a great diversity of antigenic determinants capable of mediating the agglutination reaction; and many of these determinants are identical or similar in groups of different but related cells.

the former state they are more persistent (Ch. 15, Immunogenicity).

Prozone. By analogy with the precipitin reaction it would be expected that agglutinating activity would decrease progressively with dilution of an antiserum. Curious departures from this expectation are often observed. With some sera that give effective agglutination reactions when diluted several hundred- or thousandfold, the undiluted or only slightly diluted serum does not visibly react with the antigen particles. The latter region of the titration is called the **prozone**, as in tubes 1 to 3 of the titration below.

Tube No.	1	2	3	4	5	6	7	8	9
Serum dilution	1:8	1:16	1:32	1:64	1:128	1:256	1:512	1:1024	1:2048
Clumping	0	0	0	+	+	+	+	+	0

Hence in order to achieve a high degree of specificity for a particular type or strain of cell it is nearly always necessary to adsorb antisera with sufficient amounts of appropriate cross-reacting cells.

Surface vs. Internal Antigens of Cells. The surface antigens that mediate the agglutination reaction are often called **agglutinogens**; they induce the formation of the corresponding agglutinating antibodies, sometimes called **agglutinins.** When a bacterial, fungal, or animal cell is introduced as an "immunogen" it is probably broken up in the host animal and many of its internal components (of cytoplasm and nucleus) are as immunogenic as the cell's surface components (cell wall and limiting cytoplasmic membrane). However, the only antibodies that can cause agglutination are those specific for surface determinants; the antibodies to internal components either do not penetrate the cells during the agglutination assay, or, if they do, do not constitute effective bridges between cells.

Surface antigens are much more potent immunogenically when administered as part of a morphologically intact cell than when given in purified form, possibly because in

By means of labeled antibodies, or the antiglobulin test described below, it may be shown that unagglutinated cells in the prozone actually have antibodies adsorbed on their surface. Indeed, it might be expected, on statistical grounds, that when antibody molecules are in great excess, relative to the number of functional groups on the cells, the simultaneous attachment of both sites of individual bivalent antibody molecules to different cells would be improbable. Nevertheless, the prozone phenomenon is not due simply to antibody excess, but often involves a special class of antibodies called "blocking" or "incomplete" antibodies.

Blocking or Incomplete Antibodies

In certain sera that exhibit the prozone to a pronounced degree a proportion of the total antibody appears to react with the corresponding particulate antigens in an anomalous manner: the bound antibody not only fails to elicit agglutination but actively inhibits it, as shown on subsequently mixing the particles with antiserum at a dilution that would otherwise evoke a brisk clumping reaction. These inhibitory antibody molecules are referred to as **blocking** or **incomplete** antibodies, and they are particularly evident in certain human antierythrocyte sera (anti-Rh; see Ch. 18) and in antisera to *Brucella*. Some sera, in fact, contain only blocking antibodies; their presence is revealed by the ability to inhibit specifically a standard agglutinating mixture of particles and a reference antiserum.

Under the influence of the lattice theory blocking antibodies have been widely assumed to be univalent. This assumption is inconsistent, however, with the observation that these antibodies will agglutinate the erythrocytes to which they are adsorbed if the reaction is carried out under special conditions, e.g., in the presence of serum albumin at high concentration (instead of in conventional dilute salt solution) or if the red cells are first treated with a proteolytic enzyme (trypsin or ficin).

Blocking antibodies are reminiscent of the nonprecipitating antibodies discussed above in connection with precipitin reactions; both types apparently combine normally with antigenic determinants but fail to bring about aggregation. The molecular basis for this anomalous behavior is not understood.

The Antiglobulin Test. An ingenious method for detecting incomplete or blocking antibodies was brought into prominence by Coombs, Mourant, and Race. Called the **Coombs**, or antiglobulin, test, it is of considerable importance in the recognition of certain hemolytic diseases. The test exploits the fact that an antibody molecule can participate simultaneously in binding to an antigen on the red cell surface and in complexing with antibody to itself (Fig. 13-28). As we shall see subsequently (Ch. 14) antibodies are globular proteins that are highly immunogenic in a foreign species.

For example, rabbits injected with human immunoglobulins (HIG) form anti-HIG molecules, regardless of the specificities of the HIG as antibodies. Hence erythrocytes with incomplete human antibodies bound specifically to their surface can be agglutinated by rabbit anti-HIG serum. Since an antibody molecule can function both as an antibody and as a ligand in two independent and simultaneous reactions, the ligand-binding sites of antibodies must be different from, or represent only a fraction of, their numerous and diverse antigenic determinant groups (Ch. 14).

Passive Agglutination

In the agglutination reactions described above the functional ligand groups are naturally occurring components of cell walls or cell cytoplasmic membranes. It has also been possible to extend the agglutination reaction to a wide variety of soluble antigens by attaching them to the surface of particles. In

Fig. 13-28 The antiglobulin (Coombs) test for incomplete antibodies. Cells coated with specifically bound, incomplete (nonagglutinating) antibodies are clumped by other antibody molecules (from another species), which react specifically with antigenic determinants of the incomplete antibodies.

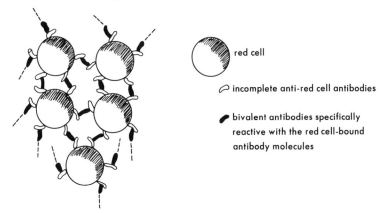

red cell

incomplete anti-red cell antibodies

bivalent antibodies specifically reactive with the red cell-bound antibody molecules

such **passive agglutination** reactions the particles most widely used are erythrocytes (**passive hemagglutination**), a synthetic polymer such as polystyrene, or a mineral colloid such as bentonite. Adsorption ordinarily depends on noncovalent bonds, and is generally achieved by simply mixing the particles with the antigens. Thus erythrocytes readily adsorb many polysaccharides. For the attachment of proteins, however, it is usually necessary first to treat the cells with **tannic acid** (whose mechanism of action is not fully established). Covalent linkage of proteins to the red cell surface has also been achieved by the use of bifunctional cross-linking reagents, e.g., bis-diazotized benzidine and toluene diisocyanate (Fig. 13-29).

As in conventional agglutination tests, passive agglutination is highly sensitive (see below), but its precision is low (at best ± 100%); and antibody levels are measured only in relative terms, not in weight units.

Passive agglutination also provides, through measurement of its inhibition, a sensitive assay for **antigens,** and it has been widely used for this purpose to measure certain hormones in plasma and urine (glucagon, growth hormone, insulin, etc.). For example, polystyrene particles or tanned red cells that have adsorbed a given purified protein or polypeptide hormone can be agglutinated by the corresponding antiserum; and added free ligand in trace amounts specifically inhibits agglutination by competing for antibody. Thus, by comparison with standard antigen solutions, the concentration of antigen in biological fluids, e.g., blood or urine, can be evaluated from their relative ability to inhibit specifically the standard passive agglutination system.

Fig. 13-29 Passive hemagglutination. Bis-diazotized benzidine is used to attach protein antigen X to the red cell surface. Red cells coated with X are specifically clumped by anti-X antibodies. The antiglobulin test shown in Figure 13-28 may be regarded as another form of passive hemagglutination, the antigen attached to the red cell surface being an adsorbed, noncovalently bound, incomplete antibody molecule. Besides benzidine, a variety of other bifunctional reagents have been used, e.g., toluene-2,4-diisocyanate (Fig. 13-33.)

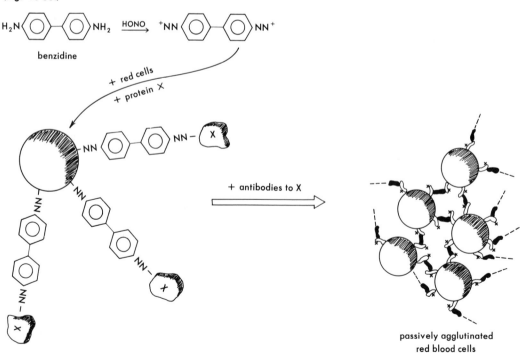

passively agglutinated
red blood cells

Differences in Sensitivity of Precipitation, Agglutination, and Other Reactions

The methods in wide use for measuring antibody levels differ considerably in sensitivity, i.e., in the minimal amounts of antibody that can be detected and measured; and of the two general methods considered so far in this chapter, agglutination is considerably more sensitive than precipitation.

Precipitin reactions in liquid media or gels are usually not observed when antisera are diluted more than 10- to 50-fold. In contrast, many antisera to bacteria or red blood cells retain agglutinating activity after being diluted many thousandfold. And passive agglutination, especially passive hemagglutination, is particularly sensitive. Some mouse antisera to hemocyanin, for example, have passive hemagglutination titers of almost 1,000,000.

This difference in sensitivity is clearly illustrated when agglutination and precipitation involve the same antigen. In one instance, for example, an antiserum to hen ovalbumin (EA) lost ability to precipitate EA when diluted 1:5, but at 1:10,000 dilution it could still agglutinate collodion particles coated with EA. These large differences are probably related to the difference in the number

TABLE 13-5. MINIMAL CONCENTRATIONS OF ANTIBODY DETECTABLE BY VARIOUS QUANTITATIVE AND SEMIQUANTITATIVE METHODS (APPROXIMATE VALUES)

Method	μg antibody/ml
Precipitin reactions in liquid media	20
Precipitin reactions in agar gel	60
Bacterial agglutination	0.1
Passive hemagglutination	0.01
Complement fixation*	1
Passive cutaneous anaphylaxis†	0.02

* See Chapter 16.
† See Chapter 17.

of particles needed for a visible reaction; e.g., about 10^7 bacterial cells, but about 6×10^{12} molecules of soluble antigen (i.e., 1 μg of a protein of M.W. 100,000). The relatively voluminous inert particle, coated with a thin layer of antigen, serves to amplify the reaction.

The several methods in wide use as routine assays for measuring antibody activity are compared in Table 13-5 with respect to sensitivity. Some of these methods are described in later chapters (complement fixation in Ch. 16, and passive cutaneous anaphylaxis in Ch. 17).

FLUORESCENCE AND IMMUNE REACTIONS

The fluorescent* properties of antibody molecules and of certain organic residues that can be attached to them provide the basis for a number of analytical methods. The most important of these is called **immunofluorescence.** Introduced by Coons and coworkers, this method is widely used for rapid identification of bacteria in infected materials and

for the identification and localization of intracellular antigens (and antibodies, Ch. 15).

Immunofluorescence

Of the several reagents that introduce fluorescent groups into proteins, the most widely used with antibodies is fluorescein isothiocyanate (Fig. 13-30). Antibodies substituted with one or two fluorescein residues per molecule are intensely fluorescent but retain their specific reactivity; hence they can specifically stain, for example, bacteria in smears and tissue sections. After a specimen on a slide has been covered for several minutes with a solution of fluorescein-labeled

---

* When molecules absorb light they subsequently dispose of their increased energy by various means, one of which is the emission of light of longer wave length. When the emission is of short duration (10^{-8} to 10^{-9} sec for return of the excited molecule to the ground state) the process is called **fluorescence.** (When the emission is of long duration the process is called phosphorescence.)

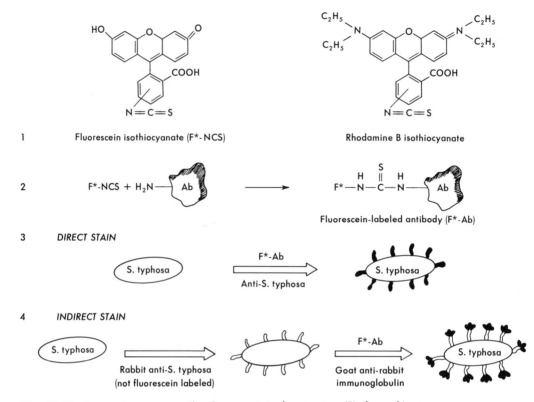

1   Fluorescein isothiocyanate (F*-NCS)   Rhodamine B isothiocyanate

2   F*-NCS + H₂N——Ab   F*——N——C——N——Ab

                                                          Fluorescein-labeled antibody (F*-Ab)

3   DIRECT STAIN

                          F*-Ab
         S. typhosa   ————————>   S. typhosa
                        Anti-S. typhosa

4   INDIRECT STAIN

                                                    F*-Ab
         S. typhosa   ————————>   ————————>   S. typhosa
                     Rabbit anti-S. typhosa   Goat anti-rabbit
                     (not fluorescein labeled)   immunoglobulin

Fig. 13-30 Immunofluorescence. The fluorescent isothiocyanates (1) form thioureas, substituted with the fluorescent group and ε-NH₂ groups of lysine residues of antibodies or other proteins (2). In the **direct** staining reaction (3) the labeled antibodies are specific for the antigen of interest. In the **indirect** reaction (4) the labeled antibodies are specific for the immunoglobulins, in general, of another species (e.g., goat anti-rabbit immunoglubulin); thus one labeled preparation can be used as a stain for a wide variety of serologically specific reactions.

antibodies (usually in the form of the globulin fraction of an antiserum), the slide is rinsed to remove unbound fluorescent protein and then examined in the light microscope, with suitable light source and filters to select the incident light. Since the emitted light (about 530 mμ) is of longer wave length than the background incident light (about 490 mμ), the antibody stands out as a sharply visible yellow-green mass (Fig. 13-31).

As with all immunological reactions it is necessary to establish the specificity of immunofluorescence with suitable controls, some of which are as follows: 1) preliminary treatment of the smear with unlabeled antibodies should saturate the antigenic determinants

and abolish subsequent staining with the fluorescent antibodies; 2) the addition of excess soluble antigen to the staining solution should also competitively block the stain.

By means of the direct and indirect reaction sequences outlined in Figure 13-30 fluorescein-labeled antibodies serve as specific stains for the detection and localization of a wide variety of antigens. In addition, differently colored fluorescent groups can be introduced into antibodies with other reagents, e.g., orange-red fluorescence with rhodamine B isothiocyanate (Fig. 13-30). This modification provides opportunities for applying immunofluorescence to a number of special problems, e.g., to the possible coexistence of

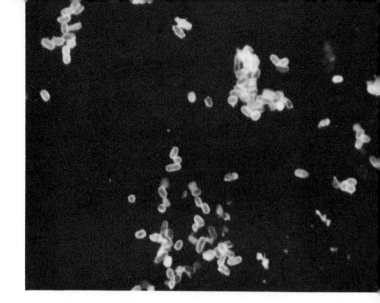

Fig. 13-31 Immunofluorescence staining. Stained with a fluorescein-labeled globulin fraction of a specific antiserum, *E. coli* 0127: B8 is clearly visible in a fecal smear from a patient with infantile diarrhea. Many other types of bacteria are abundant in the smear but are not stained. About ×1000. The photograph was kindly supplied by personnel of the National Communicable Disease Center, Atlanta, Georgia.

different antigens and antibodies in the same cell (Ch. 15, Antibody formation).

In all these applications a recurrent problem arises from the nonspecific staining of tissues, especially by labeled proteins with more than two or three fluorescein residues per molecule. To minimize this difficulty ion-exchange chromatography, and adsorption with acetone-dried tissue powders, are used to remove these highly substituted proteins. In addition, the use of high-titer antisera (e.g., > 2 mg of antibody per milliliter) reduces nonspecific staining by making it possible to work with dilute solutions of labeled protein.

Fluorescence Quenching

Like other proteins, unlabeled antibody molecules also fluoresce in the upper ultraviolet region by virtue of their aromatic amino acid residues. Antibody fluorescence is excited maximally at about 290 mμ (i.e., near the absorption maximum of tyrosine and tryptophan), and the emitted light has maximal intensity at about 345 mμ (which is characteristic of the fluorescence spectrum of tryptophan). When the binding sites in the antibody are specifically occupied by certain kinds of haptens (or antigens) the energy absorbed by the ultraviolet-irradiated tryptophan residues is somehow transferred to the bound ligand, which emits light at some still longer wave length or does not fluoresce at all. The net result of the transfer is quenching or damping of the antibody's characteristic fluorescence. Thus the binding sites of a preparation of purified antibodies can be titrated as shown in Figure 13-32; and the titrations can be used to calculate average intrinsic association constants, which agree with those determined by equilibrium dialysis. Quenching is particularly effective with those ligands whose absorption spectrum overlaps the protein's emission spectrum; but the overlap need not be extensive.

The fluorescence quenching method is not as generally useful as equilibrium dialysis, since many haptens, such as simple sugars, do not quench. However, the method offers a number of significant advantages: it is rapid, requires only minute amounts of antibody, and in special cases can be carried out with ligands that are too large to be dialyzable.

Fluorescence Polarization

When fluorescent molecules are excited by a beam of polarized light the extent of polarization of the emitted light varies with the molecule's size: small molecules, with much rotational motion, have short "relaxation" times and their emission exhibits correspondingly little polarization. If, however, the fluorescent molecule is bound to a relatively large particle, such as an antibody molecule, its relaxation time is prolonged and the polarization of its fluorescence is correspondingly increased. Hence the proportion of ligand molecules bound by antibodies can be determined from the polarization of fluorescent emission. This method, now in its early stages of development, is potentially useful with those small antigens and haptens whose fluorescence spectrum (natural or introduced by fluorescent substituents) is distinctly

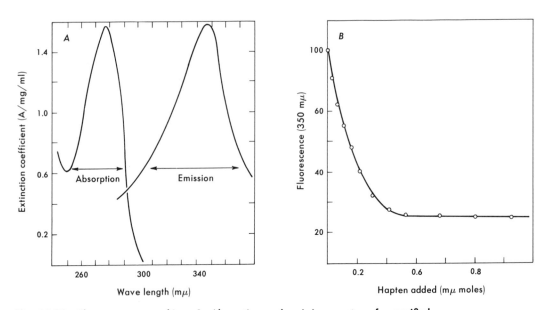

Fig. 13-32 Fluorescence quenching. **A.** Absorption and emission spectra of a purified antibody, specific for the 2,4-dinitrophenyl group. The height of the emission band maximum is set, by convention, equal to that of the absorption maximum, though only about 20% of the energy absorbed by antibodies appears as fluorescence emission. **B.** Decline in fluorescence of the antibody as it binds ε-DNP-lysine; about 75% of the fluorescence is quenched when the antibody's ligand-binding sites are saturated. (From S. F. Velick, C. W. Parker, and H. N. Eisen. Proc. Nat. Acad. Sc. 46:1470, 1960.)

different from that of antibodies (Fluorescence quenching, above).

Fluorescence Enhancement

Certain small organic molecules, such as anilinonaphthalenesulfonates, have strikingly different fluorescence spectra when they exist as free molecules in water and when bound in the active sites of antibodies, which have a much lower dielectric constant than water. It is thus possible to measure the specific binding of such ligands by the corresponding antibodies by following the appearance of fluorescence at the appropriate wavelength. The method is exquisitely sensitive and can be used with antibodies in complex media, such as serum.

APPLICATIONS OF SEROLOGICAL TESTS IN DIAGNOSIS

The etiological diagnosis of infectious diseases is usually established both by isolating the putative causative microorganism and by demonstrating antibodies to it. Several principles are involved in the use of serological tests as diagnostic procedures.

Changing Titer. The antibody formation initiated by an infectious agent, as it invades and multiplies in tissues, may continue for months or even years after the clinically apparent infection has subsided. Hence the presence of an elevated titer of antibodies to a given microbe indicates only that infection (or vaccination) has occurred at some time in the past. In order to establish that an acute illness is due to a particular agent it is desirable to show a **change** in titer to that agent during the illness, i.e., the absence of detectable antibodies during the first week, their appearance and progressive increase in titer during the second and subsequent weeks and, perhaps, their eventual decline. For practical purposes a pair of serum samples are compared, one drawn in the acute phase of the illness, the other during convalescence. If only a single serum sample is available, from late in the illness, a high titer is sometimes accepted as provisional diagnostic evidence; the critical level depends on the disease and the assay, and is determined by experience. Under these circumstances it is necessary to be sure that the high titer is not the result of prior vaccination.

In order to prove that an isolated microorganism plays an etiological role in the illness, and is not merely a symbiont, it is desirable, whenever possible, to use the isolate itself as the antigen in the serological tests.

Identification of etiological agent. Even when no likely agent has been isolated, a provisional etiological diagnosis can be established by testing the serum with antigens from different microbial strains: the antigen that elicits the highest titer reaction is assumed to be from the etiological agent. This procedure, however, can be misleading, even though it is based on the well established rule that an antiserum reacts more copiously with the immunogen than with related antigens (Cross-reactions, this chapter). Thus other antigens, not tested, might have elicited a still higher titer. Moreover, some curious cross-reactions between very different microorganisms may also serve to mislead, e.g., the classic instance in which persons with rickettsial infections form antibodies in high titer to certain *Proteus* X strains.

Time-Course of Immune Response in Infectious Disease. In the course of a given infectious disease the appearance and the persistence of antibodies to the etiological agent follow a different time-course when measured with different antigenic preparations and different assays. In brucellosis, for example, agglutination titers appear early in infection and persist at low levels for years afterward, whereas precipitin levels appear later and disappear much sooner; and in many rickettsial and viral diseases the antibody titers measured by complement fixation (Ch. 16) appear later and subside sooner than those measured by neutralization (Ch. 27).

A number of possibilities can account for these variations. 1) A given microbe is obviously an assembly of many antigens, which differ in amount, immunogenicity, and stability in the animal host. 2) There are structural and functional differences in the antibodies specific for a given antigenic determinant, and different types of antibodies are formed at different stages of the immune response, e.g., γM antibodies (Ch. 14) are formed early in the response and are especially effective in the agglutination assay (Ch. 15, Antibody formation). 3) The various serological methods differ in their sensitivity (Table 13-5), and a method that requires much less antibody will, other things being equal, detect antibody earlier and more persistently than a less sensitive assay. Though the basis for the differences between different assays is not always clear for individual infectious diseases it is important for practical purposes to be aware that such differences exist.

THE UNITARIAN HYPOTHESIS

In the last decade of the nineteenth century immunologists were confronted in rapid succession by discoveries of a bewildering variety of immune phenomena. Particularly impressive, no doubt, was the extraordinary diversity of activities displayed by a given antiserum. A serum prepared, for example, against the cholera vibrio could 1) protect guinea pigs against an otherwise lethal infection with virulent cholera vibrios, 2) agglutinate a suspension of these organisms, 3) form a precipitate with a filtrate of the broth in which they had grown, 4) specifically enhance their phagocytosis by leucocytes, etc. This wide range of phenomena gave rise to the prevailing **pluralistic** view, according to which each of these diverse activities was ascribed (even by so astute an observer as Ehrlich) to a qualitatively different molecular form; these were named agglutinins, precipitins, opsonins (promoters of phagocytosis), protective antibodies, etc.

With the improved methods of analysis developed in the 1930s, however, this view became clearly untenable. For example, Heidelberger found that all the antibody activities of antiserum to type 3 pneumococci were removed by precipitation with the organism's purified capsular polysaccharide; and the protein subsequently isolated from the precipitate duplicated the diverse activities of the antiserum. Moreover, this capsular polysaccharide is a polymer of cellobiuronic acid (Fig. 13-17); and Avery and Goebel found that a cross-reacting antiserum, prepared against a conjugated protein substituted with the *p*-azobenzyl ether of cellobiuronic acid, not only precipitated the type 3 polysaccharide and agglutinated type 3 cells, but also protected mice against lethal infection with these organisms.

From these and similar observations there emerged the **unitarian hypothesis,** according to which a given population of antibodies will, on uniting with the corresponding ligand, produce any of the diverse consequences of anti-body-antigen combination, depending on the state of the ligand and the milieu in which combination takes place: if the ligand is soluble and multivalent, precipitation; if the ligand is a natural constituent of a particle's surface or artificially attached to the surface, agglutination; if the ligand is part of the surface of a virulent bacterium, protection against infection.

These contrasting views may be epitomized by saying that with respect to capacity to elicit the total range of in vivo and in vitro manifestations of antigen-antibody complex formation, the early pluralistic view maintained that a given antibody molecule is **unipotent,** whereas the unitarian view held that the antibody molecule is **totipotent.** But while it has been clear beyond doubt since the 1940s that the pluralistic view is not valid, it is also becoming increasingly clear that the unitarian view is a gross oversimplification. As we shall see in subsequent chapters, it is now evident that among the antibody molecules specific for a given ligand group, some are competent in eliciting certain reactions, and others are not. It therefore seems reasonable to regard any given antibody molecule as being competent to elicit **many** reactions, but not necessarily **all** of them: though antibodies are multipotent to an impressive degree, they are not totipotent.

APPENDIX

Purification of Antibodies

Methods for purifying antibodies are based on the dissociability of antibody-ligand complexes. Two stages are involved in all methods. 1) Antibodies are precipitated from serum with soluble antigens, or adsorbed by insoluble antigenic materials; the latter are often prepared by coupling small haptenic groups or soluble proteins to an insoluble matrix, such as cellulose. 2) After extraneous serum proteins are washed away, antibodies are eluted from the insoluble complexes by specific or nonspecific procedures.

Specific Procedures. With aggregates whose stability depends largely on specific ionic interactions, such as those involving types 3 and 8 pneumococcal polysaccharides (Fig. 13-17), strong salt solutions (e.g., 1.8 M sodium chloride) elute purified antibodies effectively.

With precipitates in which the specific antigenic determinants are simple haptenic groups, such as 2,4-dinitrophenyl, small univalent haptens that encompass the crucial part of the determinant (e.g., 2,4-dinitrophenol) are useful for competitive displacement of the precipitating antigen or adsorbent, yielding soluble antibody-hapten complexes. Depending on the properties of the antigen, the adsorbent, and the hapten, diverse procedures are then used, first, to isolate the soluble antibody-hapten complexes, and, second, to separate the hapten from the antibody (e.g., ion-exchange resins, dialysis, gel filtration).

When small univalent haptens are employed

for specific elution of antibodies it is desirable to use those haptens that are both 1) **weakly bound** by the antibody and 2) **highly soluble.** Highly concentrated solutions of hapten can then be used to elute the antibody, and the weakly bound hapten is easily separated from the soluble hapten-antibody complex, e.g., by dialysis or gel filtration.

Nonspecific Procedures. For the isolation of antibodies to protein antigens it is usually necessary to expose specific aggregates to conditions that cause reversible denaturation of the antibody, allowing it to dissociate from the antigen. Organic acids at pH 2 to 3 are often effective; and various procedures are then used to separate the denatured antibody and antigen, depending on the properties of the antigen. Since antibodies readily regain their native structure on being restored to physiological conditions, neutralization of the antigen-free material yields active antibody.

Yields and Purity. About 10 to 90% of the antibodies in serum can be recovered in purified form by diverse procedures. And the isolated antibodies are often better than 90% pure, with purity being defined as the capacity to react specifically with a given ligand. However, the purified antibodies are usually heterogeneous with respect to affinity for their ligands (Fig. 13-2) and in some physicochemical properties to be discussed later (Ch. 14, Antibody structure).

Ferritin-Labeled Antibodies

As noted earlier, fluorescein-labeled antibodies provide specific stains for the detection and localization of antigens in the light microscope. A similar function is performed at the level of resolution of the electron microscope by ferritin-labeled antibodies. For use in the electron microscope antibodies must be rendered much more highly electron-scattering than proteins in general, and this is accomplished by attaching a molecule of ferritin to an antibody molecule. Ferritin, a protein molecule of about the same size as an antibody molecule, has extraordinarily high electron-scattering capacity because of its uniquely high iron content—about 20%. Ferritin-antibody conjugates were first introduced by Singer, who used toluene-2,4-diisocyanate to form stable covalent links between the two proteins, as is shown in Figure 13-33.

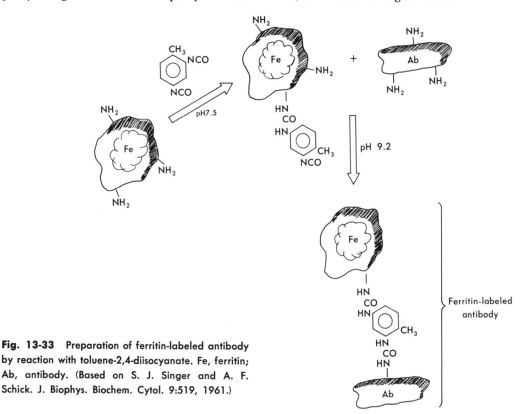

Fig. 13-33 Preparation of ferritin-labeled antibody by reaction with toluene-2,4-diisocyanate. Fe, ferritin; Ab, antibody. (Based on S. J. Singer and A. F. Schick. J. Biophys. Biochem. Cytol. 9:519, 1961.)

SELECTED REFERENCES

Books and Review Articles

HEIDELBERGER, M. *Lectures in Immunochemistry*. Academic Press, New York, 1956.

KABAT, E. A. *Kabat and Mayer's Experimental Immunochemistry*, 2nd ed. Thomas, Springfield, Ill., 1961.

KARUSH, F. Immunologic specificity and molecular structure. *Advances Immunol.* 2:1 (1962).

LANDSTEINER, K. *The Specificity of Serological Reactions*, rev. ed. Harvard University Press, Cambridge, Mass., 1945. Reprinted by Dover Publications, New York, 1962.

MARRACK, J. R. *The Chemistry of Antigens and Antibodies*, H. M. Stat. Off., London, 1938.

SINGER, S. J. Structure and Function of Antigen and Antibody Proteins. In *The Proteins*, vol. III. (H. Neurath, ed.) Academic Press, New York, 1965.

14 ANTIBODY STRUCTURE

THE IMMUNOGLOBULINS

Antibodies were first suspected to be proteins when the antibody activity of immune sera was found to precipitate with globulins. More direct evidence then became available when purified antibodies were obtained. For example, as noted in Chapter 13, specific precipitates obtained with a pneumococcal polysaccharide and its antiserum contain only the polysaccharide and protein, and the protein isolated from such precipitates interacts specifically with the same polysaccharide.

The subsequent analysis of serum proteins by electrophoresis revealed that antibodies are members of a particular class of globulins. Of the three principal electrophoretically separable globulins of vertebrate sera (α-, β-, and γ-globulins) the γ-globulins were observed by Tiselius and Kabat to be elevated in the sera of intensively immunized animals (Fig. 14-1). Moreover, the purified antibodies to various antigens, isolated from specific precipitates, were found to be indistinguishable from γ-globulins, not only with respect to chemical properties (electrophoretic mobility, solubility, amino acid composition), but also with respect to antigenicity. That is, when γ-globulin of a nonimmunized rabbit was used as immunogen in a heterologous species (e.g., in sheep), the resulting antiserum usually reacted not only with the immunogen but with purified rabbit antibodies of various specificities.

Shortly before antibodies were identified as γ-globulins Heidelberger and Pedersen had shown that some purified antibodies sedimented rapidly in the ultracentrifuge (18 to 23S), and others more slowly (7S). With the development of immunoelectrophoresis, about 20 years later, these two types of antibodies were shown to be antigenically distinguishable from each other and from an antigenically related third group of antibody globulins, present at low concentration in human sera (Fig. 14-2).

The γ-globulins are defined as those serum proteins with least anodic mobility under standard conditions of electrophoresis (e.g., barbital buffer, pH 8.6, ionic strength 0.1). It has gradually become clear, however, that some more rapidly moving serum proteins also exhibit antibody activity and are antigenically similar to γ-globulins. Hence, following Hereman's suggestion, all proteins that behave as antibodies, or that have antigenic determinants in common with antibody molecules, are now called **immunoglobulins**.

Fig. 14-1 Free-boundary electrophoresis of serum from a rabbit intensively immunized (hyperimmunized) with hen's ovalbumin, before and after removal of antibody molecules by specific precipitation with ovalbumin. (From A. Tiselius and E. A. Kabat. J. Exp. Med. 69:119, 1939.)

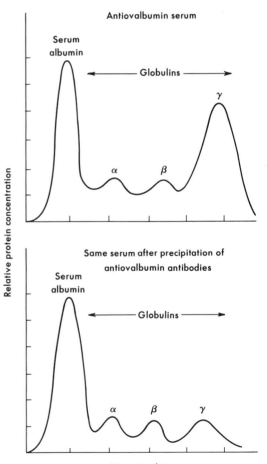

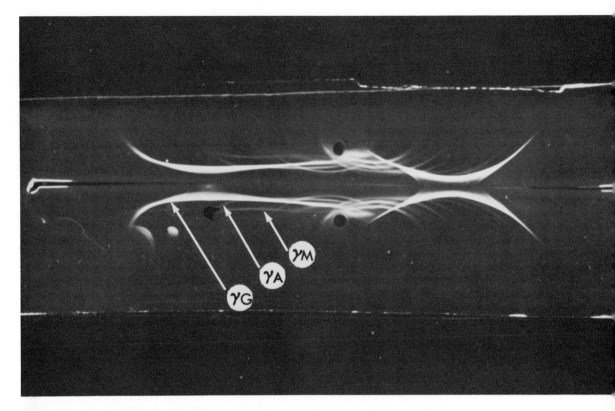

Fig. 14-2 Immunoelectrophoresis of human serum showing γG, γA, and γM immunoglobulins. Serum in the center wells was subjected to electrophoresis in agar in 0.1 M barbital,
pH 8.6. The rabbit antiserum in the long central trough, parallel to axis of migration of
the human proteins, had been prepared against unfractionated human serum. (Courtesy of
Dr. Kirk Osterland; see also Fig. 13-27, Ch. 13.)

Three major classes are now recognized on
the basis of their physical, chemical, and antigenic properties. As is shown in Figure 14-2,
they are called γG immunoglobulin, γA immunoglobulin, and γM immunoglobulin.
(For synonyms, see Appendix at the end of
this chapter.) Their differences in charge also
allow these classes to be separated by ion-
exchange chromatography.

Further subdivisions of these classes have
been recognized as a result of more refined
analyses of their antigenic properties. The
tests are performed with antisera to the various immunoglobulins; for example, purified
human immunoglobulins are injected into
rabbits and monkeys, and the resulting antisera are used as specific analytical reagents.
Four variants of γG immunoglobulin have

been recognized in man, and two or three in
several other species. The antibody molecules
specific for a given ligand group may be
found among the several classes of immunoglobulins, even in a single bleeding of one
immunized individual.

In most normal and hyperimmune individuals over 85% of the immunoglobulins are
γG proteins, and these have accordingly been
studied most extensively.* In view of this
predominance, it is understandable that many
older findings with preparations that were
called γ-globulin have turned out to be valid
for purified γG immunoglobulin.

---

* γA immunoglobulins are probably synthesized at
the same rate as γG, but they are degraded much more
rapidly, and their steady state concentration in serum is
low (Fig. 14-2 and Table 14-2).

γG Immunoglobulins

The γG immunoglobulins are often referred to as 7S γ-globulins because their sedimentation coefficient in neutral, dilute salt solution is 6.5 to 6.6 Svedberg units. Their molecular weight, determined by a variety of methods, is close to 150,000, and hydrodynamic studies (e.g., by sedimentation and viscosimetry) suggest that in aqueous solution the protein is equivalent to an elongated ellipsoid whose major and minor axes are about 240 and 50 A, respectively. These dimensions are consistent with recent studies by electron microscopy and low angle X-ray scattering.

In view of their large molecular weight extensive efforts have been made to determine whether γG antibodies can be separated into subunits or fragments that retain the intact molecule's specific ligand-binding activity. In the following paragraphs we will consider the **subunits** (i.e., polypeptide chains), and later we will consider the **fragments** obtained by enzymatic degradation.

Multichain Structure: Subunits

For proteins in general every chain has an N-terminal amino acid, i.e., a residue whose a-NH$_2$ group is free, unless substituted by an acyl group or modified in some other manner. The number of moles of N-terminal amino acids per mole of protein thus provides a minimal estimate of the number of polypeptide chains per molecule. In human γG immunoglobulin two to three N-terminal residues were found per molecule of protein (on the average), suggesting the presence of at least two to three chains. In horse γG, however, four or five different kinds of N-terminal amino acids were found, but their sum amounted to less than one residue per molecule of protein. This result suggested that the chains are chemically heterogeneous and that somehow they are also often blocked. These results were largely overlooked, however, because for many years most structural studies were carried out on antibodies isolated

from rabbits; and per molecule of rabbit γG there is, on the average, close to one residue of N-terminal alanine. Though traces of other N-terminal amino acids were noted, this evidence was widely interpreted for almost a decade to mean that the rabbit γG molecule consists of one large polypeptide chain.

γG immunoglobulin has a large number of S-S bonds (about 20 to 25 per molecule), and its subunit structure was not established until these were split. In 1959 Edelman discovered that reductive cleavage of most of the disulfide (S-S) bonds in human 7S γ-globulin led to a drop in molecular weight from about 160,000 to about 50,000, suggesting that multiple chains, i.e., subunits, are linked in the intact molecule by S-S bonds. The products obtained were unable to bind antigens or haptens and were soluble only in special solvents, e.g., 6 M urea, probably because under the reducing conditions employed many intrachain S-S bonds were cleaved in addition to S-S bridges between chains. (Rupture of intrachain S-S bonds causes polypeptide chains, in general, to become grossly denatured and insoluble.) Nevertheless, chromatography of the reduced material yielded a subunit of low molecular weight, about 20,000.

Shortly thereafter the macromolecular structure of γG immunoglobulin was greatly clarified by observations of Fleischman, Pain, and Porter: after **mild** reduction, with scission of only four or five disulfide bonds, exposure of the molecule to organic acids caused it to dissociate into subunits, which could be separated on the basis of size by gel filtration. (Evidently cleavage of only about four S-S groups was sufficient to cleave the covalent bridges between chains, and the organic acids caused the chains to separate by breaking noncovalent hydrophobic bonds and by imposing many positive charges on the chains, leading to their mutual repulsion.) Two components, designated A and B, were recovered with essentially 100% yield of the starting material (Fig. 14-3); the molecular weight of A was about 50,000 and that of B was

Fig. 14-3 Separation of heavy and light chains of γG immunoglobulin by gel filtration on Sephadex G75 in 1 M propionic acid. Prior to gel filtration the protein had been reduced (S-S to 2SH) and alkylated to prevent reoxidation, i.e., the SH groups were converted by treatment with iodoacetate to S-carboxymethyl groups (. . . S-CH₂-COOH). (Based on J. Fleischman, R. H. Pain, and R. R. Porter. Arch. Biochem. Suppl. 1, 174, 1962.)

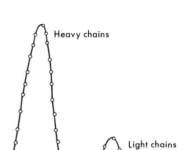

20,000 to 25,000. Since recovery was quantitative the arithmetic was simple: on the assumption that the A and B fractions were each made up of single chains, the original molecule of 150,000 molecular weight consisted of two heavy chains (2 × 50,000) plus two light chains (2 × 25,000). As will be discussed later (Localization of the active site), it is of particular interest that the heavy chains obtained in this manner retained some of the ligand-binding activity of the intact molecules from which they were derived.

The more extensively denatured subunits obtained originally by scission of most S-S bonds were called H (for heavy) and L (for light). Except for differences in extent of denaturation the subunits obtained by limited or extensive reduction are the same, i.e., **A = H and B = L**, and the terms **heavy** chain and **light** chain, respectively, are now preferred (see Appendix, this chapter).

Fragmentation with Enzymes

It has long been known that antibodies can be split by proteolytic enzymes into biologically active fragments. In fact, proteolysis of horse and rabbit immunoglobulins was used extensively in the past to reduce the frequency of allergic reactions in persons treated with immune sera (Ch. 17, Serum sickness). Early attempts to analyze the architecture of antibody molecules by enzymatic fragmentation were, however, of limited value until certain S-S bonds were also cleaved.

Papain Digestion. In 1959 Porter showed that digestion of rabbit γG immunoglobulins with papain, in the presence of cysteine, caused a decrease in sedimentation constant from 7S to 3.5S, with loss of only about 10% of the protein as small dialyzable peptides. By ion-exchange chromatography the digest separated into three fractions. These were originally called I, II, and III (Fig. 14-4); but it was subsequently recognized that I and II are parts of a large spectrum of similar fragments derived from parent γG molecules of different net electrical charge (Charge heterogeneity, below). When the I, II fragments were obtained from purified antibodies, they could be shown to retain the antibody specificity of the parent molecule but to be univalent, i.e., to contain a single ligand-binding site per fragment; and their total yield accounted fully for the ligand-binding activity of the intact bivalent antibody molecules from which they were split. These fragments are now collectively called **Fab** (antigen-binding fragments).

The third fragment (III) is different. It does not combine with antigens or haptens, and it is much the same in all rabbit γG molecules, regardless of their specificity as antibodies. Moreover, in contrast to intact antibody molecules, this fragment is crystallizable; hence it is now called **Fc** (crystallizable fragment).

Of the total digest prepared with papain, about 2/3 is Fab and 1/3 Fc; and the molecu-

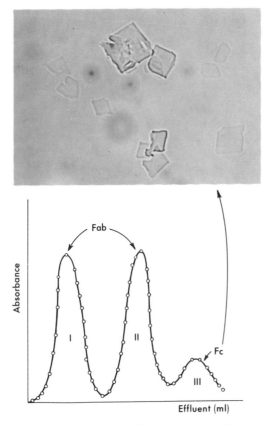

Fig. 14-4 Chromatographic separation of fragments of rabbit γG immunoglobulin produced by digestion with papain in the presence of cysteine. When the crude digest is dialyzed against dilute phosphate buffer, pH 7.0, the Fc fragment crystallizes (see above). The supernatant, containing some soluble Fc and all the Fab fragments, may then be chromatographed on carboxymethylcellulose at pH 5.2 as shown. The relative amounts of the several Fab peaks vary widely with different preparations of γG immunoglobulin. Crystallization of Fc is regularly observed with rabbit and some guinea pig γG immunoglobulins, but only with rare preparations of human immunoglobulin, and so far with no immunoglobulins of other species. (Based on R. R. Porter, Biochem. J. 73:119, 1959.)

lar weights of the fragments are about 45,000 and 50,000, respectively. The arithmetic again appears straightforward: an intact, bivalent γG antibody molecule is made up of two univalent Fab fragments joined through α-peptide bonds to one Fc fragment.

In the early use of papain cysteine was added because the activity of the enzyme depends on keeping its SH groups reduced. Subsequent work has revealed, however, that the cysteine was performing an additional, critical role, for it also reduced some S-S bonds in the immunoglobulin substrate. Thus fragmentation of γG molecules into Fab and Fc is actually the result of two independent reactions, which can be carried out concomitantly or in sequence: 1) proteolytic cleavage of a few peptide bonds (about four are sufficient), and 2) reductive cleavage of one critical and particularly labile S-S bond.

Other Proteases. Using **pepsin**, Nisonoff demonstrated that digestion of γG antibodies, in the absence of cysteine, yields a 5S bivalent fragment of molecular weight about 100,000, which can be split subsequently by reduction of one S-S bond to yield univalent fragments; the latter are indistinguishable from the Fab fragments prepared with papain with respect to sedimentation constant (3.5S), ligand-binding activity, and antigenicity. But the pepsin fragment has a molecular weight about 10% higher, and it contains some covalently linked carbohydrate. To indicate these small differences the univalent fragment obtained with pepsin is called **Fab′**, and the corresponding 5S bivalent fragment is **F(ab′)₂**. The Fc fragment is not recovered in pepsin digests because it is broken down to several smaller fragments.

A variety of other proteolytic enzymes also split immunoglobulins into a number of fragments; and until recently these fragments, obtained from many species by the use of different proteases, were described by a bewildering variety of terms. Nevertheless, a unified architectural pattern has emerged for all γG antibodies, at least of mammals and birds. In these molecules two compact globular domains (corresponding to Fab fragments) are joined to a third compact domain (corresponding to the Fc fragment) by connecting regions that are highly susceptible to attack by many proteases (Fig. 14-5). Cleavage of peptide bonds in the connecting regions yields three stable globular fragments

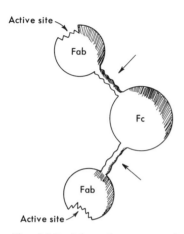

Fig. 14-5 Schematic representation of a γG immunoglobulin molecule showing three globular domains linked by regions that are highly susceptible to attack by proteolytic enzymes, shown by arrows. The active ligand-binding sites, in Fab domains, are shown to be far removed from each other to indicate that steric interference is negligible when two large antigen units, such as red blood cells, are simultaneously bound to the same antibody molecule. This scheme bears considerable resemblance to the electron micrograph of Figure 14-6. (Based on M. E. Noelken, C. A. Nelson, C. E. Buckley, and C. Tanford. J. Biol. Chem. 240:218, 1965.)

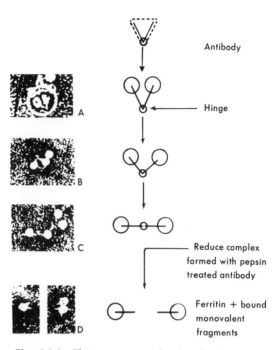

Fig. 14-6 Electron micrographs of antibody-antigen complexes. The antigen is ferritin. In **A** and **B** the large spherical ferritin molecules are linked by V-shaped antibody molecules which appear in **C** to have opened into elongated rods that bridge between ferritin molecules. In **D** the ferritin molecules bind the short, univalent Fab' fragments prepared by treating the bivalent antiferritin antibody with pepsin and a reducing agent. (From A. Feinstein and A. J. Rowe. Nature 205:147, 1965.)

that are relatively resistant to further proteolytic digestion. From hydrodynamic studies with the isolated fragments and intact γG molecules, it has been suggested that the molecule is hinged, as is indicated in Figure 14-5. Some recent electron micrographs provide independent evidence in support of this view (Fig. 14-6).

Correlation Between Subunits and Fragments

The immunogenicity of isolated proteolytic fragments has aided the analysis of antibody structure by making it possible to match fragments with dissociated chains. For example, goat antisera to the isolated Fc fragment of rabbit γG immunoglobulin form specific precipitates with isolated heavy chains, as well as with Fc, but do not react with light chains. In contrast, the corresponding anti-Fab sera form specific precipitates with both light and heavy chains (Table

14-1). These findings led Porter to formulate the schematic structure for γG immunoglobulins shown in Figure 14-7; and all information now available is consistent with this scheme.

The structural symmetry of the γG antibody molecule, with its two kinds of chains, each in duplicate, conforms with the func-

TABLE 14-1. GOAT ANTIBODIES TO HUMAN Fab AND Fc FRAGMENTS: Precipitation Reaction with Chains Isolated from Human γG Immunoglobulin

	Antisera to	
	Fab	Fc
Heavy chains	+	+
Light chains	+	−

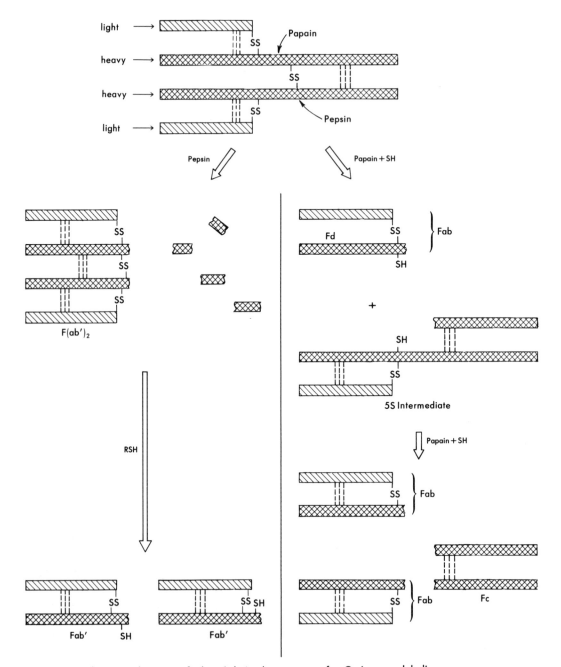

Fig. 14-7 Schematic diagram of the 4-chained structure of γG immunoglobulins showing major interchain S-S bonds and regions susceptible to attack by papain and pepsin (arrows). That portion of the heavy chain within the Fab fragment is the Fd piece; hence an Fab fragment consists of one light chain plus one Fd piece. Pepsin cleaves to the right and papain to the left of the principal SS link between heavy chains. Dashed lines represent noncovalent bonds between chains. (The scheme for pepsin is based on A. Nisonoff, F. Wissler, L. Lipman, and D. Woernley. Arch. Biochem. 89:230, 1960. The 5S intermediate in papain cleavage is based on C. A. Nelson. J. Biol. Chem. 239:3727, 1964.)

tional symmetry of these molecules, i.e., the presence of two binding sites per molecule, both specific for the same ligand.

Genetic Variations

According to the one gene–one polypeptide hypothesis the heavy and light chains should be specified by two different genes. This expectation found support in analyses of some subtle antigenic differences among rabbit γG proteins, initiated in 1956, i.e., several years before their multichain structure was appreciated.

Isoantigens. Though animals only rarely form antibodies to components of their own tissues, some substances derived from one individual are regularly immunogenic in certain other individuals of the **same** species. These substances, called **isoantigens**, will be discussed further in Chapter 18, as they are of practical importance for blood transfusions and tissue transplantation, and are also of considerable theoretical interest. Of particular relevance here is the fact, established by Oudin with rabbits, that immunoglobulins are isoantigens. The several isoantigenic forms of the immunoglobulins are called allotypes (Gr. *allos*, "other").

Rabbit Allotypes. Soluble immunoglobulins from one rabbit have little immunogenic potency in other rabbits. But with the aid of adjuvants (Ch. 15), antigen-antibody precipitates formed from one rabbit's serum can elicit in some other rabbits antibodies that react specifically with immunoglobulins of the donor and of many other rabbits. The antisera thus produced have been arranged into six main types on the basis of precipitin reactions with immunoglobulins from many individual rabbits. Each type corresponds to a particular allotypic form of rabbit immunoglobulin; and with standard sera as analytical reagents the distribution of γG allotypes in rabbit families has been studied.

The patterns of inheritance of γG allotypes reveal that they correspond to two **independently segregating** genetic loci with multiple,

codominant* alleles at each. At locus **a** the known alleles in rabbits are designated a^1, a^2, and a^3, and the corresponding immunoglobulins are a1, a2, and a3. At locus **b** the known alleles are designated b^4, b^5, and b^6, and the corresponding immunoglobulins are b4, b5, and b6. Additional alleles, of low frequency, are expected to turn up. Different allotypes produced under the aegis of different alleles at the same locus are often referred to as **allelic allotypes**: thus a1, a2, and a3 are allelic with each other, and b4, b5, and b6 form another allelic group. The total immunoglobulins of each individual contain the product of each allele it possesses at both **a** and **b** loci. Hence the serum of an individual rabbit possesses two, three, or four γG allotypes, depending on whether the animal is homozygous or heterozygous at one or both loci (Fig. 14-8).

The significance of these loci became clearer with the observation that allotype-specific sera react not only with certain γG molecules but also with chains isolated from these molecules. The light chains are precipitated only by antisera to determinants specified by alleles of the **b** locus, whereas the heavy chains (which react poorly because they tend to be denatured during isolation) precipitate only with antisera to the **a** allotypes. **Thus the a locus specifies the heavy chains, and the b locus the light chains** (Fig. 14-8).

Precipitin reactions also reveal that with heterozygous rabbits the two heavy chains in any particular γG molecule are of the **same** allotype, as are the two light chains. For example, with serum from a heterozygous rabbit with allotypes b4 and b5, successive additions of anti-4 and anti-5 sera precipitate about 60 and 30% of the γG immunoglobulins, respectively; and when the order of addition is reversed the amounts precipitated by each serum are the same. Thus anti-4 serum does not precipitate molecules carrying the "5" markers, and anti-5 does not precipi-

---

* Alleles in a heterozygous diploid animal are codominant when both are expressed, more or less equally.

tate molecules with "4" markers. Similar observations have been made with **a** allotypes. **Thus, each γG molecule contains two identical heavy chains and two identical light chains,** even when synthesized in a heterozygous animal. However, in any particular molecule any of the light-chain allotypes may be found associated with any of the heavy-chain allotypes. Thus nonallelic allotypes are paired randomly, but allelic allotypes are not (Fig. 14-8).

About 10-30% of the γG molecules in rabbit serum are not precipitated by standard antisera to light chain allotypes (b4, b5, b6). This result indicates that there is an additional locus for

Fig. 14-8 Some examples of allotypes of rabbit γG immunoglobulins. The numbers (4, 5, etc.) refer not to single antigenic determinants but to over-all antigenic character; each thus probably represents a characteristic mosaic of antigenic determinants, as with any distinctive protein antigen. The same allotypic markers have been found in rabbit γG and γM immunoglobulins. In man, however, the known allotypic markers in γG heavy chains are **not** present in γM heavy chains. (Based on S. Dray and A. Nisonoff. Proc. Soc. Exp. Biol. & Med. 113:20, 1963.)

Genotype	Phenotype	Schematic diagram of phenotype	Comment
a^1b^4	1/4	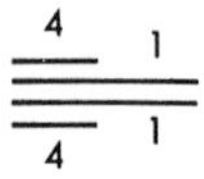	Homozygous at a and b loci
$a^1b^4b^5$	1/4,5	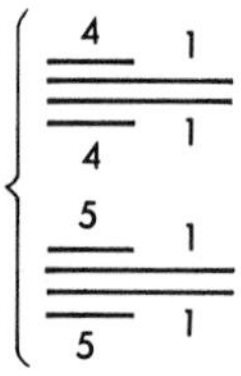	Homozygous at a, Heterozygous at b
$a^1a^2b^4$	1,2/4	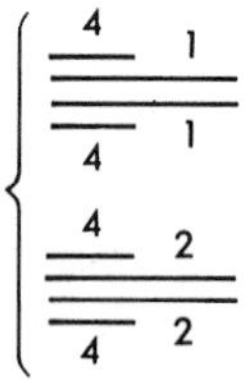	Homozygous at b, Heterozygous at a
$a^1a^2b^4b^5$	1,2/4,5	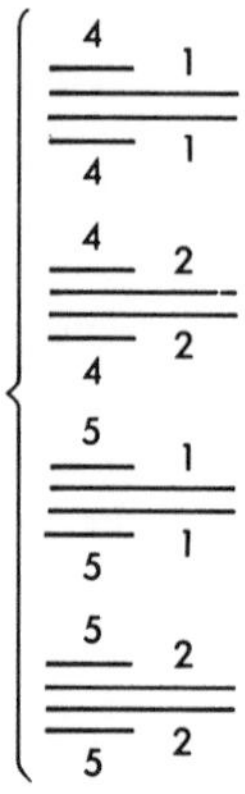	Heterozygous at both loci

lights chains, probably producing other allotypes. In addition, several of the allotypic specificities (at least a1, a2, and b5) appear to be **families** of allotypes; e.g., the immunoglobulins of each family appear as multiple precipitin bands in gel diffusion against the corresponding anti-allotype serum. Some rabbits (and their progeny) have only certain members of the a1 family, while others (and their progeny) have different members of the same family. The a1 allotype (and several others) thus appears to be governed by a multiallelic cluster of closely linked loci. It should be recalled, however, that the loci controlling light chains and those controlling heavy chains are **unlinked** (i.e., they segregate independently), suggesting that they are located on different chromosomes.

The antigenic differences between allelic allotypes might be expected to reflect differences in their amino acid sequences, and this expectation is supported by differences in the peptide maps of purified light-chain preparations of different allotypes.

In addition to the rabbit, allotypy has been found in the immunoglobulins of other mammalian species, including the mouse, guinea pig, baboon, and man.

Human Allotypes. As noted with rabbit allotypes, the immunoglobulins are ineffective isoantigens when injected as soluble proteins. Thus in man, as in rabbits, transfusions of whole blood, plasma, or soluble immunoglobulins do not induce significant formation of antibodies to the donor's immunoglobulin. Nevertheless, by a fortuitous and completely different approach based on the study of rheumatoid disease, allotypic immunoglobulins in man were discovered independently of, and simultaneously with, their initial demonstration in rabbits.

Some human sera, particularly those from patients with chronic rheumatoid arthritis, contain certain immunoglobulins, called **rheumatoid factors,** that react specifically with pooled human γG immunoglobulin. The reaction of rheumatoid factor with human immunoglobulin is revealed, among other ways, by agglutination of human erythrocytes coated with human antierythrocyte antibodies of the incomplete type (Ch. 13, Blocking antibodies; Ch. 18, Rh system). In studying such reactions Grubb observed that a given rheumatoid factor reacted with cells that had been coated with the anti-red-cell antibodies of only certain persons. Any particular agglutination reaction could, moreover, be specifically inhibited only by the serum of particular individuals. The immunoglobulins of the inhibiting sera presumably carry the same antigenic determinants as the antibody molecules adherent to the red cells, and thus the two sets of molecules compete for rheumatoid factor (Fig. 14-9).

Though the origin of rheumatoid factors is still obscure, they have proved to be valuable reagents for typing human immunoglobulins.* Through the interactions of several rheumatoid factors and serum samples from large numbers of people, several heritable types of human γG immunoglobulins have been revealed. From their distribution within families, and from the coexistence of certain types in individual sera, they are classified into two main groups, both represented in almost every person's γG immunoglobulin.

These two groups have been designated **Gm** (for γ-globulin) and **InV** (In for inhibitor and V for the patient contributing the agglutinating serum). As with rabbit **a** and **b** allotypes, the two groups are under the respective genetic control of independently segregating loci, and are localized on different polypeptide chains: **the Gm markers are found on the heavy chains of γG immunoglobulins and the InV markers on light chains.**

---

* More recently agglutinating globulins of similar specificities have been found in the serum of some normal persons. Called SNagg, for serum normal agglutinators, these are now preferred over Ragg, the rheumatoid serum agglutinators, for typing human immunoglobulins. It has been suggested that agglutinators might arise at rare events in normal persons through unintentional immunization—e.g., following blood transfusion (Ch. 18), or transfer of maternal or foetal immunoglobulins across the placenta (Ch. 15).

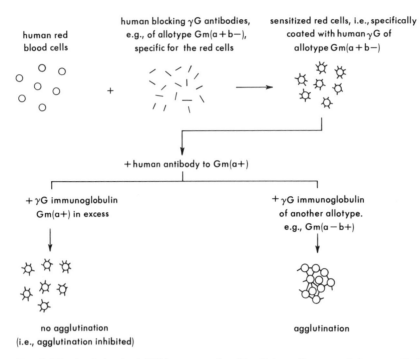

human red blood cells

human blocking γG antibodies, e.g., of allotype Gm(a+b−), specific for the red cells

sensitized red cells, i.e., specifically coated with human γG of allotype Gm(a+b−)

+human antibody to Gm(a+)

+γG immunoglobulin Gm(a+) in excess

+γG immunoglobulin of another allotype. e.g., Gm(a−b+)

no agglutination (i.e., agglutination inhibited)

agglutination

Fig. 14-9 Agglutination-inhibition assay for identifying allotypes of human γG immunoglobulins. The inhibition assay is convenient because with one batch of sensitized red cells and a specific agglutinating serum many individual human sera can be rapidly examined to determine whether they have immunoglobulins of the same allotype as the blocking antibody that coats the red cells. (Based on R. Grubb and A. B. Laurell. Acta path. et microbiol. scandinav. 39:195, 390, 1956.)

At least 16 Gm allotypes have been recognized. They fall into several allelic groups, each of which is associated with a particular subclass of γG immunoglobulins. (As described below, subclasses of human γG immunoglobulins have been clearly identified with the aid of myeloma proteins, which are unusually homogeneous immunoglobulins produced by plasma cell tumors.) For example, the allelic allotypes called Gm(a) and Gm(f) are found only in those immunoglobulins of the subclass known as γGb (also called We group or γ2b); Gm(a) and Gm(f), however, are not allelic with another group of allelic allotypes called Gm(b^{α}), Gm(b^{β}), Gm(b^{γ}), and Gm(b^3), which are found only in immunoglobulins of the γGc subclass (also called Vi group or γ2c). These and similar results emerging from extensive serologic and genetic analyses indicate that the Gm allotypes are governed by four closely linked loci, some of which (perhaps all) have multiple alleles.

Charge Heterogeneity

When purified γG immunoglobulin is subjected to electrophoresis at its isoelectric point (about pH 7) the center of the protein band remains stationary, but its boundary spreads with time. The spreading is considerably greater than that observed with other purified proteins (e.g., many crystallized enzymes) and is considerably faster than can be accounted for by diffusion. Moreover, if the electrical field is reversed (+ becomes −, and − becomes +) the boundaries come together again, at the same rate as that at which they previously separated. This phenomenon, known as **reversible boundary spreading**, is illustrated in Figure 14-10. It indicates that with a γG population as a whole at its **average** isoelectric point, some members of the population have higher iso-

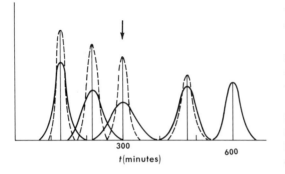

Fig. 14-10 Reversible boundary spreading of γG immunoglobulin in free electrophoresis (pH 7.2), showing heterogeneity in net electrical charge of normal human γG immunoglobulins. Solid lines are refractive index gradient curves. The superimposed dotted lines show patterns that would have been obtained if the spreading had been due to diffusion alone. The field was reversed after 300 minutes (arrow). Similar heterogeneity is observed even with purified antibody specific for a single ligand group. (From R. A. Alberty. J. Am. Chem. Soc. 70:1675, 1948.)

and diffuse zones. Thus the heavy chains are also inhomogeneous.

The light chains, on the other hand, vary in a curiously discrete fashion. They separate on gel electrophoresis into eight to ten distinct bands (Fig. 14-11). Moreover, a similar

Fig. 14-11 Multiplicity of light chains in γG immunoglobulins from rabbit (1), guinea pig (2), cow (3), horse (4), baboon (5), and human (6). The light chains were subjected to electrophoresis in 8M urea — 0.035 M glycine, pH 8, in starch gel. (The rabbit light chains separate into 8-10 discrete bands more clearly at pH 5-6, or with electrophoresis in polyacrylamide gel.) (From S. Cohen and R. R. Porter, Biochem. J., 90:278, 1964.)

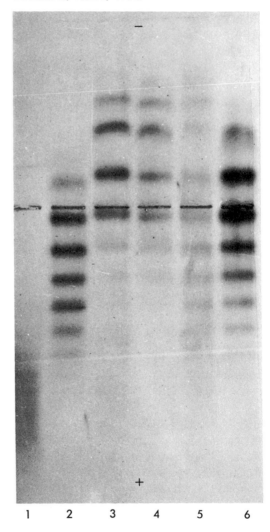

electric points than the average (and hence move to the cathode), whereas others have lower values than the average (and hence move to the anode).

Electrophoretic inhomogeneity is also observed with Fab fragments, which are expected to vary in structure since they possess diverse ligand-binding sites.

Inhomogeneity with respect to electrical charge is characteristic of γG and other immunoglobulin populations, including highly purified antibodies. It is expressed in a wide variety of circumstances, e.g., in electrophoresis in paper and agar gel (see, for example, the broad γG zone in Figs. 14-2 and 14-14) and in ion-exchange chromatography.

Charge Heterogeneity of Chains. If human γG immunoglobulins are arbitrarily separated by electrophoresis into a more rapidly and a more slowly migrating fraction, the heavy chains isolated from each fraction show corresponding differences in mobility. Moreover, they migrate as broad

set of bands is observed with light chains of the two different (InV) allotypes. Since the banding is observed in solvents that cause extensive unfolding of polypeptide chains (e.g., 8 M urea), the bands presumably differ from each other in covalent structure and not simply in aggregation or in accessibility of ionized groups.

Stability and Disulfide Bridges

γG immunoglobulins are relatively stable proteins. In serum, as well as in the form of highly purified antibodies, they are stable for years at low temperature. Moreover, as judged from spectral properties and from activity as antibodies, the conformational changes that the molecules undergo when exposed to denaturing conditions, such as heat to 70°, pH 11, pH 2, and 8 M urea, appear to be largely reversible when the molecules are returned to dilute salt solution at physiological conditions of pH and temperature.

In view of this unusual stability, it is of interest that **these proteins have no recognizable periodic structures**, such as the α-helix, which contribute to the stability of many proteins. Instead, their remarkable elasticity is largely due to their unusually large content of disulfide (S-S) groups, about 20 to 25 per molecule. These stabilize the protein by serving as covalent cross-linking bridges between various cysteine residues of the polypeptide chains. As indicated in the legend of Figure 14-7, three or four of the S-S bonds link the four chains together; the remainder are distributed within the chains, stabilizing their respective conformations. It appears that there are two disulfides within each light chain and about six within each heavy chain.

When intact γG protein is treated with a mercaptan (e.g., 0.1 M 2-mercaptoethanol) in neutral aqueous solution only about 1/4 of the disulfide bridges are reduced to SH groups. The remainder are reduced by the mercaptan only if the molecule is extensively unfolded by the presence of high concentrations of urea, guanidine, or a detergent. The fully reduced molecule is unable to combine specifically with antigen or hapten. Under most circumstances that permit S-S bonds to re-form the reoxidized protein is also inactive, presumably because incorrect pairing of SH groups leads to a permanently deranged conformation. The exceptional circumstance, under which fully reduced Fab fragments regain some activity, is discussed at the end of this chapter.

As has been observed with other disulfide-linked multichain proteins, such as insulin, the **inter**chain S-S bonds are more easily reduced than the **intra**chain S-S bonds. This fortunate difference makes it possible to separate relatively unmodified heavy and light chains after mild reduction; moreover, it is possibly of importance in the biosynthesis of these complex molecules, as we may infer from the preparation of hybrid antibodies, discussed next.

Hybrid Antibodies

In order of increasing resistance to reductive cleavage (S-S to SH), the S-S bonds of γG immunoglobulins fall into several classes: 1) those that link the heavy chains, 2) those that link light to heavy chains, and 3) those within light and heavy chains (intrachain). Under the mildest reducing conditions only the first set is reduced, splitting the molecule into symmetrical halves, each consisting of one heavy plus one light chain. The halves separate when, owing to lowered pH, they acquire large positive charges; they reassociate to form native molecules when returned to neutral pH. When their SH groups are blocked chemically, e.g., by treatment with iodoacetic acid, the halves can still associate, now without the aid of S-S bridges, to form molecules that are essentially indistinguishable from the original γG protein in sedimentation properties and antigenicity.

The association between half-molecules appears to be random. For example, when half-molecules from a preparation of purified antibodies of a particular specificity are mixed with an excess of half-molecules from non-specific γG protein, some of the reconstituted complete molecules behave in precipitin reactions as though univalent, i.e., as though formed from one antibody half-molecule plus one nonspecific half-molecule. Thus they specifically inhibit the corresponding precipitin reaction. Such reconstituted molecules are known as **hybrids** (Fig. 14-12).

Hybrid antibodies may also be prepared by mild reduction of the F(ab')$_2$ fragments obtained by pepsin digestion (p. 420); this leads to Fab' fragments, each with one ligand-binding site and one free SH group. If the fragments are prepared from two purified antibodies, of different specificity, then mixed and allowed to reoxidize, a number of hybrid bivalent fragments appear with a different ligand-binding specificity at each of the two sites. Thus, if one set of fragments is derived from anti-A and the other from anti-B antibodies, the hybrid fragments precipitate with a **mixture** of antigen A and antigen B, but not with either antigen alone (Fig. 14-12), a result neatly in accord with the lattice theory of precipitation (Ch. 13). The proportion of hybrid fragments indicates that the combination of two Fab' fragments to form one F(ab')$_2$ fragment is random.

Symmetry. Though pairing of half molecules or Fab' fragments appears to be essentially random in the test tube, there must be restrictions in vivo since naturally occurring immunoglobulin molecules, as noted above, are symmetrical: in any particular molecule the two light chains are the same, as are the two heavy chains; e.g., light chains have the same allotypic determinants and heavy chains are of the same class. This form of symmetry may also account for the homospecificity of individual γG molecules, i.e., the same specificity at its two ligand-binding sites. The biosynthetic restrictions implied by this symmetry principle could mean that each immunoglobulin-producing cell is capable of forming, at least at any one time, only one type of light chain and one type of heavy chain (Ch. 15).

Carbohydrate Content

All immunoglobulins contain covalently linked carbohydrate moieties, i.e., they are glycoproteins; and in all classes **the carbohydrate is associated with heavy chains.** The amount is much greater in γM and in γA than in γG (Table 14-2); but the carbohydrate has been most extensively studied in γG, in which it amounts to about 3% by weight. About 50% of the carbohydrate is hexose, about 40% is hexosamine, and small amounts of fucose and sialic acid are present.

The function of the carbohydrate is not known. It is not essential for binding antigens or haptens, since Fab fragments, free of carbohydrate, react just as well as intact antibodies. And it does not account for the antigenicity of immunoglobulins when these are used as immunogens in foreign species.

In rabbit γG the carbohydrate seems to be distributed between two oligosaccharide moieties attached to different parts of the heavy chain. The larger moiety is attached covalently to an aspartic acid residue in the Fc fragment. The smaller may be attached close to the points of cleavage by pepsin and papain (Fig. 14-7); it is present in Fab' fragments, and with papain digestion a small peptide bearing this oligosaccharide tends to adhere noncovalently to Fab fragments.

γG molecules appear to be heterogeneous in their carbohydrate content; the molecules with larger amounts of carbohydrate are more resistant to papain digestion than those with lesser amounts. This difference is consistent with the evidence that papain seems to cleave the heavy chains close to the site of attachment of a carbohydrate moiety.

Other Immunoglobulins

γM Immunoglobulins

As was noted above, some of the earliest samples of purified antibodies had high sedimentation values (18 to 23S). Called 19S antibodies, they were obtained from horses that had been intensively immunized with pneumococci, and were specific for the pneumococcus capsular polysaccharide. Most purified antibodies subsequently obtained were from other species and were specific for other ligands, and they proved to be γG immuno-

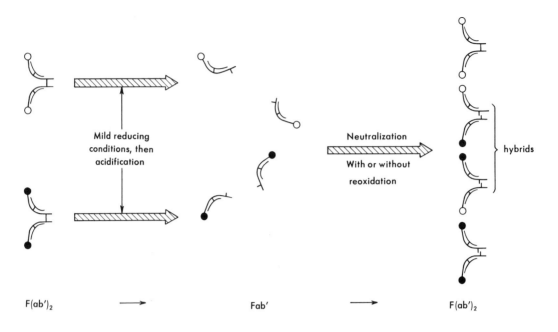

F(ab')₂ ⟶ Fab' ⟶ F(ab')₂

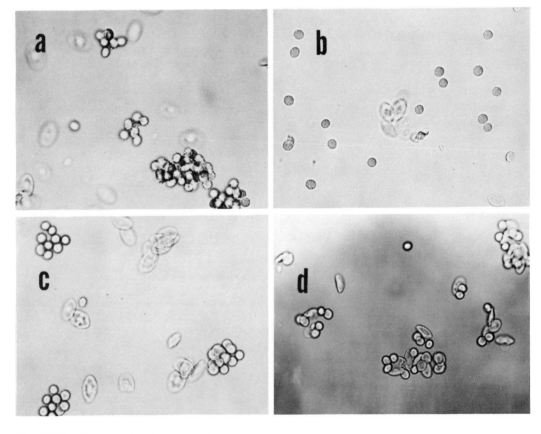

Fig. 14-12 *(See legend on facing page)*

globulins (7S). The 19S antibodies were therefore considered to be quite exceptional. Recently, however, it has become evident that in most immune responses, regardless of immunogen or species, the antibodies detected earliest, though usually transiently and in trace amounts, are of this variety (Ch. 15). Now called γM immunoglobulins, these proteins are characterized by high molecular weight (about 10^6) and higher electrophoretic mobility (at pH 8.6) than other immunoglobulins. Antigenically, the γM proteins are related to, but distinguishable from, γG and γA immunoglobulins.

Under mild reducing conditions (i.e., 0.1 M 2-mercaptoethanol at neutral pH) γM protein dissociates into 7S subunits, which are presumably locked together in the intact pro-

Fig. 14-12 Formation of hybrid bivalent antibody fragments. The principle is outlined in **A.** F(ab′)₂ fragments prepared from anti ○ and anti ● are reduced to Fab′ fragments, which are mixed and allowed to reoxidize. Twice as many hybrids are formed as bivalent fragments of the original specificity, indicating randomness in reassociation. The same procedure can be carried out with intact 7S molecules reduced to half-molecules (one light plus one heavy chain), which also appear to reassociate randomly on reoxidation to form 7S hybrids. For precipitation of hybrid F(ab′)₂ fragments it is necessary to have both antigen ○ and antigen ● present (see Fig. 13-13). **B.** Dual specificity of hybrid antibody fragments revealed by mixed hemagglutination. The Fab′ fragments were obtained from rabbit antibodies specific for chicken ovalbumin (Ea) or for bovine γ-globulin (BγG). Human red cells (small, spherical, non-nucleated) were coated with Ea, and duck red cells (large, oval, nucleated) were coated with BγG. In (**a**) reoxidized F(ab′)₂ fragments prepared exclusively from anti-Ea clump only the human cells. In (**b**) the reoxidized F(ab′)₂ fragments prepared exclusively from anti-BγG clump only the duck cells. In (**c**) a mixture of the two F(ab′)₂ fragments of (**a**) and (**b**) are seen to form **separate** clumps of human and of duck cells. In (**d**) hybrid F(ab′)₂ fragments form **mixed** clumps with both human and duck cells. (From H. Fudenberg, G. Drews, and A. Nisonoff. J. Exp. Med. 119:151, 1964.)

tein by S-S links. The 7S units retain antigen-binding activity but lose a number of other activities. For example, antisera whose activity depends on γM molecules lose ability to agglutinate red cells after exposure to mild reducing conditions; but they can specifically inhibit agglutination by intact antibodies. Since these conditions do not inactivate γG molecules the loss of activity on treatment of dilute serum with a mercaptan is sometimes used as a crude assay to distinguish between γM and γG antibodies.

If reduced γM immunoglobulin is acidified its 7S monomers separate into heavy and light chains, which are present in the same proportions as in γG molecules. Despite these similarities, however, γM is not simply a multimer of five or six γG molecules, linked by S-S bridges. The two proteins differ with respect to carbohydrate content (10% in γM and 3% in γG); and a more fundamental difference in their respective heavy chains is discussed below.

A molecule of γM immunoglobulin seems to be made up of five 7S monomers, because the molecular weights are about 900,000 and 180,000, respectively. By equilibrium dialysis (Ch. 13) a γM antibody (to benzenearsonate) has been shown to have 5 ligand-binding sites per molecule, or one per 7S monomer. This finding raises an interesting paradox, for the following reason. From the proportion of light to heavy chains in γM (see above) it is clear that each 7S monomer consists of 2 heavy chains plus 2 light chains. If in a given 7S monomer the 2 light chains and the 2 heavy chains are each identical (as in a molecule of γG immunoglobulin; see above), then each monomer should be bivalent, and the 19S molecule should have 10 binding sites, not the 5 observed. The basis for this discrepancy is not yet understood.

γA Immunoglobulins

It has long been known that certain antibodies migrate unusually rapidly to the anode under standard conditions of electrophoresis. Only recently, however, has antigenic analysis made it clear that some of these faster-moving antibodies are structurally different from both γG and γM proteins (Fig. 14-2). This special class, called γA, has a variable sedimentation coefficient: 7S, 9S, and 11S. Since the sedimentation coefficient for spherical molecules is proportional to (molecular weight)$^{2/3}$, these values suggest that γA immunoglobulins include dimers (11S), trimers, and even some higher multimers of 7S monomers.

The γA molecules resemble other immunoglobulins in being composed of heavy and light chains in the same relative proportions (about 2.5:1 by weight). Like γM, the γA species has a high carbohydrate content (about 12%), and the 7S monomers tend to form multimers via S-S links.

γA and γM proteins are also alike in that neither passes across the placenta from maternal to fetal circulation in those species, such as man, in which γG molecules are readily transmitted (Ch. 15, Transmission of maternal antibodies).

In most sera the level of γA is about 1/5 that of γG (Table 14-2); but the relative concentrations are reversed (γA greatly exceeds γG) in many secretions, e.g., tears, saliva, colostrum, and mucinous secretions of nasopharynx. The relatively high concentration of

γA antibodies in these secretions may play a role in protecting mucosal surfaces against invasion by pathogenic bacteria and viruses.

Comparison of Chains in Immunoglobulins

γG, γA, and γM Chains. In antisera prepared against γG proteins (e.g., in rabbits injected with purified 7S human γG) some antibodies are specific for heavy chains of the immunogen, and others for its light chains. By absorption with isolated light or heavy chains, antisera specific for either type of chain can be prepared. Absorbed sera specific for the light and for the heavy chains of human γM and γA immunoglobulins can be similarly prepared.

Unabsorbed rabbit antiserum prepared against human γG cross-reacts with human γA and γM. But after absorption with light chains from any of these immunoglobulins it reacts **only** with γG (Fig. 14-13). Conversely, when anti-γG is absorbed with the heavy component of γG the absorbed serum, now specific for light chains, gives reactions of identity with intact γG, γA, and γM proteins (Fig. 14-13). Similar observations with

Fig. 14-13 Double diffusion precipitin reactions in agar of human γG, γM, and γA with goat antiserum prepared against γG immunoglobulin. The antiserum is used without absorption (I), and after absorption with heavy chains (II) or light chains (III) of γG. In all patterns the center well contains the antiserum. The pattern in II shows that light chains are identical in γG, γM, and γA. The pattern in III shows that heavy chains of γG are antigenically different from those of γM and γA.

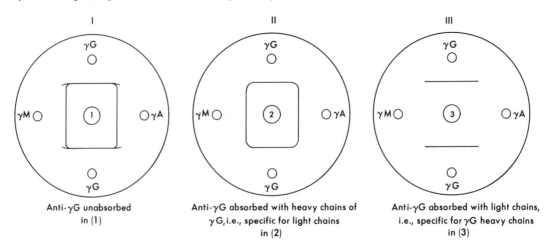

Anti-γG unabsorbed in (1)

Anti-γG absorbed with heavy chains of γG, i.e., specific for light chains in (2)

Anti-γG absorbed with light chains, i.e., specific for γG heavy chains in (3)

unabsorbed and absorbed sera to γA and γM proteins demonstrate that the **three classes of immunoglobulins have antigenically identical light chains, but each has antigenically distinctive heavy chains.** The distribution of allotypic markers is also in accord with this conclusion. The InV markers, present in light chains, are present in all classes of immunoglobulins; the Gm markers, however, are present only on heavy chains of γG molecules, and are absent in γA and γM immunoglobulins.*

γD Immunoglobulin. With the aid of special antisera prepared in rabbits against an unusual myeloma protein (p. 436), a fourth antigenic class of immunoglobulins, γD, has recently been found at very low concentrations in normal human serum (about 30 μg/ml in some sera, and not detectable in some others). The light chains of γD are also indistinguishable from those of γG, γM, and γA, but its heavy chains are distinctive.

The heavy chains from γG, γA, γM, and γD immunoglobulins have been named γ, α, μ, and δ chains, respectively. Though useful as concise designations, each of these terms embraces a family of closely related chains, as will become apparent when we consider the pathological immunoglobulins below.

γE Immunoglobulins. The human antibodies that cause certain allergic reactions in man (Anaphylaxis, Ch. 17) are inactivated by rabbit antisera to a crude mixture of human globulins, but not by monospecific antisera to γG, γM, γA, or γD. It has therefore been proposed that these particular allergy-mediating antibodies represent a special class of immunoglobulins, called γE.

Variants Among γG Heavy Chains. By means of precipitin reactions in gels and immu-

noelectrophoresis, certain antisera reveal a further variety of antigenically distinctive proteins within the γG class. For example, though rabbit antisera only differentiated γG, as a single antigenic class, from γM and γA, some monkey antisera prepared against purified human γG give three precipitin bands with the γG immunoglobulins of a single serum. And rabbit antisera prepared against various pathological immunoglobulins that resemble γG (G myeloma proteins, below) distinguish four different γG immunoglobulins in normal human sera. By using absorbed sera, rendered specific for light or heavy chains, it has been shown that these variants of γG, called γGa, γGb, γGc, and γGd, **differ in their heavy chains, but have the same light chains.**

A similar multiplicity of 7S immunoglobulins, with the same light chains but antigenically distinctive heavy chains, has been found in some other species, e.g., three in the horse and two in the guinea pig, mouse, and dog. As we shall see later, some of these variants differ in a number of biological activities, e.g., in their reactions with complement and in mediation of allergic responses (Ch. 16 and 17).

In Table 14-2 the principal properties of the major classes of immunoglobulins are summarized.

Pathological Immunoglobulins

Just as the derangements in various microbial mutants have played a vital role in elucidating the physiology of the wild-type organisms, certain human diseases provide anomalies that are crucial for understanding the normal physiology of animals in general. Long apparent in studies of the endocrine and nervous systems, this generalization has recently come to apply also to the physiology of the immune response. Thus studies of the abnormal 7S immunoglobulins produced by neoplastic plasma cells, in patients with the disease called **multiple myeloma,** have powerfully illuminated the structure of normal γG and γA immunoglobulins. The analysis of normal γM immunoglobulins has been similarly aided by studies of **Waldenström's macroglobulinemia,** another disease of lym-

---

* Consistent with their presence in γG heavy chains, most Gm determinants are also located in the Fc fragment split from γG by papain. The distribution of heavy-chain allotypes in the rabbit appears, however, to be considerably more complex: the antigenic determinants that correspond to the a (heavy-chain) locus are found in rabbit γM as well as γG, and in Fab fragments of γG.

TABLE 14-2.   PROPERTIES OF MAJOR CLASSES OF HUMAN IMMUNOGLOBULINS

Property	Immunoglobulin class			
	γG	γA	γM	γD
Approx. sedimentation coefficients	7	7, 9, 11, 13	18–32	7
Approx. molecular weight	150,000	150,000–600,000	900,000	?
Heavy chains	γ	α	μ	δ
Light chains	κ and λ	κ and λ	κ and λ	κ and λ
Allotypes				
Heavy chains	Gm	—	—	—
Light chains	InV	InV	InV	InV
Carbohydrate (%)	3	12	12	?
Average concentration in normal serum				
(mg/ml ± 1 SD, or range)	12.4(±2.2)	3.9(±0.9)	1.2(±0.35)	0.03(0–0.3)
Earliest antibody formed in immune (primary) response*	—	—	+	
Bulk of antibody formed later in primary response and in secondary response*	+	—	—	
Active in complement fixation†	+	—	—	
Transmitted across placenta*	+	—	—	
Sensitizes guinea pig skin for passive cutaneous anaphylaxis‡	+	—	—	
Reacts with rheumatoid factor	+	—	—	

* See Chapter 15.
† See Chapter 16.
‡ See Chapter 17.
Modified from J. L. Fahey. J.A.M.A. 194:71 (1965).

phoid cells in which anomalous proteins are elaborated; these proteins, called **19S macroglobulins,** resemble γM in sedimentation coefficient, molecular weight, and antigenic properties.

Reductive cleavage of the S-S bonds to SH groups modifies all these abnormal proteins in the same way as normal immunoglobulins. Thus, with mild reduction at neutral pH 19S macroglobulins are converted to 7S subunits, while the myeloma proteins continue to sediment at 6 to 7S. When these reduced proteins are exposed to organic acids (e.g., propionic acid) they all separate into heavy and light chains, which are present in the same proportions (2.5:1 by weight) as in the normal immunoglobulins.

The pathological immunoglobulins differ considerably from their normal congeners, however, in one crucial respect. **The abnormal protein from any particular patient is rela-**

tively homogeneous; for example, it migrates electrophoretically as a relatively compact band, and its dissociated light chains yield far fewer bands in gel electrophoresis than light chains of normal immunoglobulins (Figs. 14-14 and 14-15). Though the light-chain bands of the myeloma proteins from different patients differ in mobility, each seems to correspond to one of the bands obtained from normal immunoglobulins.

Patients with plasma cell tumors not only produce unusual circulating myeloma proteins, but they also often excrete in the urine massive amounts of a peculiar protein, called **Bence Jones protein** after the physician who first studied it in the mid-nineteenth century. This protein has unusual thermosolubility properties: it precipitates on being heated to 45 to 60°, redissolves on boiling, and precipitates again on cooling. In contrast, the normal and pathological serum immunoglobulins are

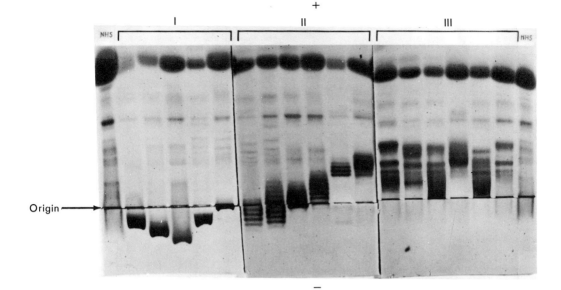

Fig. 14-14 Electrophoresis in starch gel of representative sera from patients with multiple myeloma. Normal human serum (NHS) is included at extreme right and extreme left for comparison; note the broad, diffuse band at origin, characteristic of normal immunoglobulins. G myeloma proteins in frame I appear as compact bands near the origin; they are apparently homogeneous. G myeloma proteins in frame II show periodic banding; their heterogeneity, which is much less than that of normal γG, is thought to be due to serum enzymes that remove (or possibly add) amide groups to aspartic or glutamic acid residues (-COOH to -CONH$_2$). In frame III each A myeloma protein appears as a series of bands, presumably corresponding to monomer, dimer, and higher multimers. About 70 and 80% of human G and A myeloma proteins, respectively, resemble those of frames II and III. (From J. L. Fahey. J. Clin. Invest. 42:111, 1963.)

coagulated irreversibly on heating to temperatures over 70 to 80°, as are most other proteins. Of particular interest has been the finding by Edelman and by Putnam that the **Bence Jones protein excreted by any patient is nearly always identical with the light chains of his myeloma protein** with respect to antigenic properties, amino acid composition, peptide maps, and various physicochemical features, including the curious thermosolubility properties.

Fig. 14-15 Homogeneity of light chains in myeloma proteins, in contrast to the diversity of these chains in normal immunoglobulins. Light chains isolated from normal human γG (N) and from five different myeloma proteins (M1 to M5) were subjected to electrophoresis in starch gel (8 M urea, glycine, pH 7 to 8). (From S. Cohen and R. R. Porter. Biochem. J. 90:278, 1964.)

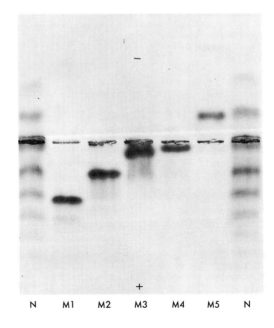

Isotopic tracer studies (feeding ^{13}C-glycine to a patient) have shown that a Bence Jones protein is not split from the myeloma protein produced by the same tumor, as was once thought; instead, it is synthesized independently of, and much more rapidly than, the myeloma protein. This suggests a regulatory defect in neoplastic plasma cells, since in normal individuals light chains, free of heavy chains, are in urine only in trace amounts.

The myeloma and Bence Jones proteins are particularly valuable for antigenic and chemical analyses: not only are they relatively homogeneous in any particular patient, but they are also available in extraordinarily large quantities. For example, a patient may have serum levels of myeloma protein as high as 10 gm / 100 ml, and may excrete up to 2 gm of Bence Jones protein per day in his urine.*

Chain Variants

Heavy-Chain Variants. Most myeloma proteins fall into two major classes with respect to their heavy chains. Those called **G myeloma proteins** react with antisera specific for heavy chains of normal human γG immunoglobulins, while those called **A myeloma proteins** react with antisera to heavy chains of normal human γA. The rare myeloma protein that reacts with neither type of antiserum presumably has still another distinctive heavy chain; and antisera to one of these unusual proteins was responsible, as noted above, for the detection of γD, a previously overlooked class of normal immunoglobulin.

The myeloma proteins have also been valuable reagents for detecting subclasses of normal immunoglobulins, as shown by the following example. It was noted before (p. 433) that monkey antisera to normal human γG immunoglobulin distinguish three antigenic subclasses,

called γGa, γGb, γGc. From these monkey antisera some G myeloma proteins absorb antibodies to the a subclass, others absorb anti-b, and still others anti-c; but no single myeloma protein absorbs the antibodies to more than one subclass. By absorption with appropriate mixtures of myeloma proteins the antisera have been rendered specific for γGa, γGb, etc.; and these subclass-specific sera have been used in turn to type a large number of other G myeloma proteins. About 10% have turned out so far not to be typable, and these anomalous proteins probably correspond to one or more additional subclasses in normal γG immunoglobulins. Indeed, with antisera prepared against some of these odd-lot G myeloma proteins a fourth subclass of normal human γG, γGd, has recently been identified. (A new nomenclature, γG1, γG2, γG3, γG4, has recently been proposed.)

Light-Chain Variants (κ and λ). In analogous fashion, Bence Jones proteins have shed considerable light on light-chain variants in normal immunoglobulins. Rabbit antisera prepared against many individual Bence Jones proteins divide all these proteins into two types. Originally called B and A, then I and II, they are now designated K and L, respectively (since they were first recognized as a result of studies by Korngold and Lipari). Any particular Bence Jones protein reacts only with anti-K sera **or** with anti-L sera, never with both (Fig. 14-16). The two corresponding kinds of light chains are now called κ and λ.

Individual myeloma proteins also have **either** κ- or λ-chains, not both; and in any particular patient the Bence Jones protein is of the same type. The normal immunoglobulin population in any person, however, includes **both** κ- and λ-chains. About 60% of the γG molecules have two κ-chains, and about 30% two λ-chains. As with allotypes, there are no naturally occurring hybrid molecules, i.e., with one κ- and one λ-chain.

The pronounced antigenic differences between K and L Bence Jones proteins are reflected in their amino acid sequences: their peptide maps have virtually no peptides in common. In view of these differences, the

---

* The production of normal immunoglobulins and antibodies is correspondingly poor in persons with multiple myeloma. Hence these patients are unusually susceptible to certain infections, and they are often first detected clinically because they suffer from repeated pneumococcal infections.

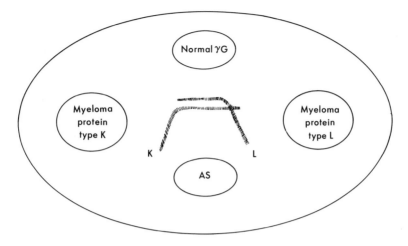

Fig. 14-16 Demonstration of the two antigenic types of light chains in human immunoglobulins. Type K and type L myeloma proteins are in the wells adjacent to normal γG immunoglobulin. The well marked AS contains a mixture of two antisera, one prepared against a type K Bence Jones protein, the other against a type L Bence Jones protein. Both κ- and λ-chains are present in normal γG immunoglobulins; but only one or the other is in a given myeloma protein. About ⅔ of all myeloma proteins are type K. A similar distribution is found by precipitin analysis of normal γG, γM, and γA; about 60% of the molecules are type K, and 30% type L. (From J. L. Fahey, J. Immunol. 91:438, 1963.)

InV allotype markers, which correspond to one locus and were previously considered to be associated with all light chains (p. 425), should be associated with only one type of chain: they are, in fact, found on Bence Jones proteins of the K type, not on those of the L type. They are also found on κ-chains, but not λ-chains, of normal immunoglobulins.

Homogeneity of Myeloma and Bence Jones Protein. The contrast between normal and pathological immunoglobulins is readily summarized by considering an individual with multiple myeloma, for example one whose plasma cell tumor produces a G myeloma protein. If he is heterozygous at loci for heavy and light chains the allotypes in his normal γG immunoglobulins may be Gm(a), Gm(y), InV(a), and InV(b); and as noted above both κ- and λ-chains will be present. In contrast, his G myeloma protein heavy chains will be **either** Gm(a) **or** Gm(y), its light chains will be **either** κ or λ, and if κ **either** InV(a) **or** InV(b). In addition, the myeloma protein light chains would, like the corresponding Bence Jones protein, appear in alkaline-urea starch gel electrophoresis as 1 or 2 bands (probably monomer and dimer forms of the same chain, see p. 438), not the 8 to 10 bands formed by the light chains of his normal immunoglobulins (Figs. 14-11 and 14-15).

Finally, with conventional electrophoresis in dilute buffers the normal immunoglobulins migrate at diverse rates and thus appear as a diffuse smear, whereas most myeloma proteins move as a relatively compact band. The majority of myeloma proteins are, however, not completely homogeneous; i.e., they exhibit a variety of electrophoretic inhomogeneities, as shown in Figure 14-14.

Variable and Constant Regions of Individual Chains

The homogeneity of Bence Jones proteins has made it possible to approach one of the major goals of immunology—the total amino acid sequence of an antibody molecule. For this purpose ordinary antibody molecules, even those specific for one small ligand group and of one immunoglobulin class, have been far too heterogeneous. Sequence analyses of a few Bence Jones proteins, however, have recently revealed a fundamental pattern, likely to be of profound significance for the structure of antibody molecules in general.

Though the primary structures (i.e., amino acid sequences) of κ and λ Bence Jones chains are different, their over-all pattern appears to be the same. For each type **the residues composing the C-terminal half of the chain are the same** in different specimens, whereas **the residues in the N-terminal half show many variations;** numerous amino acid differences in the latter region confer individual uniqueness on the chains produced by any particular tumor. This general pattern has been demonstrated most thoroughly so far with the κ-chains of three different Bence Jones proteins (Fig. 14-17).

These findings, which are unique among natural polypeptides, also represent the pattern that accounts for both the variable and the constant features of heavy chains. For example, the C-terminal halves of heavy chains of rabbit γG (Fc fragment) seem to be the same in all molecules of this class. In contrast, the N-terminal halves of γ chains (Fd piece in the Fab domain) show considerable variations, even in the fragmentary data available (Fig. 14-18).

The Chain-Linking Cysteine Residue of Light Chains. Study of the Bence Jones proteins has also led to the identification of the particular residue on light chains that provides the links to heavy chains. In urine and in dilute salt solutions individual Bence Jones proteins exist as monomers (M.W. about 20,000 to 25,000), or as dimers, and rarely as higher multimers (M.W. up to 90,000). In dissociating solvents, such as 8 M urea or 1 M propionic acid, some of the dimers dissociate and others do not. These variations have been accounted for by the behavior of a particular cysteine residue, located at the C-terminal end of κ-chains or next to the C-terminal serine of λ-chains. In monomers and in dissociable dimers this cysteine residue is blocked by a disulfide bridge with another cysteine residue; whereas in stable dimers, the same cysteine residues join two identical chains through

Fig. 14-17 Amino acid sequence in a human Bence-Jones protein, type K. Amino acid residues, abbreviated in the conventional way, are numbered from one, the N-terminal aspartic, to 212, the C-terminal cysteine. Arrows mark points of cleavage by tryspin, at -CO- side of lysyl and arginyl residues. Two intrachain disulfide bonds (-S-S-) link cysteine residues 32 to 93 and 132 to 192. The terminal cysteine (212) contributes its SH to form the -S-S- bond linking light to heavy chains in the corresponding 4-chained structure (see Fig. 14-19). Residues 106-212 are same in different type K Bence-Jones proteins (**constant region,** outlined by straight lines), except for an interchange of val and leu at position 189. (Allotype specificity InV a is exhibited by chains with val at 189 and InV b by those with leu.) In contrast, about 65 residue positions in the sequence 1-106 differ in different type K chains (**variable region,** outlined by undulating lines). (Based on N. Hilschmann and L. C. Craig, Proc. Nat. Acad. Sc. 53:1403, 1965; and K. Titani, E. Whitley, Jr., L. Avogardo, and F. W. Putnam, Science 149:1090, 1965.)

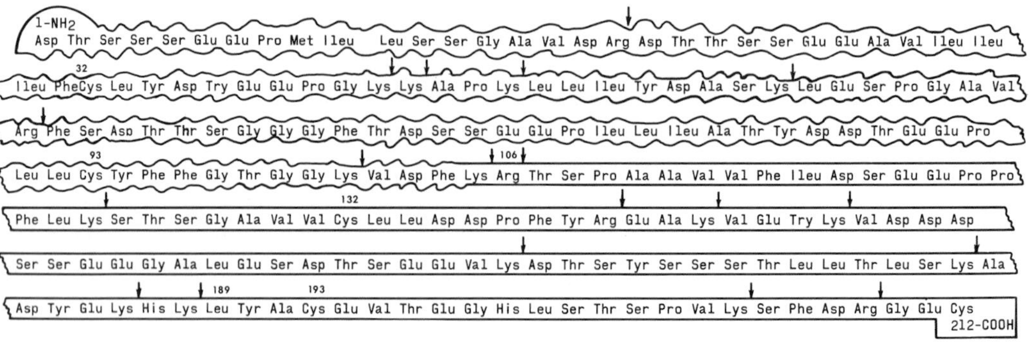

1-NH2
Asp Thr Ser Ser Ser Glu Glu Pro Met Ileu   Leu Ser Ser Gly Ala Val Asp Arg Asp Thr Thr Ser Ser Glu Glu Ala Val Ileu Ileu

32
Ileu PheCys Leu Tyr Asp Try Glu Glu Pro Gly Lys Lys Ala Pro Lys Leu Leu Ileu Tyr Asp Ala Ser Lys Leu Glu Ser Pro Gly Ala Val

Arg Phe Ser Asp Thr Thr Ser Gly Gly Gly Phe Thr Asp Ser Glu Glu Pro Ileu Leu Ileu Ala Thr Tyr Asp Asp Thr Glu Glu Pro

93
Leu Leu Cys Tyr Phe Phe Gly Thr Gly Gly Lys Val Asp Phe Lys Arg Thr Ser Pro Ala Ala Val Val Phe Ileu Asp Ser Glu Glu Pro Pro
                                                          106

132
Phe Leu Lys Ser Thr Ser Gly Ala Val Val Cys Leu Leu Asp Asp Pro Phe Tyr Arg Glu Ala Lys Val Glu Try Lys Val Asp Asp Asp

Ser Ser Glu Glu Gly Ala Leu Glu Ser Asp Thr Ser Glu Glu Val Lys Asp Thr Ser Tyr Ser Ser Ser Thr Leu Leu Thr Leu Ser Lys Ala

                189   193
Asp Tyr Glu Lys His Lys Leu Tyr Ala Cys Glu Val Thr Glu Gly His Leu Ser Thr Ser Pro Val Lys Ser Phe Asp Arg Gly Glu Cys
                                                                                        212-COOH

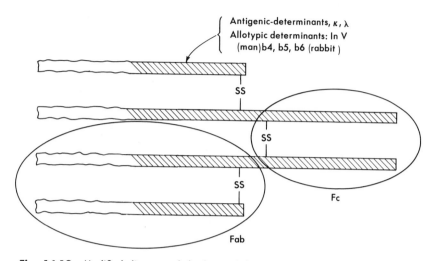

Fig. 14-18 Modified diagram of the basic 4-chain structure of immunoglobulins, showing the variable (unshaded) and relatively constant (striped) portions of heavy and light chains.

an S-S bridge (Fig. 14-19). The chains are probably synthesized as monomers and stabilized by the attachment of an S-S linked cysteine residue; possibly the stable dimers are formed subsequently through interchange in the residues that constitute the S-S bridges (disulfide interchange).

The same C-terminal peptides, ending in cysteine or in cysteinyl-serine, have been found in hydrolysates of pooled normal immunoglobulins. Since the SH groups of these residues do not seem to be involved in intrachain S-S bridges (in contrast to the other SH groups of light chains), these groups are probably involved in the S-S bridges that link light to heavy chains in all human immunoglobulins and antibodies (Fig. 14-19). Comparable cysteine residues at or next to the C-terminii of μ chains (heavy chains of γM) seems to provide the SH groups that join 7S monomers, in forming γM immunoglobulins.

Individuality of Myeloma Proteins

As noted above, individual myeloma proteins can be classified on the basis of antigenic determinants in their heavy chains as A proteins or as one of the four G proteins. They are also readily classified serologically as having either κ or λ light chains. In addition, more detailed analyses, with rabbit antisera to individual myeloma proteins, reveal that each of these proteins has what appear to be **individually unique antigenic determinants.** These are revealed simply as spurs of cross-reaction (Ch. 13) when, for example, two myeloma proteins of the same antigenic group or subgroup are compared in agar diffusion precipitin reactions (Fig. 14-20).

When antimyeloma sera are absorbed with modest amounts (e.g., 2 to 10 mg/ml antiserum) of pooled normal immunoglobulin or of myeloma proteins other than the immunogen the residual antibodies are highly specific for the particular protein used as immunogen; even after absorption with huge amounts of pooled immunoglobulins (up to 100 mg/ml antiserum) antibodies specific for a myeloma protein may persist. With some other antisera to individual myeloma proteins, however, absorption with normal immunoglobulins appears to remove all antibodies to the immunogen.

These results have been interpreted in different ways. Some have suggested that the myeloma proteins are pathological products, synthesized only by neoplastic plasma cells and thus unique for each patient's tumor; hence myeloma proteins are not present at all in populations of normal immunoglobulin molecules, though they cross-react with these

Type K

stable monomer: NH$_2$...lys ser phe aspNH$_2$ arg gly glu cys COOH
                                                              S
                                                              S
                                                              cys

stable dimer: NH$_2$...lys ser phe aspNH$_2$ arg gly glu cys COOH
                                                            S
                                                            S
                 NH$_2$...lys ser phe aspNH$_2$ arg gly glu cys COOH

Normal immunoglobulin: NH$_2$...lys ser phe aspNH$_2$ arg gly glu cys COOH
                                                                    S
                                                                    S
                                                                    Heavy chain

Type L

stable monomer: NH$_2$...lys thr val ala pro thr glu cys ser COOH
                                                          S
                                                          S
                                                          cys

stable dimer: NH$_2$...lys thr val ala pro thr glu cys ser COOH
                                                        S
                                                        S
                 NH$_2$...lys thr val ala pro thr glu cys ser COOH

Normal immunoglobulin: NH$_2$...lys thr val ala pro thr glu cys ser COOH
                                                                  S
                                                                  S
                                                                  Heavy chain

Fig. 14-19 The C-terminal amino acid sequence in κ and λ light chains in monomer and dimer forms of Bence Jones proteins and in normal immunoglobulins. Monomers can also associate noncovalently to form unstable dimers and higher multimers that separate in dissociating solvents, such as 8 M urea. (From C. Milstein. Nature 205:1171, 1965.)

molecules. The alternative view, currently more favored, regards the normal immunoglobulins as a heterogeneous population of molecules made up of a large number (e.g., thousands) of homogeneous subpopulations, each corresponding to some particular myeloma protein. Thus any particular pathological protein would be identical with only a very small proportion of the molecules in a preparation of normal immunoglobulins; hence the difficulties in absorbing the myeloma-specific antibodies with normal immunoglobulins. The cellular counterpart of this view, discussed in Chapter 15, regards the normal immunoglobulin-forming cells of the body as a heterogeneous collection of clones, each capable of producing one or perhaps a few immunoglobulins; and each of the latter

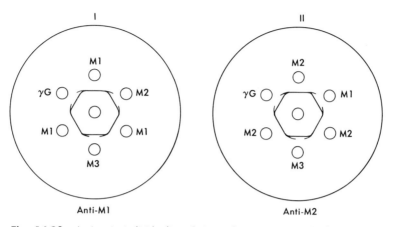

Fig. 14-20 Antigenic individuality of G myeloma proteins. Idealized double diffusion precipitin reactions in agar. M1, M2, and M3 are G myeloma proteins from three patients; γG is normal γG immunoglobulin. The center wells contain rabbit antiserum to M1 in I, and to M2 in II. The spurs in I, corresponding to reactions of partial identity, show that M1 has some unique antigenic determinants that are lacking in M2, M3, and normal γG, as well as antigenic determinants in common with these proteins. Similarly, from the pattern in II it is seen that M2 has some unique determinants, as well as shared determinants with M1, M3, and γG.

is visualized as being homogeneous (like a myeloma protein) and specific (in its antibody function) for some particular antigenic determinant.

The foregoing views can be epitomized in terms of possible mutations. If myeloma proteins are not normal immunoglobulins, the mutation in a clone of neoplastic plasma cells would involve a **structural** gene for immunoglobulin. If each myeloma protein represents overproduction of a particular normal immunoglobulin, the lesion in the neoplastic cells would involve **regulatory** genes—either a gene that controls the rate of cell proliferation and over-all protein synthesis or one that controls the rate of immunoglobulin production in particular. Further discussion of these possibilities is deferred until we have considered whether a given plasma cell has the genetic potential to form all or only a few of the normal immunoglobulins and antibodies (Ch. 15).

Myeloma Proteins in the Mouse. The valuable tools provided by human plasma cell tumors are likely to be extended by the recent discovery that plasma cell tumors can be readily induced in certain strains of mice. It was unexpectedly found that when plastic chambers were implanted in the peritoneal cavity some mice subsequently developed plasma cell tumors. Similar tumors were then found by Potter to appear within 6 months in 50% of mice (of a particular strain) that are simply injected intraperitoneally with mineral oil. The plasma cell tumors can be perpetuated indefinitely by serial transplantation in normal mice of the same inbred strain. (The necessity for using inbred, genetically homogeneous strains of animals is considered in Chapter 18, which deals with the homograft reaction.) The tumor cells of any particular nodule seem to represent a distinctive clone; they produce distinctive myeloma and Bence Jones proteins with essentially the same structural features found in the human disease.

Amino Acid Sequences and the Origin of Immunoglobulins

As noted above, the use of normal and myeloma immunoglobulins as antigens made it possible to distinguish 9 types of heavy chains and

2 types of light chains (see summary in Appendix, this chapter); peptide fingerprint technics (peptide "mapping") have shown that differences in antigenicity are associated with differences in amino acid sequence. However, antigenic analysis and peptide maps tend to emphasize **differences** among polypeptides. Determination of the actual amino acid sequence, in contrast, makes it possible to see **similarities** between polypeptides, as well as their relations to their genes. Begun initially with Bence Jones proteins (because of their homogeneity, abundance, and small size) amino acid sequences have already been established for substantial parts of a few myeloma heavy chains, and even for the C-terminal half of normal rabbit γG (Fc fragment). As is indicated in the examples given below, these studies have revealed a number of interesting and striking similarities among all the immunoglobulin chains, and even between different segments of a given chain.

Chains in Different Species. Of the 107 C-terminal residues of mouse and human κ chains 60% are identical, and differences in another 30% can be accounted for by single base changes in nucleotide triplets in DNA, assuming that the genetic code established for *E. coli* is applicable to vertebrates. A comparable level of likeness has been found among the 30 C-terminal residues of human, horse, and rabbit γ chains. These resemblances are similar in extent to those observed among the various hemoglobins, cytochrome C's, and insulins of phylogenetically related species.

Classes of Light Chains. As noted above, human κ and λ light chains cross-react little if at all in serologic reactions, and their peptide maps have almost no common peptides. However, they exhibit many similarities in amino acid sequences especially over their respective "constant" regions (Fig. 14-17). Eleven (40%) of their 28 C-terminal residues are identical; 11 out of another stretch of 14 residues in the "constant" region are also identical; and most of the nonidentical residues correspond to nucleotide triplets that differ in a single base. This degree of similarity is comparable to that between closely related polypeptides that seem to have arisen by duplication of a common ancestral gene, such as the α and β chains of hemoglobin.

Heavy and Light Chains and Comparison of Different Segments within a Chain. Human light chains (both κ and λ) also share many similar

sequences with rabbit heavy (γ) chain. For example, 21 (60%) of the 35 C-terminal residues of these chains are identical or similar (e.g., serine substitutes for threonine, or glutamic acid for aspartic acid). And within the rabbit Fc fragment (C-terminal half of the γ chain) 40% of the C-terminal 107 residues are identical or similar to the correspondingly positioned residues in the next 107 of the same chain, proceeding towards the N-terminus.

These striking homologies have led to the proposal that all of the present-day genes for immunoglobulin chains evolved from a primordial gene that coded for a polypeptide of about 107 residues (M.W. about 12,000), corresponding to about half a light chain, or ¼ a heavy γ chain. By duplications and fusion this hypothetical gene may be envisioned as having given rise to a primitive light chain and to a primitive heavy chain, and these in turn, through further duplication, could have yielded multiple copies of genes for light and heavy chains. The latter, through mutation and selection, could then have led to the present-day polymorphism, with its approximately 9 types of heavy chains and 2 types of light chains. Some of the possible processes by which the very much larger number of different individual chains are formed within each type will be considered under Theories of antibody formation (Ch. 15).

"Variable" Regions. As noted before (Fig. 14-17), all Bence Jones proteins of a given type (e.g. κ) have virtually identical sequences in their 107 C-terminal residues ("constant" region), but those produced by different tumors differ from each other by many substitutions in the N-terminal "variable" half (107-112 residues long, depending on the particular protein). Nevertheless, about half of the residues in the "variable" region are identical in the 3 or 4 most extensively analyzed chains, and differences in 20% of the residues correspond to single base changes in DNA. The differences in almost all of the remaining residues correspond to 2 base changes; but even these could have arisen as single base changes in a common ancestral nucleotide. For example, the substitution of isoleucine for alanine is associated with a triplet change from AUX to GCX. If, however, in a hypothetical antecedent chain this residue was valine (GUX), 2 single step mutations could account for the present residues (AUX← GUX→GCX). Thus the pattern of variability

in the "variable" half of diverse light chains seems to be compatible with frequent single base changes in DNA, along with occasional deletions and additions. Variability does not appear to have arisen, at least commonly, from inversions or translocations of nucleotides, or from frame shifts. The frequent amino acid substitutions in the variable regions (which seem somehow to be associated with differences in antibody specificity; see below) appears to be the result of mutational processes resembling those that account for the evolution of differences between the corresponding chains of different species. The significance of these finding will be discussed further in connection with Theories of antibody formation (Ch. 15).

THE STRUCTURAL BASIS FOR ANTIBODY FUNCTION

An antibody molecule functions in two ways. First, in its **specific** function it selectively binds a particular ligand (antigen or hapten). Second, regardless of this specificity, antibody molecules participate in a limited number of **general** reactions—precipitation, complement fixation, allergic responses, etc.

These diverse functions are exercised through various sites in different regions of the antibody molecule. As was noted earlier, the sites responsible for the specific function, called **active sites** by analogy with the catalytic sites of enzymes, are localized in the Fab domains. In contrast, most of the general functions are due to various sites within the Fc domain; the evidence for, and consequences of, this localization will be considered in chapters that deal with various general functions: complement fixation (Ch. 16), binding to mast cells and mediation of certain allergic reactions (Ch. 17), and transmission across the placental membranes (Ch. 15).

The Problem of the Active Site: Folding vs. Sequence

An antibody molecule's specific function is a consequence of the unique spatial arrangement and chemical nature of the amino acid residues in the active site. As was noted in Chapter 13, geometrical and chemical complementarity between these residues and atomic groupings of the ligand provides the basis for the multiple weak interactions whose cumulative effect determines the stability of the antibody/ligand complex.

The number of unique conformations of active sites in the universe of antibody molecules must be almost astronomical. One popular guess is that there are 10^4 different kinds of sites. However, the number could well be 10^6, or even more, when one considers that specific antisera can be prepared against almost any protein in Nature, as well as against vast numbers of other natural and synthetic macromolecules and simple chemicals; moreover, the antibody molecules to a given antigenic determinant vary widely in affinity. Nonetheless, all antibody molecules have, as repeatedly noted, a strong familial resemblance: their gross macromolecular architecture is the same, and they have so many common physical, chemical, and antigenic properties that it required decades of careful study to recognize the differences among them.

The question therefore arises: how can such great variability in the active sites be provided for within the limitations imposed by so much structural uniformity? The cogency of this question is emphasized by contrasting antibodies to enzymes. Both bind specifically an almost limitless number and variety of ligands; but enzymes are enormously diversified in structure and composition, while antibodies are monotonously alike (Table 14-3).

Folding Hypothesis. The first serious attempt to answer this question, by Haurowitz, Pauling, and others, proposed that all antibody molecules consist of the same polypeptide, which could fold into an almost infinite number of different conformations in the region of the active site, each stabilized by secondary (noncovalent) bonds between amino acid residues. This hypothesis was subsequently modified by Karush when the large number of S-S bridges in antibodies were found, and their importance for stability was recognized. According to this modified hypothesis different cysteine residues can pair to form stable S-S bonds, each pairing arrangement imposing a unique conformation on the active site. Since antibodies have 20 to 25 S-S bonds per molecule, the number of statistically possible unique pairing patterns is large enough ($>10^6$) to accommodate the vast number of specificities in the totality of antibodies.

Both of these folding hypotheses have had considerable influence for many years, but recent experiments have shown them to be untenable. For example, after antibody molecules and Fab fragments have been extensively unfolded in denaturing solvents they can regain considerable ligand-binding specificity (see below). In addition, the number of S-S groups found in an Fab fragment is so small that only a small number of different conformations could arise from their variable pairing.

Sequence Hypothesis. The alternative hypothesis is based on the general principle that the gross and fine details of the shape of a protein molecule are a direct consequence of its amino acid sequence; i.e., given a particular amino acid sequence, thermodynamic forces lead the polypeptide to assume one energetically favored conformation (Ch. 8, Genetic determination of protein structure). The conformation will change with alterations in pH, temperature, etc., but for any set of conditions it is still determined by the amino acid sequence. For enzymes it is well established that specific catalytic function, and hence the conformation of the active site, is determined by the amino acid sequence of the polypeptide(s). If antibodies are similarly constructed from polypeptides with self-determining conformation, rather than from more plastic polypeptides, molecules with different ligand-binding specificities should have different amino acid sequences; and if the differences are large enough they should be revealed as differences in over-all amino acid composition.

Early analyses failed to reveal differences in the amino acid content of several different purified rabbit antibodies; and indeed these

TABLE 14-3. CONTRAST BETWEEN STRUCTURAL DIVERSITY OF ENZYMES
AND GROSS STRUCTURAL UNIFORMITY OF ANTIBODIES

Enzymes	Molecular weight	No. of chains	γG Antibodies specific for	Molecular weight*	No. of chains
E. coli alkaline phosphatase	80,000	2	Diphtheria toxin	150,000	4
RNase	13,700	1	Bacteriophage T2	150,000	4
Phosphorylase a	495,000	4	Lysozyme	150,000	4
Yeast enolase	67,000	1	Azophenyl-β-lactoside	150,000	4
Aldolase	142,000	3	2,4-Dinitrophenyl	150,000	4

The molecular weight values found by different methods range from 135,000 to 180,000. The variations are inherent in the methods, e.g., the extent to which they are biased by small amounts of aggregated or contaminating protein.

were indistinguishable from total rabbit γ-globulin (probably over 95% γG immunoglobulin). With the development of more precise analytical methods, however, small but significant differences have been consistently found among almost all purified antibody preparations examined (Table 14-4).

Strong support for the sequence hypothesis has been provided by the observation that after an Fab fragment has been completely unfolded in a denaturing solvent (7 M guanidine) and had all of its S-S bonds reduced, it can spontaneously regain some measure of its original ligand-binding specificity following oxidation by air and annealing (refolding) in dilute solutions at physiological conditions of pH and ionic strength.

It therefore appears that antibodies are like other proteins: the covalent structure of the polypeptide chain, i.e., the amino acid sequence, determines the molecule's stable conformation and hence its activity. With antibody molecules it is the particular amino acid

sequence within the Fab domain that dictates the conformation of the active site, and hence the ligand-binding specificity.

Localization of the Active Site

An Fab fragment has one active site, and is made up of one light chain plus about half of a heavy chain (the Fd piece, Fig. 14-7). Is the active site formed by one chain or by both chains acting cooperatively?

With chains isolated from purified antibodies it is now clear that the isolated heavy chains can bind the corresponding ligand, though considerably less strongly than do the intact parent molecules. The isolated light chains, in contrast, bind much less, if at all. Nonetheless, there is considerable evidence that light chains contribute to the active site. For example, light chains from antibodies of different specificities differ in electrophoretic mobility in denaturing solvents, indicating that they differ in amino acid composition (Fig. 14-21). Moreover, the specific binding

TABLE 14-4. DIFFERENCES IN AMINO ACID COMPOSITION OF TWO RABBIT ANTIBODIES

Amino acid	Moles of Residue per 160,000 gm	
	Anti-p-azobenzenearsonate	Anti-p-azophenyl-β-lactose
Lysine	70.0	70.8
Histidine	16.5	16.9
Arginine	44.6	44.6
Aspartic acid	**105**	**112**
Threonine	161	163
Serine	148	143
Glutamic acid	122	121
Proline	110	110
Glycine	109	109
Alanine	79.8	77.3
Valine	128	129
Methionine	13.5	13.6
Isoleucine	48.1	47.2
Leucine	89	89
Tyrosine	**56.3**	**50.9**
Phenylalanine	44.2	44.5

Both antibodies were isolated by dissociation of specific precipitates. Tryptophan and 1/2 cystine residues were not determined. The numbers are moles amino acid residue per mole antibody, normalized to a leucine content of 89. Significant differences are in boldface.

From M. E. Koshland, F. M. Englberger, and R. Shapanka. Science 143:1330 (1964).

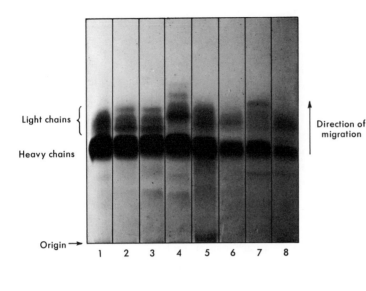

Fig. 14-21 Variations in light chains from guinea pig antibodies of different specificities. Normal guinea pig γ-globulin (predominantly γG) and purified antibodies were reduced, alkylated, and subjected to starch gel electrophoresis in 8M urea, formate buffer. In (1) the protein is γ-globulin of a nonimmunized animal. In the remaining columns the antibodies were specific for: (2) 2,4-dinitrophenyl; (3) 2,4,6-trinitrophenyl; (4) p-toluene-sulfonyl; (5,6) ovalbumin; (7) bovine serum albumin; and (8) p-azobenzenearsonate. (From G. M. Edelman, B. Benacerraf, Z. Ovary, and M. D. Poulik. Proc. Nat. Acad. Sc. 47:1751, 1961.)

of ligand by heavy chains from the appropriate antibody molecules is augmented when light chains from the same antibodies are permitted to form stable complexes with the heavy chains. Light chains from other sources are less effective in enhancing the binding activity of heavy chains.

Additional evidence is provided by the method called **affinity labeling**, in which chemically reactive small molecules are used as haptens. These reagents are first bound specifically by noncovalent bonds in the active site, as are haptens generally; but then they react with susceptible amino acid residues in or close to the site, introducing easily identifiable, covalently linked substituents. For example, by a cross-reaction antibodies to the 2,4-dinitrophenyl group can bind m-nitrobenzene-diazonium salts; once localized in the active site the diazonium salts can form stable azo derivatives of neighboring tyrosine residues. After subsequent separation of subunits the azo derivative has been found on both light and heavy chains, indicating that amino acid residues of light chains are part of, or close to, the active site.

Though currently available evidence is still tentative, two conclusions appear warranted:

1) the active site is probably constructed predominantly, from part of the heavy chain (Fd fragment); 2) the light chains either contribute some amino acid residues directly to the active site or contribute indirectly to the activity of the site through specific interaction with, and stabilization of, the neighboring heavy chain.

Light-Chain–Heavy-Chain Interaction. Isolated heavy chains readily aggregate and become insoluble in neutral dilute salt solutions, but their solubility is increased as they form complexes with added light chains. When heavy and light chains are separated, and the SH groups that constituted their S-S links are blocked chemically (with iodoacetate to form S-carboxymethyl substituents), they can still reassociate through noncovalent bonds. The reconstituted molecules resemble native 7S antibodies in their physical and chemical properties; they even yield Fab fragments when treated with papain, and as noted above they bind antigens specifically, though weakly. Thus, the light and heavy chains must have considerable mutual affinity: they spontaneously form the characteristic four-chain structure of immunoglobulins, even when prevented from forming S-S linkages;

and while the disulfide links between chains stabilize the molecule, they are not essential for the specific structure.

Light and heavy chains associate readily, even when derived from quite different immunoglobulins. For example, Bence Jones protein can pair with heavy chains of normal human immunoglobulin, and even with rabbit heavy chains to form 7S immunoglobulins. Heavy and light chains derived from γG antibodies of different specificities also form 7S molecules. Nevertheless, the chains of any particular natural immunoglobulin (homologous chains) seem to have a greater mutual affinity than chains from different molecules (heterologous chains).

Size and Composition of the Active Site

Regardless of whether one or both chains form the active site, two other questions may be considered: how large are these sites and from what particular amino acid residues are they formed?

Size of the Active Site. The size of the active site has been estimated from binding studies with homologous series of ligands of increasing size. For example, antibodies to dextran (poly-D-glucose, mostly linked α-1:6) bind with increasing strength glucose oligosaccharides of increasing size up to a maximum of about 6 residues. However, the disaccharide and trisaccharide are bound almost as well as the larger oligosaccharides, and the increment in binding becomes progressively less with each additional residue. Similar results have been obtained with antibodies to polythymidylic acid or to polyalanine. With all these systems binding appears to be maximal with oligomers consisting of 4, 5, or 6 residues. The active sites of the corresponding antibodies are thus assumed to be just large enough to surround determinants of this size. If the active site were shaped as an invagination making contact on all sides with an extended 4- to 6-membered oligomer, 15 to 30 of the approximately 1300 amino acid residues of an antibody molecule

might be involved in each of its active sites. The affinity of antibodies for their ligand, however, is far from uniform (Ch. 13): among antibody molecules of a given specificity some exhibit maximal binding with smaller ligands than others. This could mean that active sites vary in size, even with antibody molecules of a given specificity.

Though binding studies seem a direct way to map the size of the active site, their simplicity is deceptive, for the structure of even well characterized simple ligands is by no means always clear. Nor is it always clear that the dimensions and shape of ligands are the same when surrounded by water and when localized in the relatively apolar region of an antibody's active site. Moreover, the question arises whether the better binding of a hexamer than a trimer means that the active site must be at least as large as the hexamer; increased binding could, for example, be accounted for if there were more statistical possibilities for finding 3 favorably oriented residues in a 6-membered oligomer than in a 3-membered structure. The dimensions of the active sites are likely to remain somewhat uncertain until they can be described unambiguously by X-ray diffraction of antibody-ligand complexes, as has been accomplished recently with a few enzyme-substrate complexes.

The Residues in the Active Site. One approach to this question with antibodies, as with enzymes, is to determine the loss of activity following treatment with reagents that act selectively on certain kinds of amino acid residues, e.g., acetylation of lysine ε-amino and tyrosine hydroxyl groups with acetic anhydride. There are well known limitations to this approach. First, most reagents are less selective than assumed, i.e., they combine with more than one kind of amino acid. Second, substitution of residues **outside** the active site may indirectly decrease activity by causing a change in the conformation of the molecule as a whole, including the conformation of the active site.

One means of deciding whether loss of activity is due to a direct or an indirect effect on the active site is to protect active sites by carrying out the reaction in the presence of a large excess of the appropriate ligand, which reversibly occupies the active sites. The amino acid residues in the sites are thus shielded from attack by derivatizing reagents. Exploitation of this principle, called **hapten protection**, has been combined with the use of labeled reagents. For example, in the presence of protective hapten amino acids outside of the active site are substituted with an unlabeled reagent; then the hapten is removed (e.g., by dialysis) and the same reagent, now labeled with a radioisotope, is used to substitute and thereby to identify the corresponding amino acids, previously shielded by bound hapten. By this means a tyrosine residue has been found in the active site of antibody to benzoic acid, and a lysine residue in antibody to diphtheria toxin.

A number of other methods exploit the selective binding of haptens to identify residues in the active site, e.g., the affinity-labeling method referred to above (p. 446). By this means a tyrosine residue has been found in, or at least close to, the active sites of anti-2,4-dinitrophenyl antibodies and anti-*p*-azobenzenearsonate antibodies.

The current status of exploration of the active site can be summarized most simply by pointing out that the methods used are more interesting than the information they have yielded so far. A good deal of information has been obtained, but a firmly established "map" of any single active site has yet to be even closely approximated. Such explorations have been difficult enough to carry out with enzymes, which at least have uniform active sites. With antibody molecules the difficulties are greatly compounded, for even those purified molecules of one immunoglobulin class, specific for one small ligand group, exhibit a wide range of affinities for the corresponding ligand (Cl. 13, Intrinsic association constants). The active sites must, therefore, be correspondingly diversified in structure despite their common specificity.

Perhaps the main hope for detailed chemical analysis of an active site rests on finding the selective ligand-binding (i.e., antibody) activity of myeloma proteins, or on discovering a means of obtaining antibody molecules that are as uniform structurally as myeloma proteins. A hopeful beginning in this direction is provided by recent observations that the antibody molecules formed after mild antigenic stimulation are much more uniform in structure than those formed after intensive and prolonged immunization (Ch. 15).

CODA

Until less than a decade ago antibodies were identified with γ-globulins, and γ-globulins were characterized simply by their slow electrophoretic mobility, their high cystine content, and especially their antigenic properties, which seemed virtually identical in all the γ-globulin molecules of any particular vertebrate species. In recent years this view has been radically altered, largely as a result of the introduction of new analytical procedures, e.g., splitting these proteins into proteolytic fragments and polypeptide subunits, measuring amino acid content with high precision, and immunoelectrophoresis. Some of the most illuminating analyses have emerged from the use of antibody molecules themselves as reagents for the study of other antibodies and their degraded products, an example, perhaps, of the old adage that it takes a thief to catch a thief.

It is now clear that all molecules with antibody activity, or with antigenic determinants in common with known antibody molecules, are members of an immensely diversified family of proteins, the immunoglobulins. All members of this family share a common structural plan: the fundamental molecular unit consists of four chains, two heavy plus two light, linked together via S-S bonds between cysteine residues.

On the basis of antigenic differences in heavy chains, as well as differences in size and charge, human immunoglobulins are divided into four principal classes (γG, γA, γM, and γD); and the preponderant class, γG, has been further subdivided, on the basis of antigenicity, into at least four subclasses. Further subdivisions are recognized on the basis of isoantigenic or allotypic determinants (within a given species), e.g., the Gm allotypes on certain heavy chains and the InV allotypes on certain light chains. And still other tests have distinguished between κ and λ light chains. In fact, from the uniqueness of the myeloma and Bence Jones proteins formed by individual tumors, and the prevailing belief that each of these homogeneous proteins represents the overproduction of a normal immunoglobulin, it is widely suspected that the number of different sets of molecules in the total immunoglobulin population of any one individual is vast, numbering in the thousands or more.

Though the isolated heavy and light chains from different immunoglobulins appear to pair almost at random in the test tube, naturally occurring immunoglobulins exhibit symmetry; each molecule appears to have identical light chains and identical heavy chains. Correspondingly, bivalent antibody molecules are homospecific, i.e., they have the same ligand-binding specificity at each of the two active sites.

Recent studies have shown that Bence Jones proteins of a given antigenic type have the same amino acid sequences in the C-terminal half of the chains, but individual specimens differ in many amino acid residues in the N-terminal half. It is reasonable to assume a similar pattern—constancy in one region and variability in another—for the light chains of normal immunoglobulins; and such a pattern also appears to account grossly for the physicochemical and immunological properties of normal heavy chains. These features would seem to provide a structural basis for reconciling the two outstanding characteristics of this family of molecules: 1) their uniformity with respect to many general properties and functions, and 2) their extraordinary diversity with respect to the selective binding of antigens and haptens. The elucidation of the biosynthetic and genetic processes responsible for elaborating this vast array of similar yet different molecules presents a challenge of formidable dimensions.

APPENDIX

Nomenclature of Human Immunoglobulins

Because of the rapid discovery, in several laboratories, of various classes, subclasses, subunits, and fragments of immunoglobulins, a variety of competing designations were introduced. The field appears to have been rescued from terminological chaos, at least temporarily, by the recommendations of a Committee on the Nomenclature of Human Immunoglobulins. These recommendations, incorporated in Table 14-5, are now being widely adopted. Whenever possible similar terms are used for the immunoglobulins of other species.

TABLE 14-5. NOMENCLATURE OF HUMAN IMMUNOGLOBULINS*

Major classes† (differ in molecular weight, carbohydrate content, and antigenicity of heavy chains)	γG immunoglobulin or **IgG** (γ, 7Sγ, γ₂, γ$_{ss}$)	γA immunoglobulin or **IgA** (β₂A, γ₁A)	γM immunoglobulin or **IgM** (β₂M, γ₁M, 19Sγ, γ-macroglobulin)
Subclasses of γG immunoglobulin (based on minor differences in antigenicity of heavy chains)	γG1, γG2, γG3, γG4	γAa, γAb	
Types of molecules (based on differences in primary structure and antigenicity of light chains)	**type K** (B, I, 1) **type L** (A, II, 2)		
Notation for polypeptide chains (subunits)	heavy chain of γG immunoglobulin = γ **chains** heavy chain of γA immunoglobulin = α **chains** heavy chain of γM immunoglobulin = μ **chains** heavy chain of γD immunoglobulin = δ **chains** light chains of type K immunoglobulins = κ **chains** light chains of type L immunoglobulins = λ **chains**		
Molecular formulas (some examples)	γ₂ κ₂ = **γGK** or **IgGK** (7Sγ-type I) γ₂ λ₂ = **γGL** or **IgGL** (7Sγ-type II) α₂ κ₂ = **γAK** or **IgAK** (γ₁A-type I) α₂ λ₂ = **γAL** or **IgAL** (γ₁A-type II) μ₂ κ₂ = **γMK** or **IgMK** (γ₁M-type I) μ₂ λ₂ = **γML** or **IgML** (γ₁M-type II) κ or κ₂ or λ or λ₂ = urinary light chains in monomer or dimer form		

Proteolytic fragments of γG immunoglobulin	Produced by papain	**Fab fragments**	(human: S,A,C) (rabbit: I, II, I-II)
		Fc fragments	(human: F,B) (rabbit: III)
		Fd (A-piece)	
	Produced by pepsin	**F(ab')₂ fragment** (bivalent; not reduced) **Fab' fragment** (univalent; reduced)	

Pathological immunoglobulins	a) **G myeloma protein:** Same sedimentation coefficient as normal γG immunoglobulin, and reacts with antisera specific for γG immunoglobulins
	b) **A myeloma protein:** Reacts with antisera specific for γA immunoglobulins
	c) **M macroglobulin:** Reacts with antisera specific for γM immunoglobulin and has high sedimentation coefficient (18–25S)
	d) Proteins consisting only of light chains:
	    1. **Bence Jones proteins,** if they have characteristic thermosolubility properties (solutions become turbid on heating to 50–60°, clear on being brought to 100°, and become cloudy again on cooling)
	    2. **Light chains,** if they lack the special thermosolubility properties of Bence Jones proteins

Recommended usage in boldface; older terminology and explanatory comments in parentheses.

†*γD immunoglobulin or IgD has been omitted here, because it is present only in trace amounts in most human sera (see Table 14-2).*

Based on Bull. World Health Organ. 30:447 (1964).

SELECTED REFERENCES

Review Articles

Antibodies. *Cold Spring Harbor Symp. Quant. Biol. 32:* 1967 (in press).

COHEN, S., and PORTER, R. R. Structure and biologic activity of immunoglobulins. *Advances Immunol.* 4:287 (1964).

FAHEY, J. Heterogeneity of γ-globulins. *Advances Immunol.* 2:42 (1962).

FLEISCHMAN, J. The immune globulins. *Ann. Rev. Biochem.* 35:835 (1965).

LENNOX, E. S., and COHN, M. Immunoglobulins. *Ann. Rev. Biochem.* in press (1967).

OUDIN, J. Genetic regulation of immunoglobulin synthesis. *J. Cell. Physiol. 67* (Suppl. 1), (1966).

Specific Articles

COHEN, S. Properties of the peptide chains of normal and pathological human γ-globulins. *Biochem. J. 89:*334 (1963).

EDELMAN, G. M., BENACERRAF, B., and OVARY, Z. Structure and specificity of guinea pig 7S antibodies. *J. Exp. Med. 118:*229 (1963).

EDELMAN, G. M., and GALLY, J. A. The nature of Bence Jones proteins: Chemical similarities to polypeptide chains of myeloma globulins and normal γ-globulins. *J. Exp. Med. 116:*207 (1962).

FLEISCHMAN, J., PORTER, R. R., and PRESS, E. M. The arrangement of the peptide chains in γ-globulin. *Biochem. J. 88:*220 (1963).

GREY, H. M., MANNIK, M., and KUNKEL, H. G. Individual antigenic specificity of myeloma proteins. *J. Exp. Med. 121:*561 (1965).

HABER, E. Recovery of antigenic specificity after denaturation and complete reduction of disulfides in a papain fragment of antibody. *Proc. Nat. Acad. Sc. 52:*1099 (1964).

HILL, R. L., DELANEY, R., FELLOWS, R. E., and LEBOVITZ, H. E. The evolutionary origins of the immunoglobulins. *Proc. Nat. Acad. Sc. 56:*1762 (1966).

HILSCHMANN, N., and CRAIG, L. C. Amino acid sequence studies with Bence Jones proteins. *Proc. Nat. Acad. Sc. 53:*1403 (1965).

METZGER, H., and MANNIK, M. Recombination of antibody polypeptide chains in the presence of antigen. *J. Exp. Med. 120:*765 (1964).

OUDIN, J. Allotypy of rabbit serum proteins. I. Immunochemical analysis leading to the individualization of seven main allotypes. *J. Exp. Med. 112:*107 (1960).

PUTNAM, F. W., and HARDY, S. Proteins in multiple myeloma. III. Origin of Bence Jones proteins. *J. Biol. Chem. 212:*361 (1955).

ROCKEY, J. H., KLINMAN, N. R., and KARUSH, F. Equine antihapten antibody. I. 7S, β_{2A} and 10S γ_1 globulin components of purified anti-β-lactoside antibody. *J. Exp. Med. 120:*589 (1964).

TITANI, K., WHITLEY, E., JR., AVOGARDO, L., and PUTNAM, F. W. Immunoglobulin structure: Partial amino acid sequence of a Bence Jones protein. *Science 149:*1090 (1965).

WHITNEY, P. L., and TANFORD, C. Recovery of specific activity after complete unfolding and reduction of an antibody fragment. *Proc. Nat. Acad. Sc. 53:*524 (1965).

15 ANTIBODY FORMATION

For about 50 years after the discovery of antibodies interest in their formation was largely oriented toward their use in the prevention and treatment of infectious diseases. Prophylactic immunization procedures were developed for the control of diphtheria and tetanus, and immune sera—prepared in horses and rabbits—were successfully used to treat these diseases as well as those due to pneumococci, meningococci, *Hemophilus influenzae,* and streptococci. The need to improve and extend the vaccines available has persisted, and during the past 20 years effective vaccines have been developed against polio, typhus, yellow fever, pertussis, and measles.

Meanwhile, several other considerations have generated increasing interest, especially since the 1940s, in antibody synthesis. For practical purposes its inhibition is sought in order to control allergic responses, especially to transplanted tissues (Chs. 17 and 18). And in theoretical biology antibody synthesis is attracting attention as an example of differentiation that is accessible to study at a molecular level: in response to an immunogen* certain cells alter their morphology and are apparently induced to synthesize a novel protein, the corresponding antibody. In addition, regulation of synthesis of specific proteins in bacteria (Ch. 9) has provided a possible model for the shifts of specific protein synthesis seen in antibody formation.

In the sections that follow we shall consider the properties of antigens that correlate with immunogenicity, the factors that influence antibody formation by the intact animal (including the prevention of antibody formation under certain circumstances, e.g., immunological tolerance), antibody synthesis at the cellular and subcellular levels, and theories of antibody formation.

PROPERTIES OF ANTIGENS RELATED TO IMMUNOGENICITY

Foreignness

In general, an animal does not form antibodies to a substance that is part of its own body ("self"). We do not know how the antibody-forming apparatus distinguishes between indigenous and foreign constituents, but it is nevertheless clear that **a substance must ordinarily be recognized as alien in order to induce the synthesis of antibodies.** This principle, and the exceptions to it, are discussed further under Immunological tolerance in this chapter (see also Ch. 17, Autoallergy).

Degrees of foreignness are impossible to quantitate, but they must exist since immunogenicity is strongly influenced by the phylogenetic relation between the source of an antigen and the responding species. A serum protein from man, for example, generally stimulates more antibody formation in guinea pigs than in monkeys; probably only a few of the protein's potential antigenic determinants are foreign in monkeys, whereas many

more are foreign in guinea pigs. (In contrast, antibodies specific for only a restricted group of determinants on a given immunogen are more readily obtained when the antigen and the responding animal are closely related. For example, antibodies to the determinants that characterize a given allotype of rabbit γG immunoglobulin are readily obtained from rabbits that lack this allotype, but not from guinea pigs, in which these antibodies would probably be only an insignificant proportion of those formed to the many other determinants of the rabbit protein.)

Chemical Characteristics

Antibodies can be formed to almost any biological macromolecule. Proteins, however, are outstandingly potent as immunogens. Vir-

---

* In this and in subsequent chapters the term **immunogen** will often be used as a synonym for antigen when it is desirable to emphasize the antigen's immunogenic function (see Ch. 13).

tually all purified proteins can stimulate antibody formation, and a vast number of simple substances (M.W. less than 1000) become immunogenic only when coupled covalently to proteins. Many purified polysaccharides and all purified nucleic acids fail to stimulate antibody formation unless they are administered in special ways, usually as stable complexes with proteins.*

Polysaccharides. When polysaccharides are administered in combination with proteins, as in intact bacterial cells, antipolysaccharide antibodies are usually formed in abundance. For example, after intensive immunization of rabbits with encapsulated pneumococci antibodies to the capsular polysaccharide often attain serum levels of 1 to 10 mg/ml, and occasionally reach the extraordinary level of 50 mg/ml. Artificially conjugated proteins with hexose or oligosaccharide substituents also induce antibodies to the small carbohydrate groups; e.g., the lactose group in glycosidic linkage with *p*-hydroxyaniline, coupled by the diazo reaction to proteins:

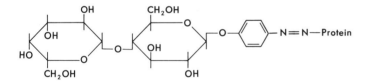

However, only a few purified polysaccharides are appreciably immunogenic when injected alone, and only in certain species where they elicit low levels of antibodies: e.g., pneumococcal capsular polysaccharides in humans and mice, and dextrans (polyglucose) and levans (polyfructose) in humans.

Nucleic Acids. Possibly because of nuclease activity in vivo nucleic acids, injected alone, do not evoke antibody formation. However, antibodies to nucleic acids have been elicited by 1) synthetic protein conjugates with covalently linked nucleic acid bases or nucleotides or oligonucleotides, and 2) naturally occurring nucleic acid–protein complexes, such as ribosomes and bacteriophages.† In addition, antibodies to nucleic acids are formed in response to complexes made with DNA and methylated serum albumin. The latter is highly cationic because its carboxyl groups are esterified; hence it forms a large number of ionic bonds per molecule with the phosphate groups in a nucleic acid. Though these complexes do not involve covalent bonds they are evidently sufficiently stable to induce antibodies to the nucleic acid moieties.

Small molecules, in contrast, cannot form enough noncovalent bonds to establish stable complexes with proteins, and their immunogenicity depends on forming covalent bonds with protein (Chs. 12 and 13; Ch. 17, Contact skin sensitivity). On the basis of experience with nucleic acids, other acidic polymers, such as purified teichoic acids of bacterial cell walls, have also been rendered immunogenic by injecting them as complexes with methylated serum albumin.

Proteins and Synthetic Polypeptides. The basis for the nearly universal immunogenicity of proteins is not known. The traditional approach of degrading a substance to establish the structural basis for its function has contributed little to the understanding of the immunogenicity of proteins because small polypeptides usually are not immunogenic, and the larger fragments, which remain active, are still highly complex structures.

---

* The statement that a substance is not immunogenic is always provisional. Many substances reported not to be immunogens have been found subsequently to induce antibody formation, at least in certain individuals under particular conditions of immunization, i.e., with appropriate choices of dose, route, and adjuvant.

† Antibodies that react with denatured DNAs from many sources, and with oligonucleotides, are often formed by persons with the disease known as disseminated lupus erythematosus, but the immunogen (if there is one) is not known.

Recently, a new approach to the problem has arisen with the development of elegant methods for synthesizing polypeptides (Fig. 15-1). These methods make it possible to synthesize linear or branched polymers of almost any desired amino acid composition and size, ranging from a few residues to molecules of several hundred thousand molecular weight. When prepared with a mixture of N-carboxyanhydrides of several amino acids the products have random amino acid sequences; hence though their composition is simpler they are in some ways more complex than natural proteins, which can often be isolated as a ho-

Fig. 15-1 Preparation of immunogenic synthetic polypeptides. **A.** Synthesis of N-carboxyanhydrides of an amino acid by reaction with phosgene. **B.** Polymerization is initiated by a nucleophilic group, such as an hydroxyl ion or an amine. **C.** When polypeptides are grown as branches on a protein or on a linear synthetic polypeptide the terminal α-NH2 group and the ε-NH2 groups of lysine residues serve as initiators. (Based on E. Katchalski, M. Sela, H. I. Silman, and A. Berger. In *The Proteins*, 2nd ed., vol. 2. (H. Neurath, ed.) Academic Press, New York, 1964.)

A. Preparation of N-carboxyanhydrides of amino acids

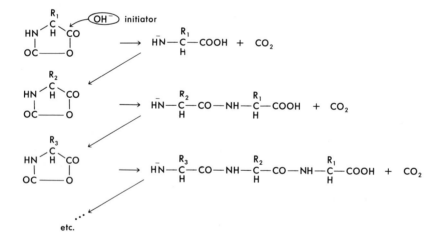

B. Polymerization

C. Growth of a polypeptide branch on a pro·ein

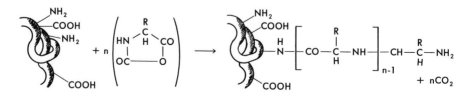

mogeneous population of identical molecules.

Though limited as general models for protein antigens the synthetic polypeptides, used alone and as substituents on natural proteins, have shed much light on the properties of proteins as immunogens. For example, gelatin (denatured collagen) is exceptionally ineffective as an immunogen. This protein becomes much more potent when certain synthetic polypeptides are attached to its free NH$_2$ groups. Polytyrosine and polyphenylalanine are effective substituents, as are also polycyclohexylalanine (cyclical but not aromatic) and polycysteine. Evidently unmodified gelatin is too "flabby" (i.e., it has too little secondary and tertiary structure) to be immunogenic, but when a rigid conformation is imposed on it by certain substituents it becomes immunogenic.

Because unmodified gelatin is markedly deficient in aromatic amino acids these residues were formerly thought to play an essential role in immunogenicity, but the efficacy of polycysteine substituents argues against this view. The nonessentiality of aromatic residues has been more directly demonstrated by the observation that linear polymers made up only of L-lysine plus L-glutamate are immunogenic. A wide variety of other nonaromatic polypeptides, each consisting of combinations of two or more L-amino acids, have also been immunogenic. In general, however, their effectiveness is increased if they contain aromatic amino acids. Homopolymers (made up of only one amino acid) are somehow ineffective,* but they can serve as carriers for various substituents: for example, 2,4-dinitrophenyl-poly-L-lysine evokes antibodies to the DNP group. Many of the polymers succeed in provoking not only synthesis of circulating antibodies but also other manifestations of the immune response, such as delayed-type hypersensitivity (Ch. 17) and immunological tolerance.

Synthetic polymers made up of D-amino acids (e.g., D-glutamate plus D-lysine) seem not to be immunogenic by themselves,† in contrast to comparable polymers made of the corresponding L-amino acids. Yet some highly anionic D-polymers become definitely immunogenic when given, like the nucleic acids, as a stable complex with methylated serum albumin or with highly cationic polymers made up of L-amino acids. In addition, D-amino acids and their oligopeptides are effective immunogenically when attached covalently as haptenic groups on natural proteins, and the antibodies to them are stereospecific. The relative ineffectiveness of D-amino acid polymers is thus not due to a lack of determinant groups.

These observations suggest that some stereospecific enzymatic reaction is obligatory for initiating antibody formation, and that proteins, but not other macromolecules, are generally effective substrates. However, any such reaction involving a prospective immunogen would not be likely to alter the molecule drastically, since the subsequent interactions with the antibodies that are induced often depend exquisitely on the fine structure of the native immunogen.

Molecular Weight. The most highly immunogenic substances are globular proteins of high molecular weight: e.g., bacterial toxins, immunoglobulins, hemocyanin. There is not a strict correlation, however, between molecular weight and immunogenicity, and even pancreatic ribonuclease (M.W. 14,000) stimulates the formation of copious amounts of antibody. Polypeptides as small as glucagon (M.W. 2500) are feebly immunogenic, and their effectiveness is usually much increased if they are first coupled to proteins.

The smallest immunogen so far recognized is a heptapeptide made up of seven L-lysine residues with one dinitrophenyl group on the ter-

---

* Though poly-L-lysine and poly-L-glutamate are individually ineffective, the aggregates formed on mixing them are immunogenic.

† Recent studies indicate that when small amounts of D-amino acid polymers are given (by themselves) over a prolonged period they can elicit a small antibody response; but in slightly larger amounts they readily induce immunological paralysis.

minal α-amino group. Peptides of the same composition but with less than seven lysine residues were not immunogenic. It is possible that the larger peptide, but not the smaller ones, can form stable noncovalent complexes in vivo with some highly anionic protein. In general, however, the effectiveness of noncovalent complexes makes it impossible to determine, at present, which substances are authentic immunogens, and which ones only become immunogenic after forming complexes in vivo.

While studies with synthetic polypeptides and a variety of other substances are thus beginning to yield a great deal of information, the fundamental reasons for the immunogenic primacy of proteins are still obscure. It is sometimes apparent why one protein is a better immunogen than another (e.g., it is more foreign or more stable), but more often the reasons for wide variations in the immunogenicity of different proteins are not known.

ANTIBODY FORMATION IN THE WHOLE ANIMAL

Route of Administration of Immunogen

Natural Immunization. Under natural conditions infection by microorganisms with some degree of tissue invasion is generally the most potent means for initiating immune responses. Thus animals reared under sterile (germ-free) conditions have low levels of circulating immunoglobulins and marked hypoplasia of lymphoid tissue, which contains the cells that make antibodies. But inhalation (e.g., of plant pollens), ingestion (e.g., of foods and drugs), and skin contact (e.g., with catechols of poison ivy plants, and antibiotic ointments) are all occasionally effective means by which a prospective immunogen can enter the body.

Deliberate Immunization. In order to initiate antibody formation deliberately the most effective means of introducing the immunogen is to inject it into the tissues or the blood stream.* Feeding is ordinarily not effective, because most antigens are proteins and are digested in the intestinal tract. However, the oral route may be successfully utilized under special circumstances. Ingestion of attenuated polio virus is effective, because the virus can invade the intestinal wall and be disseminated widely; antibodies to salmonella O antigens (lipopolysaccharides of the cell wall) can also be formed in response to ingestion of dead

microorganisms; and doubtless allergic responses to foods are often due to earlier antigenic stimulation by ingestion of the same substances. Inhalation can also be used to initiate antibody formation, as, for example, by the aerosol administration of attenuated strains of *Pasteurella tularensis*. Even direct application to the skin has been effective with certain substances of low molecular weight (Ch. 17).

Adjuvants

The immunogenic potency of soluble proteins is usually enhanced if they can be made to persist in tissues for prolonged periods. For example, repeated small subcutaneous inoculations of diphtheria toxoid evoke a greater antibody response than the same total amount of toxoid given as a single injection. Accordingly, a widely used method of immunization involves the administration of inorganic gels (e.g., alum, aluminum hydroxide, or aluminum phosphate) to which soluble immunogens are adsorbed; the slow release of the bound immunogen serves to maintain it in the tissues for prolonged periods. These gels are called **adjuvants, a term which applies broadly to any substance that increases the response to the immunogen with which it is injected.**

Probably the most effective adjuvants are the water-in-oil emulsions developed by Freund, particularly those in which living or dead mycobacteria are suspended. The anti-

---

* Intradermal, subcutaneous, intramuscular, and intraperitoneal injections are all occasionally used; the choice is usually based on experience with a particular immunogen, and is influenced by the volume to be injected.

gen, contained in water droplets dispersed within mineral oil, diffuses slowly into the surrounding tissues. After a single subcutaneous or intramuscular injection (e.g., 0.5 ml in a rabbit) antibody formation can be detected as early as 4 or 5 days later, and it may continue for 8 or 9 months (Fig. 15-2). Droplets of emulsion metastasize widely from the site of injection, and intense, chronic inflammatory responses develop around the inoculum and its metastases. The intense inflammation evoked by these emulsions precludes their use in man. However, the emulsions from which mycobacteria are omitted ("incomplete" Freund's adjuvant) are much less irritating and have been used effectively for human immunization; their enhancing effect is appreciable, but less than that of "complete" Freund's adjuvant (i.e., with mycobacteria).

Most adjuvants seem to have two features in common: 1) they retard the destruction of antigen and permit relatively prolonged maintenance of low but effective levels in the tissues; 2) they provoke inflammatory responses, the cells of which may play a role in antibody formation. The detailed mechanisms of adjuvant action are, however, not known.

Dose of Immunogen

The minimal effective dose of an immunogen depends on the method of administration. Thus 100 μg of a typical immunogen, such as human serum albumin, will usually not evoke detectable antibody formation when injected intravenously in a rabbit, whereas the same dose is likely to be highly effective if injected subcutaneously in Freund's adjuvant; with the adjuvant as little as 10μg, or even 1 μg, might represent the threshold. In addition, as we shall see below, the threshold dose is often much lower in animals that have been previously stimulated by the same immunogen (see The secondary response).

Once the threshold is exceeded, increasing amounts of immunogen over a broad range lead to increasing, but generally less than proportionate, responses. (Responses extend over an approximately 1 million-fold range:

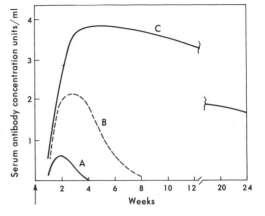

Fig. 15-2 Idealized representation of the influence of adjuvants on the amount of antibody synthesized by a rabbit in response to one injection (arrow) of a globular protein, such as bovine γ-globulin, in dilute salt solution (A), adsorbed on precipitated alum (B), and incorporated in a water-in-oil emulsion containing mycobacteria (Freund's complete adjuvant) (C).

from ca. 0.01 μg of antibody per milliliter, usually the lowest concentration that can be detected in serum, to ca. 10 mg per milliliter, about as high as is observed in animals that are intensively immunized with extremely potent immunogens.) Few detailed dose-response studies have been carried out, largely because individuals vary widely in response to identical stimuli. While this variability is probably due in part to genetic differences, it is observed even among highly inbred mice.

Excessively high doses not only fail to stimulate antibody synthesis, but can establish a state of specific unresponsiveness, which is discussed further under Immunological tolerance.*

The Primary Response

With most antigens the initial exposure evokes a smaller antibody response than do subsequent identical exposures; moreover, the antibodies differ in reactivity. These differences are of cardinal importance in resistance to microbial infections, and they constitute a

---

* The unresponsive state may be impossible to establish with some immunogens because of toxic side effects of large doses.

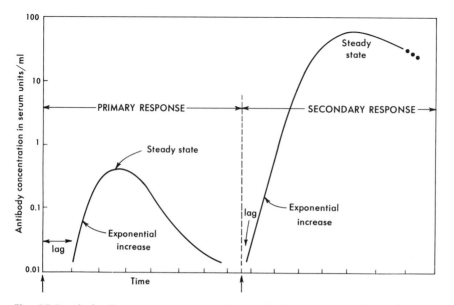

Fig. 15-3 Idealized representation of the changing levels of serum antibody following injections of an immunogen (arrows). Note the logarithmic scale for antibody concentration.

fundamental feature of the immune response.

The first introduction of the immunogen is called the **primary stimulus,** and the response to it the **primary response.** Various stages are shown schematically in Figure 15-3, where time units are left unspecified to indicate the high degree of variability encountered with different immunogens under different conditions. Following a primary injection anti-bodies may be first detectable after 1 to 30 days, or sometimes even later. The more sensitive assays, of course, detect antibody sooner; but it is also clear that the lag period before the appearance of antibody varies with the dose, the route of injection, the particulate or soluble nature of the immunogen, and the type of adjuvant used, if any. No firm generalizations are possible, but it is common for

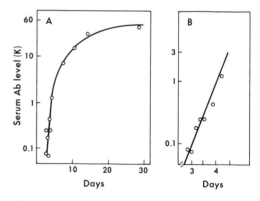

Fig. 15-4 A. The primary response in a guinea pig injected at zero time with 6×10^8 bacteriophage ϕX174 (about 0.01 µg protein). **B.** The first 4.5 days shown in A is repeated with an expanded scale to demonstrate that the increase is clearly exponential. The short lag and the exponential increase are both brought out unusually well because the phage is highly immunogenic, permitting the use of an exceptionally small dose; and the assay for its antibodies (phage neutralization) can measure γM antibodies, which are readily detected at low levels (see Fig. 15-16). With more conventional immunogens (such as heterologous serum proteins) large doses must be injected, and residual free antigen tends to mask the antibodies formed initially. In addition, when assays are restricted to the measurement of γG antibodies the exponential phase is probably completed by the time the measurements can be made (e.g., days 6 to 9). The phage neutralization assay actually measures antibody "activity" (K), which is assumed to parallel the concentration of antibody. (From J. W. Uhr, M. S. Finkelstein, and J. W. Baumann. *J. Exp. Med.* 115: 655, 1962.)

antibodies to be detected 3 to 4 days after injection of erythrocytes, 5 to 7 days after soluble proteins, and 10 to 14 days after bacterial cells.

The kinetics of the response to one injection of a soluble immunogen may be illustrated with the bacteriophage ϕX174. The antibodies to this small virus are measured by a sensitive assay, based on the ability to prevent infection of *Escherichia coli* by a phage particle (Ch. 23). In contrast to most antigens, the phage evoked detectable antibodies as early as 24 hours after an intravenous injection (Fig. 15-4). The antibody activity in serum increased thereafter for the next 4 to 5 days at an **exponential rate;** i.e., the rate of increase at any time was proportional to the level of activity at that time. During this period the doubling time for serum antibody activity in serum was as short as 6 hours, possibly shorter than the doubling time of the cells that synthesize antibodies.

The time required to attain maximal antibody levels also varies with different immunogens and different methods of immunization. The peak titer in serum may be reached 4 or 5 days after an injection of red cells, but 9 to 10 days after an injection of soluble protein is common, and diphtheria toxoid in man commonly requires as long as 3 months.

The duration of the peak titer likewise varies with the antigen, its dose, route of administration, and other conditions: for example, after injection of a soluble protein the concentration of the corresponding antibodies in serum may begin to decline within 1 or 2 days after reaching the maximum, whereas after the same immunogen is given in Freund's adjuvant the antibody level may remain elevated for many months (Fig. 15-2).

Antibody Turnover and Distribution. When the concentration of an antibody in serum is constant with time the antibody is in a steady state; i.e., it is being synthesized and degraded at equal rates. During this steady state antibodies of a given specificity behave, with respect to turnover and distribution, like the total mass of the corresponding nonspecific immunoglobulins. The site at which immunoglobulins are degraded is not known, but like other serum proteins they are broken down exponentially; i.e., a constant proportion of the total mass is degraded per unit time. Studies with isotopically labeled proteins have shown that ca. 25% of the circulating γG immunoglobulin diffuses out of the vascular compartment per day, while an equal amount is being returned via the lymphatics; and the total mass of these proteins is about the same in circulating plasma and in extravascular fluids.

The serum antibody concentration falls when the rate of synthesis is less than the rate of degradation (Fig. 15-5). When synthesis

Fig. 15-5 Turnover of serum antibodies. A rabbit immunized with type 3 pneumococcus was fed ^{15}N-glycine for 3 days. Antipneumococcal antibodies, isolated from serum at various intervals, were then analyzed for ^{15}N content. The initial incorporation of ^{15}N and its subsequent replacement by unlabeled amino acids shows that antibody was being synthesized continuously, even though its total level in serum was declining. (Based on R. Schoenheimer, S. Ratner, D. Rittenberg, and M. Heidelberger. *J. Biol. Chem.* 144:545, 1942.)

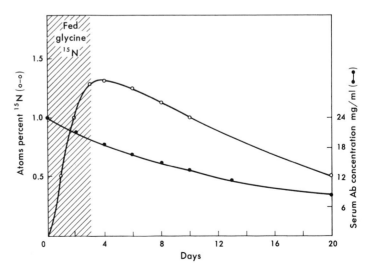

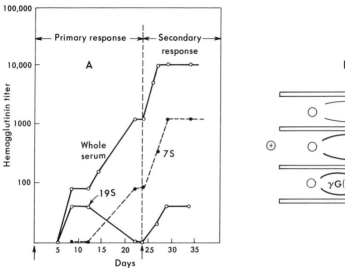

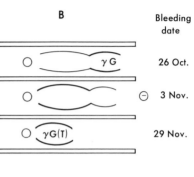

Fig. 15-6A. Sequential changes in the type of antibody made after immunization. At various intervals after injections of alum-precipitated diphtheria toxoid (arrows) serum samples from a rabbit were subjected to sucrose density gradient centrifugation, and fractions corresponding to γM and γG immunoglobulins were assayed by passive hemagglutination (using red cells coated with diphtheria toxoid). Note that hemagglutinin titers are logarithmic. Similar changes were observed following immunization with human serum albumin and with hemocyanin. (From D. C. Bauer, M. J. Mathies, and A. B. Stavitsky. *J. Exp. Med. 117:889, 1963.*)

Fig. 15-6B. Change in type of antibody with time, shown by immunoelectrophoresis of serum obtained at intervals after immunizing a horse with tetanus toxoid. After electrophoresis of whole antiserum the troughs were filled with purified toxoid. The earliest precipitating antitoxin was a γG immunoglobulin. Originally called T protein (for antitoxin), the antitoxin of greater anodic mobility appears later, and it was called γG(T), because it and γG are very similar antigenically and have a similar amino acid sequence at the C-terminal region. (From M. Raynaud. In *Mechanisms of Hypersensitivity.* [J. H. Shaffer, G. A. LoGrippo, and M. W. Chase, eds.] Little, Brown, Boston, 1959.)

ceases altogether the rate of decline is characteristic of the animal's rate of "turnover" of his immunoglobulins. This rate is usually determined experimentally from the decline in serum concentration of an injected sample of immunoglobulin, which is identified by isotopic label or by its activity as antibody.

Some typical rate constants for the degradation of immunoglobulins (expressed as half lives) are given in Table 15-1. Antibodies of the γM and γA variety are broken down in vivo more rapidly than γG antibodies. For example, γM antibodies have a half life of ca. 3 to 4 days in the guinea pig and rabbit, whereas in both species γG antibodies have a half life of ca. 6 to 9 days. **Thus the rate at which an individual synthesizes anti-**

TABLE 15-1. RATES OF DEGRADATION OF CIRCULATING IMMUNOGLOBULINS

Species	Approximate half life (days)
Man	25*
Rabbit	6*
Rat	7*
Guinea pig 7S	7–9†
Guinea pig 19S	4†

Given for γ-globulin, the values doubtless apply to γG immunoglobulins. The half life is obtained from the first-order rate constant (k in days^{-1}) by the relation: $t_{1/2} = 0.693/k$. Based on H. S. Anker. In The Plasma Proteins, vol. II. (F. W. Putnam, ed.) Academic Press, New York, 1960.

†From S. Svehag and B. Mandel. J. Exp. Med. 119:1 (1964).

bodies can vary widely, but the rate at which antibodies are exponentially degraded is characteristic for a given class of immunoglobulin in a particular species.

Changes in the Kinds of Antibodies Made

The character of the antibodies made at various times after immunization changes in two ways: 1) in the type of immunoglobulin, and 2) in the affinity for antigen.

Changes in the Type of Immunoglobulin. Though exceptions occur (see below), with most immunogens and in most animal species the antibodies first detected after immunization are γM immunoglobulins, and γG antibodies are detected shortly afterward. The γM antibodies are usually detectable within the first week after the immunogen is injected (Fig. 15-6A). They are ordinarily at such low levels that the most sensitive assays are required for their detection, e.g., passive hemagglutination, or neutralization of infectivity of a virus. The γG antibodies commonly become detectable while γM antibodies are still present, and the two can usually be distinguished by treating dilute serum with mercaptoethanol, which in most species inactivates the γM but not the γG antibodies.* γG antibodies then continue to increase in concentration, while the γM antibodies usually become difficult to detect after 1 to 2 weeks. With prolonged and intensive immunization the antibodies formed in some species seem, in some instances, increasingly to resemble the γA variety (Fig. 15-6B).

There is no doubt that γM antibodies are usually made within a few days of the initial injection of the immunogen. However it is not absolutely clear that γM antibodies are actually made before γG antibodies, because at low levels the measurement of antibodies depends to a considerable extent on their avidity, i.e., the capacity to form stable complexes with antigen (Ch. 13). Since γM antibodies appear to have five or six binding sites per molecule, in contrast to the two sites per γG molecule, they tend, for a given intrinsic affinity (per site), to be more avid and more readily detected.

The synthesis of γM antibodies usually ceases 1 to 2 weeks after immunization, when the level of γG antibodies is usually still increasing. These observations suggested that γG antibodies, by some kind of direct "feedback" process, inhibit synthesis of γM antibodies; and it was then found that an injection of 7S (mostly γG) antibodies can shut off abruptly the synthesis of γM molecules of the same specificity. The formation of γM antibodies seems to depend on relatively high levels of immunogen, and it is possible that passively infused γG antibodies exert their effects in a more indirect manner by reducing the level of free immunogen (see discussion of Immune elimination, p. 469).

There are a number of exceptions to the apparent rule that the order of appearance of antibodies is γM, γG, γA. Some of the more notable are the following:

1) In horses repeatedly immunized with pneumococci the antipolysaccharide antibodies continue to be synthesized as γM immunoglobulins for many months and even years; γG antibodies are formed only late, if at all.

2) In rabbits immunized with sheep red cells the antibody formed to one of the constituents of the red cell stroma (the Forssman antigen; Chs. 16, 17, and 18) is predominantly γM and remains so indefinitely; the same is true for rabbit antibodies to the lipopolysaccharide antigen of *Salmonella*.

3) In rabbits immunized with proteins γA antibodies are hardly detectable in serum, if at all, even after intensive and prolonged immunization. (γA antibodies may, however, be abundant in rabbit colostrum.) In rabbits most antibodies to most antigens are γG immunoglobulins.

---

* As noted before (Ch. 14), reducing agents, such as mercaptoethanol, cause γM immunoglobulins to dissociate into 7S subunits. Though the subunits retain the ability to bind antigens they are apparently unable to cause hemagglutination or virus neutralization, suggesting that the high multiplicity of binding sites per γM molecule is critical for detecting low concentrations of these antibodies. With γG antibodies, in contrast, even though some of the S-S bonds are cleaved by mercaptoethanol the chains do not dissociate and the molecules retain their activity in neutral solution (Ch. 14). In chicken sera, however, γG antibodies lose some activity after reduction.

The significance of these changes with time is not clear. It has been suspected from the exclusive synthesis of γM antibodies by the newborn human, and from the early appearance of this immunoglobulin in the immune response in adults, that it might represent the phylogenetically most primitive type of antibody molecule. This view is supported by the reports that the antibodies present in some primitive vertebrates, such as sharks, seem to be exclusively of one type and to resemble γM immunoglobulins.

Changes in Binding Properties. It is commonly observed that the antisera obtained with increasing time after the primary stimulus are able to form increasingly stable complexes with the antigen. In addition, the sera tend to become progressively less specific; i.e., they exhibit more cross-reactions with heterologous ligands. These changes take place over a period of several weeks, and they are readily seen after a single injection of immunogen in Freund's adjuvant, which causes a protracted response.

Two mechanisms can account for both these changes. 1) It has been shown that of the antibodies specific for a given antigenic determinant those synthesized initially have low intrinsic binding constants (i.e., low affinity per active site), whereas the antibodies synthesized later have much higher affinity (Table 15-2). These changes are observed

among γG antibodies, and are unrelated to the shift from γM to γG. 2) Because a given immunogen, such as a native protein, usually consists of many different antigenic determinants, it is possible that the corresponding populations of antibody molecules appear after different lag periods. Thus with increasing time an increasing number of populations, each specific for a different determinant, might accumulate in the serum. Perhaps it is for this reason that antigens tend to function as though they have more binding sites per molecule with a late antiserum than with an early one (Fig. 15-7), and that the antigen-antibody complexes formed by late antisera tend to be less dissociable. The increase in

Fig. 15-7 Sequential changes in antiserum reflected in the increasing number of functional groups on the antigen. Rabbits were immunized with several courses of injections of hen's ovalbumin (Ea) adsorbed on precipitated alum. Precipitin reactions carried out with Ea and the sera obtained after courses I, II, and III show, from the limiting mole ratio in extreme antibody excess (intercept on ordinate), that with time the serum antibodies react with an increasing number of sites on Ea. (Based on M. Heidelberger and F. Kendall. *J. Exp. Med.* 62:697, 1935.)

TABLE 15-2. SEQUENTIAL CHANGES IN AFFINITY OF THE ANTI-2,4-DINITROPHENYL ANTIBODIES (γG IMMUNOGLOBULINS) MADE WITH INCREASING TIME AFTER IMMUNIZATION

Rabbit No.	Average intrinsic association constants for binding ϵ-DNP L-lysine at		
	2 weeks	5 weeks	8 weeks
1	0.60	32	—
2	1.6	27	—
3	0.32	1.6	20
4	1.0	5.9	250
5	0.78	1.5	80

Rabbits were injected at zero time with 5 mg 2,4-dinitrophenyl bovine γ-globulin. The haptenic group of the immunogen is ϵ-DNP-L-lysine. Association constants are in liters mole^{-1} $\times$ 10^{-6}.

From H. N. Eisen and G. W. Siskind. Biochemistry *3:996 (1964).*

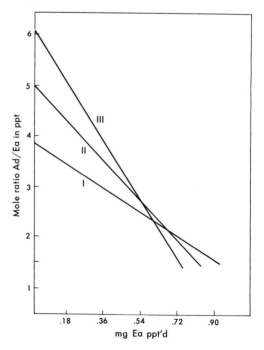

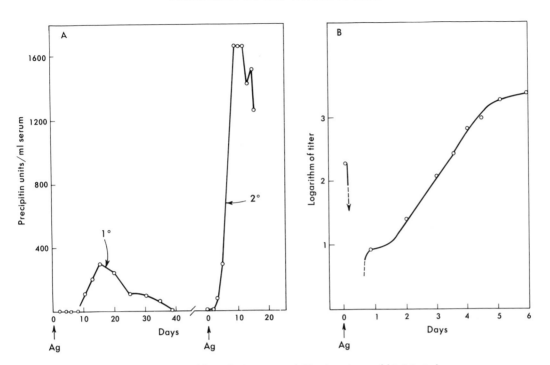

Fig. 15-8 Secondary response in rabbits. **A.** Serum precipitin titers in a rabbit injected once (1° = primary response), and in another rabbit injected with the same antigen about 4 weeks after a series of priming injections (2° = secondary response). **B.** A rabbit previously immunized with staphyloccocal toxoid was given a second large dose intravenously. Note the initial drop in titer ("negative phase") followed by the exponential increase: the doubling time is approximately 9 hours, about the same as in the primary (and secondary) responses of rabbits to bacteriophage ϕX174 (see Fig. 15-4). (**A.** based on H. R. Dean and R. A. Webb. *J. Path. Bact.* 31:89, 1928. **B.** based on F. M. Burnet. Monograph No. 1, Walter and Eliza Hall Institute, 1941.)

number of functional sites per antigen molecule could, however, also follow from an increase in the intrinsic affinity of antibodies, without an increase in the number of antibody populations (Ch. 13).

The Secondary Response

When antibody levels have decreased after an initial exposure to an immunogen, even to the point where serum antibody is no longer detectable, a subsequent encounter with the antigen will often evoke an enhanced response, called the **secondary or anamnestic or memory response** (Gr. *anamnesis*, "recall"). By comparison with the initial response, secondary responses as a whole are characterized by 1) lowering of the threshold dose of im-

munogen,* 2) shortening of the lag phase, 3) a higher rate, and 4) longer persistence of antibody synthesis (Fig. 15-8). In addition, the antibodies formed soon after the secondary stimulus have a much higher affinity for the corresponding determinant than those synthesized at a comparable time after the primary stimulus (Table 15-3).

Though the amount of antibody produced per unit time is usually greater in the secondary response the doubling time appears to be about the same as in the primary response (cf. Figs. 15-4 and 15-8). This can come about

---

*The minute amount of diphtheria toxoid injected intradermally in a man in the Schick test (0.003 μg) is usually enough to cause a secondary response in the production of antitoxin, though it is far too little to cause a primary response.

for several reasons: 1) the antibody level may already be substantial when the exponential increase in the secondary response begins (Fig. 15-8B); 2) the secondary exponential phase may begin sooner and last longer. These differences are probably due to a great increase, following the primary stimulus, in the number of cells that can respond specifically to the immunogen: with reexposure there would thus be many more cells engaged in forming antibodies, though the synthetic rate per cell is probably the same as in the primary response.

The capacity to elicit a secondary response differs with different immunogens, and some, such as pneumococcal polysaccharides, do not evoke them at all. With others pronounced secondary responses can be evoked many years after the primary stimulus, e.g., 10 to 20 years (in man) after primary immunization with tetanus toxoid. And the secondary response to the 2,4-dinitrophenyl (DNP) group can be elicited in rabbits 2 years after a primary injection with DNP bovine γ-globulin (Table 15-3).

TABLE 15-3. INCREASED AFFINITY OF THE ANTI-BODIES FORMED IN THE SECONDARY RESPONSE

Group	Rabbit No.	Average intrinsic association constant for binding 2,4-dinitrotoluene (liter mole^{-1} × 10^{-6})
I. Bled 14 days after primary stimulus	1	0.14
	2	.03
	3	.20
	4	.15
II. Bled 8 days after secondary stimulus	5	34.
	6	84.
	7	>500.

Rabbits were injected with 1 mg 2,4-dinitrophenyl hemocyanin in Freund's adjuvant and anti-DNP antibodies were isolated 14 days later (group I, primary stimulus). Seven months later animals with less than 100 µg anti-DNP antibody per milliliter of serum were reinjected with 1 mg of the same immunogen: 7 to 8 days later the level of anti-DNP antibodies had increased to 2 to 6 mg/ml, and their affinity for ε-DNP-L-lysine, the haptenic group of the immunogen, was too high to measure. Hence affinity was measured with 2,4-dinitrotoluene, a less strongly bound analog.

From H. N. Eisen, J. R. Little, L. A. Steiner, and E. S. Simms. Unpublished data.

The capacity to give a secondary response can thus provide long-lasting immunity against infection. When the level of antibody has decreased greatly—after an earlier infection or after prophylactic immunization—even to the point where antibodies are no longer detectable, the immunogen introduced as part of a new infection can evoke unusually prompt synthesis of relatively large amounts of highly efficient antibodies. In contrast, the primary response affords much less protection because antibodies appear more slowly and because their over-all combining power is relatively poor, at least initially.

The magnitude of the secondary response depends on many variables, including the interval between injections of immunogen, the level of serum antibodies at the time of the secondary stimulus, the nature of the immunogen, and the kind of antibodies formed in the primary response. If the interval is either too short or too long a secondary response is not elicited. The optimal period is commonly just long enough for the antibody level to drop below detectability. When antigen is introduced for the second time into an individual who already has a substantial level of the corresponding antibodies, much of the antigen is rapidly bound to form specific complexes, and the free antibody concentration is decreased temporarily (an effect referred to sometimes as the "negative phase"; Fig. 15-8B). The immunogen may then be not at all effective, especially if the dose is relatively small, probably because it is phagocytized and degraded ("immune elimination"; p. 469).

Effect of Passively Transferred Antibody. Secondary responses are sometimes simulated superficially by the passive transfer of antibodies to nonimmune individuals just before, or together with, the immunogen. When the amount of antibody is large the effectiveness of the immunogen is depressed or even abolished.* However, when the amount is small

* The "blanketing" effect of passively transferred antibody is of practical importance. In early neonatal life the passively acquired maternal antibodies to some immunogens (e.g., measles virus) can block induction; hence active immunization is postponed until 6 to 9 months of age (see discussion of Ontogeny of the immune response).

the induction of antibody synthesis is sometimes enhanced.

During the 1920s, in fact, it was commonplace to immunize humans against diphtheria toxin by injecting nontoxic toxin-antibody mixtures. In addition, antiserum plus virulent virus are now given to animals for prophylactic immunization against some diseases, such as hog cholera and canine distemper. The results range from typical attacks of disease with ensuing immunity through suppression of disease but failure to induce immunity. Unless very carefully selected doses are given the simultaneous administration of antibody is more likely to hinder than to enhance the antigen's immunogenicity.

These results suggest that the potency of an immunogen in the secondary response may depend, in part, on the kinds of antibody-antigen complexes it forms in vivo. Complexes like those observed in the antibody-excess zone of the precipitin reaction (several antibody molecules per antigen molecule) diminish immunogenicity. And it has been suggested that low concentrations of high affinity antibodies, persisting below the level of detectability after the primary response has apparently stopped, could form binary 1:1 Ab-Ag complexes, which might be especially effective in enhancing the antigen's immunogenicity (see Immunological tolerance).

The strongly binding antibodies formed so copiously in the secondary response are 7S and predominantly γG immunoglobulins. Enhanced synthesis of γM immunoglobulins also seems to occur, but not so regularly or conspicuously. It also appears that when the initial response consists entirely of γM antibodies a clear secondary response is not elicited; and even when 7S antibodies are formed in the primary response not all of the features of the secondary response cited above are always recognized: for example, the peak titer may not be particularly persistent.

"Doctrine of Original Antigenic Sin." A secondary response can sometimes be elicited with an immunogen that resembles the primary immunogen. Most of the antibodies made will then react more strongly with the first than with the second immunogen. This phenomenon, called the "doctrine of original antigenic sin," was first recognized in epidemiological studies with cross-reacting strains of influenza virus. An example is shown in Table 15-4, where the secondary response evoked with 2,4,6-trinitrophenyl (TNP) proteins in rabbits that had been primed many months before with an injection of a 2,4-dinitrophenyl (DNP) protein consisted primarily

TABLE 15-4. DOCTRINE OF ORIGINAL ANTIGENIC SIN ILLUSTRATED IN THE SECONDARY RESPONSE
TO 2,4-DINITROPHENYLATED (DNP) PROTEIN AND TO 2,4,6-TRINITROPHENYLATED (TNP) PROTEIN

Rabbit No.	Primary stimulus	Secondary stimulus	Affinity of antibodies formed 7–8 days after secondary stimulus		Ratio of affinities DNT/TNT
			For 2,4-dinitrotoluene (DNT) (liters mole^{-1} $\times$ 10^{-7})	For 2,4,6-trinitrotoluene (TNT) (liters mole^{-1} $\times$ 10^{-7})	
1	DNP-BγG	TNP-BγG	25.	0.49	50.
2	DNP-BγG	TNP-BγG	17.	.85	20.
3	DNP-BγG	TNP-BγG	34.	.84	40.
4	TNP-BγG	DNP-BγG	0.20	0.30	0.7
5	TNP-BγG	DNP-BγG	0.62	1.0	0.6

The primary stimulus was 1 mg DNP bovine γ-globulin (DNP-BγG) or 1 mg TNP-BγG; 8 months later animals with no detectable antibody in serum were reinjected with the immunogen shown, and they produced antibodies in abundance. In control rabbits given DNP-BγG in both injections the ratio of affinities for DNT/TNT ranged from 2 to 100 (i.e., they formed anti-DNP antibodies). In other controls given TNP-BγG in both injections this ratio ranged from 0.2 to 0.9 (i.e., they made anti-TNP molecules). Thus the antibodies produced within 1 week of the secondary stimulus in rabbits 1 to 5 had binding properties that reflected the primary rather than the secondary stimulus.

Based on H. N. Eisen, J. R. Little, L. A. Steiner, and E. S. Simms. Unpublished data.

of anti-DNP, rather than anti-TNP, molecules. According to one theory of antibody formation (see Clonal selection theory) this result would be due to the specific stimulation—by TNP proteins—of an enlarged population of anti-DNP-producing ("memory") cells remaining after the primary response to DNP proteins.

This principle has been exploited in "serological archeology," testing human sera during an influenza epidemic with diverse strains of the virus. A given patient's serum tends to react less strongly with the strain that causes his current illness than with a strain that caused his first attack of influenza in some previous epidemic. From the study of sera from very elderly patients it has thus been possible to identify strains that probably caused major epidemics in the past, e.g., in 1918, long before the influenza virus was discovered.

Competition Among Immunogens

It is of considerable practical importance in the prophylactic immunization of large human or animal populations to combine as many different immunogens as possible in a single vaccine. However, the response to one immunogen is sometimes reduced when seemingly unrelated antigens are injected at the same time. For example, ferritin and hemocyanin reduce the response to bovine γ-globulin; and bovine γ-globulin diminishes the level of antibodies formed to ferritin.

This interference is also evident at the level of different antigenic determinants within a given immunogenic molecule: for example, animals immunized with poly-D-alanyl proteins or with poly-L-alanyl proteins form antibodies to D- or L-alanyl peptides, respectively, but a mixture of the two immunogens, or even a single protein substituted with poly-DL-alanyl groups, evokes essentially only the formation of antibodies to the D- residues. Similarly, polyphenylalanyl determinants block the response to polyalanyl substituents, though phenylalanyl (Phe) and alanyl (Ala) peptides do not cross-react with the antibodies

formed to the appropriate singly substituted immunogens (i.e., poly-Ala proteins and poly-Phe proteins, respectively). The reasons for competition among different determinants are not known.

In contrast to these competitive effects, some immunogenic materials actually enhance the response to others, and certain mixtures are highly effective; for example, a "triple" vaccine widely used in man is a mixture of tetanus toxoid, diphtheria toxoid, and heat-killed *Bordetella pertussis*,* all adsorbed on precipitated alum.

Fate of Injected Antigen

Following the intravenous injection of an antigen the decline in its concentration in serum exhibits three sharply distinguishable phases, as is shown in Figure 15-9. 1) There first occurs a brief phase of **rapid diffusion** into the extravascular space. 2) Then, after equilibration of the body fluids, there follows a period in which the antigen is degraded, apparently by the same mechanisms that break down the animal's own serum proteins. During this period of "metabolic decay" the decline in serum antigen concentration is exponential; i.e., the rate is proportional to the concentration at any given time. This phase lasts until shortly before antibodies begin to accumulate in the serum, i.e., from several days to several weeks. During this period the rate constant for the disappearance of the antigen is usually expressed as a half life (the time required for the concentration in serum to drop from a given value to half that value). The half life is distinctive for each substance in a particular species (Table 15-5). 3) Finally, a phase of **rapid elimination** begins with, and has been used to identify, the onset of antibody formation. During this terminal phase the antigen exists in the serum in the form of **soluble antibody-antigen complexes**. At the

---

* *B. pertussis* is an adjuvant for many immunogens in mice. In the human "triple" vaccine it is probably both an adjuvant and an important immunogen, leading to increased resistance to pertussis.

Fig. 15-9 Accelerated elimination of antigen as an index of antibody formation in rabbits injected intravenously at zero time with 75 mg ^{131}I-labeled bovine γ-globulin (BγG). The vertical bars represent serum antibody levels. Control animals (**A**) show a short initial period of rapid decline due to antigen diffusion into extravascular fluids ("equilibration"). During the period of accelerated decay on days 4 to 7 ("immune elimination") the circulating antigen exists as soluble antibody-antigen complexes. Antibody becomes detectable when antigen is no longer found in blood (day 7). **B.** Accelerated elimination begins at time zero when BγG is injected into animals that have circulating anti-BγG antibodies; and it begins after an abbreviated lag in previously immunized rabbits that make a secondary response (**C**). X-irradiation (500 r before administration of BγG blocks both antibody formation and accelerated elimination (**D**). (Based on D. W. Talmage, F. J. Dixon, S. C. Bukantz, and G. J. Dammin. *J. Immunol.* 67:243, 1951.)

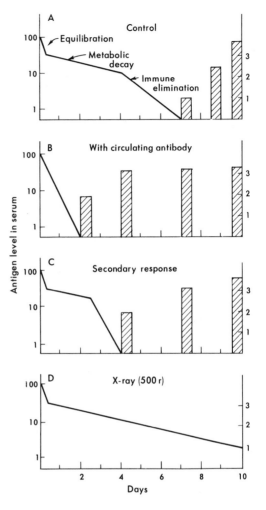

TABLE 15-5. HALF LIVES OF SOME ANTIGENS IN SERUM

Species	Antigen	Approximate half life (days)
Rabbit	Human serum albumin	4.3
	Bovine γ-globulin	3.0
Guinea pig	Rabbit serum albumin	2.2
	Human γ-globulin	1.9
Rat	Bovine serum albumin	1.3
	Bovine γ-globulin	3.0
Mouse	Human serum albumin	1.5
	Rabbit γ-globulin	5.3

The values given were obtained before an immune response was evident. Once antibodies appear the heterologous proteins disappear more rapidly (see Fig. 15-9).

Based on H. S. Anker. In The Plasma Proteins, *vol. II. (F. W. Putnam, ed.) Academic Press, New York, 1960.*

end of the rapid elimination phase, when the antigen is no longer detectable, free antibody generally appears (Fig. 15-9).

The use of ^{131}I-labeled protein as antigen has shown that during the period of rapid elimination from serum there occurs a brisk increase in the rate of urinary excretion of ^{131}I-labeled peptides, indicating extensive proteolysis of the antigen as a consequence of its complexing with antibody. The rapid clearance of antigen from blood in this phase has, therefore, been referred to as **immune elimination** of antigen. (The fate of the antibody in the circulating complexes is not yet established, but from studies with ^{131}I-labeling it also appears to be degraded.)

The drop in serum antigen below the level

of detectability does not mean, of course, that the antigen has been eliminated from the body. There is considerable evidence that antigen fragments persist for prolonged periods in tissues and within various cells. For example, when the antigen is a conjugated protein with intensely colored azo substituents the colored proteins (or fragments of them) remain in phagocytic cells of the reticuloendothelial system for a prolonged period: e.g., about 4 months in liver Kupffer cells of mice, where they were shown to have retained some of the antigenic determinants of the intact protein.

Particulate antigens, such as bacteria or red cells or bacteriophages, do not exhibit the initial phase of rapid decrease in serum concentration after intravenous injection because they do not diffuse into the extravascular space. These particles are much more rapidly cleared from the blood than are soluble proteins, because they are more readily phagocytized.

Genetic and Other Host Factors

Genetic Factors.   Wide variations are usually observed in the amounts of antibody formed by different individuals of the same species in response to a given immunogenic stimulus. Though individual differences are almost equally evident among animals of essentially identical genetic background (e.g., in highly inbred strains of mice) it appears that some of the differences are heritable. For example, one strain of guinea pigs, that can make antibodies normally to many immunogens, does not make anti-DNP antibodies in response to DNP-polylysine, whereas other strains do. The responses of the F_1 ("responders" × "nonresponders") and F_2 hybrids indicate that responsiveness to this immunogen is inherited as a single dominant gene. However, the animals incompetent to respond to DNP-polylysine (nonresponders) can make anti-DNP antibodies when immunized with DNP bovine γ-globulin. Hence the gene involved governs induction by DNP-polylysine, not the formation of anti-DNP molecules per se.

Another example of genetic control is provided by inbred strains of mice, some of which make copious amounts of antibody to certain synthetic polypeptides, while others make only small amounts. The F_1 hybrids form intermediate amounts, suggesting that several genes regulate the amount of antibody formed to these immunogens (Fig. 15-10).

In a third example the ability to make an antibody is inherited as a single Mendelian recessive trait that governs the formation of a "self-antigen." Thus certain strains of inbred mice lack a serum protein (the fifth component of complement, C′5, see Ch. 16), and when immunized with it they form the corresponding antibodies. The only animals that can respond, however, are those that are homozygous for the defective gene for this protein. More familiar examples of this type are represented by the blood groups of man: the ability of humans to make antibodies to these substances depends on the absence of the genes that govern the synthesis of the corresponding antigens (Ch. 18, ABO blood groups).

Though several examples of genetic control of antibody formation have thus been well documented, there are as yet no instances known in which a gene dictates the formation of a particular antibody by specifying the amino acid sequence that determines the antibody's active site and specificity. Such genes would be of particular interest in connection with theories that ascribe the ability to form particular antibodies to conventional genes, transmitted by gametes (p. 503).

Dietary Factors.   Calorie deprivation and specific dietary deficiencies seem to have virtually no effect on the ability to form antibodies. Even in extremely malnourished individuals, and in cachectic persons with metastatic carcinoma, antigenic stimulation usually evokes the normal range of responses. Pyridoxine deficiency, however, is exceptional. In rats deprived of this vitamin, or fed a pyridoxine analog, there is a marked inability to form antibodies to many immunogens, or to display other manifestations of the immune response, such as delayed-type hypersensitivity or rejection of foreign tissue grafts (Ch. 18). The reason for the pyridoxine requirement is not known.

Vaccination Against Microbial Antigens

Immunology's most significant contribution so far has doubtless been the development of practical procedures for increasing the resistance of human populations to infectious dis-

Fig. 15-10 Genetic control of antibody formation in inbred strains of mice. The immunogen was a synthetic polypeptide: a poly-L-lysine backbone on which were grown poly-DL alanyl branches that terminated in mixed sequences of poly-L-tyrosine plus poly-L-glutamate [(T,G)-A--L]. Antibody response was measured as per cent radioiodine-labeled antigen that specifically precipitated with the animals' γ-globulins. C-57 mice responded well and CBA mice poorly; their F₁ hybrids and back-crosses gave intermediate responses. (From H. O. McDevitt and M. Sela. J. Exp. Med. 122:517, 1965.)

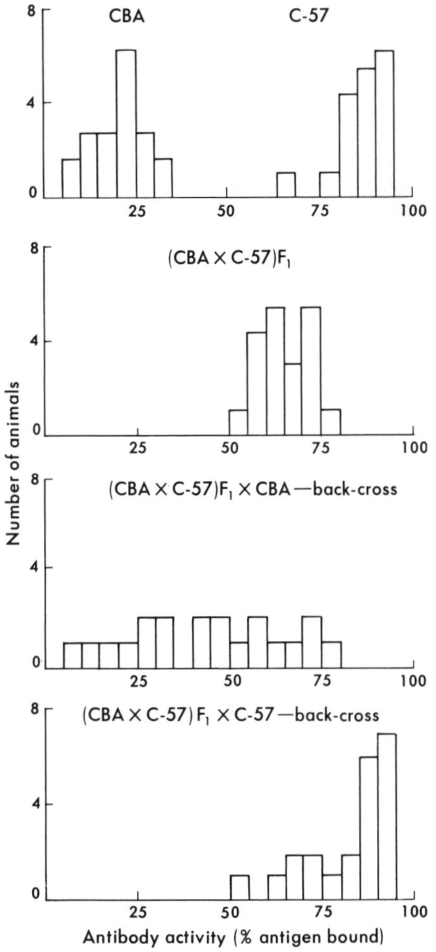

eases (Table 15-6). As Edsall has put it: "Never in the history of human progress has a better and cheaper method of preventing illness been developed than immunization at its best." Unfortunately, the development of the best procedure for a given microbe is a laborious and almost entirely empirical process: useful generalizations are pitifully meager. As noted before, some of them are the following.

Number of Injections. Multiple injections of immunogen at appropriately spaced intervals (commonly 1 to 6 months apart) are usually necessary to establish the ability to give an effective secondary response, when either natural infection occurs or a subsequent ("booster") injection is given, e.g., tetanus toxoid after possible infection with *Clostridium tetani*.

Soluble vs. Insoluble Antigens. An immunogen adsorbed on alum or some other gel is usually more effective than the soluble immunogen. As already noted, Freund's complete adjuvant is too irritating for use in man, and the safety of the incomplete adjuvant (without mycobacteria) for use in large human populations is still under consideration.

TABLE 15-6. SOME VACCINES CURRENTLY USED TO PREVENT INFECTIOUS DISEASE IN MAN

Disease against which vaccine is directed	Immunogen
Diphtheria	Purified diphtheria toxoid
Tetanus	Purified tetanus toxoid
Smallpox	Infectious (attenuated) virus
Yellow fever	Infectious (attenuated) virus
Measles	Infectious (attenuated) virus
Polio	Infectious (attenuated) virus
	or
	Inactivated virus
Influenza	Inactivated virus
Typhus fever	Killed rickettsiae (*Rickettsia prowazekii*)
Typhoid and paratyphoid fever	Killed bacteria (*Salmonella typhi, S. schottmulleri*, and *S. paratyphi*)
Pertussis	Killed bacteria (*Bordetella pertussis*)
Cholera	Crude fraction of cholera vibrios
Plague	Crude fraction of plague bacilli
Tuberculosis	Infectious (attenuated) mycobacteria (bacillus Calmette-Guerin or BCG)

Living vs. Killed Vaccines. Ideally, immunization against an infectious agent should be carried out with a single purified immunogen of particular relevance for the microbe's pathogenicity. The only ideal immunogens, in this sense, are still those which were first discovered (in the 1890s) to be of practical value—tetanus and diphtheria toxins and toxoids. Pneumococcal polysaccharides are also effective (in man) but they are not ordinarily useful because pneumococcal infections are not a large-scale threat. For all other currently used procedures the immunogen consists of crude bacterial fractions or whole bacteria or viruses, either "killed" (noninfectious) or "live" (infectious strains of attenuated virulence; Table 15-6).

Live vaccines seem generally to be more effective. For example, the immunity induced by the killed vaccines for epidemic typhus and for influenza is substantial but not absolute: infections can occur in immunized persons, but are relatively mild. In contrast, with several live vaccines (e.g., smallpox and yellow fever) the immunity induced is much more effective and infections are almost completely prevented. In accord with this difference is the common observation that the immunity following recovery from natural infection is also more effective and more enduring than that induced by killed vaccines. It may be that the process of inactivating a microbe destroys some of the prospective immunogens that are of particular importance for pathogenicity. In addition, the development of solid immunity is probably favored by long persistence of immunogen in the body, and infectious (but attenuated) agents probably tend to persist longer, because they are self-replicating, than noninfectious substances.

Live vaccines, however, are subject to the risk of mutation to virulence, a possibility which is infinitesimally small with those in wide use, such as BCG and polio virus (the Sabin vaccine). Moreover, many killed vaccines are of definitely established value, e.g., polio virus (the Salk vaccine). Thus, the choice between a killed and a live vaccine is often difficult to make, and it has led to some bitter controversies.

In evaluating the effectiveness of an immunization procedure it should be realized that measurements of antibody levels in immunized individuals are relevant only when the antibody is directly concerned with protection, such as antitoxin. In general, the most significant index of effectiveness is protection against infection in experimental animals and ultimately in large populations under natural conditions.

ANTIBODY FORMATION AT THE CELLULAR LEVEL

Sites of Antibody Synthesis

When an immunogen is inoculated into tissues (e.g., skin, subcutaneous tissue, muscle) it is carried through lymphatic channels to neighboring (regional) lymph nodes. If the immunogenic stimulus is intense these nodes become markedly hyperplastic and increase several-fold in weight within the following 1 to 2 weeks. Similarly, after an intravenous injection of immunogen the spleen often becomes hyperplastic. Such observations focused attention very early on the possibility that antibodies are synthesized in lymphoid tissues, and evidence from a variety of sources has firmly established this conclusion. For example, when extracts of lymph nodes were analyzed soon after serum antibodies were first detected the antibody levels were found to be greater in regional lymph nodes than in serum or in distant lymph nodes. Moreover, the efferent lymph from the regional node contained more antibody than the afferent lymph entering it (Fig. 15-11). Finally, when

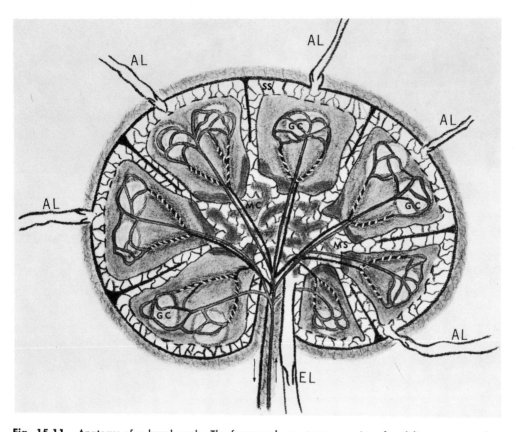

Fig. 15-11   Anatomy of a lymph node. The framework, or stroma, consists of a delicate sponge of reticular fibers (wrapped in reticular cells) that enclose the free cells of the node in a labyrinthine space. The reticular framework within sinuses is obvious (black lines), but within dense lymphoid tissue it is obscured by free cells. Together, dense lymphoid tissue and sinuses appear to form a single, intercommunicating vascular space, connected through interruptions in the inner wall of the subcapsular sinus (SS): similar interruptions have not been observed in the walls of medullary sinuses (MS).

The free cells consist chiefly of lymphocytes, plasma cells, large round pyroninophilic cells (blast cells) and macrophages. Large lymphocytes, blast cells, and macrophages make up the large, pale foci (germinal centers; GC) in the periphery of the cortex. Small lymphocytes fill most of the remainder of the cortex; and plasma cells are found in the medullary cords (MC).

Antigens enter the node, along with lymph, through afferent lymphatics (AL) that are equipped with valves to prevent backflow. The lymph traverses subcapsular (SS) and medullary sinuses (MS) to emerge from the node in the efferent lymphatic (EL), but most particulate antigens are ingested by macrophages and by phagocytic reticular cells lining or straddling the sinuses. Antigens also enter germinal centers, perhaps through the interruptions in the inner wall of the subcapsular sinus (SS), and accumulate within or on the surfaces of phagocytic reticular cells. Proliferative activity in germinal centers is increased by the administration of antigen, but the plasma cells that make antibody lie chiefly within medullary cords.

Blood enters and leaves the node at the hilum (arrows). Arterioles penetrate the cortex and supply blood to capillary plexuses that permeate the germinal centers. The venules that return the blood through the inner cortex (diagonally striped) have tall endothelial cells through which small lymphocytes migrate from the blood stream into the dense lymphoid tissue of the inner cortex; this appears to be the chief route by which lymphocytes recirculate from blood to lymphoid tissue and the major source of cells entering the lymph node. The inner region of the cortex is reported to hypertrophy during the development or delayed-type hypersensitivity (Ch. 17) and to be particularly susceptible to the depleting effect of thymectomy. (Courtesy of S. L. Clark, Jr.; from S. L. Clark, Jr. Am. J. Anat. 110:217, 1962.)

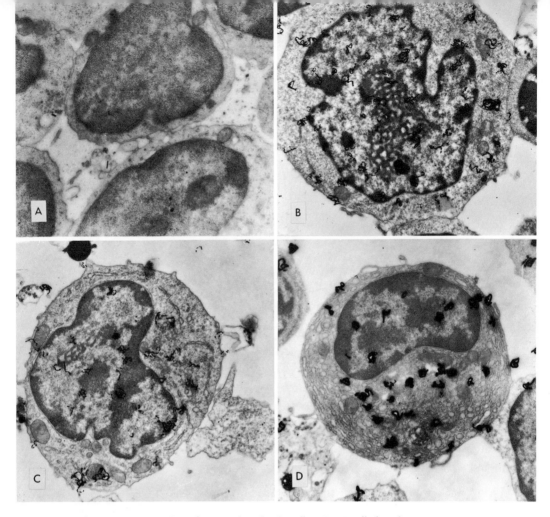

Fig. 15-12 Electron micrographs of some lymphoid cells. **A.** Small lymphocytes from the cortex of mouse lymph node. Note the scanty cytoplasm and paucity of mitochondria and ribosomes. **B.** A blast cell. Note large nucleolus and abundant ribosomes. **C.** An immature plasma cell. Note nucleolus and sparse rough endoplasmic reticulum. **D.** A mature plasma cell. The nucleolus is condensed and eccentric; the abundant rough endoplasmic reticulum is arranged in concentric lamellae; and the Golgi complex is prominent. The cells in **B, C,** and **D,** had been incubated briefly in ³H-leucine before fixation, and their radioautographs were then examined in the electron microscope. The dark irregular bodies are grains in the emulsion, corresponding to ³H-leucine in cell proteins. × ca. 13,000 (reduced). (Courtesy of S. L. Clark, Jr.; from S. L. Clark, Jr. *Am. J. Anat.* 110:217, 1962, and *Am. J. Anat,* in press.)

cells isolated from the regional lymph nodes (or from the spleen after an intravenous injection of immunogen) were inoculated into a nonimmune animal of the same species, the recipient's serum soon contained antibodies of the appropriate specificity.

Subsequent extensions of this work have unequivocally shown that isolated lymph node cells synthesize and do not merely contain antibodies. Thus, the antibody molecules that appear in a recipient animal's serum are the same as those that the cells would have produced within the donor animal, i.e., they are of the same allotype and have the same avidity characteristics as the corresponding molecules of the donor's serum. And the amount of antibody formed in the recipient can actually exceed the total weight of protein in the transferred cells. Furthermore, as is detailed below, when suspensions of cells isolated from lymph nodes of immunized donors are maintained in synthetic media they continue to synthesize antibodies for many hours; isolated fragments of lymph nodes have even continued to synthesize antibodies for up to 2 months.

Lymphoid tissues contain a great variety of morphological cell types, and at various times different ones have been held responsible for the synthesis of antibodies and immunoglobulins. In the 1930s macrophages of the reticuloendothelial system were favored; and in the 1940s, lymphocytes. In the past 15 years, however, a considerable body of evidence has shown that plasma cells are particularly active. For example:

1) As lymphoid tissues become hyperplastic in response to immunogenic stimulation, plasma cells become conspicuous. They are particularly numerous when antibody production is at its height.

2) In intensively immunized animals the amount of antibody extractable from various tissues correlates roughly with the plasma cell content.

3) Plasma cells in tissues are unusually prominent in a variety of diseases in which serum immunoglobulins are markedly elevated (plasma cell tumors, various chronic infectious diseases, cirrhosis of the liver, and some diseases of unknown origin, such as Boeck's sarcoid).

4) Plasma cells are virtually absent, even after the administration of immunogens, in persons with a heritable inability to synthesize immunoglobulins and antibodies (congenital agammaglobulinemia).

Although plasma cells are usually discussed as though they can be identified with precision in the light microscope there is often considerable difficulty in distinguishing them from some other lymphoid cells. Some morphologists maintain that electron microscopy provides the only reliable means for their identification (Fig. 15-12).

Histological Localization of Antibodies and Antigens. A direct means of identifying antibody-forming cells is provided by the immunofluorescent staining procedures introduced by Coons (Ch. 13). The cells that form anti-X antibodies are identified by treating tissue sections with antigen X and then, after washing, with fluorescein-labeled antibody to X. Cells that contain anti-X bind X specifically; since X is a multivalent ligand it will also bind the fluorescent anti-X. The reasonable assumption is made that a cell whose cytoplasm contains enough antibody molecules for detection must have synthesized them. A variation of this powerful method also permits visualization of antigens in cells, which are simply stained with the corresponding fluorescein-labeled antibody. By means of these methods the distribution of antigen and that of the antibodies it induces can be followed in lymphoid tissue at various intervals after immunization.

Within 1 day after an initial injection of diphtheria toxoid in the toepad of a rabbit, sections of the homolateral regional (popliteal) lymph node revealed antigen, or antigenic fragments, within hundreds of large macrophages in the medulla. Over the course of several days the antigen became progressively less conspicuous and antibody then appeared within a few plasma cells (Fig. 15-13).

When a second injection of immunogen was given, after a lapse of several weeks, there rapidly appeared a large number of plasma cells whose cytoplasm stained intensely for antibodies. The number of positive cells per unit area of tissue was much greater than that observed after the primary injection. These results are thus qualitatively in accord with the kinetics of the primary and the secondary responses mentioned before: the rate of increase in serum antibody concentration is greater in the secondary response because more antibody-forming cells are present, whereas the doubling time of the serum antibody concentration is the same, presumably because the cell division time (and the activity per cell) is essentially the same in both responses.

Although the lymph node cells that contain antibody are designated as plasma cells by most observers, other cells also occasionally contain antibodies, e.g., large and small lym-

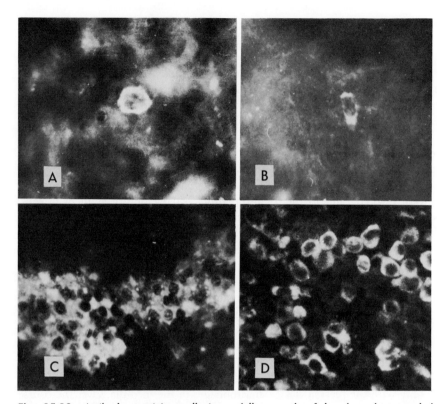

Fig. 15-13 Antibody-containing cells in medullary cords of lymph nodes revealed by immunofluorescence. Following footpad injections with diphtheria toxoid or bovine serum albumin (BSA) sections of regional lymph nodes were treated with the antigen (toxoid or BSA) and then with fluorescein-labeled globulins from a corresponding antiserum. **A** and **B** show rare antibody-producing cells 4 days after the first injection; **C** and **D** show clusters of antibody-producing cells 4 days after the second injection. (From E. H. Leduc, A. H. Coons, and J. M. Connolly. *J. Exp. Med. 102:61, 1955.*)

phocytes and large cells of the germinal follicles (Fig. 15-20). The latter have been given a variety of names, including reticular cells, and it has been suggested that they might differentiate into plasma cells.

Cellular Differentiation

In the resting lymph node ca. 80% of the cells are small lymphocytes (about 7 μ diameter); most of the remainder might be called large lymphocytes. Plasma cells are rare. After antigenic stimulation, however, the incidence of plasma cells increases—in one study to ca. 3% of the total cells in the primary response and to as much as 30% at the height of the secondary response.

From what precursor cells do the plasma cells arise? The answer has been sought by various approaches, such as the administration of ^{3}H-thymidine followed by radioautography to identify the cells that incorporate the labeled compound. Incorporation shows that DNA synthesis has occurred, and provides presumptive evidence of cell division.* In animals whose lymph nodes contain plasma cells it has been found, following a single injection (pulse) of ^{3}H-thymidine, that the mature plasma cell does not detectably incorporate the nucleoside. It is therefore inferred that these cells do not divide. (This finding fits the general rule that highly

* Failure to incorporate labeled thymidine may not, however, exclude cell division, because thymidine triphosphate, which is directly incorporated into DNA, is largely derived by methylation and phosphorylation of deoxyuridylic acid (dUMP); see Chapter 4.

differentiated cells—such as reticulocytes, muscle cells, and neurons—do not proliferate; they appear to lose the ability to synthesize DNA and undergo mitosis.)

However, almost all the large, "primitive lymphocytes" (>11 μ in diameter) do incorporate ³H-thymidine. In both resting and antigenically stimulated nodes, the generation time of these rapidly dividing cells has been estimated, from the rate at which the label is subsequently lost, to be ca. 10 hours. If a nonimmune animal is given ³H-thymidine for only a brief period, say 2 hours, and is then given a primary injection of antigen, label is subsequently found in the nuclei of the plasma cells appearing ca. 3 or 4 days later, which include virtually all the antibody-containing cells. It has therefore been suggested that the immunogen stimulates the rapidly dividing large "lymphocytes" to differentiate into antibody-forming plasma cells. However, these results are of questionable validity, because of the possibility that ³H-thymidine, administered as a "pulse," is available for incorporation (or reincorporation) for a prolonged period.

Other studies, utilizing different approaches, suggest, in contrast, that small lymphocytes, most of which are "resting" cells with a generation time in excess of 3 months (in rats), are the cells that respond to an immunogen and differentiate into antibody-forming cells. For example, purified populations of small lymphocytes (less than 1 in 2000 cells was a large lymphocyte), obtained by cannulation of the thoracic duct, can confer on immunologically unresponsive, heavily X-irradiated animals the capacity to form antibodies, and to express other manifestations of the immune response, such as rejection of foreign tissue grafts (Ch. 18). Small lymphocytes, labeled in RNA with ³H-adenosine, also appear to differentiate, after immunogenic stimulation, into large "transitional" cells, which are presumed eventually to form antibody. Moreover, it has been found that in lymph node fragments from animals previously immunized with both antigen X and antigen Y the capacity to form anti-X in vitro is destroyed by simultaneously exposing fragments to X and to 5-bromodeoxyuridine (a thymidine analog which blocks cell division if incorporated in sufficient amount into DNA), whereas the potential to form the second antibody, anti-Y, was unaffected. This result also indicates that the immunogen reacts with a resting cell which is then stimulated to divide rapidly, rather than with one that is already dividing rapidly before immunogenic stimulation.

The above findings indicate that the small lymphocyte is probably the cell type that responds initially to the immunogen, by differentiating into a large, ribosome-rich, rapidly dividing cell, called (among other things) an "immunoblast."* It has further been proposed that the immunoblasts divide asymmetrically, one line of descendents differentiating, after further proliferation, into cells that resemble plasma cells (more-or-less, see Fig. 15-20), which synthesize the corresponding antibodies; and the other line, after further proliferation, differentiating back into small, resting lymphocytes that persist for long periods without further division as dormant "memory" cells for the corresponding immunogen (Fig. 15-14). In connection with the long persistence of immunological memory it is notable that in studies of chromosomal aberrations of cells from patients who were heavily X-irradiated many years previously some small, circulating lymphocytes appear to be able to persist without division for at least 10 years.

Secretion of Antibody

Animal cells seem to secrete macromolecules in one of three ways: 1) by cell lysis, with indiscriminate discharge of cellular contents (holocrine secretion); 2) by periodic shedding of specialized parts of the cell in which the secretory products are concentrated (apocrine secretion); or 3) by a highly selective process in which only a particular kind of molecule is extruded, the cell remaining viable and retaining all its other components (merocrine secretion). When lymph node cells from immunized animals are incubated in the presence of an isotopically labeled amino acid, it is easy to follow the synthesis and secretion of proteins. Though immuno-

* All lymphoid cells involved in the immune response, from small lymphocytes through transitional forms to plasma cells, have been collectively called **immunocytes**.

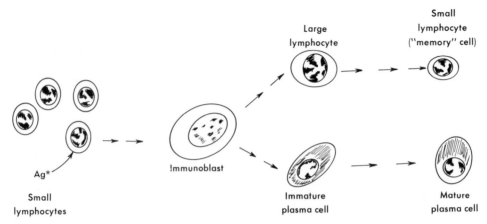

Fig. 15-14 Possible sequence of changes in lymphoid cells following immunogenic stimulation. Ag*, an "activated" antigen from a macrophage, stimulates certain lymphocytes to differentiate into rapidly dividing "immunoblasts." The latter supposedly divide asymmetrically. One daughter presumably gives rise to plasma cells, which produce most of the circulating antibodies to Ag; whereas the other daughter presumably gives rise to lymphocytes, which can persist as resting "memory" cells.

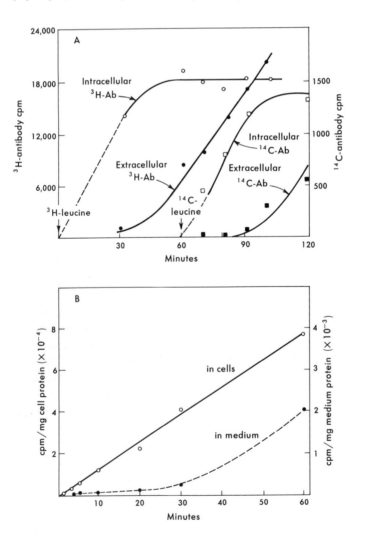

Fig. 15-15 **A.** Lag in the secretion of labeled antibody shown by the addition of labeled L-leucine to a suspension of lymph node cells isolated from an immunized rabbit. Samples removed at various times were assayed for labeled (i.e., newly synthesized) antibodies in the cells and in the incubation medium. There is a 20- to 30-minute lag before newly synthesized antibodies appear in the medium. **B.** Synthesis and secretion of light chains by a suspension of mouse myeloma cells that produce only light chains (Bence Jones protein). The cells were incubated with ^{14}C-amino acids. About 10% of the total protein made was labeled light chains. The secretory lag is the same as in **A.** (A from E. Helmreich, M. Kern, and H. N. Eisen. *J. Biol. Chem.* 236: 464, 1961. B from E. L. Kuff, M. Potter, K. R. McIntire, and N. E. Roberts. *Biochemistry* 3:1707, 1964.)

globulins represent only a minority of the proteins synthesized by these cells, they are essentially the only ones secreted into the medium. The secretion of immunoglobulins and antibodies is therefore merocrine. The proportion of the secreted immunoglobulins that are antibody molecules of a particular specificity varies with the state of immunization, and has been as high as 60% at the height of a secondary response.

The isolated cell system makes it possible to study the kinetics of antibody synthesis and secretion. Labeled amino acids are incorporated promptly into immunoglobulins in the cells, but the newly synthesized molecules appear in the extracellular medium only after a lag (Fig. 15-15). The intracellular labeled antibody quickly reaches a constant level, the rate of secretion then matching the rate of synthesis. The "transit" time from synthesis of an antibody molecule to its appearance in the medium is about 20 minutes, and a similar lag has been observed after an immunized animal has been injected with labeled amino acids, before labeled antibodies are detected in the serum. It has been suggested that the gap between synthesis and secretion is a consequence of an "assembly line" process in which the older immunoglobulin molecules are secreted systematically before the newer ones.

In comparable studies on the secretion of enzymes by pancreatic cells, supported by elegant electron micrographs, vesicles of the endoplasmic reticulum are seen to enlarge and develop into zymogen granules, which contain the newly synthesized enzymes that are destined to be secreted. The granules approach the outer cell membrane, fuse with it, and discharge their contents outside the cell. In plasma cells the kinetics of antibody secretion are similar; hence it is of interest that intracellular "granules" of immunoglobulins are occasionally observed by immunofluorescent stains (Fig. 15-16). (These granules have long been known as Russell bodies, though their immunoglobulin nature was not previously appreciated, and the cells that contain them as Russell body or Mott-type plasma cells. In most plasma cells, however, the stained immunoglobulins are diffusely spread through the cytoplasm.) Furthermore, the ultrastructure of mature plasma cells (Fig. 15-12), with their intricate and highly developed endoplasmic reticulum, closely resembles that of other cells that are also specialized to secrete particular proteins: e.g., pancreatic acinar cells (digestive enzymes) and hen oviduct cells (ovalbumin).

In the older anatomical literature lymph nodes were referred to as **lymph glands.** In retrospect this is a remarkably apt name, although in view of the product secreted an even more appropriate (but less euphonious) term would be "immunoglobulin gland."

Macrophages and Antibody Formation

After its injection antigen is most conspicuous in macrophages of the reticuloendothelial system, and after unusually large doses it can also be detected in many other cells (e.g.,

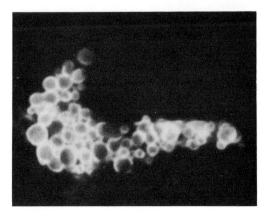

Fig. 15-16 A Russell body type plasma cell in a human lymph node. Stained with fluorescent rabbit anti-human γ-globulin, the cell's immunoglobulin appears to lie within vesicular structures of irregular size. (Compare with E in Fig. 15-20.) ×2550 (reduced). (From L. G. Ortega and R. C. Mellors. *J. Exp. Med.* 106:627, 1957.)

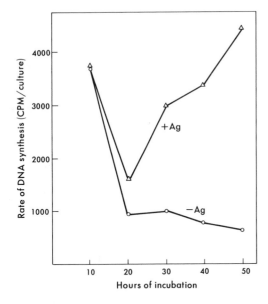

Fig. 15-17 Antigen-dependent stimulation of DNA synthesis. Lymph node cells of a previously immunized rabbit show an increased rate of ³H-thymidine incorporation into DNA when incubated with the homologous antigen (Ag). Rate of DNA synthesis was measured as ³H-thymidine uptake over a 10-hour incubation period. The enhanced synthesis corresponds to a secondary response in vitro, since the antigen does not stimulate cells from an unimmunized animal. Radioautographs of stimulated cultures showed ³H-thymidine incorporation into large "undifferentiated" cells, composing 1 to 4% of the total cell population. (From R. W. Dutton and J. D. Eady. *Immunology* 7:40, 1964.)

parenchymal cells of liver, kidney, adrenal). There is no evidence, however, by fluorescence staining or by other methods, that these cells form antibodies. On the other hand, plasma cells, which clearly can form antibodies, are not phagocytic, and they seldom contain antigen. In fact, recent studies with highly radioactive antigens (¹³¹I-labeled) show that there are fewer than 10 molecules per cell, and perhaps none at all, in the plasma cells that contain (i.e., are synthesizing) antibodies to these antigens. It appears possible, therefore, that susceptible cells might be stimulated to differentiate into plasma cells and to form antibodies by surface contact with the corresponding antigen, or perhaps with antigen that has first been processed by macrophages and somehow activated.

A cooperative interaction between macrophages and lymphocytes was suggested about 30 years ago, from histological evidence, and is consistent with recent observations on cells in vitro. When lymphoid cells from a previously immunized animal are exposed to the immunogen in vitro both antibody formation and incorporation of ³H-thymidine into DNA are stimulated, indicating that a secondary response has been initiated (Figs. 15-17 and 15-18). However, the induction of a primary response in vitro is much less consistently achieved, suggesting that antigen in some activated form may be necessary for this phase of the immune response. It is of interest, therefore, that an RNA-rich fraction from macrophages that have been incubated with a bacteriophage appears to stimulate antiphage

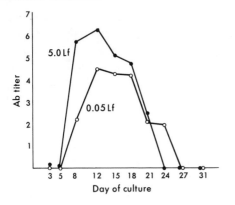

Fig. 15-18 Induction of a secondary response in vitro. A rabbit was immunized with 185 Lf diphtheria toxoid (D); 6 months later its lymph nodes were removed, and fragments were incubated for 2 hours in culture with 5.0 or 0.05 Lf of D (1 Lf = 0.8 µg protein). Diphtheria toxoid did not induce antibody formation in vitro in lymph node cells from unimmunized animals. (From M. C. Michaelides and A. H. Coons. *J. Exp. Med.* 117:1035, 1963.)

Fig. 15-19 Junction between a lymphocyte (L) and a macrophage (M) with an apparent protoplasmic bridge between them. Top, × 11,580; bottom × 39,500. From M. D. Schoenberg, V. R. Mumaw, R. D. Moore, and A. S. Weisberger, Science, *143*, 964, 1963.)

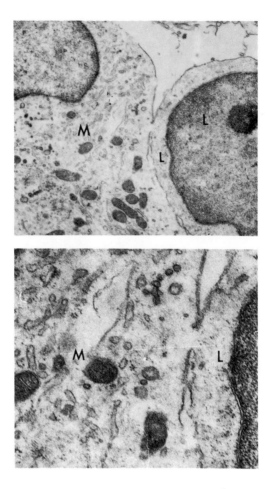

antibody production in isolated lymphoid cells (predominantly lymphocytes) from nonimmunized rats. Rather than necessarily serving as a source of specific information for antibody formation, the RNA is conceivably effective because it is associated with some antigenic fragments. In other studies, in fact, an RNA fraction that is clearly associated with antigenic fragments has been isolated from liver tissue of immunized rabbits, and has been found to be more immunogenic than the original antigen. Though RNA may have only some sort of adjuvant effect these observations provide a hint that activation of the immunogen in macrophages, by linking it perhaps to a form of RNA, may be necessary for inducing antibody formation.

Anatomical studies also provide evidence for a role for macrophages in the induction of antibody formation. Lymphocytes tend to cluster around macrophages that contain phagocytized material; and not only do pseudopods of the lymphocytes appear to make prolonged contact with the macrophage surface, but bridge-like connections are formed between the two cells, as though to facilitate the transfer of activated antigen or of some type of informational macromolecule (Fig. 15-19). It is possible that macrophages do not modify the immunogen chemically, but only serve as effective vehicles for conveying it to plasma cell precursors.

Antibody Formation by Single Cells

As was previously pointed out, a myeloma protein is a homogeneous immunoglobulin produced by a plasma cell tumor, which presumably arises from a single neoplastic progenitor cell (Ch. 14). It would not be surprising therefore if a normal plasma cell were also to produce a homogeneous immunoglobulin—i.e., were to form only one kind of heavy chain and one kind of light chain—and if the immense heterogeneity of the normal immunoglobulins formed by one individual were due to a corresponding diversity of his lymphoid cells. This possibility is strongly supported by studies of single cells.

Immunofluorescence. When lymphoid tissues are stained with pairs of fluorescent antisera, each tagged with a differently colored

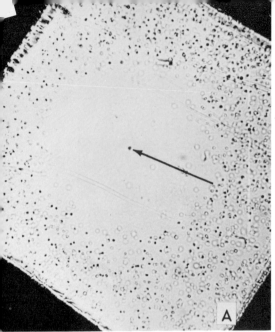

Fig. 15-20 Varied morphology of isolated cells that produce anti—red cell antibodies in vitro and form hemolytic plaques. **A.** Appearance of a plaque with an antibody-producing cell in the center. ×100 (reduced). **B.** An antibody-producing small lymphocyte. Mitochondria (M) and endoplasmic reticulum (ER) are more conspicuous in this cell than in most small, "resting" lymphocytes, which probably do not form antibodies. ×24,000 (reduced). **C.** An antibody-producing large lymphocyte. Note narrow channels of endoplasmic reticulum and the conspicuous nucleolus (NOS). ×21,600 (reduced). **D.** Antibody-producing immature plasma cell. Note lamellar arrangement of channels of endoplasmic reticulum. ×19,000 (reduced). **E.** An antibody-producing plasma cell with dilated endoplasmic reticulum filled with granular material (cf. Fig. 15-16). ×17,000 (reduced). (From T. N. Harris, K. Hummeler, and S. Harris. *J. Exp. Med. 123*:161, 1966. Morphological variation among the antibody-producing cells that form plaques in vitro has also been described by A. Bussard and C. Hannoun. *J. Exp. Med. 123*:1035, 1966.)

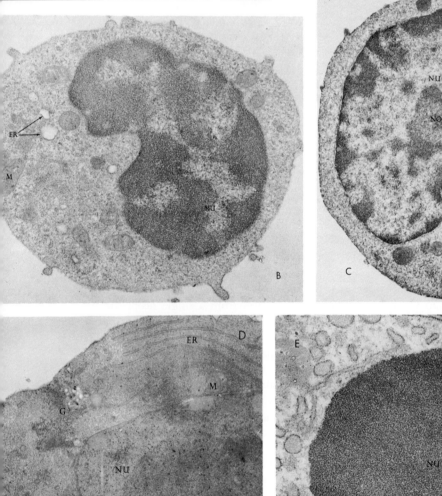

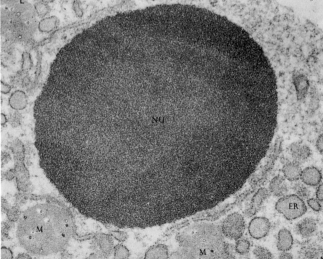

fluorescent substituent, individual immuno-globulin-producing cells have been found to contain γG or γM or γA or, rarely, γD immunoglobulins, but not more than one kind. A given cell thus appears to synthesize only one type of heavy chain (γ or μ or α or δ), at least at any particular time. Similar tests show that a given cell will produce κ or λ light chains, but not both. And in animals heterozygous for light and heavy chain allotypes any particular lymphoid (plasma) cell will stain for one allotype or another, but not for both.* **Thus in a given individual different cells produce different kinds of immunoglobulins, and any given cell synthesizes only one kind, at least at any one time.** These findings imply that only one of several heavy chain genes and only one of several light chain genes can function in a given cell, and that only one allele for each of the functioning genes is expressed at a given period. (A comparable degree of "allele exclusion" occurs rarely, if at all, with other gene systems: for example, in the heterozygous person who produces normal and sickle-type hemoglobins both molecules are made in the same reticulocyte.)

The basis for the **one cell–one immunoglobulin** rule is not known. Its operation accounts for the absence of natural "hybrid" immunoglobulins (with different light or different heavy chains); and it probably also accounts for the homospecificity of antibodies, i.e., the same specificity at each of the ligand-binding sites of a given antibody molecule. It should be noted, however, that the evidence for this principle is based on those properties of the immunoglobulin chains that are localized in their constant (C-terminal) regions—such as the markers for κ, λ, γ, μ, etc. It is not yet clear that a similar restriction applies to the variable N-terminal regions. If it does, the

dictum would be: one cell–one antibody. As we shall see later, however, there is some evidence that a single cell can form antibodies of different specificities (p. 506).

The frequency of a given immunoglobulin-producing cell in lymphoid tissues seems to be roughly proportional to the level of the corresponding protein in serum, provided allowance is made for differences in half life. Thus there are ca. 3 to 6 cells that produce δ-chains per 1000 that produce γ-chains, in accord with the much lower level of γD than γG in serum. And cells that form α-chains are about equal in frequency to those that produce γ-chains, which fits with the shorter half life and lower concentration of γA in serum. Reasonable shifts also occur following immunization: after injection of salmonella in footpads of rabbits, for example, the popliteal lymph nodes exhibit a large increase in the number of cells that form μ-chains, in agreement with the production of γM antibodies (p. 463). It thus seems likely that differences in the serum levels of different immunoglobulins reflect the **number of cells** that synthesize each of these proteins, rather than differences in the rates of synthesis per cell.

Plaque Technics. While immunofluorescent staining serves admirably for the detection and rough enumeration of antibody-forming cells, more quantitative plating methods have recently been devised by Jerne and, independently, by Ingraham and Bussard. Dilute suspensions of lymphoid cells from animals immunized with foreign red cells are plated in agar or in a methylcellulose gum, along with the red cells that served as immunogen. During incubation the lymphoid cells synthesize and secrete antibodies, which combine with surrounding red cells. When complement (Ch. 16) is subsequently added the antibody–red cell complexes lyse, leaving clear **plaques** resembling those produced by phage-infected bacterial cells on a lawn of susceptible bacteria. In addition, at the center of the immune plaque the antibody-producing cell can be clearly visualized, allowing its morphology to be evaluated (Fig. 15-20).

---

* Some reports have indicated that two types of heavy or of light chains can be found within single cells of germinal follicles. However, studies of lymph nodes after infusions of extraneous allotypes have indicated that circulating, extracellular immunoglobulins tend to stick to cells of the germinal follicles: hence the doubly stained cells are probably artifacts.

γM antibodies to red cells are much more efficient than γG antibodies in causing hemolysis (Ch. 16) and, if used without further modification, the plaque technics are limited largely to measurement of γM-producing cells. Thus, the rapid appearance and disappearance of plaque-forming cells from the spleen of a mouse that has received a single immunizing injection of sheep red cells is in accord with the transient formation of γM antibodies to this immunogen (see also Fig. 15-6A). γG-producing cells can be detected by an indirect test. Their incipient plaques are brought out by adding to the plate an antiserum specific for γG immunoglobulins and then complement: when anti-γG antibodies bind to the red cells coated specifically with anti–red cell (γG) antibodies the addition of complement causes hemolysis. (If the antiserum added is monospecific for a particular allotype it is also possible to distinguish the cells producing anti–red cell antibodies of that particular allotype.)

The plaque technics are now dependent on antibodies to red cells. However, intensive efforts are currently being made to extend this approach to various simple antigens and haptens by attaching them to red cells (Ch. 16, Passive hemolysis).

Microdrop Technics. Another method for studying antibody formation by single cells is based on the immobilization of motile salmonella or the neutralization of infectious bacteriophage when added to a microdrop (e.g., 10^{-6} ml) containing a single lymphoid cell. These methods are of particular value for determining whether or not one cell can produce antibodies of different specificities; some of the results obtained are discussed later (Theories of antibody formation).

A recently developed modification of the microdrop technic is based on the findings that 1) some phages remain infectious when labeled with a haptenic group (mononitroiodophenyl, NIP), and 2) infectivity is lost on combination with antibody to the haptenic group. By testing individual cells in microdrops with two different phages (e.g., T2 and T4), each labeled with a cross-reactive hapten (mono- and dinitroiodophenyl,

NIP and NNP), it has been found that some cells from animals immunized with NIP-bovine γ-globulin form antibodies that neutralize NIP-phage but not NNP-phage, whereas other cells form antibodies that neutralize both. Thus the heterogeneity of purified antihapten antibodies (Ch. 13) finds its cellular counterpart in the heterogeneity of the cell population that synthesizes these molecules.

The Thymus and Other Lymphoepithelial Structures

The thymus gland is populated mainly by cells that are morphologically indistinguishable from lymphocytes; it has therefore long been suspected of having a role in the immune response. Isolated thymus cells, however, form little, if any, immunoglobulin; and those from immunized animals do not form detectable antibodies in recipient animals or in vitro. Moreover, when the thymus atrophies (as in many chronic diseases and in older persons),* or is removed surgically from a normal adult, the ability to form antibodies is not detectably impaired.

Recent studies have shown, however, that the maturation of peripheral lymphoid tissue (in lymph nodes, spleen, and elsewhere) and their acquisition of immunological competence is greatly influenced by the thymus and some other lymphoepithelial structures, i.e., the bursa of Fabricius in birds, and possibly also the tonsils. Each of these structures arises embryologically as an outpouching of the gut wall and eventually consists of masses of lymphocytes in close proximity to epithelial cells of endodermal origin (Fig. 15-21). When the thymus is removed from a newborn mouse, or the bursa plus the thymus from a newly hatched chick, the peripheral lymph nodes re-

---

* The thymus becomes atrophic in response to adrenal cortical steroids, even more rapidly than lymphoid tissue elsewhere. Hence a decrease in thymic weight has been widely used as an index of involution of lymphoid tissue during many stressful situations, such as starvation and fever.

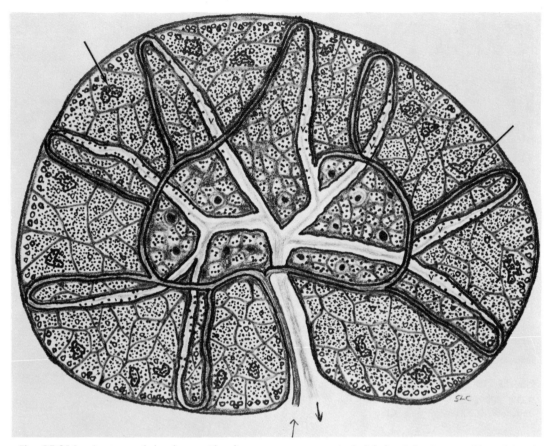

Fig. 15-21A Anatomy of the thymus. The diagram represents a single lobule of the thymus, with peripheral cortex and centrally placed medulla. Lymphatic vessels (not depicted) are found only within interlocular septa and the cuffs of connective tissue surrounding large blood vessels.

In the cortex, small lymphocytes (dots) are numerous and epithelial cells (gray lines) form an attenuated network. Large, proliferating lymphocytes (circles) are scattered throughout, but lymphopoiesis is particularly active in a narrow subcapsular zone. Also present are large macrophages filled with dead lymphocytes and other debris (upper arrows).

In the medulla, where lymphocytes are less numerous, epithelial cells (gray areas) possess abundant cytoplasm and appear to be actively secretory. Cytoplasmic granules and mucoid droplets are present within some epithelial cells, and there are extracellular accumulations of amorphous material within cystic spaces surrounded by epithelial cells (dark bodies in medulla). Hassall's corpuscles appear to develop from these cysts through a process of degeneration of the surrounding epithelial cells.

Blood enters the lobule chiefly through arteries that penetrate to the medulla before supplying the cortex (lower arrow). From arterioles skirting the medulla, capillaries run radially through the cortex and form loops just beneath the capsule. Venules return the blood centripetally through the cortex to the medulla. Cortical capillaries are closely invested in epithelial cells and their basement membranes, but the venules are surrounded by a relatively broad connective tissue cuff in which lymphocytes are numerous. In some places the venular endothelium consists of tall cells through which lymphocytes appear to be migrating, as in the postcapillary venules of lymph nodes (Fig. 15-11). Gaps in the surrounding epithelial barrier are occluded by lymphocytes, suggesting an additional pathway for migration of lymphocytes between thymic parenchyma and the blood stream. Through most of the organ, however, epithelial cells (gray areas) and their basement membranes form a continuous barrier separating lymphoid cells from connective tissue and the blood stream. Antigens penetrate this barrier to a limited degree. (Courtesy of S. L. Clark, Jr.; from S. L. Clark, Jr. In *Ciba Foundation Symposium on the Thymus* (G. L. W. Wolstenholme and R. Porter, eds.) Churchill, London, 1966.)

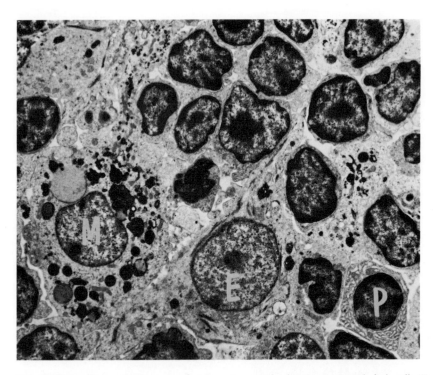

Fig. 15-21B Mouse thymus. An electron micrograph showing an epithelial cell (E), a macrophage (M), a rare plasma cell (P), and many lymphocytes (unlabeled). ×20,000 (reduced). (Courtesy of S. L. Clark, Jr.)

main aplastic, the blood lymphocyte count drops, the animal fails to make antibodies to many immunogens, and it is deficient with respect to "cellular immunity," e.g., it accepts foreign tissue grafts (allografts) remarkably well (Ch. 18). These defects are all alleviated when the animal receives a graft of thymus tissue from a donor of the same inbred strain.

In the normal newborn mammal, which has only very small amounts of peripheral lymphoid tissue, mitotic figures are numerous in thymus lymphocytes. In contrast, mitoses are rare in small lymphocytes of peripheral tissues and blood. These observations suggest that in embryonic development the thymus may serve as a central reservoir in which lymphocytes multiply, and from which they spread peripherally to populate lymph nodes, spleen, etc. However, the following observations, based on thymus grafts to thymectomized animals, suggest that the thymus also acts, perhaps predominantly, by elaborating a

hormone. A thymus graft, as noted before, will alleviate the immunological deficiencies of an animal that has been thymectomized at birth. When the donor of the graft has a distinctive chromosomal marker, which distinguishes grafted from host cells, it is observed that most of the mitotic figures in the peripheral lymph nodes of the alleviated host have the chromosomal pattern of the host cells. Moreover, the alleviation occurs even when the thymus graft is enclosed within a plastic chamber whose walls are impermeable to cells but permeable to solutes.

It is therefore thought that the thymus and other lymphoepithelial structures contribute in the neonatal period to the maturation of the body's lymphoid system in two ways: 1) by forming lymphocytes that spread out and populate the peripheral lymphoid tissues, and 2) by elaborating some sort of hormone that regulates the maturation of the peripheral cells.

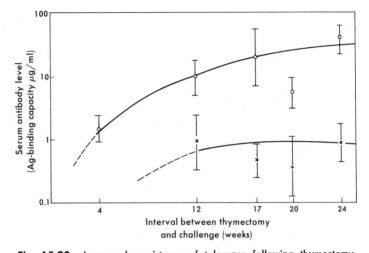

Fig. 15-22 Increased persistence of tolerance following thymectomy. Mice were first made tolerant by multiple injections of bovine serum albumin (BSA); then half were thymectomized. Loss of tolerance (=recovery of responsiveness) was determined by giving a challenging injection of BSA in Freund's adjuvant at intervals up to 24 weeks after thymectomy. Animals were bled 20 days after challenge. Symbols refer to average values for groups of 5 to 8 mice with standard deviation: x-tolerant, thymectomized; ○-tolerant, not thymectomized. Control mice (not tolerant and not thymectomized) had a titer of about 10. Hence nonthymectomized mice had apparently recovered responsiveness by 12 weeks, whereas the thymectomized ones had not recovered by 24 weeks. (From R. B. Taylor. *Immunology 7:595, 1964.*)

When adult animals are rendered tolerant of a foreign antigen (by one or a few large doses) the tolerance ordinarily wanes, but it tends to be more persistent if the thymus is removed (Fig. 15-22). It has thus been suggested that the thymus in adults may continue to provide an important mechanism whereby the immunologically uncommitted ("virgin") lymphocyte acquires the specific ability to respond to a particular immunogen (see Clonal selection theory). In addition, the finding of lesions in the thymus of persons with certain autoimmune diseases has led to the suggestion that the thymus may also be involved in the destruction of lymphoid cells that acquire the ability to form antibodies to self-antigens; i.e., some mechanism in the thymus is supposed to guard against the emergence of "forbidden" clones (see below, and Chapter 17).

INTERFERENCE WITH ANTIBODY FORMATION

Immunological Tolerance

The remarkable capacity of an individual's immune response to distinguish between his own and alien molecules has long been recognized. Since the 1890s it has, in fact, been held as axiomatic that an individual vertebrate can normally form antibodies to an almost unlimited number and variety of foreign substances, but not to components of his own tissues. This doctrine, called *"horror auto-toxicus"* by Ehrlich in 1900, has been recently designated "self-tolerance" by Burnet.

Attempts to evaluate this doctrine experimentally have disclosed that certain self-antigens are exceptions. Some of them (e.g., eye lens, spermatozoa, neural tissue, or thyroglobulin) are normally restricted to some anatomically confined site that prevents them from having access to antibody-forming lymphoid cells. When removed from an animal and injected back into the same animal (using a dose, route, and adjuvants as though it were a foreign material), these materials provoke antibody formation with considerable regularity. Antibodies may also be formed to those circulating self-constituents that acquire foreignness as a consequence of structural alterations in vivo (e.g., enzymatic fragmentation, or denaturation). These and other exceptions will be further discussed under Autoallergy in Chapter 17. For the present, however, it must be taken for granted that the Doctrine of Self-Tolerance is valid for the bulk of self-constituents.

Some insight into the mechanisms responsible for self-tolerance has emerged from studies of tolerance to foreign antigens. As was pointed out previously, immunogens in general exert two opposing effects: in moderate doses they stimulate antibody synthesis; whereas in very large doses they can establish a state of **unresponsiveness** during which antibodies to their determinant groups are not induced, even by subsequently administered doses that are ordinarily immunogenic. This dose-dependence was clearly demonstrated in the 1930s by Felton and associates. They observed that mice injected with 0.01 to 1.0 μg of a pneumococcal polysaccharide, say of type 1, became resistant to infection with type 1 pneumococci and produced antibodies to the polysaccharide; but if given 1000 μg of the same polysaccharide they failed to become resistant and did not form detectable antibodies. Such mice were said to be immunologically **paralyzed.** Their unresponsiveness was persistent and specific: though they failed to yield antibodies to type 1, they responded normally to stimulation with immunogenic doses of the capsular polysaccharides associated with other types of pneumococci.

The significance of this observation was not, however, widely appreciated until nearly 20 years later, when elegant experiments by

Billingham, Brent, and Medawar focused attention again on tolerance. They used the reaction to foreign tissue grafts as an immune assay (Ch. 18), and found that the transfer of viable cells from one individual to a genetically dissimilar newborn animal of the same species conferred on the recipient lifelong unresponsiveness to the cellular antigens of the donor. Detailed description of these experiments must be deferred for a general discussion of the immune reaction to grafts (Ch. 18).

The unresponsive state thus induced was called **tolerance,** apparently in the belief that it differed from the paralysis established by massive doses of polysaccharides, and was more relevant for self-tolerance. Subsequent studies have cast doubt on this distinction. For example, unresponsiveness has been induced with a variety of more conventional immunogens (e.g., serum proteins) in both the newborn and adult; and it has been shown that the duration of unresponsiveness depends on persistence of the immunogen. When the antigen is readily degraded in vivo (as are serum proteins), unresponsiveness established by a single large dose (or by repeated smaller ones) lasts only a few weeks or months, and repeated administration is required to prolong it. Pneumococcal polysaccharides, however, are unusually persistent in mammalian tissues, probably because degradative enzymes are lacking; and the unresponsiveness induced by one injection in a mouse can last a lifetime. Similarly, there is evidence (Ch. 18) that the viable foreign cells inoculated in the newborn period continue to proliferate, and they undoubtedly produce their immunogens continuously in the tolerant host. Thus it seems reasonable to regard all forms of unresponsiveness as fundamentally the same, regardless of the immunogen and the animal's age at which tolerance is established. We shall, accordingly, consider the terms unresponsiveness, tolerance, and paralysis as synonymous.

Though it was suspected for a time that the apparent unresponsiveness induced by large amounts of foreign antigen might represent only thorough neutralization of circulating antibodies that were formed, such a continuing synthesis and elimination of antibodies should lead to accelerated elimination of labeled antigens, which could not be observed. Moreover, intracellular antibodies to tolerated antigens have not been detected in lymphoid cells by immunofluorescence, though other intracellular antibodies can be seen. **Hence tolerance of an immunogen signifies the absence of synthesis of the corresponding antibodies.**

The following generalizations have emerged from studies of tolerance induced with foreign antigens; it is assumed that they also apply to tolerance of self-antigens.

1) **Establishment.** The establishment of tolerance ordinarily requires large amounts of immunogen, usually several hundredfold greater than the minimum for induction of antibody synthesis. Some exceptions, in which repeated injections of a small dose also establishes tolerance, are discussed below.

2) **Maintenance.** While maintenance of tolerance does not require as high a level of antigen as is required for its establishment, continued tolerance depends on persistence of the antigen above a critical but as yet undefined level. Tolerance is thus an intrinsically unstable state. If the antigen declines sufficiently it may eventually reach an immunogenic level. It is therefore not surprising that as tolerance disappears antibodies may be formed spontaneously; i.e., without the administration of additional antigen.

Recent studies indicate, however, that the need for persistent high levels of antigen may be due to the continuing emergence, possibly under the influence of the thymus, of new lymphoid cells that are potentially able to make antibodies to the tolerated antigen, and high levels are required to make these new cells tolerant. Thus, as noted before, when a tolerant animal is thymectomized its tolerant state tends to be more persistent, without further administration of antigen (Fig. 15-22).

3) **Diversity.** Tolerance has been established to the entire range of chemical structures that induce antibody formation: proteins, poly-saccharides, synthetic polypeptides, and simple groups, such as 2,4,6-trinitrophenyl.

4) **Specificity.** Tolerance is as specific as are immune reactions in general. When established to one antigen, such as bovine serum albumin, it does not extend to another, such as ribonuclease.

The relations among cross-reacting antigens, however, are of considerable interest: when an animal rendered tolerant of one antigen (such as bovine serum albumin) is immunized with a cross-reacting antigen (such as human serum albumin) tolerance of the first appears to be terminated. One explanation would be that some of the antibodies to the second antigen form complexes with the tolerated antigen and accelerate its degradation ("immune elimination"). Another possibility is that in the presence of antibody to one determinant of an antigen, the formation of antibodies to its other determinants is enhanced.

5) **Newborn vs. adult.** Tolerance of an antigen is much more readily established in the fetal or newborn animal than in the adult. This difference is particularly striking with viable cells: their injection into the newborn readily yields lifelong tolerance (Ch. 18), whereas in adults tolerance of alien cells is difficult to establish, and requires extreme immunosuppressive measures at about the time the alien antigens are administered.

The difficulty in establishing tolerance in the immunologically mature animal is possibly explained by the observation that **once antibody formation has been initiated** (by an immunogenic dose) **tolerance becomes more difficult to establish** (with a tolerance-inducing dose). It generally takes several days for a large quantity of injected antigen to achieve a uniformly high level in tissue fluids, and during this period the levels may be adequate in certain tissues to initiate antibody formation. However, in adults that have received massive X-irradiation or treatment with immunosuppressive drugs induction of tolerance is much easier since they are almost completely depleted of antibody-forming cells (as is the normal fetus or newborn). Another view, based on a proposed key role of macrophages in the induction of antibody formation, attributes the relative ease in establishing tolerance in irradiated adults and in the newborn period to a special defect in the ability of macrophages to "activate" immunogens in both situations.

Whatever the actual mechanism may be, the ease with which tolerance can be established in the fetal and neonatal period is a singularly advantageous feature of the immune system. Unresponsiveness during this critical period of growth and differentiation permits the gradual build-up of self-antigens to the high levels required to perpetuate tolerance of them during adult life.

Interpretations. A number of interpretations of tolerance to foreign and self-antigens have been proposed.

One view, the **"forbidden clone" hypothesis,** is based on the clonal selection theory, which assumes the cells that form antibodies to a particular immunogen to be clonally related: i.e., to be the progeny of a given cell. This hypothesis proposes that at some critical stage in the differentiation of a clone its reaction with the corresponding antigen leads somehow to death of the clone. Self-tolerance is thus ascribed to the

Fig. 15-23 Some immunosuppressive drugs.

Alkylating agents

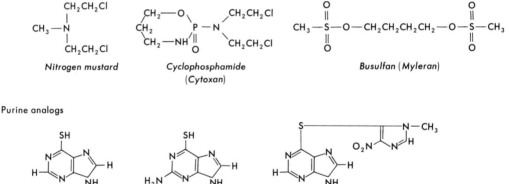

Nitrogen mustard   Cyclophosphamide   Busulfan (Myleran)
                          (Cytoxan)

Purine analogs

6-Mercaptopurine   6-Thioguanine   Azathioprine (Imuran)

Pyrimidine analogs

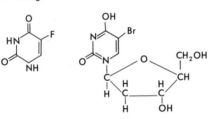

5-Fluorouracil   5-Bromodeoxyuridine (BUDR)

Folic acid analog

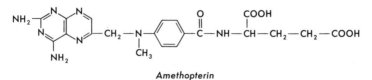

Amethopterin

elimination of the cells that can form antibodies to self-antigens; these antigens monitor lymphoid cell populations continually, destroying the "forbidden clones" as they arise (presumably by mutation). It has also been suggested that the progenitor cells for these clones continually arise during an individual's lifetime, and are destroyed, in the normal thymus (Ch. 17).

Another view regards the induction of tolerance and the induction of antibody formation as competitive reactions of the same cell. It is assumed that tolerance is established when the antigen makes direct contact with hypothetical antibody-like receptor sites on appropriate plasma cell precursors (see "sentinel antibodies," below); whereas antibody formation is induced if the antigen is first ingested by a macrophage which then somehow delivers it, perhaps in "activated" form, to the plasma cell precursor. Thus when antigen levels are high the former process supposedly takes precedence and tolerance is induced; tolerance would also be favored if macrophages do not function normally, as in the normal newborn and in recently irradiated adults. In fact, Mitchison has found that very low doses of antigen (repeated injections of 1 to 10 μg of many protein antigens, which is below their threshold for induction of antibody formation in mice) induce tolerance in irradiated or newborn mice. And one antigen that is phagocytized poorly (bovine serum albumin) induces tolerance in normal adult mice when given in these small doses, which are too low to cause antibody formation.

In a third hypothesis it is assumed that binary (1:1) antigen-antibody complexes, formed in vivo by conventional (bivalent, homospecific) "natural" antibodies (or those induced by previous immunization), are essential for activating lymphoid cells to form the corresponding antibodies; whereas unbound antigen, or antigen bound in the type of complexes formed by excessive levels of antigen (Ag-Ab-Ag), are unable to stimulate the cells. Thus moderate levels are immunogenic and high doses cause tolerance. In a modification of this view it has been speculated that a cell capable of making a particular antibody carries some molecules of it at the surface as "sentinels," by means of which an immunogen reacts specifically with that cell: 1:1 immune complexes at the surface membrane would supposedly stimulate the cell to proliferate and to differentiate into plasma cells that form

the corresponding antibodies, whereas 2:1 complexes (excess antigen) would specifically block these changes and maintain the precursor cell in its dormant state.

Though a substantial amount of descriptive information has been accumulated, and several plausible hypotheses have been proposed, the cellular and molecular bases for tolerance of self as well as of foreign antigens remains one of the major unsolved problems in immunology. And some of the most elementary questions are still unanswered: for example, does the individual tolerant of antigen X possess lymphoid cells that can form anti-X, but which are held in an unresponsive state, or are all prospective anti-X forming cells absent from the body while tolerance of X is in force?

Immunosuppressive Agents

The suppression of the immune response is of considerable importance for controlling autoimmune diseases and for enhancing the survival of foreign tissue grafts (Ch. 18). Many chemical agents, and X-rays, have been tested for the ability to prevent or to arrest antibody formation; and their effectiveness varies with the time at which they and the immunogen are administered. The most promising chemical agents are highly diversified in structure (Fig. 15-23) and in metabolic activity, and their potency and toxicity often differ considerably in different species. While their mechanisms of action are not yet understood in detail, the following tentative general conclusions seem warranted.

1) When given at the appropriate time the immunosuppressive agents can **prevent the initiation** of antibody formation. Several are sufficiently selective (i.e., relatively nontoxic at inhibitory doses) to be clinically useful.

2) When antibody synthesis is underway, in contrast, **it cannot be interrupted** by any of these agents, given in tolerable doses.

3) All the agents are more effective in blocking the primary than the secondary response: perhaps with the greater number of cells that respond to the secondary stimulus

there is a greater probability that some will escape inhibition.

4) The most extensively studied agents fall into two main groups. a) The **lympholytic agents** cause prompt and massive destruction of lymphocytes, including, it is thought, prospective responders to the immunogens of interest. These agents, of which X-rays are the paradigm, include the alkylating drugs (Fig. 15-23) and 11-oxycorticosteroids. X-rays and alkylating agents also damage DNA and their effects are particularly pronounced on many rapidly dividing cells, such as hematopoietic stem cells and intestinal epithelium. Thus their effectiveness seems to be due not only to reduction in the total pool of small lymphocytes, but also to their impairing the capacity of many surviving cells to undergo multiplication in response to antigenic stimulation.

b) The **antimetabolites**, which include purine analogs, pyrimidine analogs, and folic acid antagonists (Fig. 15-23), affect nucleic acid metabolism and are particularly damaging to actively dividing and differentiating cells, including those responding to immunogenic stimulation.

In contrasting various immunosuppressive agents it is useful to consider the optimal times for their administration in regard to the three phases into which the antibody response may be divided: 1) the **preinductive** phase, before an immunogen is administered (1 to 30 days, depending on the duration of a particular agent's effect); 2) the **inductive** phase, between immunogen administration and appearance of the corresponding serum antibodies; and 3) the **productive** phase, when antibodies are being synthesized vigorously. The lympholytic agents are effective immunosuppressors when given in the preinductive phase, and the antimetabolites are probably most effective in the inductive phase. All the immunosuppressive agents so far studied appear to be ineffective in the productive phase, unless given in doses that are severely cytotoxic for cells in general. While this schematic division is a formal convenience it is actually a gross oversimplification, for the lymphoid cells do not respond synchronously: some cells can still be in the inductive phase while others (e.g., plasma cells) are already productive, and others (preinductive) are still to be stimulated by the immunogen, which doubtless remains active for some time after its injection.

X-rays. Whole body irradiation with sublethal doses of X-rays (400 to 500 r) can depress the response to most immunogens for many weeks, but usually not permanently. The effects on the **primary response** are as follows: 1) When irradiation is given 12 hours to 50 days before the primary stimulus there is either complete prevention of antibody formation or a long delay in the appearance of antibodies, with reduction in peak titers. Suppression is greatest when the interval is 24 to 48 hours (Fig. 15-24). 2) If irradiation is given within 12 hours before to 1 day after the immunogen, the onset of antibody formation is usually also delayed, but peak titers are generally in the normal range. 3) If irradiation is given 2 days after the immunogen the

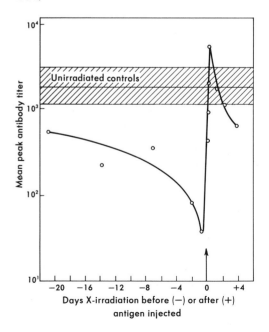

Fig. 15-24 Effect of 500 r X-irradiation of rabbits at various times before and after immunization (arrow) with sheep red cells. (Based on W. H. Taliaferro and L. G. Taliaferro. *J. Infect. Dis.* 95:134, 1954.)

peak titer may even, occasionally, be higher than in unirradiated controls.

Immediately following whole body X-irradiation massive disintegration of lymphocytes is observed and the capacity to undergo normal mitosis is markedly inhibited, the duration depending on the dose. After a large dose (e.g., 500 r) active proliferation of lymphoid cells is resumed after ca. 3 to 4 weeks, and lymph nodes appear normal shortly thereafter. If an immunogen is given after irradiation the formation of antibodies is delayed until the capacity for mitotic activity is recovered. The decline in the level of immunogen during this period probably accounts for the reduction of the peak titer, and for its absence if the immunogen disappears rapidly. If, however, the immunogen has stimulated some cellular proliferation just before irradiation, the cells can apparently continue their differentiation and they eventually form antibodies. Cells that are already actively synthesizing antibodies continue to be active even after massive irradiation. Indeed, it is even possible that having once proliferated and begun to differentiate the responding cells are more active than normally, because the lymphoid tissues are then depleted by the irradiation of so many other cells; this effect could account for the increased antibody formation sometimes seen in animals irradiated 1 to 2 days **after** immunization.

In spite of the unresponsiveness of irradiated animals to ordinary immunization it has been reported that they form antibodies to salmonellae when injected with viable macrophages (from nonirradiated donors) that had phagocytized the bacteria in vitro. If, however, the macrophages are themselves obtained from recently irradiated donors they are ineffective, though they phagocytize the bacteria in an apparently normal manner. These findings suggest that the unresponsiveness of irradiated animals may be due in part to some defect in their macrophages; and additional evidence is thus provided for the participation of macrophages in the induction of antibody formation, at least in the primary response.

The **secondary response** is relatively resistant to X-irradiation. The appearance of antibody may be delayed but peak titers are usually normal. Antibody formation may actually be unusually persistent, especially if the immunogen is given before irradiation; and more antibody is then formed than in control animals. As with the comparable situation in the primary response, the stimulated "memory" cells responsible for the secondary response appear to be more than normally active in lymphoid tissues depleted of many other cells by irradiation.

Alkylating agents, such as the nitrogen mustards, block cell division by cross-linking strands of DNA; they also alkylate proteins. Often called **radiomimetic drugs,** their biological effects resemble those of X-irradiation, and they cause massive destruction of lymphocytes. However, recovery from their effects is more rapid than after X-rays, and these drugs are therefore usually given at frequent intervals (e.g., 2 to 3 times per week) for sustained immunosuppression.

Corticosteroids. In therapeutic doses the 11-oxycorticosteroids inhibit inflammation, whether due to allergic reactions (Ch. 17) or to nonspecific chemical irritants, such as turpentine. In large doses they also cause extensive destruction of small lymphocytes. These drugs are therefore widely used to suppress various allergic reactions, especially of the delayed type (Ch. 17). In the rabbit large doses given with, or just before, an immunogen also decrease the amount of antibody formed; but in man and some other species such doses barely affect antibody synthesis.

Antimetabolites. Many of the antimetabolites that inhibit proliferation of neoplastic and other rapidly dividing cells have been found to inhibit the immune response when given with immunogen. However, the margin between immunosuppression and serious toxicity for hematopoietic tissues and intestinal epithelium is usually exceedingly narrow. A few of these drugs can, nevertheless, be used for prolonged periods in man; and one of them, imidazolyl thioguanine (Imuran, Fig. 15-23), appears to enhance the survival of kidney grafts (Ch. 18).

In contrast to X-rays, which are most inhibitory when given just **before** the immunogen, 6-mercaptopurine, a representative purine

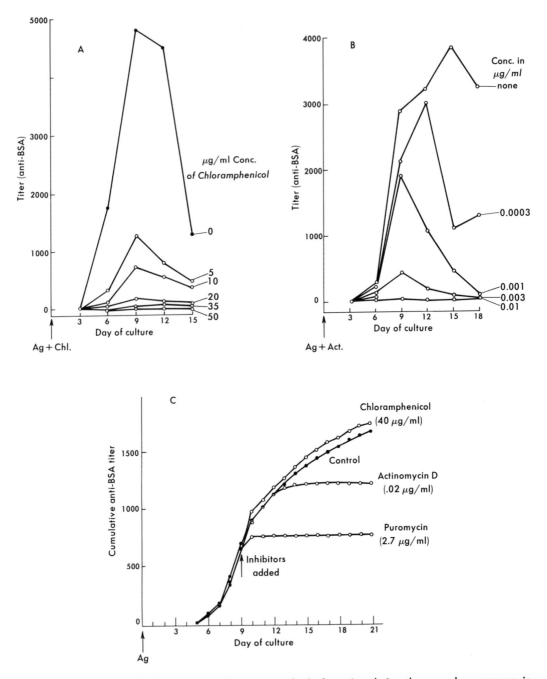

Fig. 15-25 Effects of some metabolic inhibitors on antibody formation during the secondary response induced in vitro. Lymph node fragments from rabbits immunized 3 to 12 months previously with bovine serum albumin (BSA) were incubated with the antigen at time zero, and inhibitors were added at varying times. **A.** Chloramphenicol (Chl) was inhibitory when present from day 0 to day 15. **B.** Actinomycin D (Act) was inhibitory when present from day 0 to day 15. **C.** When added **after** antibody production was underway chloramphenicol did not inhibit, and actinomycin D had a delayed effect. As expected, puromycin has an immediate effect when it is added, because it promptly blocks all protein synthesis. (From C. T. Ambrose. *Bact. Rev.* 30:408, 1966. Based in part on C. T. Ambrose and A. H. Coons. *J. Exp. Med.* 117:1075, 1963.)

analog (Fig. 15-23) suppresses antibody formation best when its administration is begun about 2 days **afterward,** probably because the cellular proliferation induced by the immunogen is then particularly active. Similar results are obtained with 5-bromodeoxyuridine, which is incorporated into DNA, and at a sufficient level blocks DNA replication and cell division. As with X-irradiation the antimetabolites are more effective in blocking the primary than the secondary response.

Other Immunosuppressive Drugs. Some antimicrobial drugs also inhibit antibody formation. **Chloramphenicol** in relatively high doses inhibits the primary response in intact animals; in cell cultures this drug also inhibits the secondary response if added with the immunogen to cells from a previously immunized animal (Fig. 15-25). If, however, the cells are already forming antibodies in vitro the addition of chloramphenicol has little effect.

Antibody formation can persist for many days in the presence of **actinomycin D** (Fig. 15-25), suggesting that the corresponding messenger RNA is relatively stable. However, if this drug is added together with the immunogen to cultured lymph node fragments from a previously immunized animal, or is given with a primary injection of immunogen in an intact animal, the formation of antibody is partially or totally inhibited, presumably because the synthesis of new mRNA is required for initiation of antibody synthesis.

Drug-Induced Tolerance. One of the more promising aspects to the practical use of the immunosuppressive agents arises from their ability, when given with large doses of immunogen, to establish immunological tolerance for an unusually prolonged period. For example, when 6-mercaptopurine was given with 70 mg of bovine serum albumin (per rabbit) not only was there suppression of antibody formation, but the animals remained tolerant when challenged some months later with this protein (Fig. 15-26). Similarly, the administration of large doses of immunogen at the time of X-irradiation can establish in adult animals a tolerant state that is long-lasting, though not permanent.

Complications of Immunosuppression. The use of immunosuppressive agents for prolonged periods is dangerous not only because of their toxicity but because they increase susceptibility to serious infections with various microbes, including those that ordinarily have little pathogenicity. Thus infection with "opportunistic" fungi is frequent in patients treated intensively with corticosteroids and X-rays (Ch. 21).

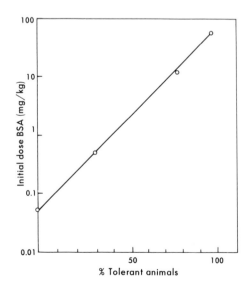

Fig. 15-26 Immunolgical tolerance induced in adult animals with the aid of an immunosuppressive agent. Rabbits received 6-mercaptopurine (10 mg/kg of body weight) over a 2-week period, beginning the day the antigen (bovine serum albumin, BSA) was given. They were tested 1 to 3 months later for their ability to make anti-BSA antibodies in response to immunization with conventional doses of BSA. The proportion of tolerant animals increased with the initial dose of BSA. (From R. S. Schwartz. *Progr. Allergy* 9:246, 1965.)

Agammaglobulinemias

Genetic defects that seriously hinder the formation of antibodies to immunogens in general should be lethal mutations. Since the 1950s, however, a number of individuals with such defects have been enabled to survive for long periods, through the vigorous use of antimicrobial chemotherapy and the frequent administration of pooled normal human immunoglobulins (which contain antibodies to common pathogens). These defects appear to fall into several groups.

Congenital Sex-Linked Agammaglobulinemia. This defect is found in boys who suffer from recurrent bacterial infections that usually begin at ca. 5 to 6 months of age, when the maternal immunoglobulins received transplacentally have virtually disappeared (Fig. 15-27). When subjected to immunization procedures these patients do not form detectable antibodies or plasma cells, but they can develop delayed-type hypersensitivity (Ch. 17). Their thymuses are not unusually atrophic, and they actually can form immunoglobulins to a very limited extent, the serum concentrations usually being ca. 1% of the normal level. Several of these young subjects, constituting a significant proportion of the total number recognized, have died of malignant tumors of lymphoid tissue (lymphomas), which seems more than coincidental because agammaglobulinemia and lymphomas in childhood are both rare diseases. Since the lymphomas may have a viral origin it seems possible that these tumors represent another example in these patients of inordinate susceptibility to infections.

These patients, however, are not especially susceptible to a number of common virus infections.

Agammaglobulinemia and Lymphopenia. This defect, the so-called Swiss type of agammaglobulinemia, is more severe than the above. Sex linkage is evident in some of the affected families, and infants with the disease begin to have severe infections even before 1 month of age. They are highly susceptible to viral and fungous as well as bacterial infections. They form neither antibodies nor plasma cells when immunized; and they do not exhibit delayed-type hypersensitivity. The thymus and peripheral lymphoid tissues are markedly atrophic, and these patients lack lymphocytes almost completely.

Acquired Agammaglobulinemia. These disorders differ from the above in that they first appear in adult life, after the subjects have been apparently well, with normal immunoglobulin levels and normal ability to respond to immunogens. Once the disability occurs, however, serum concentrations of immunoglobulins drop to very low levels, including all major classes of these proteins; moreover, the response to immunization becomes exceedingly weak or nondetectable. The disease tends to occur in families, suggesting that the defect may be heritable. In some patients, however, the defect is not familial but is associated with various neoplastic diseases, such as chronic lymphatic leukemia. It seems possible that a replacement of normal lymphoid cells by the neoplastic ones could account for the disorder in the latter group, since the neoplastic cells do not form immunoglobulins (except in rare instances).

ONTOGENY AND PHYLOGENY OF THE IMMUNE RESPONSE

Ontogeny

Synthesis of immunoglobulins begins shortly before or after birth in most mammals, but some time lapses before protective levels of antibodies to common pathogens can be attained. The newborn would therefore be extremely vulnerable to infection were it not for the maternal antibodies it receives, by passive transfer, before or shortly after birth. This is achieved in mammals by 1) transfer from maternal to fetal circulation in utero, or 2) suckling of colostrum, which is rich in γA and γG immunoglobulins. In some species (cattle, pigs) the fetus receives no immunoglobulins in utero, but the newborn absorbs large amounts by suckling colostrum. In others (rabbits, mice, other rodents) maternal immunoglobulins are transferred both in utero and by suckling. In man and higher primates absorption from colostrum is probably of minor importance, while maternal immunoglobulins are mainly transferred to the fetus directly across the placenta. When intrauterine transfer occurs in other mammals it apparently takes place across the yolk sac (Table 15-7).*

Maternal γG immunoglobulins, but not γM or γA, are transmitted freely to the human fetus in utero. Experiments in rabbits suggest that sites on the Fc domain are required, because Fc fragments are transferred as well as are intact γG molecules, and much more rapidly than Fab fragments. This finding accounts for the observation in humans that pepsin digestion of horse antibodies to diphtheria toxin (which degrades the Fc domain, Ch. 14) destroys its ability to be transferred from the maternal to the fetal circulation.

The changing levels of the major immunoglobulins in the human newborn are shown in Figure 15-27A. γM and γA, which are lacking at birth because they are not transmitted from the mother, are synthesized almost immediately, whereas the synthesis of γG is not detectable until ca. 1 to 3 months later. Hence the newborn's total γG level falls, as the maternal protein is degraded, until 8 to 10 weeks

---

* In chickens (and presumably in other birds) β-globulins containing antibodies are transmitted from hen to ova via follicular epithelium, and are stored in the yolk sac, from which these proteins are eventually absorbed into the fetal circulation shortly before hatching.

of age, when it rises again as a result of active synthesis, reaching the normal adult level at ca. 2 years of age. (In agammaglobulinemic infants, however, the level drops continuously, falling below 10% of the normal adult value by 5 to 6 months (Fig. 15-27B). It is at this time that many of these infants begin to suffer from severe and recurrent infections; see Congenital sex-linked agammaglobulinemia.)

The response of the newborn to antigenic stimulation depends, in part, on the nature of the immunogen and on how much maternal antibody of the corresponding specificity is present in its circulation. If the level of antibody is high the immunogen is likely not to evoke antibody formation, because it is rapidly eliminated. Thus immunization of infants with measles virus is usually postponed until 6 to 9 months of age, i.e., after the corresponding maternal antibodies have disappeared. In addition, those immunogens that evoke (in adults) mainly γG antibodies are ineffective in the newborn, because these immunoglobulins are not synthesized at birth. However, immunogens that evoke readily detectable γM antibodies (such as flagella of enteric bacteria and bacteriophages) can induce antibody (γM) formation at birth, even in those born prematurely.

Careful studies of the immune response in fetal lambs, which are carried in utero about 150 days, revealed that they can synthesize antibodies long before birth, and that the abil-

---

TABLE 15-7.   RELATION OF PLACENTAL STRUCTURE AND MODE OF PASSIVE TRANSFER OF IMMUNOGLOBULINS TO THE FETUS

Species	Tissue layers between maternal and fetal circulation at term	Placental or amniotic transmission	Importance of transmission via colostrum
Pig	6	—	+++
Ruminants	5	—	+++
Carnivores	3	±	+
Rodents	2	+ (yolk sac)	+
Man	2	+++ (placenta)	—

From R. A. Good and B. W. Papermaster. Advances Immunol. 4:1 (1964). Based on B. Vahlquist. Advances Pediat. 10:305 (1958).

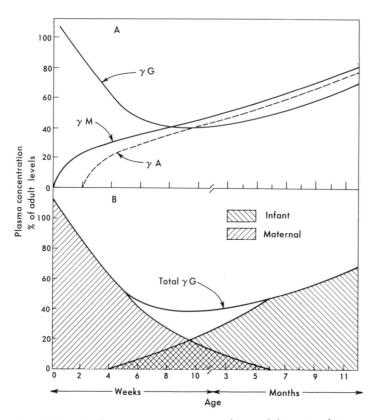

Fig. 15-27 A. Changing concentrations in plasma of the major classes of immunoglobulins in the human infant. **B.** Disappearance of the mother's γG immunoglobulins and appearance of the infant's γG immunoglobulins account for the changing plasma level of these proteins during the first 6 months. Note change in time scale on abscissa. (Based on D. Gitlin. *Pediatrics 34:198, 1964.*)

ity to respond to various immunogens appears in a fixed time sequence. When immunized at various times (in utero) they form antibodies to bacteriophage ϕX174 by day 41 of gestation, to ferritin at ca. day 66, to egg albumin at day 125, and to diphtheria toxoid only some days after birth. A somewhat different sequence is followed in fetal monkeys. The time elapsed between intrauterine inoculation of phage and the appearance of antiphage antibodies was the same in the fetus as in the adult, with γM antibodies being detected initially. The responses of fetal monkeys to immunization are in accord with the ability of the prematurely born human infant to respond to some immunogens.

Phylogeny

The immune response appears to have originated in evolution with the vertebrates. Invertebrates show none of the adaptive immune responses: they do not display accelerated clearance of antigens from their circulation; they do not form antibodies or exhibit allergic responses; and they readily accept foreign tissue grafts (allografts).* One of the

---

* In many invertebrates, however, macrophages phagocytize foreign particles, and in this sense they could be regarded as having a rudimentary immune response—especially if it turns out that the ingestion of an immunogen by a macrophage is an essential step in the induction of antibody formation.

most primitive of present-day vertebrates, the California hagfish, lacks recognizable immunoglobulins and seems not to possess immunological capability. However, the lamprey eel, which is believed to be a slightly more advanced form, has immunoglobulins (Fig. 15-28) and displays most features of the immune response, though rather feebly. It rejects allografts, forms antibodies to some immunogens but not to others, and has small lymphocytes in its blood and in its gut wall; however, plasma cells have not been recognized in this species and the thymus is rudimentary.

Beginning with the more advanced elasmobranchs, and continuing on up to mammals, essentially all features of the immune response are present in all species of vertebrates: antibody formation, appearance of plasma cells in response to immunization, allograft rejection, and a fully developed lymphoid system, including the thymus and other lymphoepithelial structures. As noted before, however, there seems to be less diversity among the immunoglobulins of some primitive vertebrates. For example, the heavy chains formed by the dogfish shark seem to be of only one class, resembling mammalian μ chains. The evolutionary origins of immunoglobulins are just now coming under intensive study (see discussion of comparative amino acid sequences of different chains, Ch. 14).

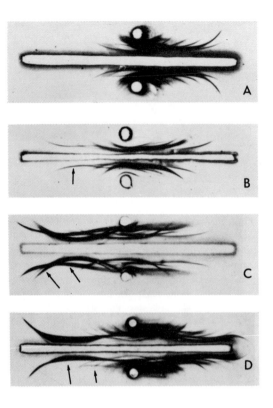

Fig. 15-28 Immunoelectrophoresis of serum from several vertebrates, showing evolutionary development of immunoglobulins. Proteins with electrophoretic characteristics of immunoglobulins (arrows) are absent in the hagfish (**A**), present in small amount in the lamprey eel (**B**), and abundant in the bowfin, a fresh water dogfish (**C**), and in man (**D**). (From B. W. Papermaster, R. M. Condie, J. Finstad, and R. A. Good. *J. Exp. Med. 119*:105, 1964.)

ANTIBODY FORMATION AT THE MOLECULAR LEVEL

Biosynthesis of Antibodies

The genetic loci for light and heavy chain allotypes are distributed randomly among the offspring of mating experiments with rabbits (Ch. 14), showing that these loci are not linked, and may well be on different chromosomes. Hence different mRNA molecules should specify the synthesis of light and of heavy chains. This expectation has recently been supported by preliminary findings that nascent light chains, labeled by incubating lymphoid cells with radioactive amino acids, are associated with small polyribosomes (ca. 190S), while nascent heavy chains are associated with much larger polyribosomes (ca. 240S) (Fig. 15-29). By exposing cells to labeled amino acids for about 1 minute and then to unlabeled amino acids for various periods it was possible to follow the rate at which the labeled polypeptides are completed and released from their polyribosomes. In ac-

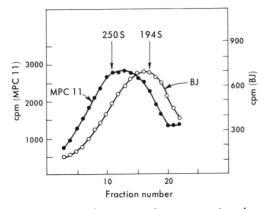

Fig. 15-29 Preliminary evidence suggesting that light chains are made on small and heavy chains on large polyribosomes. Sucrose density gradient centrifugation was carried out with extracts of mouse myeloma tumor cells previously incubated with labeled amino acids. The position of the labeled nascent protein indicates the size of the poly-ribosomes (and the mRNA) on which they are made. In a tumor that made only light chains (BJ, Bence Jones protein) the nascent protein sedimented on relatively small polyribosomes (194C); whereas in a tumor that made light and heavy chains (MPC 11) there was more nascent protein associated with larger polyribosomes (250S). (From M. D. Scharff, A. L. Shapiro, J. V. Maizel, Jr., and J. W. Uhr. Symposium on differentiation and growth of hemo-globin- and immunoglobulin-synthesizing cells. *J. Cell. Physiol.* 67, Suppl. 1. 1966.)

cord with the difference in molecular weight (and in chain length) the light chains appeared to be completed about twice as fast as heavy chains (about 30 vs. 60 seconds). Since light chains are turned out more rapidly they are found free of heavy chains in the cell sap and are secreted into the medium as free chains (or perhaps as light chain dimers; see Ch. 14). In addition, the larger polyribosomes with attached heavy chain seem to bear some light chains. It is thought therefore that im-munoglobulin molecules (or half-molecules made of one light plus one heavy chain) are assembled through the attachment of free light chains to polyribosome-bound heavy chains, which are then released. The process thus appears to resemble hemoglobin synthe-sis in reticulocytes, where free β-chains, which are made more rapidly than α-chains, combine with ribosome-bound α-chains, releasing he-moglobin molecules.

Detailed analysis of antibody biosynthesis is handicapped by the diversity of cell types in suspensions of normal lymphoid cells: the total immunoglobulins made range from 1 to 40% of the total protein formed, depending on how intensively the cells have previously been stimulated by antigen. Hence myeloma tumors, which yield homogeneous suspensions of plasma cells, have much to offer as models, even though the immunoglobulins they pro-duce in large amount (up to ca. 40% of the total protein made) have not been shown to have antibody activity. Many of these tumors, however, have regulatory anomalies that lead to wide discrepancies in the rates at which the light and heavy chains are made. In one mouse myeloma tumor, for example, light chains are completed four times faster than heavy chains, while some others produce only light chains (see Fig. 15-15B). (When made in sufficient excess the secreted light chains are detected in urine as Bence Jones protein; see Ch. 14.) And one line of human lym-phoma cells is claimed to produce only heavy chains. This finding suggests that light chains are not essential for the release of nascent heavy chains from polyribosomes, though they apparently speed up this process in normal cells.

Theories of Antibody Formation

Various theories of antibody formation ascribe different roles to the immunogen dur-ing immunization. According to **selective theories** the immunogen reacts selectively with specific biosynthetic units (cells or subunits within cells), stimulating them to make greater amounts of the antibody molecules they were already making at a low level, or were capable of making, in advance of immu-nization. **Instructive theories,** in contrast, as-sume that the immunogen helps to shape the corresponding antibodies, which could not be made in its absence, except as a rare and for-tuitous event.

The first detailed theory proposed, by Ehrlich in 1900, was selective (Fig. 15-30). Cells were supposedly covered by antibody-like receptors; and in combining with the appropriate ones the immunogen was supposed somehow to stimulate the cell to synthesize them in great excess, and to shed them into the circulation. This theory was gradually abandoned by the 1920s, when the increasing number of immunogenic substances, including a large number of synthetic organic chemicals, suggested that the diversity of antigens is almost limitless: it seemed beyond belief that the corresponding antibodies could all preexist.

In place of Ehrlich's selective hypothesis an instructive theory then came to be favored widely. Formulated independently and almost simultaneously by several persons in the 1930s (Breinl and Haurowitz, Mudd, and Alex-

Fig. 15-30 Ehrlich's selective theory of antibody formation, showing hypothetical multiplication and shedding of natural cellular receptors following their combination with the immunogen. (From P. Ehrlich. *Proc. Roy. Soc. s. B* 66:424, 1900.)

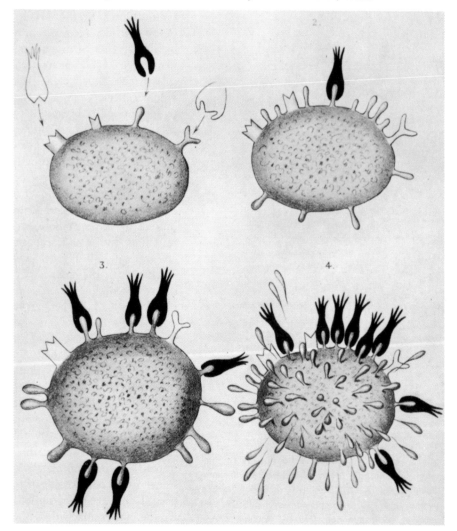

ander), this viewpoint, the **antigen-template** theory, postulated that antigenic determinants act as templates at biosynthetic sites. In molding itself around the immunogenic determinant a flexible nascent globulin molecule was supposedly stamped with a complementary conformation at its active sites (Fig. 15-31). A central assumption in this theory was that the specificity of an antibody molecule was

determined not by its amino acid sequence, but by the immunogen's presence at the site of the protein's synthesis. As was pointed out elsewhere, however, the specificity of an antibody molecule—and thus the conformation at its active site—seems now to be due directly, like the specificity of an enzyme, to its amino acid sequence (Ch. 14); an antigenic template is thus gratuitous. In addition, antigen appears to be absent from cells that are making the corresponding antibodies. These findings have, therefore, made the antigen-template theory untenable.

Clonal Selection Theory. Even before the antigen-template theory encountered serious difficulties a novel selective theory, substantially different from Ehrlich's, was proposed by Burnet. Its formulation was encouraged by the success of mutation-selection in explaining microbial adaptations. According to this theory, called **clonal selection,** an individual can elaborate a large number of different antibodies because his total population of lymphoid cells is composed of a correspondingly large number of different classes of cells, each able to synthesize antibodies of one, or perhaps a few, specificities. Each class is presumed to be a clone, made up of the descendants of a progenitor cell that had acquired, by some random process of somatic mutation, the genetic capacity to synthesize an antibody of a particular structure and specificity. In the absence of the immunogen the corresponding clone is supposedly made up of few cells. When an antigen is introduced into the body it presumably reacts selectively with the cells of the corresponding clones, stimulating their proliferation and thereby increasing the production of only those immunoglobulins that these cells are capable of synthesizing. Clonal selection thus requires a mechanism of antibody synthesis within the cell identical with that of protein synthesis in general; but the antigenic determinant, in its immunogenic activity, must somehow recognize cells of the proper clone, possibly by means of antibody or antibody-like receptors attached to their surfaces (cf. Fig. 15-30).

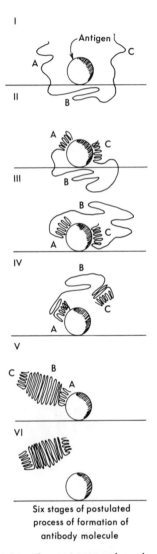

Six stages of postulated process of formation of antibody molecule

Fig. 15-31 The antigen-template theory. The immunogen supposedly reacts with a nascent immunoglobulin chain (A-B-C), causing it to fold in such a way that its ends are complementary to determinant groups of the immunogen. (From L. Pauling. *J. Am. Chem. Soc.* 62:2643, 1940.)

The clonal selection theory requires that only a few structural genes for immunoglobulins be transmitted by germ cells (perhaps one for each type of chain, such as κ, λ, γ, μ, and for each allotype), because they can presumably become sufficiently diversified by mutations in somatic (lymphoid) cells to generate the vast amount of genetic information required to code for all the different antibody molecules a given animal can make. Thus a given lymphoid cell and its progeny (**clone**) would come to have a unique set of genes for immunoglobulins (Ig genes); though these genes would be few **per cell**, their total number and variety in the body would be immense because of the great number of different clones.

Various processes have been suggested by which a large amount of genetic diversity could be achieved in the short time between fertilization of the ovum and the end of the neonatal period, when the ability to make many different antibodies is usually fully developed. Some possibilities are 1) an extremely high rate of mutation at certain intragenic sites as in certain "hot spots" of the bacteriophage genome (Ch. 9), and 2) intragenic inversions, duplications, and deletions. Others might be imagined; for example, some unusual DNase's, together with repair enzymes (Ch. 9) that make "mistakes" with a high frequency, might act on the Ig genes at some stage in the maturation of lymphoid cells. Though a somatic mechanism for generating diversity in Ig genes is still entirely speculative, the existence of such a process is attractive, for it would permit a modest investment in a relatively small number of nucleotides to accumulate immensely diversified genetic reserves that could be tapped on demand, as it were, with the formation of antibodies to all sorts of immunogens.

In addition to being consistent with the evidence for genetic determination of antibody specificity, the clonal selection theory can account for some other features of the immune response. Thus "natural" antibodies would be those produced at a low level before exposure to the immunogen; and self-tolerance—as well as induced tolerance to foreign antigens—would be due to the destruction of clones, instead of their stimulation, when the prospective immunogen became available under conditions which are still only vaguely perceived. The existence of clones is particularly satisfactory in accounting for the differences between the primary and secondary responses, e.g., the differences in kinetics, and the phenomenon called the "doctrine of original antigenic sin" (p. 467).

There are, however, several difficulties with this theory. One is the finding that the ability to synthesize antibodies of different specificities appears during fetal development in a fixed time sequence, rather than at random (p. 498). Another is the mutual interference during immunization between antigens that appear to be immunologically unrelated, i.e., which do not cross-react with the respective antibodies (see Competition among immunogens); this effect suggests that different immunogens may direct the same cells to differentiate in different ways and produce different antibodies. And studies with single cells (p. 506) still do not exclude the possibility that an individual lymphoid cell can form antibodies to many different antigenic determinants.

Germ Line Theories. Is it possible, in contrast to the clonal selection theory, that the structural genes for all the antibodies that an individual can make are transmitted in germ cells, and are present, therefore, in each of his lymphoid (and other somatic) cells? Since an individual mammal could conceivably form distinctive antibodies for perhaps 10^6 different antigenic determinants, the one gene–one polypeptide hypothesis would thus require that a given cell have 10^6 structural genes for immunoglobulins (Ig genes), or even twice this number if the specificity of a given antibody depends on both unique light and heavy chains (Ch. 14). (The number of Ig Genes required, however, would be only 10^3, i.e., $(10^6)^{1/2}$, if any light chain and any heavy chain could pair, and each pair were to provide a unique specificity; but this possibility is not attractive in view of tentative evidence that the light and heavy chains dissociated from a given antibody have much greater affinity for each other than for the chains from other immunoglobulin molecules.) It is necessary, therefore, to ask whether there is enough DNA in a cell to accommodate 10^6 Ig genes.

A typical mammalian mononuclear diploid cell has ca. 1×10^{-11} gm DNA, which can code for about 10^7 polypeptides of M.W. 50,000 each, assuming the triplet code and a molecular weight of 600 for each nucleotide pair.* Thus if each light chain (M.W. 20,000 to 25,000) and each heavy chain (M.W. 50,000) were represented by a separate gene they would preempt ca. 15% of the total genome. While this seems an almost absurdly large proportion it cannot be dismissed lightly because of the immense survival value of the immune response: in underdeveloped human societies perhaps 1/4 of all children die of infectious diseases before puberty, and it is entirely possible that microbial and parasitic infections have exacted a similarly severe toll among animals throughout evolution.

An early form of the germ line theory, modeled after induced enzyme formation in bacteria, proposed that all of an individual's Ig genes are present in each of his lymphoid cells. Low levels of intracellular immunoglobulins were then supposed to act as repressors for their genes, until an immunogen penetrated the cell and combined specifically with its antibody (repressor), derepressing its gene to yield induced synthesis of the corresponding antibody. This view is now seen to entail an immense amount of genetic redundancy, because the C-terminal halves of immunoglobulin chains are virtually invariant among antibodies that belong to a given class of immunoglobulins despite great diversity in their active sites (Ch. 14). Moreover, the

Mendelian inheritance of the allotype determinants would then demand that enormous numbers of these genes be handled in recombination as a single genetic unit; for if these genes segregated independently all allotypic markers would tend to be present in each individual, and their recognition would have been impossible.

The foregoing difficulties are avoided in another germ line theory, recently proposed by Dreyer and Bennett. This theory postulates that the gene for a given Ig chain is assembled during maturation of the cell from two half-genes, one corresponding to the constant (C-terminal) region of the chain, the other to the variable (N-terminal) region. In its primitive, immunologically uncommitted form, the cell is supposed to contain one half-gene for the constant region of each class of Ig chains (κ, λ, γ, μ, a, etc.) and a vastly larger number of variable-region half-genes (Fig. 15-32). As the lymphoid cell matures (i.e., supposedly becomes phenotypically restricted to form only one or a few kinds of Ig molecules) one of the large pool of variable-region genes becomes integrated with one of the constant-region genes, perhaps by a mechanism analogous to that by which a phage genome is incorporated into the genome of a bacterial cell (Ch. 24).† Thus out of an immense number of different possibilities a lymphoid cell would become restricted (at random) to form antibodies of only one or a few specificities.

This theory avoids redundancy, and is compatible with the heritability of allotypes. In addition, it provides for clonal variation among the lymphoid cell population. However, in assuming that all the Ig genes are

---

* $1 \times 10^{-11}/3 \times 600 = 6 \times 10^{-15}$ moles amino acid residue-equivalents; $6 \times 10^{-15} \times 6 \times 10^{23} = 36 \times 10^8$ amino acid residues in proteins. With ca. 450 residues in a polypeptide of M.W. 50,000 this amounts to ca. 10^7 polypeptides ($36 \times 10^8/450$).

† It is conceivable, of course, that "half-genes" might be transcribed and translated as though they were conventional genes. In this event each immunoglobulin chain would be formed from two smaller chains, the terminal a-COOH of one being joined via peptide linkage to the terminal a-NH₂ of the other. However, it has been inferred from the sizes of the polyribosomes on which the chains appear to be made that the mRNAs for each type of chain correspond to genes that are large enough to code for polypeptide chains of M.W. 25,000 or 50,000.

Ring of DNA coding for
N-terminal halves of
Ig chains

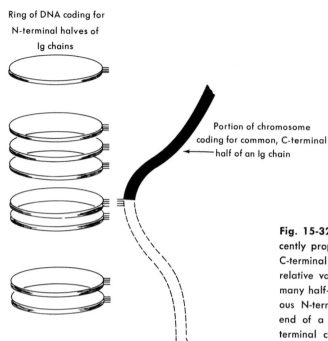

Portion of chromosome
coding for common, C-terminal
half of an Ig chain

Fig. 15-32   One of several genetic mechanisms recently proposed to account for the constancy of the C-terminal halves of immunoglobulin chains and the relative variability of the N-terminal halves. One of many half-genes that supposedly code for the numerous N-terminal sequences becomes inserted at the end of a half-gene that codes for a particular C-terminal constant region. (From W. J. Dreyer and J. C. Bennett. *Proc. Nat. Acad. Sc.* 54:864, 1965.)

transmitted via germ cells, it implies that their preservation throughout evolution is governed by the same rules that apply to other genes, e.g., selection for survival value, and loss following mutation to forms that confer no benefits. It is difficult to see, however, what advantages accrue from the preservation of genes for the synthesis of antibodies to many recently synthesized organic chemicals—such as *p*-aminobenzoate, 2,4-dinitrobenzene, etc. —which have no obvious resemblance to microbial pathogens. The preservation of so much excess genetic baggage through eons of time, before their targets came into existence, seems hardly credible.

Translational Variability. Since the differences among the variable regions of different heavy chains (or of different light chains) involve only a small number of residues, it has been suggested that these differences may be achieved without mutation, and without redundancy, by having the differentiating lymphoid cells develop new and different ways of translating the unchanged codons for these special sites. This variation could be achieved, for ex-

ample, by eliminating the normal tRNAs for these codons and by synthesizing (through the activation of appropriate genes) other tRNAs, which translate these codons in an unusual way, falling outside the normal genetic code. (The special codons, of course, would not be present in the genetic regions specifying the constant portions—i.e., C-terminal halves—of the immunoglobulin chains.) While this mechanism could (in principle) account for the diverse amino acid substitutions in different Bence Jones proteins, it could not explain the deletions or additions of amino acid residues, which account for other differences among the chains (Ch. 14).

The Number of Antibodies Produced by Single Cells. In order to evaluate various theories of antibody formation it is important to establish the **genotype** of antibody-forming cells, e.g., to determine whether each is potentially able to form antibody molecules of one specificity or of as many different specificities as the whole animal can produce. Experimentally, however, it is only possible at present to determine a cell's **phenotype**, i.e., the specificities of the antibodies it synthesizes following exposure to a variety of immunogens. The distinction between genotype and phenotype is especially important because the regulatory mechanism responsible for the one cell–one immunoglobulin rule (p. 483) might also restrict a cell to the formation of antibody of one specificity even if it possessed all the genetic information necessary for making antibodies of many different specificities. If, however, a cell that has been exposed to many immunogens were to make antibodies to all of them its genetic potential would obviously be so great as to rule out present clonal theories. Because of these considerations the types of antibodies produced in single cells, studied mostly by the microdrop methods described above, are of great interest.

In one series of studies by Nossal *et al.* animals received two to four different kinds of motile salmonellae and the specificity of the antiflagellar antibodies formed by single cells isolated from their lymph nodes was determined. Of the antibody-producing cells 98% formed antibodies to only one kind of bacteria, 1% to two kinds, and no cell to more than two kinds. These findings are consistent with the clonal selection theory. Because of two considerations, however, they do not establish its validity. 1) These findings do not necessarily mean that a cell (or clone) has a limited capacity, fixed before immunization, to form only a particular antibody; for as we have seen from the one cell–one immunoglobulin rule a cell with the potential capacity to form many different immunoglobulin chains is somehow restricted to the synthesis of only one heavy chain and one light chain. 2) Since a given protein contains a diversity of antigenic determinants the antibodies to it are usually a mixed population of molecules of different specificities (Ch. 13). Hence, when a cell makes antibodies to only one of several flagellar proteins it could be forming many different antibody molecules—whose structures and specificities are as different, for example, as antidinitrophenyl and antilactose.

In another series of studies, by Attardi *et al.*, rabbits were immunized against three antigenically distinctive bacteriophages. It was found that a large proportion of the cells that formed antibodies to one phage also formed antibodies to a second. Though no cells formed antibodies to all three phages, the observed frequency of double producers, compared with the frequencies of single producers, was high enough to be consistent with the possibility that the response of a cell to one phage was independent of any response it might have made to an unrelated phage. These findings are an exception to the one cell–one immunoglobulin rule. For several reasons, however, they are not necessarily incompatible with the clonal selection theory. 1) It is possible that with successive exposures to different immunogens (A and B) anti-B producers might have been selected for among the population of anti-A producers, yielding double producers as in the stepwise selection of bacteria for two independent mutations. 2) The recent demonstration that mammalian cells can fuse to form heterokaryons (Ch. 21) raises the possibility that double producers could arise from the fusion of different single producers. Thus these studies do not distinguish between the extreme alternatives: that the potentiality of the individual lymphoid cell to respond to immunogens is severely limited, or that the potentiality is the same as that of the whole animal.

Taken as a whole, the evidence from these and other elegant studies of antibody formation by single cells is still too limited to support or to invalidate the clonal selection or alternative genetic theories. Nevertheless, in view of the recent success of the classic Darwinian doctrine of mutation-selection in accounting for the heritable adaptive responses of microbial populations (Ch. 6) it is understandable that the clonal viewpoint, which applies this principle to adaptive lymphoid cell populations, should have great appeal. The finding that individual lymphoid cells produce relatively homogeneous immunoglobulins is in accord with this view. But the contention that there are different clones of lymphoid cells, each able to respond to only one or a few antigenic determinants, is still not established.

CODA

On superficial examination the synthesis of antibodies in vertebrates and that of adaptive enzymes in bacteria appear to be alike: a susceptible cell is stimulated, by immunogen or inducer, to synthesize the corresponding protein: antibody or induced enzyme. There are, however, several fundamental differences. The induced enzyme is homogeneous (in structure and in reactivity with substrate), and when the inducer is removed the bacterial culture soon reverts to its previous state. In the immunized animal, however, the antibodies to a given ligand are a heterogeneous population of protein molecules that differ in structure (size, charge, amino acid composition) and in affinity for the ligand; and the population made at any period changes with time after the primary stimulus. The antibodies detected first are 19S immunoglobulins and those made later are 7S; and the γG molecules made soon after immunization have low affinity for the ligand, whereas those made later have high affinity. Moreover, after the primary response has come to a halt (presumably when the immunogen is no longer effectively present) the animal does not usually return to its preimmunized state; instead it retains the ability to respond much more effectively to a second encounter with the same immunogen. The duration of immunological "memory" differs with different immunogens, and with some it can persist for a lifetime. In addition to these differences the immunogen, unlike the inducer of bacterial enzymes, causes the responding cells to become altered morphologically and to multiply rapidly.

The earliest steps in the induction of antibody formation have been the most difficult to elucidate. Some observations with synthetic polypeptides suggest that there may be a critical stereospecific reaction, which could account for the outstanding potency of proteins (and synthetic polypeptides made of L-amino acids) as immunogens, and as carriers of other molecules that, by themselves, are not immunogenic. Related, perhaps, are other observations which suggest that in one of the earliest steps the immunogen is "activated" by macrophages; but it is not clear whether this process involves a chemical change (e.g., in the immunogen's covalent structure) or a physical one, whereby the unaltered immunogen is merely transferred effectively from the macrophage that has ingested it to a susceptible lymphoid cell.

A mounting body of evidence indicates that the first cells to be stimulated specifically by an immunogen (activated or not) are small lymphocytes, whose generation time is on the order of many months, and possibly many years (in man). From their paucity of ribosomes and mitochondria, as well as their long generation time, most of these cells seem to be relatively inert or "resting." Once stimulated by immunogen, however, they are thought to differentiate into rapidly dividing, large, ribosome-rich cells, called transitional or blast cells or immunoblasts, which (supposedly) ultimately differentiate further into plasma cells, and perhaps also back into small resting lymphocytes that persist as "memory" cells, primed to respond efficiently to another encounter with the same immunogen, or a closely related one.

Of all lymphoid cells the plasma cell is most active in synthesizing and secreting antibodies. Nevertheless, it seems clear from studies with viable single cells that variously sized lymphocytes can also produce antibodies.

The clonal selection theory provides, at present, a more satisfying interpretation than other theories of the structural and functional heterogeneity of antibodies and of the differences between primary and secondary responses. But though lymphoid cells are indeed phenotypically diversified, as is required by this theory (e.g., different cells produce different immunoglobulins), there is still no direct evidence that clones exist; nor is it known whether there are only a small number of genes for immunoglobulins subject to a high mutation rate in lymphoid cells, or whether the number of immunoglobulin genes per cell equals the number of different antibodies the individual can make, or whether a small number of invariant genes can be transcribed, recombined, or translated in many different ways.

The development of more insight into antibody formation and its genetic basis is blocked at present by severe technical problems: foremost is the inability to isolate and maintain cultures of homogeneous lymphoid cells that respond in vitro as they do in the intact ani-mal. Though the induction of antibody formation by microbial antigens continues to provide the most effective prophylactic procedure yet developed for protecting human and animal populations against infectious diseases, the number of qualifications required in this summary makes it evident that many of the cellular and most of the molecular and genetic bases for the response to immunization are still largely obscure.

SELECTED REFERENCES

Books and Review Articles

BURNET, F. M. *The Clonal Selection Theory of Acquired Immunity*. Vanderbilt University Press, Nashville, 1959.

GOOD, R. A., and PAPERMASTER, B. W. Ontogeny and phylogeny of adaptive immunity. *Advances Immunol.* 4:1 (1964).

GOWANS, J. L., and MC GREGOR, D. D. Immunological activities of lymphocytes. *Progr. Allergy* 9:1 (1965).

Molecular and Cellular Basis of Antibody Formation. Proceedings of a Symposium. (J. Sterzl, ed.) Czechoslovak Academy of Sciences, Prague, 1965.

NOSSAL, G. J. V. Genetic studies on immunologically competent cells. *Advances Immunol.* 2:163 (1962).

SCHWARTZ, R. S. Immunosuppressive drugs. *Progr. Allergy* 9:247 (1965).

SELA, M. Immunological studies with synthetic polypeptides. *Advances Immunol.* 5:29 (1966).

SMITH, R. T. Immunological tolerance of non-living antigens. *Advances Immunol.* 1:67 (1961).

Symposium on differentiation and growth of hemoglobin- and immunoglobulin-synthesizing cells. *J. Cell. Physiol. 67*, Suppl. 1 (1966).

The Thymus in Immunobiology. (R. A. Good and A. E. Gabrielsen, eds.) Hoeber, New York, 1964.

Specific Articles

ATTARDI, G., COHN, M., HORIBATA, K., and LENNOX, E. S. Antibody formation by rabbit lymph node cells. *J. Immunol.* 92:335 (1964).

COONS, A. H., LEDUC, E. H., and CONNOLLY, J. M. Studies on antibody production. I. A method for the histochemical demonstration of specific antibody and its application to a study of the hyperimmune rabbit. *J. Exp. Med. 102*:49 (1955).

EISEN, H. N. The immune response to a simple antigenic determinant. *Harvey Lect.* 60:1 (1966).

FISHMAN, M., and ADLER, F. L. Antibody formation initiated *in vitro*. II. Antibody synthesis in X-irradiated recipients of diffusion chambers containing nucleic acid derived from macrophages incubated with antigen. *J. Exp. Med. 117*:595 (1963).

HARRIS, T. N.. and HARRIS, S. Lymph Node Cell Transfer in Relation to Antibody Formation. In *Cellular Aspects of Immunity*. A Ciba Foundation Symposium. (G. E. W. Wolstenholme and M. O'Connor, eds.) Little, Brown, Boston, 1960.

LEDERBERG, J. Genes and antibodies. *Science 129*:1649 (1959).

LEVINE, B. B., and BENACERRAF, B. Genetic control in guinea pigs of immune responses to conjugates of haptens and poly-L-lysine. *Science 147*:517 (1965).

SILVERSTEIN, A. M., UHR, J. W., KRANER, K. L., and LUKES, R. J. Fetal response to antigenic stimulus. II. Antibody production in the fetal lamb. *J. Exp. Med. 117*:799 (1963).

16 COMPLEMENT

Shortly after the discovery that immunity to diphtheria is due to serum antibodies (Ch. 12), a curious observation led to the disclosure of another remarkable group of substances in serum that seemed also to contribute to host defenses, through modifying the behavior of diverse antibody-antigen complexes. Pfeiffer and Issaeff observed in 1894 that cholera vibrios disintegrated when injected into the peritoneal cavity of a guinea pig that had been previously immunized against the organism. Bordet then showed that the vibrios were also lysed within a few minutes in vitro when added to serum from the immunized animals. However, if the serum had been previously heated to 56° for a few minutes, or simply allowed to age for a few weeks, it lost its lytic activity, though its antibodies were retained; and the addition of fresh **normal** serum to the inactivated antiserum restored its bacteriolytic capacity. Hence lysis appeared to require **both** specific antibody and a complementary, labile, nonspecific factor present in normal (as well as in immune) serum. Originally called **alexin** (Gr., "to ward off"), the unstable factor was subsequently named **complement**; it is commonly referred to simply as C'.

Over the past several decades it has become apparent that complement is a collective term for a group of proteins, of which 11 have now been identified in human serum. These proteins are not immunoglobulins, and they are not increased in concentration by immunization. They react with a wide variety of antibody-antigen complexes. When the antigen is part of a cell's cytoplasmic membrane the participation of complement in the antibody-antigen reaction can lead to irreversible cell damage and, finally, to cell lysis. Because of this cytotoxic effect the reactions of complement appear to have far-reaching physiological consequences: certain bacteria are lysed, phagocytosis of some antibody-coated particles is enhanced, red cells and tissue cells are damaged or lysed, and inflammatory changes are initiated, as in certain allergic reactions (Ch. 17).

The cytotoxic effect on erythrocytes has re-ceived particular attention. Because red cell lysis is so simple to measure, the antibody–red cell–complement system is widely used as a model for analyzing complement reactions. It also provides the basis for an important laboratory procedure for detecting and measuring antibodies and antigens, the C'-fixation assay.

The Complement-Fixation Assay

Almost any particulate or soluble antigen, but only certain kinds of antibodies, can be used in the complement-fixation assay. In addition to the test antigen and antiserum the assay requires a number of standard reagents (which have been referred to as the immunological zoo): **sheep** red blood cells, **rabbit** antibodies to sheep cells (these antibodies are also often called *hemolysins*),* and fresh **guinea pig** serum as a source of complement. Guinea pig serum, which is a more active source of complement than serum from other species, is used promptly after it is collected, or it may be stored at −40° or lyophilized.

If sheep erythrocytes in neutral isotonic salt solution are optimally coated with nonagglutinating amounts of rabbit antibodies, the addition of complement, in the presence of adequate concentrations of Mg^{2+} or Ca^{2+}, promptly causes the cells to lyse. The extent of lysis is easily evaluated, either qualitatively by inspection, or quantitatively by determining the concentration of supernatant hemoglobin after sedimentation of intact cells and stroma. Antibody-coated ("sensitized") eryth-

---

* Rabbits immunized with intact sheep red cells form two kinds of hemolysins: **isophile** antibodies, which are species-specific (for the determinants on red cells of sheep), and **heterophile** antibodies, which are specific for the so-called Forssman antigen, a substance found in the red cells and tissue cells of many species in addition to sheep, and even in some bacteria (Ch. 18). In order to obtain more uniformly effective antiserum it is preferable to immunize rabbits with boiled stromata of sheep red cells, which evoke only the anti-Forssman (heterophile) antibody. The latter antibody is almost entirely a 19S immunoglobulin, whereas the isophile antibodies are both 7S and 19S immunoglobulins. As noted later (p. 516), the 19S are more efficient than the 7S hemolysins.

Fig. 16-1 Complement-fixation assay. Ab=antibody; Ag=the corresponding antigen; C′=guinea pig complement; EA=sheep erythrocytes complexed with rabbit antibodies to the cells (sensitized red cells) as indicator for active complement. C′-fixation has occurred in reaction (1) but not in reactions (2) or (3).

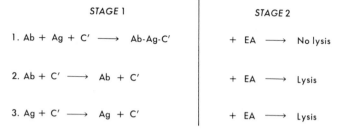

	STAGE 1		STAGE 2	
1. Ab + Ag + C′	⟶	Ab-Ag-C′	+ EA ⟶	No lysis
2. Ab + C′	⟶	Ab + C′	+ EA ⟶	Lysis
3. Ag + C′	⟶	Ag + C′	+ EA ⟶	Lysis

rocytes thus become indicators to detect active complement.

When antibodies combine with antigen in the presence of complement some components of complement are bound and inactivated. As a result, complement activity, i.e., ability to lyse sensitized red cells, is lost. Complement-fixation assays are therefore performed in two stages. **In stage 1** antiserum and antigen are mixed in the presence of a carefully measured amount of complement and then incubated, usually for 30 minutes at 37° or overnight at 2 to 5°. If the appropriate antibody-antigen complexes are formed complement is inactivated or "fixed." **In stage 2** a suspension of sensitized red cells is added to determine whether or not active complement has survived. **Hemolysis** indicates that complement persists and, therefore, that an effective antibody-antigen reaction **has not** occurred in stage 1. Conversely, **absence of hemolysis** indicates that complement has been fixed and, therefore, that an antibody-antigen reaction **has** occurred in stage 1 (positive complement-fixation reaction). These steps are outlined in Figure 16-1. With a known antigen the assay can be used to detect (and measure) antibodies in unknown sera; and with a standard antiserum (to a known antigen) it can be used to detect the corresponding antigen in complex biological materials.

Amount of Complement. If the amount of complement used in the assay is excessive, some active complement may persist and cause hemolysis even though an antibody-antigen reaction has taken place in stage 1. On the other hand, if the amount of comple-

ment added is insufficient, its deterioration may lead to the absence of lysis in stage 2 even if an antibody-antigen reaction has not occurred in stage 1. Accordingly, just the right amount of complement is required. Usually 5 units is an effective compromise in conventional assays (10^8 sensitized cells in a total reaction volume of 1.5 ml). The unit of complement is discussed below.

Controls. The interpretation of the complement-fixation assay depends on the outcome of a number of control procedures. For example, the antigen and the antiserum must be individually tested to ascertain that they are not "anticomplementary," i.e., that each does not inactivate complement without the other.* To provide a margin of safety anticomplementarity is tested with antigens or antiserum at a higher concentration than that used in the assay, and complement is reduced to an amount that is just sufficient to lyse the indicator cells (Table 16-1). It is also essential to ascertain that the red cells do not lyse spontaneously, and that complement survives stage 1 in the absence of an authentic antibody-antigen reaction.

Dependence on Mass and Ratio of Antibody-Antigen Complexes. The amount of complement fixed depends not only on the

---

* The most common artifact arises from anticomplementary properties of antigens and antisera. Particularly frequent with antigens prepared from homogenates of animal tissue, this difficulty is especially troublesome with complement-fixation assays in the serological diagnosis of diseases due to viruses, rickettsiae, and chlamydia, in which antigenic material is obtained from infected tissue. Undiluted or slightly diluted antisera are also frequently anticomplementary, usually owing to some denatured and aggregated immunoglobulins (p. 514).

TABLE 16-1. COMPLEMENT-FIXATION TEST FOR ANTIBODIES IN HUMAN SERUM TO POLIOVIRUS*

Virus dilution	Serum dilution								Control with	
	1:10	1:20	1:40	1:80	1:160	1:320	1:640	1:1280	5 C'H$_{50}$	3 C'H$_{50}$
1:20	0	0	0	1/2	4	4	4		4	4
1:40	0	0	0	0	2	4	4	4	4	4
1:80	0	0	0	0	0	3 1/2	4	4	4	4
1:160	0	0	0	0	0	0	4	4	4	4
1:320	0	0	0	0	0	0	2	4	4	4
1:640	0	0	0	0	0	0	1	4	4	4
1:1280	1/2	1/2	1/2	1/2	1/2	1/2	3	4	4	4
1:3200	4	3	3	3	3	3	4	4	4	4
1:6400	4	4	4	4	4	4	4	4	4	4
Control with										
5 C'H$_{50}$	4	4	4	4	4	4	4	4		
3 C'H$_{50}$	4	4	4	4	4	4	4	4		

* *Assay with 5 C'H$_{50}$ units of complement; fixation at 2 to 5° for 20 hours before addition of sensitized indicator red cells. 0 = no lysis (positive C'-fixation); 4 = complete lysis (negative C'-fixation). The highest dilution of antigen (virus) that gives positive C'-fixation is 1:1280. A 1:640 dilution of serum gives positive C'-fixation with dilute virus (1:640), but with more concentrated virus the system is then in antigen excess and it is necessary to use higher antibody concentrations, i.e., less dilute serum. The antigen alone and the serum alone are not anticomplementary at any dilution examined, even when tested in controls with only 3 C'H$_{50}$ units of complement.*
From M. Mayer et al., J. Immunol. 78:435 (1957).

mass of antibody-antigen complexes formed, but on their antibody/antigen ratio. When the ratio corresponds to that in the antibody-excess or the equivalence regions of the precipitin curve (Ch. 13) complement is fixed most effectively. When antigen is present in excess, however, fixation is less; and with antigen in extreme excess complement is not fixed at all (see Fig. 16-3). Since information about optimal proportions is not generally available, complement-fixation tests are best carried out by means of a "checkerboard titration," in which both antigen and antiserum concentrations are varied as shown in Table 16-1.

Measurement of Complement

The proportion of sensitized red cells that are lysed increases with the amount of complement added (Fig. 16-2). Because 100% lysis is approached asymptotically it is convenient to **define the unit of complement (the C'H$_{50}$ unit) as that amount which lyses 50% of sensitized red cells** under conditions that are arbitrarily standardized with respect to

the concentration of sensitized cells, the concentration and type of sensitizing antibody, the ionic strength and pH of the solvent, the concentrations of Mg^{2+} and Ca^{2+}, and the temperature of the incubation mixture.

The dose-response curve of Figure 16-2 follows the von Krogh equation,

$$x = K\left(\frac{y}{1-y}\right)^{1/n},$$

in which x is the amount of C' added (i.e., milliliters of guinea pig serum), y is the proportion of cells lysed, and n and K are constants. The curve described by this equation (which was arrived at empirically) is sigmoidal when $1/n < 1$; for fresh normal guinea pig sera $1/n$ is usually about 0.2. In estimating the number of C'H$_{50}$ units per milliliter of guinea pig serum it is convenient to plot $\log x$ vs. $\log y/1-y$. The data thus fall on a straight line,

$$\log x = \log K + \frac{1}{n}\log\left(\frac{y}{1-y}\right),$$

in which the intercept at 50% lysis ($y = 1-y$; $\log y/1-y = 0$) gives the volume of guinea pig serum that corresponds to one C'H$_{50}$ unit.

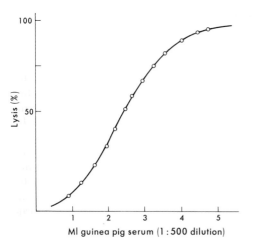

Fig. 16-2   Dose-response curve of immune hemolysis. The proportion of sensitized cells lysed increases with the volume of guinea pig serum (complement) added. The curve follows the empirical von Krogh equation (see text).

The Quantitative Complement-Fixation Assay

The amount of complement fixed in a reaction between soluble antigen and antibody can be determined as the difference between the amount added and the amount remaining after the reaction has gone essentially to completion. It is thus possible to follow the reaction between a given amount of antiserum and increasing amounts of antigen, as is shown in Figure 16-3. The amount of complement fixed varies like the amount of precipitate in the precipitin reaction, increasing over the antibody-excess region to a maximum at the equivalence zone and then decreasing in the antigen-excess zone. The complement reaction can thus be used as an alternative to the precipitin reaction, e.g., to measure quantitatively the concentrations of antibody or of antigen, or to compare closely related antigens for their reactivity with a standard antiserum. Complement fixation offers the important advantage that it can be used with high precision to measure very small amounts of antibody or antigen, detecting as little as 0.5 μg of antibody in 0.1 ml of serum. However, it has two disadvantages: it measures the reactivity of only certain classes of immunoglobulins (see below), and it measures concentrations in relative rather than absolute weight units.

Competent and Incompetent Complexes

Antibodies.   Not all antibodies are capable of fixing guinea pig complement, which is used universally in routine assays. For example, antibodies from cattle and many species of birds are ineffective. Moreover, in species with competent antibodies only those molecules that belong to certain classes of immunoglobulins are effective: γM and many γG **antibodies can fix complement, but γA antibodies cannot.** The difference between various classes of immunoglobulins has been brought out especially forcibly in those species, such as the guinea pig, whose 7S immunoglobulins are separable electrophoretically into two antigenically distinguishable classes, called γ1 and γ2 (Chs. 14 and 17): with guinea pig antibodies of the same specificity (anti-2,4-dinitrophenyl) those of the γ2 type can fix guinea pig complement, whereas the γ1 type cannot.

Fig. 16-3   Fixation of complement by varying quantities of chicken ovalbumin (OA) and 12.5 μg antibody from rabbit antiserum to OA. Note resemblance to precipitin curves of Chapter 13, with decreasing C'-fixation in the region of antigen-excess. (From A. G. Osler and M. Heidelberger. J. Immunol. 60:327, 1948.)

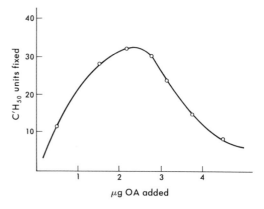

Since the various immunoglobulin classes have the same kinds of light chains, but each has a distinctive type of heavy chain (Ch. 14), it seems likely that the sites involved in complement fixation are localized in the heavy chains of the competent antibody molecules. These sites seem, furthermore, to be contained primarily within the Fc region, since digestion of γG antibodies with pepsin, which degrades heavy chains only in the Fc region (Ch. 14), destroys almost entirely their ability to fix complement, without impairing their ability to bind antigen.

Ligands. The small soluble complexes formed by antibodies and univalent ligands do not fix complement. Even the somewhat larger complexes formed by small bivalent ligands fix complement poorly, if at all (e.g., bis-DNP-lysine with anti-DNP antibodies; see Ch. 12, Fig. 12-2). Multivalent antigens, however, are regularly effective; and the effectiveness of antigens of diverse chemical nature, size, and charge, suggests that it is the antibody moiety of antibody-antigen aggregates that reacts with complement. Indeed, **when immunoglobulins in the absence of antigen are simply aggregated by heating, or by other denaturing conditions, they fix complement in the same way as antibodies that are aggregated by specific combination with multivalent antigen.** Perhaps interactions between contiguous, closely packed antibody molecules produce conformational changes, and these expose the sites on heavy chains (in the Fc domain) that initiate complement fixation. These postulated changes would be analogous to the changes that many multichain enzymes undergo upon binding substrates or regulators (Ch. 9, Allosteric transitions).

Components of Complement

A variety of treatments can destroy the complement activity of guinea pig serum, and when certain of the inactive preparations are combined the activity is restored: hence complement must consist of more than one substance. For example, dialysis of serum against water yields some precipitated and some soluble protein ("euglobulin" and "pseudoglobulin," respectively): each fraction is itself inactive, but together they are active. Similarly, serum inactivated by adsorption with "zymosan," a polysaccharide preparation from yeast cell walls, forms an active mixture with serum that has been inactivated by ammonia or by hydrazine (N_2H_2). From the behavior of these preparations it was inferred in the 1920s that there are at least four C′ components, which were called C′1, C′2, C′3, and C′4, in the chronological order of their recognition.

C′1 referred to the fraction of C′ in the euglobulins that precipitate when serum is dialyzed against water at pH 5.

C′2 referred to the fraction in the proteins that remain soluble under these conditions.

C′3 referred to the substance that is inactivated when serum is shaken with zymosan. (As noted below, "C′3" actually consists of at least six different proteins.)

C′4 referred to the substance that is inactivated when serum is treated with ammonia or hydrazine. This was the first of the classic components to be purified and characterized physiochemically (see Table 16-2).

C′1 and C′2 are extremely heat-labile, being inactivated in a few minutes at 56°, whereas C′3 and C′4 require another 20 to 30 minutes at this temperature.

For several decades after they were recognized, the several components of complement could be studied only indirectly with the aid of so-called R-reagents: serum preparations that lack one of the components. But progress has been greatly accelerated more recently as purified components have been isolated, following the intensive exploitation of chromatography, preparative electrophoresis, and other methods of protein fractionation. The number of recognized components has thus increased; for example, C′3 actually consists of six proteins, called, in human serum, C′3, C′5, C′6, C′7, C′8, and C′9.* Some properties of a number of the more highly purified pro-

---

* These proteins correspond, respectively, to those originally called C′3c, C′3b, C′3e, C′3f, C′3a, and C′3d in guinea pig serum.

TABLE 16-2. PROPERTIES OF SOME PURIFIED COMPLEMENT COMPONENTS
ISOLATED FROM HUMAN SERUM

Component	C'1q	C'1s	C'4	C'2	C'3	C'5	C'6
Synonyms	11S component	C'1 esterase	β_{1E}-globulin	—	β_{1C}-globulin	β_{1F}-globulin	—
Sedimentation constant	11S	4S	10S	6S	9.5S	8.75	5S
Concentration in serum (μg/ml)	20–30		30–50	<10	300–400	30–50	<10
Thermolability (56°, 30 min)	+	+	0	+	0	+	0
Inactivated by		DFP	N_2H_2, NEM	p-CMB	N_2H_2		

DFP $=$ diisopropylphosphofluoridate; N_2H_2 $=$ hydrazine; NEM $=$ N-ethylmaleimide; p-CMB $=$ p-chloro-mercuribenzoate.
From M. J. Polley and H. J. Müller-Eberhard. Chemistry and Mechanism of Action of Complement. In Progress in Hematology, vol. 5. (E. Brown and C. V. Moore, eds.) Grune & Stratton, New York, 1966.

teins are summarized in Table 16-2. Analysis of the order in which these components react, and of the consequences of their reactions, has constituted a formidable problem. However, as a result of intensive studies, carried out in the past 15 years in relatively few laboratories, considerable progress has been made, as is indicated in the following section.

The reaction sequence summarized in Figure 16-4 has been established for the lysis

of sensitized red cells (**immune hemolysis**), and the same sequence almost certainly applies also to the lysis of antibody-coated bacteria and other cells. The same order is also followed, though not necessarily to completion, in the reaction of complement with antibody-antigen aggregates formed from soluble antigens. The individual steps are reviewed below, using the same abbreviations as in Figure 16-4.

Fig. 16-4 Sequence of reactions in immune hemolysis. E=sheep red cells. A=rabbit antibodies to sheep red cells. EDTA=ethylenediaminetetraacetate (Versene), a chelating agent used to remove Ca^{2+}. Both EAC'1a,4,2a and EAC'4,2a are unstable and tend to lose C'2a (reactions 5a and 5b).

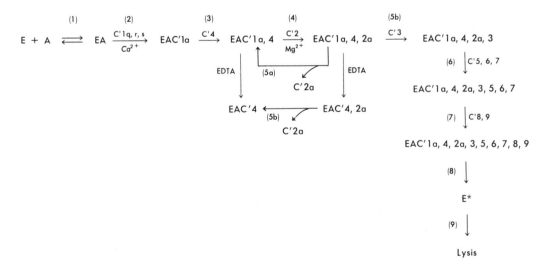

Reaction Sequence in Immune Hemolysis

1) E $+$ A $\rightarrow$ EA. The first step in immune hemolysis is the specific binding of antibodies (A) of appropriate type to the red cell (E) surface. Because the appropriate antibodies have not been available in sufficient purity it has not been possible to measure directly the number of molecules required to sensitize a red cell. However, there is much indirect evidence, discussed below in connection with the "one-hit" theory of hemolysis, that **the binding of one γM or one pair of γG antibody molecules per red cell is sufficient to sensitize a cell** for the subsequent reactions with complement, leading to lysis. In accord with this view, when excessive and varying numbers of red cells are mixed with a given concentration of γM antibody the number of sensitized cells remains constant, but if the antibody is a γG immunoglobulin fewer cells are sensitized as the total number of cells increases. Thus, when relatively large numbers of red cells are exposed to a limiting concentration of antibody the **γM antibodies tend to be much more efficient than the γG antibodies** in sensitizing the cells. As noted before, γA antibodies seem to be entirely ineffective.

The necessity for pairing γG molecules implies that the corresponding antigenic determinants on the red cell surface must be closely spaced. This requirement could account for the ineffectiveness of antibodies for certain red cell antigenic groups, for if the groups were widely spaced and the antibodies to them were γG molecules the EA complex would not react with complement. These considerations might explain the inability of antibodies to the Rh and many other isoantigens to sensitize red cells for immune hemolysis (Ch. 18).

The antigenic determinants involved in the binding of sensitizing antibodies need not be natural constituents of the red cell membrane. Thus in the process called **passive hemolysis** red cells are sensitized by complexing with antibodies to a variety of soluble antigens, and even to haptenic groups, that have been attached artificially to the red cell membrane.

2) EA $+$ C′1 $\xrightarrow{Ca^{2+}}$ EAC′1a. The over-all reaction between complement and red cells requires Ca^{2+} and Mg^{2+}, and the rate is much greater at 37° than at 0°. These observations suggested that at least some of the complement proteins are enzymes; and it was subsequently established that **after C′1 is bound to EA it becomes capable of splitting the ester bond** of such amino acid esters as *p*-toluenesulfonylarginine methyl ester (TAME).

In addition, both the hemolytic and the esterase activities of activated C′1 are blocked by diisopropylphosphofluoridate (DFP), which also inhibits a number of proteases with amino acid esterase activity, such as chymotrypsin. (The inhibition of the proteases, and presumably also of activated C′1, is due to substitution of a diisopropylphosphoryl group in a critical serine residue at the catalytic site of these enzymes.)

C′1 actually consists of three proteins, whose association into a single macromolecular complex depends on Ca^{2+}. Removal of calcium, by Versene or other chelating agents, causes the complex to dissociate into three chromatographically separable proteins, called C′1q, C′1r, and C′1s (Fig. 16-5). **Only the C′1 complex, and not the separated subunits, can be activated by EA to form C′1a, thus accounting for the absolute requirement for Ca^{2+} in immune hemolysis.** Ultracentrifugation has shown that C′1q can bind to native γG immunoglobulin, though it is likely to have much greater affinity for aggregated than for native, soluble immunoglobulins. It thus appears that the C′1 complex is bound to sensitized red cells through sites on C′1q. In contrast, the catalytic site is localized in the C′1s subunit: if Ca^{2+} is removed from the EAC′1a complex by treatment with Versene the bound C′1a dissociates, and of the subunits released into solution only the C′1s has esterase activity.

3) EAC′1a $+$ C′4 $\rightarrow$ EAC′1a,4. It is thought that the C′4 component is modified by C′1a (presumably functioning as a protease rather than an esterase), and then binds avidly to receptor sites on the red cell membrane or on antibody. (The modified C′4 tends also to form complexes with other proteins, including soluble immunoglobulins and

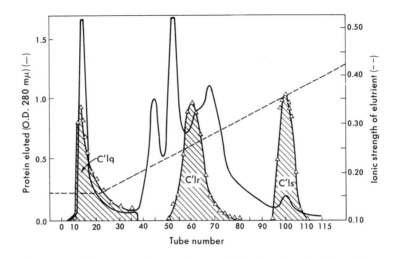

Fig. 16-5 Chromatographic resolution of C′1 into three fractions, C′1q, C′1r, and C′1s, on DEAE-cellulose in a buffer containing Versene, which binds Ca^{2+}. The contents of each tube were inactive, suggesting the loss of C′1 on the column. However *combinations* of different tubes localized three activities (cross-hatched areas) that together, with Ca^{2+}, formed EAC′1a from EA. (From I. H. Lepow, G. B. Naff, E. W. Todd, J. Pensky, and C. F. Hinz, Jr. J. Exp. Med. 117:983, 1963.)

native C′4.) The hypothetical, activated form of C′4 is believed to be labile, however, and it is thought to deteriorate rapidly into an inactive form (C′4i) if it is not bound by a suitable acceptor almost immediately after its formation.

Isotopic studies have shown that when C′4 is activated by EAC′1a some of it is attached directly to the membrane, since it can remain on the red cell after removal of antibody and C′1a.

4) $EAC′1a,4 + C′2 \xrightarrow{Mg^{2+}} EAC′1a,4,2a.$ This reaction takes place in two steps. First, in a reaction that requires Mg^{2+}, C′2 is bound **reversibly** to the EAC′1a,4 complex (Fig. 16-6). Second, in a temperature-dependent step, the C′1a esterase cleaves the adsorbed

Fig. 16-6 Reversible binding of C′2 to EAC′1a,4 or to EAC′4. The results indicate that C′2 is adsorbed to C′4, which is fixed to the red cell. It is not certain that the difference in slopes is significant. The ordinate is the reciprocal of bound C′2/red cell complex (r), and the abscissa is the reciprocal of the free C′2 concentration (c). The plot thus resembles those used in Chapter 13 for the binding of haptens by antibodies. The intercept on the ordinate (0.002) indicates that there are 500 sites per EAC′4 complex to which C′2 can be absorbed. (From G. Sitomer, R. M. Stroud, and M. M. Mayer. Immunochemistry 3:57, 1966.)

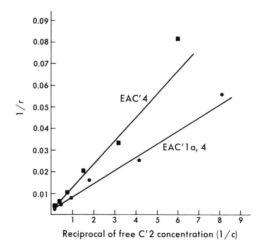

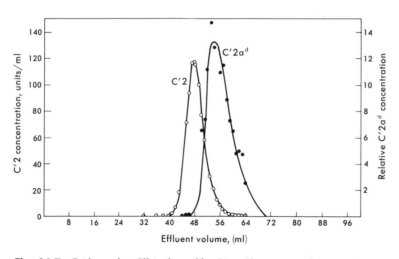

Fig. 16-7 Evidence that C'2 is cleaved by C'1a. Chromatography on Sephadex G-100 of a mixture of C'2 and its split product. The latter was recovered by allowing EAC'1a,4,2a to decay into EAC'1a,4 and the derivative of C'2 called C'2a^d, which was detected by its reaction with antibodies prepared against C'2. The molecular weight of C'2a^d is about 2/3 that of C'2 (see text, reaction 4). (From R. M. Stroud, M. M. Mayer, J. A. Miller, and A. T. McKenzie. Immunochemistry 3:163, 1966.)

C'2 into an active and an inactive fragment; the former, C'2a, becomes **firmly** attached to the previously bound C'4 molecule while the other, C'2i, probably goes into the fluid phase.

The molecular weight of guinea pig C'2 is 130,000, while that of C'2a is 80,000 (Fig. 16-7). The cleavage of C'2 by C'1a also occurs when these factors are incubated together in the absence of EAC'4. TAME inhibits competitively the enzymatic cleavage and fixation of C'2 by C'1a (Fig. 16-8). Thus, C'2 is almost certainly a natural substrate of the enzyme C'1a. It is

thought that the cleavage of the C'2 molecule is an activation which exposes a reactive group on the C'2a fragment. According to this hypothesis, if the cleavage occurs close to the C'4 molecule, C'2a becomes fixed to this component. On the other hand, if C'4, the natural acceptor, is not closely accessible, the reactive group on C'2a is lost very rapidly, perhaps by a reaction with water.

5a) EAC'1a,4,2a → EAC'1a,4 + C'2a.
The EAC'1a,4,2a complex undergoes two competing reactions (steps 5a and 5b). In

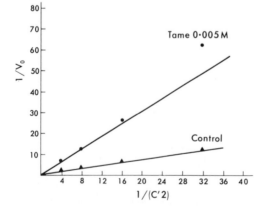

Fig. 16-8 Catalysis of C'2 fixation by C'1 esterase. The Lineweaver-Burk plot shows that the conversion of EAC'1a,4 to EAC'1a,4,2a is competitively inhibited by p-toluenesulfonylarginine methyl ester (TAME). The ordinate is reciprocal of maximal velocity of this reaction and abscissa is reciprocal of C'2 concentration. (From R. M. Stroud, K. F. Austen, and M. M. Mayer. Immunochemistry 2:219, 1965.)

one, which hinders the efficiency of the hemolytic sequence, the complex suffers loss of $C'2a$, with decay to $EAC'1a,4$. This reaction accounts for the marked instability of the $EAC'1a,4,2a$ complex at elevated temperature; for example, its half life at $37°$ is about 10 minutes.

5b) $EAC'1a,4,2a + C'3 \rightarrow EAC'1a,4,2a,3$. In this competing reaction, which is necessary for hemolysis, it is thought that the $EAC'1a$, $4,2a$ complex activates $C'3$, which is then also bound. The $C'1a$ is no longer required for this step, since the $EAC'4,2a$ complex, freed of $C'1a$ esterase by removal of Ca^{2+}, can also activate and bind $C'3$, and can then be lysed by the remaining complement components. According to this hypothesis, if the activated $C'3$ is not rapidly bound it deteriorates into a hemolytically inactive form, $C'3i$.

It has been shown with ^{131}I-labeled $C'3$ that several hundred $C'3$ molecules are bound to red cells per molecule of bound $C'4$, suggesting that the $C'4,2a$ complex acts catalytically on $C'3$. Moreover, electron micrographs with ferritin-labeled antibodies to $C'3$ have shown that this component is bound to the edges of the holes that eventually appear in the membrane at the end of the entire reaction sequence (Fig. 16-9).

The role of $C'2$ has been studied also with purified components in solution. A mixture of purified $C'1$ esterase, $C'4$, $C'2$, and Mg^{2+} can inactivate $C'3$. The inactivation proceeds smoothly if the $C'1$ esterase is allowed first to react with $C'4$ and then with $C'2$, but it is blocked if the order of reactions is reversed. These results, extended by studies of complexes in the ultracentrifuge, indicate that the $C'2a$, formed by the action of $C'1$ esterase on $C'2$ (and required for inactivation of $C'3$), is extremely labile unless it is also promptly bound by $C'4$.

6) $EAC'1a,4,2a,3 + C'5,6,7 \rightarrow EAC'1a,4,2a$, $3,5,6,7$. Ultracentrifugal studies with purified components have shown that $C'5$ forms dissociable complexes with $C'6$ and with $C'7$. All three components are required for a step that converts $EAC'1a,4,2a,3$ from a thermolabile to a thermostable form. The detailed mechanisms of this reaction have not yet been established.

7) $EAC'1a,4,2a,3,5,6,7 + C'8,9 \rightarrow E^* \rightarrow$ lysis. The terminal stages of lysis are incompletely understood. Components $C'8$ and $C'9$ are both required, and $C'9$ activity disappears after reaction with the active EAC' complex. Following the reaction of $C'8$ and $C'9$ the red cell, now called E^*, is inexorably destined to lyse, and it eventually develops small holes, each about 100 A in diameter, through which hemoglobin escapes (Fig. 16-9).

The Role of Antibodies

Antibodies on the red cell membrane are obligatory **only** for the binding and activation of $C'1$. By various procedures, however, some C' components can be activated in solution; and though they react inefficiently, because of their lability, they can nonetheless cause hemolysis of **nonsensitized** red cells. For example, after $C'4$ and $C'2$ are activated by $C'1$ esterase in solution they can be bound by nonsensitized red cells, which then lyse on addition of the remaining C' components. Similarly, activated $C'3$ in solution can react with the $C'5,6,7$ complex, which will then bind to nonsensitized red cells; addition of $C'8$ and $C'9$ then causes lysis.

The One-Hit Theory

As indicated above, the complement proteins act at discrete sensitized sites (SA) on the red cell membrane, each site normally being established by the binding of one or a pair of antibody molecules. The subsequent reaction of complement proteins at the sensitized site leads to the formation of a damaged site, S^*, through which escape the cell's contents—hemoglobin from erythrocytes, and essential cofactors, metabolites, and macromolecules from other cells.

Is one S^* site sufficient for cell lysis, or does lysis require the accumulation of many damaged sites per cell? The sigmoidal dose-response curve (Fig. 16-2) suggested that the accumulation of many S^* sites was necessary, and in one estimate the minimal number was

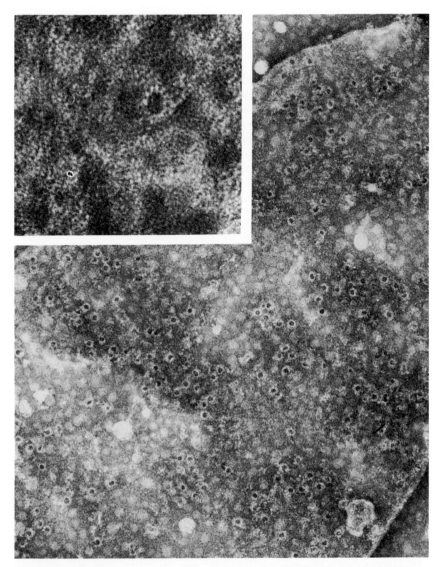

Fig. 16-9 Electron micrograph of the membrane of a sensitized sheep red cell lysed by complement. Many holes in the membrane are evident. ×187,000 (reduced). Inset shows a representative hole at greater magnification (×720,000, reduced). Preparations by R. Dourmashkin. (From J. H. Humphrey and R. R. Dourmashkin. In *Complement*. Ciba Foundation Symposium. (G. E. W. Wolstenholme and J. Knight, eds.) Little, Brown, Boston, 1965.)

calculated to be 10 per cell. Recently, however, Mayer and his colleagues have provided evidence that hemolysis is a one-hit process, i.e., one S* lesion per red cell is sufficient for lysis. Thus with a limiting amount of complement the extent and velocity of hemolysis is **independent** of the total number of sensi-

tized cells in the reaction mixture. Moreover, with EA, or with EAC'1a, or with EAC'1a,4, the average number of lytic lesions per cell is linearly related to the concentration of C'1, or C'4, or C'2, respectively, indicating that one molecule of each of these components per cell is sufficient for lysis (provided the cell then reacts with the other C′ components).* Similarly, the activation and binding of C′1 has been found to be related linearly to the concentration of γM anti-red-cell antibodies, and to the square of the concentration of the corresponding γG antibodies. These latter findings provide the most direct evidence available that the S* site is initiated by the binding of one γM or one pair of γG antibodies at the cell surface.

It thus appears that one lesion per cell, requiring one or two antibody molecules and one molecule each of C′1, C′4, and C′2, is sufficient for lysis (after the remaining C′ components react). However, with most lysing cells there undoubtedly are a large number of damaged sites, many of which lead eventually to the formation of holes in the membrane (Fig. 16-9).

The sigmoidal shape of the hemolytic dose-response curve (Fig. 16-2), which had constituted the principal basis for interpreting immune hemolysis as a multi-hit or cumulative process, has been reconciled with the one-hit theory by considering the properties of EAC′1,4,2a. As noted above (steps 5a and 5b), this complex undergoes two competing reactions: one hindering hemolysis, with loss of C′2a; and the other, by activating C′3, producing the next complex required in the chain of steps to hemolysis. The loss of C′2a is a unimolecular reaction, with a fixed half life at a given temperature, whereas

---

* The average number of lytic lesions per red cell is calculated from the proportion of red cells that are **not** lysed, by applying the Poisson distribution (Ch. 22).

the rate of reaction with C′3 is exponentially dependent on the C′3 concentration, and is greatly augmented by high concentrations of this component. Qualitatively, at least, this relation appears to account for the sigmoidal shape of the dose-response curve.

Other in Vitro Reactions of Complement

The reactions mediated by complement in vitro are listed in Table 16-3. Immune cytolysis was discussed above with red cells as a model. Some of the other reactions, and their less extensive requirements for C′ components, are commented on briefly below.

Bactericidal Reaction. Gram-negative bacteria coated with specific antibody are lysed by complement, apparently by the same reaction sequence as in red cell lysis. **Gram-positive bacteria and mycobacteria, however, are not susceptible to the action of complement,** and the basis for their resistance is not understood. A cytotoxic reaction is also used in clinical diagnosis to detect antibodies to the treponemes that cause syphilis. Here, however, the reaction leads not to immediate lysis but to immobilization of these characteristically motile organisms (*Treponema pallidum* immobilization, or TPI, test.)

Immune Adherence. This term refers to the adherence of antibody-antigen-C′ complexes to the surface of certain nonsensitized particles, such as primate red cells, platelets, and starch granules. The adherent complexes also increase the susceptibility of bacteria and

---

TABLE 16-3. COMPLEMENT COMPONENTS INVOLVED IN SOME BIOLOGICAL REACTIONS

Components*	Reactions
M-A-C′1a	
M-A-C′1a,4	Immune conglutination
M-A-C′1a,4,2a,3	Opsonization, immune adherence, conglutination, immune conglutination
M-A-C′1a,4,2a,3,5	Anaphylatoxin production, C′-dependent histamine release
M-A-C′1a,4,2a,3,5,6,7	Leucocyte chemotaxis
M-A-C′1a,4,2a,3,5,6,7,8,9	Cytolysis of red cells, gram-negative bacteria, etc.

*M = cell membrane; A = antibody.
Courtesy of H. J. Müller-Eberhard.

viruses to phagocytosis in vitro. Immune adherence requires only the first four complement components (Table 16-3).

Leucocyte Chemotaxis. Antibody-antigen complexes can attract polymorphonuclear leucocytes in vitro after certain complement components are bound: activation by $C'3$ of the $C'5,6,7$ complex is required. The requirement for $C'6$ is borne out by the inability of serum from $C'6$-deficient rabbits (see below) to promote the accumulation of granulocytes around antibody-antigen complexes. The leucotactic activity of immune complexes is of particular importance in certain immediate-type allergic vascular responses (Ch. 17, Arthus reaction).

Histamine Release. The reaction of $C'3$ and $C'5$ with the activated $C'4,2a$ complex leads to the appearance of a substance that can cause release of histamine from mast cells, and therefore some of the manifestations of anaphylaxis (Ch. 17). Called **anaphylatoxin**, the active substance appears to be a polypeptide fragment cleaved from $C'5$ or from $C'3$.

A related phenomenon is seen with rat mast cells, which normally are coated with adsorbed rat γ-globulins. When these cells are exposed to antibodies for these globulins they release some of their histamine, without undergoing cytolysis. This reaction also requires only the first five C' components (Table 16-3).

The release of histamine from mast cells is also brought about by a mechanism that does not appear to involve C', but depends on a special type of immunoglobulin with high affinity for the mast cell surface. This mechanism is of particular importance for anaphylaxis, and will be considered in Chapter 17.

Conglutination. Antibody–red cell–C' complexes are agglutinated by a protein, **conglutinin**, which is present in the normal serum of certain mammalian species (cattle and other ruminants). The level of conglutinin is not increased by immunization, and this protein bears no structural similarity to the immunoglobulins. Conglutinin, whose biological significance is unknown, is specific for some sugar residues of $C'3$, a glycoprotein, and the reaction requires Ca^{2+}.

Immune Conglutination. A variety of antibody-antigen-complement complexes are specifically precipitated by **"immune conglutinin,"** an antibody specific for $C'3$ and $C'4$. Present in low titer in most normal sera, the level of immune conglutinin increases with infectious disease and after immunization with many antigens. This anti-C' antibody is directed against determinant groups that are hidden in native $C'3$ and $C'4$ but become exposed when these proteins are activated and bound by antigen-antibody complexes. Immune conglutinin is usually a γM immunoglobulin. Since a given individual's immune conglutinin reacts with his own complement, the immune conglutinin is, by definition, an autoantibody (Ch. 17).

Heritable Deficiencies in Complement

The physiological functions of complement in vivo have been difficult to establish directly because it has not previously been possible to produce chronic deficiencies in these proteins. Recently, however, this approach has become available with the discovery of several specific heritable deficiencies.

Deficiencies in Animals. In two strains of rabbits the serum lacks $C'6$ and therefore hemolytic and bactericidal activity. Both strains can form antibodies to the $C'6$ protein isolated from other rabbits. These animals appear, therefore, to lack $C'6$ altogether, or perhaps they possess an inactive form of this protein, analogous to CRMs in bacterial mutants.

The ability of these animals to survive experimental infections with gram-negative and other bacteria has not yet been established, but many appear normal in size and vigor, and have a normal life expectancy. Preliminary studies indicate that they do not give Arthus and delayed-type tuberculin reactions (Ch. 17), and that they sometimes accept skin homografts (Ch. 18) unusually well, suggesting that complement-mediated reactions are important in these allergic responses.

In the sera from several inbred strains of mice hemolytic activity is lacking but can be restored by adding purified C′5 from human serum. These mice also do not appear to be unusually susceptible to natural infections.

C′2 Deficiency in Man. In several human families the serum has markedly diminished bactericidal activity, and the C′2 is reduced to about 5% of the normal value. Affected persons, however, are clinically well. It is not yet clear whether their apparently normal resistance to infection depends on the trace amounts of C′2 in their sera.

Hereditary Angioneurotic Edema. Humans with this disease are deficient not in complement but in **a serum inhibitor of C′1 esterase:** serum from an affected person has about 10% of the inhibitor activity of normal serum. These individuals suffer periodically from acute and transitory local accumulations of edema fluid, which can become life-threatening when localized in the larynx, with obstruction of the tracheal airway. During an attack the level of C′1 esterase rises in the serum and causes increased capillary permeability, possibly by activating C′4, C′2, C′3, and C′5, with the formation of anaphylatoxin (see above). The deficiency is due in some families to a low level of the normal inhibitor protein, and in others to the presence of an inactive analog.

Properdin

The properdin system has been the subject of much controversy. As originally described by Pillemer *et al.* in 1954 this system consisted of a serum factor called properdin, which, together with Mg^{2+} and some complement components, reacted with zymosan (a cell wall preparation from yeast), inactivating C′3. The system seemed especially interesting because of its apparent involvement in certain antimicrobial activities of normal human serum, such as the killing of *Shigella dysenteriae* and neutralization of some viruses. Thus when normal serum was depleted of properdin, by absorption with zymo-

san at 17°, it lost these antimicrobial activities though it retained all known complement components; and partially purified properdin restored the activities. Hence properdin appeared to be a novel factor that participates nonspecifically, like complement, in some antimicrobial activities of normal serum.

It was subsequently suggested that properdin might be an antibody to zymosan; hence the reaction leading to C′3 inactivation might be merely a standard complement-fixation reaction. Moreover, since the killing or neutralization of susceptible bacteria and viruses by normal serum was found to be due to "natural" antibody (Ch. 12), the participation of properdin in these reactions could reflect cross-reactions between it and these microbes. The original concept of properdin as some special nonspecific factor thus seemed highly tenuous.

In more recent studies, however, it appears that properdin has been isolated in highly purified form, and that it has been found not to react with antisera to any of the known immunoglobulins, and not to behave as a specific antibody to *Shigella*. Properdin therefore might be, as originally claimed, a distinct serum protein that, like the complement components, participates in various immunologically specific reactions. Properdin, however, has been involved so far in only relatively few immunological reactions, and its action is poorly understood.

Coda

The complement system consists of a group of about 11 proteins which normally exist in serum in inactive form. When γM or certain γG immunoglobulins are specifically aggregated by antigens, or are bound to appropriate antigenic determinants on the surface of erythrocytes, bacteria, or other cells, it appears that the heavy chains of the bound antibody become capable of binding one of the complement components, C′1, which then becomes catalytically active (C′1a). Though C′1a has esterase activity it probably functions normally as a protease, attacking two other components, C′4 and C′2, mediating their fixation near the site created by bound antibody and C′1a. Other components of the system then react in sequence at this site in a biological chain reaction, each component being activated by one or more of those that reacted previously. When all components have reacted, the surface membrane becomes irreversibly damaged, holes appear, and the cell lyses. The cytotoxic effects of complement are almost entirely confined to those cells with antibodies specifically bound to their membrane. Neighboring cells, without bound antibody, are spared because the activated complement components deteriorate rapidly in solution, though they are relatively stable when bound to a cell surface.

Some of the other biological effects of the complement system require the participation of only some of the components, e.g., C'1 through C'3 in immune adherence, and C'1 through C'5 in anaphylatoxin formation.

It has been generally assumed from its bac-teriolytic power that complement augments host defenses against infections. It has been difficult, however, to substantiate this view by direct observations in vivo, because individuals with chronic deficiencies in complement have not previously been available for study. In fact, their very scarcity has been construed to mean that complement might be vital for survival. However, several strains of rabbits and mice and some human families with genetic deficiencies in various complement components have recently come to light. Preliminary studies of these mammalian mutants indicate that complement plays an important role in various allergic responses, but its role in vivo in host defenses against microbial infections still remains to be established.

SELECTED REFERENCES

Books and Review Articles

LEPOW, I. H. Serum Complement and Properdin. In *Immunological Diseases*. (M. Samter and H. L. Alexander, eds.) Little, Brown, Boston, 1965.

MAYER, M. In *Kabat and Mayer's Experimental Immunochemistry,* 2nd ed. Thomas, Springfield, Ill., 1961.

MAYER, M. Development of the One-Hit Theory of Immune Hemolysis. In *Immunochemical Approaches to Problems in Microbiology.* (M. Heidelberger and O. Plescia, eds.) Rutgers University Press, New Brunswick, N.J., 1961.

POLLEY, M. J., and MÜLLER-EBERHARD, H. J. Chemistry and Mechanism of Action of Complement. In *Progress in Hematology,* vol. 5. (E. Brown and C. V. Moore, eds.) Grune & Stratton, New York, 1966.

WOLSTENHOLME, G. E. W., and KNIGHT, J. (eds.). *Complement.* Ciba Foundation Symposium. Little, Brown, Boston, 1965.

Specific Articles

BECKER, E. L. Concerning the mechanism of complement action. V. Early steps in immune hemolysis. *J. Immunol. 84*:299 (1960).

BORSOS, T., and RAPP, H. J. Complement fixation on cell surfaces by 19S and 7S antibodies. *Science 150*:505 (1965).

MÜLLER-EBERHARD, H. J., and BIRO, C. E. Isolation and description of the fourth component of human complement. *J. Exp. Med. 118*:447 (1963).

STROUD, R. M., MAYER, M. M., MILLER, J. A., and MCKENZIE, A. T. C'2a^d, an inactive derivative of C'2 released during decay of EAC'4,2a. *Immunochemistry 3*:163 (1966).

17 HYPERSENSITIVITY

Far from being uncomplicated defensive adaptations, immunologic reactions can give rise in animals to a wide variety of pathologic effects, called **hypersensitive** or **allergic reactions.** The hypersensitive reactions were formerly divided into two classes, **immediate** and **delayed,** on the basis of the time lag between administration of antigen and appearance of the allergic response—several minutes in one class and several hours or even days in the other. These terms are still retained, but they are now endowed with a different meaning. The reactions that appear within minutes, and also some of the more slowly evolving ones, are clearly mediated by antibodies. To emphasize this common feature, both responses are now called **immediate-type,** indicating that "immediate" is not to be taken literally. In contrast, the **delayed-type** are those slowly evolving responses in which the role of antibodies has not been demonstrated. Studies of their mechanisms are now widely interpreted to mean that the delayed-type responses are mediated by "sensitized" lymphocytes or macrophages, perhaps with antibodies or antibody-like molecules attached to their surface.

TABLE 17-1. CLASSIFICATION OF ALLERGIC RESPONSES*

Immediate-type	Delayed-type
Systemic anaphylaxis	Due to microbial antigens
Cutaneous anaphylaxis	Due to purified proteins
Arthus reaction	Due to simple chemicals
Serum sickness	(allergic contact dermatitis)
syndrome	

◄─────────Allergy to drugs─────────►
◄──Allergy to self-antigens (autoallergy)──►

* **Reactions to transfused red cells** *(Ch. 18) are mediated by serum antibodies and could be regarded as another example of immediate-type hypersensitivity.* **Rejection of a foreign tissue** *seems to be more often a manifestation of delayed-type than of immediate-type hypersensitivity (Ch. 18).*

In previous chapters the administration of an immunogen to stimulate antibody formation was called immunization. Within the context of the allergic response, however, the immunogen or antigen is often referred to as the **allergen** or **sensitizer,** and immunization as **sensitization;** and the immunized individual, previously called immune, is often called **sensitive or hypersensitive or allergic.** Some of the most important and best studied allergic responses are listed in Table 17-1.

IMMEDIATE-TYPE RESPONSES

Anaphylaxis

Except for some toxins, soluble antigens can be injected into a normal guinea pig with impunity, but when they are injected into a previously immunized animal an explosive response often occurs within 2 to 3 minutes: smooth muscles contract and capillaries dilate and became excessively leaky. If the antigen is injected intravenously the response, called **systemic or generalized anaphylaxis,** can lead to shock, vascular engorgement, asphyxia due to bronchial constriction, and other changes. However, if the antigen is injected into the dermal layer of skin the response, called **cutaneous anaphylaxis,** is characterized by lo-

cal swelling and redness. In both systemic and cutaneous anaphylaxis the response is **transient** and recovery is usually complete within ca. 30 to 60 minutes, unless death occurs promptly, as often happens in generalized anaphylaxis.

Generalized Anaphylaxis

Anaphylaxis resembles antigen-antibody reactions in general: it can be evoked with almost any immunogen and with many haptens, and the response is specific; i.e., it is elicited only by the inducer, or by a structurally related cross-reacting substance. In addition, multivalents ligands, whether or not immunogenic, can specifically elicit anaphylaxis, whereas univalent ligands usually inhibit it, just as they inhibit the precipitin reaction.

The dependence on antibodies has been demonstrated directly by **passive anaphylaxis,** in which an animal is first injected with antibodies and then with the corresponding antigen. As a procedure for determining the types and amounts of antibodies required for anaphylaxis, **passive sensitization** by an injection of well characterized antisera or purified antibodies is superior to the study of **active sensitization,** in which animals are sensitized by a prior injection of the immunogen.

Fixation of Antibodies. In order to evoke passive anaphylaxis several hours must elapse between injecting antibodies and then the corresponding antigen. This **latent period** is required for the antibodies to become bound or "fixed" to certain tissue or cellular receptors, on which the subsequent specific reaction with antigen takes place.*

The selectivity of the fixation process accounts for the inability of many antibodies to mediate passive anaphylaxis. For example, guinea pigs are sensitized by antibodies of only certain immunoglobulin types from guinea pigs, rabbits, and humans (see Special cytotropic antibodies responsible for anaphylaxis, below) and not by any antibodies from chickens, goats, cattle, and horses.

The receptors that bind antibodies are still uncharacterized, but evidence cited below indicates that many at least are located on mast cells and platelets.

Passive anaphylaxis can also be evoked by **reversing** the order of injections if the anti-

gen, which is now injected first, is itself an immunoglobulin of the type that is readily bound to guinea pig tissue receptors (such as rabbit γG immunoglobulin). After a latent period the intravenous injection of antiserum (specific for the immunoglobulin used as antigen) can then cause anaphylaxis. This procedure, called **reverse passive anaphylaxis,** is not effective with other antigens, because they do not bind to the appropriate target cells.

Desensitization. A variety of procedures can prevent or diminish anaphylaxis. a) The repeated, closely spaced injections of small amounts of antigen can bring about temporary desensitization; if 100 μg of an antigen, injected intravenously, is required to evoke fatal shock, the same quantity given in ten 10 μg doses at 0.5 hr. intervals would not elicit shock. Moreover, if the full dose were then given all at once shortly after the last small injection, shock would probably still not be elicited. Presumably insufficient unreacted antibody would remain to allow the rapid build-up of the required critical mass of complexes. b) A somewhat more durable desensitization appears also to be brought about by the repeated injections of small immunogenic quantities of antigen that lead, presumably, to the formation of "blocking" or "protective" antibodies (p. 534).

Pharmacological Mediators

Following the observation by Dale, in 1911, that injections of histamine duplicate the manifestations of anaphylaxis, a number of vasoactive substances were found to be released from tissues in response to antigen-antibody complexes. The direct action of these substances on blood vessels and on smooth muscle accounts for most, and perhaps all, of the manifestations of anaphylaxis.

So far, five active substances have been recognized: two primary amines, **histamine** and **serotonin,** preexist in cells and are promptly released by appropriate antibody-antigen complexes (Fig. 17-1); two basic polypeptides, **bradykinin** and **lysyl-bradykinin,**

---

* If an exceptionally large amount of antibody is injected into an animal shock can be elicited immediately afterwards by injecting the antigen. This type of reaction, elicited without a latent period, has been called "aggregate anaphylaxis" to indicate that its detailed mechanisms probably differ in some details from *cytotropic anaphylaxis,* in which the latent period is required for binding of antibodies to special receptors (p. 533).

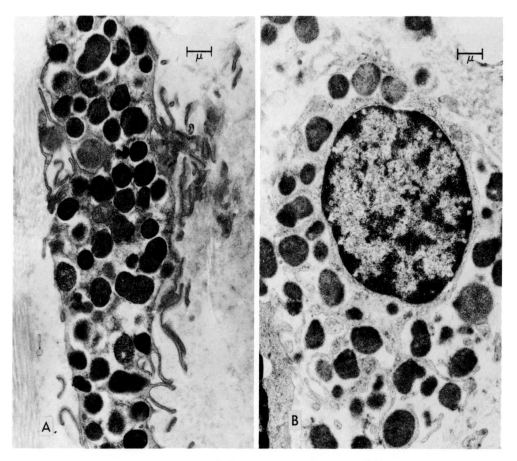

Fig. 17-1 Electron micrographs of mast cells from rat dermis. The intact cell (**A**) contains small, dense granules, each enclosed in a membranous sac. Each granule is about the size of a mitochondrion. Mitochondria, which are generally scarce in mast cells, are not visible. The nucleus also is not visible in this section. The degranulating cell (**B**) contains larger, paler granules, presumably more hydrated than those in the intact cell. The release of granules, associated with the release of histamine, involves fusion of the membrane surrounding each granule with the cell membrane, releasing intact but swollen granules into the extracellular space. ×7000. (Courtesy of S. L. Clark, Jr.; based on E. M. Singleton and S. L. Clark, Jr. *Lab Invest.* 14:1744, 1965.)

are produced only after the complexes are formed. The fifth substance, SRS-A (for slowly reactive substance-anaphylaxis), is uncharacterized chemically and is also produced after immune complexes are formed in the tissues. The structures, sources, and some properties of these substances are shown in Fig. 17-2.

The specific blocking of histamine by certain drugs, the **antihistamines,** is the basis for their therapeutic efficacy in preventing and treating anaphylaxis and some other mani-

festations of immediate-type hypersensitivity. The antihistamines do not antagonize the other mediators and are thus not always highly effective.

Species Variations. Guinea pigs are preferred for the study of anaphylaxis because they react intensely and uniformly. The same response has been provoked in many other mammals, in fish, and in chickens, and can probably be elicited in most vertebrates. It is occasionally elicited inadvertently in man, e.g. by foreign sera (as from horse or rabbit),

MEDIATOR	STRUCTURE	SOURCE	PROPERTIES USED FOR IDENTIFICATION

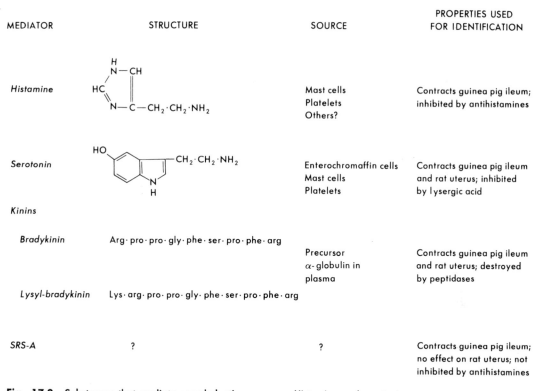

Histamine — Mast cells, Platelets, Others? — Contracts guinea pig ileum; inhibited by antihistamines

Serotonin — Enterochromaffin cells, Mast cells, Platelets — Contracts guinea pig ileum and rat uterus; inhibited by lysergic acid

Kinins

Bradykinin — Arg·pro·pro·gly·phe·ser·pro·phe·arg — Precursor α-globulin in plasma — Contracts guinea pig ileum and rat uterus; destroyed by peptidases

Lysyl-bradykinin — Lys·arg·pro·pro·gly·phe·ser·pro·phe·arg

SRS-A — ? — ? — Contracts guinea pig ileum; no effect on rat uterus; not inhibited by antihistamines

Fig. 17-2 Substances that mediate anaphylactic responses. Histamine and serotonin are produced by specific decarboxylases acting on L-histidine and L-tryptophan, and by enzymatic hydroxylation of the phenyl ring at 5-C in serotonin. The structures for brady-kinin and lysyl-bradykinin are given with conventional abbreviations for amino acids, the terminal α-NH_2 groups being at the left. SRS-A (slow reactive substance-anaphylaxis) has not been characterized chemically.

by penicillin and other immunogenic drugs, and following some insect stings, especially of wasps and hornets. The gross pathological manifestations differ widely in various species (Table 17-2), and the differences arise largely from species variations in distribution and susceptibility to the pharmacologically active mediators released during anaphylaxis.

Manifestations also differ when the antigen is injected by different routes. In a sensitized guinea pig, for example, intravenous injection of antigen leads to constriction of bronchi with asphyxia, with the lungs at autopsy appearing bloodless and greatly distended by air (emphysema); whereas after antigen is given subcutaneously or intraperitoneally, hypotension and hypothermia, rather than respiratory obstruction, are prominent, and death occurs only after many hours with

engorged blood vessels in abdominal viscera as the main gross finding.

Mode of Administration of Antigen. Anaphylactic shock is elicited most intensely when immune complexes form rapidly, because the released pharmacologically active mediators are rapidly degraded. Hence intravenous injection of antigen is most effective. Inhalation of antigens dispersed as aerosols can also provoke fatal shock, but subcutaneous and intraperitoneal injections elicit more protracted and less intense reactions, which are less often fatal.

Cutaneous Anaphylaxis in the Guinea Pig

As with generalized anaphylaxis, the local reaction in the skin can be active or passive. In **active cutaneous anaphylaxis** the animal rendered sensitive (by administration of im-

TABLE 17-2.　ANAPHYLAXIS IN DIFFERENT SPECIES

Species	Principal site of reaction (shock organ)	Pharmacologically active agents implicated	Principal manifestations
Guinea pig	Lung (bronchioles)	Histamine Kinins SRS-A	Respiratory distress; bronchiolar constriction; emphysema
Rabbit	Heart Pulmonary blood vessels	Histamine Serotonin Kinins SRS-A	Obstruction of pulmonary capillaries with leucocyte-platelet thrombi; right-sided heart failure; vascular engorgement of liver and intestines
Rat	Intestines	Serotonin Kinins	Circulatory collapse; increased peristalsis; hemorrhages in intestine and lung
Mouse	?	Serotonin Kinins	Respiratory distress; emphysema; right-sided heart failure; hyperemia of intestine
Dog	Hepatic veins	Histamine Kinins ? Serotonin	Hepatic engorgement; hemorrhages in abdominal and thoracic viscera
Man	Lung (bronchioles) Larynx	Histamine ? Kinins SRS-A	Dyspnea; hypotension; flushing and itching; circulatory collapse; acute emphysema; laryngeal edema; urticaria on recovery

Based mostly on K. F. Austen and J. H. Humphrey. Advances Immunol. 3:1 (1963).

munogen 1 week to several months previously) is injected intradermally with the antigen. Swelling and redness appear within a few minutes at the injected site, but the response is made much more conspicuous by injecting the animal intravenously, a few minutes before the skin test is performed, with an intensely colored dye, such as Evans blue, which is strongly bound by serum albumin. At the site of the response serum proteins rapidly pour out into the dermis, carrying the dye as a marker. The response thus appears as an irregular circle of stained skin, its area being an index of the intensity of the reaction.

In **passive cutaneous anaphylaxis (PCA)** an antiserum (or purified antibody) is injected intradermally. After a latent period of several hours the corresponding antigen, mixed with dye, is injected intravenously. A response is again revealed by the prompt accumulation of dye at the injected skin site (Fig. 17-3). Multiple tests can be performed simultaneously in an individual animal, and only small amounts of material are required; hence in its

simplicity, economy, and opportunities for controlled observations, PCA is preferred over systemic anaphylaxis or active cutaneous anaphylaxis for comparing various antibodies and preparations of allergens for their competence in eliciting anaphylactic responses.

The following lines of evidence, based largely on the work of Ovary and co-workers, indicate that in PCA, as in systemic anaphylaxis, antibodies must react both with the corresponding ligands and with receptor sites in skin.

1) A **latent period** must elapse between injection of antibodies into the skin and antigen intravenously. Usually 3 or 4 hours suffice.

2) If the antigen is itself a particular type of immunoglobulin (see Special cytotropic antibodies responsible for anaphylaxis, below) the order of injections may be reversed, introducing the antigen intradermally and then the corresponding antiserum, mixed with indicator dye, intravenously **(reverse PCA).**

3) As in passive systemic anaphylaxis, antisera from certain species (guinea pig, rabbit,

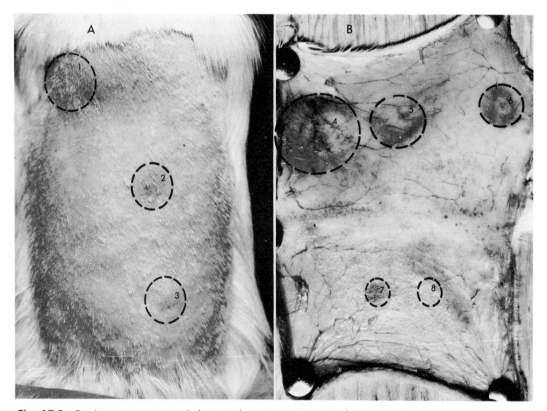

Fig. 17-3 Passive cutaneous anaphylaxis in the guinea pig. In **A** the guinea pig was injected intradermally at 3 sites with 0.1 ml containing 1) 100 μg rabbit anti-chicken ovalbumin (Ea), 2) 10 μg anti-Ea, and 3) buffered saline. Four hours later 1.0 ml containing 2 mg Ea and 5 mg Evans Blue was injected intravenously, and the photo was taken 30 min later. Note blueing at 1 and at 2, and the absence of blueing at the control site (3).

In **B** a similar sequence was followed except that 30 min after the intravenous injection of Ea the animal was sacrificed and skinned. The photo was taken of the skin's undersurface. The amount of rabbit anti-Ea injected initially were 100 μg (at 4), 10 μg (at 5), 1 μg (at 6), and 0.1 μg (at 7). The control site, which did not turn blue (8), had been injected with buffered saline. Another site (not shown) had been injected with 0.01 μg anti-Ea and it also failed to react.

man) can sensitize guinea pig skin; those from other species (chicken, horse, goat, sheep) cannot.

4) Considerable diversity also exists among the antibodies from a particular species. With effective antibodies (see cytotropic antibodies, below) as little as 0.01 μg is sufficient; other antibodies are ineffective at many times this level.

Cutaneous Anaphylaxis in Man

Cutaneous anaphylaxis in man begins 2 or 3 minutes after an allergen is injected intradermally: itching at the injected site is followed within a few minutes by a pale, elevated, irregular wheal, surrounded by a zone or erythema (**hive** or **urticarium**). This reaction, called the **wheal-and-erythema response,** attains maximal intensity ca. 10 minutes after the injection, persists for an additional 10 to 20 minutes, and then gradually subsides (Fig. 17-4).

Most humans can be actively sensitized to give wheal-and-erythema responses; for example, persons injected with a sufficient quantity of horse serum usually become responsive to horse serum, and those recovering from pneumococcal pneumonia react to the appropriate pneumococcal polysaccharide. These responses can usually be elicited only with antibody levels above a critical value, which for antidextran seems to be ca. 30 $\mu g/ml$ of serum.*

Atopy. In contrast, a special group of persons, constituting perhaps 10% of the population in the United States, can display wheal-and-erythema responses without a high level of serum antibody. These individuals tend to become sensitive spontaneously (i.e., without deliberate inoculation) to a variety of environmental allergens, such as airborne pollens of ragweed, grasses, and trees, and also to fungi, animal danders, house dust, and foods. When they inhale or ingest the appropriate allergen their response is prompt: most frequent and prominent among the manifestations are rhinitis, asthma, and hives. The tendency to develop this form of human allergy, called **atopy** (Gr., "out of place"), is familial and probably heritable. Atopy has also been recognized in dogs and in cattle.

Passive Transfer. Until the development of highly sensitive assays, such as passive hemagglutination (Ch. 13), the sera of atopic persons usually gave no detectable reactions with allergens in vitro. Characteristically, however, these sera can quite regularly sensitize passively the skin of almost all normal persons. Passive sensitization is performed by injecting ca. 0.1 ml (or less) of serum from the sensitive donor into the skin (dermal layer) of a nonsensitive recipient. From 1 day to as long as 6 weeks later, injection of the corresponding allergen into the same site elicits the wheal-and-erythema response. This transfer reaction is called the **Prausnitz-Küstner or P-K reaction,** after the investigators who first described it.†

To elicit the P-K reaction it is necessary to allow at least several hours between injection of serum and the corresponding allergen; mixtures of the two do not elicit responses. As with other forms of anaphylaxis, during

Fig. 17-4 Cutaneous anaphylaxis (wheal-and-erythema response) in man. Fifteen minutes before the photograph was taken the subject was injected intradermally with 0.02 ml containing about 0.1 µg protein extracted from guinea pig hair. Note the irregularly shaped wheal, with striking pseudopodia. The surrounding erythema is not easily visible. No reaction is seen at the control site, about 5 cm above the wheal, where 0.02 ml of buffer alone was injected.

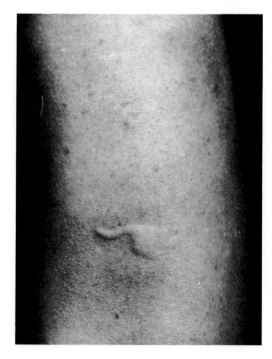

---

* The skin responses that depend on such relatively high levels of serum antibody probably represent examples of "aggregate anaphylaxis" (p. 534).

† As described in their paper in 1921, Küstner was extremely sensitive to certain fish, but his serum gave no detectable reaction with extracts of these fish and did not sensitize guinea pigs for passive anaphylaxis. Prausnitz therefore injected a small amount of the serum into a normal person's skin, and injected the skin site 24 hours later with the fish extract; the immediate appearance of a wheal-and-erythema response provided the basis for much of the clinical and experimental work on allergy of the succeeding decades.

this **latent period** antibodies presumably become fixed to receptor sites in skin.

Special (Cytotropic) Antibodies Responsible for Anaphylaxis

Homocytotropic Antibodies in the Guinea Pig. The 7S antibodies of the guinea pig and several other species are separable electrophoretically into two fractions, $\gamma 1$ and $\gamma 2$. For convenience they may be regarded as subclasses of γG immunoglobulin. Only guinea pig antibodies of the $\gamma 1$ fraction can passively sensitize guinea pig skin (Fig. 17-5). Similarly, the rat, rabbit, dog, and mouse are passively sensitized for PCA by a special subset of their 7S antibodies, resembling guinea pig $\gamma 1$, not $\gamma 2$. With specific fluorescein-labeled antibodies to $\gamma 1$ and $\gamma 2$ it has been shown that only the $\gamma 1$ molecules adhere firmly to tissue mast cells.

Fig. 17-5 Separation of homocytotropic from other antibodies of the same specificity. Purified 7S guinea pig antibodies, specific for the 2,4-dinitrophenyl (DNP) group, were subjected to electrophoresis in starch (arrow marks point of application). Fractions eluted from ½-inch cuts of the starch block were then tested for ability to mediate PCA in guinea pigs. The more anionic anti-DNP molecules, called $\gamma 1$ (fractions 11 to 15), mediated PCA, whereas the less anionic antibodies, called $\gamma 2$ (fractions 1 to 7), did not. By means of immunoelectrophoresis and a rabbit antiserum to whole guinea pig serum, the $\gamma 1$ and $\gamma 2$ fractions were distinguished antigenically, as well as electrophoretically. (Redrawn from Z. Ovary, B. Benacerraf, and K. J. Bloch. *J. Exp. Med.* 117:951, 1963.)

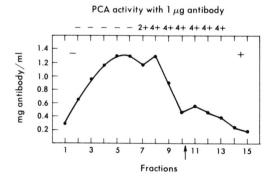

Purified guinea pig anti-DNP-antibody

PCA activity with 1 μg antibody

As with other types of immunoglobulins (Ch. 14), $\gamma 1$ and $\gamma 2$ have indistinguishable populations of light chains but different heavy chains, and antigenic differences are evident in their Fc fragments, isolated after papain digestion. **The capacity of certain antibodies to mediate anaphylactic responses thus seems to depend on a distinctive structural feature of the Fc portion of their heavy chain, which is responsible for the affinity of these antibodies for membranes of mast cells, and probably of platelets.** Once the antibody is bound to the cell surface, subsequent reaction with the corresponding ligand apparently leads to the release of vasoactive amines.

The antibodies that bind to target cells and thus sensitize for anaphylaxis have been called **cytotropic** antibodies; and the $\gamma 1$ antibodies of the guinea pig have been called **homocytotropic,** because they sensitize guinea pig mast cells. Paradoxically, however, $\gamma 2$ antibodies of the guinea pig can sensitize the skin of other species, such as man and mouse, presumably because they fortuitously can bind to mast cells of these species. The guinea pig $\gamma 2$ antibodies have thus been called **heterocytotropic.** Similarly, the other mammalian species examined also have distinguishable homocytotropic antibodies, that sensitize the homologous species, and heterocytotropic antibodies, that only sensitize a number of foreign species.

Antibodies of the γM immunoglobulin class do not sensitize animals of the same or of other species.

Homocytotropic (Skin-Sensitizing) Antibodies in Man. The antibodies of atopic sera that mediate the wheal-and-erythema (P-K) response have been called **skin-sensitizing antibodies, atopic reagins,** simply **reagins,** or **reaginic antibodies.** They can sensitize the skin of monkeys but not of guinea pigs or of other species, for local anaphylactic responses; they may thus be classified as homocytotropic. Though they have not been purified, some of their characteristics have been deduced from the properties of whole sera, especially those from persons allergic to ragweed and other pollens. As is shown in Table 17-3,

TABLE 17-3. COMPARISON OF HUMAN SKIN SENSITIZING AND BLOCKING
ANTIBODIES TO POLLEN ANTIGENS*

	Skin-sensitizing antibodies†	Blocking antibodies‡
Immunoglobulin class	?γE	Probably γG
Stability		
To heat (56°, 4 hr)	Labile	Stable
To reducing agents		
(0.1 M 2-mercaptoethanol)	?	Stable
Activity in Prausnitz-Küstner test	Yes	No (inhibits)
Persistence in normal human skin (P-K reaction)	Up to 6 weeks	Up to 2 or 3 days
Transfer across human placenta	No	Yes
Passive sensitization of guinea pigs for anaphylaxis	No	Yes
Detection in conventional in vitro assays	Possibly by passive hemagglutination	Yes

* *Highly purified protein antigens have been isolated from ragweed and grass pollen extracts by ion-exchange chromatography. Several active fractions have been obtained from each extract, and different fractions are active in different persons. As little as 10^{-4} μg of some ragweed fractions evoke specific skin responses in sensitive humans.*

† *Homocytotropic antibodies.*
‡ *Heterocytotropic antibodies.*

these antibodies are relatively heat-labile and they differ in many other respects from the heterocytotropic antibodies (of the same specificity) in the same sera.

Ishizaka has shown that the skin-sensitizing activity of atopic human sera is precipitated by antisera to crude globulin fractions, but not by monospecific antisera to γA, γG, or γM immunoglobulins. It thus seems possible that these antibodies may be associated with a unique class of immunoglobulins; though evidence for their existence is still tenuous, these proteins are called γE immunoglobulins.

Blocking Antibodies in Man. If ragweed extract is injected repeatedly into nonatopic human volunteers, antiragweed antibodies appear in serum and may be detected by various in vitro assays, such as passive hemagglutination. However, these deliberately induced antibodies are not capable of sensitizing human skin for wheal-and-erythema responses. In fact, their addition to pollen extract, before its injection, specifically prevents it from evoking a response in a sensitive person. These antibodies, called **blocking antibodies,** are predominantly γG immunoglobulins. Since they can sensitize guinea pigs and other species for anaphylaxis they are heterocytotropic (Table 17-3).

Other Forms of Anaphylaxis

The in vivo reactions discussed above, called **cytotropic anaphylaxis,** are all mediated by cytotropic antibodies, and a latent period is required for attachment of antibody to cell receptors. In contrast, a latent period is not required for another type of reaction, called **"aggregate anaphylaxis,"** which also appears within minutes after antigen is injected. This reaction seems to be caused by relatively large amounts of soluble antibody-antigen complexes. For example, a single intradermal injection of soluble complexes, prepared by dissolving a specific precipitate in a concentrated solution of antigen, can evoke cutaneous anaphylaxis in a normal guinea pig.

Guinea pigs also undergo fatal shock when injected intravenously with antisera that have been incubated for a few minutes with antigen.* And even heat-aggregated γ-globulins of rabbit and man, without an antigen, can elicit cutaneous anaphylaxis, suggesting that the essential role of the antigen is to serve as a cross-linking agent for aggregating antibody molecules. The aggregates presumably fix complement in vivo, leading to formation of anaphylatoxin, which releases histamine from mast cells (Ch. 16). In accord with this view, the effective soluble complexes are those (e.g., with an average molar composition of about Ag₃Ab₂) that fix complement, while those that do not fix complement are ineffective (e.g., Ag₂Ab complexes, which are formed in extreme antigen excess; see Ch. 16).

Anaphylactic Responses in Isolated Tissues

Many organs and cells from a sensitized animal respond specifically to the corresponding antigen in vitro. In the **Schultz-Dale reaction,** for example, the uterus from a sensitized guinea pig, bathed in a balanced salt solution, contracts promptly when the antigen is added, because the antigen causes histamine release, presumably from tissue mast cells and trapped platelets. Similar reactions are obtained with isolated segments of ileum, gallbladder wall, and sections of arterial wall (Fig. 17-6). Moreover minced fragments of lung from a sensitized guinea pig release measurable amounts of vasoactive substances. These responses can also be elicited by antigens in tissues removed from passively sensitized animals, and in isolated tissues that are sensitized passively by perfusion with, or simply soaking in, an antiserum. The reactivity of the isolated tissue is retained after exhaus-

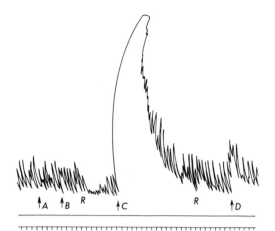

Fig. 17-6 Smooth muscle contraction in vitro in response to antigen (Schultz-Dale reaction). A uterine horn, excised from a guinea pig 13 days after one injection of a horse serum euglobulin fraction, was suspended in Ringer's solution to which various protein fractions from horse serum were added, as indicated by arrows. At A, 1 mg of pseudoglobulin was added; at B, 10 mg of pseudoglobulin; at C and at D, 10 mg of euglobulin (the immunogen). Following the specific response at C the muscle is almost totally desensitized, because the tissue-bound antibodies are saturated with antigen or because the histamine content is depleted. Time scale markers are at 30-second intervals. R refers to change in Ringer's solution. (From H. H. Dale and P. Hartley. Biochem. J. 10:408, 1916.)

tive washing; hence once the appropriate antibodies are bound, they adhere tenaciously.

Participation of Complement in Anaphylaxis

Homocytotropic antibodies do not fix complement in vitro. In addition, passive cutaneous anaphylaxis has been evoked with mouse antibodies in mice that were depleted temporarily of complement activity. Thus complement does not seem to be involved in the type of anaphylaxis that occasionally occurs (inadvertently) in man. However, complement fixation in vivo is probably required for some of the experimental responses evoked with heterologous antibodies: for example, temporary depletion of complement in rats inhibits the passive cutaneous anaphylaxis elicited with rabbit γG antibodies.

---

* Normal serum becomes similarly toxic after brief incubation at 37° with suspensions of various particles (kaolin, talc, barium sulfate, inulin, agar), which apparently activate some serum proteases, resulting in the formation of vasoactive peptides that resemble anaphylatoxin (Ch. 16). The response to these incubated sera (without antigen) is sometimes called **anaphylactoid shock.**

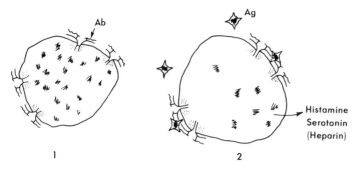

Fig. 17-7 Schematic diagram of cytotropic anaphylaxis. **1.** Bivalent antibodies with strong affinity for the membrane of mast cells are represented as being bound by noncovalent bonds (fine dots) involving heavy chains in the Fc domain. **2.** Binding of multivalent ligand by the mast-cell-bound antibodies results in discharge of granules and release of soluble vasoactive amines. Platelets, blood basophils, and perhaps other cells also bind cytotropic antibodies and release vasoactive amines following the interaction with antigen.

It also appears that complement fixation in vivo is essential for aggregate anaphylaxis, because there is a consistent correlation between ability of aggregates to fix complement in vitro and their ability to evoke anaphylaxis (p. 535). In addition, when guinea pigs are injected intradermally with purified C'1 esterase, the first product of the reaction between complement and antigen-antibody complexes (Ch. 16), they give a prompt response, inhibitable with antihistamines, which is indistinguishable from cutaneous anaphylaxis. In all the anaphylactic reactions in which complement is involved it is probable that anaphylatoxin is formed and causes release of histamine (Ch. 16).

Summary of Cytotropic Anaphylaxis

These reactions range from wheal-and-erythema in the skin to fatal shock. They have in common the following properties (Fig. 17-7).

1) The responses appear promptly and are transient. Recovery is complete unless the outcome is fatal, as it may be in systemic anaphylaxis.

2) Antibodies can mediate a response only if they bind to certain target cells, and the binding depends on sites in the Fc region of the heavy chains of a special class of antibody molecules.

3) The binding sites on the target cells have not been characterized, but some at least must be localized on the surface of mast cells and platelets.

4) The effective specific complexes are, at a minimum, probably small multimolecular aggregates. Hence, the responses are usually inhibited specifically by univalent ligands.

5) The physiological effects of the competent antibody complexes are due to the release of one or more pharmacologically active agents: e.g., histamine, serotonin, bradykinin, and SRS-A.

6) The responses are inhibited by drugs that antagonize the pharmacologically active mediators.

7) Desensitization is readily achieved, but is usually temporary. A variety of procedures are effective: e.g., a) neutralizing the reactive antibodies through repeated inoculation of small amounts of allergen; b) depleting tissue stores of histamine or serotonin with unrelated antibody-antigen systems, or with histmine-releasing agents; c) stimulating the production of blocking antibodies, which compete for antigen but which are themselves unable to mediate anaphylaxis.

Arthus Reaction

First described by Arthus, a French physiologist, another kind of immediate-type reaction occurs when antibody levels are sufficiently high. These reactions are usually studied in the skin, but can be evoked as local responses in almost any tissue, such as pericardial sac or synovial space.

In the **passive Arthus reaction** an antiserum is first injected intravenously into a nonsensitive recipient animal, and the corresponding antigen is then injected into its skin. In the **reverse passive Arthus reaction,** antiserum is injected into the recipient's skin and antigen is then injected into the same dermal site or intravenously.

The main features of the Arthus reaction, defined largely by means of these passive reactions, differ greatly from anaphylaxis. Some of the properties of the Arthus reaction that differentiate it from anaphylactic responses are listed below:

1) Arthus responses appear more slowly and are more persistent, appearing 1-2 hours after injection of antigen and lasting for several hours.

2) Antibodies of almost any class of immunoglobulins, and from almost any species, can mediate the passive Arthus response.

Fig. 17-8 The passive Arthus reaction in a rat, showing localization of antigen and complement in the wall of an affected blood vessel. The skin site was excised 2 to 3 hours after an intradermal injection of 300 μg of rabbit antibodies to bovine serum albumin (anti-BSA) and an intravenous injection of 6 mg of BSA. (The antibody was injected intradermally, and the antigen intravenously, in order to conserve antibodies.) **A.** Note intense polymorphonuclear leucocyte infiltration in and around the wall of a small blood vessel adjacent to skeletal muscle. **B.** The section was stained with fluorescent rabbit antibody to a purified component of rat complement (C'3 or β_{1c}; see Ch. 16). **C.** The section was stained with fluorescent anti-BSA to localize the aggregated antigen in the blood vessel wall and in the adjacent perivascular connective tissue. The same result would be obtained by staining the aggregated antibody (rabbit anti-BSA) with fluorescent anti-rabbit γ-globulin. (From P. A. Ward and C. G. Cochrane. *J. Exp. Med. 121:* 215, 1965.)

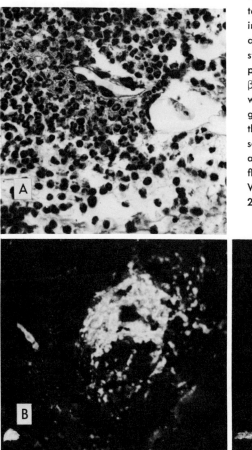

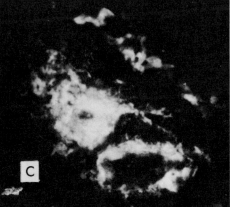

3) Exceptionally large amounts of antibody are required for the Arthus response, e.g., 100 μg when injected into a rabbit's skin, whereas as little as 0.01 μg of a cytotropic antibody can mediate cutaneous anaphylaxis, at least in the guinea pig.

4) Pharmacologically active mediators are not involved; e.g. antihistamines do not inhibit, and there is no latent period in the passive Arthus reaction.

5) The tissue changes in the Arthus response are those of classical inflammation (Fig. 17-8) whereas the histological changes in anaphylaxis are limited to vasodilation with few if any inflammatory cells.

Pathogensis. By means of immunofluorescence, antibody-antigen aggregates and some of the complement proteins (C′3, see Ch. 16) are demonstrable within blood vessel walls at the site of an Arthus reaction (Fig. 17-8). The aggregates are also visible in polymorphonuclear leucocytes and within the macrophages that ingest necrotic leucocytes. It is thus thought that the Arthus reaction depends on the following sequence: antigen-antibody complexes, formed in blood vessel walls, fix some of the complement components and thereby attract leucocytes which surround and ingest the complexes (C′1 to C′6; Ch. 16, leucotactic activity). The release of lysosomal enzymes, perhaps from necrotic leucocytes, then causes focal necrosis of the blood vessel wall and the other inflammatory

changes. From the release of acid-soluble peptides (from ^{131}I-labeled antigens) it appears that lysosomal enzymes of polymorphonuclear leucocytes degrade the ingested antigen-antibody complexes. Thus the Arthus reaction may have evolved as a mechanism for eliminating immune complexes from blood vessels.

Serum Sickness Syndrome

This reaction usually becomes evident 7 to 14 days after the initial injection of antigen. During this interval the antigen can persist at a fairly high level, while antibodies are synthesized. This combination permits soluble antigen-antibody complexes to form and to initiate focal inflammatory lesions. Serum sickness is thus usually observed only after exceptionally **large** amounts of foreign protein are injected, e.g., 25 gm of bovine serum albumin in man, or 1 gm in a rabbit. However, in a previously sensitized individual, with an accelerated (anamnestic) antibody response, the reaction appears earlier and therefore requires much less antigen: for example, serum sickness can become evident 3 or 4 days after 1 ml of horse serum is injected into a previously immunized person.

As the manifestations of serum sickness appear, the decline in the level of free antigen is accelerated (Fig. 17-9). During this period

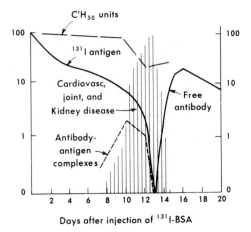

Fig. 17-9 Serum sickness in the rabbit. Changes in serum levels of free antigen (^{131}I-labeled bovine serum albumin), free antibody (anti-BSA), antigen-antibody complexes, and complement activity (C′H50 units, see Ch. 16) following the injection of rabbits with 250 mg of ^{131}I-BSA per kilogram of body weight. Ordinate (log scale) refers to ^{131}I-BSA in total blood volume, as per cent of the amount injected; anti-BSA in terms of micrograms of antigen bound per milliliter of serum; complement as per cent of normal serum. The incidence of cardiovascular, joint, and kidney lesions (Fig. 17-13), shown by shaded area, reached 100% on day 13. (From F. J. Dixon. In *Immunological Diseases.* (M. Samter, ed.) Little, Brown, Boston, 1965.)

soluble antibody-antigen complexes can be detected in serum if ^{131}I-labeled bovine serum albumin is used as antigen. Free antibody becomes detectable and the inflammatory lesions regress as the soluble complexes disappear.

At the height of the syndrome the level of **complement** is depressed, because it is fixed by the antigen-antibody complexes that form in situ. As in the Arthus reaction, one of the complement components (C'3; Ch. 16) is detectable by immunofluorescence in the immune aggregates within the focal blood vessel lesions. Since the rise and fall of soluble complexes parallels the evolution of the lesions, it is not surprising that injection of complexes formed in vitro causes the characteristic lesions to develop in rabbits. The most effective complexes are those prepared in moderate antigen excess (Ag_3Ab_2). Complexes formed at equivalence are ineffective, probably because they are generally particulate and tend to be rapidly cleared from the circulation. Complexes formed in extreme antigen excess (Ag_2Ab) are also ineffective, probably because they fail to fix complement.

Relation to Other Allergic Reactions. The histological appearance of the focal vascular lesions, the requirement for antigen-antibody aggregates, and the participation of complement suggest that the serum sickness syndrome is essentially a disseminated form of the Arthus reaction, with the same injected substance serving first as immunogen and then as reacting antigen. However, among the antibody molecules formed there doubtless are some that tend especially to be bound by mast cells and platelets. Very likely these are responsible for the urticarial skin lesions that are also prominent in this disorder in man. Moreover, after a person has recovered from the serum sickness syndrome he will generally give a wheal-and-erythema response to an intradermal injection of the responsible antigen. It thus seems reasonable to regard this syndrome as an expression of both Arthus and anaphylactic responses (Table 17-1).

DELAYED-TYPE RESPONSES

Recognized in many species of vertebrates, delayed-type allergy has been most extensively studied in man and in the guinea pig. The response to proteins of the tubercle bacilli has been studied especially extensively, because of a suspected role in the pathogenesis of tuberculosis; it serves as a model for delayed-type hypersensitivity to microbial antigens in general.

Koch observed in 1890 that viable tubercle bacilli inoculated subcutaneously into previously infected guinea pigs evoke a much more intense inflammatory reaction than in uninfected animals (Koch phenomenon). Since a similar result was obtained with killed tubercle bacilli, he examined bacterial extracts and found that they, as well as culture filtrates of **Mycobacterium tuberculosis,** were also effective: injected in non-toxic amounts they elicited after many hours an inflammatory response in tuberculous but not in normal animals. After concentration by boiling, the culture filtrate was called tuberculin (now called "old tuberculin" or OT). Similar preparations from various other bacterial and fungal cultures also elicit delayed-type responses in those infected by the corresponding organism (Table 17-4). These allergic skin reactions are now widely used in the diagnosis of many infectious diseases and for population surveys to detect those with previous or current infections.

Cutaneous Reaction

After 0.1 μg of tuberculin (PPD) is injected **intradermally** into a sensitized individual no change is observed at the inoculated site for at least 5 to 10 hours. Erythema and swelling then gradually appear and increase progressively; maximal intensity and size (up to ca. 7 cm diameter) are reached in 24 to 72 hours, and the response then subsides over a period of several days. In the most severe reactions hemorrhage and necrosis appear at the peak of the response.

TABLE 17-4. SOME DELAYED-TYPE CUTANEOUS RESPONSES USED AS DIAGNOSTIC
TESTS AND FOR EPIDEMIOLOGICAL SURVEYS

Disease	Type of etiological agent	Antigenic preparation used in skin test
Tuberculosis	Bacteria	Tuberculin
Leprosy	Bacteria	Lepromin
Brucellosis	Bacteria	Brucellin
Psittacosis	Bacteria	Heat-killed organisms
Lymphogranuloma venereum	Bacteria	Extract of chorioallantoic membrane of infected chick embryo
Mumps	Virus	Noninfectious virus from yolk sac of infected chick embryo
Coccidioidomycosis	Fungus	Concentrated culture filtrate
Histoplasmosis	Fungus	Concentrated culture filtrate
Blastomycosis	Fungus	Concentrated culture filtrate
Leishmaniasis	Protozoan	Extract of cultured leishmania
Echinococcosis	Helminth	Fluid from hydatid cyst
Contact dermatitis	Simple chemical	Patch tests with simple chemical

Fig. 17-10 Delayed-type allergic reaction in guinea pig skin. The animal was sensitized by injecting 5 μg of hen's egg albumin (HEA) in complete Freund's adjuvant into its toepads. Six days later it was injected intradermally with 5 μg of HEA in saline. The skin site was excised 24 hours later, when induration and redness (which had probably first become evident at about 12 hours) were maximal. **A.** ×64; **B.** ×355. (From J. E. Coe and S. B. Salvin. *J. Immunol. 93:495, 1964.*)

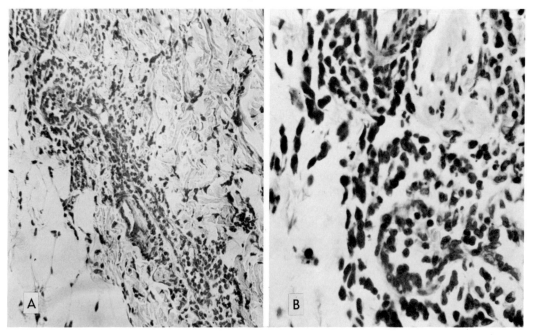

Histologically, the delayed-type response to tuberculin is characterized by a massive accumulation of inflammatory cells. Initially (e.g., at 12 hours), granulocytes are abundant about small blood vessels, but by 24 hours the lesions are populated almost exclusively by lymphocytes and macrophages (Fig. 17-10).

Comparison Between Arthus and Delayed-Type Skin Reactions.

The Arthus reaction sometimes simulates the delayed-type response. It should be recalled, however, that the Arthus reaction usually appears ca. 2 hours after a test dose of antigen is injected into the skin, is maximal at 4 or 5 hours, and subsides by 24 hours (p. 537). It is also more boggy than indurated, reflecting a large amount of edema fluid and only a modest accumulation of inflammatory cells, which are mainly polymorphonuclear leucocytes. In contrast, delayed-type reactions do not usually appear before 10 or 12 hours, reach a maximum at about 24 hours (sometimes as late as 48 to 72 hours), and they are especially indurated because of the intense accumulation of mononuclear cells.

Sometimes both responses follow a single test injection, with a bimodal inflammatory reaction, one maximal at 4 hours (Arthus) and the other at 24 hours (delayed-type reaction). The situation is, however, often more complex, and a severe Arthus reaction, which can be hemorrhagic and necrotic, can remain conspicuous for 24 hours or more. The distinction from the delayed-type reaction is then hardly possible by either gross or microscopic inspection.

Noncutaneous and Systemic Reactions

Delayed responses also occur in tissues other than the dermal layer of skin. Even in the avascular normal **cornea** tuberculin can cause severe inflammation and necrosis in highly sensitized guinea pigs.

A systemic response, **tuberculin shock,** ensues when a sensitized guinea pig is injected intraperitoneally with a relatively large amount (e.g., 5 mg) of tuberculin. Prostration develops after 3 to 4 hours, body temperature falls ca. 4 or 5°, and death may follow in 5 to 30 hours. A systemic reaction, only very rarely fatal, also occurs in highly sensitized persons who are injected with excessive amounts of tuberculin in the skin, or who inhale aerosols while working with tuberculin.

Tuberculous individuals exposed to large amounts of tuberculin also develop **focal** reactions: exaggerated inflammatory reactions in infected lesions in lungs and elsewhere. These reactions resemble histologically the responses elicited in the skin with tuberculin; they may be due to a high concentration of specifically reactive lymphoid cells in the infected lesions (p. 548). Similar systemic responses have been evoked with antigens of histoplasma, brucella, vaccinia, and pneumococci in persons with delayed-type sensitivity to these organisms.

Induction of Sensitivity

Delayed responses to tuberculin can be elicited about 2 weeks after infection with either virulent or attenuated tubercle bacilli.

Injections of tuberculin, in contrast to viable bacilli, do not establish delayed-type sensitivity: instead, they induce appreciable levels of circulating antibodies, associated with the capacity to give anaphylactic responses to tuberculin, and even Arthus reactions after protracted immunization. Attempts to induce sensitivity by simpler means than infection have established that certain lipids of acid-fast bacteria are unusually potent adjuvants (Ch. 15; see Freund's adjuvant).

The role of the mycobacterial lipid is not understood; and, in fact, this lipid is not actually obligatory. As indicated before, infections with many other microbes, that lack mycosides or other waxes, also regularly establish delayed sensitivity to the corresponding antigens. Even the intradermal injection of minute amounts of many soluble proteins or other allergens, in simple aqueous solution, can induce delayed-type hypersensitivity. It has been suggested, therefore, that some unknown lipids in skin or in the inflammatory cells at foci of infection might serve the same function as the mycobacterial lipid.

Cell Transfer

Nearly all attempts to transfer delayed-type hypersensitivity with serum from a sensitive donor to an insensitive recipient have failed, and the few reported successes have not been convincing. Chase discovered in 1942, however, that delayed sensitivity to tuberculin can be transferred to a normal guinea pig with viable lymphoid cells from a tuberculin-sensitive animal. Since then similar transfers, involving many other antigens, have been accomplished so consistently that **transfer by viable lymphoid cells (from lymph nodes, spleen, blood, or peritoneal exudates) is now regarded as an essential characteristic of delayed-type hypersensitivity.** (However, it is not an exclusive attribute, because the lymphoid cells from an intensively immunized donor continue to form circulating antibodies in a recipient animal [and even in vitro; Ch. 15], and thus they probably can also transfer immediate-type allergy.)

In laboratory experiments with rodents **only viable cells** have been effective, and the persistence of sensitivity in recipients parallels continued survival of the transferred cells, or perhaps their progeny. For example, sensitivity persists for many weeks when the recipient and the donor are genetically similar, but it usually disappears after 2 or 3 weeks when they are genetically dissimilar, the recipient then destroying the transferred cells by an allograft reaction (Ch. 18).

The transfer of delayed hypersensitivity (or any other immune capacity) by viable cells is often called **adoptive immunity** or sensitivity), to distinguish it from the **passive immunity** (or sensitivity) confered by a transfer of antibody molecules.

Transfer Factor. An interesting exception to the requirement for viable cells has been seen in humans. Lawrence has shown that extracts of blood leucocytes from a tuberculin-sensitive person can confer typical delayed-type sensitivity on tuberculin-negative persons. Extracts of human white blood cells have similarly been shown to transfer delayed hypersensitivity to other antigens (e.g., from streptococci and *Coccidioides immitis*), and to transfer the specific capacity for accelerated rejection of tissue grafts, also regarded as a manifestation of delayed-type hypersensitivity (Ch. 18).

The active component, called "transfer-factor," has been difficult to characterize since it can be assayed only in humans.

Sensitivity of Cells in Vitro

In an effort to study delayed-type allergy in a less complex system than the whole animal, blood and tissue cells from tuberculous animals have been examined for cytopathic changes after incubation with tuberculin in vitro. The addition to the medium of tuberculin at low concentrations inhibits the movement of cells derived from tuberculous animals, but not that of cells from normal animals. Macrophages and lymphocytes are particularly vulnerable; epithelial cells are unaffected.

Similar results have been obtained with cells from animals with delayed-type hypersensitivity to other antigens (e.g., streptococcal proteins, diphtheria toxoid). In contrast, cells from animals with immediate-type hypersensitivity, and from those who are briskly forming antibodies, do not respond in this manner (Fig. 17-11).

Drug Suppression

Delayed-type responses are not inhibited by antihistamine drugs, but they are readily suppressed by moderate doses of 11-oxycorticosteroids (cortisone, hydrocortisone, etc.). Conversely, the steroids do not inhibit anaphylactic responses, unless given in the unusually high dosage required to suppress antibody formation (Ch. 15). The suppression of delayed reactions is not specific, however, since these adrenal steroids block inflammatory reactions to a variety of nonallergic stimuli. Inhibition of delayed-type responses with steroids is temporary; several days after administration of drug has been stopped the response can again be elicited.

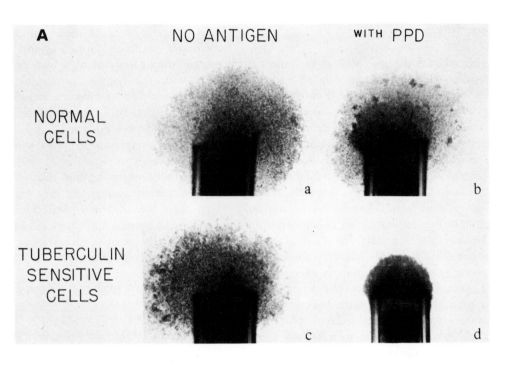

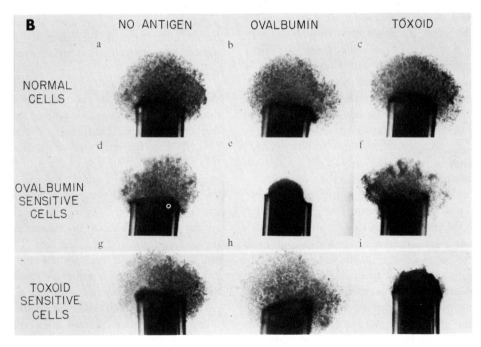

Fig. 17-11 Cytotoxic reaction in vitro of lymphoid cells from peritoneal exudates of guinea pigs with delayed-type hypersensitivity. Note inhibition by antigen of migration of cells from sensitive animals. **A.** Cells from normal and tuberculin-sensitive guinea pigs. **B.** Cells from normal, ovalbumin-sensitive and diphtheria toxoid-sensitive guinea pigs. (From J. R. David, S. Al-Askari, H. S. Lawrence, and L. Thomas. *J. Immunol.* 93:264, 1964.)

Specificity

Microbial Antigens. Most of the microbial antigens used for eliciting delayed responses are inadequately characterized chemically. In addition, quantitation of responses is limited to imprecise estimates of the diameter of the erythemaotus zone and thickening of skin. Though detailed evaluation of specificity has thus not been possible, even qualitative tests have been informative. For example, guinea pigs infected with *M. tuberculosis* respond strongly to skin tests with tuberculin from this organism but only feebly, if at all, to "tuberculin" from *M. kansasii,* whereas the reverse is observed in animals infected with *M. kansasii.* Antisera to diverse mycobacteria, in contrast, cross-react extensively, and even cross-react with actinomycetes (Ch. 20). **Thus, delayed responses to infectious agents and their antigens seem to be even more specific than antigen-antibody reactions in general.** Nonetheless, some cross-reactions are troublesome in diagnostic skin tests, e.g., among extracts from such fungi as Histoplasma, Blastomyces, and Coccidioides.

Soluble Proteins and Carrier Specificity. Hapten-protein conjugates have been particularly useful for studying the specificity of delayed-type hypersensitivity.

In guinea pigs sensitized with picryl (2,4,6-trinitrophenyl)-bovine γ-globulin, a typical hapten-protein conjugate, the delayed responses elicited with the immunogen (picryl-BγG) were more intense than those elicited with the unsubstituted carrier protein (BγG), and no responses were evoked with conjugates of the picryl group and an unrelated carrier, such as picryl-ovalbumin. Hence it appeared that the response is specific for the picryl group plus other determinants of the immunogen, presumably amino acid residues surrounding the haptenic group: that is, the response was **carrier-specific.** Many observations of this type indicate that small determinants, of the size of the picryl group, are insufficient by themselves to elicit the delayed-type response: reenforcement wtih other residues of the inducing agent is required.

In contrast, many of the serum antibody molecules eventually formed against hapten-protein conjugates can be shown readily to react with the haptenic group alone; for example, antipicryl antibodies, formed in response to picryl-BγG, precipitate picryl-ovalbumin, bind ε-picryl-lysine, and mediate anaphylactic responses to picryl-ovalbumin. Thus delayed-type responses to proteins **appear to be directed against relatively large antigenic determinants;** and they tend to be even more specific than antibody-mediated reactions in general since they exhibit fewer cross-reactions to small determinant groups shared by different antigens.

Though carrier specificity is conspicuous in delayed reactions it can also be demonstrated in other immune responses. For example, with antisera prepared against hapten-protein conjugates, absorption studies show that some of the antibody molecules also exhibit carrier specificity, forming specific precipitating complexes only with the immunogen, and not with the protein moiety alone or with the haptenic groups attached to an antigenically unrelated protein.

An approach to understanding carrier specificity is afforded by considering conventional antibody-antigen reactions involving defined, haptenic antigenic determinants (Fig. 17-12). For any antibody-antigen reaction to be discernible a critical mass of specific complexes must be formed, and this requires that some minimal proportion of the active sites of the antibody and of the ligand populations combine. These proportions depend on the concentrations of the reactants (antibody and ligand) and on their mutual affinity (Ch. 13). In addition, each antigenic determinant can be considered to be composed of several parts, each of which makes a **partial** contribution to the total mutual affinity between the whole determinant and the corresponding population of antibody molecules. When the total affinity and the concentrations of antibody and ligand are barely sufficient to form the mass of complexes required to provoke a detectable reaction, an analog with less than the complete structure of the inducer would

Immunogen
(inducer)

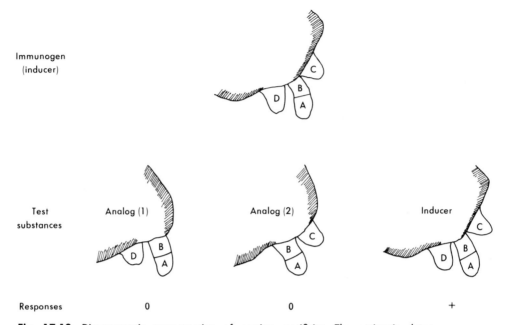

Test
substances   Analog (1)   Analog (2)   Inducer

Responses   0   0   +

Fig. 17-12 Diagrammatic represenation of carrier specificity. The antigenic determinant (ABCD) of the immunogen (inducer) is visualized as made up four parts,
with A representing an extrinsic group (such as 2,4-dinitrophenyl) attached covalently to
amino acid residue B (e.g., lysine); C and D represent other amino acid residues of
the carrier protein. Test substances, made by attaching the same extrinsic group (A)
to lysine residues (B) of other proteins (analogs 1 and 2), lack either C or D in the correct
position and fail to elicit a positive response.

probably not interact strongly enough to support a visible reaction. **Hence carrier specificity is likely to be conspicuous in those in
vitro and in vivo reactions in which the concentrations of the reactants, or their mutual
affinity are marginal.** Though it is unusually
conspicuous in some experimental forms of
delayed-type allergy, carrier specificity is not
unique to this manifestation of the immune
response.

Delayed-Type Responses to Small
Molecules: Contact Skin Sensitivity

In this allergic disorder sensitization, like
elicitation, is nearly always evoked simply by
contact of the sensitizing agent with the skin.
The capacity to respond to a percutaneous
application of sensitizer (i.e., on the skin surface) is called **contact skin sensitivity;** and

the allergic response to such an exposure,
whether from a test or from accidental contact, is called **allergic contact dermatitis** (Fig.
17-13).

Induction. Contact skin sensitivity is induced either by percutaneous application or
by intradermal injection of the sensitizer.
Only one means is available for by-passing
the skin: injection of the sensitizer in complete Freund's adjuvant into deeper tissues.
As noted before, it has been suggested that
skin lipids might exert an adjuvant effect
comparable to the mycoside of *M. tuberculosis* (p. 539).

Elicitation. Beginning 4 to 5 days after the
sensitizing exposure application of a dilute
solution of the sensitizer almost anywhere on
the skin surface elicits a delayed inflammatory
response.

Time-course. After a lag of ca. 10 to 12 hours erythema and swelling appear and increase to a maximum at ca. 24 to 48 hours. Recovery is slow.

The capacity of simple substances to evoke allergic skin reactions is consistent with the rule that immunogens are usually macromolecules, especially proteins (Ch. 15), for only those simple substances that form covalent derivatives of proteins in vivo are effective. Since sensitizers usually react indiscriminately with most proteins, and thus are potential irritants, they must be used at low concentrations in eliciting responses, to avoid provoking nonspecific inflammation. The maximal nonirritant concentration is determined by testing nonsensitized individuals. With many potent sensitizers 0.01 M solutions are suitable.

Adoptive Transfer. As with other forms of delayed-type allergy, contact skin sensitivity is transferable by viable lymphoid cells, especially those from lymph nodes that drain sites where the inducer had been injected. Serum and purified antibodies are not effective.

Reactions with Protein in Vivo. In accord with the general requirements for immunogenic activity (Ch. 15), the simple substances that evoke contact responses do not appear themselves to be the actual immunogenic agents. Instead, it is necessary that they form covalent derivatives of tissue proteins in vivo, and the protein conjugates are immunogenic. Thus, among a group of 2,4-dinitrobenzenes, those with -F, -Cl, -Br, and SO_3H on C-1 are active, while those with -H, -CH_3, and -NH_2 are not; only the members of the first group form dinitrophenyl proteins in vivo (as well as in vitro).*

Specificity. Contact skin reactions are more highly specific than serological reactions (Fig. 17-13). For example, guinea pigs sensitized with 2,4,6-trinitrochlorobenzene (picryl chloride) react intensely to this substance but do not react to 2,4-dinitrochlorobenzene (DNCB). In addition, these responses seem to exhibit carrier specificity. Thus contact sensitivity to picryl chloride can be induced by injecting guinea pigs with trinitrophenyl (TNP) conjugates prepared from guinea pig skin or plasma proteins but not with the corresponding conjugates prepared from proteins foreign to the guinea pig. Evidently it is necessary in the skin test with picryl chloride that this allergen form the same TNP-conjugates in vivo as those which had induced the sensitized state. The essential nonhaptenic residues have not been identified, because it has not yet been possible specifically to inhibit contact responses with chemically characterized substances, such as picryl peptides.

Coexistence of Contact and Immediate-Type Sensitivity. The coexistence in one individual of immediate-type and delayed-type hypersensitivity for the same determinant is readily demonstrated in individuals with contact skin sensitivity. Consider a guinea pig that has been injected intradermally with 2,4-dinitrochlorobenzene (DNCB): 1 to 2 weeks later a drop of DNCB on its skin elicits a response, which is clearly specific for the 2,4-dinitrophenyl group because 2,4,6-trinitrochlorobenzene elicits little if any response and 2,6-dinitrochlorobenzene elicits none at all. At the same time the guinea pig may exhibit systemic (or cutaneous) anaphylaxis if injected intravenously (or intradermally) with 2,4-dinitrophenyl- (DNP) protein, and these responses are also DNP-specific since they are specifically inhibited by univalent DNP ligands. Hence the animal possesses both immediate- and delayed-type hypersensitivity directed to determinants with a common structural element—the DNP group. However, as noted in the preceding section, the determinants of the delayed-type response also involve additional residues of the carrier proteins, with which the sensitizers conjugate in vivo.

---

* As noted elsewhere, certain macromolecules, such as denatured nucleic acids, become immunogenic on forming extremely stable **noncovalent** complexes with proteins (Ch. 15). Because of their small size, however, the simple inducers of contact sensitivity can form only few noncovalent bonds per molecule. Thus they probably cannot form sufficiently stable noncovalent complexes, and the formation of covalent derivatives is obligatory.

Tolerance has been established by tube-feeding guinea pigs with large amounts of picryl chloride, particular care being taken to avoid contamination of the animal's skin surface. Animals so treated cannot be subsequently induced to develop contact skin sensitivity to the picryl group, at least for a prolonged period; in addition, they do not form antibodies or exhibit immediate-type sensitivity for the picryl group.

Persistence. Once established in guinea pigs or humans, contact skin sensitivity probably persists for years, though it tends to wane. A patch test carried out to evaluate its persistence can serve as an effective stimulus, which boosts the level of sensitivity. The unusually long persistence of sensitivity in some cases may be related to the absence of enzymes that modify or degrade many of the exotic substances that establish contact skin sensitivity.

Mechanisms in Delayed-Type Hypersensitivity

The properties of the several forms of delayed-type allergy described above are summarized and compared with immediate-type allergy in Table 17-5. The units that determine the specificity of delayed-type responses are generally thought to be "sensitized" lymphocytes or macrophages whose specific interaction with antigenic determinants somehow leads to the localized accumulation of non-specific inflammatory mononuclear cells, and, in extreme reactions, to tissue necrosis. Briefly stated, the evidence for this view is 1) the

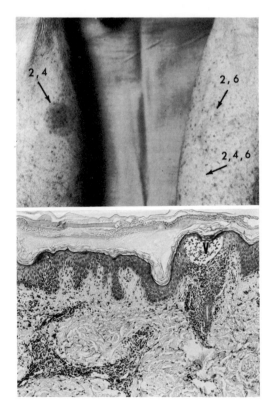

Fig. 17-13 Allergic contact dermatitis in man. The subject was sensitized by exposure to 2,4-dinitrofluorobenzene (DNFB) and then tested with 2,4 dinitrochlorobenzene (2,4), 2,6-dinitrochlorobenzene (2,6), and 2,4,6-trinitrochlorobenzene (2,4,6). The positive response was evident at 24 hours and photographed at 72 hours. The specificity of this delayed-type response is shown by the strong reaction to 2,4-dinitrochlorobenzene, and the absence of a reaction to the 2,6 and to the 2,4,6 analogs. DNFB and all the Cl-substituted analogs form dinitrophenyl (or trinitrophenyl) derivatives of skin proteins in vivo. Histology of the reaction in human skin is shown below. Note the characteristic intraepidermal vesicle (V) and the dense infiltration of parts of dermis and epidermis by lymphoid cells.

TABLE 17-5.   COMPARISON OF IMMEDIATE-TYPE AND DELAYED-TYPE ALLERGY

Property	Immediate-type	Delayed-type
Responses specified and mediated by	Antibodies	? "Sensitized" lymphocytes and macrophages; ? a special class of high-affinity antibodies
Procedures for inducing the allergic state	As varied as those for inducing antibody formation	Favored by small doses of immunogen (few μg), especially in inflammatory foci (e.g., in infected lesions, or with Freund's complete adjuvant)
Passive transfer with serum	Yes*	No
Adoptive transfer with viable lymphoid cells	Probably yes	Yes*
Inhibited by antihistamine drugs	Anaphylaxis, yes Arthus, no	No
Inhibited by cortisone	No (unless prolonged use of high doses inhibits antibody formation)	Yes
In vitro cytotoxic effects	No (except for degranulation of mast cells)	Yes (lymphoid cells)
Inducers	Any immunogen	Virtually any immunogen; polysaccharides seem relatively inactive
Specificity	Cross-reactions common; carrier specificity only occasionally evident	Cross-reactions relatively restricted; carrier specificity conspicuous

These transfers are sometimes unsuccessful because serum antibody levels are too low, or because of technical difficulties in handling the cells. Extracts of human white blood cells transfer delayed-type allergy only in man (see Transfer-factor).

regularity with which lymphoid cells transfer delayed allergy, 2) the consistent failure of serum to do so, 3) the frequent lack of detectable antibodies in serum of individuals with intense delayed allergy, and 4) the cytotoxic effect of the allergen in vitro on lymphoid cells from those with delayed-type allergy, but not on cells from those with immediate-type allergy or with vigorous antibody production.*

Many features of delayed-type allergy, however, are shared with antibody-mediated responses. For example:

1) The induction period is commonly 4 to 5 days, about the same as for the appearance of antibodies in the primary response to many immunogens.

2) The incorporation of an immunogen into Freund's adjuvant enhances its capacity to induce delayed allergy, as well as antibody formation.

3) Substances that induce delayed allergy are practically as numerous and chemically diversified as those that induce antibody formation: virtually all proteins; many natural and synthetic polypeptides; and a host of small molecules, provided they are covalently linked to proteins. (Polysaccharides as a class, however, appear less competent for inducing delayed hypersensitivity than antibody formation.)

4) Populations of lymphoid cells transfer both delayed-type allergy and the capacity to form antibodies. A dichotomy is apparent, however, because plasma cells are particularly

*In addition, the profusion of lymphoid cells in the inflammatory lesions of delayed allergy has long been regarded as evidence for the central role of "sensitized" cells. Similar infiltrations, however, are seen in a wide variety of subacute and chronic nonallergic inflammatory reactions.

active in the formation and secretion of antibodies, but do not seem to be involved in delayed-type allergy.

5) Self-tolerance is just as apparent in delayed-type hypersensitivity as in antibody formation. And when large amounts of a foreign antigen specifically induce tolerance to that antigen, induction of both delayed-type allergy and antibody formation is blocked.

6) The capacities to form antibodies and to develop delayed-type allergy appear to have had a parallel evolutionary development, for they seem to have the same phylogenetic distribution: both are absent in invertebrates and in the hagfish, one of the most primitive vertebrates, but are present in higher vertebrates, from the lamprey eel up.

Antibody formation thus provides an impressive model for speculation about the possible molecular mechanisms responsible for delayed-type allergy. In addition, no substances other than proteins are known to exhibit the exacting and varied specificity displayed by these responses, making it difficult to escape the notion that the delayed-type reaction is mediated by an antibody or an antibody-like protein, whose formation is induced by the sensitizer. The hypotheses proposed thus fall into two groups, involving 1) **antibodies** or 2) **antibody-like molecules** that are part of the surface membrane of sensitized lymphoid cells.

Antibody Models. Several variants of the first hypothesis have been suggested. Though antibodies are often not detected in the serum of those with delayed-type allergy, one model suggests that serum antibodies are present below the level of detectability (usually ca. 0.01 μg/ml) and mediate directly the delayed response. At such low concentrations the antibodies could build up a critical mass of specific complexes with the administered antigen if the antibodies 1) had exceedingly high affinity for the corresponding ligand, and 2) were synthesized continuously, so as to maintain the steady-state concentration of free antibody. The requirement for continued antibody synthesis is consistent with the effectiveness of viable lymphoid cells, but not serum, in trans-ferring sensitivity. And the requirement for high affinity provides an explanation for two features of delayed responses: 1) the tendency of the antigenic determinants to be larger than those involved in serological reactions and in immediate-type allergy, and 2) the inability of delayed hypersensitivity to be evoked with most polysaccharides (whose specific interactions with antibodies are characterized by relatively low intrinsic association constants; Ch. 13). In addition, low levels of immunogens favor the formation of high-affinity antibodies (Ch. 15), which is consistent with the unusual effectiveness of small doses of sensitizer in inducing delayed-type hypersensitivity.

In a second variant, a special class of serum antibodies is postulated to have high affinity for the surface membrane of macrophages and lymphocytes. These **"cytophilic"** antibodies would thus be analogous to the "cytotropic" antibodies that bind to the surface membrane of mast cells and mediate anaphylactic responses (p. 527). And in a third variant of the antibody model it is postulated that in eliciting a delayed response the test antigen actually stimulates lymphoid cells in its immediate vicinity to form and secrete minute amounts of antibody that interact locally, thereby accounting for the slow evolution of inflammation and the effectiveness of cells, but not serum, in transferring delayed hypersensitivity.

Cellular Model. In the alternative hypothesis, cells are postulated to be specifically sensitized by forming antibody-like molecules that are somehow incorporated into their surface membranes, rather than being secreted and then adsorbed from without. There is some evidence that lymphoid cells from sensitized individuals can specifically bind antigens. However, this effect is not consistently related to delayed-type hypersensitivity, and the cells may conceivably have adsorbed the antibody molecules from serum. This model has long been attractive, because it implies that some as yet unrecognized type of molecule determines the specificity of a ubiquitous class of immune reactions. Moreover, since the response to an immunogen may involve, in different stages, different cellular responses and the formation of different classes of antibodies (Ch. 15), many investigators have been intrigued by the notion that at one end of this range is a class of cells whose antibodies never leave the cell, thus providing a primitive,

slow response to a subsequent antigenic challenge.

The molecular and cellular basis for delayed-type hypersensitivity is thus largely an unsolved problem; and its role in resistance to infections is also much debated.

ALLERGY TO DRUGS

A survey of hypersensitivity would be incomplete without mention of drug allergy, particularly since penicillins and other antimicrobial drugs are currently among the more common causes of allergy in man. Most of the principles involved are those noted or implied in earlier sections.

Since drugs are small molecules it appears that in functioning as sensitizers they must, like the inducers of contact skin sensitivity, form stable, covalent derivatives of proteins in vivo (p. 544). Once these conjugates are formed they can induce antibody formation and virtually any type of hypersensitivity.

Most drugs in wide use do not introduce

haptenic groups into proteins under physiological conditions; if they did, they would be too toxic to be useful. If, however, the rate of reaction with protein is sufficiently slow a drug may be tolerably nontoxic, and yet may substitute enough active groups into protein to become an effective inducer. For most drugs that cause allergic reactions, however, it is more reasonable to assume that reactive contaminants, or reactive metabolic derivatives formed in vivo, are responsible for the formation of protein conjugates. The mechanisms involved are well illustrated in the allergic responses to penicillins, which have been analyzed in considerable detail.*

AUTOALLERGY

It has become clear, from clinical observations and from experimentation in animals, that immune responses are occasionally induced to one's own antigens (i.e., self-antigens): the law of self-tolerance as originally formulated is thus not absolute, and a substantial number of exceptions have been carefully studied. While these reactions are now receiving increasing attention their importance in disease is still difficult to estimate.

It is useful to distinguish several aspects of the phenomenon. 1) An **autoimmune response** is that condition in which an individual forms demonstrable antibodies to a self-antigen, or exhibits an allergic reaction on being tested with it. 2) An **autoimmune disease** refers to the overt pathological effects

caused by an autoimmune response. 3) Since self-tolerance is apparently characteristic only of those self-antigens that normally have access to immunologically competent cells (Ch. 15), some autoimmune responses may result from an **altered distribution of a self-antigen, rather than from a failure of the mechanisms responsible for self-tolerance.** For example, auotsensitivity to antigens of the central nervous system, or to those of the thyroid, does not necessarily indicate impairment of the mechanism responsible for tolerance of self-antigens. These antigens, and some others to

---

* A discussion of mechanisms in penicillin allergy is given in Chapter 17 of the parent volume—"Microbiology," Hoeber Medical Division, Harper & Row, New York, 1967.

which autoallergy can be established (e.g., lens and uvea of eye, spermatozoa), are normally blocked anatomically from interacting with immunologically responsive cells. The primary event leading to induction of the autoimmune response would thus seem to be some process, such as infection or trauma, that allows these antigens to make contact with lymphoid cells. In addition, the response may well be self-perpetuating: once the autoimmune response is initiated, allergic inflammation in the target organ may lead to penetration by immunologically competent (inflammatory) cells and to further interaction with the antigen, causing further induction of the hypersensitive state.

True Abrogation of Self-Tolerance. In contrast, autoimmune responses to freely circulating antigens, such as those on the surface of red cells and platelets, do imply a breakdown in self-tolerance. The mechanisms involved are not established. Some possibilities, however, are suggested by the ways in which artificially established tolerance to foreign antigens can be terminated (Ch. 15). For example, high levels of antigen usually seem necessary for the maintenance of tolerance. Hence if a particular self-antigen were no longer synthesized tolerance to it would be expected to decline, and the gradual reappearance of the antigen might then stimulate an immune response.

Delayed-Type Versus Immediate-Type Allergy in Autoimmune Disease. Some of the spontaneously occurring autoallergies are clearly mediated by serum antibodies (e.g., those involving breakdown of red cells and platelets). In contrast, many others, especially those produced experimentally, appear to involve delayed-type allergy. This is not surprising with the experimental diseases, because they are usually produced by injecting animals with small amounts of tissue antigens in Freund's adjuvant, which favors the induction of delayed-type allergy.

Considerable stress has been placed on the ineffectiveness of serum antibodies in transferring many experimental autoimmune disorders. This finding, however, could be due to the heterogeneity of antibodies, which is possibly just as pronounced with antibodies to self-antigens as it is with those to foreign antigens (Chs. 13 and 14); self-antigens, unlike foreign antigens, are likely to be consistently present and therefore to be unusually effective in removing autoantibodies with highest affinity for them. The circulating, free autoantibody molecules might thus be those with least physiological activity. Like the peak of an iceberg they could perhaps be easily detectable indicators of their concealed, more menacing congeners.

Pathological Consequences of Autoantibodies and Autoallergy

When autoantibodies were first discussed, at the turn of the century, they were imagined to occur either not at all or with disastrous consequences. However, as these antibodies became identified in subsequent decades they came to be regarded as rare, but not necessarily catastrophic. Now, with the development of increasingly sensitive and reliable assays for antibodies and for hypersensitivity, it has come to be appreciated that autoimmune responses are actually quite common, especially in certain connective tissue diseases, such as disseminated lupus erythematosus. Usually, however, their pathological effects remain conjectural, with three possibilities to be considered. 1) The autoimmune response can be innocuous. For example, though the anti-cardiolipin (i.e., Wassermann) antibodies in a person with syphilis can react with cardiolipin extracted from his own tissues, they do not appear to be pathogenic: they may be present at high titer in healthy persons, after recovery from active syphilis. Presumably cardiolipin is buried within membranes and is thus inaccessible to antibodies. 2) The response can be secondary to another disease (e.g., anti-thyroglobulin antibodies following the trauma of partial thyroidectomy); but it may then be responsible for continuing disease, as has been suggested for the chronic hepatitis that sometimes follows viral hepatitis, or the demyelinating encephalitis that may follow a viral encephalitis. 3) The response can be the main causal factor in disease, e.g., as in acquired hemolytic anemia or idiopathic thrombocytopenic purpura.

The spectrum of allergic effects is so wide —from hemolysis to demyelinating inflammatory lesions—that autoimmune processes are now commonly invoked to account for many diseases of unknown etiology; and a search for autoantibodies or autoallergy frequently yields positive results. However the significance of such findings is not self-evident. In an effort to provide guidelines, Witebsky has suggested some criteria, reminiscent of Koch's postulates for the proposed bacterial etiology of a disease. In effect, Witebsky's criteria are as follows: an autoimmune response should be considered as the cause of a human disease if 1) it is regularly associated with that disease; 2) immunization of an experimental animal with the antigen from the appropriate tissue causes it to make an immune response (form antibodies or develop allergy); 3) associated with this response the animal develops pathological changes that are basically similar to those of the human disease; and 4) the experimental disease can be transferred to a nonimmunized animal by serum or by lymphoid cells.

CODA

In this chapter we have seen that the immune response, like many other biological adaptations, can also have a wide variety of pathogenic effects. Though nearly 70 years have elapsed since these reactions first came into prominence, progress toward understanding their molecular basis has been slow. They are still usually defined rather vaguely as intensified responses to substances, specifically induced by prior exposure. Nevertheless, progress has been almost sufficient to justify an explicit definition of allergic reactions as **structural and functional aberrations in animal cells and tissues caused by antigen-antibody complexes.** Even now, however, this simple statement is not quite warranted because in delayed-type hypersensitivity it is still not clear whether antibodies or antibody-like components of lymphoid cells are involved.

Allergic responses are highly varied with respect to several factors: the types of immunoglobulin molecules that can participate, the requirements for complement, and the ancillary cells that are involved, such as mast cells in anaphylaxis and granulocytes in the Arthus reaction; in the delayed-type responses lymphocytes and macrophages are involved, perhaps as carriers of immunological specificity.

Allergic reactions to microbial antigens probably occur commonly in the course of most infectious diseases. It seems likely that the inflammatory changes with which they are associated favor host defenses by mobilizing leucocytes and macrophages, as well as serum antibodies and complement, at the site of the reaction. Sometimes, however, these responses seem harmful to the host, as when severe inflammatory reactions to the tubercle bacillus facilitate the spread of infection in certain tissues. Nevertheless, the total effect of allergic responses is probably favorable, which would account for the evolutionary persistence of allergic reactivity, along with antibody formation, throughout the vertebrate kingdom.

Currently, the allergic reactions that attract most attention are directed not to microbial agents but to two other groups: environmental allergens (such as pollens), and self-antigens (such as red cells and thyroglobulin) in the so-called autoimmune diseases. In addition, allergic reactions to synthetic chemicals, including drugs, are becoming increasingly conspicuous as these substances become more commonplace in man's environment.

And some of the best studied allergic responses arise from other highly artificial situations in which blood is transfused, or organs are transplanted, from one individual to another. These responses to foreign cells are sufficiently complex to merit special attention, and they are therefore considered in the next chapter.

SELECTED REFERENCES

Books and Review Articles

AUSTIN, K. F., and HUMPHREY, J. H. In vitro studies of the mechanisms of anaphylaxis. *Advances Immunol.* 3:1 (1963).

BECKER, E. L., and AUSTEN, K. F. Anaphylaxis. In *Immunopathology*. (H. Mueller-Eberhard and P. Miescher, eds.) Little, Brown, Boston, 1967. In press.

Cellular and Humoral Aspects of the Hypersensitive States. (H. S. Lawrence, ed.) Hoeber, New York, 1959.

CHASE, M. W. Delayed hypersensitivity. *Med. Clin. N. Amer.* 49:1013 (1965).

GELL, P. G. H., and BENACERRAF, B. Delayed hypersensitivity to simple protein antigens. *Advances Immunol.* 1:319 (1961).

Immunological Diseases. (M. Samter, ed.) Little, Brown, Boston, 1965.

KUNKEL, H. G., and TAN, E. M. Autoantibodies and disease. *Advances Immunol.* 4:351 (1964).

LEVINE, B. B. Immunochemical mechanisms of drug allergy. *Ann. Rev. Med.* 17:23 (1966).

Mechanisms of Hypersensitivity. Henry Ford Hospital Symposium. (J. H. Shaffer, G. A. LoGrippo, and M. W. Chase, eds.) Little, Brown, Boston, 1959.

OVARY, Z. Passive Cutaneous Anaphylaxis. In *Immunological Methods*. (J. F. Ackroyd, ed.) Davis, Philadelphia.

PATTERSON, P. T. Experimental allergic encephalomyelitis and autoimmune disease. *Advances Immunol.* 5:131 (1966).

UHR, J. W. Delayed hypersensitivity. *Physiol. Rev.* 46:359 (1966).

Specific Articles

BOREK, F., and SILVERSTEIN, A. Specificity of guinea pig antibodies and delayed hypersensitivity. *Nature* 205:299 (1965).

BROCKELHURST, W. E. Pharmacological Mediators of Hypersensitivity Reactions. In *Clinical Aspcts of Immunology*. (P. G. H. Gell and R. R. A. Coombs, eds.) Davis, Philadelphia, 1962.

DIXON, F. J. The role of antigen–antibody complexes in disease. *Harvey Lect.* 58:21 (1963).

LAWRENCE, H. S. Some Biological and Immunological Properties of Transfer Factor. In *Cellular Aspjects of Immunity*. Ciba Foundation Symposium. (G. E. W. Wolstenholme and M. O'Connor, eds.) Little, Brown, Boston, 1960.

LICHTENSTEIN, L. M., and OSLER, A. G. Histamine release from human leucocytes by ragweed pollen antigen. *J. Exp. Med.* 120:507 (1964).

KAPLAN, M. H. Induction of auto-immunity to heart in rheumatic fever by streptococcal antigen(s) cross-reactive with heart. *Fed. Proc.* 24:109 (1965).

OVARY, Z., BENACERRAF, B., and BLOCH, K. J. Properties of guinea pig 7S antibodies. II. Identification of antibodies involved in passive cutaneous anaphylaxis and systemic anaphylaxis. *J. Exp. Med.* 117:951 (1963).

WHITE, R. G., JENKINS, G. C., and WILKINSON, P. C. The production of skin sensitizing antibody in the guinea pig. *Int. Arch. Allergy* 22:156 (1963).

WITEBSKY, E., ROSE, N. R., TERPLAN, K., PAINE, J. R., and EGAN, R. W. Chronic thyroiditis and autoimmunization. *J.A.M.A.* 164:1439 (1957).

18 MAMMALIAN ISOANTIGENS: BLOOD GROUP SUBSTANCES AND TRANSPLANTATION ANTIGENS

This chapter deals with the immunology of two groups of antigens: blood group substances on red cells, which are of practical importance in the transfusion of blood, and transplantation antigens on diverse cells, which are responsible for the reactions that limit the survival of transplanted organs and tissues. Immunological concepts and technics have made important contributions in both areas, and they, in turn, have contributed, experimentally and conceptually, to our insight into the immune response.

The blood group and transplantation antigens are **isoantigens,** which may be defined as **those antigens that segregate within a species,** i.e., are present in some individuals and absent in others. They are identified operationally as those substances which, when derived from certain individuals, are immunogenic in some members of the same species, but not in the donor.

Isoantigens were first recognized, in erythrocytes, over 60 years ago (see below). Isoantigens of nucleated cells were similarly long believed to exist, but have only more recently been shown to account for the general observation that tissues transplanted from one individual to another are ultimately rejected, unless donor and recipient are genetically identical (**syngeneic,** see p. 567). Though isoantigens were thought for many years to be peculiar to cells, several soluble proteins have recently also been recognized as isoantigens (e.g., haptoglobins, transferrins, and some β-lipoproteins). As we have seen with the immunoglobulins (Ch. 14), their isoantigens, known as allotypes, have been exploited to great advantage in establishing the multichain structure of these molecules.

BLOOD GROUP SUBSTANCES

The ABO System

Beginning with Harvey's discovery of the circulation of the blood in the seventeenth century, repeated attempts were made to transfuse blood from one individual to another. Disastrous reactions in the recipients were so frequent, however, that this procedure was abandoned until the basis for the failure was established in 1900, when Landsteiner discovered the isoantigens of human red blood cells.

Stimulated by the observation, in the 1890s, that closely related animal species could be distinguished by the reactions of their red cells and serum proteins with specific antisera, Landsteiner sought to determine whether individuals of the **same species** could be distinguished in the same way. In the course of his initial study individual samples of serum and erythrocytes from

22 human subjects were mixed in all possible combinations, and the red cells of some persons were found to be clumped by the sera of certain other individuals. On the basis of these reactions the subjects were classified into three groups, A, B, and O; and within 1 year a less common fourth group, AB, was also recognized (Table 18-1).

TABLE 18-1. DIVISION OF HUMAN POPULATIONS INTO FOUR BLOOD GROUPS ON THE BASIS OF RED CELL AGGLUTINATION BY NORMAL HUMAN SERA

Serum from group:	Red cells from group:			
	A	B	O	AB
A	0	+	0	+
B	+	0	0	+
O	+	+	0	+
AB	0	0	0	0

+ = clumping; 0 = no clumping.

The conclusions drawn by Landsteiner were as follows: 1) two different isoantigens or blood group substances, A and B, are associated with human red cells, and one, both, or neither may be present in any given individual's cells; 2) antibodies for these isoantigens (often called **isoantibodies**) are regularly present in the sera of those individuals who lack the corresponding isoantigen, and never present in the sera of those who possess it. These observations were extended and confirmed in vast numbers of humans, and they contributed greatly to the early acceptance of the doctrine of self-tolerance (Chs. 15 and 17).

The **blood groups** or types in the population are named for these red cell isoantigens: group A has the A isoantigen, group B has the B isoantigen, group O has neither, and in group AB **each** red cell has both A and B. The corresponding serum isoantibodies are anti-A in group B persons and anti-B in group A; group O has both anti-A and anti-B, while group AB has neither.

When anti-A sera are adsorbed with cells from certain A persons (A_2), making up about 20% of the A population, they lose their ability to clump these cells but retain their ability to clump A cells from the remaining 80% (A_1). On the other hand, adsorption of these sera with A_1 cells abolishes their capacity to agglutinate all A cells. Thus there are two kinds of A antigens: A_1 adsorbs anti-A antibodies completely, and A_2 adsorbs only some of these antibodies. Correspondingly, there are two types of AB cells: A_1B and A_2B.

Genetic Determination of the Isoantigens

Family studies established clearly the heritability of blood cell isoantigens. Analysis of data from large populations led Bernstein to propose that there are three allelic genes, A, B, and O, with A and B being dominant over O. Since man is diploid, the two alleles per individual provide the six genotypes and four phenotypes shown in Table 18-2.

TABLE 18-2. GENOTYPES AND PHENOTYPES IN THE ABO BLOOD GROUP SYSTEM

Genotype	Phenotype
AA	A
AO	
BB	B
BO	
OO	O
AB	AB

Since each allele has the same probability of being inherited, the Bernstein theory accounts for the distribution of blood groups within families. For example, of the children of an O and an AB parent (OO $\times$ AB) approximately 50% are A (genotype **AO**) and 50% are B (genotype **BO**); none are AB or O. The large number of families examined are consistent with the foregoing scheme; the small proportion of inconsistent results (less than 1%) are reasonably ascribed to illegitimacy, technical errors in typing, or possibly mutations.

H-Antigen. Though the A gene controls the formation of the A substance, and the B gene the B substance, the O gene is an "amorph," i.e., it does not specify a particular red cell isoantigen. Nevertheless, O cells have a distinctive antigen which has been recognized from the agglutination of these cells by some normal animal sera (from eels and cattle), by certain antisera (goat anti-shigella), and by some plant proteins (extracted from the seeds of *Ulex europeus*). Moreover, this antigen (as well as the A and the B isoantigens) is lacking in the red cells of certain rare humans, first recognized in Bombay; and such Bombay-type individuals can form antibodies in high titer to the characteristic antigen of O cells, either spontaneously or in response to injections of O cells. The O-cell antigen is present not only in man, but also in a variety of other species; i.e., it is **hetero-**

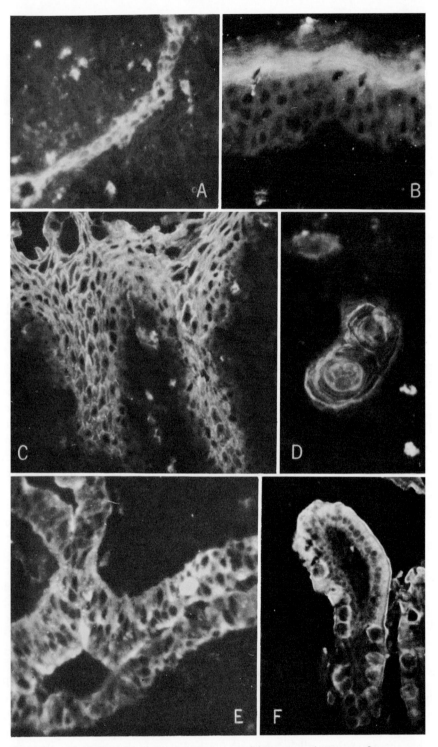

Fig. 18-1 Localization of A and B isoantigens in human tissue by immunofluorescence. The A substance is shown in lymph node (**A**), epidermis (concentrated in stratum corneum) (**B**), Hassal's corpuscle of the thymus (**D**), and the goblet cells of a villus in the small intestine (**F**). The B substance is shown in squamous epithelium of the tongue (**C**) and in transitional epithelium of renal calyces (**E**). (From A. E. Szulman. J. Exp. Med. 111:789, 1960.)

genetic;* it is therefore called **H substance.** This antigen cannot, however, be considered the product of the O gene since it is also detectable, with anti-H sera, on the red cells of persons who **lack** the O gene, such as A₂B or homozygous A₂ individuals.

As we shall see below from the chemical properties of the A, B, and H substances, there are good reasons for believing that 1) the gene for H substance (H gene) is independent of the ABO allelic genes, and 2) the H substance provides an essential macromolecular precursor to which the A and B antigenic groups are attached. Hence **in O individuals the H substance is exposed and fully expressed.** Partial expression in red cells of other types is revealed by reaction with monospecific anti-H sera, the order of reactivity being O $>>$ A₂ $>$ A₂B $>$ B; the sera react weakly with some A₁ and A₁B cells, and, as noted above, not at all with Bombay-type. In Bombay-type persons a mutation in the H gene has apparently led to the absence of H substance, and thereby of A and B determinants as well (see below).

Distribution of the Isoantigens in the Body: Secretors

The A, B, and H substances are not confined to red cells, but are widely though unevenly distributed in various tissues. They are present as **surface components** of many human epithelial cells and virtually all endothelial cells, but are lacking in connective tissue and muscle cells (Fig. 18-1). Their isolation and characterization has been aided immensely by their presence in water-soluble

---

* An antigen is called heterogenetic when it is formed by a variety of phylogenetically unrelated species. The best known examples are the **Forssman** antigens, one of which is of clinical importance in the diagnosis of infectious mononucleosis. These antigens, defined by their ability to induce rabbits to form hemolytic antibodies to sheep red blood cells (sheep hemolysins), are found in many animal and some bacterial species, e.g., in tissues of guinea pig, horse, cat, and chicken, but not rat or rabbit. The anti-Forssman antibodies, sometimes called **heterophile antibodies,** are of two types, differing in their ability to distinguish human A and AB from O and B cells.

form in many secretions, e.g., saliva, gastric mucin, ovarian cyst fluid, meconium, pancreatic secretions, and sweat. About 75% of all persons are **secretors;** they contain abundant quantities of A, B, or H substances in saliva, depending on their blood type.†

Lewis Factors. Before considering the chemical structure of the A, B, and H antigens, it is necessary to call attention to a set of closely related blood group substances, the **Lewis a and b factors** (Leᵃ and Leᵇ). These antigens are thought to be specified by one of a pair of allelic genes, **Le** and **le,** that segregate from the ABO genes. The Leᵃ antigen is specified by the Le gene, whereas the Leᵇ antigenic activity (which was once thought to be controlled by the allele le) is accounted for by the combined presence of the Leᵃ and H determinants (Fig. 18-3).

The 25% of humans who are **nonsecretors** (i.e., of A, B, and H) usually have Leᵃ substance in saliva. In about 1% of the nonsecretors, however, the saliva lacks even Leᵃ, and has in its place a polysaccharide that cross-reacts extensively with the capsular polysaccharide of pneumococcus type 14. These seemingly disconnected observations have been integrated into a scheme, outlined below, which has been proposed by Morgan, Watkins, Ceppellini, and others for correlating the chemistry and the genetics of the ABO and Le blood group substances.

Chemistry of the A, B, H, and Le Isoantigens

In the purification and characterization of blood group substances particular attention has been devoted to those that are water-soluble and abundantly available in mucinous secretions. Serologically they are indistinguishable from those that are firmly attached to red cell membranes (and therefore very difficult to isolate in quantity); the few

---

† This secretion is controlled by a pair of allelic genes, called **Se** and **se.** In the absence of Se (i.e., in persons homozygous for se) the A, B, and H substances are not detectably changed on the red cell, but they do not appear in the saliva.

known differences do not appear relevant for antigenic specificity.* The following description applies to substances isolated from secretions (e.g., ovarian cyst fluid). The assays used in their purification and in structural analyses are based on the ability of these substances, and some of their fragments, to inhibit specifically the corresponding isoantibodies, e.g., in agglutinating red cells or precipitating the soluble blood group substances.

Molecular Weight and Composition. Purified substances with A, B, H, and Le[a] activity are large mucopeptides (M.W. 200,000 to 1,000,000) and remarkably alike in over-all composition. By weight they are 85% carbohydrate and 15% peptide, the two moieties being covalently linked. Five sugars account for the carbohydrate content: L-fucose (i.e., 6-deoxy-L-galactose), D-galactose, N-acetyl-D-glucosamine, N-acetyl-D-galactosamine, and N-acetylneuraminic (sialic) acid. (The sialic acid is present in variable amount and does not appear to contribute to the immunological activity.) In the peptide moiety 15 L-amino acids have been identified. From enzymatic and chemical degradation it appears that the polypeptide constitutes the backbone, from which project many oligosaccharide branches that terminate in nonreducing sugars.

In individuals whose saliva contains both A and B substances (type AB) precipitation of A activity with anti-A serum (from rabbits) also precipitates all the B activity, and vice versa. Similarly, when H activity is present with A or with B the precipitation of one activity with a monospecific antiserum precipitates all the others. Thus, these diverse antigenic structures are present on the **same** macromolecule.

Degradation Products. The various mucopeptides not only are alike in amino acid and sugar composition, but they all also yield on partial degradation (enzymatic or by mild acid hydrolysis) nondialyzable polysaccharides that show increased cross-reactivity.

For example, by stepwise enzymatic degradation of sugars from the nonreducing ends of branches it is possible to remove some determinant groups and to expose others that were previously detected only feebly or not at all. Thus, when purified A substance is digested with a crude enzyme preparation from certain clostridia the A activity is lost, and H activity appears or increases. Similarly, when purified B substance is digested with an enzyme from *Trichomonas foetus,* or with an α-glucosidase from coffee, the B activity is lost and H activity appears. Furthermore, when the H-active mucopeptides derived from these procedures (or isolated directly from O individuals) are treated with still another crude enzyme preparation, the H-substance activity disappears, and the capacity to react with antibodies to the Le[a] determinant and with antibodies to type 14 pneumococcal polysaccharide, appears. Finally, with further degradation Le[a] activity is lost and only the cross-reaction with type 14 pneumococcal polysaccharide remains (Fig. 18-2).

Structure and Biosynthesis of the Antigenic Determinants. The foregoing relations have led to the view that the blood group macromolecule of the ABO and Lewis systems is

---

* For example, peptides are absent in the blood group substances isolated from red cell membranes, but present in those isolated from saliva.

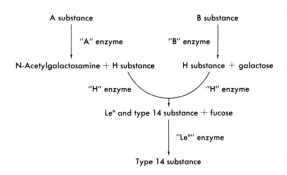

Fig. 18-2 Antigenic determinants of blood group mucopeptides revealed by sequential enzymatic removal of terminal sugar residues from A and B substances. (From W. M. Watkins. Science 152:172, 1966.)

Fig. 18-3 Suggested structures for the precursor carbohydrate chains in A, B, O, and Lewis blood group substances. The residues are specified by the H and Le genes. Gal=D-galactose; GNAc=N-acetyl-D-glucosamine; GalNAc=N-acetyl-D-galactosamine; Fuc=L-fucose. (Based on W. M. Watkins. Tenth Congress of International Society of Blood Transfusions, Stockholm, 1964.)

The type II chain has just been found to contain another fucosyl residue, linked 1⟶3 to GNAc. It is not known if the additional fucose is specified by Le or an as yet unidentified gene.

Carbohydrate Chains in Precursor Substance

Type I β-Gal-(1→3)-β-GNAc-(1→3)-β-Gal-(1→3)-GalNAc . . .

Type II β-Gal-(1→4)-β-GNAc-(1→3)-β-Gal-(1→3)-GalNAc . . .

Additions to Nonreducing Ends of Precursors

Gene	Chain	Structure at nonreducing end	Antigenic specificity
—	I	β-Gal-(1→3)-GNAc . . .	—
	II	β-Gal-(1→4)-GNAc . . .	Type 14 pneumococcus polysaccharide
H	I	β-Gal-(1→3)-GNAc . . . ↑α1,2 Fuc	H
	II	β-Gal-(1→4)-GNAc . . . ↑α1,2 Fuc	H
Le	I	β-Gal-(1→3)-GNAc . . . ↑α1,4 Fuc	Le^a
	II	β-Gal-(1→4)-GNAc . . .	Type 14 pneumococcus
H and Le	I	β-Gal-(1→3)-GNAc . . . ↑α1,2 ↑α1,4 Fuc Fuc	Le^b
	II	β-Gal-(1→4)-GNAc . . . ↑α1,2 Fuc	H

built from a single large mucopeptide, on which the various antigenic determinants of the Le^a, H, A, and B characters are added sequentially under the aegis of enzymes specified by the corresponding genes. As each determinant is added it introduces a new specificity, which replaces the previous one.

There are two types of carbohydrate chains (I and II) common to all A, B, H, and Le blood group substances (Fig. 18-3); they are the precursors to whose nonreducing ends the various sugar determinants are added. The chains differ only in that in type I the terminal D-galactose residue is linked 1 → 3 to N-acetylglucosamine; in type II the linkage is 1 → 4. The type II chain cross-reacts more strongly than the type I chain with antibody to type 14 pneumococcal polysaccharide.

Under the influence of the H gene an L-fucose residue is added (in α-linkage) to the C-2 posi-

tion of the terminal galactose, forming the H determinant (Fig. 18-3). The expression of the H gene in the salivary mucopolysaccharide is apparently controlled by another gene, called Se (for secretor). When the H gene is inactive, the Le^a determinant is formed under the influence of the Le gene by adding, via α-linkage, a fucose residue to the C-4 position of the penultimate N-acetylglucosamine group of the type I chain. However, the type II chain is also present, and it cannot be similarly substituted because the C-4 position is already occupied. Hence substances with Le^a activity also show extensive cross-reactivity with antibody to type 14 pneumococcal polysaccharide (Fig. 18-3). If, however, both H and Le genes are active it has been suggested that two fucosyl residues are attached to type I chains and one fucosyl residue to type II chains, forming, as is shown in Figure 18-3, a blood group substance with both Le^b and H antigenic activity.

The A and B genes can function, if present,

Gene	Structure at nonreducing ends of chains	Antigenic specificity
O	β-Gal-(1→3 or 1→4)-GNAc... ↑α1,2 Fuc	H
A	α-GalNAc-(1→3)-β-Gal-(1→3 or 1→4)-GNAc... ↑α1,2 Fuc	A
B	α-Gal-(1→3)-β-Gal-(1→3 or 1→4)-GNAc... ↑α1,2 Fuc	B

Fig. 18-4 The H-active chains and the residues specified by the A and B genes. For abbreviations and source see Figure 18-3. The crucial difference between the A and B isoantigenic determinants (underlined) is due to the N-acetyl galactosamine residue in A, and the galactose residue in B.

only if the H determinant has already been formed. The A gene leads to addition of a terminal N-acetylgalactosamine residue, and the B gene to addition of a galactose residue instead (Fig. 18-4). Thus the immunological difference between the A and B determinants, of vast clinical importance for blood transfusions, is influenced in a crucial way by the small structural difference in the terminal sugar residues of these huge and complex blood group mucopeptides. However, from the reactivity of various oligosaccharides with anti-A and anti-B antibodies it appears that the A and B determinants are at least as large as the terminal trisaccharides shown in Figure 18-4.

It may be supposed that the blood group genes specify a variety of hexose transfer enzymes. In the Bombay-type blood described above the absence of the α-fucosyl residues of the H determinant—due, presumably, to a defective H gene—prevents the addition of the characteristic terminal residue of the A or the B determinants. The O gene apparently produces an inactive enzyme for these additions, or perhaps none at all.

From the foregoing description it appears reasonable to hypothesize that both allelic (A, B) and nonallelic (H, Le) genes cooperate in effecting the sequential addition of different sugar determinants on a complex heteropolymer. The whole process resembles the complex interaction of genes that determine the numerous different specificities of the cell wall antigens (O polysaccharides) in the salmonellae (Ch. 20).

Origin of the AB Isoantibodies

The isoantigens and the accompanying isoantibodies were long thought, because of their strict correlation, to be determined by a single gene: for example, the A gene would control the formation of both the A isoantigen and the anti-B isoantibodies in individuals with type A blood. From our current vantage point, of course, it seems naive to consider that a single gene might control the synthesis of **both** an oligosaccharide determinant and an immunoglobulin of a particular specificity. Nevertheless, the origin of the isoantibodies remains an unsolved question.

The most plausible explanation is based on the wide distribution of polysaccharides having A- and B-like characteristics in various bacteria and plants. It seems likely that the corresponding "natural" antibodies (Ch. 12) arise from inconspicuous immunogenic stimulation provided by these exogenous substances, whether in intestinal flora, ingested food, or inapparent infection. Because of self-tolerance (Ch. 15), an individual would form only those natural antibodies that are specific for the isoantigens he lacks; for example, a person of type A forms anti-B isoantibodies, but not anti-A.

Evolution. It has been suggested that severe infectious diseases have served as selective agents in the evolution of blood group substances. Thus, if the A-like substance present in egg-grown vaccinia virus contributed to the virion's infectivity, persons of groups B or O, possessing anti-A antibodies, would be more resistant to smallpox than those of groups A or AB, and have a greater chance of surviving and reproducing. This could account, for example, for the relatively high incidence of group B persons in India, where smallpox is recurrent (Table 18-3). The same idea could also account for the relatively low incidence of group O in India, since plague is also endemic in that country and *Pasteurella pestis* is said to possess an H-like antigen. However, the A-like substance in vaccinia virus preparations has been shown to be a contaminant of the chick embryo tissue in which the virus is cultivated, and anti-A antibodies do not neutralize the virus' infectivity. Moreover, the frequency of different blood groups among persons with smallpox, and the severity of the disease among patients of different blood groups, provide little support for the view that groups B and O offer an advantage over groups A and AB. Nevertheless, the notion that the evolution of differences in distribution of ABO blood types among various ethnic groups (Table 18-3) has been influenced by past epidemic diseases remains an attractive suggestion.

Types of Immunoglobulin. Natural anti-A and anti-B antibodies are predominantly 19S immunoglobulins in persons of groups B and A, but they are both 19S and 7S immunoglobulins in those of group O. The antibodies formed in response to intensive antigenic stimulation by injections of A and B substance are largely γG immunoglobulins.*

Other Red Cell Isoantigens

The discovery of the ABO system was facilitated by the fortunate presence of anti-A and anti-B isoantibodies in most normal human sera. Since then many other red cell isoantigens have been recognized, but different means were required for their detection, because the corresponding natural isoantibodies are not found in normal human sera. One approach was through the use of skillfully adsorbed animal antisera to human red cells. Another, which has been especially fruitful, is provided by the accidental finding of diverse antibodies in 1) persons who have received multiple blood transfusions, and 2) women who have had multiple pregnancies. The latter situation arises because a fetus may inherit from the father isoantigens that are absent in its mother; such an antigen, arising early in embryonic life, can stimulate maternal antibody formation, provided it enters the maternal circulation. These several approaches are illustrated with the blood group systems described below.

MNSs Blood Groups

MN Antigens. About 25 years after the ABO system was recognized Landsteiner and Levine found that occasional rabbit antisera to human blood would, after adsorption with red cells from certain persons, agglutinate many but not all human erythrocytes, regardless of their ABO type. The adsorbed antisera were thus specific for an additional red cell isoantigen, which they called M. When the

TABLE 18-3. FREQUENCY OF ABO BLOOD TYPES
IN VARIOUS ETHNIC GROUPS

Population	Phenotypes (%)			
	O	A	B	AB
Scotland (Stornoway)	50	32	15	3
Sweden (Uppsala)	37	48	10	6
Switzerland (Berne)	40	47	9	4
Pakistan (N.W. frontier province)	25	33	36	5
India (Hindus in Bombay)	32	29	28	11
United States (Chippewa Indians)	88	12	0	0
Eskimos (Hudson Bay)	54	43	1.5	1.5

Based on A. E. Mourant. The Distribution of the Human Blood Groups. Thomas, Springfield, Ill., 1954.

---

* Purified A and B substances are sometimes injected deliberately to raise the antibody titer, as in the preparation of typing sera (p. 565). In addition, A and B are also sometimes injected inadvertently in mismatched blood transfusions, or in bacterial vaccines that contain A- and B-like substances, either as part of the bacterial cells or (more often) as contaminants of the culture media.

rabbit antisera subsequently evoked with various samples of M-positive cells were adsorbed with M cells from certain persons, the expected loss of agglutinating activity was often observed, but some adsorbed sera were still able to react strongly and selectively with still other red cells, regardless of ABO type; the latter antisera must therefore have contained antibodies for still another red cell isoantigen, which was called N.

All human red cells react with either anti-M or anti-N sera, or with both. From the distribution of the M and N antigens in many human families, it has become clear that these antigens are governed by a pair of allelic genes that segregate from the ABO locus. Irrespective of an individual's ABO type, his cells will also have M or N, or both. The MN alleles are codominant, and so genotypes MM, NN, and MN correspond to phenotypes M, N, and MN.

By a similar approach, adsorbing rabbit antisera to human blood with red cells from different individuals, Landsteiner and Levine subsequently recognized another independent system, the **P group** of red cell isoantigens, for which several allelic forms (P_1, P_2, p) have been found at a locus that segregates both from MN and from ABO.

Ss Antigens. Some years after the MN system was described a human serum (from a woman who had formed antibodies to her fetus' red cells) was found to agglutinate the red cells of many persons, but the reactions did not correspond with antisera to the then known isoantigens. The new isoantigen thus detected was called S; and an allelic form, called s, was subsequently discovered. The Ss antigens are of particular interest because they illustrate in a simple manner **genetic linkage** to other isoantigens—a relation which is of considerable interest with the Rh factors, discussed below. Thus the S antigen was found more frequently on M and MN than on N cells, but its distribution was unrelated to the ABO or other isoantigens. Crossing over between MN and Ss loci must be very rare;

otherwise genetic equilibrium would have led the S antigen (and the s) to be as frequently associated with M as with N (see footnote of Table 18-4).

The observed association of S with M and N suggested that S might represent a mutation in M, and less frequently in N, that added a determinant but left the original antigens still reactive. However, Race and Sanger preferred the view that the S gene was separate from, but closely linked to, the MN locus. If so, they predicted, an allele for S, called s, might become identifiable if an anti-s serum could be found. A few such human sera were subsequently found: i.e., these sera agglutinated all cells (presumably ss) that were not clumped by anti-S. In addition, many human cells were clumped by both anti-S and anti-s: i.e., the Ss antigens behave as though governed by a pair of allelic, codominant genes.

Linkage of Ss to MN was demonstrated by family studies. For example, the child of homozygous MS and Ns parents (MMSS × NNss) would be MNSs, but he would contribute to each of his offspring **either** the MS **or** the Ns genes, as though they were inseparable.

Rh Factors

The discovery of the Rh factors provides a striking example of the significance of maternal isoantibodies to fetal red cells. In 1939 Levine and Stetson reported a case in which a mother gave birth to a baby with a hemolytic disease, called **erythroblastosis fetalis,** and then suffered a serious transfusion reaction upon receiving blood from her husband. Both parents had the same ABO blood type, but further study showed that the mother's serum agglutinated the husband's red cells and also those of 80% of other persons. Fortunately, just at the time of these observations Landsteiner and Wiener reported that rabbit and guinea pig antisera to *Rhesus* monkey red cells clumped the red cells of approximately 85% of individuals (Rh^+) in New York City, but not those of the remaining 15% (Rh^-). It was soon demonstrated that in Levine and Stetson's case these anti-Rhesus sera clumped the father's cells, but not the mother's; and the mother's serum also contained anti-Rh antibodies, much like those of the animal anti-Rh sera. In similar cases studied subsequently the erythroblastotic babies born to such parents (Rh⁻ mother × Rh⁺ father) were also Rh-positive. Evidently, then, a baby's red cells, carrying a paternal antigen foreign to the mother, can cross the placenta and immunize the mother; and her isoantibodies can then enter the fetal circulation and react with the baby's red cells, causing massive clumping and hemolysis and erythroblastosis fetalis.

Multiplicity of Rh Antigens. The study of many other cases of fetal-maternal incompatibility soon provided many additional maternal antisera, which revealed several different, novel red cell isoantigens. When the patterns of transmission were studied in many human families four of these antigens were found to be specified by very closely linked genes. Hence, though these genetically related antigens are serologically distinctive, and do not all react with anti-Rh serum, they are said to make up the "Rh group."

Two of the four antisera were then recognized by R. A. Fisher, the noted English geneticist, to be **antithetical,** i.e., any red cell sample that failed to react with one of these antisera always reacted with the other, and vice versa. It was proposed, therefore, that the corresponding antigens are specified by a pair of allelic genes, called C and c: virtually everyone's red cells react with anti-C, or with anti-c, or with both, depending on whether his genotype is CC, cc, or Cc. The remaining two types of antisera were not so related, and their antigens were called D and E.

Fisher was thus led to postulate that the Rh locus consists of three allelic pairs of closely linked genes, Cc, Dd, and Ee, and he predicted the eventual discovery of the two other antisera, anti-d and anti-e, required to identify the missing antigens and alleles. Anti-e, identified by its antithetical relation to anti-E, was indeed found shortly afterward, but no unambiguous anti-d has yet been found.

However, as antisera from the mothers of erythroblastotic babies became more numerous they disclosed an increasing variety of heritable antigenic determinants genetically linked to, or part of, the Rh locus. The Fisher scheme has therefore been contested, especially by Wiener, who prefers to regard all the genes that specify the Rh antigens as being allelic, each allele governing a single large antigenic structure that encompasses multiple smaller antigenic determinants.

Whether or not the Fisher scheme is valid, it has provided an extremely useful and relatively simple approach for systematizing a mass of serological and genetic data. This information has been especially difficult to interpret because it is not yet supported by chemical characterization of the kind available with the ABO isoantigens.

Blood Typing

The identification of red cell isoantigens, called **blood typing** or **grouping,** is required for blood transfusions. In addition, it is commonly used for genetic analysis in cases of disputed paternity, and for anthropological surveys of human populations. Blood typing has even been used in archeological work, since the red cell antigens are extraordinarily stable: they have apparently been identified (by inhibition of specific agglutination reactions) in Egyptian mummies thousands of years old.*

Blood typing is performed by agglutination reactions, unknown red cells being typed with known antisera and unknown isoantibodies with red cells of known type. The C'-fixation test is not used, not only because it is so much more laborious than the agglutination assay, but because red cells coated by isoantibodies to most isoantigens are not lysed by comple-

---

* Blood typing and other serological procedures are widely used in **forensic medicine:** to distinguish human from animal blood; to identify human blood types in blood stains, semen, or saliva; to distinguish horse meat from beef; etc.

ment. The failure to lyse might be due to a peculiar distribution of most isoantigens on the red cell surface, or to the possibility that most of the blood group isoantibodies are types of immunoglobulin that do not react with complement (Ch. 16).

Uniqueness of the Individual's Red Cell Isoantigens. So many different blood group

isoantigens have now been identified (at least 60) that no two individuals are likely to be found with identical combinations, except for monozygotic twins.

In the face of this extreme diversity one might well wonder that blood transfusions are ever successful. In fact, they **are** extraordinarily successful, even when recipients un-

TABLE 18-4. INCIDENCE OF SOME RED BLOOD CELL PHENOTYPES IN THE UNITED STATES*

Blood group system	Phenotype	Frequency (%)	
ABO	O	44	
	A (A_1 + A_2)	42	
	B	10	
	AB (A_1B + A_2B)	4	
MN	M	27	
	N	24	
	MN	50	
Ss†	S	11	
	s	45	
	Ss	44	
P	P_1	80	
	P_2	14	
	p	rare	
Rh‡	DCe (Rh_1, R_1)	54	⎫
	DCE (Rh_z, R_z)	15	⎬ 85% react with anti-D
	DcE (Rh_2, R_2)	14	⎬ (= "Rh-positive")
	Dce (Rh_0, R_0)	2	⎭
	dce (rh, r)	13	⎫
	dCe (rh', R')	1.5	⎬ 15% do not react with anti-D
	dcE (rh", R")	0.5	⎬ (= "Rh-negative")
	dCE (rh_y, R_y)	rare	⎭
Lutheran	Lu^a	6	
	Lu^b	94	
Kell	K^+	6	
	K^-	94	
Lewis	Le^a	22	
	Le^b	78	
Duffy	Fy^a	38	
	Fy^b	28	
Kidd	Jk^a	83	
	Jk^b	17	

 * *Based on* Zinsser's Microbiology, *13th ed. (D. T. Smith, N. F. Conant, and J. R. Overman, eds.) Appleton, New York, 1964.*
 † *The incidence of S, s, and Ss is from R. Race and R. Sanger.* Blood Groups in Man, *2nd ed. Blackwell, Oxford, 1954. Anti-S sera agglutinate 73% of M, 54% of MN, and 32% of N cells.*
 ‡ *From P. Levine, M. Stroup, and W. Pollack. In* Bacterial and Mycotic Infections of Man, *3rd ed. (R. J. Dubos, ed.) Lippincott, Philadelphia, 1958.*

dergo multiple transfusions from many different donors. Aside from the care exercised in the selection of prospective donors, through scrupulous typing procedures, the infrequency of transfusion reactions appears to be ascribable to the fortunate fact that **most red cell isoantigens are only feebly immunogenic.** Moreover, transfused red cells survive for only a limited time (an average of perhaps about 3 to 4 weeks), so that even

if antibody formation should be stimulated in the recipient the transfused cells are likely to be few in number by the time his isoantibodies reach an effective level; the clumping or hemolysis of a small number of cells is not likely to be serious. As we shall see below, however, the Immunological Gods are not quite so benevolent in the immune response to the isoantigens of transplanted tissues.

TRANSPLANTATION IMMUNITY: THE ALLOGRAFT REACTION

It seems appropriate to close the chapters on the immune response with a discussion of the transplantation of tissues. The immunological mechanisms underlying these reactions are difficult to decipher because of the complexity of the materials involved; but the possibility of effectively suppressing these reactions offers hope that organ transplantation may become as feasible in the future as blood transfusions are at present. Hence transplantation reactions are among the most challenging problems in immunology today.

Definitions

Four terms are used to describe tissue grafts.

1) **Autografts** are transplants from one region to another of the same individual.

2) **Isografts** are transplants from one individual to a genetically identical individual. These are possible only between monozygotic twins or between members of certain lines of mice and other rodents that have been so highly inbred (by brother-sister matings) as to be **syngeneic** or **isogenic,** i.e., genetically identical.†

3) **Homografts** or **allografts** are transplants from one individual to a genetically noniden-

tical (i.e., **allogeneic**) individual of the same species.

4) **Heterografts** or **xenografts** (Gr. *xenos,* "foreign") are transplants from one species to another.

In these four types of grafts the donors are designated respectively as autologous, isologous, homologous, or heterologous with respect to the recipient.

Unfortunately the prefix **iso** in red cell immunology (as in "isoantigen") is tantamount to **homo** in transplantation, both referring to genetically different individuals of the same species; whereas **iso** in transplantation refers to genetically identical individuals. The confusion is somewhat mitigated by the recent tendency to use allograft (emphasizing the difference of antigen), rather than homograft (emphasizing the sameness of species), for the third of the above four groups.

The Allograft Reaction as an
Immune Response

Among vertebrates autografts and isografts are usually enduring, but allografts (and heterografts) are regularly rejected.* In investigating the mechanisms of the allograft reaction skin grafts have been used most extensively, because of technical advantages: they are easy to prepare, and their acceptance or rejection is easily observed and evaluated.

---

† **Syngeneic** in the transplantation field refers operationally to the absence of any discernible tissue incompatibility, i.e., to genetic identity with respect to the genes controlling these antigens. It is a special case of the classic genetic concept of **isogenic** individuals, who are identical with respect to all their genes.

---

* Allografts are regularly accepted by invertebrates, which do not display any of the known immune responses (see Ch. 15).

However, the same principles are clearly involved in grafts of other tissues and cells.

The Second-Set Reaction

The immune nature of the transplanation reaction is suggested by the following observations. When an allograft of skin is placed on a recipient animal, in a bed created by excising a piece of skin of about the same size, the graft at first becomes vascularized and appears to flourish; but after about 10 days or 2 weeks, or sometimes even longer, it quite abruptly becomes the seat of intense inflammation, withers, and is sloughed. If a second graft is then made to the same recipient, with another piece of skin from the same donor, it is rejected much more rapidly than the first graft, perhaps in 5 to 6 days. This accelerated rejection, the **"second-set" reaction,** is specific for the particular donor: if after the accelerated rejection another donor, antigenically unrelated to the first, provides skin grafts to the same recipient, first- and second-set reactions to successive grafts are again seen. Thus, the capacity to reject an allograft **(transplantation immunity)** is **acquired** by virtue of exposure to the donors tissue; and it is **specific** for transplantation antigens (histocompatibility antigens) in that donor. The shorter survival of the second graft results from persistence of the immunity acquired from the first graft or, perhaps, from an anamnestic response.

The second-set reaction to a skin graft can be induced not only by a prior skin graft, but just as well by prior inoculation of various other cells from the same donor, e.g., spleen cells. In fact, virtually all cells suffice to induce transplantation immunity except erythrocytes, which apparently lack the critical isoantigens, at least in effective form.

Transfer of Allograft Immunity

Adoptive Transfer. Not only is the second-set reaction acquired and specific but, like other immune responses, it can be transferred from an immunized donor to a nonimmune recipient. The transfer is regularly accomplished with viable **lymphoid cells.** Thus if an A-strain mouse is immunized with a graft from a B-strain mouse, and viable lymphoid cells from the immune A animal are inoculated into a nonimmunized A mouse, the latter then responds as does the donor, giving a second-set reaction specifically to a B graft.

The sensitivity (or immunity, the words often being used interchangeably) acquired from inoculation with the viable lymphoid cells from a sensitized donor has been called "adoptive" immunity, to distinguish it from active and passive immunity. Thus, in active immunity the individuals own cells respond to an antigenic stimulus; with passive immunity he is the recipient of antibody molecules that were synthesized in another individual; but with adoptive immunity he harbors another individual's lymphoid cells and they, rather than his own cells, respond to the immunogenic stimulus. The duration of adoptive immunity depends on the persistence of the transferred cells and their progeny. When donor and recipient are syngeneic persistence can be enduring; when they are allogeneic the adoptive immunity is terminated early by an allograft reaction to the donor's lymphoid cells.

Antisera have only rarely, if ever, transferred the ability to give a second-set reaction; but some antisera from highly immunized donors can interfere specifically with the healing-in process of a fresh graft, such as skin, and cause what appears to be unusually rapid rejection (the so-called "white-graft" reaction). However, grafted suspensions of allogeneic lymphoid cells are readily destroyed in animals that are passively sensitized with antisera (see below for the regular susceptibility of normal and neoplastic lymphoid cells to the cytotoxic action of isoantibodies plus complement).

Delayed- vs. Immediate-type Allergy

The rejection of an allograft is generally considered to be an expression of delayed-type hypersensitivity. This belief is based upon 1) the effectiveness of lymphoid cells in transferring the capacity for accelerated rejection,

2) the usual ineffectiveness of serum, and 3) the histology of the inflammatory lesion.* In addition, in some species, such as the guinea pig, lymphoid cells from a sensitized animal can elicit a delayed cutaneous reaction if injected into the skin of the animal to whose tissues it is sensitive. An animal that has rejected a skin allograft will often also have circulating antibodies for various cellular iso-antigens of the donor; but these antibodies usually appear late and their levels do not bear a consistent relation to the intensity or rapidity of the graft rejection.†

Nevertheless, there are also clear indications that some allograft reactions are mediated by serum antibodies. For example, lymphocytes can be destroyed in vitro and in vivo by serum of allogeneic individuals previously sensitized to these cells, and complement is required for the reaction in vitro. Moreover, as noted above, high-titer serum from some allograft-sensitized animals can occasionally cause the white-graft reaction to skin allografts. Broadly speaking, therefore, it appears that rejection of an allograft, like allergic reactions to most antigens, can be a manifestation of either immediate- or delayed-type hypersensitivity (Ch. 17).

Tolerance of Allografts

Under a number of exceptional circumstances allografts are not rejected.

Privileged Sites. There are a few special ("privileged") sites where allografts may flourish for prolonged periods without inducing immunity, such as the meninges of the brain and the anterior chamber of the eye. Lymphatic drainage is lacking in these sites; hence stimulation of immunologically competent cells of lymphatic tissue is minimal.

Pregnancy. Transplantation antigens are formed early in embryonic life, and many of these antigens, inherited from the father, are alien to the mother. Hence in man and other mammals the intrauterine fetus is actually an allograft. Its success is probably explained by the absence or masking of transplantation antigens in the special fetal cell layer (trophoblast) at the placental interface between the embryo and its maternal host.

Induction of Immunological Tolerance. The induction of immunity to allografts has dose-response features that resemble those of immune responses in general, but they are not readily quantitated. With respect to threshold levels, the frequent success of corneal transplants in man (which are routinely allografts) may be due in part to the small amount of tissue transplanted, but probably depends largely on the relative avascularity of the transplantation site. At the other extreme, large doses of allogeneic cells can establish tolerance to allografts, especially when introduced around the time of birth (see below).

Current interest in immunological tolerance in general may be fairly said to have begun with experiments on allograft tolerance, which grew out of certain curious observations on red cell isoantigens in cattle twins. Heritable blood groups are found in cattle, just as in man and many other species. With nonidentical twin calves, however, Owen observed in 1945 that each individual often had two kinds of red cells, as different antigenically as, say, A and B red cells of man; and these mixtures persisted as the twins grew to maturity. Since nonidentical cattle twins frequently have anastomoses of their placental blood vessels, and therefore a common circulation in utero, it was inferred that hematopoietic stem cells from each twin had settled in the marrow of the other during intrauterine life and then survived in the genetically foreign soil, producing through the animal's lifetime a type of red cell that was, properly speaking, its twin's. In addition, each twin produced red cells with its own characteristic isoantigens. Such individuals, with mixtures of genetically different cells, are called **chi-**

---

*The site of an allograft undergoing rejection is intensely infiltrated with lymphocytes and histiocytes; granulocytes and plasma cells are much less conspicuous.

† These serum antibodies give easily visible reactions with red cells and lymphoid cells of the donor, and adsorption studies have shown that these antibodies can also react with almost all cells of the donor.

meras, after the monster in Greek mythology with a lion's head, a goat's body, and a serpent's tail.

Surmising that such twins might also be generally tolerant of each other's tissues, Billingham and Medawar then demonstrated that they accepted skin grafts from each other without an allograft reaction. By taking advantage of the fact that mice of a given isogeneic strain are exact genetic replicas, it was subsequently shown, in a series of elegant experiments, that mice of one strain (A) could be rendered permanently tolerant of skin allografts from a genetically alien strain (CBA) if **embryonic or newborn** A mice were inoculated with viable cells (e.g., of spleen) from CBA animals. When the inoculated animals matured they accepted allografts permanently from CBA donors, though they rejected grafts from any other strain in a perfectly normal manner.

The newborn appears to develop allograft tolerance with ease because its immune apparatus is relatively immature, and it therefore cannot reject the foreign cells by an allograft reaction. Once established, the tolerance persists because the foreign cells continue to proliferate and to maintain a sufficient level of the tolerated transplantation antigens. An individual rendered tolerant in this manner is, therefore, a chimera, carrying the genetically alien cells in advance of the allograft that reveals his tolerance.* Since tolerance of allografts depends on an adequate level of foreign transplantation antigens (i.e., allogeneic cells) it seems to be fundamentally the same as the tolerance that can be established to "inanimate" antigens, such as globular proteins and polysaccharides (Ch. 15).

The immunological balance in the chimera can be readily tipped, and the tolerance abrogated, by introducing immunologically competent cells that recognize the tolerated tissue

as genetically alien. Thus when a mouse of strain A, rendered tolerant as a newborn to tissues of strain B, carries a successful and enduring B graft, the graft can be made to undergo prompt rejection by inoculating the tolerant host with viable lymphoid cells from another strain A animal that had previously been immunized against B (Fig. 18-5). The rejection can also be elicited by inoculating the tolerant A animal with lymphoid cells from a normal, **nonimmune** animal of strain A, but the effect requires more cells and takes longer to develop.

Adult animals have also been rendered tolerant of allografts by inoculation of viable cells from prospective donors, but special measures are required: the adult is first converted temporarily to a state of immunological incompetence, resembling that of the newborn period, by intensive X-irradiation or treatment with cytotoxic drugs (Ch. 15), and multiple injections of the allogeneic cells are then usually given.

The ease with which tolerance is established, especially in an adult animal, depends on whether "weak" or "strong" transplantation antigens are involved in a particular donor-recipient pair. Tolerance is readily established to the weak antigens, and a single dose of allogeneic cells may be sufficient (see below, for example, the weak isoantigens associated with the male Y chromosome).

Histocompatibility Genes

The evidence that transplantation immunity is based upon the genetic makeup of donor and recipient is reenforced by experience with hybrids of certain highly inbred strains of mice. The latter are homozygous at virtually all genetic loci. If a mouse of one such strain (AA) is mated to a mouse of another (BB), the F₁ hybrid (AB) will accept homografts from **either** parent, whereas each parent will reject grafts from the F₁ offspring: since the F₁ animal carries the antigenic markers of both parents it is tolerant of them,

---

* The chimerism can be demonstrated by using spleen or white blood cells from such a tolerant animal (A strain tolerant of CBA) as immunogens to induce in other mice allograft sensitivity to **both** A and CBA.

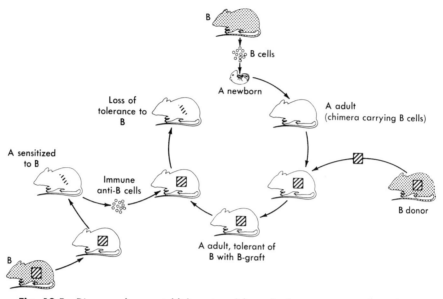

Fig. 18-5 Diagram shows establishment and loss of tolerance to transplantation antigens. Newborn A was injected with B cells. A subsequent injection of the tolerant A animal (shown carrying a B skin graft) with lymphoid cells from a B-sensitive A donor leads to adoptive immunity, with rejection of the previously tolerated graft.

but each parent can react to the alien determinants in the hybrid.

The antigens that determine the response to transplantation are governed by **histocompatibility (H) genes.** In inbred strains of mice and rats at least 14 independently segregating genetic loci for transplantation (histocompatibility) isoantigens, located in separate linkage groups, have been recognized.* At each of these loci there also seem to be multiple alleles: for example, at the locus that specifies the immunogenically most potent determinants in the mouse, the H-2 locus, 18 alleles appear so far to have been identified. Others undoubtedly exist. Hence in rodents the number and variety of transplanation antigens are huge, and they are doubtless at least as extensive in man. The number of

different combinations of these isoantigens is astronomical, which accounts for the **uniqueness of individuals** with respect to their transplantation antigens. These isoantigens vary considerably in immunogenic potency, however, and many are quite weak.

The sensitivity of the allograft response to small genetic differences is quite remarkable. Within an isogenic strain, for example, skin transplanted from a female donor to a male recipient is tolerated permanently, but the reciprocal transplant, from male to female, is eventually rejected. Similar nonreciprocity is observed with grafts of spleen, thymus, thyroid, and parathyroid. Male tolerance of female cells results from the presence of X chromosomes in both sexes, but products of the male Y chromosome are evidently recognized as foreign by the female recipient. Transplantation antigens associated with the Y chromosome are weak; tolerance of them is readily established, by, for example, simply transplanting an extra large piece of skin from a male to an otherwise isogenic female.

Transplantation antigens are as yet only poorly characterized chemically, but their accessibility to reactions with antibody (or with "sensitized"

---

* The minimum number of histocompatibility genes that differ in two inbred strains is determined by crossing them and mating their F_1 progeny to yield F_2 progeny. Animals of the F_2 generation are then used as recipients of grafts from the inbred parental strains, and the number of different histocompatibility genes, n, is determined from the proportion of grafts accepted, x, through the relation: $x = (3/4)^n$.

lymphocytes, if these should be the vectors of delayed-type hypersensitivity), and their reactivity with fluorescent antibodies, indicate that they are localized at the cell surface. Moreover, preliminary observations with butanol and detergent extracts of cells suggest that the transplanation antigens are associated with lipoproteins of cytoplasmic membranes.

Graft-vs.-host reaction

In establishing tolerance by injecting a newborn animal with viable allogeneic cells the inoculum is most conveniently prepared as a suspension of lymphoid cells from spleen or lymph nodes. When these cells are derived from an adult animal they are, of course, immunologically competent. They may therefore react with the isoantigens of the neonatal host.

Though such reactions were not observed in the donor-recipient strains used in the original discovery of induced tolerance to allografts, they have since been observed with other allogeneic donor-recipient pairs. In these reactions the inoculated newborn animal fails to gain weight normally, develops skin lesions and diarrhea, and dies after a few weeks. This symptom complex is known as the **runting syndrome** or the **graft-vs.-host reaction.** It has also been seen when immunologically competent cells from allogeneic donors are injected into another kind of unresponsive animal—an adult depleted of lymphoid tissue by X-irradiation or cytotoxic drugs.

SELECTED REFERENCES

Books and Review Articles

AMOS, B. Transplantation antigens in mouse, rat, and man. *Progr. Med. Genet. 3*:106 (1964).

HELLSTROM, K. E., and MOLLER, G. Immunological and immunogenetic aspects of tumor transplantation. *Progr. Allerg. 9*:158 (1965).

KABAT, E. A. *Blood Group Substances: Their Chemistry and Immunochemistry.* Academic Press, New York, 1956.

MEDAWAR, P. B. The immunology of transplantation. *Harvey Lect. 52*:144 (1956–57).

MEDAWAR, P. B. *The Uniqueness of the Individual.* Basic Books, New York, 1958.

MORGAN, W. T. J. Croonian lecture: A contribution to human biochemical genetics: The chemical basis of blood group specificity. *Proc. Roy. Soc., S.B. 151*:308 (1960).

RACE, R. R., and SANGER, R. *Blood Groups in Man.* Thomas, Springfield, Ill., 1962.

WATKINS, W. M. Blood-group substances. *Science 152*:172 (1966).

Specific Articles

BILLINGHAM, R. L., BRENT, L., and MEDAWAR, P. B. Quantitative studies on tissue transplantation immunity. III. Actively acquired tolerance. *Phil. Tr. Roy. Soc., London, S.B. 239*:357 (1956).

LANDSTEINER, K. Cell antigens and individual specificity. *J. Immunol. 15*:589 (1928).

OWEN, R. D. Immunogenetic consequences of vascular anastomoses between bovine twins. *Science 102*:400 (1945).

SNELL, G. D. Methods for the study of histocompatibility genes and isoantigens. *Meth. Med. Res. 10*:1,8 (1964).

SZULMAN, A. E. The histological distribution of blood group substances in man as determined by immunofluorescence: The A and B antigen. *J. Exp. Med. 111*:789 (1960); The H antigen. *J. Exp. Med. 115*:977 (1962).

19 PATHOGENIC PROPERTIES OF BACTERIA

PATHOGENIC PROPERTIES OF BACTERIA

There are two basic mechanisms by which bacteria cause disease: 1) the **invasion of tissues** and 2) the **production of toxins.** Whereas the invasive process leads to demonstrable damage of host cells only in the immediate vicinity of the invasion, soluble toxins transported by lymph and blood may cause cytotoxic effects at tissue sites remote from the original lesion. Some species of bacteria appear to owe their pathogenicity to invasiveness alone (*Diplococcus pneumoniae*), while others are almost solely toxigenic* (*Clostridium tetani*). Many species are clearly invasive and toxigenic (*Streptococcus pyogenes*).

Rarely, however, are invasiveness and toxigenicity completely separable since invasiveness may involve factors of short-range toxicity, and toxigenicity must require at least some degree of bacterial multiplication in the tissues.† Nevertheless, it is useful to distinguish between the two processes whenever possible in considering the pathogenesis of bacterial diseases.

Invasiveness

Intracellular vs. Extracellular Parasitism

Pathogenic bacteria may be conveniently divided into two additional categories: those that are capable of surviving, and even multiplying, within the phagocytic cells of the host, and those that are promptly destroyed by phagocytes. The factors which lead to ultimate destruction of the former (*Mycobacterium tuberculosis, Brucella abortus, Salmonella typhosa,* etc.) are only partially understood; undoubtedly, they relate to complex metabolic and enzymatic interactions between the ingested bacterium and the cyto-

plasmic environment of the phagocyte. When in proper balance, these interactions permit a state of intracellular parasitism to persist. When out of balance, they lead to destruction of either the parasite or the host cell, or perhaps in certain situations to the death of both. Bacteria that behave as **intracellular parasites** frequently give rise to relatively chronic diseases, such as tuberculosis.

In contrast, those species that are promptly destroyed when phagocytized (*Diplococcus pneumoniae, Klebsiella pneumoniae, Streptococcus pyogenes,* etc.), damage the tissues of the host only so long as they remain outside the phagocytic cells. The manner in which they are disposed of following phagocytosis is now fairly clear.‡ Since their presence in the tissues usually stimulates the production of opsonizing antibodies, which render them susceptible to phagocytosis, the diseases they produce are likely to be acute and of relatively short duration (e.g., pneumococcal pneumonia). In these diseases in which the bacteria behave as **extracellular parasites,** phagocytosis per se is a critical event in the host-parasite relation.

Antiphagocytic Capsules

Pathogenic bacteria that behave as extracellular parasites owe their virulence to **antiphagocytic surface components,** often demonstrable as definite **capsules** (Fig. 19-1A and B). These surface structures, consisting of hydrophilic gels, tend to protect the organisms from being ingested by phagocytic cells. The chemical structures of the capsular gels of a number of bacterial species have been identified. The capsule of type 3 pneumococcus, for example, is composed of a high molecular weight polymer of glucose and glucuronic acid, while that of *Bacillus anthracis* contains a polypeptide of D-glutamic acid. Capsules of some bacteria (e.g., *Bacillus megaterium*) contain both protein and carbohydrate (Fig. 19-1B).

That such capsular structures may indeed interfere with phagocytosis, and thus contribute to virulence, is clearly exemplified by

---

* Synonymous with toxinogenic.

† Toxic products may also be released from damaged cells.

‡ For a discussion of the biology of phagocytes, see Chapter 19 of the parent volume—"Microbiology," Hoeber Medical Division, Harper & Row, New York, 1967.

Diplococcus pneumoniae. If the behavior of a fully encapsulated S (smooth) strain is compared with that of a nonencapsulated R (rough) strain, the former is found to resist phagocytosis (in the absence of antibody) and is highly virulent for mice, whereas the latter is readily phagocytized and is virtually avirulent. Enzymatic removal of the capsular gel, as may be readily accomplished in the case of type 3 pneumococci, likewise renders the organisms both nonpathogenic and susceptible to phagocytosis. Similarly, antibody to the capsular polysaccharide combines specifically with the gel and destroys its antiphagocytic properties. Furthermore, the variations in capsular size that occur during different phases of the growth cycle affect pneumococcal virulence. During the exponential phase of growth, when the rate of polysaccharide synthesis is maximal, the capsules are largest and the organisms most virulent. In the later stationary phase of growth, polysaccharide synthesis slows, the capsules become smaller, and the organisms are less virulent. This difference must obviously be borne in mind when measuring the virulence of a given strain.

In contrast, information concerning the physicochemical forces at the capsule-phagocyte interface that prevent phagocytosis is woefully deficient. Although the cytoplasmic membranes of polymorphonuclear leucocytes are known to be composed primarily of lipoproteins, the chemical groups exposed at their outer surfaces have not been identified. Since some of the surface groups may be of a lipid nature, it has been postulated that they impart to the membrane a hydrophobic character which prevents the pseudopod of the leucocyte from forming a sufficiently intimate contact with the hydrated capsular gel to allow phagocytosis to take place (Fig. 19-1C to F). Conclusive evidence for this hypothesis, however, is lacking. Attempts to relate the antiphagocytic

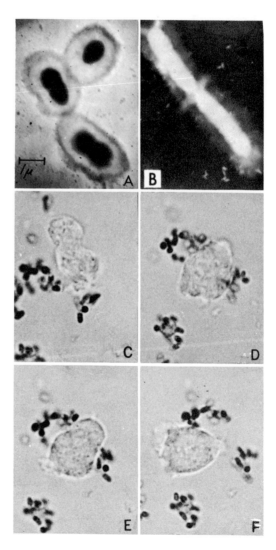

Fig. 19-1 A. Electron micrograph of *D. pneumoniae*, type 1. Capsule has been reacted with type 1 antibody to accentuate its visibility (quellung reaction). × 10,500, enlarged. **B.** Similar photograph of capsule of *B. megaterium* reacted with homologous polysaccharide antiserum. The specific anticarbohydrate antibody increases the visibility of the transverse septa of the capsule, which are composed of polysaccharide, but does not affect the rest of the capsule, which is made up of protein. × 2600, enlarged. **C–F.** Series of photomicrographs taken at 30-second intervals showing failure of granulocyte in hanging drop to phagocytize encapsulated Friedländer's bacilli (*K. pneumoniae*), despite their direct contact with the cell's advancing pseudopod. × 1250, enlarged. (**A** from S. Mudd, F. Heinmets, and T. F. Anderson. *J. Exp. Med.* 78:327, 1943. **B** from G. Baumann and J. Tomcsik. *Schweis. Ztschr. Path. u. Bakt.* 21:906, 1958. **C–F** from M. R. Smith and W. B. Wood, Jr. *J. Exp. Med.* 86:257, 1947.)

effect of the capsule to electrostatic charges have been unsuccessful. An answer to this fundamental question will probably have to await further knowledge of the chemistry of leucocytic membranes.

Adaptation to Microenvironment

Since the surfaces of many potentially invasive bacteria are not antiphagocytic, it is evident that factors other than resistance to phagocytosis must be responsible for their virulence. One property, as yet poorly understood, enables nonencapsulated pathogenic bacteria to resist enzymatic attack in the microenvironment of phagocytic vacuoles. By and large, bacterial species that are easily phagocytized and do **not** possess this property of intracellular survival are noninvasive (e.g., *Staphylococcus albus*); unless toxigenic they are incapable of producing disease. Other species, though readily phagocytized, resist intracellular destruction and are virulent (e.g., *Salmonella typhi*). The biochemical characteristics that enable one bacterial strain and not another to survive phagocytosis are not yet known, though some of the mechanisms involved in the killing of ingested bacteria have been elucidated.*

Invasive strains of bacteria, whether resistant to phagocytosis or not, must also be capable of multiplying in the deeper tissues of the host. Characterization of the biochemical environments provided by the various organs of the body is so fragmentary that little is known of the metabolic properties that enable invasive strains to thrive in certain tissues. It is clearly established, however, that many bacteria are **organotropic** in the sense that they are highly selective in regard to the tissues they invade. For example, both meningococcus (*Neisseria meningitidis*) and pneumococcus (*Diplococcus pneumoniae*) are frequently present in the human

---

*Some strains of pathogenic bacteria that behave essentially as intracellular parasites also form capsules that contribute to their virulence, e.g., *Salmonella typhimurium*, the causative agent of mouse typhoid.

nasopharynx, yet of the two only pneumococcus invades the lower respiratory tract to cause pneumonia. How is this fact explained? Is it due to special metabolic capacities that permit pneumococci to thrive in mucous secretions within the bronchial tree where the pneumonic lesion originates?

A high degree of selectivity is also involved in the habitation of superficial tissues by specific bacteria. Whereas *Neisseria meningitidis* infects only the upper respiratory tract of man, the closely related species, *N. gonorrhoeae*, characteristically invades the genitourinary tract. Similarly, in healthy individuals staphylococci tend to inhabit the skin and the vestibule of the nose, whereas pneumococci are usually confined to the throat.

The phenomenon of bacterial organotropism has been subjected to experimental analysis in a remarkable series of observations made by Buddingh and Goodpasture in chick embryos. When the chorioallantoic membrane of the 15-day-old embryonated egg, for example, is infected with *Bordetella pertussis* (the agent of whooping cough), the microorganisms, in addition to producing a local lesion on the membrane, frequently invade the embryo and eventually localize on the ciliated epithelium of the bronchial mucosa. If they are injected into the amniotic cavity, which provides direct access to the respiratory tract, the same localization results. When, on the other hand, the experiments are performed with 12- or 13-day embryos, in which ciliated cells have not yet appeared in the bronchi, infection of the bronchial epithelium fails to occur. *B. pertussis* appears, therefore, to have a special predilection for the environment provided by ciliated epithelial cells of the bronchi, a fact entirely in keeping with the pathology of whooping cough. Likewise, *Neisseria meningitidis*, which causes acute meningitis in man, localizes in the meningeal tissues of the embryo, and *Streptobacillus moniliformis*, the causative agent of rat-bite fever (a human disease characterized by severe polyarthritis) invades the embryonic joints.

Equally interesting are experimental findings relating to the proliferation of bacteria in the same organ of different hosts. When virulent bovine tubercle bacilli, for example, are injected intravenously (or even intrarenally) into guinea pigs, the kidneys remain free of progressive lesions. In contrast, the kidneys of rabbits treated in the same fashion become riddled with tubercles. It has been suggested that the greater susceptibility of the rabbit kidney to invasion by the tubercle bacilli may be due to the absence of a tuberculocidal polyamine, spermidine, which is present in the renal tissues of the guinea pig.

Finally, in **different parts of the same organ of the same host** the invasiveness of a single strain of bacteria may vary over a wide range. Such differences have been most clearly demonstrated in the rabbit kidney, where the tissues of the medulla are far more susceptible to experimentally induced staphylococcal and *Escherichia coli* diseases than are those of the cortex. A possible explanation for this difference lies in the fact that the inflammatory response in the medullary tissues (probably for anatomical reasons) is definitely slower than in the cortex. The resulting delay in mobilization of phagocytic cells appears to be sufficient to allow the bacteria invading the medulla to establish a firm foothold. Other more subtle factors may also be involved.

Production of Extracellular Enzymes

A number of bacterial species elaborate extracellular enzymes to which their invasive properties* have been attributed. Many grampositive bacteria, for example, produce **hyaluronidase**. Originally referred to as "spreading factor," this enzyme† promotes diffusion through connective tissue by depolymerizing hyaluronic acid in the ground substance. Although it has been assumed to facilitate bacterial invasion, there is no conclusive evidence that it does so. In fact, in experimental *Clostridium perfringens* infections the administration of antihyaluronidase antibodies fails to

influence the spreading of the lesion. Furthermore, in the special case of *Streptococcus pyogenes,* the hyaluronidase released by the growing organism may degrade its hyaluronate capsule and thereby suppress, rather than enhance, its invasiveness.

Equally unconvincing is the evidence concerning the pathogenetic role of staphylococcal coagulases, which clot plasma by a thrombokinase-like action. To these enzymes, which are produced by most virulent strains, there have been attributed two principal effects: 1) the laying down of the fibrin barrier that characteristically surrounds and appears to localize acute staphylococcal lesions and 2) the formation of antiphagocytic fibrin envelopes about the cocci themselves. Since pathogenic non-coagulase-producing strains have been identified, which produce identical tissue lesions and are no more readily phagocytized by leucocytes, it seems unlikely that coagulases per se account either for staphylococcal virulence or for the tendency of staphylococcal lesions to remain relatively circumscribed.

Streptococci and staphylococci also elaborate kinases (streptokinase and staphylokinase) that catalyze the lysis of fibrin. Whether these fibrinolytic enzymes actually influence the invasiveness of the organisms is also uncertain, although it has long been assumed that the relative absence of fibrin in spreading streptococcal lesions may be due to the action of streptokinase.

Evidence is reasonably convincing, on the other hand, that the collagenases of *Clostridium histolyticum* and *C. perfringens,* which break down the collagen framework of muscles (leaving the fibers intact), facilitate extension of the forms of gas gangrene due to these organisms.

Toxigenicity

The idea that bacteria may cause disease by producing toxins was first suggested in 1884 by the classic experiments of Loeffler. Having injected a large number of guinea

---

*Bacterial extracellular enzymes known to be cytotoxic are usually classified as toxins and are discussed in the next section.

† Or group of enzymes.

pigs subcutaneously with diphtheria bacilli, he noted that when they died a few days later, all had widespread systemic lesions in which no bacilli could be found. He concluded that the bacilli growing at the primary site of infection had generated a soluble poison, which became widely disseminated by the blood stream. This conclusion was confirmed 5 years later when injection of bacteria-free filtrates was shown by Roux and Yersin to produce an essentially identical disease. Once the principle of toxigenicity had been established, other species of pathogenic bacteria were found to be toxigenic (Table 19-1).

The diffusible toxins produced by certain gram-positive bacteria (and an occasional gram-negative species) are referred to as **exotoxins,** since they are present in the filtrates of growing cultures in which no appreciable autolysis has occurred. Their concentration in the culture medium often parallels the growth of the organisms. All that have thus far been characterized chemically have been found to be proteins. Toxins of a quite different sort, called **endotoxins,** are produced by many gram-negative bacteria. They are complex lipopolysaccharides of the bacterial cell wall and are released into the surrounding medium only if the organisms become autolyzed or are artificially disrupted by mechanical or chemical means. Endotoxins are generally less potent and less specific in their action than exotoxins.

Exotoxins

The most thoroughly studied exotoxins are those of *Corynebacterium diphtheriae, Clostridium tetani,* and *Clostridium botulinum* (type A). All three have been highly purified and two (tetanus and botulinus) have been crystallized. Relatively heat-labile proteins, they share with the neurotoxin of *Shigella dysenteriae* (Shiga) the distinction of being the most powerful poisons known. From the figures listed in Table 19-1 it will be seen that a milligram of tetanus (or botulinus) toxin is enough to kill more than 1,000,000

guinea pigs. It has been suggested that the somewhat lower potency of diphtheria toxin, as estimated by its median lethal dose (LD_{50}) in guinea pigs, may be due to its affinity for body cells in general, in contrast to the highly selective actions of the tetanus and botulinus toxins on specific cells of the central nervous system. Even so, 1 oz of diphtheria toxin would be more than enough to kill everyone in the city of New York.

Toxicity estimates of this kind are obviously inexact. Indeed, one of the most striking characteristics of bacterial exotoxins is the degree to which their potencies vary when measured in animal hosts of different species. Men, horses, and guinea pigs, for example, are much more susceptible to diphtheria toxin than mice or rats, and are far more sensitive to tetanus and botulinus toxins than dogs. Rabbits (per unit of body weight) are 10,000 times as susceptible as guinea pigs to the lethal action of shigella neurotoxin. The pharmacological and biochemical bases for these striking differences in species susceptibility are not known, although recent studies on the comparative metabolic effects of diphtheria toxin on cultured mouse and human cells suggest that species-specific components of the protein-synthesizing system may be involved.

Since bacterial exotoxins are proteins, it is not surprising that the molecular bases of their poisonous actions have not yet been elucidated. Type A botulinus toxin, as usually isolated, has a molecular weight of approximately 1,000,000, but has been dissociated into smaller subunits (M.W. 70,000) which retain activity. The amino acid compositions of tetanus (M.W. 67,000) and botulinus toxins have failed to reveal any unusual features, but neither the amino acid sequences nor the spatial configurations of the molecules are known. Even when these have been determined, it is likely that the critical reactive groups of exotoxin molecules will remain difficult to define, just as they have with enzymes and antibodies.

Exposure of exotoxin to heat, acid, or proteolytic enzymes (e.g., in the gastrointestinal tract) causes marked losses in toxicity.* In

---

* Paradoxically, the potency of type E botulinus toxin is enhanced by proteolysis.

Bacterial species	Disease	Toxin	Action	Toxicity per mg, expressed as LD_{50}^{kg}*
Clostridium botulinum	Botulism	Six type-specific neurotoxins	Paralytic	1,200,000 (G)
Clostridium tetani	Tetanus	Tetanospasmin	Spastic	1,200,000 (G)
		Tetanolysin	Hemolytic cardiotoxin	
Clostridium perfringens	Gas gangrene	α-Toxin†	Lecithinase: necrotizing, hemolytic	200 (M)
		β-Toxin		
		γ-Toxin		
		δ-Toxin		
		ε-Toxin	Necrotizing	
		η-Toxin		
		θ-Toxin	Hemolytic cardiotoxin	
		ι-Toxin	Necrotizing	
		κ-Toxin	Collagenase	
		λ-Toxin	Proteolytic	
Clostridium septicum	Gas gangrene	α-Toxin	Hemolytic	
Clostridium novyi	Gas gangrene	α-Toxin	Necrotizing	50,000 (M)
		β-Toxin	Lecithinase: necrotizing, hemolytic	
		γ-Toxin	Lecithinase: necrotizing, hemolytic	
		δ-Toxin	Hemolytic	
		ε-Toxin	Lipase: hemolytic	
		ζ-Toxin	Hemolytic	
Corynebacterium diphtheriae	Diphtheria	Diphtheritic toxin	Necrotizing	3,500 (G)
Staphylococcus aureus	Pyogenic infections	α-Toxin	Necrotizing, hemolytic, leucocidic	50 (M)
		Enterotoxin	Emetic	
		Leucocidin	Leucocidic	
		β-Toxin	Hemolytic	
		γ-Toxin	Necrotizing, hemolytic	
		δ-Toxin	Hemolytic, leucolytic	
Streptococcus pyogenes	Pyogenic infections and scarlet fever	Streptolysin O	Hemolytic	0.5 (M)
		Streptolysin S	Hemolytic	
		Erythrogenic	Causes scarlet fever rash	
		Streptococcal DPNase	Cardiotoxic, leuco-toxic (?)	
Pasteurella pestis	Plague	Plague Toxin	Necrotizing (?)	25 (M)
Bordetella pertussis	Whooping cough	Whooping cough toxin	Necrotizing	
Shigella dysenteriae	Dysentery	Neurotoxin	Hemorrhagic, paralytic	1,200,000 (R)

* LD_{50}^{kg} denotes median lethal dose (LD$_{50}$, p. 649) per kilogram of guinea pig (G), mouse (M), or rabbit (R).

† The designation of toxins by Greek letters is purely arbitrary and is based on the order in which they were identified.

Modified from W. E. van Heyningen. In General Pathology, p. 754. (H. W. Florey, ed.) Saunders, Philadelphia, 1962.

addition, a variety of reagents, including iodine, ketene, diazonium salts, and formaldehyde, introduce substituent groups into various amino acid residues of exotoxin molecules. The resulting denatured proteins lose their toxicity but retain much of their original antigenicity. Such modified protein toxins are referred to as **toxoids.** Those prepared from cultures of *Corynebacterium diphtheriae* and *Clostridium tetani* are widely used to induce active immunity in man. The change from toxin to toxoid, which is accomplished industrially by treatment with dilute formaldehyde, tends to occur spontaneously even at low temperatures.†

The **pharmacological actions of the known bacterial exotoxins** are comparatively slow, some requiring several days. As already mentioned, diphtheria toxin in susceptible hosts inhibits protein synthesis and thus damages a wide variety of cells. The α-toxin of *Clostridium perfringens* is a lecithinase, which likewise acts upon many different kinds of body cells, including erythrocytes, affecting primarily their membranes. When injected intravenously in laboratory animals, it causes hemolysis, but in human *C. perfringens* infections hemolytic reactions are rarely observed. The actions of the neurotoxins of botulinus and tetanus, on the other hand, are restricted to cells of the central nervous system. Although both seem to depress the

formation and/or release of acetylcholine, botulinus toxin affects both pre- and post-ganglionic synapses of the peripheral autonomic system, as well as cholinergic mechanisms in peripheral motor nerves, whereas tetanus toxin appears to act only on motor cells within the cerebrospinal axis where, according to Eccles, it causes spasm by blocking the function of inhibitory synapses.

There has been much disagreement as to how tetanus toxin reaches the central nervous system from the local site of infection. One school of investigators has favored the hematogenous route; another has claimed that the toxin travels within the axons of peripheral nerves. A third currently preferred view is that the toxin is propelled centripetally in the interneuronal tissue spaces of the peripheral nerves by muscular contractions, and that it is thus carried to the interstitial fluid of the spinal cord and brain, where it acts exclusively on motor neurons.

The "shiga neurotoxin" of *Shigella dysenteriae* differs from botulinus and tetanus toxin in that it acts only secondarily upon the central nervous system. Its primary action is a vascular one, which is remarkably limited to small blood vessels in the brain and spinal cord.

Not all bacterial exotoxins have been shown to play a role in the production of disease. The pathogenic properties of diphtheria, tetanus, and botulinus toxins, staphylococcal enterotoxin, and the erythrogenic toxins of *Streptococcus pyogenes,* have been conclusively established. The evidence is also convincing that the exotoxin of *Bordetella pertussis* is responsible for the deep bronchial wall lesions in whooping cough. Similarly, observations implicating the α-toxin of *Staphylococcus aureus,* the neurotoxin of *Shigella dysenteriae,* the lethal toxin of *Bacillus anthracis,* and the plague and cholera exotoxins are reasonably decisive. The pathogenetic role of the necrotoxic proteases elaborated by certain of the gas gangrene organisms (e.g., *Clostridium histolyticum*) also seems fairly clear. Regarding the numerous other exotoxins produced by gram-positive bacilli and cocci, however, including

---

† The following reasoning may be relevant to the chemistry of toxoid formation:

1) Bacterial exotoxins have many properties in common with enzymes; indeed, some have been identified as enzymes.

2) Enzymes of the approximate size of certain exotoxins (M.W. 50,000 to 100,000) contain only a few (probably one or two) catalytically active sites per molecule.

3) Each protein molecule of this size (including enzymes) possesses many antigenically active groups which collectively determine its immunological specificity.

4) Hence chemical modification of the exotoxin molecule which affects its few active (toxic) sites without causing drastic configurational changes would be expected to yield toxoid, i.e., an atoxic derivative retaining substantial immunological cross-reactivity with the native toxin.

streptococcal leucotoxin and the various leuco-cidins which tend to damage polymorphonuclear leucocytes in vitro, there is yet no conclusive evidence that any of them are pathogenically active in vivo.

Endotoxins

The following properties of bacterial en-dotoxins distinguish them from exotoxins:

1) They are produced primarily, if not solely,* by gram-negative bacteria.

2) They are complex macromolecules con-taining both phospholipid and polysaccharide moieties.

3) They make up an integral part of the bacterial cell wall and are released only if the integrity of the cell is disturbed.

4) In comparison to protein exotoxins they are relatively heat-stable.

5) They are less potent poisons than most exotoxins† and are less specific in their cyto-toxic actions.

6) Their toxicity appears to reside in the phospholipid fractions, whereas their specific antigenic determinants reside in the polysac-charide moieties.

7) They do not form toxoids.

The chemical structures of bacterial endo-toxins are extremely complicated. Originally isolated as phospholipid-polysaccharide-pro-tein complexes identical with the somatic O antigens of bacterial cells, their biological activity has been shown, principally by West-phal, to reside in a lipopolysaccharide fraction which can be separated by phenol extraction from most of the phospholipid and all of the protein of the original complexes. The re-maining phospholipid of the active fraction, termed **lipid A,** appears to be responsible for most, if not all, of the toxicity,‡ whereas the structure of the polysaccharide moiety, which contains dideoxyhexoses (Ch. 20), Antigenic structure) not known to occur anywhere else in Nature, determines the specific antigenicity of the molecule. Although endotoxins were originally obtained only from smooth strains of gram-negative bacteria possessing demon-strable O antigens, they have now been ex-tracted from rough strains as well, which lack O antigens. The product isolated from smooth strains has been found to contain certain hexoses not detectable in endotoxins from rough strains. These additional hexose residues are believed to account for the O-antigenicity of the smooth strains. Further details of the chemistry of O antigens and of lipid A are discussed in Chapter 20.

The **biological effects of bacterial endo-toxins** are numerous. When injected in suffi-cient amounts they cause within an hour or two an irreversible state of shock, usually accompanied by severe diarrhea. At autopsy a few hemorrhages in the wall of the gastro-intestinal tract are often the only discernible lesions. In smaller doses they cause fever, transient leucopenia followed by leucocytosis, hyperglycemia, hemorrhagic necrosis of tu-mors, abortion, altered resistance to bacterial infections (see below), a wide variety of cir-culatory disturbances, and vascular hyper-reactivity to adrenergic drugs. When prop-erly administered, they are also capable of eliciting the **Shwartzman phenomenon.***

---

* Pathogenic gram-negative bacteria from which endo-toxins have been isolated include such species as *Sal-monella typhi, Shigella dysenteriae, Vibrio cholerae, Bru-cella melitensis, Neisseria gonorrhoeae,* and *Neisseria meningitidis.* Endotoxins have also been obtained from relatively avirulent gram-negative species, e.g., *Escherichia coli.* Although the presence of a rather weak endotoxin in extracts of the gram-positive species *Streptococcus pyogenes* has been reported, its nature and biological properties have not been well characterized.

† LD_{50}^{kg} (see Table 19-1) $= 0.1$ to 0.2/mg (M).

‡ This point is still in dispute.

* When endotoxins are injected subcutaneously into rabbits, in doses of a few micrograms, a mild inflamma-tory reaction occurs in the skin. If, 24 hours later, an intravenous injection of the same, or another, endotoxin is given in the same amount, the originally injected skin site becomes hemorrhagic within a few hours. Histo-logically it is characterized by the presence of leucocyte-platelet thrombi, particularly in venules. Indeed, the reaction, first described by Shwartzman in 1928, will not occur unless a sufficient number of leucocytes are

If animals are given repeated injections of an endotoxin they become relatively unresponsive to its pyrogenic and other biological effects. This state, known as **tolerance,** is nonspecific, i.e., it affects the response to other endotoxins. Furthermore, it subsides within a week or two after the course of repeated injections is terminated and therefore does not correlate with the much longer persistence of active immunity. Although tolerance results primarily from an enhanced clearance of the injected endotoxin by cells of the reticuloendothelial system and can be nullified by "reticuloendothial blockade" with such agents as Thorotrast or India ink, there is evidence that the process also involves humoral factors detectable by passive transfer. Besides being refractory to endotoxin-induced fever, tolerant animals exhibit an increased resistance to many other noxious stimuli, e.g., traumautic shock, radiation damage.

The three properties of bacterial endotoxins that have aroused the most interest among experimental pathologists have been those relating to their pyrogenicity, their ability to cause irreversible shock, and their effect upon nonspecific immunity. 1) Much evidence has accumulated that the pyrogenic action is indirect and that it is mediated through an endogenous pyrogen released from polymorphonuclear leucocytes. 2) Regarding hemorrhagic shock, Fine and his coworkers have reported extensive experimental findings indicating that its terminal irreversibility is due in large part to the absorption of bacterial endotoxins from the bowel. Although this conclusion has been contested on the grounds that irreversible hemorrhagic shock

may be produced in axenic animals, quantitative studies of comparative susceptibility have not been performed, and the possibility that the axenic animals* may be sensitized to endotoxins contained in their food has not been excluded. 3) How prior treatment with endotoxin influences nonspecific immunity to bacterial infections is only partially understood. Whereas large doses of endotoxin depress both resistance to infection and phagocytosis, small doses enhance them. Indeed, if an appropriate dose of endotoxin is given, a biphasic response occurs, in which resistance and phagocytosis are first depressed and later enhanced.

Despite the many biological effects of bacterial endotoxins, their role in the pathogenesis of bacterial diseases remains poorly defined.

Virulence

Measurement

The virulence of a bacterial strain, whether due primarily to invasiveness, toxigenicity, or a combination of the two, is ordinarily measured in terms of the median dose that will kill within a stated period of time 50% of the animals inoculated. The number of bacteria required to accompilsh this result is known as the **LD$_{50}$.*** The principal reason for measuring the LD$_{50}$ rather than the minimum lethal dose (M.L.D.), i.e., the smallest dose needed to kill all the animals injected, is revealed by the shape of the characteristic dose-response curves depicted in Figure 19-2. In graphs A and B the doses of bacteria injected, expressed in logarithms to the base 10, are plotted on the abscissa, and the mortalities observed in separate groups of animals receiving each dose are plotted in percentages on the ordinate. It will be noted that the rates of change in mortality (graphs C and D) are greatest in the middle portions of the

---

present in the circulation. If both injections are given by vein, the animal usually dies with 24 hours after the second, and at autopsy bilateral cortical necrosis of the kidneys is regularly found. Neither this generalized Shwartzman reaction (which is accentuated by cortisone), nor the localized form, has ever been satisfactorily explained in immunological terms; in fact, both appear to be essentially toxic in nature and are considered by many immunologists to be only "mad cousins of proper immune reactions."

---

* Germ free.

* LD, lethal dose. The LD$_{50}$ is most readily measured by the Reed-Muench method (see Appendix at end of Ch. 22).

curves and are smallest at the extremes. Therefore, it is obviously possible to determine with much greater accuracy the dose which will kill 50% of a group of animals than that which will kill 100%. Furthermore, if the dose-response curve is relatively steep, as in B, the LD_{50} can be measured more precisely with a given number of animals than when the slope changes more gradually, as in A.

The sigmoid shape of the dose-response curve is thought to be due both to the heterogeneity of the animal population injected and to the statistical distribution of chance events in the infection. When animals of the same age, weight, sex, and inbred strain are used, the heterogeneity factor may be minimized, and the dose-response curve will thus be made steeper. Since the susceptibilities of different strains, as well as species, of animals for a given organism may vary over a wide range, and since the severity of the disease produced may depend to a large extent on the site of inoculation, these two variables must always be defined. In addition, the state of the culture to be injected must be rigidly controlled because of the variations in virulence that occur in the different phases of the growth cycle (p. 575). Finally, when the LD_{50} values of different bacterial strains are to be compared, sufficiently large numbers of animals must be injected to provide statistically valid results.

Fig. 19-2 Examples of dose-response curves used to measure bacterial virulence (for explanation see text). Quantitative measurements of the lethal effects of toxins (in contrast to viable organisms) result in much the same kind of dose-response curves. (From *Topley and Wilson's Principles of Bacteriology and Immunology*. [G. S. Wilson and A. A. Miles, eds.] Williams & Wilkins, Baltimore, 1964.)

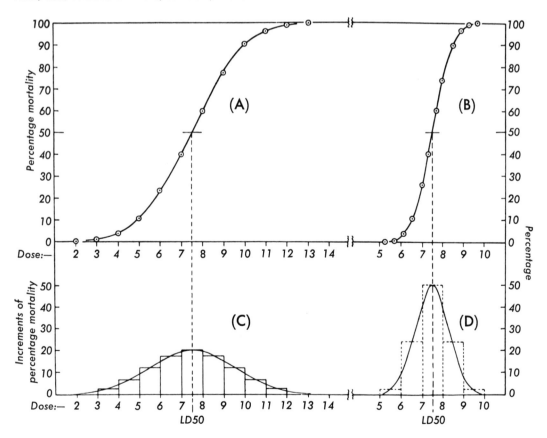

Similar technics may be employed to measure the LD_{50} **of a bacterial toxin** or the **transmissibility** of a bacterial strain to a given animal host. The endpoint in the latter type of test is determined by measuring the dose required to cause a demonstrable infection (usually detected by cultural methods) in 50% of the animals exposed. The dose required, known as the ID_{50} (I.D., infectious dose), will depend in part upon the method of exposure, i.e., by aerosol, by intravenous injection, by intraperitoneal inoculation, etc. Therefore, as in measurements of the LD_{50}, the precise manner in which the infectious agent is introduced into the test animal must be specified.

Variation

Alterations in the virulence of a bacterial strain may result either from mutations or from changes in the organism's environment. Virulence, however, it should be remembered, is not determined solely by genotypic or phenotypic properties of the microorganism; rather it is a property of the host-parasite pair (or system). Hence variation in virulence may result from changes in the parasite, in the host, or in both.

Genotypic Variations. The best-studied example of a mutational change affecting bacterial invasiveness is that involving encapsulation of pneumococci. In multiplying populations of smooth (S) fully encapsulated pneumococci, unencapsulated, one-step, rough (R) mutants spontaneously arise. Conversely, one-step R → S mutations occur in populations of rough pneumococci. Which of the two variants (S or R) will eventually predominate in a given population depends upon the conditions under which the organisms multiply. If, for example, pneumococci originally in the S form are repeatedly subcultured on an artificial medium which selectively favors the growth of the R variant, the unencapsulated rough form will finally overgrow the culture. When, on the other hand, a population containing both variants is injected

into a susceptible laboratory animal, such as a white mouse, the unencapsulated R cells will be rapidly destroyed by the phagocytic defenses of the host, while the S cells will be protected from the phagocytes by their capsules and will continue to multiply and eventually kill the mouse. The pneumococci cultured from the blood at postmortem will, therefore, be of the virulent encapsulated variety. The virulence of the progeny of a given strain of pneumococcus may thus vary depending upon the selection of mutants. Furthermore, the virulence of each pneumococcal cell depends not only on the presence or absence of a capsule but also on its size. Intermediate (I) variants may arise which produce only small capsules and therefore are less virulent than fully encapsulated S cells, but more virulent than unencapsulated R cells. Any one of the three genotypes (S, I, or R) may be obtained by transformations performed in vitro. Similar genetic variations of other pathogenic capsule-bearing bacteria (e.g., *Streptococcus pyogenes, Klebsiella pneumoniae, Pasteurella pestis*) affect invasiveness in the same manner.

The toxigenicities of virulent bacterial species are likewise subject to genotypic variation. Of particular interest is the fact that toxin production by diphtheria bacilli depends upon **lysogeny,** i.e., only those bacilli infected by a specific temperate bacteriophage, known as the β-phage, generate diphtheria toxin. In lysogeny the DNA of the temperate phage becomes associated with the chromosome of the bacterial cell and during cell division is transmitted to the daughter cell (Ch. 24). Its presence affects the cell's synthetic capabilities and enables it to generate one or more chemical constituents which it is unable to make in the absence of the virus. In *Corynebacterium diphtheriae* the lysogenic β-phage controls the synthesis of toxin, for when the virus is removed, the cells are no longer toxigenic. Since lysogeny is a heritable phenomenon, its influence on toxigenicity may justifiably be defined as genotypic. Lysogeny also controls the production of the scarlet fever toxin by *Strepto-*

coccus pyogenes, and it seems likely that temperate phages will be found to affect the toxigenicities of other pathogenic bacteria.

Phenotypic Variations. Modifications in both invasiveness and toxigenicity may also result from metabolic changes controlled by factors of environment rather than heredity. As already mentioned, pneumococci produce larger capsules and thus are more virulent during the exponential phase of growth than during later stages of the growth cycle. They also form more generous capsular envelopes when cultured in a carbohydrate-rich medium than when grown in a carbohydrate-deficient medium. Similarly, toxigenic strains of *Corynebacterium diphtheriae* and *Clostridium tetani* elaborate their toxins only when cultured in media in which the iron content is critically controlled, and *Bordetella pertussis* thrives in vivo only in the special microenvironment provided by ciliated epithelial cells of the bronchial mucosa. Other examples might be cited, but the foregoing should suffice to indicate how **both genotypic and phenotypic factors influence the virulence of bacteria.**

III SELECTED MICROORGANISMS

20 SELECTED BACTERIA

ENTERIC BACILLI: GENERAL PROPERTIES

No part of bacteriology is more confusing than that dealing with the intestinal tract. The sheer mass of organisms in the bowel (ca. 10^{10} bacteria per gram of feces), the variety of "species" present, and the metabolic and genetic interactions among them all make the intestinal flora exceedingly complicated. Among the myriads of mutants that arise, only the hardiest and most adaptable survive the constant pressures of **bacterial antagonism.** Many potentially virulent strains are thus held in check and, even when one manages to gain a foothold in the bowel wall, it may still succumb to the antibacterial defense of the host.

The situation is further complicated by a chaotic system of species classification. The unfortunate custom of giving a species name (usually derived from the geographic locality where the organism was first isolated) to each newly discovered antigenic variant has led to a list of specific names so long as to be virtually meaningless. Happily the tide of taxonomic confusion is beginning to ebb, primarily as the result of new developments in microbial metabolism and genetics.

Contemporary biochemists and geneticists have tended to study intestinal bacteria rather than other kinds for several reasons: they are particularly easy to handle in the laboratory; they are known to include hundreds of readily identifiable genetic variants; and they were the first organisms to exhibit conjugation and transduction. Accordingly, the story of molecular genetics has been largely a story of intestinal microbes. As a welcome byproduct has come a clearer understanding of the chemical subtleties of antigenic variations and a new insight into how the synthesis of each specific antigen, as well as the fermentation and other biochemical hallmarks of each strain of organism, are genetically controlled. From this new genetic base a more orderly system of **bacterial speciation** is bound to emerge.

Among the bacteria that naturally inhabit the gastrointestinal tract of man is a large and heterogeneous group of gram-negative bacilli, collectively referred to as the "enteric bacilli" (Table 20-1). Although they are formally classified under several genera (and even families), they have many properties in common and are best discussed together. Not only do they produce overlapping patterns of disease, but many of them also share common antigens and are genetically interrelated.† Other bacteria that make up the normal intestinal flora include enterococci and members of two anaerobic genera, *Clostridia* and *Bacteroides.* Organisms of the latter genus rarely produce disease but frequently outnumber all others in the bowel and therefore will be considered in this chapter.

In their virulence for man, the enteric bacilli fall into three general categories (Table 20-1). The first includes the coliform

TABLE 20-1. THE ENTERIC BACILLI

Groups, genera, and species	Pathogenicity
Coliform bacilli	
Escherichia coli	
Aerobacter aerogenes	Pathogenic only
Klebsiella pneumoniae	under special
Paracolon bacilli	circumstances
Proteus group*	
*Pseudomonas aeruginosa**	
*Alcaligenes faecalis**	
Salmonellae	Enteric fever, septicemia, gastroenteritis
Shigellae	Bacillary dysentery
*Vibrio cholerae**	Cholera

Not members of the family Enterobacteriaceae.

---

† The DNA base ratios (AT/GC) of the coliform bacilli, the salmonellae, and the shigellae are virtually identical (0.92), suggesting that these organisms are close genetic relatives. All are classified in the family *Enterobacteriaceae*. The base ratios of the proteus and pseudomonas organisms, on the other hand, are quite different (1.47 and 0.54).

bacilli, the proteus organisms, *Pseudomonas aeruginosa*, and *Alcaligenes faecalis*. These common inhabitants of the normal human gastrointestinal tract are ordinarily nonpathogenic, causing disease (most often of the urinary tract) only under special circumstances. The second group contains the salmonellae, highly invasive pathogens, some of which characteristically give rise to systemic infections such as typhoid fever. The third is composed of the shigellae and *Vibrio cholerae*, relatively noninvasive microbes, which produce the superficial though disabling intestinal lesions of bacillary dysentery and cholera.

Common Morphological Features

None of the enteric bacilli form spores, and all are relatively small gram-negative rods,

measuring 2 to 3 μ in length and 0.4 to 0.6 μ in breadth. Only the shigellae and certain strains of the coli-aerogenes group are nonmotile (Table 20-2); the rest have peritrichous flagella, except for *Vibrio cholerae*, each cell of which has a single polar flagellum. Many enteric bacilli also possess fimbriae (or pili), which must be distinguished from flagella. Their structural features and the role played by the specialized F pili in chromosomal transfer during bacterial conjugation are discussed elsewhere (Ch. 7, Conjugation). Smooth variants of all species form shiny convex colonies on agar, whereas those of rough strains are granular. Capsule production (e.g., by *Klebsiella pneumoniae, Aerobacter aerogenes,* and some strains of *Escherichia coli*) gives rise to large mucoid colo-

TABLE 20-2. PHYSIOLOGICAL CHARACTERISTICS OF ENTERIC BACILLI

Organism	Motility*	Fermentation of				H₂S	Urease	Indole produced	MR	VP	Citrate utilization
		Glucose	Sucrose	Lactose	Mannose						
Escherichia coli	+ (−)	AG	AG	AG	AG	−	−	+	+	−	−
Klebsiella-Aerobacter	− (+)	AG	AG	AG	AG	−	−	−	−	+	+
Proteus vulgaris	+ (S)	AG	AG	−	−	+	+	+	+	−(+)	−(+)
Pseudomonas aeruginosa†	+	−	−	−	−	−	−	−	−	−	+
Proteus mirabilis	+ (S)	AG	AG (late)	−	−	+	+	−	−	+(−)	+(−)
Proteus morgani	+ (S)	AG	−	−	−	−	+	+	+	−	−
Alcaligenes faecalis	+	−	−	−	−	−	−	−	−	−	−
Salmonella typhosa	+	A	−	−	A	+	−	−	+	−	−
Salmonella paratyphi A	+	AG	−	−	AG	−	−	−	+	−	−
Salmonella schottmulleri (para B)	+	AG	−	−	AG	+	−	−	+	−	+
Shigella dysenteriae	−	A	−	−	−	−	−	−(+)	+	−	−
Shigella paradysenteriae (flexneri)	−	A	−	−	A	−	−	+(−)	+	−	−
Vibrio cholerae	+	A	A	−	A	+(slow)	−	+	−	−	−

* *Nonmotile variants may occur in all species that are usually motile.*
† *Produces pigment.*
AG, produces acid and gas.
A, produces acid but no gas.
MR, methyl red test.
VP, Voges-Proskauer reaction.

\+ (−) *Occasional strains are negative.*
− (+) *Occasional strains are positive.*
(S) *Swarm on 1 to 2% agar.*

nies that are easily distinguished from the usual smooth variety.

Metabolic Characteristics

The enteric bacilli grow readily on ordinary media under both aerobic and anaerobic conditions. All are cultivable in simple synthetic media and many will grow with a single carbon source. The capacities of different species to utilize (ferment) specific carbohydrates are ordinarily quite stable and hence provide a basis for tentative group (or species) identification. The fermentation tests commonly employed are listed in Table 20-2. The coli-aerogenes organisms, which dominate the facultative gram-negative bacilli of the normal intestinal flora, are initially identified as lactose fermenters; on solid media containing lactose and an appropriate acid-base indicator (e.g., neutral red) they form easily identified, colored colonies. *E. coli* in turn may be differentiated from *A. aerogenes* by other biochemical tests, referred to in Table 20-3 and discussed in the section dealing with the coliform bacilli. The principal groups of "nonlactose fermenters," most of which are pathogens, may likewise be differentiated by their utilization of glucose, sucrose, mannitol, etc. and by their ability to produce hydrogen sulfide and urease (Table 20-2). The relatively avirulent species, *Pseudomonas aeruginosa,* is recognized by its production of pigment.

Screening Media. A variety of ingenious media have been empirically devised to reveal in a single culture tube many of the differential characteristics of these organisms. One such medium, known as triple-sugar-iron agar (T.S.I.) is widely used in the preliminary "screening" of enteric bacilli. Its formula is as follows:

Peptone	20 gm
Sodium chloride	5 gm
Lactose	10 gm
Sucrose	10 gm
Glucose	1 gm
Ferrous ammonium sulfate	0.2 gm
Sodium thiosulfate	0.2 gm
Phenol red	0.025 gm
Agar	13 gm
Distilled water	1000 ml

pH 7.3

The agar medium is allowed to solidify in tubes so as to form slants, and the inoculum (picked from a single colony on an original isolation plate)* is stabbed through the butt and streaked onto the surface of the slant. T.S.I. agar reveals not only the fermentation of lactose, glucose, and sucrose, but also the production of hydrogen sulfide, which reacts with the ferrous ion in the medium to form black ferrous sulfide. In addition the production of gases (e.g., hydrogen and carbon dioxide) causes bubbles to form in the agar.

The detection of the fermentation reactions, which generate organic acids and "decolorize"† the phenol red indicator, depends upon the following factors: 1) a delicate balance of the concentrations of the several sugars and the nitrogenous constituents of the medium; 2) inclusion of approximately 10 times

---

* Although it is permissible for diagnostic purposes to "fish" a colony on an original isolation plate, a second subculture on agar should always be made before inoculating a culture to be stored for future reference.

† Note that the acidic form of phenol red is yellow, whereas the alkaline form of neutral red is colorless.

TABLE 20-3. IMVIC REACTIONS

Organism	Indole formation	Methyl red	Voges-Proskauer	Citrate utilization
E. coli	+	+	—	—
A. aerogenes	—	—	+	+

as much lactose and sucrose as glucose (see formula); 3) slow diffusion through the agar of the acid products of the fermentations and the alkaline products of nitrogen metabolism; and 4) greater production of acid in the anaerobic environment of the butt (fermentation) compared with the aerobic surface of the slant (respiration).

Thus an organism that ferments glucose only (e.g., *S. typhosa*) will produce detectable amounts of acid in the butt of the medium (anaerobic), but not on the surface of the slant (aerobic) where the nitrogenous bases formed will fully neutralize the less acid endproducts of respiration. Species that ferment the more concentrated lactose or sucrose (e.g., *E. coli* or *P. vulgaris*), on the other hand, will generate in the butt enough acid to diffuse throughout the medium and thus acidify it even at the surface (Table 20-2).

Although multiple sugar media of this sort are reasonably satisfactory for preliminary identification of enteric bacilli,* the fermentation reactions observed should be confirmed by tests with appropriate liquid media, each containing a single sugar as the sole source of carbohydrate. To recognize gas formation (Table 20-2) an inverted, small test tube is submerged in the medium to trap a portion of any gas that is generated. During sterilization in the autoclave the air initially present in the inverted tube is expelled and replaced by medium.

Selective Media. Other metabolic properties of the enteric bacilli that have been exploited for diagnostic purposes include their relative resistance to the inhibitory action of certain bacteristatic dyes (e.g., brilliant green) and surface-active compounds (e.g., deoxycholate) as compared with most gram-positive bacteria. Selective media containing appropriate concentrations of such substances (e.g., deoxycholate agar) greatly facilitate the isolation of enteric bacilli from cultures of feces.† Furthermore, among the enteric bacilli the intestinal pathogens (shigella and salmonella) are less sensitive than the coliform organisms (escherichia and aerobacter) to in-

hibition by citrate.‡ Deoxycholate agar containing a high concentration of citrate is therefore used for selective cultivation of pathogenic species and is commonly referred to as SS (**Salmonella-Shigella**) agar. For primary isolation it is best to use both the deoxycholate media since some strains of shigellae are inhibited by the citrate.

Antigenic Structure

Although many of the principal varieties of enteric bacilli can be tentatively identified by fermentation and other metabolic reactions in differential media, final identification of individual species is usually based on highly specific differences in antigenic structure. Strains with the same antigenic structure may occasionally exhibit different metabolic reactions; these are referred to as fermentative variants.

Surface Antigens

As is shown diagrammatically in Figure 20-1A, there are three kinds of specific surface antigens (H, O, and Vi)§ which deter-

---

* Mixed cultures will obviously give misleading results.

† Since deoxycholate is a constituent of bile, to which enteric bacilli are exposed in the bowel, it is not surprising that the wild-type strains that selectively survive this exposure should be deoxycholate-resistant.

‡ The mechanism of inhibitory action of the citrate is not known; the possibility that it acts as a chelating agent and binds essential divalent cations would seem reasonable.

§ The term H is derived from the German *Hauch*, meaning "breath." It was first used to describe the thin film of growth of proteus bacilli on the surfaces of moist agar plates. The film produced by the swarming of this highly motile organism resembles the light mist caused by breathing on glass. The designation O comes from the German *ohne*, meaning "without." First applied to nonswarming (i.e., nonflagellated) forms of proteus, it is now used as a generic term for the **lipopolysaccharide somatic antigens** of all coliform bacilli and more specifically for their antigenically active polysaccharide components. The term Vi was adopted to designate an additional surface antigen of *S. typhosa*, originally thought to be primarily responsible for virulence. Its precise relation to pathogenicity is still not clear.

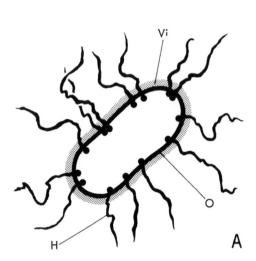

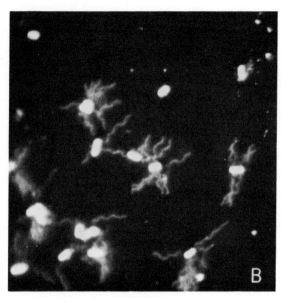

Fig. 20-1 **A.** Schematic diagram of cellular locations of H, O, and Vi antigens of enteric bacilli. **B.** *S. typhosa* stained with fluorescein-labeled immune serum containing anti-H, anti-A, and anti-Vi antibodies. ×3500, reduced. Note that the flagella of different bacilli have in some cases become agglutinated with one another. Note also, however that the presence of the flagella has prevented the bodies of the bacilli from coming close enough together to agglutinate, despite the presence of the antisomatic (Vi and O) antibodies in the serum. The interflagellar agglutinate is, therefore, understandably less densely packed than if the flagella had been absent and intersomatic agglutination had occurred. (From B. M. Thomason, W. B. Cherry, and M. D. Moody. *J. Bact. 74:*525, 1957.)

mine the interaction of the organism with homologous specific antiserum. If motile species are treated with formalin the labile protein **H antigens** of their **flagella** are preserved, and the cells will be agglutinated only by specific antiflagellar (anti-H) antibodies. The resulting agglutination reaction, for the reasons suggested by Figure 20-1B, will form a light, fluffy precipitate. When interacted only with antibody to their **somatic O antigen** (i.e., in the absence of anti-H antibody) such bacilli will not agglutinate because their numerous peritrichous flagella hold them apart. When, on the other hand, flagella are absent from a strain or are denatured by heat (100° for 20 minutes), acid, or alcohol, the somatic O antigen at the surfaces of adjacent bacilli can be linked by anti-O antibody. The resulting agglutination yields closely packed, granular clumps.

In certain species, as diagrammed in Figure 20-1A, a third kind of surface antigen, designated **Vi antigen,** may form an outer coat which prevents the cells from being agglutinated by anti-O antibody. Strains possessing this external carbohydrate layer, which acts as a K antigen,* will agglutinate only in serum containing anti-H or anti-Vi antibodies (Fig. 20-1B). However, Vi-coated bacilli will still adsorb anti-O antibody, even though not agglutinated by it, suggesting that the coating of Vi polysaccharide does not "cover up" the O antigen but rather holds the cells far

---

* Though usually not present in sufficient amounts to form a visible capsule, the Vi antigen is not inactivated by the alcohol treatment that destroys H antigen, but is inactivated by boiling for 2 hours, which permits preservation of most of the O antigen. The letter K (from the German *Kapsel*) refers to capsular antigens.

enough apart to prevent them from being linked by the divalent O antibody molecules.

R Antigens. Rough strains of enteric bacilli have none of these three specific surface antigens, tend to agglutinate spontaneously, and are referred to as R variants.* The polysaccharide antigens extractable from their cell walls are known as **R antigens** and are apparently covered up by the O antigens in smooth (S) cells (Fig. 20-1A). As indicated below, certain R variants, though devoid of O and Vi antigen, may still possess flagella.

Preparation of Specific Antisera

When animals are immunized with formalin-killed motile strains of enteric bacilli the antisera contain both anti-H and anti-O antibodies as well as anti-R antibodies. The titer of the H antibody is usually higher than that of the O antibody † If the immunizing strain also possesses a capsular (Vi) antigen, the antiserum will contain, in addition, anti-Vi antibody. In other words, since the immunizing organisms are lysed or digested (Ch. 19, Phagocytosis) in the host, all their major antigens, regardless of location in the intact bacilli, are immunogenic.

When, on the other hand, intact bacilli serve as antigens in agglutination tests, or are used to absorb antibodies from antisera, only those antigens exposed at the surfaces of the organisms react with the corresponding antibodies in the antiserum. For example, anti-H antibody may be selectively removed from antiserum by adsorption either with suspensions of flagella (mechanically removed from motile bacilli) or with suspensions of mutants possessing flagella but neither Vi nor O antigen (i.e., flagellated R variants). Similarly, anti-O or anti-Vi antibodies may be selectively

removed by appropriate antigenic extracts or by suspensions of bacilli with the corresponding surface antigen (i.e., O but not Vi, and Vi but not O). As already noted, bacilli possessing O antigen but coated with Vi antigen will still adsorb O antibody and therefore cannot be used to adsorb Vi antibody alone because their O antigens are still "exposed."

Kauffmann-White Classification of the Salmonellae

The antigenic complexities of the enteric bacilli have been most thoroughly documented in the genus *Salmonella*. Largely as a result of the systematic studies of Kauffmann in Denmark and White in England, approximately 700 varieties have been distinguished on the basis of specific H, O, and Vi antigens, identified by exhaustive cross-adsorption and cross-reaction tests. The manner in which such tests are performed is illustrated by the following example.

Let us assume that two strains of salmonella, **a** and **b**, have been isolated, each from a separate outbreak of salmonellosis. Antisera prepared to them (anti-a and anti-b) are first reacted with standardized suspensions‡ of each strain, and the intensity of the reactions is recorded in roughly quantitative terms (see below). Each serum is then adsorbed with the heterologous strain (i.e., anti-a with b, and vice versa). The adsorbed sera are similarly reacted with the standardized suspensions, and the results are measured in the same manner. If the agglutination reactions observed were as follows

Antisera	Organisms	
	a	b
Anti-a, unadsorbed	4+	2+
Anti-b, unadsorbed	2+	4+
Anti-a, adsorbed with b	2+	0
Anti-b, adsorbed with a	0	2+

it would be concluded that **a** and **b** each has unique, as well as shared, antigenic determi-

---

* When suspended in media of proper ionic strength R cells can be prevented from agglutinating spontaneously and thus can be used to test for anti-R antibody.

† This difference may be due in part to the greater immunogenicity of the protein H antigen, as compared with the polysaccharide O antigen, and in part to the greater sensitivity of the H agglutination test.

‡ Standardized to contain a fixed number of organisms.

nants. Using an arbitrary numbering system, **a** might be said to possess determinants 1, 2, and **b** determinants 2, 3. If, on the other hand, strains **a** and **b** were equally effective in removing **all** the agglutinating antibody from the two antisera, they would be considered antigenically identical. Every new strain isolated would be similarly tested with the existing antisera (anti-a and anti-b, both adsorbed and unadsorbed) and with antiserum to the new strain itself, before and after adsorption. Whenever a new determinant was detected, it would be given a new number, and according to the Kauffmann-White scheme the organism possessing it would be designated a new "species."

Application of this technic to H, O, and Vi agglutination reactions has resulted in identification of the more than 700 salmonella types. Only in large salmonella typing centers (Copenhagen, London, Atlanta, etc.) are the necessary collections of specific antisera available for such work. In most diagnostic laboratories salmonella strains are merely grouped by means of fermentation tests and agglutination reactions performed with group-specific antisera (see below).

The antigenic properties of the O lipopolysaccharides alone yield about 60 distinguishable types. Many of the O antigens, however, cross-react with one another, indicating that their complex polysaccharide determinants share common reactive groups. It is on the basis of these cross-reactions (Table 20-4) that Kauffmann and White have classified the salmonellae into major **groups** designated by the letters A to I. More than 95% of strains isolated from natural sources fall into the first five groups (A to E).

In the Kauffmann-White scheme, as shown in Table 20-4, the individual O determinants are designated by numbers. It will be noted that all species in a given group possess at least one O determinant in common. This common factor (**bold face** in the table) is referred to as the **major determinant** of the group. In group C, for example, the major determinant is factor 6 and in group E it is factor 3 (cf. Tables 20-4 and 20-5). Additional divisions within a group may be made on the basis of the minor O determinants.

The members of each O antigen group may be differentiated still further into species on the basis of their protein flagellar (H) antigens. A given strain may form at different times either one of two kinds of H antigen. The first kind, known as **phase 1 flagellar antigens,** are shared with only a few other species of *Salmonella*; the second kind, **phase 2 antigens,** are less specific. In the Kauffmann-White classification the former are indicated by small letters and the latter by numbers (Table 20-4). Although the organisms in a given culture may be entirely in one phase (monophasic culture), they are frequently capable of giving rise to mutants in the other phase (diphasic culture); the shift from phase 1 to 2 occurs particularly if the culture is incubated for more than 24 hours. This kind of phase variation, which is genetically controlled, can also be accentuated by growing the organisms in serum containing antibodies to their flagellar antigen, thereby selectively favoring the growth of mutants with the alternate (allelic) antigen which does not react with the antiserum.

Elaboration of the polysaccharide Vi antigen* by a species is indicated in the Kauffmann-White schema by the letters Vi, placed by convention after the numbers indicating the individual O antigens (e.g., *S. typhosa* in Table 20-4). Since the coating of Vi antigen on the somatic surface prevents agglutination with homologous anti-O antibody (p. 594), Vi-producing strains cannot be easily differentiated on the basis of their somatic agglutinins.

Chemical Nature of Antigenic Determinants

As is true of protein antigens in general, little is known about the chemical determinants of the H antigen. Vi antigen, on the other hand, has been identified as a simple carbohydrate composed of repeating units of

---

* Vi antigens elaborated by *S. typhosa* and certain strains of *E. coli* and paracolon bacilli are immunologically indistinguishable, but differ from those of other salmonellae, e.g., *S. schottmulleri*.

TABLE 20-4. KAUFFMANN-WHITE CLASSIFICATION OF COMMON SALMONELLA SPECIES

Species	Group	O Antigens	H Antigens Phase 1	H Antigens Phase 2
S. paratyphosa	A	(1), **2**,* 12	a	—
S. schottmülleri	B	(1), **4**, (5), 12	b	1,2
S. typhimurium	B	(1), **4**, (5), 12	i	1,2
S. hirschfeldii	C$_1$	**6**, 7, Vi	c	1,5
S. choleraesuis	C$_1$	**6**, 7	c	1,5
S. oranienburg	C$_1$	**6**, 7	m,t	—
S. montevideo	C$_1$	**6**, 7	g,m,s	—
S. newport	C$_2$	**6**, 8	e,h	1,2
S. typhosa	D	**9**, 12, Vi	d	—
S. enteritidis	D	(1), **9**, 12	g,m	—
S. gallinarum-pullorum	D	1, **9**, 12	—	—
S. anatum	E	**3**, 10	e,h	1,6

Parentheses indicate that antigenic determinant may be difficult to detect (see p. 599).

* *Boldface number signifies major determinant of group. (N.B. Roman rather than Arabic numerals are sometimes used to designate O determinants.)*

TABLE 20-5. ANTIGENIC CLASSIFICATION OF GROUP E SALMONELLAE

Species	O Antigen	Group
S. anatum	**3**,* 10	E$_1$
S. newington	**3**, 15	E$_2$
S. minneapolis	(**3**), (15), 34	E$_3$
S. senftenberg	1, **3**, 19	E$_4$

* *Boldface number signifies major determinant of group.*
Parentheses indicate that determinant may be difficult to detect (see p. 599).

N-acetyl galactosaminuronic acid. Because of its free carboxyl groups it presents a highly acid surface.

The O antigens of the cell wall are also polysaccharides but are more complex. The systematic investigations, particularly of Westphal, of Staub, and of Robbins, have provided a unified picture of O antigen structure which appears to account for both cross-reactions within groups and the specificity of individual O determinants (see below).

The R antigens extractable from rough variants of all salmonellae are indistinguishable, both immunologically and chemically.* Furthermore, brief acid hydrolysis of O antigens has yielded haptens that react with anti-R as well as anti-O antibody. It therefore appears that the specific O antigenic determinants are built upon a common chemical substructure, the R antigen which

is in fact the core of the O antigen and has the structure indicated in Figure 20-2. The terminal side chains (or "whiskers"; Figs. 20-2 and 20-5) attached to this basic substructure determine both the broad group reactions and the extremely specific species reactions of the smooth phase O antigens (cf. streptococcal C antigens).

Chemical data concerning the O determinants are fairly complete for group E (Table 20-5). As is depicted in Figure 20-3, the group E determinant is composed of repeat-

---

* Recent evidence suggests that R antigen may exist in one of two forms, R$_I$ and R$_{II}$. The R$_{II}$ form is believed to lack only the S (smooth) specific side chains, whereas the R$_I$ form seems to be deficient in one or more of the deeper monosaccharide units. Similarly, **semirough** (SR) variants have been described that synthesize only the innermost portion of the specific side chains of the smooth phase organisms (cf. intermediate strains of pneumococci).

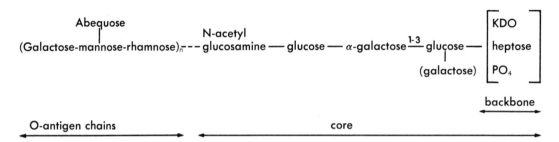

Fig. 20-2 Antigenic polysaccharide of *S. typhimurium*. R antigen is made up only of the core, whereas the complete O antigen contains in addition the outer O-antigen chains (See Figs. 4-33 and 20-5). KDO=keto-deoxyoctulonate through which the polysaccharide is believed to be glycosidically linked to the lipid A of the lipopolysaccharide. (Modified from M. J. Osborn, S. M. Rosen, L. Rothfield, L. D. Zelesnick, and B. L. Horecker. *Science 145:783, 1964.*)

ing trisaccharide units containing D-galactosyl-D-mannosyl-L-rhamnose sequences. The precise number of repeating trisaccharide units per side chain is not known but is believed to be about as shown in Figure 20-5.

The structures of three of the specific group E antigens listed in Table 20-5 are drawn in Figure 20-3 for comparison. Antigen 3,10 is represented by the α-O-acetyl-D-galactosyl-D-mannosyl-L-rhamnose trisaccha-

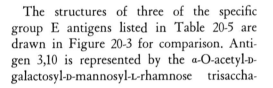

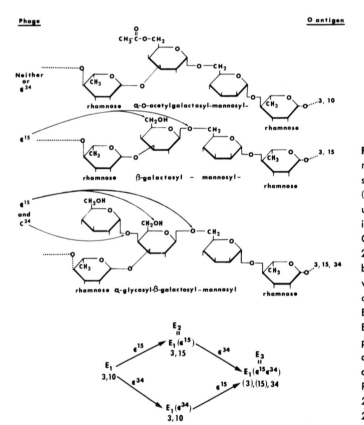

Fig. 20-3 Structures of determinant trisaccharide units of O polysaccharides of group E salmonella (Table 20-5). The relation of the underlying R antigen to the repeating trisaccharide units of the specific O determinants is shown in Figure 20-5. The changes in structure brought about by lysogenic conversions of determinant 3,10 (*S. anatum*, E_1) to 3,15 (*S. newington*, E_2), and to 3,15,34 (*S. minneapolis*, E_3) by phage ε^{15} and phages ε^{15} plus ε^{34}, respectively, (see bottom diagram), are indicated by the curved arrows. (Modified from P. W. Robbins and T. Uchida. *Fed. Proc. 21:702, 1962,* and *J. Biol. Chem. 240:375, 1965.*)

ride (top); antigen 3,15 is shown as the corresponding trisaccharide having β-D-galactosyl-D-mannosyl linkages (middle); and antigen 3,15,34 contains the β-galactosyl-mannosyl linkages and in addition has D-glucosyl units attached through α linkages to all the galactose units (lower) except the terminal one (see Fig. 20-5).* From this example it is clear that the immunological specificities of O antigens may be determined by relatively minor structural differences in the side chains of otherwise identical polysaccharides.

The modifications that have been observed in closely related antigens include: 1) changes of position of linkages, i.e., 1-4 vs. 1-6; 2) al-

---

* The results of serological inhibition analysis with haptens (Ch. 13, Applications of precipitin reaction) indicate that determinants 3 and 10 of antigen 3,10 each represent different (though probably overlapping) segments of the repeating trisaccharide unit as depicted in the following formula:

$$
\text{(O-ac-gal} \underset{10}{\overset{\overset{3}{\overbrace{}}}{\underbrace{\overset{\alpha}{}}}} \text{man} \overline{} \text{rh)}_n \overline{} \text{R}
$$

Similarly, the corresponding formula for antigen(3), (15),34 (Table 20-5) may be written as:

$$
\begin{array}{c}
\text{gluc 34} \\
| \quad \overset{\beta}{} \quad \overset{(3)}{\overbrace{}} \\
\text{(-gal} \overline{} \underbrace{\text{man} \overline{} \text{rh)}_n}_{(15)} \overline{} \text{R}
\end{array}
$$

The parentheses around the 3 and 15 indicate that the addition of the glucose (determinant 34) to the repeating trisaccharide has weakened antigenic determinants 3 and 15 to the point where they are difficult to detect (see footnotes to Tables 20-4 and 20-5).

tered anomeric configurations; i.e., α vs. β linkage; 3) attachment of additional monosaccharides, such as glucose, at different points on the repeating sequence; 4) deletion of, or substitution for, one of the monosaccharides in the basic trisaccharide units; and 5) presence or absence of acetyl groups on one type of sugar residue. Such modifications can easily account for the more than 60 known O antigens of the salmonellae. The determinants of groups A, B, D, and E, for example, all contain the repeating galactosyl-mannosyl-rhamnose sequence, and differ only in their anomeric configurations and in the monosaccharides attached to the basic trisaccharide.

Among the latter are the 3,6-dideoxyhexoses **abequose, tyvelose, paratose,** and **colitose** shown in Figure 20-4. These four sugars, not known to exist in Nature except in enteric bacilli, have been shown to occur as groups on the polysaccharide side chains of specific salmonella antigens (Table 20-6). Colitose is also a major component of the O antigen of other enteric bacilli, including strain O-111 of *E. coli*, while the other three dideoxyhexoses are known to occur only in salmonellae of groups A, B, and D. It is of interest that enteric bacilli containing these unusual sugars in their O antigens tend to be relatively virulent. From salmonellae of the less common groups, O antigens have been isolated which lack mannose and/or rhamnose and contain other monosaccharides such as fucose.

TABLE 20-6. SALMONELLA DIDEOXYHEXOSES

Dideoxyhexose	Structure	Group	Determinant*
Colitose	3,6-dideoxy-L-galactose	O	35
Abequose	3,6-dideoxy-D-galactose	B	4
Tyvelose	3,6-dideoxy-D-mannose	D	9
Paratose	3,6-dideoxy-D-glucose	A	2

* The sugars listed are best regarded as essential residues in the corresponding determinant; but undoubtedly other neighboring residues contribute, though to a lesser extent, to the over-all energy of interaction between the whole determinant and the homologous antibody. All strains possessing the determinant listed are designated as members of the corresponding group.

From P. W. Robbins and T. Uchida. Fed. Proc. 21:702 (1962).

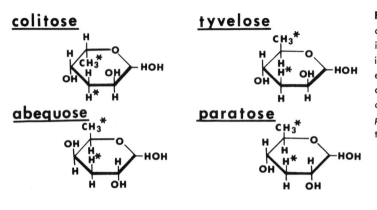

Fig. 20-4 Structural formulas of the 3,6 dideoxyhexoses listed in Table 20-6. The name of each is derived from the species of enteric bacilli from which it was originally isolated, i.e., *E. coli, S. abortus equi, S. typhosa,* and *S. paratyphosa.* The deoxy positions are indicated by asterisks.

Endotoxins

The lipopolysaccharides that form an integral part of the lipid-rich cell walls of the gram-negative enteric bacilli and contain their antigenic O polysaccharides are typical bacterial endotoxins. The varied biological properties of these toxic macromolecules have already been discussed in the chapter on host-parasite relations (Ch. 19, Endotoxins). The lipopolysaccharide may be extracted from the bacterial cell walls by treatment with 45% phenol at 90°. The crude colloidal suspension thus obtained is both toxic and antigenic. On mild acid hydrolysis it splits into a nonimmunogenic lipid fraction (lipid A), believed to carry the chemical grouping responsible for toxicity, and a polysaccharide fraction which contains the O antigens.* The chemistry of the O polysaccharide has been described above and in Chapter 4 (Lipopolysaccharides).

From the lipid fraction phosphorylated basic units of molecular weight 1700 have been isolated which contain glucosamine, instead of glycerol, and are rich in β-hydroxymyristic acid. Evidence that this fraction contains the entire toxic component of the intact endotoxin molecule is not yet conclusive; nevertheless it is certain that the toxic and antigenic groups of the whole molecule are not identical. This conclusion is based on the observations that 1) the toxicity/antigenicity ratio of the complex varies over a wide range depending upon the method of extraction, and 2) endotoxin can be extracted from R cells which possess only the core of the O antigen polysaccharide devoid of its specific terminal oligosaccharide side chains (Fig. 20-2).

Although bacterial endotoxins would be expected on theoretical grounds to have great pathogenic significance, their role in the production of enterobacillary diseases remains largely a matter of speculation.

Colicins

In addition to possessing endotoxins which are capable of injuring cells of the host, some enteric bacilli release highly specific proteins called colicins, which kill other enteric bacilli. These substances attach to specific receptors on susceptible bacilli, as do bacteriophages, but do not cause bacteriolysis. A variety of colicins have been identified which kill sensitive bacteria by different mechanisms: blocking of oxidative phosphorylation, inhibition of protein synthesis, degradation of bacterial DNA, etc. The reversibility of the killing action of some colicins by trypsin suggests that they remain at the bacterial surface and act primarily on the bacterial membrane. This suggestion implies that important metabolic processes within bacterial cells may be controlled from specific receptor sites on their surface membranes.

---

* As stated in Figure 20-2, the lipid is believed to be bound by glycosidic linkage to the keto-deoxyoctonate residue of the O polysaccharide.

The producion of colicins (colicinogeny) is controlled by **episomes** which act independently of the bacterial chromosomes and may be transmitted to other enteric bacilli by transduction or conjugation (Ch. 24). Responsible for a special form of **bacterial antagonism,** colicinogeny undoubtedly helps to stabilize the microbial population in the adult intestinal tract.

Phage Typing

Since practically all freshly isolated strains of *S. typhosa* elaborate a single type of Vi antigen, they are often subjected to an additional typing procedure involving susceptibility to lysis by specific bacteriophages. Phage typing (cf. staphylococci) permits recognition of at least 72 subtypes of Vi strains and is, therefore, useful in tracing the sources and progress of epidemics.

All the phages used to type Vi strains of *S. typhosa* are descended from a single strain of bacteriophage, some being mutants and others host-modified variants (Ch. 23, Host-controlled modification). The phage susceptibilities of the Vi (bacterial) strains, on the other hand, are determined by lysogeny with type-determining temperate phages, by nonlysogenic heritable traits, or by a combination of both.

Genetic Interrelations

That different strains of enteric bacilli should exhibit such a bewildering array of metabolic and antigenic variations is doubtless due to the complexity of the bacterial and viral populations of the gastrointestinal tract. Many of the bacterial species reach high population densities (10^8 to 10^{10} cells per gram) in the richly nutritious medium of the feces, thus affording frequent opportunities for **spontaneous mutations.** A significant proportion of them also harbor bacteriophages, which likewise may mutate at relatively high rates. Furthermore, genetic material from one strain of bacillus may be transmitted to another by

transduction, by **lysogenization,** and by **conjugation** (Ch. 7). Because of the frequency with which genetic recombinations must occur under these conditions, it is only natural that so many overlapping patterns of metabolism and antigenicity should be found among the enteric bacilli.

Since these processes of genetic recombination have already been discussed in detail (Ch. 7 and 8; see also Ch. 24), only two examples of special interest will be mentioned here. The first illustrates the alteration of somatic antigens by lysogenic conversion. In the example given in Figure 20-3, *S. anatum* is converted to another antigenic species by infection with phage ϵ^{15},* and to still another by double infection with phages ϵ^{15} and ϵ^{34}. The resulting molecular changes occurring in the polysaccharide side chains of the O antigens are indicated schematically in Figure 20-5. Two points are noteworthy: 1) formation of the β-linked 3,15 antigen requires persistence of lysogeny with ϵ^{15} phage, indicating that the process involved is one of lysogenic conversion rather than transduction, and 2) the addition of the D-glucosyl residue to position 4 of the galactose, brought about by the lysogenic effect of the ϵ^{34} phage, occurs only in cells that are already infected with ϵ^{15} phage. The presence of the latter phage in the cell 1) blocks acetylation of the galactose residues of the 3,10 antigen and 2) causes conversion of its D-galactosyl-mannose bridge to the β-linkage characteristic of antigen 3,15. Only after these subtle changes have been made is the glucosylating enzyme controlled

---

* The manner in which phage ϵ^{15} was discovered is of interest. In studying the interrelations of the O determinants of salmonella group E (Table 20-5), investigators in Japan employed an anti-10 serum to promote selection of 3,10 cells treated with DNA from 3,15 cells (transformation, Ch. 7). The resulting transformation was shown by appropriate control experiments to be due neither to the DNA (as expected) nor to the anti-10 antibody, but rather to a bacteriophage adventitiously contributed to the anti-10 antiserum by 3,15 cells used to adsorb it and thus render it monospecific. The phage isolated from the antiserum carries the gene for the enzyme that causes the cell to produce determinant 15 instead of 10 (Fig. 20-3); accordingly it was named ϵ^{15}.

O antigen

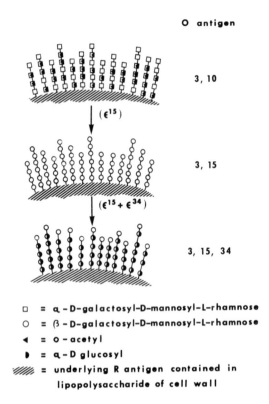

3, 10

(ϵ^{15})

3, 15

($\epsilon^{15} + \epsilon^{34}$)

3, 15, 34

□ = α – D – galactosyl – D – mannosyl – L – rhamnose
○ = β – D – galactosyl – D – mannosyl – L – rhamnose
◀ = o – acetyl
▶ = α – D glucosyl
▨ = underlying R antigen contained in lipopolysaccharide of cell wall

Fig. 20-5 Schematic diagrams of determinant side chains of O antigens of group E salmonellae, showing their terminal relation to the core R polysaccharide (see Fig. 20-2) and indicating the nature and approximate number of repeating trisaccharide units in each side chain. (Modified from P. W. Robbins, and T. Uchida. Fed. Proc. 21:702, 1962, and J. Biol. Chem. 240:375, 1965.)

by the ϵ^{34} phage able to add the terminal D-glucosyl residue of the 3,15,34 antigen. The extreme precision involved in the biosynthesis of each specific O antigen is thus apparent.

The second example of genetic interaction relates to the resistance of shigella to antibiotics. In Japan treatment with sulfonamide drugs at the close of World War II led to a striking decrease in the incidence of bacillary dysentery (shigellosis), only to be followed by the emergence of sulfonamide-resistant strains and a return of high morbidity rates. When in the mid-1950s streptomycin, chloramphenicol, and the tetracyclines became available, the number of cases again declined. In 1955, however, a

shigella strain resistant to all these antibiotics, as well as to sulfonamides, was isolated from a dysentery patient recently returned from Hong Kong. Shortly thereafter an increasing number of epidemics were reported due to shigellae resistant to all four of the drug types. Not all of the patients in each epidemic, however, were infected with the resistant organisms, even when the strains isolated were antigenically identical; in fact, a few patients were found to shed both drug-sensitive and drug-resistant shigellae of the same antigenic type. It seemed quite impossible, therefore, that the drug resistance could have resulted from the usual mechanisms of genetic variation, since the quadruply resistant strain would have to have undergone a series of four more or less simultaneous mutations.

Strains of *E. coli* resistant to the several drugs were also isolated from some of the dysentery patients, and in 1959 Akiba* made the novel suggestion that the multiple drug resistance of the shigellae was acquired from multiply resistant *E. coli* already present in the patients' gastrointestinal tracts. Shortly thereafter, transfer of the resistance from *E. coli* to shigellae was accomplished, first in mixed cultures grown in vitro, and then in the intestinal tracts of human volunteers. Subsequently it was found that similar transfers could be made to (and between) salmonellae, cholera bacilli, and many species of coliform bacteria. Since the transfers required cell to cell contact, they evidently involved **conjugation.** The factor responsible for the conjugation was shown to be an **episome** (Ch. 24, Episomes), designated the "resistance transfer factor" or **RTF.** Attached to the RTF are genes for resistance to the different drugs. Each gene can be segregated genetically and several have been shown to produce enzymes that inactivate the drugs. Thus the RTF is in reality a sex factor analogous to (but specifically different from) the F factor (Ch. 7, Conjugation); and with its genes for drug resistance attached, it behaves like F.

* See Wanatabe (1963).

The medical implications of these findings are obvious. If individuals who have ingested multiply drug-resistant *E. coli* continue to harbor them in their intestinal tracts and are later infected with pathogenic salmonellae, shigellae, or cholera vibrios, the disease-producing strains in their feces may acquire the multiple resistance factor (RTF) and become potential sources of serious epidemics. Although transfer of the multiple resistance factor is partially inhibited in the human intestinal tract by fatty acids and other as yet undefined inhibitors, its effect on the bacterial population is certain to be accentuated by the selective pressure of antimicrobial therapy.

Genetic advances of the kind illustrated by the foregoing examples have cast new light on the complex interrelations of the enteric bacilli. Above all, they emphasize the extraordinary genetic instability of intestinal bacteria. They reveal that **species** differentiation among intestinal pathogens (equivalent, it should be noted, to antigenic **type** differentiation among

respiratory pathogens) is based primarily on differences in antigenic structure which may involve only minor modifications of a single kind of macromolecule. These precise molecular configurations could hardly be expected to remain stable in the microbe- and virus-laden environment of the intestinal tract, where opportunities for genetic recombination abound. Likewise, it may be anticipated that the metabolic characteristics of a given immunological type will at times vary. A striking example of such a variation is the recent identification of lactose-fermenting strains of *S. typhosa* cultured from patients with undoubted typhoid fever.* Here, even the time-honored lactose fermentation method, universally used as a provisional test to differentiate pathogenic from nonpathogenic enteric bacilli, proved unreliable. Indeed, the possibility cannot be dismissed that genetic recombination in the intestinal tract may even cause harmless enteric bacilli occasionally to become virulent.

ACTINOMYCETES

General Characteristics

The actinomycetes* are gram-positive organisms that tend to grow slowly as branching filaments. In some genera filaments readily segment during growth and yield pleomorphic, club-shaped cells that resemble corynebacteria and mycobacteria; and some are even acid-fast. The resemblance of actinomycetes to fungi is also particularly striking: their filamentous growth leads to mycelial colonies (Ch. 21), and the chronic subcutaneous granulomatous abscesses caused by some actinomycetes are clinically indistinguishable from the mycetomas caused by some fungi (Ch. 21). For these reasons the actinomycetes were long regarded as fungi, and their name, **ray-fungus,** reflects this view (Gr. *aktino,* "ray," and *mykes,* "mushroom or fungus").

The term ray refers to the characteristic radial arrangement of club-shaped elements formed in infected tissues by microcolonies of the major human pathogen of this group, one of the first actinomycetes to be discovered.

Nevertheless, the following more fundamental biological properties establish the actinomycetes as bacteria.

1) They are prokaryotic (i.e., lack a nuclear membrane).

2) The diameter of their filaments is 1 μ or less, i.e., smaller than yeast cells and much narrower than the characteristic tubular structures (hyphae) of molds (Ch. 21). The filaments of the more fragile actinomycetes readily segment into bacillary and twig-like forms, with typical dimensions of bacteria.

3) Their cell walls contain muramic acid and diaminopimelic acid (lysine in some species), which are characteristic of bacterial walls (Ch. 2); and they lack chitin and

*In this chapter we follow the practice of referring to all members of the order Actinomycetales, except for the mycobacteria, as actinomycetes (see Table 20-7).

TABLE 20-7. MEMBERS OF THE ORDER ACTINOMYCETALES

Actinomycetes	Family: Mycobacteriaceae—mycelium absent or rudimentary
	    Genus: *Mycobacterium*
	Family: Actinomycetaceae—grow as fragile branching filaments that readily fragment into bacillary and twig-like elements
	    Genus: *Actinomyces*—anaerobic or microaerophilic; not acid-fast
	    Genus: *Nocardia*—aerobic; some species somewhat acid-fast
	Family: Streptomycetaceae—grow as stable, branching filaments; form aerial mycelia with spores; filaments not readily fragmented; not acid-fast, except for spores in some species
	    Genus: *Streptomyces**—spores formed in chains

Five other genera are also classified as Streptomycetaceae, and a third family, Actinoplanaceae, including two other genera, is also classified with the actinomycetes.
Based on the classification system of S. Waksman and A. Henrici.

glucans, characteristic of cell walls of molds and yeasts (Ch. 21).

4) Their growth is inhibited by penicillins, tetracyclines, sulfonamides, and other antibacterial drugs, all of which are innocuous for fungi.

5) They are insensitive to the polyenes, which are effective fungicidal agents (Ch. 21).

6) Genetic recombination has been observed in one group, *Streptomyces,* and involves a transmissible fertility factor and the formation of merozygotes, rather than the zygote formation seen with fungi.

In addition, some actinomycetes can be infected by viruses (actinophages), whereas viral infections of fungi have not been recognized.

Together with mycobacteria, the actinomycetes make up the order Actinomycetales (Table 20-7). *Actinomyces* and *Nocardia* (named for Nocard, the French microbiologist) both tend to grow as branching filaments when freshly cultivated. However, in older cultures and in infected lesions increased septation leads to spontaneous fragmentation into bacillary and even coccoid elements of irregular diameter, indistinguishable from diphtheroids; and those species of *Nocardia* that are acid-fast resemble mycobacteria. *Streptomyces* species are more fungus-like: their filaments do not fragment spontaneously in the course of growth, they form aerial mycelia and at the tips of the filaments they develop chains of asexual

spores, called conidia, like the corresponding structures of fungi (Ch. 21).

Up until 25 years ago only a small number of soil microbiologists were interested in the streptomycetes. However, beginning with the isolation by Waksman et al. of actinomycin in 1940, and streptomycin in 1943, the streptomycetes have received a phenomenal amount of attention. Innumerable isolates from soil samples, taken from all parts of the world, have been systematically scrutinized for production of antibiotics. To date various species of *Streptomyces* have produced upward of 500 different antibiotics. And except for penicillins and griseofulvin, which are obtained from various species of the fungus *Penicillium,* almost all other antibiotics of practical value are produced by cultures of *Streptomyces*; these amount annually to several million pounds, worth almost one billion dollars. Thus, unlike the other organisms considered in this volume, the streptomycetes are medically significant not so much for their pathogenic effects, which are relatively rare, but for their contribution to the control of other microbial pathogens.

Equally important, streptomycetes and some other actinomycetes are widespread scavengers in soil. By breaking down proteins, cellulose, and other organic matter (including waxes, rubber, and paraffin), they probably contribute as much as all other bacteria and fungi to the fertility of soil and to the geochemical stability of the biosphere.

MYCOPLASMAS

History

Early in the eighteenth century a highly contagious pulmonary disease of cattle appeared in Europe causing enormous losses. Because it was characterized by large amounts of serous fluid in the lungs and pleural cavities, it bceame known as **pleuropneumonia.** Injection of a drop of the serous fluid into the skin of a healthy animal was later found to produce a rapidly spreading edematous lesion; yet no bacteria could be found in the fluid. The causative agent was finally cultivated in 1898 on serum-enriched media. The colonies produced were very small and difficult to detect, and the tiny organisms stained poorly and were extremely pleomorphic.

In the intervening years a number of microorganisms with similar morphological and cultural properties have been isolated: some from animals, others from the mucous membranes of man, and still others from soil and sewage. Unlike other bacteria they possess **no cell walls** and (except for certain saprophytic species) require sterols for growth. Indeed, they are the smallest known free-living organisms. Originally referred to as pleuropneumonia-like organisms, or **PPLO** for short, they have recently been assigned the generic name *Mycoplasma*. The one human disease of proved mycoplasmal etiology is a form of **primary atypical pneumonia.**

Morphology and Mode of Replication

Because they have no rigid cell wall mycoplasmas not only stain poorly but are also much more plastic and pleomorphic than other bacteria (hence the term mycoplasma). They are bounded by a limiting membrane, which is 75 to 100 A in width and resembles, in electron photomicrographs, the cytoplasmic membranes of animal cells. Within the cell ribosomes and "nuclear strands" can be identified, and in some strains amorphous material on the outer surface of the membrane suggests the existence of a capsule or rudimentary wall.

Replication. The absence of a rigid cell wall is associated with a pattern of replication quite different from that of typical bacteria, whose division starts with the formation of a well-defined septum. Though the mechanism of division in mycoplasmas has not been unequivocally established, sequential microscopic observations suggest the cycle of morphological changes depicted diagrammatically in Figure 20-6. The particle sizes of the smallest reproductive units are difficult to measure because of their plasticity, but some are capable of passing filters with an average pore diameter of 150 mμ. These small units are believed to grow into much larger cells from which new small units, formed either in the cytoplasm or by budding (Fig. 20-7), are eventually separated. Thus the cycle seems to be perpetuated. The extreme plasticity of the large cells permits them to assume, particularly in fluid media, bizarre shapes such as those depicted in Figure 20-6. Since septum formation is believed to be controlled by mesosomes, it has been suggested that the absence of mesosomes in mycoplasmas accounts for their relatively haphazard replicative cycle.

Colonial Morphology. On solid media mycoplasmas form minute, transparent colonies which are difficult to detect without a hand lens, even when stained. After several days' incubation the colonies range in size from 10 to 600 μ in diameter and usually appear as tiny, round structures with granular surfaces and a dark central nipple (Fig. 20-8). The latter, which gives the colony a "fried egg" appearance, is due to a central zone of deep growth beneath the surface of the agar. Many colonies, however, lack the lighter peripheral zone of surface growth and exhibit only the dark center. The colonies of most human strains cultured aerobically on blood agar are surrounded by zones of either α- or β-hemolysis.

When grown in liquid media mycoplasmas produce little turbidity.

Metabolism

Mycoplasmas are the smallest free-living cells that have thus far been discovered. Indeed, it has been calculated, on theoretical grounds, that their smallest forms are just about large enough to contain the necessary macromolecular machinery for extracellular reproduction. Therefore they are of great interest to molecular biologists.

As might be expected, mycoplasmas require a rich medium for growth. The most widely used basal medium consists of 10 gm of peptone, infusion prepared from 500 gm of beef heart, 5 gm of sodium chloride, and 14 gm of agar per liter. Each liter of basal medium is usually supplemented with 200 ml of horse serum and 100 ml of 25% yeast extract.* The

final pH is adjusted to the range of 7.6 to 8.0.

Most mycoplasma species require both a steroid and serum protein. Since steroids are not known to be essential nutrients of other bacterial species, their requirement by mycoplasmas is of major interest. Parasitic human mycoplasmal species contain 10 to 20% total lipid, 50 to 65% of which is nonsaponifiable; no nonsaponifiable lipid can be detected in saprophytic species grown without steroids (e.g., *M. laidlawii*).† An important function

---

* The final concentration of agar is only about 1%, making the medium somewhat softer than that used for routine bacterial cultures. Because of the high concentrations of serum in the medium pseudocolonies may form, composed of calcium and magnesium soaps; these must not be mistaken for mycoplasmal colonies.

† When *M. laidlawii* is grown in the presence of cholesterol, however, it becomes sensitive to polyene antibiotics (Ch. 10, Polyenes), indicating that the exogenous sterol is incorporated into the cell membrane.

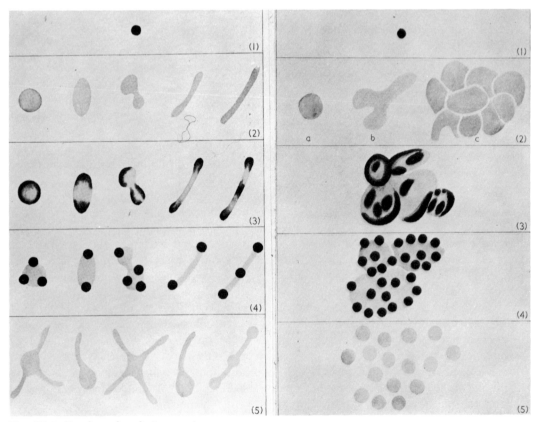

Fig. 20-6 *(See legend on facing page)*

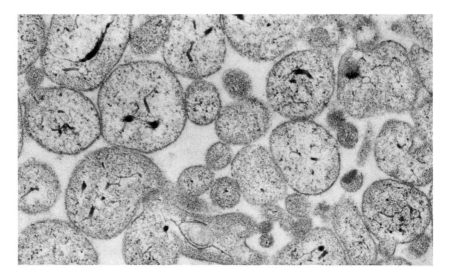

Fig. 20-7 Cell culture (HeLa) of *M. pneumoniae*, fixed in 2% osmic acid, showing pleomorphism and apparent bud formation. The osmiophilic strands in the centers of many of the organisms are believed to be composed of DNA. ×38,000. (From Zucker-Franklin, D., Davidson, M., and Thomas, L. *J. Exp. Med. 124:*521, 1966.)

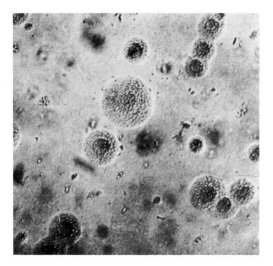

Fig. 20-8 Colonies of human strain of mycoplasma on surface of solid medium. Note fried egg appearance due to growth penetrating surface of agar in center of each colony. ×100. (From E. Klieneberger-Nobel. *Pleuropneumonia-like Organisms (PPLO) Mycoplasmataceae.* Academic Press, New York, 1962.)

Fig. 20-6 Diagrams of mycoplasmal replication in liquid (**left**) and solid (**right**) media: (1) minimal reproductive unit; (2) pleomorphic mycoplasmal cells; (3) concentrations of opaque cytoplasm at margins of cells; (4) appearance of reproductive granules within cells; (5) new generation of cells arising from granules. (From E. Klieneberger-Nobel. *Pleuropneumonia-like Organisms (PPLO), Mycoplasmataceae.* Academic Press, New York, 1962.)

of the serum protein as a growth factor is also believed to relate to lipid metabolism, since a required component of the horse serum supplement is α-1 lipoprotein which contains esterified cholesterol and phospholipid. When lipid is extracted from the horse serum neither the lipid nor the lipid-free fraction alone will support growth, whereas in combination they will do so. The protein growth factor therefore probably regulates the uptake of sterols essential for growth. The special growth factor in yeast extract required by *M. pneumoniae* and *M. orale* is dialyzable but has not been identified.

Some human species, and the saprophytic species *M. laidlawii,* ferment glucose, whereas most others do not. All have a relatively low content of nucleic acids as compared with other bacteria (p. 605). Most require nucleic acid precursors (guanine, uracil, and cytosine) in the medium, as well as a number of vitamins. Whereas most species indigenous

to man can be cultivated aerobically, some grow well only in nitrogen with 5 to 10% carbon dioxide.

Many strains of mycoplasmas can also grow on the chorioallantoic membrane of chick embryos and in tissue cultures. In 12- to 13-day-old embryos *M. pneumoniae* causes inapparent infections confined primarily to the mucous layer of the bronchial epithelium. In monkey kidney tissue cultures its colonies may be seen both on and within the cells.

Mycoplasmas are resistant to the antimicrobial actions of the sulfonamides, penicillin, and thallium acetate,‡ but are generally sensitive to tetracyclines and to kanamycin. They are more susceptible than walled bacteria to killing by distilled water, physiological saline, and surface-active agents including soaps.

---

‡ Thallium acetate (1:1000) is highly bacteristatic for aerobic spore-forming bacteria and for gram-negative bacilli.

SELECTED REFERENCES

Books and Review Articles

AJELLO, L., GEORG, L. K., KAPLAN, W., and KAUFMAN, L. *Laboratory Manual for Medical Mycology.* P.H.S. Publ. No. 994. U.S. Government Printing Office, Washington, D.C., 1963.

CONANT, N. F., SMITH, D. T., BAKER, R. D., CALLOWAY, J. L., and MARTIN, D. S. *Manual of Clinical Mycology,* 2nd ed., Ch. 2. Saunders, Philadelphia, 1954.

CUMMINS, C. S., and HARRIS, H. Studies on the cell-wall composition and taxonomy of Actinomycetales and related groups. *J. Gen. Microbiol. 18*:173 (1958).

ROSEBURY, T. Bacteria Indigenous to Man. In *Bacterial and Mycotic Infections of Man,* Ch. 14. (R. J. Dubos and J. G. Hirsch, eds.) Lippincott, Philadelphia, 1965.

ROSEBURY, T. *Microorganisms Indigenous to Man,* Ch. 3. McGraw-Hill, New York, 1962.

WAKSMAN, S. *The Actinomycetes,* vols. 1, 2, and 3 (with H. A. Lechevalier). Williams & Wilkins, Baltimore, 1962.

21 FUNGI

CHARACTERISTICS OF FUNGI

The fungi (L. *fungus,* "mushroom") have traditionally been regarded as "plant-like" (for taxonomic position, see Ch. 1). Most species grow by continuous extension and branching of twig-like structures. In addition, they are immotile (except for flagellated gametes in some aquatic species), and their cell walls resemble those of plants in thickness and, to some extent, in chemical composition and in ultramicroscopic structure.

The fungi grow either as single cells, the **yeasts,** or as multicellular filamentous colonies, the **molds** and **mushrooms.** The multicellular forms have no leaves, stems, or roots, and are thus much less differentiated than higher plants. However, in comparison with bacteria most species of fungi are capable of a striking degree of differentiation. A single uninucleated cell can yield filamentous multinuclear strands, yeast cells, fruiting bodies with diverse spores, and cells that are differentiated sexually (in many species). Moreover, a few species form remarkable traps and snares for capturing a variety of microscopic creatures, e.g., amebae, nematodes.

Fungi are abundant in soil, on vegetation, and in bodies of water, where they live largely on decaying leaves or wood. Because of their ubiquitous airborne spores they are frequently troublesome contaminants of cultures of bacteria and mammalian cells. In fact, it was just such a contaminant in a culture of staphylococci that eventually led to the discovery of penicillin (Ch. 10).

Though we shall be concerned mainly with those few fungi that cause diseases of man, other fungi have had an even more adverse effect on human welfare as causes of plant diseases: for example, the potato blight led to death from starvation in Ireland alone of over 1 million persons in the period 1845 to 1860. Nevertheless, the over-all effects of fungi on man's condition are probably more benign than malignant. As scavengers in soil they make a major contribution to the chemical stability of the biosphere (Ch. 1), and their biosynthetic capabilities are used in the industrial production of penicillins,

corticosteroids, and numerous organic acids (e.g., citric, oxalic). Moreover, through their role in the production of certain cheeses, bread, and ethanolic beverages, the fungi help provide more than calories to man's food supply.

Structure and Growth

Molds. The principal element of the growing or vegetative form of a mold is the **hypha** (Gr. *hyphe,* "web"), a branching tubular structure, about 2 to 10 μ in diameter, i.e., much larger than bacteria. As a colony, or **thallus,** grows, its hyphae form a mass of intertwining strands, called the **mycelium** (Gr. *mykes,* "mushroom"). Hyphae grow by elongation at their tips (apical growth) and by producing side branches.

Those hyphae that penetrate into the medium, where they absorb nutrients, are known collectively as the **vegetative mycelium,** while those that project above the surface of the medium constitute the **aerial mycelium;** since the latter often bear reproductive cells or spores they are also referred to as the **reproductive mycelium.** Most colonies grow at the surface of liquid or solid media as irregular, dry, filamentous mats. Because of the intertwining of the filamentous hyphae the colonies are much more tenacious than those of bacteria. At the center of mycelial colonies the hyphal cells are often necrotic, owing to deprivation of nutrients and oxygen, and perhaps to accumulation of organic acids.

In most species the hyphae are divided by cross-walls, called **septa** (L. *septum,* "hedge, partition"; Fig. 21-1). The nonseptate mycelia are obviously **coenocytic,** i.e., their many nuclei are obviously embedded in a continuous mass of cytoplasm. However the septa have fine, central, pores; hence even septate hyphae are coenocytic.

Yeasts. Yeasts are unicellular oval or spherical cells, usually about 3 to 5 μ in diameter. Sometimes yeast cells and their progeny adhere to each other and form chains or "pseudohyphae."

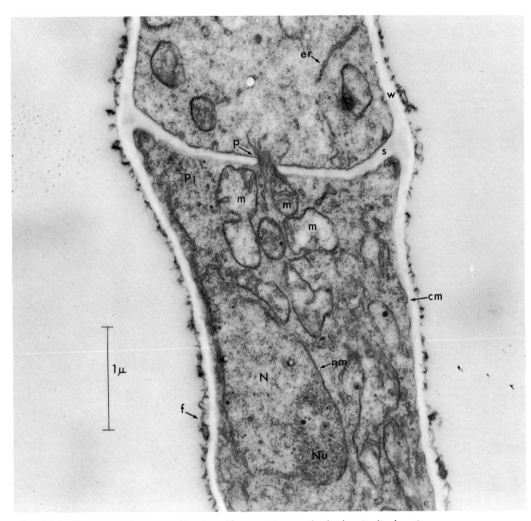

Fig. 21-1 The coenocytic nature of hyphae. Electron micrograph of a longitudinal section through 2 cells of *Neurospora crassa* partially separated by a septum (s). Note the streaming of mitochondria (m) through the septal pore (p). Other labelled structures are cell wall (w), outer frayed coat of the cell wall (f), cell membrane (cm), nucleus (N), nucleolus (Nu), nuclear membrane (nm), ribosomal particles (p$_1$), and endoplasmic reticulum (er). Fixed with OsO$_4$ and stained with uranyl nitrate. $\times$47,000, reduced. (From A. J. Shatkin and E. L. Tatum, J. Biophys. and Biochem. Cytology, 6, 423, 1959.)

Cytology. Yeasts and molds resemble higher plants and animals in the anatomical complexity of their cells. They are eukaryotic, with several different chromosomes and a well defined nuclear membrane, and they possess mitochondria and an endoplasmic reticulum (Fig. 21-2). Moreover, their membranes contain sterols, thus resembling higher forms rather than bacteria.

Cell Wall

The cell wall of a fungus, like that of a bacterium, lies immediately external to the limiting cytoplasmic membrane, and in some yeasts it is surrounded by an external capsular polysaccharide. However, unlike bacteria, whose cell walls often contain brick-like structural units (Ch. 2), fungus cell walls

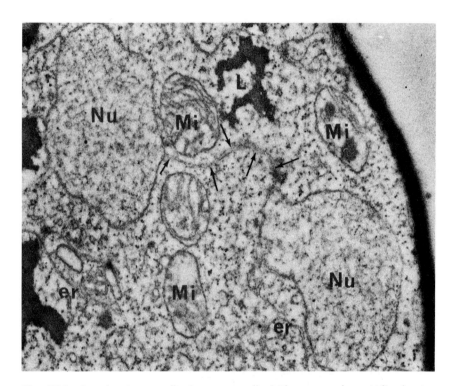

Fig. 21-2 Cytoplasmic organelles in a yeast cell of *Blastomyces dermatitidis*, showing two nuclei (Nu), each surrounded by a nuclear membrane. Also seen are mitochondria (Mi), vesicles and ribosomes of endoplasmic reticulum (er), and lipid droplets (L). Arrows point to membranous connections between nuclei. Osmium-fixed, thin sections. ×35,000, reduced. (From G. A. Edwards and M. E. Edwards, Am. J. Botany 47:622, 1960.)

appear thatched (Fig. 21-3). Polymers of hexoses and hexosamines provide the main structural wall elements of fungi. In many molds and yeasts the principal structural macromolecule of the wall is **chitin,** which is made up of N-acetylglucosamine residues. These are linked together by β-1,4-glycosidic bonds, like the glucose residues in cellulose, the main cell wall material in higher plants.

Chitin also makes up the principal structural material of the exoskeleton in crustacea. Hence this substance represents, at a molecular level, an interesting example of convergent evolution, in which distantly related organisms have developed, presumably by an independent evolutionary sequence, similar or identical structures to serve similar needs.

In yeasts extraction of the wall with hot alkali leaves an insoluble **glucan,** made up of β-1,6-linked D-glucose residues, with β-1,3-linked

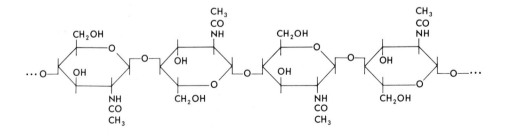

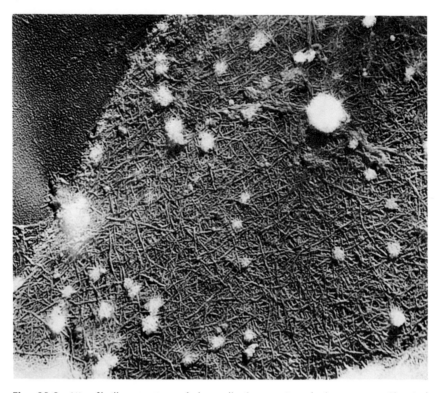

Fig. 21-3 Microfibrillar structure of the wall of a species of phycomycete. Chemical analysis and X-ray diffraction showed the thatched fibrils to be chitin. Electron micrograph shadowed with Pd-Au. ×30,000, reduced. (From J. M. Aronson and R. D. Preston. Proc. Roy. Soc. s. B 152:346, 1960.)

branches arising at frequent intervals. (Glucan resembles cellulose in its insolubility and rigidity.) An additional, soluble polysaccharide is **mannan,** an α-1,6-linked polymer of D-mannose with α-1,2 and α-1,3 branches.

As with bacteria (Ch. 4), the cell wall polysaccharides of fungi are synthesized from various sugar nucleotides (UDP-N-acetylglucosamine, GDP-mannose, etc.). Chitin synthetase is particle-bound in extracts of *Neurospora* and is probably attached to the cell membrane in the intact cell. It requires a primer in vitro, which must contain at least six or seven residues connected as in chitin.

In a number of yeasts complexes of polysaccharide with protein have been identified. In these proteins cystine residues are abundant, and the reversible reduction of -S-S-

bonds has been implicated in the formation of buds. In some yeasts lipids, containing phosphorus and nitrogen, are also abundant in the wall (up to 10% of dry weight).

Fungus cell walls can be digested by enzymes contained in the digestive juices of the snail *Helix pomatia*. These juices contain over 30 recognized enzymatic activities, including glucanase, chitinase, and mannanase. Bacteria that produce lytic enzymes for these walls have also been isolated from soil samples, by application of the enrichment technic (Ch. 3, Genotypic adaptation) with purified cell walls as carbon source.

As expected from the behavior of bacteria, when the walls of yeast or molds are digested in hypertonic solution viable **protoplasts** are left. Protoplasts are also produced by growth

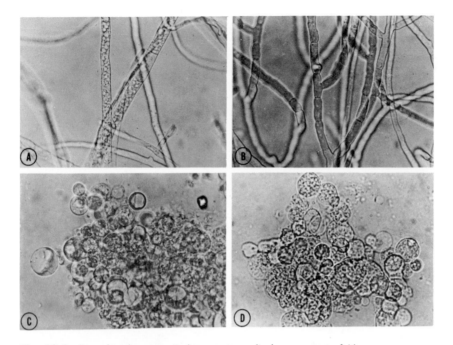

Fig. 21-4 Protoplast formation in hypertonic media by a mutant of *Neurospora crassa* with defective synthesis of cell wall. Cultures were grown in minimal medium with sorbose 0% (**A**), 5% (**B**), or 10% (**C** and **D**). Branching hyphae with septa are evident in **A** and in **B**. Protoplasts with occasional cell wall fragments are present in **C** and **D**. Similar results were obtained with equimolar concentrations of glucose, sucrose, and fructose. (From J. G. Hamilton and J. Calvet. J. Bact. 88:1084, 1964.)

in media that inhibit cell wall synthesis (Fig. 21-4). Yeast protoplasts are deficient in some of the hydrolases of the intact cells, such as invertase and β-fructosidase activity. These observations suggest that as in bacteria (Ch. 5) secreted enzymes are located in the cell wall or, more likely, between cell wall and cytoplasmic membrane.

Metabolism

Fungi are sharply distinguished from algae by their **lack of chlorophyll.** All fungi are heterotrophic (Ch. 3), requiring organic food-stuffs, and most are obligate aerobes. Some, however, are facultative; but none are obligate anaerobes. Except for the absence of auto-trophs or obligate anaerobes, the fungi as a group exhibit almost as great a diversity of metabolic capabilities as the bacteria. Many species of fungi can grow in minimal media,

given an organic carbon source and nitrogen as NH_4^+ or even NO_3^-. Thermophilic species can grow at temperatures as high as 50° and above; some can flourish in the high-salt media of cured meats, and others in highly acidic media. And some fungi can hydrolyze even the most complex organic substances, such as wood, bone, tanned leather, chitin, waxes, and even synthetic plastics.

Fungi can be induced by appropriate substrates and analogs to form the corresponding degradative enzymes, and their regulatory mechanisms for controlling enzyme synthesis and activity appear similar to those in bacteria, but differ in some interesting details.

Like bacteria, yeasts show induction, repression, and catabolite repression; in fact the glucose effect on enzyme induction (Ch. 9) was first observed in yeast, at the turn of the century. In contrast to bacteria, however, the structural genes for a given metabolic pathway (e.g., histidine synthesis) are scattered over the genome, and operator genes and operons have, accordingly, been difficult to identify. Since fungi are eukaryotic and yet can be handled with almost as much ease as bacteria, they are attractive for extending knowledge of molecular genetics and regulatory mechanisms to higher forms.

Reproduction

In addition to growing by apical extension and branching, fungi reproduce by means of sexual and asexual cycles, and also by a parasexual process. We shall consider asexual reproduction and the parasexual process in particular detail, since the vast majority of fungi that are pathogenic for man lack sexuality.

Asexual Reproduction

The vegeative **growth** of a coenocytic mycelium involves nuclear division without cell division, the classic process of mitosis ensuring transmission of a full complement of chromosomes to each daughter nucleus. The further addition of cell division leads to asexual (vegetative) **reproduction,** i.e., the formation of a new clone without involvement of gametes and without nuclear fusion. Three mechanisms are known: 1) sporulation, followed by germination of the spores; 2) budding; and 3) fragmentation of hyphae.

Asexual spores in general are sometimes referred to as **conidia;** more often, however, the term is reserved, as in this chapter, for those asexual spores that form at the tips and the sides of hyphae. Other asexual spores (chlamydospores and arthrospores) develop **within** hyphae. The spores germinate when planted in a congenial medium, i.e., they become enlarged, and, if destined to become a mold, send out one or more germ tubes (Fig. 21-11). The tubes elongate into hyphae and give rise to a new colony.

Chlamydospores, which can be formed by many fungi, are thick-walled and unusually resistant to heat and drying; they are probably formed like bacterial spores, by true endosporulation (Ch. 5), and they similarly promote survival in unfavorable environments. In contrast, **arthrospores,** which form by fragmentation of hyphae, and **conidia,** which form by a process akin to budding, are not unusually resistant; they probably function to promote aerial dissemination.

Spores, which contain one or several nuclei, vary greatly in color, size, and shape. Their morphology and their mode of origin constitute the main basis for classifying fungi that lack sexuality. Some species produce only one kind of spore, and others as many as four different kinds. Various common asexual spores, and their distinctive features, are listed in Table 21-1 and illustrated in Figures 21-5

TABLE 21-1. ASEXUAL SPORES FORMED BY FUNGI

Conidia (Gr. *konis*, "dust")	This term is used sometimes generically for all asexual spores, or sometimes more specifically for spores borne singly or in clusters along sides or at tips of hyphae or of specialized hyphal branches (**conidiophores**). Highly diversified in shape, size, color, and septation. Large (usually multinuclear) and small (usually uninuclear) conidia are called **macroconidia** and **microconidia**, respectively.
Arthrospores (Gr. *arthron*, "joint"; *sporos*, "seed")	Cylindrical cells formed by double septation of hyphae. Individual spores are released by fragmentation of hyphae, i.e., by disjunction.
Blastospores (Gr. *blastos*, "bud, shoot")	Buds that arise from yeast and yeast-like cells.
Chlamydospores (Gr. *chlamys*, "mantle")	Thick-walled, round spores formed from terminal or intercalated hyphal cells.
Sporangiospores (Gr. *angeion*, "vessel")	Spores within sac-like structures (**sporangia**) at ends of hyphae or of special hyphal branches (**sporangiophores**). Characteristically formed by species of *Phycomycetes*.

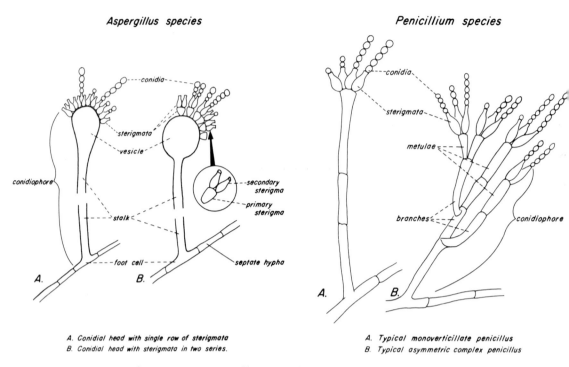

A. Conidial head with single row of sterigmata
B. Conidial head with sterigmata in two series.

A. Typical monoverticillate penicillus
B. Typical asymmetric complex penicillus

Fig. 21-5 Diagram of some representative filamentous fungi and their asexual spores (conidia). (From L. Ajello, L. K. Georg, W. Kaplan, and L. Kaufman. Laboratory Manual for Medical Mycology, P.H.S. Publ. No. 994. U.S. Government Printing Office, Washington, D.C., 1963.)

and 21-6. They should not be confused with sexual spores (see below).

Budding is the prevailing asexual reproductive process in yeast, though some species divide by fission (fission yeast). Whereas in fission (the usual reproductive process of almost all bacteria) a parent cell divides into two daughter cells of essentially equal size, in budding the daughter cell is initially much smaller than the mother cell. As the bud bulges out from the mother cell the nucleus of the latter divides, and one nucleus passes into the bud; cell wall material is then laid down between bud and mother cell, and the bud eventually breaks away (Fig. 21-7). A **birth scar** on the daughter cell's wall, and a **budding scar** on the mother's wall, are visible in electron micrographs (Fig. 21-8). As a result of repeated budding old yeast cells bear many budding scars, but they have only a single birth scar.

Fragments of hyphae are also capable of

forming new colonies. Thus when a colony is fragmented by teasing fragments implanted in fresh medium it can form a new mycelium. This capacity is often exploited in the cultivation of fungi, but it is probably not important in Nature.

Sexual Reproduction

Fungi that carry out sexual reproduction go through the following steps. 1) A haploid nucleus of a donor cell (male) penetrates the cytoplasm of a recipient (female) cell. 2) The male and female nuclei fuse to form a diploid zygotic nucleus. 3) By meiosis the diploid nucleus gives rise to four haploid nuclei, some of which may be genetic recombinants. In most species the haploid condition is the one associated with prolonged vegetative growth, and the diploid state is transient; but in other species, as in higher animals, the opposite is true.

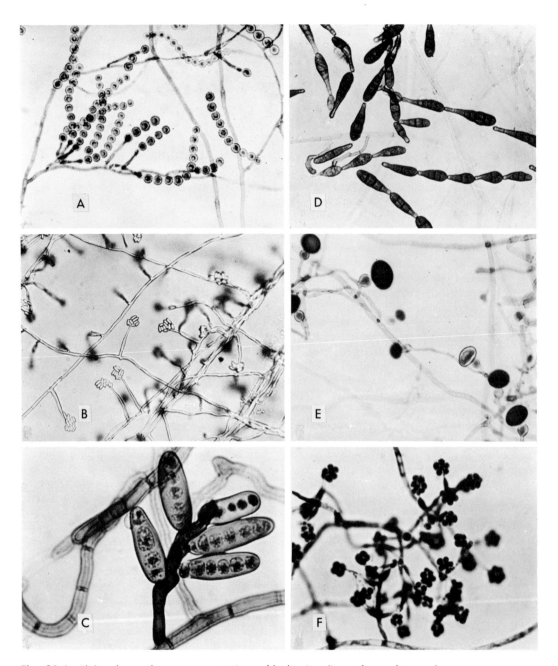

Fig. 21-6 Slide cultures of some representative molds showing diverse forms of asexual spores (conidia), which aid in identifying species, particularly with members of the class *Fungi imperfecti* (Deuteromycetes). (From L. Ajello, L. K. Georg, W. Kaplan, and L. Kaufman. A Manual for Medical Mycology, P.H.S. Publ. No. 994. U.S. Government Printing Office, Washington, D.C., 1963.)

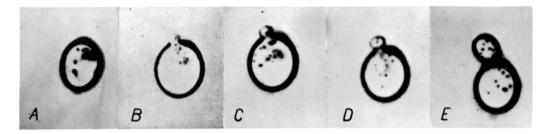

Fig. 21-7 Budding in a yeast cell (*Saccharomyces cerevisiae*). The wall-less bud in **B** was extruded in the 20-second interval between the photos in **A** and **B**. The subsequent photos were taken at approximately 15-minute intervals. The bud in **E** is nearly mature. (From W. J. Nickerson. Bact. Rev. 27:305, 1963.)

In **homothallic** species the cells of a single colony (arising from a single nucleus) can engage in sexual reproduction. In some homothallic species (hermaphrodites) male and female cells are anatomically differentiated, but in others they are indistinguishable. In **heterothallic** species the cells that engage in sexual reproduction must arise from two different colonies, of opposite mating type. The reproductive cells of heterothallic species may be anatomically distinguishable as male and female (**diecious**), or may not, in which event they are only functionally differentiated into sexually compatible mating types. Among fungi with a sexual stage the anatomy of sex organs and the mating procedures are highly diversified but are characteristic

Fig. 21-8 Thin section of an osmium tetroxide-fixed yeast cell (*Saccharomyces cerevisiae*), showing the concave birth scar at one pole and a convex bud scar at the other, ×29,000, reduced. (From H. D. Agar, and H. C. Douglas. J. Bact. 70:247 1955.)

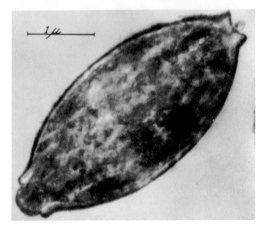

for any particular species; hence they are important for taxonomy.

Sexual cycle in Neurospora. The sexual process in some fungi has played so vital a role in the development of biochemical genetics, as in the classic studies of Beadle and Tatum in *Neurospora crassa*, that a brief description of a representative cycle is warranted.

Neurospora contains in its nucleus seven different chromosomes, each a single copy (i.e., the vegetative organism is haploid). The haploid state is maintained during mycelial growth and during asexual reproduction (i.e., the formation of conidia). Sexual reproduction occurs when two cells (hyphae or conidia) of different mating type fuse to form a **dikaryotic** cell; the two kinds of haploid nuclei coexist in the same cytoplasm and for a time divide more or less in synchrony. If a cell initiates an ascus, however, two different haploid nuclei fuse and form a diploid nucleus, containing pairs of **homologous** chromosomes (Fig. 21-9).

The diploid cell then initiates the process of **meiosis.** The homologous chromosomes pair (synapse) with each other (i.e., assume parallel, closely adjacent positions), and each chromosome divides without duplicating its centromere (whose attachment to a spindle fiber subsequently guides its migration to one pole or other during anaphase). Each chromosome thus becomes a pair of identical **chromatids** connected by a centromere (a bivalent), and each pair of homologous bivalents constitutes a **tetrad.** One or more exchanges of parts (crossing-over) may then occur at random among the four chromatids of the tetrad, resulting in genetic recombination.

Two meiotic divisions follow. In the first there are no divided centromeres to separate (as in mitosis); instead, one member of each pair of homologous chromosomes (in the form of a bivalent) is drawn after its centromere to each daughter nucleus. In the second meiotic division the chromosome is already divided into two chromatids, and only the centromere divides; one product then migrates (as in mitosis) to each pole, drawing its chromosome with it. Thus the four chromatids of each tetrad are distributed to four different cells, each of which ends up with a haploid set of chromosomes. The individual members of each set are thus derived at random from either parent, and are further scrambled by the genetic recombination occurring at the tetrad stage (Fig. 21-9).

One further feature of this process is that the four haploid cells resulting from the meiosis remain together in the same sac (**ascus**); and in *Neurospora* (though not in all Ascomycetes) before the ascus is fully matured each cell divides mitotically into two identical spores. In the ascus, which is shaped as a narrow pod, the eight resulting **ascospores** are held in a linear array, whose order reflects the meiotic segregation of their chromosomes.

Analysis of the genetic constitution of all four pairs of spores in the same ascus (**tetrad analysis**) allows the most complete possible description of the genetic events occurring during meiosis: the products of reciprocal recombination can be identified, rather than merely deduced (as with higher organisms) from the statistical distribution of genetic markers among the progeny. Moreover, the haploid nature of the vegetative phase eliminates the complicating effect of dominance on the relation between genotype and phenotype.

Parasexual Cycle (Mitotic Recombination)

Some fungi go through a cycle that imparts some of the biological advantages of sexuality (i.e., recombination of parental DNA) without involvement of specialized mating types or gametes. This process of parasexuality, first demonstrated by Pontecorvo with *As-*

Fig. 21-9 Sexual reproduction in *Neurospora crassa*. **A.** Mating leads to formation of a dikaryon and then eventually, by fusion of nuclei, to a diploid cell. **B.** Meiotic divisions with recombination, followed by mitosis, produces eight haploid ascospores linearly arranged in a narrow pod (ascus).

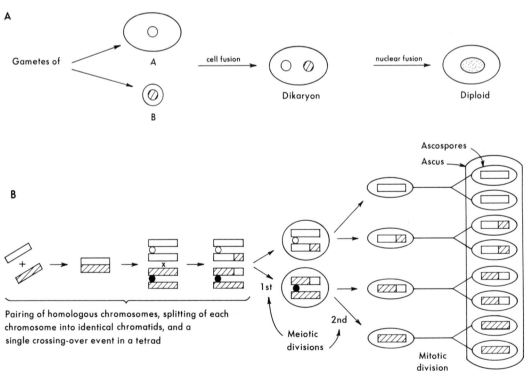

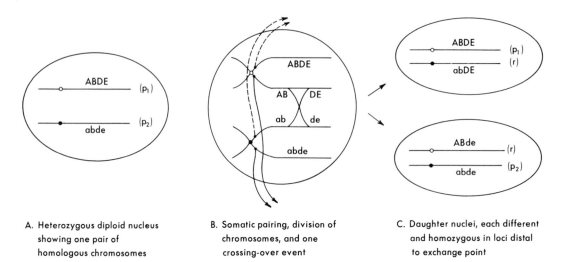

A. Heterozygous diploid nucleus
showing one pair of
homologous chromosomes

B. Somatic pairing, division of
chromosomes, and one
crossing-over event

C. Daughter nuclei, each different
and homozygous in loci distal
to exchange point

Fig. 21-10 Somatic pairing and mitotic recombination in the parasexual cycle of fungi. After fusion of genetically different hyphae to form a heterokaryon, the unlike haploid nuclei occasionally fuse to yield the heterozygous diploid nucleus depicted in **A**. Rare somatic pairing and recombination give rise, through the daughter nuclei depicted in **C**, to partially homozygous lines of diploid cells, as shown. These occasionally also segregate haploid strains, half of which are recombinant (compared with the original haploid parents) in respect to loci dD and eE. p, parental chromosome; r, recombinant chromosome.

pergillus, involves the following steps (Fig. 21-10). 1) By **hyphal fusion** different haploid nuclei come to coexist in a common cytoplasm. The **heterokaryon** thus formed can be stable, the two sets of nuclei dividing at about the same rate. 2) Rare **nuclear fusion** will yield heterozygous diploid nuclei. These are usually greatly outnumbered by the haploid nuclei, but once formed they tend to divide at about the same rate as the latter; and stable diploid strains may be isolated. 3) Though homologous chromosomes are usually arranged independently on the equatorial plate in the mitosis of a diploid cell, rarely (ca. 10^{-4} per mitosis) sufficient **somatic pairing** will occur to permit crossing-over, as in meiosis.

The result of such mitotic recombination between heterozygous homologous chromosomes is to make the products **homozygous for genes distal to the exchange point.** Thus two diploid daughter cells with different properties result, each homozygous for some alleles for which the diploid parent cell is heterozygous (Fig. 21-10). Further phenotypic changes appear when these new diploid strains yield haploid progeny: as can be seen from Figure 21-10, half of these will be parental in genetic composition and half will be recombinant.

Mitotic recombination has provided unique opportunities for genetic analysis of asexual molds. Its possible application to the study of the genetics of somatic diploid cells, such as human cells in tissue culture, is of great interest, and could contribute to our understanding of many problems of cell physiology and genetics in man. With the limited range of genetic markers available thus far in human cells, however, the recombination rate has been low, but sufficient to be encouraging.

Though recombinants are infrequent in a parasexual cycle, compared with a sexual cycle, the process may be significant for the evolution of asexual fungi.

Taxonomy

The four major classes of fungi are summarized in Table 21-2.

TABLE 21-2. CLASSES OF FUNGI

Class	Asexual spores	Sexual spores	Mycelia	Representative genera or groups
Phycomycetes	Endogenous (in sacs)	Anatomy variable	Nonseptate	*Rhizopus, Mucor,* watermolds (aquatic)
Ascomycetes	Exogenous (at ends or sides of hyphae)	Ascospores, within sacs or asci	Septate	*Neurospora, Penicillium, Aspergillus,* true yeasts
Basidiomycetes	Exogenous (at ends or sides of hyphae)	Basidiospores, on surface of basidium	Septate	Mushrooms, rusts, smuts
Deuteromycetes (Fungi Imperfecti)	Exogenous (at ends or sides of hyphae)	Absent	Septate	Most human pathogens

The **Phycomycetes** have nonseptate hyphae; their asexual spores (sporangiospores) are contained in sacs (sporangia) that form at the end of specialized stalks (sporangiophores). Different species have different sexual cycles and those that live in aquatic environments (Gr. *phyco,* "seaweed") have **flagellated gametes.** Each flagellum contains nine parallel fibers arranged circumferentially about two central fibers, thus resembling cilia of protozoa and higher animals, rather than bacterial flagella (Ch. 2).

The **Ascomycetes** are distinguished from other fungi by the **ascus,** a sac-like structure containing sexual spores (**ascospores**). The ascospores are the endproduct of mating, fusion of male and female nuclei, two meitoic divisions, and usually one final mitotic division, as described above for *Neurospora.* There are thus usually eight ascospores in an ascus. The true yeasts are ascomycetes, though they generally do not grow as molds (see Dimorphism, below).

The **Basidiomycetes** are distinguished by their sexual spores, called **basidiospores,** which form on the surface of a specialized structure, the **basidium.** They include the edible mushrooms. Basidiomycetes cause a variety of serious diseases of plants, including those of cereals and grains, but do not cause infectious diseases of man. However, some species of mushrooms synthesize toxic alkaloids, which can cause fatal poisoning in man. Some mushroom alkaloids are of major pharmacological interest (e.g., ergotamine, muscarine).

The **Deuteromycetes (Fungi Imperfecti)** are particularly important for medicine as they include the vast majority of human pathogens. Because no sexual phase has been observed, they are often referred to as imperfect fungi. Their hyphae are septate, and conidial forms are very similar to those of the ascomycetes; they have therefore long been suspected of being **special ascomycetes,** whose sexual phase is either extremely infrequent or has disappeared in evolution. Indeed, typical ascomycetous sexual stages have recently been observed in several species of this class (Table 21-3). Superficially, the reversible change from sexual to asexual form resembles phase

TABLE 21-3. SOME PATHOGENIC IMPERFECT FUNGI DISCOVERED TO HAVE A SEXUAL (PERFECT) STAGE

Name of imperfect "species"	Perfect form
Microsporum gypseum	{ *Nannizia incurvata* { *N. gypsea*
M. fulva	*N. fulva*
M. nanum	*N. obtusa*
M. cookei	*N. cajetana*
M. vanbreuseghem	*N. grubyia*
Keratinomyces ajelloi	*Arthroderma uncinatum*
Trichophyton terrestre	*A. quadrifidum*

The "species" listed are dermatophytes: they infect the epidermis, nails, and hair of mammals. Only the asexual (imperfect) form is found in infected skin. Conversion to the sexual (perfect) form was facilitated by growth on sterilized soil enriched with keratin (e.g., hair, feathers). The perfect stages were then identified as Ascomycetes by observing production of fruiting bodies when compatible "imperfect" forms were mated (e.g., + and − strains). (A fruiting body contains many asci with their enclosed ascospores.)

variations in bacteria (Ch. 6), suggesting that the imperfect fungi are mutants in genes that specify sexual development.

The provisional status of species designations for imperfect fungi is emphasized by a recent finding with *Microsporum gypseum,* which causes skin infections in man: this classic "species" is the imperfect stage of **two** species of ascomycetes, in which heterothallism (p. 618) is controlled by a pair of allelic genes (Table 21-3).

Dimorphism

Some species of fungi grow only as molds, and others only as yeasts; many species, how-ever, can grow in either form, depending on the environment. **The capacity for growth in alternative forms is known as dimorphism.*** It is important clinically, since most of the more pathogenic fungi (in man) are dimor-phic: they usually appear in infected tissues as yeast-like cells, but when cultivated under conventional conditions in vitro they appear as typical molds (Figs. 21-11 and 21-12).

Dimorphism can be experimentally con-trolled by modifying cultural conditions, a single factor sometimes being decisive. For

---

* The alternatives are not limited to yeast and mold forms. One of the most virulent human pathogens, *Coccidioides immitis,* is dimorphic, growing in infected tissues as spherules and in conventional cultures as a mold. The alternatives apply to a given **cell;** a given **culture** can have a mixture of alternative forms.

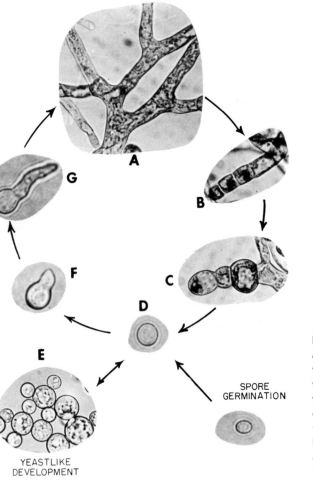

SPORE
GERMINATION

YEASTLIKE
DEVELOPMENT

Fig. 21-11 Mold-yeast dimorphism in *Mucor rouxii.* Note absence of septa, typical of phycomycetes, in hyphae of the mold at **A.** Arthrospores are being formed in **B** and **C.** At **D** an isolated arthrospore is shown developing into yeast-like cells (**E**), or into a mold (**A**) by outgrowth of a filamentous tube (**F** and **G**). (From S. Bartnicki-Garcia. Bact. Rev. 27:293, 1963.)

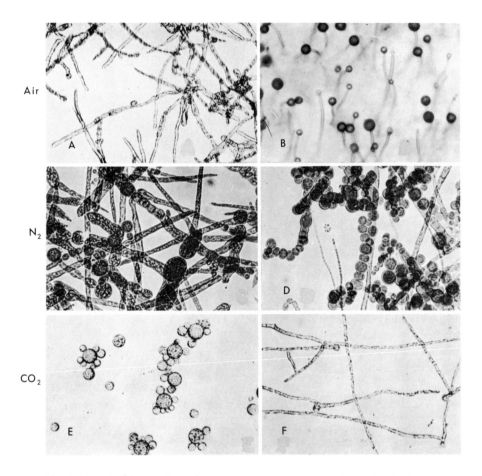

Fig. 21-12 Mold-yeast dimorphism in *Mucor rouxii*, growing in yeast extract–peptone–glucose medium. Air phase for incubation is shown at left. **A.** Filamentous growth is submerged culture. **B.** Surface growth with active spore formation. **C.** Filamentous growth at low concentration of glucose (~ 2%). **D.** Arthrospore formation stimulated by high concentration of glucose (10%). **E.** Yeast-like cells. **F.** Inhibition of yeast-like growth by a chelating agent (diethylene-triamino-pentaacetic acid). All the forms shown can develop under appropriate conditions from a single uninucleated cell (Fig. 21-11). (From S. Bartnicki-Garcia. Bact. Rev. 27:293, 1963.)

example, the human pathogen *Blastomyces dermatitidis* grows as a mycelium at 25° but as yeast cells at 37°; and anaerobiosis promotes the yeast phase of many fungi.

The effect of anaerobiosis on dimorphism has been known for almost a century and has played an important role in establishing the capacity of microorganisms to adapt to their environment. Thus Pasteur, studying variations in microbial physiology in the presence and absence of oxygen (*la vie sans l'air*), was struck by the fact that

Mucor (a common mold, very rarely pathogenic for man) grows at the surface of broth in mycelial form, but in the depths as yeast cells. Recently this difference has been shown to depend upon carbon dioxide: as its tension increases, growth switches from mycelial to yeast-type. There is no gross change in the over-all growth rate, but the cell wall becomes relatively enriched in mannan-protein complexes, and it composes a much larger fraction of total cell weight (about 30% of the yeast cell, but only about 10% of the hyphae).

For most dimorphic fungi parasitism in animals is an incidental and rare event, if it occurs at all. Hence it seems unlikely that infected tissues could have exerted significant selective pressure in the evolution of these fungi. It seems possible that mycelial forms have evolved for growth at surfaces, and yeast forms for growth in the depths of a liquid.

Comparison with Bacteria

Fungi resemble bacteria with respect to their role in maintaining the geochemical stability of the biosphere, the methods used for their isolation and cultivation, their capacity to cause infectious diseases, and the many applications of their fermentations to industrial processes. Fungi differ greatly from bacteria, however, in their reproductive processes, their growth characteristics (e.g., budding, branching filaments), the greater size of the cell, the greater anatomical complexity of their cytoplasmic architecture, their somewhat less

diversified metabolic activities (none are photosynthetic, autotrophic, or obligately anaerobic), the composition and ultrastructure of their cell walls, and the chemotherapeutic agents to which they are susceptible. In addition, dimorphism is not recognized among bacteria but is common among fungi. Finally, as we shall see below, the human diseases caused by fungi are much less common and less varied than those caused by bacteria.

Genetic, biochemical, and antigenic differences have been studied much less among fungi than among bacteria (Table 21-4). And although modern biochemical genetics had its inception in the classic studies of Beadle and Tatum with the mold *Neurospora crassa,* no mating has been discovered (as yet) in most of the fungi pathogenic for man, nor have they been found to be susceptible to viral infection. Hence the genetics of the medically important fungi remains virtually unexplored.

TABLE 21-4. CONTRAST BETWEEN FUNGI AND BACTERIA

Property	Fungi	Bacteria
Cell volume (μ^3)	Yeast: 20–50 Molds: Not definable because of indefinite size and shape and coenocytic form; but much greater than yeast	1–5
Nucleus	Eukaryotic (well-defined membrane)	Prokaryotic (no membrane)
Cytoplasm	Mitochondria, endoplasmic reticulum	No mitochondria or endoplasmic reticulum
Cytoplasmic membrane	Sterols present	Sterols absent (except for *Mycoplasma* grown on sterols)
Cell wall	Glucans; mannans; chitin; glucan- and mannan-protein complexes No muramic acid peptides, teichoic acids, or diaminopimelic acid	Muramic acid peptides; teichoic acids; some have diaminopimelic acid residues No chitin, glucans, or mannans
Metabolism	Heterotrophic, aerobic, facultative anaerobes; no known autotrophs or obligate anaerobes	Obligate and facultative aerobes and anaerobes; heterotrophic and autotrophic
Susceptibility to virus infection	None known	Bacteriophages
Sensitivity to chemotherapeutic agents	Sensitive to polyenes and griseofulvin (dermatophytes); not sensitive to sulfonamides, penicillins, tetracyclines, chloramphenicol, streptomycin	Often sensitive to penicillins, tetracyclines, chloramphenicol, streptomycin; not sensitive to griseofulvin or polyenes
Dimorphism	A distinguishing feature of many species	Absent

SELECTED REFERENCES

Books and Review Articles

AINSWORTH, G. C., and SUSSMAN, A. S., eds. *The Fungi, an Advanced Treatise,* vols. I and II. Academic Press, New York, 1965 (vol. I), 1966 (vol. II).

AJELLO, L., GEORG, L. K., KAPLAN, W., and KAUFMAN, L. *Laboratory Manual for Clinical Mycology.* P.H.S. Publ. No. 994. U.S. Government Printing Office, Washington, D.C., 1963.

ALEXOPOULOS. C. J. *Introductory Mycology,* 2nd ed. Wiley, New York, 1964.

CONANT, N. F., SMITH, D. T., BAKER, R. D., CALLAWAY, J. L., and MARTIN, D. J. *Manual of Clinical Mycology,* 2nd ed. Saunders, Philadelphia, 1954.

DALLDORF, G. (ed.). *Fungi and Fungous Diseases.* Thomas, Springfield, Ill., 1962.

EMMONS, C. W., BINFORD, C. H., and UTZ, F. P. *Medical Mycology.* Lea & Febiger, Philadelphia, 1963.

HILDICK-SMITH, G., BLANK, H., and SARKANY, I. *Fungus Diseases and Their Treatment.* Little, Brown, Boston, 1964.

LARGE, E. C. *The Advance of the Fungi.* Dover, New York, 1962.

Opportunistic fungus infections: An international symposium. *Lab. Invest.,* vol. 11, no. 11, part 2, 1962.

PHAFF, H. J. Cell wall of yeasts. *Ann. Rev. Microbiol.* *17*:15 (1963).

PONTECORVO, G. The parasexual cycle in fungi. *Ann. Rev. Microbiol.* *10*:393 (1956).

SALVIN, S. Immunologic aspects of the mycoses. *Progr. Allergy* 7:213 (1963).

Symposium on biochemical bases of morphogenesis in fungi. *Bact. Rev.* 27:273 (1963).

Specific Articles

KINSKY, S. C., LUSE, S. A., and VAN DEENEN, L.L.M., Interaction of polyene antibiotics with natural and artificial membrane systems, *Fed. Proc.* 25:1503 (1966).

WEITZMAN, I. Variations in *Microsporum gypseum.* I. A genetic study of pleomorphism. *Sabouraudia* 3:195 (1964).

IV VIROLOGY

22 THE NATURE OF VIRUSES

Viruses are a unique class of infectious agents. They were originally distinguished because they are especially **small** (hence the original term "filtrable viruses"), and because they are **obligatory intracellular parasites.** These properties, however, are shared by some small bacteria, and the truly distinctive features of viruses are now known to lie in their simple organization and composition and their mechanism of replication. A complete viral particle, or **virion,** may be regarded as a bloc of genetic material surrounded by a coat, which protects it from the environment and serves as a vehicle for its transmission from one host cell to another.

Distinctive Properties

Composition. The composition of a virus was first determined in 1933 by Schlesinger, who demonstrated that a bacteriophage contained only protein and DNA. A few years later Stanley crystallized tobacco mosaic virus, which was shown to be made up of RNA and protein. Extensive work with many viruses in recent years has confirmed and generalized these findings. It is now accepted that all viruses contain **a single type of nucleic acid,** either DNA or RNA, and a **protein** coat surrounding the nucleic acid. In addition, some viruses contain lipids and carbohydrates. Virions lack constituents fundamental for growth and multiplication, e.g., ribosomes, transfer RNA, enzyme systems required for synthesis of nucleic acids and proteins, and systems generating ATP.

Size and Structure (Fig. 22-1, Table 22-1). The **size** of virions was first estimated by W. J. Elford, using filtration through collodion membranes of known pore diameter. Viral sizes are also determined by analytical ultracentrifugation and by electron microscopy. The latter technic is the most accurate and it will be given preference in presenting measurements.

Most viruses are smaller than bacteria; the larger viruses (e.g., vaccinia), however, are as large as certain small bacteria (e.g., myco-plasma, rickettsia, or chlamydia). The chlamydiae were for a time regarded as large viruses because they also are obligatory intracellular parasites, but their more fundamental kinship to bacteria has been established with the recognition that they have a cellular type of organization (including both DNA and RNA, a variety of biosynthetic enzymes, and wall components characteristic of bacteria).

Virions display a limited range of morphological types, which are highly characteristic and are therefore used as the basis for classification. Since the number of distinctive morphological classes is small, however, viruses with quite different biological properties may appear morphologically indistinguishable. Hence morphology by itself is not adequate for identifying viruses.

Mode of Replication. Since the virions do not contain within their coats the machinery required for replication, but must use enzymes and precursors provided by the host cell, **viruses multiply by separate synthesis and then assembly of their components.** After the protein coat has been shed the viral nucleic acid comes in contact with the appropriate cell machinery, where it causes the synthesis of proteins specified by viral genes, which are required for its own replication. The viral nucleic acid is then itself replicated, the subunits of the viral coat are formed, and these components are finally assembled. This mode of multiplication accounts for the **obligatory intracellular parasitism.**

Viruses multiply only in particular **host cells** and are accordingly subdivided into three main classes: **animal viruses, bacterial viruses** or **bacteriophages,** and **plant viruses.** The host range is determined mainly by the specificity of attachment of the virions to the host cells, and depends on properties of both the coat of the virion and specific receptors of the cell surface. The naked viral nucleic acid has a much broader, and perhaps unlimited, host range because its association with cells is not restricted by the specificity of the cell receptors.

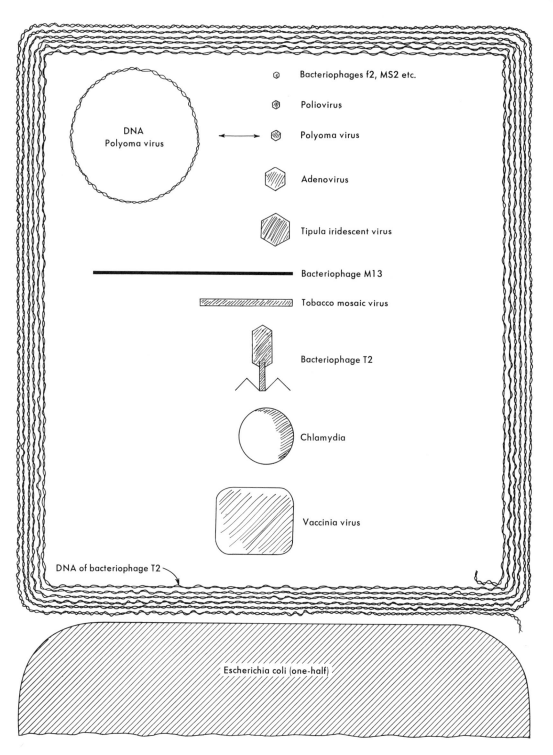

DNA
Polyoma virus

Bacteriophages f2, MS2 etc.

Poliovirus

Polyoma virus

Adenovirus

Tipula iridescent virus

Bacteriophage M13

Tobacco mosaic virus

Bacteriophage T2

Chlamydia

Vaccinia virus

DNA of bacteriophage T2

Escherichia coli (one-half)

Fig. 22-1 Comparative sizes of virions, their nucleic acids, and bacteria. The profiles, as well as the length of the DNA molecules, are reproduced on the same scale.

TABLE 22-1. CHARACTERISTICS OF VIRUSES

Morphological class	Viruses	Size of capsid (A)	No. of capsomers	Size of virions of enveloped viruses (A)	Special features
		Viruses containing DNA (double-stranded unless otherwise specified)			
Helical capsid Naked	Coliphage fd	50 × 8000			Single-stranded DNA
Enveloped (complex)	Poxviruses*				
	Vaccinia virus			2500 × 3000	Brick shape
	Contagious pustular dermatitis of sheep			1600 × 2600	Flat cylinder
Icosahedral capsid Naked	Adeno-satellite virus	200	12		
	Coliphage φX174	220	12		Single-stranded DNA
	Polyoma virus	450	72		
	Papilloma virus	550	72		
	Adenoviruses	600–900	252		
	Tipula iridescent virus (insects)	1400	812		
Enveloped	Herpesviruses, e.g., herpes simplex virus	1000	162	1800–2000	
Capsids of binal symmetry (i.e., some components icosahedral, others helical)					
Naked	Large bacteriophages, e.g., coliphages T2, T4, T6	Modified icosahedral head, 950 × 650; helical tail, 170 × 1150			
		Viruses containing RNA (single-stranded unless otherwise specified)			
Helical capsid Naked	Many plant viruses				
	Tobacco mosaic virus	175 × 3000			
	Beet yellow virus	100 × 8000			
Enveloped	Myxoviruses	90 diameter		900–1000	
	Paramyxoviruses	180 diameter		1250–2500 and over	
	Vesicular stomatitis virus of cattle*			680 × 1750	Bullet shape
Icosahedral capsid Naked	Coliphage f2 and others	200–250			
	Picornaviruses, e.g., poliovirus	280	32		
	Many plant viruses, e.g., turnip yellow mosaic	280	32		
	Reoviruses (man) Wound tumor (plants)	700	92		Double-stranded RNA
Unknown Enveloped	Arbovirus A			450–480	

Assignment is tentative, since the structure of capsid is not known.

Viruses as Infectious Agents

Two properties of viruses, intimately connected with their obligatory intracellular parasitism, explain why they are infectious pathogenic agents: virions produced in one cell can invade other cells and thus cause a spreading infection; and viruses cause important functional alterations of the invaded cells, often resulting in their death.

The role of viruses as infectious agents was recognized long before their true nature was understood. In 1898 Loeffler and Frosch proved that the agent of foot-and-mouth disease in cattle can be transmitted by a cell-free filtrate; cell-free transmission for a plant virus was demonstrated even earlier (Ivanovsky, 1892). These findings paved the way for the recognition of many other viral agents of infectious disease. Soon the tumor-producing ability of viruses was also indicated by the discovery of the viral transmission of fowl leucosis (Ellerman and Bang, 1908) and of a chicken sarcoma (Rous, 1911). The discovery of bacteriophages, made independently by Twort in England and D'Herelle in France in 1917, was of great significance for the development of virology as a science because it afforded an important model system for investigations of basic virology (Ch. 23).

Are Viruses Alive?

Life can be viewed as a complex set of processes resulting from the actuation of the instructions encoded in nucleic acids. These instructions determine the structure and function of all the cellular enzymes, and consequently the structure, multiplication, and function of the cells. Instructions encoded in the nucleic acids of living cells are actuated all the time; in contrast, those encoded in the nucleic acid of a virus are actuated only when the viral nucleic acid, upon entering a host cell, causes the synthesis of virus-specific enzymes and structural proteins. Viruses are thus "alive" when they replicate **in the cells** that they infect. From the point of view of infectious disease, also, viruses are "alive," since they can cause infection, in appropriate hosts, just as well as cellular agents of infection. **Outside of cells,** however, viral particles are metabolically inert and are no more alive than fragments of DNA (e.g., the DNA used in bacterial transformation, Ch. 7).

When Stanley, in 1935, crystallized tobacco mosaic virus, there followed extensive debates on whether such a crystallizable substance was a living being or merely a nucleoprotein molecule. As Pirie pointed out, these discussions showed only that some scientists had a more theological than operational view of the meaning of the word "life." Just as physicists recognize light either as electromagnetic waves or as particulate photons, depending on the context, so biologists can profitably regard viruses both as exceptionally simple microbes and as exceptionally complex chemicals.

THE ANALYSIS OF VIRUSES

Preparation of Samples

Physical and chemical determinations usually require fairly large amounts of virus in highly purified form. With many bacterial and plant viruses the preparation of such material is easy, but with animal viruses it is usually more difficult, though it has become simpler in recent years through the use of tissue cultures. The process of purification consists of separating the virus from the constituents of the host cells in which it multiplies.

The following methods of purification have proved to be especially valuable.

Differential centrifugation separates particles markedly different in mass, since at a centrifuge speed causing the heavier, larger particles to be pelleted to the bottom of the centrifuge tube most of the smaller ones remain in the supernatant. In viral purification low-speed centrifu-

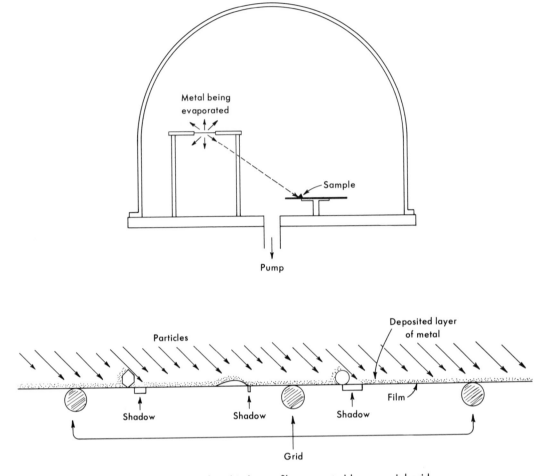

Fig. 22-2 Shadowcasting. A sample is first dried on a film supported by a special grid. The grid is placed in an evaporator chamber, which is evacuated. Metal atoms are projected from a glowing filament in every direction and impinge at a predetermined angle on the sample-carrying film, where they form a relatively uniform layer of metal. The grid is then examined in the electron microscope. Particles present on the film cause the formation of "shadows," i.e., areas where the metal layer does not form. The length and the shape of the shadows provide information on the three-dimensional shape of the particles.

gation first removes cell debris from crude virus preparations, and then high-speed centrifugation separates viral particles from small molecules.

Zonal sedimentation in a linear density gradient, which is described in Chapter 8, separates particles of different sedimentation constants (dependent upon particle size, shape, and density).

Density gradient equilibrium (isopycnotic) centrifugation, also described in Chapter 8, separates particles according to buoyant density, and

is used to separate virions of different types from each other and from cellular debris.

Methods that separate particles according to surface properties include: **chromatography through columns of ion exchangers** and **electrophoresis,** which separate particles primarily according to number and distribution of charges on their surface; **chromatography through columns of neutral substances** (calcium phosphate, silica gel, etc.); **partition between two polymer solutions** (such as dextran and methylcellulose);

and **extraction with solvents** (such as fluorocarbon), which removes from the water phase a considerable proportion of cellular degradation products but leaves many viruses unaltered.

How Pure is a Purified Viral Preparation? The goal of purification is to increase the ratio of virions to contaminating material, and its results, therefore, can be evaluated by determining the ratio of number of virions to total protein or total nitrogen. This ratio may be hundreds or thousands of times greater in purified than in crude virus. Whereas the **relative degree of purification** can thus be determined, there is no way to determine the **absolute purity** of a viral preparation. In fact, whereas the removal of a substance without altering the viral biological properties proves that it is a contaminant, its persistence after extensive purification does not demonstrate that it is a constituent of the virions; it is difficult, for instance, to remove contaminants adsorbed to the viral particles. Considerable judgment must therefore be exercised in deciding what may belong to the virions and what may not.

Danger of Contamination with Other Viruses. In contrast to bacteria, which are propagated in sterile media, viruses are propagated in cells, which often harbor unrecognized viruses. One must therefore be alert to the danger that a viral preparation may contain contaminant viruses in addition to the inoculated ones, and that the former may be preferentially enriched during viral purification. This danger can be minimized by ensuring that the particles retained during the various steps of viral propagation and purification have the same physical, immunological, and biological properties.

Electron Microscopic Technics

The use of X-ray diffraction and electron microscopy has elucidated only recently the architectural properties of viruses, which are of considerable importance for understanding their function and their evolution. The electron microscopic technics employed will be briefly reviewed in order to help appreciate the significance of the results obtained.

Shadowcasting (Fig. 22-2). A metal vapor, projected at an angle onto a membrane to which dried viral particles are attached, coats it with an electron-opaque layer of metal. Metal deposition is thick on the side of the particles exposed to the vapor, and strengthens their outlines; it is absent on the opposite side, where a "shadow" forms. The size and shape of the particles can be deduced from a study of the outlined parts and of the shadows.

Negative Staining (Fig. 22-3). The viral particles are mixed with a solution of a salt highly opaque to electrons, usually sodium phosphotungstate. The mixture is then spread in a thin layer on a carbon membrane and dried. The parts of the particles that are not penetrated by the salt stand out as electron-lucent areas on an opaque background. This method allows a study

Fig. 22-3 Negative staining. The sample is mixed with a solution of a salt having high electron opacity (e.g., sodium phosphotungstate), and a thin layer is spread on the supporting film and dried. The salt solution surrounding the particles penetrates between particles and film and also into indentations in the surface of the particles, as shown in **A**. When the preparation is examined in the electron microscope, surface projections appear as transparent areas on an opaque background, as shown in **B**.

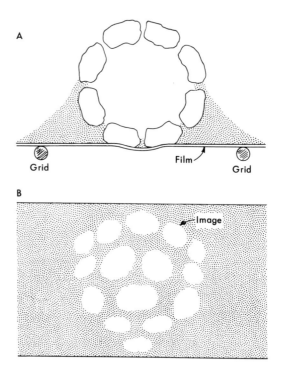

of the details of surface structures because the salt penetrates between protruding parts and makes them visible. The side of the particles against the carbon membrane often contributes the predominant detail.

Positive Staining. Certain components of viruses can be stained by salts that become selectively adsorbed. Uranyl acetate stains the viral nucleic acid and other components; antibodies conjugated to an electron-opaque molecule such as ferritin stain the proteins for which they have specificity. Positive staining can be associated with negative staining to improve the resolution.

Thin Sectioning. This is used to study viral particles in cells or in centrifugal pellets.

The different methods do not yield identical sizes. The size of a virion will be maximal in shadowed preparations, which enhance the contrast at the periphery of the particles; it will be smaller in negatively stained preparations, since the phosphotungstate penetrates the surface details; and it will be even smaller in sections, where the action of the knife tends to collapse the particles. Furthermore, the values obtained by all these methods are less than the size of the particles in water, since drying, as required for electron microscopic examination, causes shrinkage by as much as 30% in linear dimension.

ARCHITECTURE OF VIRAL PARTICLES

General Morphology

Electron microscopy shows that virions have a characteristic anatomy. Each virion has a protein coat, the **capsid**, which closely surrounds the **nucleic acid** to form the **nucleocapsid**. The nucleocapsid, in turn, may be either naked or surrounded by an **envelope**. Virions of the morphological types described below can be recognized (Fig. 22-4).

1) Some virions resemble small crystals. Extensive studies, especially by Klug and Caspar, have shown that these virions are icosahedral and that their shape is determined by the capsid. (The icosahedron is a regular polyhedron with 20 triangular faces and 12 corners.) These virions are called **icosahedral virions.** Examples are polioviruses, adenoviruses, and papilloma viruses (Fig. 22-5A).

2) Some virions form long rods. Their capsid is a hollow cylinder, on the outside of which a fine helical structure can be discerned by high-resolution electron microscopy. They are called **helical virions.** Examples are tobacco mosaic virus (Fig. 22-5B) and bacteriophage M13.

3) Virions of more complicated morphology possess an internal nucleocapsid—in some cases icosahedral, in others helical—surrounded by a loose membranous envelope. Enveloped virions are roughly spherical but highly pleomorphic (i.e., of varying shapes), because the envelope is not rigid. An example of an **enveloped icosahedral** virus is herpes simplex virus (Fig. 22-5C). In **enveloped helical** viruses, such as influenza virus (Fig. 22-5D), the nucleocapsid is coiled within the envelope.

4) Virions of more complex structure belong to two groups. Those illustrated by vaccinia virus (Fig. 22-5E) do not possess clearly identifiable capsids but have several coats around the nucleic acid; while certain bacteriophages (Fig. 22-5F) have a capsid to which additional structures are appended.

The morphological types of the representative viruses are given in Table 22-1.

Location of the Nucleic Acid

In **icosahedral nucleocapsids** the nucleic acid constitutes a central core, as shown by the electron microscopic appearance of **empty capsids,** without nucleic acid (Fig. 22-6). These are present (along with nucleocapsids) in most preparations of icosahedral viruses, both with and without envelopes; and since they have a lower buoyant density they can

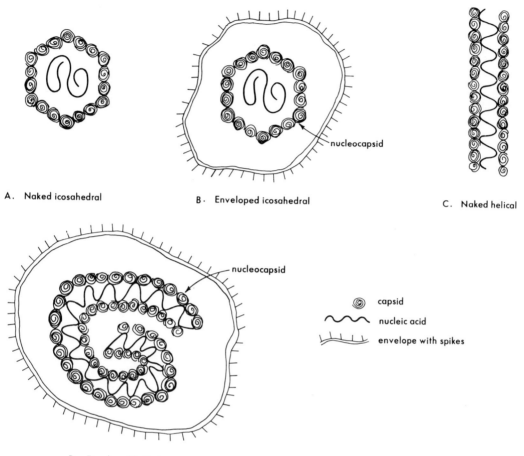

A. Naked icosahedral

B· Enveloped icosahedral

C. Naked helical

nucleocapsid

D. Enveloped helical

⊚ capsid

〜 nucleic acid

⊔⊔⊔ envelope with spikes

Fig. 22-4 Schematic diagram of simple forms of virions and of their components. The naked icosahedral virions resemble small crystals; the naked helical virions resemble rods with a fine regular helical pattern in their surface. The enveloped icosahedral virions are made up of icosahedral nucleocapsids surrounded by the envelope; the enveloped helical virions are helical nucleocapsids bent to form a coarse, often irregular coil, within the envelope.

be separated from the nucleocapsids by equilibrium density gradient centrifugation. In negatively stained preparations both types of particles show a similar external conformation, but in the empty capsids the stain also reveals the hollow center. Although the organization of the nucleic acid in the virion is not known in detail, it has been shown to follow to a certain extent the symmetry of the capsid.

In **helical nucleocapsids** the nucleic acid is located in a helical groove on the inside of the cylindrical capsid (Fig. 22-7). This orderly relation between nucleic acid and capsid has been clearly shown for tobacco mosaic virus (TMV)* by X-ray diffraction studies of nucleocapsids and empty capsids. It has been confirmed by electron microscopic observations of virions in which limited lengths of the capsid, but not the RNA, are removed by

---

* This virus has been a model for the study of the structure of helical viruses, because it can be easily prepared in large amounts and in a highly purified form.

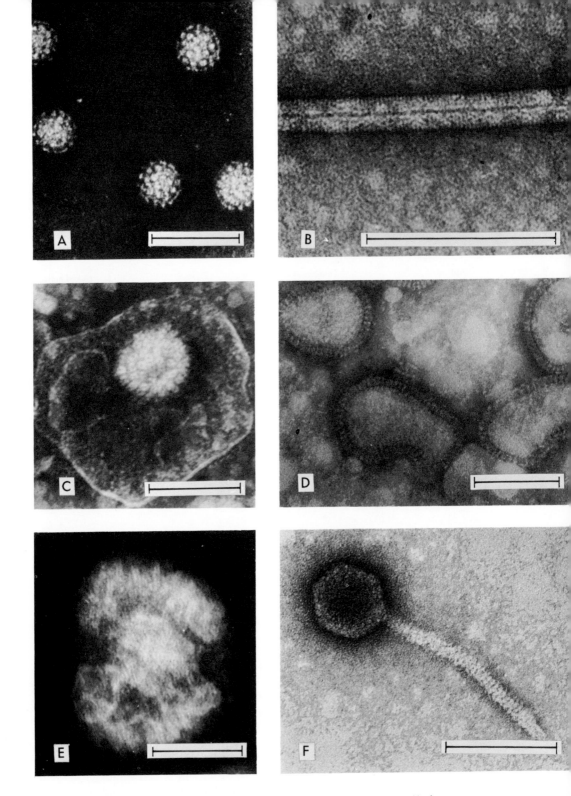

Fig. 22-5 Electron micrographs of representative virions, with negative staining. Markers under each micrograph are 1000 A. **A.** Naked icosahedral: human wart virus. **B.** Naked helical: a segment of tobacco mosaic virus. **C.** Enveloped icosahedral: herpes simplex virus. **D.** Enveloped helical: influenza virus. **E.** Complex virus: vaccinia virus. **F.** Coliphage lambda. (**A** from W. F. Noyes. Virology 23:65, 1964. **B** from J. T. Finch. J. Molec. Biol. 8:872, 1964. **C** courtesy of P. Wildy. **D** from P. W. Choppin and W. Stockenius. Virology 22:482, 1964. **E** courtesy of R. W. Horne. **F** courtesy of F. A. Eiserling.)

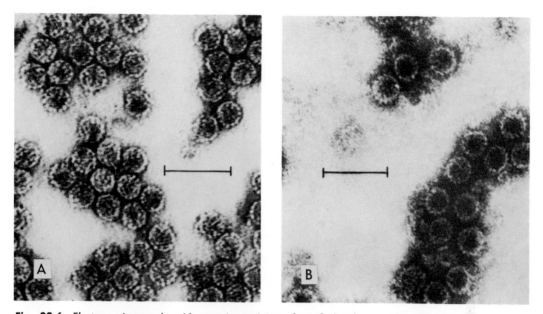

Fig. 22-6 Electron micrographs with negative staining of purified polyoma virus. The full virions, on the left (**A**) are not penetrated by the stain and show only the pattern on the surface of the capsid; the empty capsids, on the right (**B**), are penetrated by the stain. Markers, 1000 A. (From E. Winocour. Virology 19:158, 1963.)

detergents. The RNA protrudes from the center of the residual rods in the form of RNase-sensitive threads (Fig. 22-8).

The existence of empty capsids shows that packing around the nucleic acid is not essential for capsid assembly. However, interaction between the two components stabilizes the nucleocapsid, as empty capsids fall apart much more easily (see also Ch. 25, Maturation).

Structure of the Capsid

The principles underlying the structure of viral capsids have been revealed by chemical and X-ray diffraction studies, which show that both icosahedral and helical capsids are large

multimeric proteins (Ch. 8). In those viruses whose chemical constitution has been sufficiently studied (i.e., the small plant viruses)

Fig. 22-7 Drawing of a segment of tobacco mosaic virus showing the helical nucleocapsid. In the upper part of the figure two rows of protein monomers have been removed to reveal the RNA. This drawing is based on results of X-ray diffraction studies. (From A. Klug and D. L. D. Caspar. Advances Virus Res. 7:225 1960.)

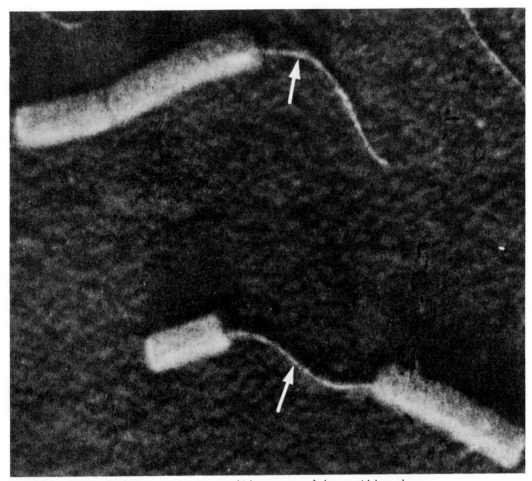

Fig. 22-8 Virions of tobacco mosaic virus in which segments of the capsid have been digested away by detergent. Threads, indicated by arrows, protrude from the center of the remaining capsid segments; they can be destroyed by RNase, and represent the viral RNA centrally located in the nucleocapsid. (From M. K. Corbett. Virology 22:539, 1964.)

the capsid is found to contain a single type of **monomer,** also called the **structural unit,** which has turned out to be constituted by a single type of polypeptide chain 20,000 to 30,000 daltons in molecular weight; the capsids of poliovirus, adenovirus and of other icosahedral animal viruses contain several different polypeptide chains; whether they are incorporated in the same or in different structural monomers is not yet known.

As pointed out by Crick and Watson, the multimeric nature of the capsid is a necessity

because its mass is several times that of the enclosed nucleic acid; and a nucleic acid can at most specify a protein about 1/10 its own weight (a coding triplet with a molecular weight of about 1000 specifies an amino acid of a molecular weight about 100; Ch. 8, The genetic code). Furthermore, only a fraction of the viral nucleic acid specifies the capsid protein because other proteins required for viral multiplication must also be specified (Chs. 23 and 25). For instance, the capsid of tobacco mosaic virus is built with monomers each containing 158 amino acids, and it therefore uses only 574 of the 6000 nucleotides of the viral nucleic acid.

As is the rule with multimeric proteins, the monomers are regularly arranged in the capsid: being identical, they must establish identical reciprocal contacts.

Icosahedral Capsids

In electron micrographs of negatively stained preparations icosahedral capsids display regularly spaced rings or knobs separated by interstices revealed by the electron-dense stain. These rings or knobs are called **capsomers** (Fig. 22-9). Each capsomer is an oligomer composed of a small number of monomers (Fig. 22-10). Theoretical considerations, discussed below, require two types of capsomers: **pentagonal capsomers** (pentamers) made up of five monomers, and **hexagonal capsomers** (hexamers) made up of six monomers. In either type of capsomer the monomers form polygonal rings with central holes of various diameters, up to 40 A. When the central hole is too small to be resolved in the electron microscope the capsomers appear as solid knobs.

The capsid is constructed by assembling the capsomers according to a rigorous geometrical pattern, in which the pentamers constitute the corners of the icosahedron and the

Fig. 22-9 Electron micrograph of GAL virus (chicken adenovirus) by negative staining, showing capsomer structure. The arrowed capsomers are situated on the fivefold axes. Marker, 1000 A. (From P. Wildy and J. D. Watson. Cold Spring Harbor Symp. Quant. Biol. 27:25, 1962.)

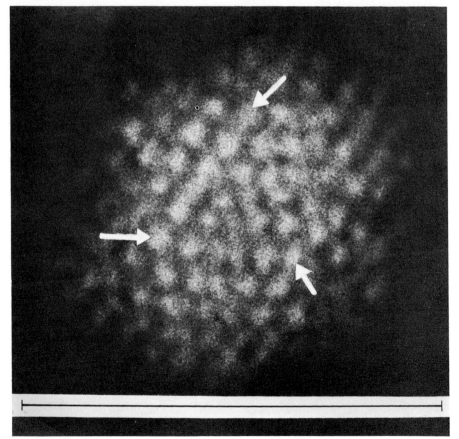

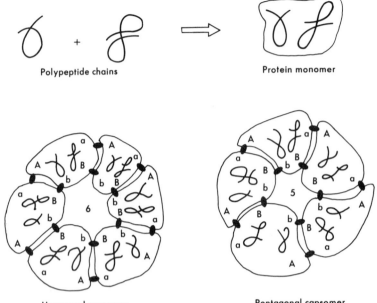

Polypeptide chains

Protein monomer

Hexagonal capsomer

Pentagonal capsomer

Fig. 22-10 Constitution of the viral capsid. The protein monomers of the capsid, also called the structural units, are made up of one or more polypeptide chains; in the diagram they are constituted by two polypeptide chains. In the icosahedral capsids the monomers constitute oligomers, of either five or six monomers, called capsomers. In the capsomers every monomer establishes bonds with two neighboring monomers, always through the same chemical groups (diagrammatically indicated as A-a and B-b). Each monomer also has other contacts with neighboring capsomers in the complete capsid, which are depicted in Figure 22-11.

hexamers are arranged in between (Fig. 22-11). We cannot specify the bonds that hold the monomers together in the individual capsomers, and the capsomers together in the capsid, but presumably they are not covalent. The bonds between the monomers **within** a capsomer appear to be stronger than those **between** capsomers, because the capsid of some viruses tends to disintegrate into intact capsomers during purification (Fig. 22-12).

Number of Capsomers. The arrangement of the capsomers in icosahedral capsids follows rules derived from the laws of crystallography. These rules permit only certain numbers of capsomers to be present in an icosahedral capsid. The minimum number is 12: each capsomer is then pentagonal and is located at a corner of the icosahedron. The next permissible number is 32, then 42, 72, 92, etc. Of these, 12 are pentamers and are located at the corners, while the

others are hexamers. The observed numbers of capsomers are 12, 32, 72, 92, 162, 252, and 812 (Table 22-1). The possible numbers of capsomers are given by $10T + 2$, where T is Pf^2; f is 1, 2, 3, 4, . . . ; and P is $h^2 + hk + k^2$, h and k being any pair of integers without common factors. In known viruses the following values of P have been found: $1(h = 1, k = 0)$, $3(h = 1, k = 1)$, and $7(h = 1, k = 2)$.

Of the numbers of capsomers observed in viruses, all except two are obtained by taking $P = 1$, with different values of f, as follows:

$$f = 1, \quad 2, \quad 3, \quad 4, \quad 5, \quad 6, \quad 7, \quad 8, \quad 9$$
$$T = 1, \quad 4, \quad 9. \ 16, \ 25, \ 36, \ 49, \ 64, \ 81$$

Number of capsomers $= 10T + 2 =$
$$12, 42, \mathbf{92}, \mathbf{162}, \mathbf{252}, 362, 492, 642, \mathbf{812}$$

The numbers found are in boldface. The remaining two observed numbers (32 and 72) are obtained by taking $P = 3$ or 7. With $P = 3$ and $f = 1$, $T = 3$ and the number of capsomers is 32; with $P = 7$ and $f = 1$, $T = 7$ and the

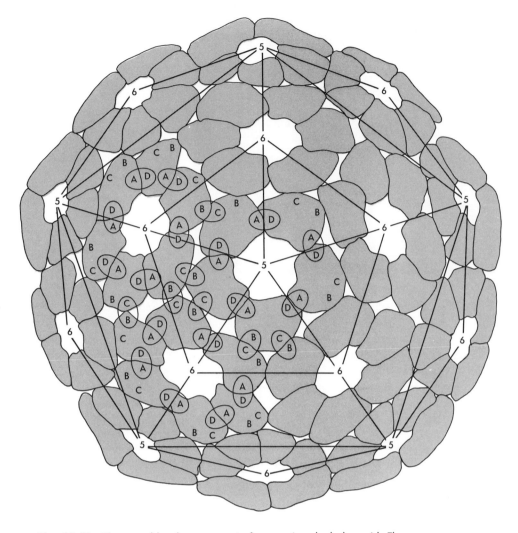

Fig. 22-11 The assembly of capsomers to form an icosahedral capsid. The capsomers are shown with reference to the edges between triangular faces of the polyhedron. The icosahedron depicted here contains 42 capsomers, of which 12 are pentagonal and 30 hexagonal: all are constituted of identical monomers. The number in the center of each capsomer refers to the number of monomers it contains. The hypothetical chemical groups involved in the bonds between monomers are indicated by letters (A, B, C, D). All monomers establish an identical set of bonds with neighboring units: two in the same capsomer (involving groups A and D), and two in different capsomers (involving groups B and C).

number of capsomers is 72. In all cases, the number of capsomers in a capsid is $(12 \times 5) + [6 \times 10(T-1)] = 60\ T$, since 12 capsomers are pentagonal, the others hexagonal. Thus the total number is either 60 or a multiple thereof.

Symmetry Axes. The basic symmetry of the icosahedron is revealed by the study of

certain ideal axes, drawn through its center; the properties of these axes depend on where they cross the surface. Axes through the corners are **fivefold axes** of rotational symmetry, as can be seen by viewing the icosahedron along one of these axes as the line of sight (Fig. 22-13): every time the icosahedron is rotated around this axis, by 1/5 of a turn,

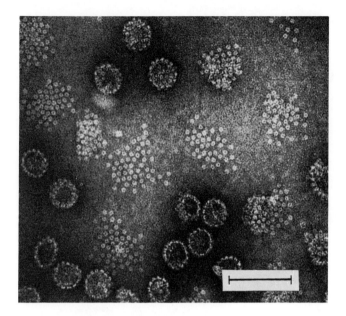

Fig. 22-12 Preparation of rabbit papilloma virus containing mostly empty capsids, i.e., devoid of nucleic acid. Some of the capsids have disintegrated into capsomers during the preparation of the specimen for electron microscopy, each producing a small puddle of capsomers (not all the capsomers of the original capsid are present in a puddle, some having been lost). The angular polygonal shape of the capsomers is evident, but it is not possible to differentiate hexamers from pentamers. Marker, 1000 A. (From C. Breedis, L. Berwick, and T. F. Anderson. Virology 17:84, 1962.)

it gives rise to an identical figure. Thus, in one complete rotation the figure reproduces itself five times. The other symmetry axes of the icosahedron are either **threefold axes** of rotational symmetry, located in the center of each triangular face, or **twofold axes,** located in the middle of each edge. The icosahedron is thus often referred to as a solid with a **5:3:2 rotational symmetry.**

Since the capsomers must conform to the symmetry of the icosahedron, those placed at the corners must be pentagonal. Those located at all other points must be hexagonal to provide the proper relation with the two- and

Fig. 22-13 Rotational axes in the icosahedron. The edges of the icosahedron, which limit the triangular faces, are drawn as heavy lines. The outlines of the capsomers are in thin lines.

A. The icosahedron of Figure 22-12 is seen looking down the center of a pentagonal capsomer which corresponds to the corner of the polyhedron. Rotating the figures by 1/5 of a rotation reproduces the same figure. A fivefold rotational axis, therefore, passes through the center of the pentagonal capsomer.

B. The same icosahedron seen looking down the center of a triangular face. Through this point passes a threefold rotational axis which is situated between three hexagonal capsomers; rotating the figure by 1/3 of a rotation reproduces the same figure.

C. The same icosahedron seen looking down the middle of an edge between two triangular faces. This is an axis of twofold rotational symmetry and is situated in the center of a hexagonal capsomer.

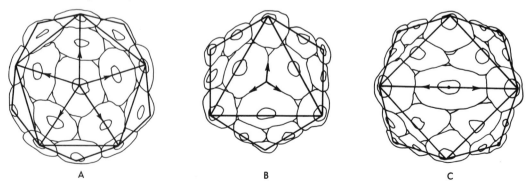

A

B

C

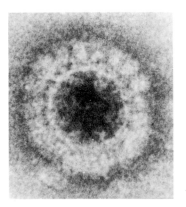

Fig. 22-14 The capsid of a reovirus particle examined with negative staining. The capsid is seen to be composed of two layers: the capsomers are especially evident in the outer layer. The capsid appears to be empty since it is penetrated by the stain. (From S. Dales and P. J. Gomatos. Virology 25:193, 1965.)

determined by the properties of its constituent polypeptide chains, and ultimately by the information contained in the viral gene(s) that specify these chains.

A special problem is posed by the capsid of reovirus, which is made up of two layers of monomers (Fig. 22-14). Two layers can satisfy the requirements of an icosahedral capsid, provided each does so independently. A similar problem derives from the attachment to some viruses of special structures, such as the small fibers of adenovirus and of bacteriophage φX174. These fibers must be arranged according to icosahedral symmetry. This is clearly true in adenovirus, in which the fibers are located at the 12 corners of the icosahedron, in connection with the pentagonal capsomers. Since the fibers are located on the fivefold axes, they probably possess fivefold rotational symmetry.

Helical Capsids (Fig. 22-15)

The structure of the roughly cylindrical helical capsid is much simpler than that of

threefold axes. The dimensions of the icosahedron depend on the size and number of its monomers; the capsid, therefore, is uniquely

Fig. 22-15 Constitution of the helical capsid. All monomers are identical and establish identical bonds with their neighbors. The monomers assemble to constitute a ribbon (by forming bonds between the hypothetical groups d and D), which then coils into a helix, stabilized by lateral bonds (between hypothetical groups a and A, b and B).

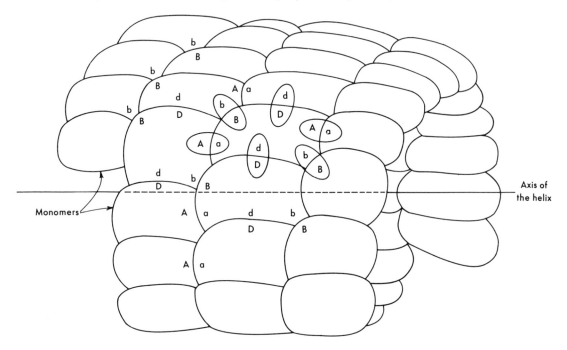

the icosahedral capsid because the helix has a single rotational axis, coincident with the axis of the cylinder. For this reason, the monomers of the capsid are not regularly grouped in capsomers, but they are bound to each other so as to form a ribbon-like structure (using the bonds between hypothetical groups d and D, Fig. 22-15). Since the monomers are thicker at one end than at the other end, the ribbon tends to curve into a helix; bonds between the units of successive turns stabilize the helix in the form of a hollow cylinder. The number of monomers present in each turn of the helix is usually not an integer, thus allowing each monomer to establish bonds with two monomers on each adjacent turn (as in Fig. 22-15, bonds between hypothetical groups a and A, and b and B). This increases the stability of the structure.

The diameter of the helical capsid is determined by the size and shape of its constituent monomers; its length, however, is undetermined. In the complete virion the length is determined by the length of the nucleic acid.

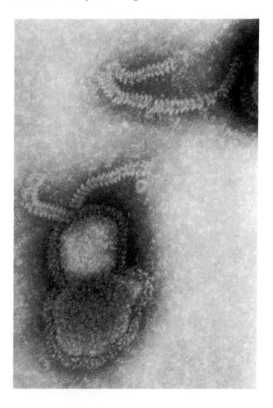

The capsids of naked helical viruses (e.g., tobacco mosaic virus) are very tight and the turns of the helix are difficult to resolve with the electron microscope (Fig. 22-5B). In contrast, the capsids of enveloped viruses are very flexible, as they have to coil within the envelope; and the turns of the helixes are easily demonstrable in the electron microscope (Fig. 22-16).

Theoretical Considerations

As already noted, the monomers of a helical or icosahedral capsid are arranged in a regular way dictated by their **uniformity** and their **lack of internal symmetry.** (The latter property follows from the fact that a monomer is often made up of a single polypeptide chain.) These monomers can assemble only through identical contacts with their neighbors. How these conditions lead to a **helical** capsid is directly understandable from examination of Figure 22-15.

It is not equally obvious how these conditions lead to the formation of an **icosahedral** capsid (although the formation of capsomers and their reciprocal attachment can be readily understood, as shown in Figures 22-10 and 22-11). In order to understand this process the laws of crystallography must be used. Consider first the two-dimensional problem of making a ring on a sheet of paper with a number of identical, asymmetrical monomers. Figure 22-17 shows how this can be done with five monomers; the figure obtained has rotational symmetry with a fivefold axis passing through its center. By extending the reasoning from a two- to a three-dimensional object, it can be deduced that the capsid must be a solid with only rotational symmetry. Solids of this type are said to have **cubic symmetry** because the cube is one of the regular polyhedrons that can be so generated. Cubic symmetry is found in three classes of regular

Fig. 22-16 The helical capsid of a myxovirus with negative staining. Two particles of the simian myxovirus SV 5 are seen: from both particles segments of the helical capsid protrude, probably owing to rupture of the envelope. Note the loose arrangement of the monomers and the hole along the axis of the helix. The envelopes are covered by the characteristic spikes. (From P. W. Choppin and W. Stockenius. Virology 23:195, 1964.)

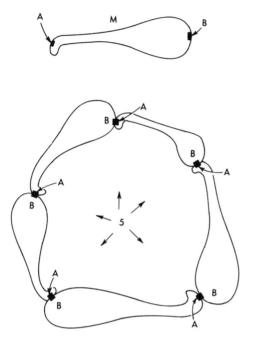

Fig. 22-17 Formation of a closed ring by using five asymmetrical monomers, M, in which group B can form a bond with group A. Since the distance between successive A-B bonds, and the angle of the A-B bonds to the axis of the monomer, are constant, a closed ring is formed which has fivefold rotational symmetry around an axis through its center.

solids, the prototypes of which are the tetrahedron, the octahedron, and the icosahedron. In all these solids two different types of capsomers would be required in order to build a closed shell: those located at the corners and those located in the flat faces of the polyhedron. The capsomers of the faces would always be made up of six monomers, while those of the corners would be made up of five monomers in the icosahedron, of four in the octahedron, and of three in the tetrahedron. Hexagonal capsomers by themselves can form flat sheets or an open-ended cylinder which arises from the rolling of the sheet. Indeed, such cylinders are often found in preparations of icosahedral viruses, and can be attributed to the self-assembly of hexagonal capsomers made in excess during viral multiplication (Fig. 22-18).

Two properties appear to explain why viruses use only icosahedral rather than octahedral or tetrahedral capsids.

1) An icosahedral shell contains more monomers than a tetrahedral or an octahedral shell, and therefore, for a given volume, the monomers can be smaller; this favors economy of genetic information.

2) Capsids containing face capsomers and corner capsomers made up of the **same** monomers have the greatest stability if they are icosahedral (Fig. 22-19). This is because the bonds between monomers are formed between similar chemical groups of the monomers, and so the angles they form with internal bonds of the monomers differ, depending on the number of monomers in the capsomer. The difference of bond angles from those of the hexamer, and therefore the stress, is less for pentamers (in the icosahedron) than for tetramers (in the octahedron) or for trimers (in the tetrahedron). The

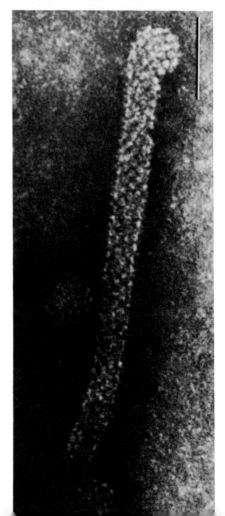

Fig. 22-18 Very long filamentous capsid of human wart virus, together with two regular virions. The filament, of a diameter close to that of the virions, is made up of hexagonal capsomers. Marker, 1000 A. (From W. F. Noyes. Virology 23:65, 1964.)

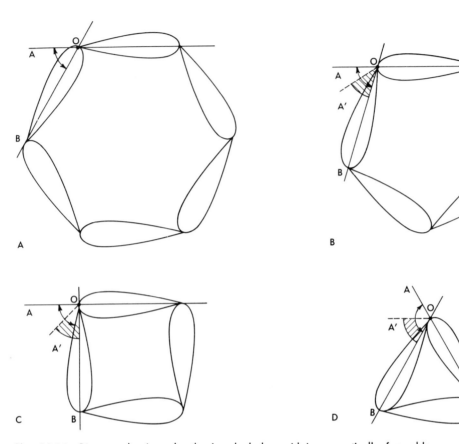

Fig. 22-19 Diagram showing why the icosahedral capsid is energetically favorable over other possible capsids with cubic symmetry. The possible capsomers made by monomers of a single type are reproduced schematically. **A** is a hexagonal capsomer, used as face element in all cubic polyhedra; **B**, **C**, and **D** are pentagonal, tetragonal and triangular capsomers, used as corner elements in the icosahedron, octahedron, and tetrahedron, respectively. The difference of bond angles AOB in the various corner capsomers increases relative to the angle A'OB of the hexagonal capsomer, as the number of monomers decreases.

stress in the latter two solids may be incompatible with the formation of a stable shell.

The Envelope

The envelope that surrounds certain animal viruses is a membrane 100 to 150 A thick, covered with **spikes,** clearly visible with negative staining (Figs. 22-5D, 22-16, and 22-20). These are characteristic of the viral envelope since they are absent on the surface membranes of uninfected cells. The spikes of myxoviruses are about 100 A long and located 70 to 80 A apart. The envelope is made

up of lipids, proteins, and carbohydrates, and can therefore be disrupted by ether and other lipid solvents. On theoretical grounds, it seems likely that the envelope, like the capsid, consists of very few kinds of virus-specified monomers.

However, little is known about the molecular organization of the envelope. That of myxoviruses contains subunits endowed with hemagglutinating activity (hemagglutinins*)

---

* These hemagglutinins should not be confused with hemagglutinating antibodies, which are often referred to by the same name.

and molecules of neuraminidase. The hemagglutinins appear to be connected with the spikes, whereas the enzyme may be on or between them.

The presence of the lipids makes the envelope loose and flexible; hence particles of an enveloped virus are highly variable in size and shape, although they contain identical nucleocapsids. Pleomorphism is especially pronounced with enveloped viruses containing helical nucleocapsids. Changes in osmolarity (e.g., during the drying of specimens for electron microscopy) cause them to assume a bizarre tadpole-like shape, presumably because one end of the nucleocapsid becomes unraveled and pushes the envelope out. This artifact, until recognized, erroneously suggested a similarity to large bacteriophages.

Relation Between Viral Envelope and Host Cell Membrane

Since the envelope of many viruses is synthesized in continuity with the cell membrane (Ch. 25), the question arises whether these two membranes have any common components. There is no doubt that the viral membrane often contains characteristic components absent in the uninfected host, such as

Fig. 22-20 Vesicular stomatitis virions with negative staining. In **A** the external outline is seen: note the spikes. In **B** the helical filament, present in a deeper layer, is visible in two particles. Markers, 1000 A. (From A. F. Howatson and G. F. Whitmore. Virology 16:466, 1962.)

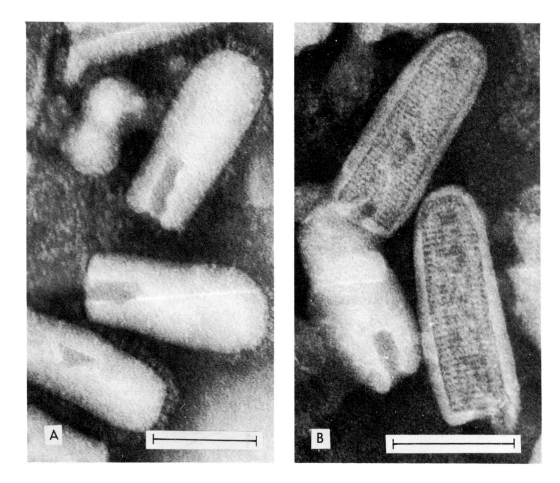

the hemagglutinins and the spikes of influenza virus. And while neuraminidase is also present in the uninfected cell, it differs both antigenically and physically from that of the virus.

However, purified preparations of many enveloped viruses also contain antigens, enzymes, or other chemical constituents present in the membranes of their uninfected host cells, and often it is not known whether they are intrinsic parts of the virions or are adsorbed to them. An example of an enzyme adsorbed to viral particles is alkaline phosphatase, which is present in partially purified preparations of vaccinia virus, but can be removed on further purification. It seems clear, however, that some intrinsic components of the viral membrane derive from the host cell membrane, e.g., its phosphatides, as shown by isotopic studies (Ch. 25). The envelope of herpesviruses, especially, appears to contain a considerable proportion of material derived from the pre-existing host cell membrane.

The incorporation of cellular material into the viral envelope causes differences in the physical properties of virions of the same virus propagated in different cells, a phenomenon known as **host-induced modification** (Ch. 25).

Complex Viruses

Poxviruses. In some members of this group the virions are brick-shaped; others are ovoid or resemble flattened cylinders. The viral DNA is contained in a nucleoid, shaped like a biconcave disc, surrounded by several layers containing proteins and lipids. A layer of coarse fibrils near the outer surface gives the virions a characteristically striated appearance in negatively stained preparations (Fig. 22-5E).

Vesicular Stomatitis Virus. This virus is noticed for its peculiar bullet-shaped virions. Negative staining reveals a series of transverse striations on the cylindrical part of the virions, possibly produced by a long fibril wound in the form of a coil in the outer layer of the particle (Fig. 22-20). Rabies virus has a similar morphology.

Large Bacteriophages. Some bacteriophages, such as the even-numbered coliphages, T2, T4, and T6, have the most complex structures (Fig. 22-21), including a **head** and a **tail**. The head, which contains the DNA, is equivalent to the capsid of icosahedral viruses, and has the shape of two halves of an icosahedron connected by a short hexagonal prism; in other phages, such as salmonella phages P1 and P2, and other coliphages, the head is strictly icosahedral (Fig. 22-5F). The **tail** varies greatly in dimensions and structure. In its simplest form it is composed of a **tube** (through which the viral DNA passes during cell infection), probably helical in structure. In the T-even coliphages the tube is surrounded by a **sheath,** which reaches from the head to near the tip of the tail, and is connected to a thin disc, or **collar,** at the head end, and to a **plate** at the tip end. With negative staining the sheath shows 25 striations, formed by parallel rows of protein monomers. The sheath is capable of contraction and plays an important role in infection (Ch. 23). The plate of T-even coliphages is hexagonal, has a **pin** at every corner, and is connected to six very long thin **tail fibers.** The fibers are the organs of attachment of the bacteriophage to the wall of the host cell. Coliphages T1 and T5 have a sheathless tail terminating in rudimentary fibers; coliphages T3 and T7 have a short stubby tail which terminates in a structure resembling a base plate.

Bacteriophages with tails are said to have

Fig. 22-21 Micrographs of bacteriophage T2 with negative staining. **A,** extended sheath; **B,** contracted sheath. In **A,** the head contains the DNA; in **B** the head is empty. (Courtesy of E. Boy de la Tour.)

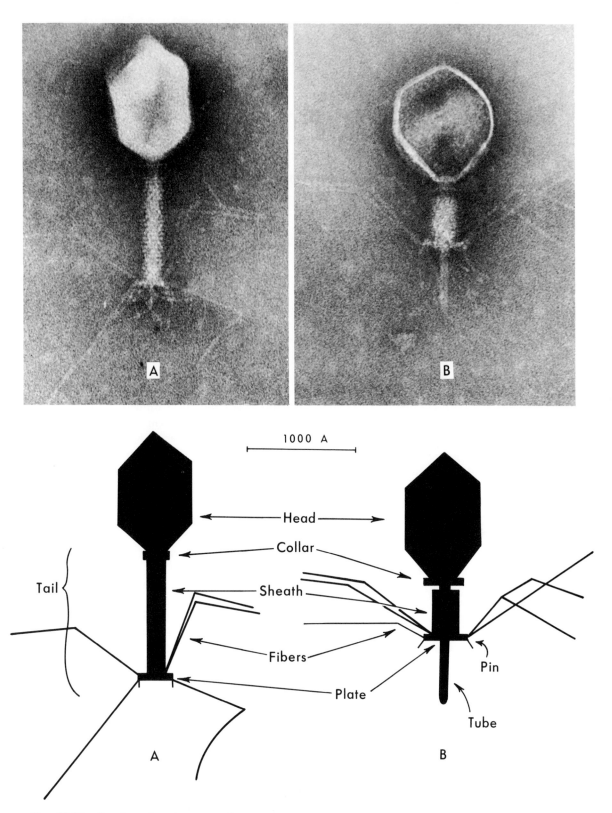

Fig. 22-21 *(See legend on facing page)*

binal symmetry because they have components with both icosahedral and helical symmetry within the same virion.

The arrangement of the DNA in the phage head is unknown; since, however, it does not show much preferential orientation by X-ray diffraction, it is probably similar to a ball of yarn. This arrangement, by avoiding sharp bends, would favor the packing of the relatively rigid filament in a very small space.

CHEMICAL COMPOSITION OF VIRUSES

All virions contain nucleic acid and protein. The nucleic acid may be either DNA or RNA, but never both. Some viruses contain unusual nucleic acids, such as single-stranded DNA or double-stranded RNA. Lipids and carbohydrates may also be present in the more complex viruses.

The proportions of the various constituents show large variations. Nucleic acid varies from about 1% for influenza virus to about 50% for certain bacteriophages, and lipid (when present) from about 5% for vaccinia virus to 50% for arboviruses. The amount of nucleic acid per viral particle is an index of the genetic complexity of the virus; it varies from a few thousand nucleotide units (i.e., single nucleotides for single-stranded nucleic acids and nucleotide pairs for double-stranded nucleic acids) in many small viruses, to about 250,000 in large bacterial or animal viruses. If 1000 nucleotide units is taken as the size of an average gene, small viruses contain very few genes and large viruses contain several hundred. The number of different virus-specific proteins synthesized in the infected cell varies accordingly.

The **proteins** of the virion surround the nucleic acid, protecting it from the nucleases in biological fluids and favoring attachment to susceptible cells. The outer coat of many virions (either capsid or envelope) is highly resistant to attack by some proteolytic enzymes, such as trypsin, but some viruses are susceptible (Ch. 26). The components of the outer coat of the virions are effective immunogens and elicit production of antiviral antibodies in the infected animals. The evolution of animal viruses has not eliminated this disadvantageous property, presumably because a virus must have surface configurations **complementary** to those of the cells it infects (Chs. 23 and 25) and is therefore necessarily foreign to its host.

In addition to the coat proteins, complex viruses contain **internal proteins** whose functions are obscure. The T-even coliphages contain an acid-soluble peptide and an internal "head protein" antigenically different from the coat proteins.

Bacteriophages and plant viruses contain **polyamines** such as spermine, spermidine, and bis-(3-aminopropyl)-amine (Fig. 22-22). Polyamines may be present in animal viruses as well, but they have not been reported. These basic compounds with their multiple cationic groups can establish multiple ionic bonds with the acidic phosphate groups of nucleic acids. Polyamines favor the folding of the nucleic acid by linking together different loops and therefore facilitate packing of the nucleic acid within the tight volume of the capsid. The internal head protein of T-even coliphages is also basic and may serve a similar function.

The proteins, lipids, carbohydrates, and polyamines are all dispensable under certain conditions, since after their removal the naked

Fig. 22-22 Polyamines present in virions. Spermine and spermidine have been found in bacteriophages; bis-(3-aminopropyl)-amine in plant viruses.

$$NH_2 \cdot (CH_2)_3 \cdot NH \cdot (CH_2)_4 \cdot NH \cdot (CH_2)_3 \cdot NH_2$$

Spermine

$$NH_2 \cdot (CH_2)_3 \cdot NH \cdot (CH_2)_4 \cdot NH_2$$

Spermidine

$$NH_2 \cdot (CH_2)_3 \cdot NH \cdot (CH_2)_3 \cdot NH_2$$

Bis-(3-aminopropyl)-amine

nucleic acid can still infect cells, though with a markedly reduced efficiency (Ch. 25).

Types of Nucleic Acids

There are four possible types of nucleic acids in respect to strandedness and composition: single- and double-stranded DNA and RNA. Although only double-stranded DNA and largely single-stranded RNA have been found in any cells, all four have been found in animal viruses. So far, plant viruses have been found only with RNA (double- or single-stranded), whereas bacterial viruses occur with all types of nucleic acid except double-stranded RNA.

Double-Stranded DNA

Molecular Weight. The molecular weight of viral DNA can be determined by the methods discussed in Chapter 8, and also chemically from the amount of DNA and the number of virions present in a purified virus sample, assuming one molecule per virion. The most reliable estimates of the molecular weight of the largest viral DNAs, those of the T-even coliphages, have been obtained by radioautography (Fig. 22-23) and electron microscopy (Ch. 8). The measured lengths were 52 and 49 μ, respectively, which correspond to 1.41 $\times$ 10^5 nucleotide pairs, respectively (assuming an internucleotide distance of 3.46 A along the axis of the helix). Since the average molecular weight of a nucleotide pair in these phages is 730, the calculated molecular weights of the DNA are 110 $\times$ 10^6 and 103 $\times$ 10^6, respectively. These values are in good agreement with those estimated chemically from the DNA content of a virion; hence even in viruses with a large DNA

Fig. 22-23 Radioautograph of molecules of DNA of bacteriophage T2. A specially prepared glass slide was drawn through a solution containing T2 DNA heavily labeled with ^{3}H-thymidine, mixed with a large excess of unlabeled T2 DNA. This procedure caused some DNA molecules to stick to the glass in an oriented fashion. The preparation was then dried, overlaid with sensitive photographic film, and exposed for 2 months. Electrons released by the decaying ^{3}H atoms initiated formation of silver grains in the emulsion, which were made visible by photographic development and fixation. The marker shows 50 u. (Courtesy of J. Cairns.)

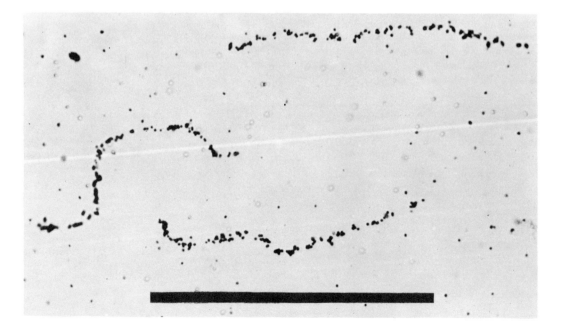

complement a virion contains a single nucleic acid molecule.

A similar conclusion derives from the study of many other viruses. With vaccinia virus (a poxvirus), however, the molecular weight (80×10^6) is only about half the DNA complement per virion. Since it seems unlikely that there are two molecules of DNA per virion, this difference may derive from technical errors (e.g., in counts of viral particles or in fragmentation of DNA before the physical determinations).

The molecular weights of a number of double-stranded DNAs are given in Table 22-2.

Cyclic Forms. The DNAs of polyoma virus, SV 40, and papilloma viruses have cyclic molecules, i.e., in the form of rings, as shown by electron microscopy (Fig. 22-24). The two ends of each strand are linked to each other by a **covalent bond** of unknown nature. Coliphage λ contains linear DNA molecules in its virions; these molecules, however, contain complementary single-stranded

TABLE 22-2. MOLECULAR WEIGHTS OF DOUBLE-STRANDED VIRAL DNAS

Virus	Molecular weight
Poxviruses	160×10^6
Bacillus subtilis bacteriophage SP8	130×10^6
Coliphages T2, T4, T6	120×10^6
Herpesviruses	ca. 60×10^6
Coliphage λ	31×10^6
Coliphage T3, T7	$20\text{--}25 \times 10^6$
Adenoviruses types 2, 4	23×10^6
Adenoviruses types 12, 18	21×10^6
Papilloma viruses	5×10^6
Polyoma virus, SV 40	3×10^6

segments at their ends, which can pair with each other under conditions leading to nucleic acid hybridization (Ch. 8), giving rise to cyclic helical molecules.

The significance of the cyclic shape of certain DNAs cannot be assessed at the moment. One hypothesis suggests that all native DNAs may be cyclic but the rings are broken during extraction and analytical procedures, except

Fig. 22-24 Electron micrographs demonstrating the cyclic structure of polyoma DNA molecules (Kleinschmidt technic). The native molecules (**A**) are twisted, for unclear reasons; the twist is maintained as long as the two strands constituting the molecule are both intact. If one of them is broken the corresponding phosphodiester bond of the other strand acts as a swivel, allowing the DNA molecule to rotate around the helix axis for a few turns, until it forms an untwisted circle (**B**). Marker, 1 μ. (From R. Weil and J. Vinograd. Proc. Nat. Acad. Sc. 50:730, 1963.)

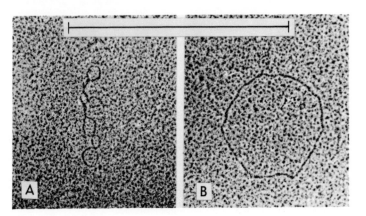

when the molecules are short and the ends are connected by covalent bonds. It should be recalled, in fact, that the ring-shape of the DNA of *E. coli* has been recognized physically only by radioautography, which involves unusually mild treatment of the molecules (Ch. 8). Alternatively, the cyclic shape may be an authentic feature of only certain DNA molecules and may entail special biological properties; this may be the case for λ DNA and perhaps polyoma DNA, as discussed in Chapter 24.

Presence of Abnormal Bases. The unusual base **5-hydroxymethylcytosine** (Fig. 22-25), as a replacement for cytosine, was discovered by Wyatt and Cohen in the DNA of T-even coliphages. This important finding made it possible to measure the replication of viral DNA in the presence of host cell DNA, which does not contain this unusual base. The problem of the origin of this base also led to the first demonstration that phage-infected cells synthesize new enzymes, absent in uninfected cells.

The hydroxymethyl group of 5-hydroxymethylcytosine is glucosylated with a different pattern in different phages (Fig. 22-25). These variations depend on the different glucosylating enzymes made in cells after infection by the corresponding phages (Ch. 23). Certain *Bacillus subtilis* bacteriophages contain **5-hydroxymethyluracil** instead of thymine (5-methyluracil).

Base Composition of Viral DNA. The G+C content of the DNA of different viruses shows considerable variation. It appears meaningful to compare the base compositions of the viral and the host cell DNA; whenever they can enter into the intimate relation of bacterial lysogeny (Ch. 24) they have a similar composition; but the converse is not necessarily true. Similarly, the DNAs of oncogenic viruses usually resemble those of the host cells in base ratio, suggesting a possible interaction of the two DNAs. In contrast, the DNAs of many animal viruses that multiply without interaction with the cellular DNA differ from the latter in base ratio. For instance, herpes-virus DNA has a much higher G+C content (60 to 70%) than the host cell DNA (42–45%).

Other Kinds of Nucleic Acids

Single-Stranded DNA. The DNA is single-stranded in the very small bacteriophages, such as the icosahedral φX174 and the helical f1 or M13. These DNAs have a molecular weight of only 1.7×10^6 and are cyclic. All the virions of phage φX174 contain the same DNA strand, which is called the **plus,** or **viral,** strand, since the purified DNA does not hybridize with itself (Ch. 8), and the base ratios do not show the characteristic pairing of double-stranded DNA.

Double-Stranded RNA. Viruses that contain single-stranded RNA in their capsids develop double-stranded RNA molecules during synthesis, which will be considered later (Ch. 25). A double-stranded RNA has been recognized **within the viral capsid,** so far, only in reoviruses of animals and in two viruses of plants (wound tumor virus and rice dwarf virus). These viruses are similar in particle size and in capsid structure. These RNAs have the usual properties of double-stranded nucleic acids and are relatively resistant to RNase, which hydrolyzes single-stranded RNA. For unknown reasons, however, double-stranded RNA appears to be much more susceptible to breakage in solution than double-stranded DNA.

Single-Stranded RNA. Single-stranded molecules have been found in most of the RNA-containing viruses so far studied, both

TABLE 22-3. MOLECULAR WEIGHTS OF SINGLE-STRANDED VIRAL RNAS

Virus	Molecular weight
Satellite tobacco necrosis virus	0.5×10^6
Coliphage R17, f2, and other small RNA-phages; broad bean mosaic virus; bromegrass mosaic virus	ca. 10^6
Influenza virus, poliovirus	ca. 2×10^6
Newcastle disease virus	ca. 7×10^6
Avian leucosis viruses	ca. 10^7

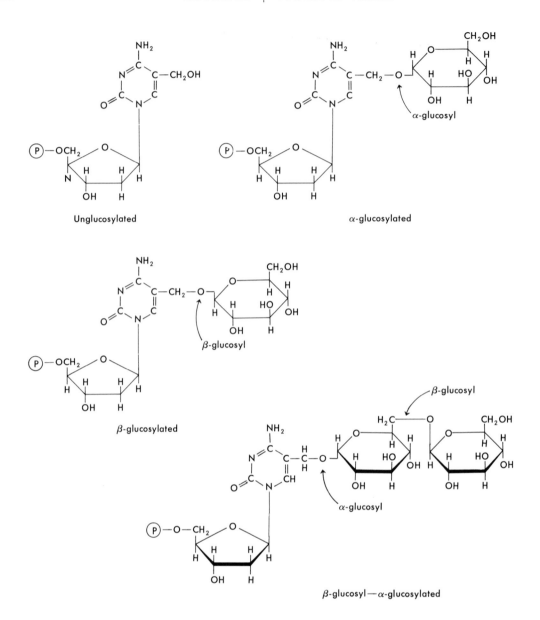

Fig. 22-25 Various forms of glucosylation of 5-hydroxymethylcytosine residues in T-even coliphages. The proportion of the residues with the various types of glucosylation is as follows:

Type of glucosylation	Bacteriophage (%)		
	T2	T4	T6
Unglucosylated	25	0	25
α-Glucosyl	70	70	3
β-Glucosyl	0	30	0
β-Glucosyl-α-glucosyl	5	0	72

(Data from I. R. Lehman and E. A. Pratt. J: Biol. Chem. 235:3254, 1960.)

helical and icosahedral. Their molecular weight varies from about 10^6 to 10^7 (Table 22-3).

The RNA of several viruses shows a compact conformation and a considerable amount of helical content, i.e., it forms base-paired segments over a considerable proportion of its length. As a consequence, these RNAs have a high sedimentation constant in relation to molecular weight, and a rather sharp melting curve with a relatively high melting temperature (Ch. 8).

Owing to their large size and high sedimentation constant, viral RNAs can be readily separated from cellular RNAs, either by chromatography on columns of methylated albumin or by zone centrifugation in sucrose gradients (Ch. 8).

ASSAY OF VIRUSES

The methods used for the assay of viruses reflect their dual nature, i.e., as both complex chemicals and living microorganisms. Viruses can be assayed either by chemical and physical methods or by the consequences of their interaction with living host cells, i.e., **infectivity.** Assays carried out by different technics can differ vastly in their significance.

Chemical and Physical Determinations

Counts of Physical Particles

Virions can be clearly recognized in the electron microscope; if a sample contains only virions of a single type their number can be determined unambiguously. Virions are counted by mixing with known numbers of polystyrene latex particles, spraying droplets of the mixture onto the specimen film, and counting the two types of particles present in the same droplet (Fig. 22-26). This technic counts the total number of viral particles; it does not distinguish between infectious and noninfectious particles.

Hemagglutination

Many viruses, from the very small ones such as foot-and-mouth disease virus, to large ones such as poxviruses, can agglutinate red blood cells. This important property, discovered independently for influenza virus by Hirst and by McClelland and Hare in 1941, affords a simple, rapid method for viral titration. Hemagglutination is usually caused by the virions themselves; in some cases, however, as with poxviruses, it is caused by hemagglutinins produced during viral multiplication, but not by the virions. Breakdown products of virions may also cause hemagglutination, e.g., the hemagglutinins released from myxoviruses by ether treatment.

Although the spectrum of red cell species that are agglutinated, and the conditions under which agglutination occurs, differ for different viruses, the phenomenon is basically similar in all cases. A virion or a hemagglutinin attaches simultaneously to two red cells and bridges them. At sufficiently high viral concentrations large aggregates, resulting from multiple bridging, are formed.

Hemagglutination Assay. The formation of aggregates can be detected in a number of ways. The simplest, **the pattern method,** is to leave the suspension of red cells and virus undisturbed in a small test tube for several hours. The nonaggregated cells sediment to the round bottom of the tube and then roll toward the center, where they form a small, sharply outlined, round pellet. The aggregates, however, sediment to the bottom but do not roll; they form a thin film, which, at the edge, has a characteristic serrated appearance (Fig. 22-27). The proportion of aggregated cells can be determined more quantitatively by observing the sedimentation in a photoelectric colorimeter, since aggregated cells sediment faster than nonaggregated ones and can be separately measured.

The assay is usually carried out by an endpoint procedure. Serial twofold dilutions of

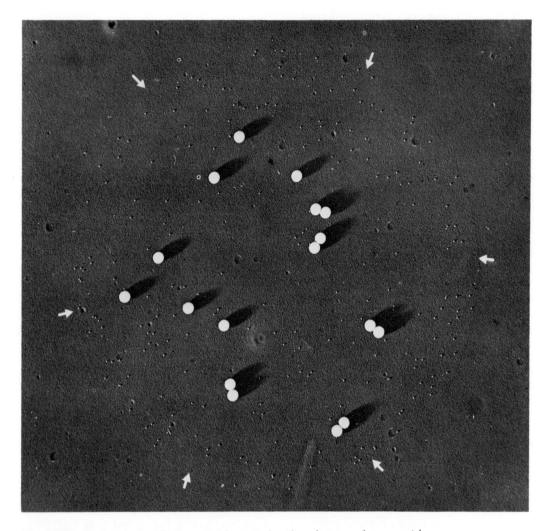

Fig. 22-26 Counting of poliovirus particles mixed with polystyrene latex particles. The mixture was sprayed in droplets on the supporting membrane, dried, and shadowed. The micrograph shows a droplet, whose outline is partly visible (arrows). The small particles are virus, the large ones latex.

There are 220 viral and 17 latex particles in the droplet. Since the latex concentration in the sample was 3.2×10^{10} particles per milliliter, the concentration of viral particles is $220/17 \times 3.2 \times 10^{10} = 4.1 \times 10^{11}/\text{ml}$. The precision of the assay based on this one droplet is only about $\pm 50\%$ (see Appendix), owing to the small number of latex particles counted. To obtain a greater precision pooled counts from many similar drops would have to be used. (Courtesy of the Virus Laboratory, University of California, Berkeley.)

the virus sample are each mixed with a standard suspension of red cells (usually $10^7/\text{ml}$). The last dilution showing complete hemagglutination is taken as the endpoint. The titer estimated by the pattern method has an inherent imprecision at least as large as the dilution step used (usually twofold); the colorimetric method removes this imprecision. The titer obtained either way is expressed in **hemagglutinating units.**

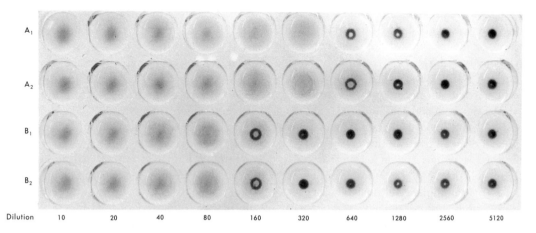

Dilution   10   20   40   80   160   320   640   1280   2560   5120

Fig. 22-27 Results of a hemagglutination assay by the pattern method with influenza virus. Two samples, A and B, were diluted serially by using twofold steps; 0.5 ml of each dilution was mixed with an equal volume of a red cell suspension, and each mixture was placed in a cup drilled in a clear plastic plate and left for 30 minutes at room temperature. Each assay was made in duplicate. Sample A causes complete hemagglutination until dilution 320; sample B until dilution 80; in either case the subsequent dilution shows still partial hemagglutination. The hemagglutinating titer of A is 320, that of B 80.

Significance of Hemagglutination. The phenomenon of hemagglutination throws considerable light on the interaction of virions with cell surfaces. It is caused by the attachment of specific sites of the virions to receptors of the membrane of the red cell. The former sites are largely uncharacterized, but a good deal is known about the receptors for myxoviruses. The nature of these receptors is indicated by several properties. 1) They are inactivated by periodate, which oxidizes glycol groups of sugar, and by the enzyme neuraminidase, which splits off N-acetylneuraminic acid (NANA) (Fig. 22-28). 2) Many sialic acid–containing mucoproteins with terminal NANA residues are present in biological fluids (e.g., blood serum, urine, submaxillary gland secretion) and bind to the virions; moreover, these mucoproteins competitively inhibit hemagglutination, and the removal of the terminal NANA by neuraminidase abolishes their activities. The receptors, therefore, are mucoproteins with terminal NANA residues.

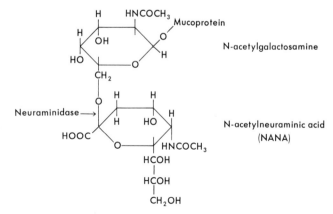

Fig. 22-28 The action of neuraminidase on a serum inhibitor. This compound contains N-acetylneuraminic acid linked to N-acetylgalactosamine, as part of the mucoprotein; the N-acetylneuraminic acid (NANA) is released by the enzyme.

The neuraminidase that splits off the NA-NA residues is obtained from filtrates of cultures of the cholera vibrio. This enzyme is commonly referred to as **receptor-destroying enzyme** (RDE) because it destroys the receptor activity for myxoviruses and paramyxoviruses on red blood cells and susceptible host cells. As noted above, neuraminidases are also present on the surface of myxovirus and paramyxovirus virions and in uninfected cells.

By splitting NANA from receptors the viral neuraminidase ultimately dissociates myxoviruses and paramyxoviruses from red cells at 37°; the virus spontaneously elutes off the red cells, which disaggregate. In contrast, at 0° the enzyme is much less active and the virion–red cell union is stable.

Adsorption to, and elution from, red cells is a useful method for viral purification, since many contaminants in crude virus preparations are not bound by red cells and can therefore be easily removed by differential centrifugation after the virus has been adsorbed.

After the virus has eluted from the cells they cannot be agglutinated again by a new batch of virus, since they have lost the receptors and cannot regenerate them: these cells are said to be "stabilized." The eluted virus, on the contrary, retains all its activities. Though cells stabilized by a given myxovirus or paramyxovirus are not agglutinable by the same virus, they can sometimes be agglutinated by another virus of these families. Indeed, it is possible to arrange the viruses in a series (called **receptor gradient**) such that any virus will exhaust the receptors for itself and the viruses preceding it in the gradient, but not for those that follow it. This result indicates that viruses differ quantitatively either in their neuraminidases or in their mode of attachment to the receptors.

Heating the virus inactivates its neuraminidase without destroying the hemagglutinating activity. This altered virus, called **indicator** virus, is useful for studying the union with receptors and mucoproteins without the complication of their enzymatic inactivation.

The nature of the receptors for other hemagglutinating viruses is known only in part. Receptors for polyoma virus, like those for myxoviruses, are destroyed by neuraminidase, but they differ from myxovirus receptors. Receptors for reoviruses may contain sugars, because they are inactivated by periodate; they are unaffected by neuraminidase. Receptors for enteroviruses and arboviruses appear to involve lipids since they are inactivated by lipid solvents.

Hemagglutination is inhibited by antiviral antibodies; hence hemagglutination-inhibition provides a convenient basis for measuring antibodies to many viruses (Ch. 27).

Assays Based on Antigenic Properties

Complement fixation or precipitation with antiserum can be used to measure amounts of virus. Owing to the low sensitivity of these methods they are used only for special purposes (Ch. 27).

Assays of Infectivity

The Plaque Method

This is the fundamental assay method of basic virology, and it is also of great importance for diagnostic purposes: it combines simplicity, accuracy, and high reproducibility. First introduced for the study of bacteriophages by D'Herelle, and perfected by the Belgian microbiologist Gratia, this method was a key factor in the spectacular advances of phage research. After the method was extended to animal viruses it also had a marked influence on the development of quantitative studies in this field.

Bacteriophages are assayed in the following way. A phage-containing sample is mixed with a drop of a dense liquid culture of suitable bacteria and a few milliliters of melted soft agar at 44°; the mixture is then poured over the surface of a Petri dish, called a **plate,** containing a layer of hard nutrient agar previously set. The soft agar, before setting, spreads in a thin layer in which bacteriophages and bacteria are evenly distributed. The virions diffuse through the soft agar until each meets and infects a bacterium in which it multiplies; after 20 to 30 minutes the bacterium lyses, releasing several hundred progeny virions. These, in turn, infect neighboring bacteria, which again lyse and release new virus. The uninfected bacteria, in the meantime, grow to form a dense, opaque lawn. A series of successive multiplication cycles results in lysis of all or most of the bacteria in a round area surrounding the initially infected cell; after a day's incubation the area stands out as a transparent **plaque** against the dense background of bacterial growth (Fig. 22-29A). The soft agar permits the diffusion of phage to nearby cells, but prevents the convection to other regions of the plate; hence secondary centers of infection cannot form.

Animal Viruses. With animal viruses it is possible to use a similar method by replacing bacteria with a suspension of cells cultivated in vitro (Ch. 25). More commonly, however, monolayers of cells growing on a solid substrate are used. The nutrient medium is removed from the cultures and substituted with a solution containing the viral sample, which is left in contact with the cells for an hour or longer to allow attachment of the virions to the cells. Soft nutrient agar or some other gelling mixture is poured over the cell layer.* Plaques develop after 1 day to 3 weeks of incubation, depending on the virus (Fig. 22-29B). Certain viruses (vaccinia, herpes, simplex, and adenovirus) are not freely released from the infected cells into the medium but are transmitted to adjacent cells in a monolayer; hence plaque formation by these viruses does not require an agar overlay.

Plaques are detected in a variety of ways.

1) The virus often kills the infected cells, i.e., produces a **cytopathic effect;** the plaques are then detected by staining the cell layer, either with a dye that stains only the live cells (e.g., neutral red) or with one that stains only the dead cells (e.g., trypan blue).

2) With certain viruses the cells in the plaques are not killed, but acquire the ability to adsorb red blood cells (Ch. 25); the plaques are revealed by **hemadsorption,** i.e., by flooding the cell layer with a suspension of red cells, then removing, by washing, those not attached to infected cells.

3) The infected cells may fuse with neighboring uninfected cells to form **polykaryocytes** (i.e., multinucleated cells), microscopically detectable.

4) Often the cells of the plaques contain large amounts of viral antigens, which can be detected by **immunofluorescence.**

If too many plaques develop on a plate some fuse with others and the counts are too low. The maximum density allowable varies with the size of the plaques and the sharpness of their margins.

The titer of the viral preparation is directly calculated from the number of plaques and the dilution of the sample, as shown in Figure 22-29. As discussed in the Appendix to this chapter, the accuracy of the assay depends on the number of plaques counted. An assay estimated from n plaques will be within $2/\sqrt{n}$ of the true value (e.g., with 100 plaques the true value will be $\pm$ 20%).

The Dose-Response Curve of the Plaque Assay. The number of plaques in plates infected with different dilutions of the same viral sample is proportional to the concentration of the virus, i.e., **the dose-response curve is linear** (Fig. 22-30). As shown in the Appendix, the linearity demonstrates that **a single virion is sufficient to infect a cell,** a conclusion fundamental to virology. A direct consequence of this result is that **the viral population contained in a plaque is the progeny of a single virion,** i.e., **a clone,** provided cross-contamination from neighboring plaques is avoided. Virus isolated from a single plaque thus represents a genetically pure line, which is required for many purposes, e.g., for preparing vaccines of mutated attenuated virus, which must be free of unmutated virulent virus. Often visible characteristics of the plaques, such as size, shape, and turbidity provide useful genetic markers.

---

* Agar contains sulfated polysaccharides which, by adsorbing some viruses, prevent them from forming plaques. This complication is eliminated either by adding to the agar cationic substances, which neutralize the negative charges of the polysaccharides, or by replacing the agar with methylcellulose.

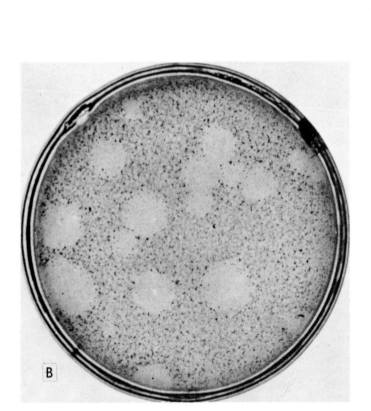

Fig. 22-29 Plaque assays.

A. Phage. The progeny of cells infected by two phage types was diluted by a factor of 10^7; 0.1 ml of the diluted virus was assayed. The plate was counted 18 hours after plating. Four different plaque types, differing in plaque size and turbidity, can be distinguished, showing the great usefulness of plaque formation for genetic work with bacteriophages. (Part of the plate is reproduced.) A total of 407 plaques could be counted on the whole plate. The titer is 4.07×10^{10}/ml in the undiluted sample. The accuracy is $\pm 10\%$.

B. Poliovirus. A sample of poliovirus type 1 was diluted by a factor of 2×10^5 and 0.1 ml was assayed on a monolayer culture of rhesus monkey kidney cells, with an agar overlay containing neutral red. The culture was incubated for 3 days at 37° in an atmosphere containing 7% CO_2, which constitutes a buffer with the bicarbonate present in the overlay. Some of the plaques show partial confluence, but they can still be identified as separate plaques. Seventeen plaques can be counted on the photograph. The corresponding titer is 3.4×10^7/ml in the undiluted sample. The accuracy is $\pm 50\%$.

Fig. 22-30 Dose-response curve of the plaque assay. The number of plaques produced by a sample of poliovirus type 1 at various dilutions was plotted versus the relative concentration of the virus (open circles); the accuracy of the assay ($\pm 2\ \sigma$) is indicated for each point. The data are in agreement with a linear dose-response curve which falls between lines 1 and 2, and, therefore, with the notion that a single particle is sufficient to give rise to a plaque. Curves 3 and 4 give the range of data that would be obtained if at least two viral particles were required to initiate a plaque, by taking the data obtained at concentration 1 as reference; the deviation is such that the hypothesis is ruled out.

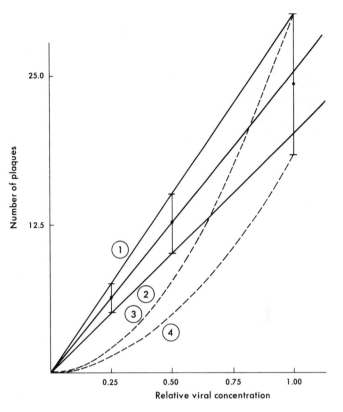

The Pock Method

When the chorionic epithelium of the chorioallantoic membrane of a chick embryo (usually 10 to 12 days of age; see Ch. 25, Fig. 25-1) is infected by certain viruses, characteristic lesions, **pocks,** appear. The counting of these pocks was introduced by Burnet and coworkers for titrating poxviruses; it has also been applied to other viruses (e.g., herpes simplex). The formation of a pock, like that of a plaque, begins with the infection of a single cell. Since the chorioallantoic membrane is complex, however, and contains several different cell types and blood vessels, the response to the local infection is also complex; it involves both cell proliferation and cell death, accompanied by edema and hemorrhage. The pocks appear after 36 to 72 hours as opaque areas, usually white and often hemorrhagic on the transparent membrane (Fig. 22-31).

Pock counting is satisfactory only for viruses that are released from the infected cells too slowly to give rise to secondary infectious centers. This method was important at the time of its introduction; now it is largely superseded by the plaque method. Under optimal conditions the virus derived from a single pock represents a genetically pure line; and viral mutants may be distinguishable by the appearance of the pocks.

Other Local Lesions

Tumor-producing viruses, such as the Rous sarcoma virus, can be assayed on monolayer tissue cultures; they produce foci of cells with altered growth properties, derived from one infected cell. Each focus is initiated by a single viral particle.

Many **plant viruses** can be titrated by counting the lesions produced on leaves rubbed with a mixture of virus and an abrasive material. The virus penetrates through ruptures of the cell walls caused by the abrasive, and the progeny spread to neighboring cells, prob-

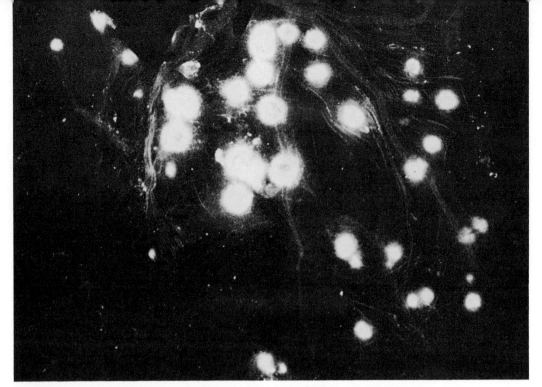

Fig. 22-31 Pocks formed by vaccinia virus on the chorioallantoic membrane of the chicken embryo. The membrane was removed, washed, and photographed in saline against a dark background. The pocks appear as brilliant white foci, whereas the membrane, which is transparent, is barely visible. (From L. L. Coriell, H. Blank, and T. F. M. Scott. J. Invest. Dermat. 11:313, 1948.)

ably through the plasmodesmata (protoplasmic bridges between cells). Recognizable spots, each started by a single virion, are thus produced.

Endpoint Method

This method was commonly used for assaying animal viruses before the advent of the plaque method. It is still employed for certain diagnostic assays and for special purposes. The virus is serially diluted and a constant volume of each dilution is inoculated into a number of similar **test units,** such as mice, chick embryos, or cell cultures. At each dilution the proportion of infected test units is scored. The following criteria of infection are used in various assays: 1) death or disease of an animal or embryo; 2) degeneration of a tissue culture; 3) multiplication of the virus to a point where it can be recognized by an in vitro method (e.g., positive hemagglutination).

Most of the test units develop signs of infection at the lower dilutions of the virus and none at the highest dilutions. A rough idea of the viral titer is given by the intermediate dilutions at which only a fraction of the test units show signs of infection. The transition is not sharp, however, and only by combining the data from several dilutions is it possible to calculate the precise endpoint at which 50% of the test units are infected. At this dilution each sample contains one ID_{50}, i.e., one infectious dose for 50% of the test units. Such interpolation can be carried out in a variety of ways, such as the method of Reed and Muench, which is discussed in Chapter 22, Appendix. Though not mathematically derived, this method yields results in good agreement with more rigorous methods.

In the Reed and Muench method the results obtained at different viral dilutions are pooled; the dilution containing one ID_{50} is obtained by interpolation between the two dilutions that straddle the 50% value of the infectivity index. The interpolation assumes that the infectivity index varies linearly with the log dilution. The accuracy of the method is usually low, since the number of test units used at each dilution is small.

When, for instance, five units are employed, as is common in diagnostic titrations, the estimated titer may vary between 1/6 and 6 times the true titer, or more (Appendix). There is, therefore, a range of uncertainty of at least 36-fold between the minimum and the maximum titer still compatible with the result obtained. Under these conditions, the titration is useful only to ascertain large differences in viral titer: a 50-fold difference is considered significant and is adequate for many routine diagnostic procedures. The precision increases as the square root of the number of test units employed at each dilution.

Viral titers obtained by the endpoint method are expressed in various units, equivalent to the ID_{50}, which describe the criterion used for detecting infection of the test units: LD_{50} (lethal dose) if the criterion is death; PD_{50} (paralysis dose) if the criterion is paralysis; TC_{50} (tissue culture dose) if the criterion is degeneration of a culture. One ID_{50} can be shown to correspond to 0.70 plaque-forming units (Appendix).

Comparison of Different Types of Assays

The focal assay methods (plaques and pocks) are most satisfactory for their simplicity, reproducibility, and economy. For example, to match the precision obtained by counting 100 plaques on a single culture one would require more than 100 test units per decimal dilution in an endpoint titration. The precision of any type of assay is adversely affected by variability of the assay units; this can be quite large in the pock assay and even larger in endpoint assays using animals.

The various methods of assay have different sensitivities and measure different properties. Assays based on infectivity are as much as a millionfold more sensitive than those based on chemical and physical properties. Chemical and physical technics, moreover, titrate not only infectious but also noninfectious virions, such as empty capsids or particles

with a damaged nucleic acid. These methods, therefore, can be useful for studies requiring measurement of the total number of viral particles. Hemagglutination can also titrate hemagglutinins separate from intact virions, e.g., those obtained from breakdown of the virions or produced during intracellular viral synthesis. Immunological methods also can titrate protein precursors of the virions, or viral subunits obtained by disruption of virions.

The quantitative relations between titers obtained by different procedures are of considerable interest. Most important is the **ratio of the number of viral particles** (determined by electron microscope counts) **to the number of infectious units.** This ratio measures the **efficiency of infection,** which varies widely among different viruses, and even for the same virus assayed in different hosts. As is shown in Table 22-4, for most viruses the ratio is larger than unity. This result is due, in part, to the presence of noninfectious particles, and in part to the failure of potentially

TABLE 22-4. RATIO OF VIRAL PARTICLES
TO INFECTIOUS UNITS

Virus	Ratio
Animal Viruses	
Poliovirus	30–1000
Foot-and-mouth disease virus	33–1600
Polyoma virus	38–50
SV 40	100–200
Papilloma virus	ca. 10^4
Reovirus	10
Semliki Forest virus (arbovirus)	1
Influenza virus	7–10
Herpes simplex virus	10
Poxviruses	1–100
Avian myeloblastosis virus	ca. 10^5
Bacterial Viruses	
Coliphage T4	1
Coliphage T7	1.5–4
Plant Viruses	
Tobacco mosaic virus	5×10^4–10^6

infectious particles to reproduce. However, even with the highest ratio of particles to infectivity infection is initiated by a single virion, since the dose-response curve remains linear.

The ratio of total viral particles to hemagglutinating units is related to the number of red cells that must be aggregated to reveal hemagglutination. Since in the hemagglutination assay each diluted viral sample is mixed with an equal volume of a red cell suspension containing 10^7 cells per milliliter, at the endpoint the virus should theoretically contain about 10^7 hemagglutinating particles per milliliter.* Indeed, experimental determinations with influenza and polyoma viruses give under optimal conditions a value close to 10^7 total viral particles per hemagglutinating unit. But because the ratio of particles to infectious units exceeds 1.0, a hemagglutinating unit corresponds to only about $10^{6.3}$ infectious units of influenza virus and 10^5 of polyoma virus.

APPENDIX

Quantitative Aspects of Infection

Distribution of Viral Particles per Cell: Poisson Distribution

In a cell suspension mixed with a viral sample individual cells are infected by different numbers of viral particles, and it is important for several purposes to know the details of this process.

Let us consider the case in which N viral particles are mixed with C identical cells, assuming that a cell is infected every time it takes up **at least one** infectious viral particle. (The validity of this assumption will be shown later.) Under these conditions each infectious particle has a certain probability (p) of infecting **a given cell,** which we single out for the sake of discussion. If at the end of the experiment a proportion (a) of the viral particles end up infecting the cells, irrespective of which cell, $p = a/C$. Under the usual experimental conditions C is very large, for instance 10^6 or 10^7, and so p is very small. Usually the number of viral particles is also large; and since each of them can infect the selected cell, the probability (P) that the latter is infected (by any viral particle) is much larger than p. We are interested in determining the probability (P), which determines the distributions of the particles among the cells.

The infection of the cells is an experiment analogous to tossing a coin many times. When the coin is tossed once the result is either heads or not heads, and when the infection experiment is performed by a single viral particle and a single cell the result is either infection or not infection of the cell; in both cases, the result obtained depends on random circumstances. If the coin-tossing experiment is repeated N times heads will be obtained a certain number of times (k). A repetition of the infection experiment consists of letting N different virus particles attempt to infect the given cell; a certain number (k) of them will succeed in doing so. In both cases the result of the N trials is expressed by the **distribution** of the number of successes, a success being heads in the coin-tossing experiment and infection of the given cell in the infection experiment. The distribution determines the probability of obtaining k successes in N trials, for various values of k.

In both cases the distribution depends on the **mean,** i.e., the average number of times a success is obtained if the series of N trials is repeated many times. The mean equals pN. The

---

* If at the endpoint of hemagglutination mostly red cell dimers were produced, there would be one viral particle for each two cells, since a single particle can form a bridge. Since larger aggregates are formed there are almost as many viral particles as red cells, for n viral particles theoretically aggregate n + 1 cells.

two types of experiments differ, however, in one important way. In the coin-tossing experiment p equals 0.5, since, on the average, heads is obtained half the times; in contrast, in the infection of the cells p is very small. In coin-tossing, on the other hand, N, the number of trials, is rarely very large, whereas in the infection it is usually large since it is equal to the total number of viral particles mixed with the cells. The different conditions call for two different forms of the same random distribution to describe the result: in the coin-tossing experiment the **binomial distribution** must be used, and in the infection experiment an asymptotic form of the binomial distribution, which is valid for small p and large N, the **Poisson distribution.**

According to the Poisson distribution the probability that a given cell is infected by k different viral particles is $P(k) = e^{-pN}(pN)^k/k!$. Since all cells are equal, two simplifications follow. $pN = a(N/C)$, the mean number of particles that infect **any cell,** and is indicated as the **multiplicity of infection** (m). Moreover, $P(k)$ is the **proportion of cells** infected by k virus particles in the whole population.

$$P(k) = \frac{e^{-m} m^k}{k!} \tag{1}$$

All the quantitative aspects of infection derived from equation (1) depend on the multiplicity of infection (m), which therefore holds a central position. The value of m can be derived directly from the known values of N and C if a can be determined, since $m = a(N/C)$. If a cannot be directly determined m can be calculated from the experimentally determinable proportion of uninfected cells, $P(0)$. By making $k = 0$ in equation (1),

$$P(0) = e^{-m}, \text{ and} \tag{2}$$
$$m = -\ln P(0), \tag{3}$$

where ln stands for the natural logarithm.

The use of equations (1), (2), and (3) will now be demonstrated with reference to two practical problems.

Problem 1. 10^7 cells are exposed to virus; at the end of the adsorption period there are 10^5 infected cells; what is the multiplicity of infection?

$$P(0) = 0.99, m = -\ln(0.99) = 0.01$$

This problem brings out the point that the mul-

tiplicity of infection can assume any value from 0 to ∞. Values smaller than unity indicate that only a fraction of the cells are infected, mostly by single viral particles.

Problem 2. What is the multiplicity of infection required for infecting 95% of the cells of a population?

$$P(0) = 5\% = 0.05, m = -\ln(0.05) = 3$$

The point of this problem is that even at very high multiplicities a certain proportion of the cells remains uninfected. The multiplicity of infection required to reduce the proportion of uninfected cells to a certain value can be calculated from equation (3).

Classes of Cells in an Infected Population

After exposure to a virus a cell population can be subdivided into classes: noninfected cells, cells infected by a single viral particle, cells infected by two viral particles, by three viral particles, and so on. Even if the multiplicity of infection is very small (i.e., much less than unity), some cells are infected by more than one particle, but their proportion is very low. The presence of these cells may not be negligible if they behave in a special way in the experiment. The sizes of the various classes are determined from equation (1), by giving various values to k. Usually only three classes of cells are considered: uninfected cells $(k = 0)$; cells infected by one viral particle (**cells with a single infection,** $k = 1$); and cells infected by more than one particle, irrespective of how many (**cells with multiple infection,** $k > 1$). The proportions are:

Uninfected cells, $P(0) = e^{-m}$
Cells with single infection, $P(1) = m\,e^{-m}$
Cells with multiple infection, $P(>1) =$
$\quad 1 - e^{-m}(m + 1)$*

If a cell is picked out of the population we cannot know a priori whether it is uninfected, or with a single or multiple infection; we only know the probability that it belongs to each of these classes.

Problem 3. To determine the various classes of infected cells if the multiplicity of infection is 10.

---

* This value is obtained by subtracting from unity (the sum of all probabilities for any value of k) the probabilities $P(0)$ and $P(1)$.

$$P(0) = e^{-m} = e^{-10} = 4.5 \times 10^{-5}$$
$$P(1) = 10 \times 4.5 \times 10^{-5} = 4.5 \times 10^{-4}$$
$$P(> 1) = 1 - 4.5 \times 10^{-5} (10 + 1) =$$
$$1 - 4.95 \times 10^{-4} = 99.95\%$$

If the cell population includes 10^7 cells there are $4.5 \times 10^{-5} \times 10^7 = 450$ uninfected cells and 4500 cells with single infection; all the others have multiple infection.

Problem 4. To determine the composition of the population of infected cells if the multiplicity of infection is 10^{-3}, or 0.001.

$$P(0) = e^{-0.001} = .9990 =$$
$$9.99 \times 10^{-1} = 99.9\%$$
$$P(1) = 0.001 \times e^{-0.001} = 10^{-3} \times 9.99 \times$$
$$10^{-1} = 9.99 \times 10^{-4} = 0.0999\%$$
$$P(> 1) = 1 - 0.9990 (0.001 + 1) =$$
$$0.000001 = 10^{-6}$$

If the cell population includes 10^7 cells there are $9.99 \times 10^{-4} \times 10^7 = 9900$ cells with single infection, and $10^{-6} \times 10^7 = 10$ cells with multiple infection; most of the cells are uninfected.

Measurement of the Infectious Titer of a Viral Sample

To measure infectious titer, a viral sample containing an **unknown** number (N) of infectious viral particles is mixed with a known number (C) of cells. N is then calculated from the proportion of cells that remain uninfected according to equation (3): $m = -\ln P(0)$; since, as defined above, $m = a(N/C)$, $N = mC/a = -C \ln P(0)/a$, or

$$aN = -C \ln P(0) \qquad (4)$$

The factor a takes into account the fact that not all potentially infectious viral particles cause recognizable cell infection, for a variety of reasons, such as adsorption to the walls of the container or to dead or unsusceptible cells, or production of abortive infection. Usually the factor a is not determinable and therefore the number (N) of infective viral particles present in the sample to be assayed cannot be calculated. In its place the product aN is obtained and is called the **number of infectious units.**

This is the basis for all measurements of the infectious viral titer. Its application is different in the plaque method and in the endpoint method.

Plaque Method

In this method m is very small, 10^{-4} or less. The equation $P(0) = e^{-m}$ can therefore be simplified by using the expansion of the exponential into a power series: $e^{-m} = 1 - m + (m^2/2!) - (m^3/3!) + \ldots$ Since $m^2/2!$ and all the following terms are much smaller than m, the asymptotic expression $e^{-m} = 1 - m$ can be used: then $P(0) = 1 - m$. The proportion of infected cells, $P(i)$, is then given by the simple equation, $P(i) = 1 - P(0) = m$. But $P(i)$ equals the ratio of the number of infected cells (C_i) to the total number of cells (C_t); thus

$$\frac{C_i}{C_t} = m = \frac{aN}{C_t},$$

and therefore $C_i = aN$. Since in the plaque method each infected cell originates a plaque, **the number of plaques equals the number of infectious units.** The actual number of cells employed in the assay is irrelevant, **provided it is in large excess** over the number of infectious viral particles, so that m is very small; uncertainties connected with the counting of the cells are therefore eliminated.

The Dose-Response Curve of the Plaque Assay. As stated above, the number of plaques that develop on a series of cell cultures infected with different dilutions of the same viral sample is proportional to the concentration of the virus. We shall now show that this linearity proves that **a single infectious viral particle is sufficient to infect a cell.**

Let us assume that more than one particle, say two particles, is required. There would then be two types of uninfected cells: those with no infectious viral particles, and those with just one such particle. According to the Poisson distribution the proportions of cells in these two classes are e^{-m} and me^{-m}, respectively. Thus, under the foregoing assumption, $P(0) = e^{-m}(1 + m)$. By using the asymptotic power expansion for the exponential for a small m, as indicated above, we have $P(0) = (1 - m + m^2/2)(1 + m)* = 1 - 1/2m^2$. Therefore $P(i) = 1/2m^2$, and the dose-response curve would be parabolic rather than linear (Fig. 22-30). If more than

---

* The term $m^2/2$ is carried in this expansion because a term in m^2 appears in the final product.

two particles were required to infect a cell, the curvature of the dose response curve would be even more pronounced.

Endpoint Method

In this method the virus to be assayed is added to a number of test units, each consisting of a large number of cells. A test unit is now equivalent to a single cell of the plaque assay. Therefore, m is the multiplicity of infection of an assay unit, rather than of a cell.

The viral titer can be calculated from the proportion of noninfected units, $P(0)$, at the endpoint dilution, according to equation (3): $m = \ln P(0)$. If at the endpoint $m = 1$, i.e., there is one infectious unit per test unit, then on the average $P(0) = 0.37$.

The multiplicity corresponding to 50% survival, which is characteristic of the ID_{50} determined by the Reed and Muench method, is calculated from the relation $e^{-ID_{50}} = 0.50$. Therefore $ID_{50} = -\ln(0.50) = 0.70$. One ID_{50} corresponds to 0.70 infectious units.

Computation of 50% Endpoints (LD_{50} or ID_{50}) by Method of Reed and Muench[†]

In biological quantitation, the endpoint is usually taken as the dilution at which a certain proportion of the test units (animals or cell cultures) reacts or dies. While a 100% endpoint is still occasionally used, its accuracy is grossly affected by small chance variations. The most desirable endpoint is one representing a situation in which half of the units react and the other half do not. The best method of determining such an endpoint is to use large numbers of test units at closely spaced dilutions near the value for 50% reaction and then to interpolate a correct value. A number of practical factors, however, militate against such an approach: 1) the cost of using large numbers of test units at every dilution point; 2) the wide variations in titer that may occur in different tests; and 3) in many instances, the unjustified application of

highly accurate statistical methods to procedures replete with uncontrolled variables.

In titrating viruses or, for example, sera for neutralizing antibody content, a series of dilutions of the test material is made, and each dilution is inoculated into a small group of test units; ordinarily 6 to 8 units are used at each dilution point. Therefore, a relatively large number of units is used in toto. Reed and Muench have devised a simple method for estimating 50% endpoints based on the large total number of test units, which gives the effect "of using, at the two critical dilutions between which the end point lies, larger groups of units than were actually included at these dilutions. By inclining to equalize chance variations, the method tends to define the point more nearly than would be possible if it were simply interpolated between the two bracketing results."

The Reed-Muench method is applicable primarily to a complete titration series; i.e., the whole reaction range, from 0 to 100% mortality (or infectivity, cytopathic effect, etc.) should be represented in the experimental data. However, the method can be utilized even if these conditions are not fulfilled, provided that the reactions occur in a uniform manner over the range of dilutions employed. If, however, the results are erratic (e.g., deaths scattered irregularly over a number of dilutions), the endpoint will be inaccurate.

This method for calculating 50% endpoints is illustrated by the example given in the table above.

Accumulated values for the total number of animals that died or survived are obtained by adding in the directions indicated by the arrows in columns c and d. The accumulated mortality ratio (column g) represents the accumulated number of dead animals (column e) over the accumulated total number inoculated (column e plus f); for example, in the 10^{-3} dilution, there were 5 deaths out of a total of 7 animals.

In the example given in the table, the mortality in the 10^{-3} dilution is above 50%; that in the next lower dilution, 10^{-4}, is considerably below 50%. Therefore, the 50% endpoint lies somewhere between the 10^{-3} and 10^{-4} dilutions of the inoculated virus. The necessary proportionate distance of the 50% mortality endpoint, which obviously lies between these two dilutions, is obtained from column h as follows:

[†] From E. H. Lennette. General Principles Underlying Laboratory Diagnosis of Virus and Rickettsial Infections. In *Diagnostic Procedures for Virus and Rickettsial Disease*, p. 45 (E. H. Lennette and N. J. Schmidt, eds.) American Public Health Association, New York, 1964. Also Reed, L. J., and Muench, H. *Am. J. Hyg.* 27:493 (1938).

Virus dilution (a)	Mortality ratio (b)	Died (c)	Survived (d)	Accumulated values		Mortality	
				Total dead (e)	Total survived (f)	Ratio (g)	% (h)
10^{-1}	6/6	6	0	17	0	17/17	100
10^{-2}	6/6	6	0	11	0	11/11	100
10^{-3}	4/6	4	2	5	2	5/7	71
10^{-4}	1/6	1	5	1	7	1/8	13
10^{-5}	0/6	0	6	0	13	0/13	0

$$\frac{\% \text{ mortality at dilution next above } 50\% - 50\%}{\% \text{ mortality at dilution next above } 50\% - \% \text{ mortality at dilution next below } 50\%} = \begin{array}{l} \text{proportionate} \\ \text{distance} \end{array}$$

or

$$\frac{71 - 50}{71 - 13} = \frac{21}{58} = 0.36 \text{ (or 0.4)}$$

Since the distance between any two dilutions is a function of the incremental steps used in preparing the series, e.g., 2-fold, 4-fold, 5-fold, 10-fold, etc., it is necessary to correct (multiply) the proportionate distance by the dilution factor, which is the logarithm of the dilution steps employed. In the case of serial 10-fold dilutions, the factor is 1 (log 10 = 1) and so is disregarded; in a 2-fold dilution series, the factor is 0.3 (log of 2); in a 5-fold series, the factor is 0.7 (log of 5), etc. In the procedure which follows, the factor is understood to be negative. Therefore, the negative log of LD_{50} endpoint titer equals the negative log of the dilution above 50% mortality **plus** the proportionate distance factor (calculated above). Therefore, in the example given, the following values obtain:

negative log of lower dilution (next above 50% mortality) $= -3.0$
proportionate distance $(0.4) \times$ dilution factor $(\log 10) = -0.4$

$$\log LD_{50} \text{ titer} = -3.4$$
$$LD_{50} \text{ titer} = 10^{-3.4}$$

Precision of Various Assay Procedures

Plaque Method. The statistical precision is measured by the standard deviation (σ) of the Poisson distribution, which is equal to the square root of the number of plaques counted. If the number of plaques counted is not too small 95% of all observations made should fall within two standard deviations from the mean in either direction (i.e., $\pm 2\sigma$). Thus 4σ is the expected range of variability of the assay. If n replicate assays are made, $\sigma = \sqrt{\bar{x}/n}$, where $\bar{x}$ is the mean value of plaque numbers in the replicate assays. The standard deviation relative to the mean (coefficient of variation) serves as a relative measure of precision: $\sigma/\bar{x}$. This is $\sqrt{x}/x = 1/\sqrt{x}$ for a single assay, and $1/.\sqrt{n\,\bar{x}}$ for n replicate assays. The smaller the coefficient of variation, the higher the precision, which therefore increases as the square root of the number of plaques.

Example. If 100 plaques are counted the standard deviation is 10. If the same assay is repeated many times its results will fall between 80 and 120 plaques in 95% of the cases; the coefficient of variation is 1/10. If 400 plaques are counted the coefficient of variation is 1/20.

Reed and Muench Method. An approximate value, empirically determined, of the standard deviation of the titer determined by this method is $\sigma = \sqrt{0.79\ hR/U}$ where h is the logarithm of the dilution factor employed at each step of the serial dilution of the virus, U is the number of test units used at each dilution, and R is the interquartile range, namely the difference between the logarithm of the dilution at which P(i) is 0.25 and 0.75, respectively. σ is expressed in logarithmic units. For the data given in Chapter 22, Appendix, with six assay units (animals) at each dilution, $h = 1.0$ and $R = 1.0$ (both in $\log_{10}$ units): $\sigma = \sqrt{0.79/6} = 0.36$ (in $\log_{10}$ units). The range of variation of the ID_{50} is therefore ± 0.72 in $\log_{10}$ units, and the highest expected value (within the 95% confidence limits) is 28 times (antilog of 1.44) the lowest value.

SELECTED REFERENCES

Books and Review Articles

ANDREWES, C. H. *Viruses of Vertebrates.* Williams & Wilkins, Baltimore, 1964.

CASPAR, D. L. D., and KLUG, A. Physical principles in the construction of regular viruses. *Cold Spring Harbor Symp. Quant. Biol.* 27:1 (1962).

GREEN, M. Chemistry of the DNA Viruses. In *Viral and Rickettsial Infections of Man.* (F. Horsfall and I. Tamm, eds.) Lippincott, Philadelphia, 1965.

HORNE, R. W., and WILDY, P. Virus structure revealed by negative staining. *Advances Virus Res.* 10:102 (1963).

KELLENBERGER, E. The genetic control of the shape of a virus. *Scient. Am.* 215:32 (1966).

SCHAFFER, F. L., and SCHWERDT, C. E. Chemistry of the RNA Viruses. In *Viral and Rickettsial Infections of Man.* (F. Horsfall and I. Tamm, eds.) Lippincott, Philadelphia, 1965.

Specific Articles

BRENNER, S., and HORNE, R. W. A negative staining method for high resolution electron microscopy of viruses. *Biochim. et biophys, acta* 34:103 (1959).

BURNET, F. M., and STONE, J. D. The receptor-destroying enzyme of *V. cholerae. Australian J. Exp. Biol. & M. Sc.* 25:227 (1947).

CRICK, F. H. C., and WATSON, J. D. Structure of small viruses. *Nature* 177:473 (1956).

DULBECCO, R. Production of plaques in monolayer tissue cultures by single particles of an animal virus. *Proc. Nat. Acad. Sc.* 38:747 (1952).

GOMATOS, P. J., and TAMM, I. The secondary structure of reovirus RNA. *Proc. Nat. Acad. Sc.* 49:707 (1963).

GOTTSCHALK, A. The influenza virus neuraminidase. *Nature* 181:377 (1958).

HIRST, G. K. The agglutination of red cells by allantoic fluid of chick embryos infected with influenza virus. *Science* 94:22 (1941).

HORNE, R. W., WATERSON, A. P., WILDY, P., and FARNHAM, A. E. The structure and composition of the myxoviruses. I. *Virology* 11:79 (1960).

HOYLE, L., HORNE, R. W., and WATERSON, A. P. The structure and composition of myxoviruses. II. *Virology* 13:448 (1961).

KATES, M., ALLISON, A. C., TYRRELL, D. A. J., and JAMES, A. T. Origin of lipids of influenza virus. *Cold Spring Harbor Symp. Quant. Biol.* 27:293 (1962).

SCHAFFER, F. L., and SCHWERDT, C. E. Crystallization of purified MEF-1 poliomyelitis virus particles. *Proc. Nat. Acad. Sc.* 41:1020 (1955).

SINSHEIMER, R. L. A single-stranded deoxyribonucleic acid from bacteriophage ϕX-174. *J. Molec. Biol.* 1:43 (1959).

STANLEY, W. M. Isolation of a crystalline protein possessing the properties of tobacco mosaic virus. *Science* 81:644 (1935).

WILDY, P., RUSSELL, W. C., and HORNE, R. W. The morphology of herpes virus. *Virology* 12:204 (1960).

WILLIAMS, R. C., and SMITH, K. M. The polyhedral form of the Tipula iridescent virus. *Biochim. et biophys. acta* 28:464 (1958).

23 MULTIPLICATION AND GENETICS OF BACTERIOPHAGES

Model Systems. Viral multiplication is a complex process constituted by many elementary acts. In order to understand this process thoroughly it is useful to study, as a model, a technically suitable virus-cell system. This approach, adopted early in the development of virology, has been an important cause for the rapid advance of knowledge in this field. It proved effective in spite of the large variety of viruses, and their marked differences in structure and abundance of genetic information, because all viruses are similar in the basic aspects of multiplication.

Bacteriophages were adopted as model systems by Burnet in Australia and by the Hungarian chemist, Schlesinger, and were later used by a large group of investigators working in close contact, which included Delbrück, Luria, and S. S. Cohen in the United States and Lwoff in France. These more recent workers concentrated on the T-phages of *Escherichia coli,* and especially the "T-even" phages (T2, T4, and T6). The choice of these bacteriophages was accidental. They would probably not be selected now as a model system because they are now known to be among

the most complex of all viruses. It must be recognized, however, that their complexity allowed the discovery of aspects of viral multiplication that would have been much harder to find with simpler viruses. The presence, for instance, of 5-hydroxymethylcytosine instead of cytosine in their DNA made it possible to follow the intracellular multiplication of the viral DNA, as noted in the previous chapter; furthermore, the presence in the infected cells of deoxycytidylate hydroxymethylase, which synthesizes the unusual base, and its absence in uninfected cells, gave the first hint that virus-specified enzymes are made in the infected cells. Moreover, these viruses are easy to purify, owing to their large size; and they have a high frequency of genetic recombination, which is beneficial for genetic studies.

Among other coliphages employed as models for special problems the most outstanding are λ, which produces the important phenomenon of lysogenization (Ch. 24); φX174, which contains single-stranded DNA; and f2, which contains RNA.

MULTIPLICATION OF BACTERIOPHAGES

As pointed out by Lwoff, bacteriophages exist in three states: **extracellular virions, vegetative phage,** and **prophage.** The properties of the extracellular virions were reviewed in the preceding chapter; those of vegetative phage will be studied in this chapter, and those of prophage in the next chapter. These studies will show that both vegetative phage and prophage are viral nucleic acid; as vegetative phage it undergoes autonomous replication, and as prophage it is inserted in and replicated with the bacterial DNA. All bacteriophages exist at some stage as vegetative phages during their intracellular multiplication, but not all can become prophages. Those able to become prophages are called **temperate,** those unable to do so are called **virulent.** The multiplication of vegetative phage will

be analyzed mostly with the virulent T-even coliphages.

Infection of Host Cells

When a suspension of phage virions is mixed with a bacterial culture two main events must occur before the bacteriophage DNA infects the cells and becomes able to multiply in them. First, the virions must attach to the host bacteria (**adsorption**), and then the DNA must separate from the viral coat and become free in the cell (**release of the nucleic acid**).

Adsorption

The attachment of a virion to a host bacterium occurs in at least two steps: the virion first collides with the cell, and then it establishes bonds with the cell surface. Under optimal conditions bacteriophage adsorption occurs rapidly: with a cell concentration of 10^8 host bacteria per milliliter 90% of the virions are adsorbed within a few minutes. The rate of adsorption depends on both the frequency of collision and the probability of forming bonds.

The frequency of collision is proportional to 1) the concentration of both virions and cells; 2) the diffusion constant of the virions; and 3) the electrostatic attraction (or repulsion) between virions and cells. The probability of forming bonds depends on the chemical structure of the surfaces of both virion and cell. Although both surfaces have over-all negative charges, attachment can take place when a virion approaches the cell surface closely and ionized groups of opposite polarities form ionic bonds. Attachment of virus and cell, therefore, depends on complementary chemical groups on the two surfaces, in much the same way as the union between an antigen and an antibody. With coliphage T1 the bonds are apparently formed between amino groups of the viral surface and acidic groups of **receptors** located on the cell surface.

Reversible adsorption of phages does not require energy from the cell, since it can occur, with both T1 and T2, at $0°$. It also does not exhibit specific ion requirements. The adsorption is abolished below pH 5 and above 12.

Irreversible adsorption always requires a favorable cation concentration: optimally 0.01 N Na^+ for T1, 0.1 N for T2, and the presence of Ca^{++} for T5. With T2 it does not require metabolic activity: it occurs even at $0°$, and it is not inhibited by azide or 2,4-dinitrophenol. With T1, in contrast, a temperature high enough for metabolic activity is required, and these inhibitors block the reaction. The mechanism of irreversible adsorption is unknown, and it is not clear whether it must be preceded by reversible adsorption. From now on we shall refer only to irreversible adsorption.

Receptors. Receptors for different phages of the T series are located in different layers of the cell wall of *E. coli* cells. The deeply located receptors are presumably accessible through holes in the more superficial layers. The receptors for phage T5 can be obtained in pure form; they are constituted by two layers, one of protein and the other of lipopolysaccharide. The receptors combine with the tip of the bacteriophage tail in vitro, as shown by electron micrographs (Fig. 23-1).

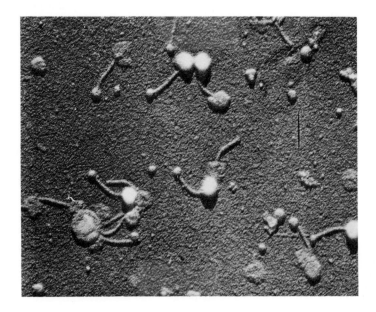

Fig. 23-1 Electron micrograph of bacteriophage T5 mixed with purified receptors. The receptors are in the form of spheres, about 300 A in diameter, some free and some adsorbed to the tip of the phage tails. Shadowed preparation. Marker, 2000 A. (From W. Weidel and E. Kellenberger. Biochim. et biophys. acta 17:1, 1955.)

The receptors for the very small coliphages f1 (DNA-containing) and f2 (RNA-containing) are present on the surface of F$^+$ cells only, and therefore are presumably related to the constituents of the cell surface that confer the male character on the cells. Indeed, the site of attachment of such phages indicates that the male surface resides in specific pili of the F$^+$ cells (Ch. 7).

Mutations Affecting Adsorption. Adsorption of a bacteriophage can be abolished by bacterial mutations that change the nature of a chemical group—such as a sugar—on the receptors; these mutations to **bacteriophage resistance** may also change the antigenic specificity of the cells. A bacteriophage-resistant mutant is indicated by a bar followed by the name of the phage: for instance, *E. coli* B/2 indicates a mutant of *E. coli* resistant to T2. If a pure culture of bacteria resistant to a given bacteriophage is exposed to a large concentration of that bacteriophage, phage multiplication occurs after a lag, and is caused by rare **host-range** (*h*) **mutants** which are able to adsorb to cells resistant to wild-type phage. These mutants played an important role in the early development of bacteriophage genetics. Moreover, the selection of such bacteriophage mutants shows the connection between viral evolution and the evolution of the host cells.

Viral Sites for Adsorption. The T-even coliphages have specialized sites for adsorption, the **tail fibers,** as shown by two types of evidence. 1) The fibers, when isolated, adsorb to bacteria and have the same host range as the intact bacteriophage from which they were derived; and 2) a fiber-specific antiserum prevents the adsorption of the phage. When the phage is absorbed the fibers become attached to the bacterial cell wall, and the virion acquires a characteristic position, perpendicular to the cell wall with the head sticking out (Fig. 23-2).

The tail fibers tend to stick to the sheath of the phage tail, with a resulting loss of adsorption. This happens regularly at a pH below 5, and for certain mutants of coliphage T4 at normal pH in the absence of tryptophan (**tryptophan-dependent mutants**). Tryptophan allows the fibers to detach reversibly, and thus "activates" the mutant. The activation can be made permanent by exposing the virion, in the presence of tryptophan, to a weak sheath-specific antiserum, which coats the sheath and thus prevents the fibers from reattaching to it.

Separation of Nucleic Acid from Coat

Separation of the viral nucleic acid from the viral coat was demonstrated in 1952 by Hershey and Chase, who studied the fate of T2 labeled either in the protein by ^{35}S or in the DNA by ^{32}P (Fig. 23-3). The bacteria were infected by the labeled phage and incubated for several minutes at 37°. They were then exposed to violent blending in a Waring Blendor, which shears the tails of the adsorbed virions, causing the head and most of the tail of each virion (except the tip) to come off the cells. The experiment yielded two results that, at the time, seemed astonishing. 1) With ^{35}S-labeled phage 80% of the label came off; but with ^{32}P-labeled phage essentially all the label remained with the cells, and since it was DNase-resistant it was **within** the cells. 2) The blended bacteria produced progeny phage as if they had not been blended.

Separation of the nucleic acid from the coat could also be demonstrated without blending, by adsorbing ^{32}P-labeled phage to cell wall fragments; the viral DNA was then injected into the medium where it was digestible by DNase. Thus, this result also showed that injection does not require energy from the cell.

These findings showed at one stroke 1) that phage DNA carries the genetic information; and 2) that infection consists of the penetration of the viral DNA into the cells. After the DNA is injected, if the cells are disrupted they do not produce plaques when plated in the usual way; but the infectivity reappears when progeny virus is formed. The temporary disappearance of infectivity is called **eclipse:** it is due to the inability of the naked viral DNA to infect bacteria under ordinary conditions, as will be discussed below.

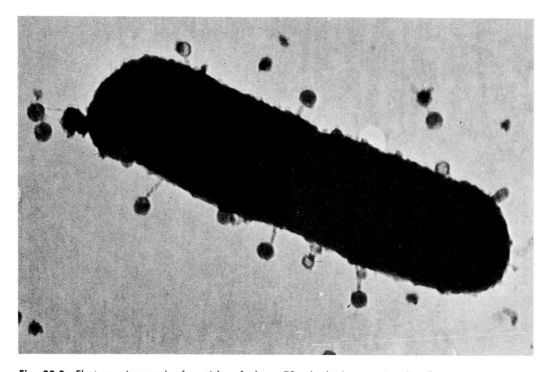

Fig. 23-2 Electron micrograph of particles of phage T5 adsorbed to an *E. coli* cell. Note that the virions attach by the tip of their tail. Note also that the heads of some particles are clear (electron-transparent) having injected their DNA into the cells; other are dark (electron-opaque) and still contain their DNA. (From T. F. Anderson. Cold Spring Harbor Symp. Quant. Biol. 18:197, 1953.)

Infection by Naked Viral Nucleic Acid

Further evidence for the essential role of the nucleic acid is afforded by the infection of bacteria with purified phage DNA. This phenomenon was discovered only recently, because bacterial cells accept infectious viral nucleic acid only under special conditions: 1) as spheroplasts, 2) as intact bacteria when competent to accept bacterial transforming DNA, or 3) when exposed at the same time to virions to which they are susceptible (**helper phage**). It is likely that all three conditions cause openings in the cell wall through which the DNA can penetrate.

By these means it could also be shown that a **whole DNA molecule** is required for infection. At very low multiplicity of nucleic acid molecules per cell, when most cells receive either a single molecule or none at all, only intact DNA molecules can infect cells. In contrast, under conditions of multiple infection **fragmented molecules** are also effective, provided the **whole genetic information** of the virus enters the cell: the fragments recombine to constitute a complete molecule.

The infectivity of a viral nucleic acid can be titrated by a modified plaque assay. If infection is caused by intact molecules the dose-response curve is linear, as with the assay of virions; if it is carried out by fragments it is not linear, since several fragments must be present in the same cell (Ch. 22, Appendix).

Injection of Nucleic Acid into the Cell

Electron microscopic observations have shown that the irreversible adsorption of the T-even coliphages is accompanied by contraction of the tail sheath. This contraction pulls

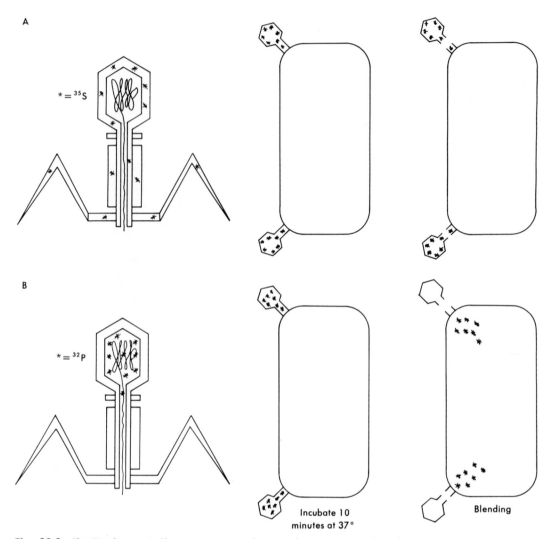

Fig. 23-3 The Hershey and Chase experiment, showing the separation of viral DNA and protein. **A.** Phage was labeled in its protein by propagation in a medium containing $^{35}SO_4^=$. **B.** Phage was labeled in its DNA by propagation in medium containing $^{32}PO_4^=$. Phage of either type was adsorbed to host bacteria for 10 minutes, then the culture was blended. Most of the ^{32}P remained associated with the cells, whereas most of the ^{35}S came off. *, radioactive atoms.

the collar and the phage head toward the plate and the tail fibers, which are held firmly against the cell surface, and therefore causes the tube connected to the head to penetrate the cell wall (Fig. 23-4). Because of this action, as well as its shape, the virion has been likened to a hypodermic syringe, and the release of the nucleic acid is called injection. It is fairly certain, however, that the tube of the

T-even bacteriophages does not penetrate the plasma membrane, because during its injection the DNA of these phages is exposed to the action of nucleases located on the membrane, as shown by the phenomenon of host-induced modification described below.

The contraction of the sheath is not generally required for releasing the DNA: many phages lack a sheath around their tail and do

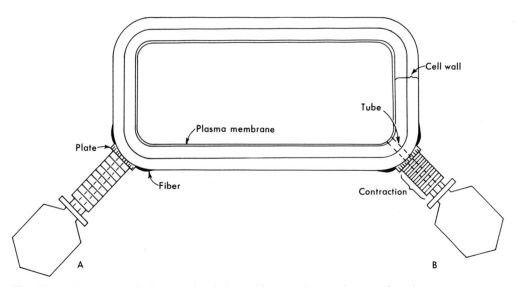

Fig. 23-4 Contraction of the sheath of T-even bacteriophages during adsorption. Since the plate is held against the surface of the bacterium (A) by the tail fibers attached to the cell's receptors, the contraction of the sheath (B) pushes the tube of the virion through the cell wall.

not contract; yet they inject their DNA into the cell. Even the small helical bacteriophage M13 releases its DNA into the cell, leaving 90% of its protein outside the cell. It should be remarked that the tube of T-even bacteriophages, the sheathless tail of many other phages, and the capsid of M13 have similar diameters. These various structures may, therefore, penetrate through holes in the cell wall, either by themselves or by syringe action, until their tip reaches the plasma membrane, where the release of DNA is triggered. There is no doubt that the DNA can then penetrate the plasma membrane by itself because naked viral DNA penetrates spheroplasts.

The sheath appears to be a useful mechanism for injection. Its contraction increases markedly the rate of penetration of the phage DNA, which is 100 times faster for T2 than for M13. The sheath, furthermore, contains the source of energy for pushing the tube through the cell wall, without depending on energy supplied by the cell, which is required by at least some sheathless phages. Indeed, in many respects, although not structurally, the sheath of the phage particle is comparable to a primitive muscle; like muscle,

it contains ATP and the enzyme ATPase, and it converts ATP to ADP during injection. As the sheath contracts it becomes shorter and thicker; the number of its discs is reduced to about half the number present in the relaxed sheath, but their spacings remain unchanged. Apparently the protein monomers present in two discs in the relaxed sheath are redistributed to form a single disc during contraction.

Enzymatic Action at the Tip of the Tail. Virions of the T-even bacteriophages are able to hydrolyze the mucopeptide of the *E. coli* cell wall, displaying an activity similar to that of lysozyme (Ch. 2). This activity is due to a phage lysozyme, specified by a viral gene and synthesized during phage multiplication. Molecules of the enzyme remain attached to the tail of the phage after its release from the cell and may help the injection of the viral DNA by drilling a hole in the mucopeptide layer of the cell wall; this may not be a strict requirement, however, since lysozyme-less phage mutants can inject their DNA. The holes of the cell wall cause a leakage of cell constituents into the medium, but in normal viral multiplication they are rapidly repaired. If, however, a large number of bacteriophages attach within a short time to the same cell, and especially if cell metabolism is impaired, the many holes drilled in the cell wall cause an immediate lysis of the cells, without viral multiplication. This phenomenon is known as **lysis from without,** to distinguish it from the lysis from within that follows viral multiplication.

The Viral Multiplication Cycle

The process of viral multiplication, initiated by the penetration into the cells of the nucleic acid of the **parent virions,** is a sequential process involving many steps which ends up in the release of the **progeny virions** produced in the cell. The sequence of steps is called the **multiplication cycle.** The study of the cycle requires many types of determinations, at precise times after infection: e.g., the number of infectious units; the amount of DNA, RNA, proteins, and other components synthesized; the activities of enzymes. These determinations require a population containing a large number of infected cells.

It is not easy to infect a cell population with a virus and at the same time maintain the characteristic sequence of events of the multiplication cycle. A common danger is that infection of the various cells is spread out over a long period of time, and that virus released from some of the cells infects other cells. Thus the multiplication cycles in various cells would be out of phase, and the sequence of events characteristic of a single cycle could not be recognized. To avoid this complication infection must be **synchronized.** This can be achieved by infecting a cell population with a large virus inoculum and removing the unadsorbed virus after a short time.

A further difficulty is introduced by the desirability of studying the multiplication cycle in cells infected by **single virions,** since if many virions infect a cell the multiplication cycle may be abnormal. Infection by single virions can be achieved by employing a low multiplicity (e.g., 0.1); but then, as seen in Chapter 22, Appendix, most cells are unin-

fected at the outset and can be infected later by virus released by the originally infected cells. This event would again destroy the single cycle character. This complication can be avoided by adopting **"one-step conditions,"** the simplest and most general of which consists in diluting the virus-cell mixture into a large volume of nutrient medium when adsorption is completed (employed in the classic bacteriophage studies of Ellis and Delbrück). The progeny virus released after dilution has much less chance of becoming adsorbed to the uninfected cells because they are so sparse.

Certain aspects of viral multiplication can also be studied by infecting cell suspensions and then isolating single cells in tubes or in small drops of medium under paraffin oil (**single-burst experiments**). The number of virions participating in the infection of a given cell is unknown, but the probability that it has a certain value can be calculated from the multiplicity of infection (Ch. 22, Appendix). If the multiplicity is low (e.g., less than 0.1) most of the virus-yielding cells are infected by single virions.

Certain aspects of viral multiplication depend on the following **parameters of infection:** the number of infectious units in the input virus (**inoculum**); the number of **productively infected cells** (those that produce progeny virus), and the **multiplicity of infection.** The measurement of infectious titer and multiplicity of infection were discussed in Chapter 22, Appendix; **productive cells** are measured as **infectious centers,** i.e., as cells able to release viral progeny and therefore to produce a plaque in the regular assay used for the virus. In these determinations the unadsorbed input phage is either removed by washing the cells or neutralized by adding antiviral antibody.

One-Step Multiplication Curve

A one-step multiplication curve describes the appearance of progeny phage in an infected culture under one-step conditions. At the end of the adsorption period unadsorbed phage is removed (e.g., by centrifuging the cells and resuspending them in a virus-free medium), and at subsequent times the infectious phage titer is assayed. Assaying the medium after centrifuging down the cells gives the **extracellular titer;** assaying the culture after disrupting the infected cells gives the **total** (extracellular plus intracellular) **titer.** Plotting these titers—usually expressed as infectious units per productive cell—versus the times of assay yields multiplication curves such as those of Figure 23-5, in which the following stages can be recognized.

1) **A to B: The eclipse period.** The total virus titer is considerably less than the concentration of productive cells. The end of the eclipse period is taken as the time, B, at which one infectious unit has been produced for each productive cell, on the average.

2) **B to C: The intracellular accumulation period.** Progeny phage accumulates intracellularly but is not spontaneously released into the medium. The end of this period, C, is the time at which one viral infectious unit per productive cell, on the average, has appeared extracellularly. The period A to C is the **latent period.**

3) **C to D: The rise period.** The extracellular phage titer increases until the end of the multiplication cycle at D. The average number of infectious units of virus per productive cell present at time D represents the **viral yield.**

The phage multiplication cycle can also be studied by following the changes in **turbidity** of a culture in which most cells are infected.

Fig. 23-5 Diagram of one-step multiplication curve of bacteriophage T2. Bacteria and phage were mixed and adsorption was allowed for 2 minutes; antiphage serum was then added to the culture. The bacteria were recovered by centrifugation and were resuspended in a large volume of medium at 37°. A sample was immediately plated to determine the concentration of productive cells. Other samples were taken from time to time and divided into two aliquots: one was shaken with chloroform to disrupt the bacteria and was then assayed (curve 1: **total** virus); the other was freed of bacteria by centrifugation and the supernatant was assayed (curve 2: **extracellular** virus). The titers are compared to the concentration of productive cells as 1.0.

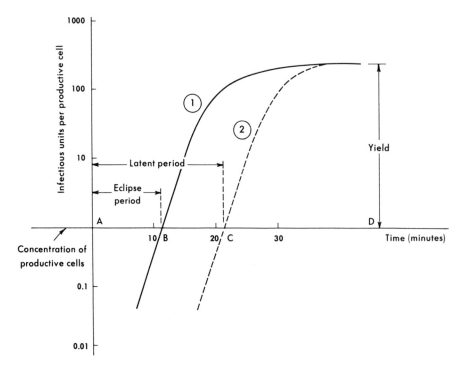

As shown in Figure 23-6, after addition of the virus inoculum the turbidity of a growing culture temporarily drops, probably owing to loss of materials from the cells through holes produced by phage particles in the cell wall and plasma membrane (see above). When the virus is released from the cells the turbidity drops rapidly because of cell **lysis.**

Lysis Inhibition. If a culture inoculated with a wild-type strain of a T-even phage is heavily reinoculated a few minutes later with the same strain the turbidity curve shows a strong deviation from the above pattern. The time of lysis is then delayed by more than 1 hour, a phenomenon called **lysis inhibition.**

Moreover, from the wild-type strains mutants lacking lysis inhibition, called **rapid lysis** or **r** mutants, can be isolated. These mutants are distinguished from the wild-type strains (r$^+$) on the basis of the shape of their plaques: r plaques are about 2 mm in diameter, clear, and with a sharp edge: r$^+$ plaques are smaller and surrounded by an opaque halo, which is formed by bacteria infected at successive times, and therefore lysis-inhibited (Fig. 23-20). This genetically controlled plaque difference has played an important role in the development of phage genetics, as noted below.

Although the mechanism of lysis inhibition is unknown, the phenomenon is a very useful tool for phage research, because all synthetic processes continue normally during this period. As a consequence, much more virus is synthesized, and

it is easier to study the time-dependent events of viral multiplication. For instance, by breaking open the infected cells at various times after the end of the eclipse period batches of virions with different times of synthesis can be obtained; and the times can be varied from about 10 minutes (length of the eclipse period at 37°) to 100 or more minutes.

Synthesis of Viral Macromolecules

Infection of bacteria by T-even phages causes an early cessation of net RNA synthesis, together with a profound rearrangement of all persistent macromolecular syntheses. The first hint of this rearrangement was gained when Hershey measured the synthesis of viral and cellular DNA in the infected cells, taking advantage of the presence of 5-hydroxymethylcytosine in the former and its absence in the latter. He showed not only that the synthesis of cellular DNA stops, but also that the preexisting cellular DNA breaks down and its components are utilized as precursors of viral DNA. Similarly, Flaks and Cohen demonstrated that a new protein, deoxycytidylate hydroxymethylase, made its appearance after infection.

After many years of biochemical investigation it has finally been realized that the cessation of RNA synthesis first observed in phage-infected cells is only one aspect of the generalized block of the synthesis of cellular macromolecules. We now know that within a few minutes after infection the synthesis of all

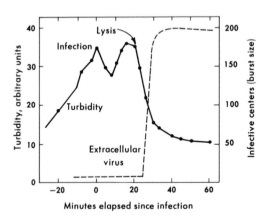

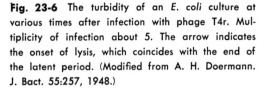

Fig. 23-6 The turbidity of an *E. coli* culture at various times after infection with phage T4r. Multiplicity of infection about 5. The arrow indicates the onset of lysis, which coincides with the end of the latent period. (Modified from A. H. Doermann. *J. Bact.* 55:257, 1948.)

cellular DNA, RNA, and protein ceases. However, the **over-all** protein synthesis continues at essentially an unchanged rate, and DNA synthesis resumes, after a brief halt, with increased rate, because viral syntheses take over after cellular syntheses cease. There is, therefore, a **shift** from cellular to viral synthesis after infection, which represents the fundamental characteristic of viral parasitism, i.e., the substitution of viral genes for cellular genes in directing the synthesizing machinery of the cell.

The inhibition of macromolecular synthesis is the consequence of the mere attachment of the viral coat to the cell, and does not require injection of the viral DNA into the cell: it occurs in bacteria infected by DNA-less phage particles or by formalin-treated phage (which does not inject its DNA). The inhibition, therefore, does not require the expression of viral genes in the cells. Its mechanism is obscure and may be similar to the inhibition caused by special proteins, called colicins, which will be discussed in Chapter 24, Episomes.

The breakdown of the cellular DNA requires more than virus attachment. It can be prevented by blocking protein synthesis with chloramphenicol, and it is presumably caused by a virus-specific DNase, as noted below. Whereas inhibition of cellular DNA synthesis is caused by many other bacteriophages, its breakdown is produced by only a few of them, endowed with the highest degree of virulence.

The over-all synthetic rate remains approximately constant because phage infection does not affect the elements that control these rates, i.e., the energy-producing machinery and the number of ribosomes (Ch. 9). Since the infection, however, blocks a further increase of both elements, the over-all rate of protein synthesis does not increase after infection, and the rate of DNA synthesis increases by an amount corresponding to the former rate of RNA synthesis, now absent.

The macromolecular syntheses in the phage-infected cells will now be examined in greater detail, by following the synthetic hier-archy: RNA synthesis first; then protein synthesis, which depends on RNA; and finally DNA synthesis, whose initiation depends on proteins (Ch. 9).

RNA Synthesis

Viral Messengers

Although the bulk of RNA synthesis stops in cells after phage infection, some can still be detected by incorporation of radioactive precursors. In 1956 Volkin and Astrakhan found that the labeled RNA fraction has a fast turnover: it rapidly acquires label when a radioactive precursor is added to the medium, and rapidly loses it when the precursor is removed. This fraction is quite small and would not readily be detectable if the synthesis of cellular RNA were not inhibited. Its base ratios, determined on the labeled material, are different from those of the bulk of the cellular RNA, but similar to those of the viral DNA. On the basis of these characteristics we now recognize this RNA fraction as the phage mRNA, the general characteristics of which were given in Chapter 9. Certain special characteristics are discussed below.

Characteristics of Phage mRNA

Synthesis and Turnover. Phage mRNA is made in infected cells even when protein synthesis is blocked by chloramphenicol at the time of infection; hence it is synthesized by a cellular enzyme already present before infection. Phage mRNA **transcribes only one of the viral DNA strands.** Thus with bacteriophage α of *Bacillus subtilis* the two DNA strands differ markedly in average base ratio, and therefore can be separated by equilibrium density gradient centrifugation in CsCl. The mRNA extracted from the phage-infected cells hybridizes with only one of the two strands (Ch. 8, DNA-RNA hybridization).

In the rapid turnover of phage mRNA its degradation products are converted to deoxynucleotides and end up in viral DNA. This flow facilitated recognition of turnover, and therefore the discovery of phage mRNA; turnover would have been more difficult to detect had the labeled breakdown products been reutilized for new mRNA synthesis.

Attachment to Pre-Existing Ribosomes. This was shown by Brenner, Jacob, and Meselson in 1961 in a classic experiment, whose details were discussed in Chapter 9, Messenger RNA.

Regulation of mRNA Synthesis. As we shall see in the next section, cells infected by T-even bacteriophages make two sets of proteins: an **early** set during the first half of the eclipse period, and a **late** set subsequently. Corresponding **early** and **late** messengers were later demonstrated. These two sets of messengers are identified by exposing infected cells to a pulse of a radioactive RNA precursor at various times after infection; their difference in composition is revealed by hybridizing the two sets to phage DNA in the presence of competing unlabeled RNA, also extracted from the cells at various times after infection. The phage DNA hybridizes with mRNA synthesized at any time after infection; however, the unlabeled "early" RNA competes effectively with the "early" RNA, but only partially with the "late" RNA. The late RNA, therefore, contains messenger molecules absent or poorly represented in the early RNA.

Protein Synthesis

The discovery of deoxycytidylate hydroxymethylase started an intense search for virus-induced enzymes in infected bacteria. This work led to the discovery, especially by Kornberg and collaborators, of many such enzymes. A striking result of these investigations was the finding that many new enzymes make their appearance in the infected cells only a few minutes after infection, and much sooner than the viral capsid protein. The **early** proteins are made **before** phage DNA; the **late** proteins together with or after phage DNA.

Early Proteins

In cells infected by T-even bacteriophages there are several types of early proteins. 1)

Enzymes required for DNA synthesis (Fig. 23-7). These compose the largest group. Some are novel and are required for the synthesis of hydroxymethylcytosine; others enhance functions already present in uninfected cells, presumably in order to allow a higher rate of DNA synthesis after infection. 2) **Glucosyl transferases,** which transfer glucosyl groups from uridine diphosphate glucose to the hydroxymethyl groups of hydroxymethylcytosine residues present in the viral DNA. The different glucosylation patterns of the DNAs of different T-even phages (Ch. 22) are determined by the specificities of the enzymes appearing in cells infected by these phages. 3) A degradative enzyme, **deoxycytidine triphosphatase,** which dephosphorylates the tri- and diphosphates of cytidine to the monophosphate. This enzyme appears necessary to prevent the incorporation of cytosine (instead of 5-hydroxymethylcytosine) residues in phage DNA, since in vitro the DNA polymerase of phage-infected cells accepts equally well cytidine or 5-hydroxymethylcytidine triphosphate. 4) An **inhibitor of the DNA-dependent RNA polymerase,** of unknown function. 5) The **internal head protein** (Ch. 22). 6) A **DNase,** which is probably responsible for the breakdown of the cellular DNA (see below). (A DNase of unusual properties appears in cells infected by temperate phage λ and may play an important biological role; see Ch. 24.)

Late Proteins

Two types of late proteins are identifiable in cells infected by T-even coliphages: the proteins of the viral coat and the phage lysozymes mentioned earlier in this chapter.

Coat proteins constitute most of the protein synthesized in the late part of the multiplication cycle, beginning shortly before the first complete progeny virions are made, and continuing throughout the intracellular accumulation period. Study of this process with a variety of technics has yielded the following results.

Labeled amino acids are first built into protein which has no recognizable characteristics of phage protein; then it acquires character-

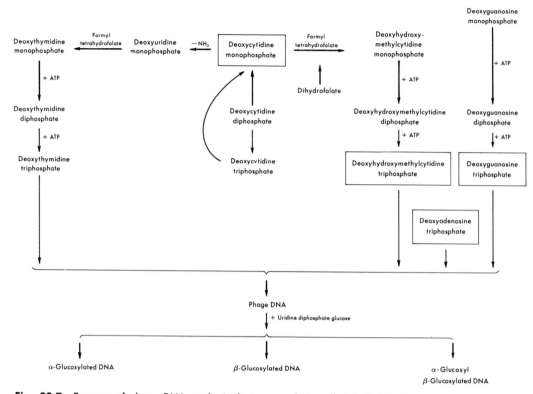

Fig. 23-7 Enzymes of phage DNA synthesis that are made in cells infected by T-even bacteriophages. Heavy arrows indicate the new enzymes.

istic sedimentability and antigenic properties; finally the label is found in morphologically recognizable structures. This sequence appears to reflect the synthesis of polypeptide chains to form subunits, which are then assembled into monomers and oligomers, where antigenicity presumably is acquired. Then the oligomers form larger structures, which are assembled into virions.

These studies have also shown that the synthesized subunits enter pools, from which elements are later withdrawn at random to form more complex structures: thus proteins labeled by short pulses are incorporated into virions finished at any subsequent times. The formation of pools is a general characteristic of the synthesis of precursors of virions, e.g., the phage DNA, as will be noted below.

Enzymes with specificity similar to that of lysozyme are synthesized in cells infected by many bacteriophages. They have the function

of weakening the cell wall, and are called **phage lysozymes** or **endolysins.** Their role in the injection of phage DNA into the cells at infection has been considered above, and their role in the release of progeny virions will be examined below.

Specification of the New Proteins

There is strong evidence that the new or enhanced enzymatic activities appearing after infection are caused by the expression of viral genes. First, these activities are produced by new enzymes, which have proved, whenever adequately purified, to differ physically and antigenically from enzymes existing before infection. Second, it is unlikely that these new enzymes are specified by cellular genes derepressed after infection, because synthesis of cellular mRNA in general ceases after infection. Finally, viral specification has been conclusively proved for a few proteins (phage lysozyme, head protein, deoxycytidylate hydroxymethylase) by correlating either amino acid substitutions or altered heat stability with mutations of viral genes.

Regulation of Synthesis of Phage Proteins

The early synthesis of some viral mRNAs and proteins, and the late synthesis of others, imply the existence of mechanisms that selectively regulate the function of various viral genes. These regulatory mechanisms remain for the most part obscure, though there is some experimental evidence on them.

For example, the cessation of the synthesis of early protein appears to be related to the replication of phage DNA, because it does not occur if this replication is prevented, either by mutation or by ultraviolet irradiation. Moreover, the initiation of synthesis of the late proteins appears to depend on the presence of functional early proteins. Thus in bacteria infected in the presence of amino acid analogs (7-azatryptophan or p-fluorophenylalanine) incorporation of the analogs causes the early proteins to be nonfunctional, and no late protein is made. When the analog is later replaced by the regular amino acid functional early proteins are made immediately, but late proteins only after a 10-minute delay.

DNA Synthesis

Origin of Components of Viral DNA

The atoms forming the DNA of the progeny virions can derive from three sources: 1) the DNA of the infecting virions; 2) materials present in the cell before infection, such as host DNA, RNA, and small molecules; and 3) the culture medium. The contributions of these precursors are determined by **transfer experiments**: at various times, either before or after infection, a sample of the cells is transferred from the regular medium to one containing a suitable radioactive marker, such as $^{32}PO_4 \equiv$. The DNA present in the progeny virions at the end of the multiplication cycle is then isolated and the specific activity of its phosphorus (i.e., the ratio of ^{32}P to total P) is determined and compared with that of the medium after transfer, which

is taken as 100. The specific activity of the isolated viral DNA is 100 if the phosphate of the DNA has all been assimilated only after transfer; if some is assimilated before transfer the specific activity is proportionally reduced.

Among coliphages of the T series host material present at the time of infection contributes about 30% of the phosphorus for the DNA of phage T2 and 90% for the DNA of phage T7, which has a lower DNA complement per virion. Other evidence shows that this phosphorus is first assimilated into the host cell DNA, and when the latter breaks down the products are utilized to make viral DNA. The remainder of the viral DNA is synthesized from precursors taken up from the medium after infection, which are incorporated into viral DNA without first going into bacterial DNA. With viruses that do not cause breakdown of the host cell DNA, such as the temperate bacteriophage λ (Ch. 24), precursors of new viral DNA come exclusively from the medium.

The Pool of Viral DNA

By using cells under conditions of lysis inhibition it can be shown that virions made early receive a larger contribution from the infecting virions, and from the host cell DNA, than those made later. This unequal distribution is understandable, since these precursors are available early after infection and are later exhausted. It is striking, however, that virions made long after these sources are exhausted continue to derive from them part of their materials. This finding is explained by the existence of a pool of intermediates, of considerable size, between source materials and virions (Fig. 23-8).

The size of the pool can be determined by introducing into it at a given time a known amount of radioactive precursor and measuring the specific activity of virions made at subsequent times. The specific activity of a virion is equal to that of the pool at the time the virion is assembled; and the ratio of the activity to that of the introduced precursor is a function of the pool size. From these data, therefore, the size of the pool can be calculated.

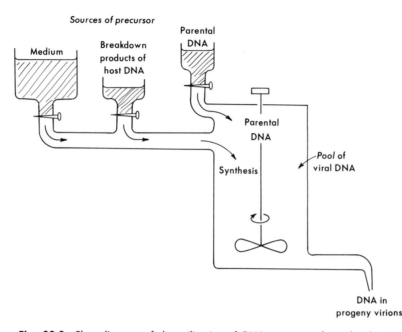

Fig. 23-8 Flow diagram of the utilization of DNA precursors from the three possible sources (parental DNA, medium, and breakdown products of cellular DNA). The parental DNA and the DNA synthesized from the other two sources of precursors are found to be mixed in the pool of phage DNA. The appearance of precursors in progeny virions is therefore much more spread out in time than their appearance in the pool.

Precursors can be introduced into the pool from any of the three sources indicated above. The clearest results are obtained by using parental virus with labeled DNA, because both its amount and the time of entry into the pool are precisely known; but results obtained by using the other two sources are in agreement.

It can be shown that the precursor pool starts building up a few minutes after infection, and by the end of the eclipse period it reaches a constant size of about 50 phage equivalents (i.e., 50 times the amount of DNA constituents present in a virion). From then on the pool size is constant, showing that precursors continue to flow in and out of it (to form virions) at equal rates.

The material present in the pool is essentially viral DNA, because the calculated pool size is equal to the chemically estimated amount of phage DNA (i.e., DNA containing 5-hydroxymethylcytosine) that is not assembled in virions. (Small molecular precursors of DNA should also contribute to the pool, but this contribution is small, because the pool size is much the same whether determined by labeling the injected viral DNA, which bypasses the small molecular intermediates, or components of the medium, which do not bypass them.) Moreover, the amount of unassembled phage DNA present in the infected cells corresponds to the number of viral genomes in the pool, as revealed by genetic experiments to be reviewed below. Thus the pool consists largely of **vegetative phages**—genetically competent molecules of phage DNA not yet assembled into virions.

Dependence of DNA Synthesis on Previous Protein Synthesis

No phage DNA is synthesized in cells infected in the presence of chloramphenicol, which inhibits protein synthesis. If chloramphenicol is added at various times after infection viral DNA synthesis continues at the rate attained when the inhibitor is added (Fig. 23-9). This result shows that phage DNA synthesis requires the formation of early phage proteins, which increase in amount throughout the eclipse period; the rate of DNA synthesis at any time is proportional to the amount of these proteins available. Some of these proteins have already been identified (Fig. 23-7).

In the presence of chloramphenicol viral capsids are not synthesized and so virions are not made; viral DNA is therefore not withdrawn from the pool, which becomes much larger than normal.

Mode of Replication of Phage DNA: Breakage and Reunion

The mode of replication of the phage DNA has been studied by transfer experiments similar to those discussed in Chapter 8, The replication of DNA. Cells were infected with phage T4 containing ^{32}P-labeled DNA and were then grown in a medium containing 5-bromouracil (5BU). This analog is incorporated in DNA in place of thymine, and owing to the heavy bromine atom it confers

on the DNA a higher buoyant density. 5BU-containing DNA can therefore be separated by equilibrium density gradient centrifugation in CsCl from thymine-containing DNA. The semiconservative mode of replication predicts that the DNA of the progeny phage should form two bands (Ch. 8, The replication of DNA): one band should contain radioactive hybrid molecules made up by one parental strand (radioactive, light) and one newly made strand (nonradioactive, heavy) and should therefore be located at an intermediate density; the other band should be made up of molecules containing no parental strand, and should be nonradioactive, with the density of 5BU-DNA (Fig. 23-10).

Surprisingly, the results did not follow this expectation; the intact progeny phage DNA yielded a single band, at the density of 5BU-DNA, and it contained all the radioactivity (Fig. 23-11). This means that the parental DNA was dispersed in the form of fragments sufficiently small so that their incorporation did not appreciably alter the density of the progeny molecules. In order to determine the size of the fragments the DNA was broken

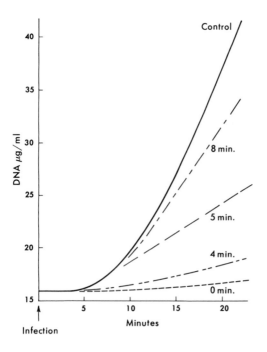

Fig. 23-9 Evidence for the role of novel proteins in the synthesis of the DNA of phage T2. Parallel cultures of *E. coli* were infected at time zero, and 30 μg/ml of chloramphenicol was added at the times (minutes) indicated near each curve. The amount of DNA present in the cultures was determined at various times. The DNA present at the moment of infection is bacterial, but phage infection stops its further synthesis almost immediately; the DNA made subsequently could be identified as viral DNA. (Modified from T. Tomizawa and S. Sunakawa. J. Gen. Physiol. 39:553, 1956.)

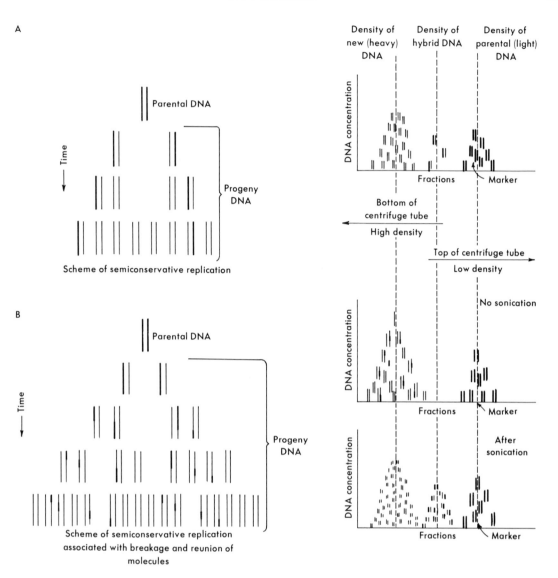

Fig. 23-10 Scheme of replication of T2 DNA. **A.** The results expected on the basis of semiconservative replication. After equilibrium centrifugation in a CsCl density gradient the parental DNA is expected entirely in a band of hybrid density. **B.** The results expected if semiconservative replication is associated with breakage and reunion. If a progeny molecule has experienced, in its line of descent, many breakage and reunion events, the parental DNA may be present in small portions distributed over a large number of molecules, which therefore would have a density only slightly less than that of new DNA. Sonication, by breaking the molecules into small fragments, allows the identification of the hybrid segments, since their lower density will not be "diluted" by attachment to nonhybrid (all new) segments.

down into pieces by sonication and banded again in CsCl. Now the two bands predicted by the semiconservative model were formed.

This means that the dispersed fragments of parental DNA were still quite large (of the order of 10% of a whole molecule).

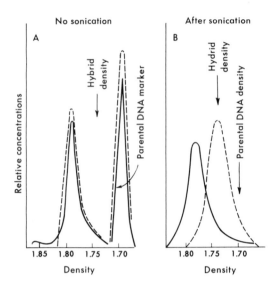

Fig. 23-11 Distribution of infecting phage DNA in progeny DNA. Cells were infected with phage containing light, radioactive DNA, and incubated in heavy, nonradioactive medium. The DNA of the progeny phage was gently extracted and centrifuged, with a sample of the labeled parental DNA added as density marker. In **A** the DNA was not sonicated; it shows dispersive replication, since the radioactivity of the infecting DNA is in the band of new DNA. In **B** the same DNA has been sonicated, and the radioactivity is mostly in the band of hybrid DNA (which is too small to yield an optical density peak). Solid line, OD$_{260}$ (measuring the amount of DNA); dashed line, radioactivity. (Modified from A. W. Kozinsky. Virology 13:124, 1961.)

The interpretation of these results is that replication of phage DNA is semiconservative but is accompanied by breakage and rejoining of molecules. For instance, a parental molecule may first replicate semiconservatively; the resulting hybrid molecules exchange fragments with entirely new molecules. The molecules thus formed replicate semiconservatively and their daughters again break and reunite with other matings. If a parental strand experiences a large number of breaks over successive replications considerable dispersion results. This inference of multiple rounds of mating in the vegetative pool is consistent with genetic evidence, to be discussed below. Breakage of the molecules appears to be caused by a virus-specified enzyme, since it does not take place in the presence of chloramphenicol.

The breakage and reunion is not essential for replication of phage DNA, since it is much less extensive in the replication of bacteriophage λ; nor is it necessarily correlated with DNA replication, since it can take place in the absence of DNA synthesis in thymine-starved cells. As will be discussed below (Phage genetics), breakage and reunion appear to be the cause of genetic recombination, since in different phages the frequencies of the two processes are correlated.

Glucosylation

Isotopic studies with T-even coliphages show that the glucosyl residues of the parental phage DNA are carried into the progeny virions. The progeny DNA is not glucosylated until the late part of the eclipse period, as shown by its density in Cs$_2$SO$_4$. By the time the first virions are formed the rate of glucosylation is rapid enough to ensure glucosylation of all DNA molecules before they mature. Unglucosylated viral DNA is produced in bacteria lacking uridine diphosphate glucose, or with viral mutants deficient in glucosylating enzymes. The significance of glucosylation, and of other substitutions on the viral DNA, is shown by studies of host-induced modification.

Host-Induced Modification

Host-induced modification is a change of the host range of a phage resulting from multiplication in special bacterial strains. The best understood case involves T2 and other T-even coliphages, grown through one cycle in UDPG-less mutant strains of *E. coli* B (Fig. 23-12), which thus lacks glucosylation of its DNA. This virus, designated as T2*, is **restricted,** i.e., it does not multiply in *E. coli* B strains, including the one in which it

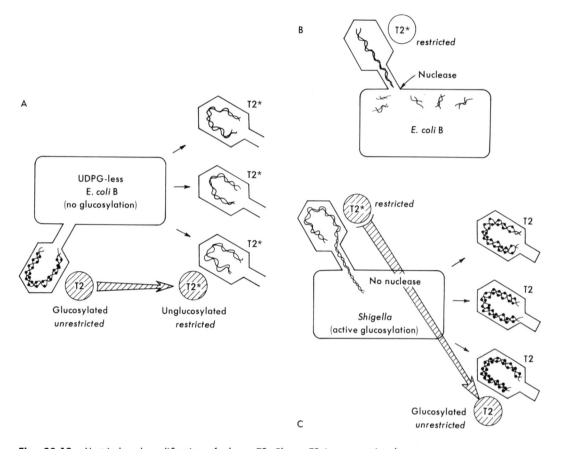

Fig. 23-12 Host-induced modification of phage T2. Phage T2 is not restricted on any of the hosts considered here. As shown in **A**, during a single cycle in UDPG-less bacteria, where the viral DNA is not glucosylated, restricted host-modified phage (T2*) is produced. In fact, when T2* tries to infect its usual host bacteria the unglucosylated DNA is broken down at injection by a surface nuclease, as shown in **B**. T2*, however, can multiply in *Shigella,* which does not have the surface nuclease, as indicated in **C**; since *Shigella* has the glucosylating system it produces T2 with regularly glucosylated DNA and is therefore unrestricted. The shaded arrows indicate the two opposite kinds of host-induced modification.

was produced. The reason is that during injection its DNA is broken down by a cellular nuclease, located on the plasma membrane, which attacks only unglucosylated DNA. T2* can, however, multiply in *Shigella,* which lacks the nuclease. Moreover, since *Shigella* possesses the glucosylating system, T2* then undergoes the reverse modification to **unrestricted** T2. In this case the nonglucosylating host carries out a host-induced modification of T2*, in making it restricted, by failure to

glucosylate its DNA; and the glucosylating host carries out the opposite host-induced modification of T2*, making it unrestricted, by glucosylating it.

In another well known case of host-induced modification the restricting and modifying influences are introduced into *E. coli* cells by bacteriophage P1, either as vegetative phage or as prophage (Fig. 23-13). P1-containing cells, for instance, restrict the regular coliphage λ. After a single multiplication cycle,

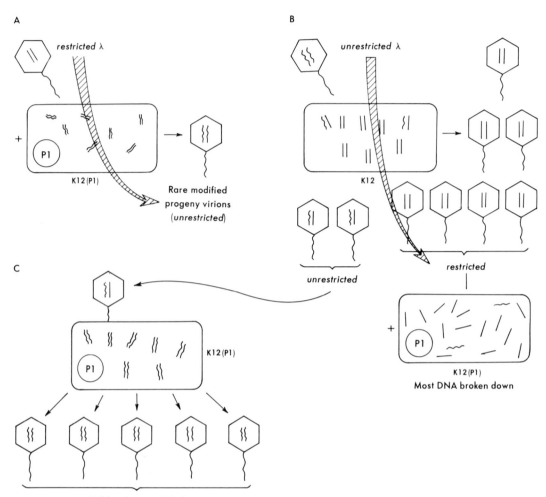

Fig. 23-13 Host-induced modification of phage λ caused by phage P1. *E. coli* K12 is the regular host and *E. coli* K12(P1), lysogenic for phage P1, the restricting host. **A.** When regular λ, which is P1-restricted, infects K12(P1) most entering DNA molecules are broken down, but a few survive and reproduce; they give rise to modified λ, which is now unrestricted, i.e., able to multiply in K12(P1). **B.** In a multiplication cycle of unrestricted λ in K12 the lack of restriction is transmitted to a small proportion of progeny virions, those that receive at least one strand from the parental phages. Straight line, restricted viral DNA strand; wavy line, unrestricted viral DNA strand. The shaded arrows indicate the two opposite kinds of host-induced modification.

however, a small proportion of the infected cells yield phage, which is modified and not restricted on subsequent multiplication in P1-containing cells. The modified unrestricted phage undergoes the reverse modification in a single multiplication cycle in cells not containing P1, and produces progeny of which

the majority are P1-restricted. A small proportion, however, are unrestricted, and by suitable isotopic experiments they can be shown to correspond to virions in which one of the DNA strands **derives directly from the unrestricted parents.** The change of DNA caused by this modification, therefore, is not lost during replication. Although the molecular basis of this modification is not clearly established, it appears to consist in an abnormal **methylation** pattern of the DNA. P1-containing cells cause restriction by breaking down the DNA of the restricted phage.

In all host-induced modifications the change from restriction to lack of restriction, and vice versa, can easily be distinguished from mutation followed by selection: 1) it occurs in a **single cycle** of multiplication in a modifying host; 2) it affects **all** the progeny virions; and 3) it is **reversed** by a single passage through another suitable host.

These reversible, nonmutational alterations of the phage were exceedingly puzzling until the chemical modifications of DNA that do not affect its genetic information were discovered: glucosylation and methylation (Ch. 8, Constitution of nucleic acids). The results obtained in the study of host-induced modification suggest that these chemical substitutions modify the susceptibility of the DNA to some cellular nucleases. Conceivably, they enable the cell to distinguish between its own and foreign DNA, allowing the selective destruction of the latter.

In the cases described above the chemical substitutions of the DNA had dramatic and easily detectable consequences. It is possible that other modifications produce biologically important effects that are less easy to recognize, and are therefore still undiscovered.

Maturation

Maturation and release are the last two acts of the process of viral multiplication. In **maturation** the various components become assembled to form an infectious virion, designated as **complete** or **mature;** in **release** the mature particles leave the infected cells. The relation between maturation and release is revealed by the one-step multiplication curves: the **total** multiplication curve describes the maturation of the virions; the **extracellular** curve describes their release.

Maturation of T-even bacteriophages involves the assembly of many components, and it therefore occurs in several steps. The first step is the condensation of individual viral DNA molecules into crystalline particles which resemble phage heads, surrounded by a thin membrane apparently different from the regular capsid (**condensates,** Fig. 23-14); these are recognizable in thin sections of infected bacteria before any mature virions are formed. The condensation is believed to result from interaction of the DNA with a "condensing principle," perhaps the internal protein or polyamines or an incomplete capsid (Ch. 22). The crystallization of capsid monomers around the DNA condensates to form the full capsid then gives rise to the phage heads, which remain unstable as long as they are not connected to the tails. In fact, if the bacterium is lysed, naturally or artificially, the DNA comes out of these heads and leaves empty head membranes, which collapse into amorphous bags, called "doughnuts."

Many aspects of phage maturation have been clarified by the study of **conditionally lethal mutants** (which will be further discussed below). These strains behave like normal phages under certain **permissive** conditions (e.g., in a certain host or at low temperature, such as 25°), but express their lethal mutations under **restrictive** conditions (e.g., in another host or at high temperature, such as 43°). These strains can be regularly propagated under permissive conditions, while the effect of the mutations can be studied under restrictive conditions.

Many of these mutants, under restrictive conditions, accumulate morphologically recognizable **precursors of phage,** just as auxotrophic mutants of bacteria accumulate biosynthetic precursors. One mutant gives rise to long, hollow cylinders of the diameter of a phage head (called **polyheads,** Fig. 23-15), but no normal heads. Polyheads may arise from assembly of monomers able to form hexamers; failure to produce heads may be attributed to lack of other monomers required for the formation of the corner elements, presumably pentamers (Ch. 22). It is likely, therefore, that at least two types of subunits constitute the phage head.

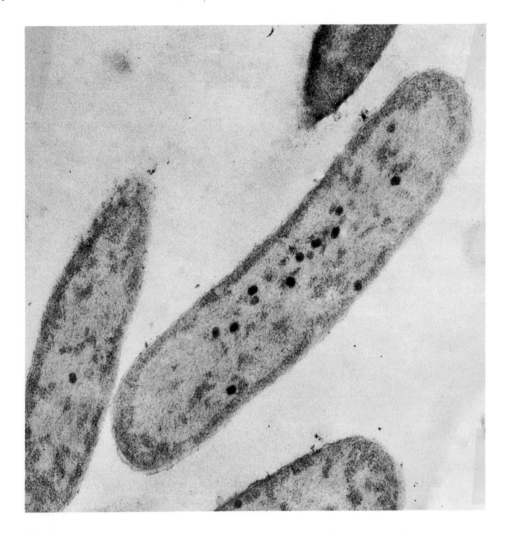

Fig. 23-14 Formation of condensates of T2 phage DNA in infected *E. coli* cells. The condensates, which are stained by uranyl acetate, are recognizable within the cells as dark crystals, with the shape of a phage head. They are not surrounded by the regular head membrane. The cells were exposed to chloramphenicol 8 minutes after infection, which caused viral DNA synthesis to proceed without maturation. Most of the phage DNA forms a very large pool filling the cell, recognizable as a filamentous, light gray mass. The darker cytoplasm is confined at the periphery of the cell. The chloramphenicol was removed at 48 minutes, and the cells were fixed at 60 minutes, thus allowing 12 minutes for phage maturation. (From E. Kellenberger, J. Sechaud, and A. Ryter. Virology 8:478, 1959.)

The manner of adding the tail elements can also be deduced from the study of mutants. A likely sequence is the following (Fig. 23-16). 1) The tube and the plate are added first to the head. 2) The extended sheath is formed around the tube; the length and shape of the sheath are probably determined by the tube, since in the absence of a tube sheaths can form monomers by self-assembly, but they always assume the contracted shape and are extremely long (**poly-sheaths;** Fig. 23-17). 3) The fibers are assembled from several subunits (since their formation is under the control of several genes) and seem to be added last.

Fig. 23-15 Electron micrograph, with negative staining, of polyheads of phage T4. These were produced by an **amber** (conditionally lethal) mutant together with a regular virion. The polyheads are comparable in width to the normal phage head shown (though they appear wider because of flattening), but they are much longer. Hexagonal capsomers can be clearly seen in the polyheads. (Courtesy of E. Boy de la Tour.)

These studies lead to the conclusion that maturation is a sequential process, in which each step recognizes and requires the previous step. Each step can be considered the equivalent of a crystallization process in which the product has a lower energy level than the unassembled components. In fact, assembly can occur in vitro when lysates containing partly assembled components are mixed together in the proper combination, e.g., one containing heads and one containing tails. Self-assembly of single components (e.g., to form polyheads or polysheaths) must be less likely than regular stepwise assembly, since it is not frequently observed in infection with normal phages.

Phenotypic Mixing

In bacteria mixedly infected by two related phages (e.g., two mutants of the same phage, such as T2 and T2h) each phage causes the formation of a complete set of protein monomers. Cells infected by phage T2h$^+$ and T2h thus contain precursor tail fibers of both h$^+$ and h specificity. During assembly either fiber can be used in any virion; hence virions of a given genotype may contain tail fibers of the same type, or the other, or a mixture of the two (Fig. 23-18). Virions in which the genotype and the phenotype are discrepant are called **phenotypically mixed.**

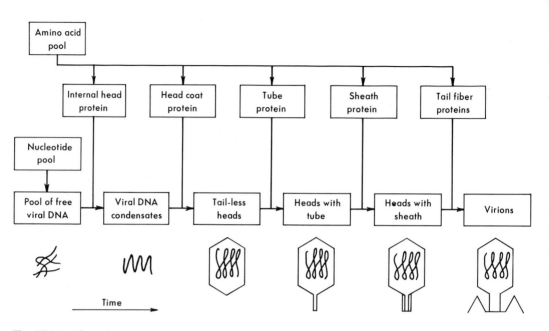

Fig 23-16 Flow sheet summarizing the maturation of T-even coliphages. (Modified from G. Stent. Molecular Biology of Bacterial Viruses. Freeman, San Francisco, 1963.)

Phenotypic mixing may affect many phage proteins, but mixing of the host-range character is the most common example. It can be detected by a two-step operation. First, the virus produced by the mixedly infected cells is propagated for a **single cycle** in *E. coli* B/2, where only **phenotypically h** phage multiplies. The **genotype** of the progeny is then determined by plating on a mixture of *E. coli* B and *E. coli* B/2 cells (**mixed indicator strains**). Since both h and h+ phages multiply in *E. coli* B, both form plaques. However, phage that is genotypically h+ produces **turbid plaques** (because the *E. coli* B/2 cells present are unaffected), whereas phage that is genotypically h produces **clear plaques** (because both B and B/2 cells are lysed).

Phenotypic mixing was discovered through aberrations in the plaque counts of phage from cells mixedly infected with T2 and T4. T2 was estimated by plating on B/4, and T4 on B/2. However, plating on the mixed indicator (B/2 + B/4) yielded many more plaques than the expected sum of the T2 and the T4 counts. The reason is that phenotypically mixed virions required one host cell type for the first cycle of infection and multiplication and the other type for subsequent cycles.

Release

Release of the progeny of all known bacteriophages—except the helical M13—occurs by **burst**: the infected bacterium suddenly explodes and releases its content of virions into the medium. This event can easily be seen in darkfield microscopy, where the particles of T-even bacteriophages are visible. The burst of the cells causes visible lysis of the infected cultures. In contrast, the helical bacteriophage leaks out of the cells, apparently without killing them, by an unknown mechanism.

The yields of individual infected bacteria can be determined in single-burst experiments (see above, The viral multiplication cycle). The yields have a broad distribution, including both very small and very large yields; the large variability may be attributed to different lengths of the period of multiplication of phage DNA in different cells (asynchrony).

Multiplication of Bacteriophage φX174 (Containing Single-Stranded DNA)

The replication of the DNA of single-stranded bacteriophages, in contrast to that of T-even phages, occurs without interference with synthesis of cellular DNA or other cellular macromolecules. Its most interesting aspect is the formation of a double-stranded **replicative form,** through synthesis of a **complementary** (or "minus") strand on the **"plus"** (viral) strand brought in by the infecting virion (Fig. 23-19). The replicative form retains the cyclic configuration of the plus strand. The two can be separated by virtue of their different buoyant densities in CsCl (Ch. 8, Physical properties of nucleic acids). The replicative form is made very shortly after

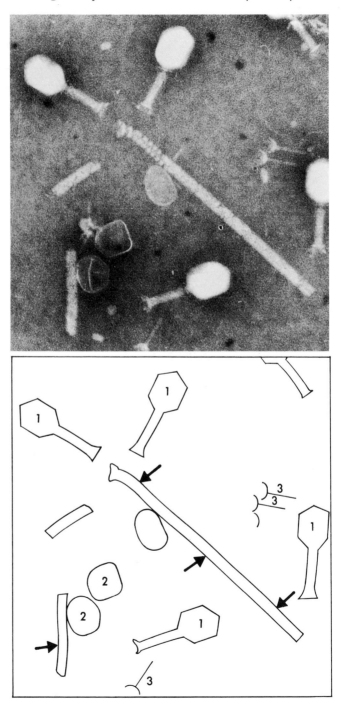

Fig. 23-17 Electron micrograph, with negative staining, of unassembled components of T4. These include polysheaths (arrows), head membranes (2), and tubes attached to plates (3). Compare with normal virion (1). The polysheath has the diameter of a contracted sheath; its helical structure is shown at one end, where it is unraveling. (From E. Boy de la Tour. J. Ultrastruct. Res. 11: 545, 1964.)

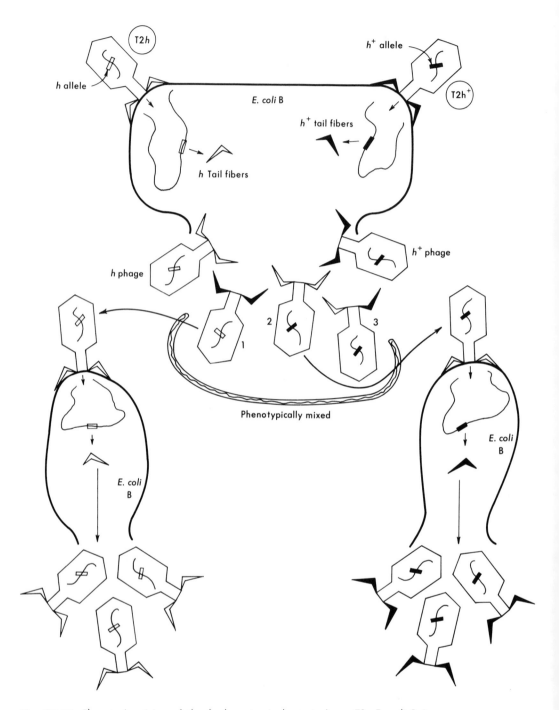

Fig. 23-18 Phenotypic mixing of the *h* character in bacteriophage T2. *E. coli* B infected by both T2*h* and T2*h*⁺ produces progeny that are in part not mixed (i.e., either *h* or *h*⁺, both genotypically and phenotypically), and in part mixed. 1 is genotypically *h*, phenotypically *h*⁺; 2 is genotypically *h*⁺, phenotypically *h*; 3 is genotypically *h*⁺ and phenotypically *h*+*h*⁺. Upon multiplication in *E. coli* B phenotypic mixing is lost, and the progeny are phenotypically true to their genotype.

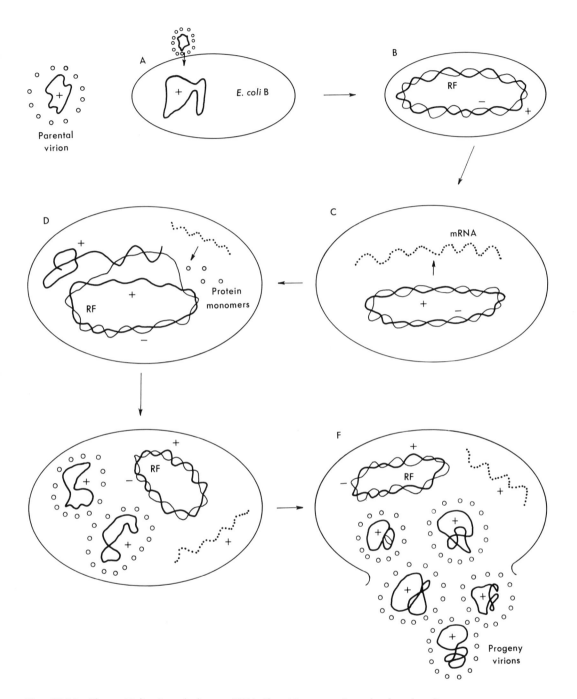

Fig. 23-19 The multiplication of phage φX174. The virions contain molecules of cyclic single-stranded DNA; this strand is designated as + . **A.** The DNA is injected. **B.** A cyclic double-stranded replicative form (RF) is made by synthesizing a − strand. **C.** The RF is transcribed into mRNA (equal to the + strand); **D.** A progeny + DNA strand is made on the RF, by copying the − strand; protein monomers are synthesized on the mRNA. **E.** The progeny + strands are assembled into virions. **F.** Lysis of the cell. The persisting RF is not incorporated into a virion.

infection even in the presence of chloramphenicol; it is therefore formed by an enzyme existing in the cells before infection.

The molecules of the replicative form multiply in the usual semiconservative manner during the whole viral multiplication cycle. The molecules containing the strands brought in by the infecting virions appear to be the main source of viral progeny DNA, because in cells infected by virus heavily labeled by ^{32}P in the DNA the decay of the isotope, even after the replicative form is made and has replicated, destroys the virus-producing ability of the cells. Moreover, studies with isotopically labeled virus show that the plus strand of an infecting virion becomes part of the replicative form and never leaves it; thus labeled parental viral DNA does not reappear in the viral progeny, in contrast to the behavior of double-stranded DNA viruses. Replication of single-stranded DNA, therefore, appears to be conservative, the stable replicative form acting repeatedly as the template for the synthesis of the plus DNA strands of the progeny virions. The synthesis of plus strands on the replicative form is prevented by chloramphenicol, and it therefore depends on the synthesis of a new, probably virus-specified, enzyme.

Viral mRNA is produced by transcription of the replicative form. It is identical in base sequence to the plus DNA strand, since it hybridizes with the DNA of the replicative form (which contains plus and minus strands) but not with the plus strand present in mature viruses.

PHAGE GENETICS

Historically, the study of phage genetics provided the main incentive for undertaking the analysis of phage multiplication. The investigators who started the "new wave" of bacteriophage work in the late 1930s recognized that genetics had to turn to simpler organisms in order to determine the molecular basis of the complex formalism previously established. For this purpose phages offer outstanding advantages: about half the total mass is genetic material; the populations conveniently studied exceed in size even those possible with bacteria; and the number of individual genes must be very limited.

The development of phage genetics in the last two decades has been an outstanding intellectual achievement. On the basis of technically simple observations, carried out with a few mutant types, a handful of investigators developed a highly sophisticated formal (i.e., mathematical) analysis of the subject. In addition, fine-structure genetics was launched through the study of mutants of a phage gene, even though its protein product was unknown. As we have seen in Chapter 8, the subsequent extension of fine-structure genetics to bacteria has led to a profound understanding of the relation between gene and protein. In recent years similar direct studies have also become possible on the phage DNA and on mutant phage proteins, and the formal and molecular aspects of phage genetics have become integrated.

Mutations

The genetics of phage, like that of all organisms, is based on the study of mutants. The types of mutations that can be recognized in these organisms are limited by their haploid nature (phages contain a single molecule of DNA; see Ch. 22). Thus lethal mutations, which have contributed considerably to genetic studies in diploid organisms, are unsuitable because the phage carrying them cannot be propagated. The permissible mutations are of two main classes: 1) those leading to production of plaques with changed morphology (**plaque-type mutants**), and 2) those with a lethal effect under certain restrictive conditions but not under permissive conditions (**conditionally lethal mutants**). As already noted above, the mutants of the latter type can be propagated under permissive conditions, and the consequence of the lethal mutation can be studied under restrictive conditions. A number of mutant types employed in genetic work with T-even bacteriophages will be briefly examined.

Plaque-Type Mutants

Rapid lysis (r) mutants (Fig. 23-20) have already been described above (One-step multiplication curve). Two classes, $r_{II}A$ and $r_{II}B$, are caused by mutations in two adjacent genes of the r_{II} locus. These mutants have been used extensively in genetic work.

Host-range (h) mutants were also described above (Adsorption). It will be recalled that they can be identified by their plaques on mixed indicator strains, where h phages produce **clear** plaques and h^+ (wild-type) phages produce **turbid** plaques.

Cofactor-requiring mutants of phage T4 produce plaques only in the presence of tryptophan (see above, Adsorption). They are also conditionally lethal, since they multiply in the presence of the cofactor but not in its absence.

Fig. 23-20 Plaques produced by cells infected by a mixture of T2r and T2r$^+$ phage. Plaques of r type are large and without a halo; those of r$^+$ type (wild-type) are small and surrounded by a halo. Cells infected by both r and r$^+$ phage produce mottled plaques with a sectored halo (dark sectors, r phage; clear sectors, r$^+$ phage). The halo is produced by infected cells with lysis inhibition caused by r$^+$ phage. (From G. Stent. Molecular Biology of Bacterial Viruses. Freeman, San Francisco, 1963.)

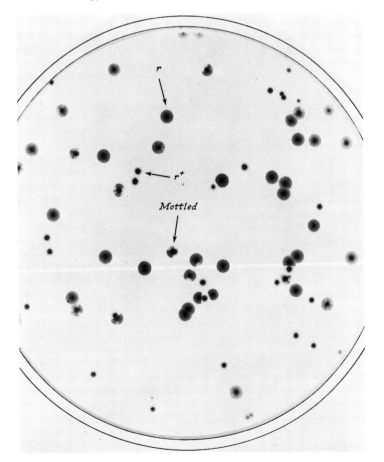

Minute plaque and **turbid plaque mutants** produce plaques described by their names.

Plaque-type mutants were extensively used in the initial investigations of bacteriophage genetics, since they could be recognized easily on inspection of the assay plates (Fig. 23-21). Two main drawbacks, however, became evident: some of these mutants do not allow the use of selective technics; and they are localized in a small number of genes, thus leaving much of the chromosome unmapped. These difficulties were overcome by the discovery that rₙₙ mutants are conditionally lethal, and by the subsequent isolation of conditionally

lethal mutations of other types, altered in essentially any phage gene (see above, Maturation).

Conditionally Lethal Mutants

rₙₙ Mutants. These strains multiply in *E. coli* B but not in *E. coli* K12(λ) (Ch. 24), whereas rₙₙ$^+$ phages multiply equally well in both hosts. The mutants are isolated on the basis of their plaque type; their conditional lethality is then used to detect minute proportions of r$^+$ virions in their populations by plating on K12(λ), where only the r$^+$ virus forms plaques. This efficient selection was

Fig. 23-21 Plaques formed by a mixture of T2 phages carrying mutations at the *h* and *r* locus, plated on a mixture of *E. coli* B and *E. coli* B/2 (i.e., resistant to T2 but sensitive to T2*h*). Phages with the *h* and those with *h*$^+$ allele produce, respectively, clear plaques (dark in the photograph) and turbid plaques (gray in the photograph); phages with the *r* allele are larger than those with the *r*$^+$ allele. Thus all four possible combinations can be distinguished: T2*h*$^+$*r*$^+$ (wild-type), T2*hr*, T2*h*$^+$*r*$^+$, and T2*hr*$^+$. (From G. Stent. Molecular Biology of Bacterial Viruses. Freeman, San Francisco, 1963.)

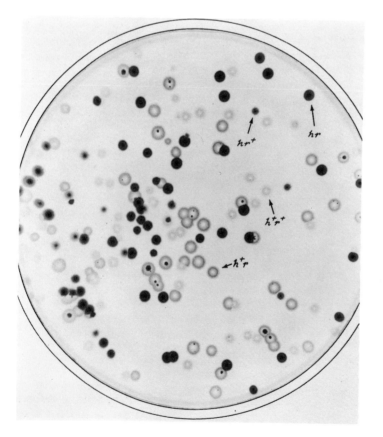

used in Benzer's pioneering studies on fine-structure genetics.

Major Classes of Conditional Lethals. Two classes of conditionally lethal mutants that are not limited to any one gene have been isolated in T phages. 1) **Amber mutants (am)** are characterized by a mutation generating the "amber" nonsense codon (Ch. 8, Genetic code) in a gene with a vital function. They can therefore multiply only in bacterial strains carrying a suppressor of that codon (Ch. 8, Suppression), i.e., they are **suppressor-sensitive (sus)** mutants. 2) **Temperature-sensitive mutants (ts)** are characterized by a mutation that prevents the expression of its gene at 43° but not at 25° (see Ch. 6 for mechanism of temperature sensitivity).

Applications of Phage Mutants

Both plaque-type and conditionally lethal mutants have been useful in studies of **recombination,** which have led to the establishment of a phage map (see below). Conditionally lethal mutants in particular have been indispensable for the development of **fine-structure** genetics, since the detection of recombination between very close sites (i.e., the resolving power of recombinational analysis) depends on the possibility of selecting a very rare recombinant from a large parental population. Such selection is readily achieved by growing conditionally lethal mutants under nonrestrictive conditions and then plating under restrictive conditions.

To define the limits of a gene the same selective technic can be applied to **complementation** studies on pairs of mutants (Ch. 8) simultaneously infecting a cell under restrictive conditions. Suppressor-sensitive mutants have been especially valuable, compared with temperature-sensitive mutants, because they do not make the protein of the mutated gene under restrictive conditions, and so the complication of intragenic complementation is absent.

Plaque-type mutants proved very useful in early studies not only of the genetics but also of the **physiology** of these viruses, as shown by the following two examples.

1) **The geometric mode of multiplication of vegetative phage.** The amount of phage DNA in infected cells increases linearly with time (except at the very beginning). Such kinetics could represent replication on a fixed number of effective templates (**linear** replication); alternatively, the number of templates could expand **geometrically** (as might be expected of semiconservative replication), but at a rate determined by some limiting reaction (e.g., energy production, precursor assimilation or synthesis). The latter pattern was established by studying the distribution of spontaneous mutants in the viral yields of individual infected cells, as in the earlier fluctuation analysis of bacterial mutants (Ch. 6).

Thus if DNA replication is exponential each mutation will produce a clone of mutants whose size is smaller the later the mutation occurs (Fig. 23-22). A mathematical theory based on these considerations predicts that a straight line should be obtained if the logarithm of the frequency of single-cell yields containing a given number of mutants or less is plotted versus the logarithm of that number (1, 2, etc.). With bacteriophage T2 this expectation is verified, thus showing that the phage genome multiplies geometrically (although from a certain time on units are continuously drawn out of the pool to form mature phage). In contrast, mutants of phage ϕX174 have a distribution compatible with linear replication of the DNA. This result, in conjunction with those reported above (multiplication of bacteriophage ϕX174) suggests that single stranded DNA replicates according to a "stamping machine" model, with the DNA of the infecting virus as template.

2) **Measurement of the pool of vegetative phage.** The size of the pool can be determined not only chemically (see above, the pool of viral DNA), but also genetically, by infecting cells first with a marked phage strain (e.g., r) and at various times superinfecting them with another allele (e.g., r^+).* The superinfecting phage DNA enters the pool established by the first infecting phage, and when the bacteria lyse they release a mixed progeny. From the ratio of the

---

* The superinfection must overcome the obstacle of interference (Ch. 26) by using sufficiently high multiplicity.

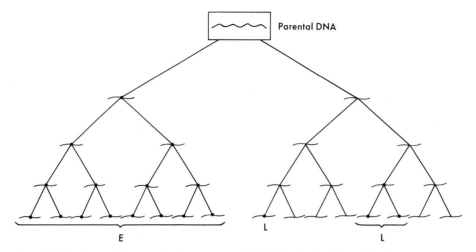

Fig. 23-22 Clones of mutants in the progeny of individual cells. A mutation is represented by a dot. Early mutations, E, cause much larger clones than late mutations, L, owing to the geometrical nature of DNA replication.

two types the number of genomes of the first phage at the moment of superinfection can be determined; the number obtained corresponds to that determined chemically.

Genetic Recombination

Special Formal Characteristics of Phage Recombination

Genetic recombination in T-even bacteriophages was discovered in 1946 by Delbrück and Bailey, and by Hershey, who performed genetic crosses by mixedly infecting bacteria with pairs of phage strains marked by different alleles of the r and h loci. The yields of these cultures contained four distinct types of particles (Fig. 23-23): two with the genetic constitution of the infecting phages (**parental**), and two with one marker from one parent and the other marker from the other parent (**recombinants**). The appearance of the new types showed that during intracellular multiplication viral genomes undergo genetic recombination, just like the chromosomes of cells.

Although the basic concept of genetic recombination is simple, its detailed study with bacteriophages turned out to involve complex statistics, because recombination takes place

in the vegetative pool with many DNA molecules participating. Indeed, recombination between vegetative phages evidently continues to occur throughout the period of multiplication, since the proportion of recombinants in a mixedly infected cell increases with the time (Fig. 23-24). This increase is clearly seen when lysis-inhibited cells are artificially lysed at various times. Furthermore, in **triparental crosses,** i.e., simultaneous infection of cells by three virus types carrying different markers (Fig. 23-25), progeny appear that individually incorporate markers from **all** the parents, a result that requires at least two independent matings. It can be calculated that T-even bacteriophages undergo four or five rounds of mating, on the average, between infection and release.

A single mating between two phage DNA molecules, therefore, cannot be studied directly. The consequence of such mating can only be inferred through statistical analysis of the consequences of the multiple, successive matings that occur in a phage cross.

Construction of a Genetic map: Distance Between Markers

The Qualitative Map. The sequence of markers is established for phage in the same

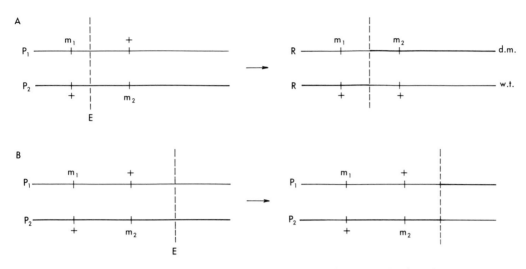

Fig. 23-23 Formal representation of recombination. P₁, P₂ = the DNA molecules of parental types; m₁, m₂ = mutant sites or markers; + = unmutated allele; E = sites of exchange; d.m. = double mutant recombinant; w.t. = wild-type recombinant. **A.** Exchange leading to recombinant-type particles (R1, R2). **B.** Exchange not leading to recombinants.

Fig. 23-24 Increase in the proportion of recombinants as a function of time after infection. E. coli cells were mixedly infected by T2h⁺r⁺ and T2hr under conditions of lysis inhibition. At various times after infection a sample was collected, the cells were broken open, and the content was assayed. The total viral yield and the proportion of hr⁺ and h⁺r recombinants were determined. The proportion of recombinants increases in parallel with the yield, showing that recombination continues to occur in the cells while their burst is delayed. (Modified from C. Levinthal and N. Visconti. Genetics 38:500, 1953.)

Fig. 23-25 The formation of a triparental recombinant. 1, 2, 3 = three differently marked phages infecting the same cell. The triparental recombinant, which contains alleles from all three parents, requires at least two matings for its formation.

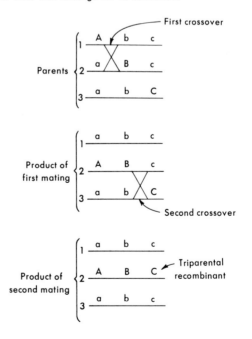

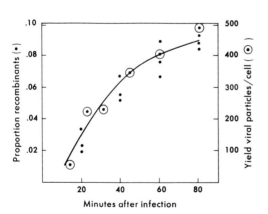

way as for higher organisms, i.e., on the basis of the proportions of different recombinants (recombination frequencies) produced in crosses. Thus in a three-factor cross (i.e., one involving two phages that differ at three markers) the frequency of recombination between the two most distant markers (outside markers) is larger than the frequencies between the other two pairs. If, for instance, of three markers, A, B, and C, A and C produce more recombinants than A and B or B and C in pairwise crossings, the order is A-B-C. By testing all the known markers three at a time they can be ordered in a unique sequence, as shown by the example of Figure 23-26. The various markers are then assigned to the same or to different genes by means of complementation tests (Ch. 8), and a **genetic map** is thus established.

The Quantitative Map. While the **ordering** of markers in phage can thus be accomplished in a conventional manner, the **distances** between markers do not have the same simple relation to recombination frequency observed in higher organisms; in particular, phage crosses exhibit **lack of additivity of recombinant frequencies.**

Thus given three linked markers, A-B-C, in higher organisms the proportion of recombinants between A and C is found equal to the sum of the proportions of recombinants between A and B and between B and C, after correcting for double crossovers within AC:

$$p_{ac} = p_{ab} + p_{bc} - 2p_{ab} \cdot p_{bc} \qquad (1)$$

where p_{ac}, p_{ab}, and p_{bc} are the proportions of the respective recombinants. In phage crosses, however, p_{ac} is lower than expected (Fig. 23-26). By following the approach of higher organism genetics one would conclude that the observed proportion of double crossovers in the AC region is higher than the proportion predicted from the proportion of single exchanges. This phenomenon has been called **negative interference**, since its consequences are opposite to those of the interference observed in higher organisms, where the proportion of double exchanges is often lower than that predicted. In the phage crosses, however, the deviation from the expected relation arises, not from an excessive frequency of double

crossovers, but from the special characteristics noted above (i.e., the statistics of multiple rounds of mating in a vegetative pool, and the statistics of multiple infection).

The specific cause of such negative interference is the presence of DNA molecules that do not mate or that undergo fewer than the average number of rounds of mating. Indeed, within the same cell population various molecules undergo different numbers of matings with genetically different molecules, for several reasons: 1) some cells are infected by a higher proportion of one or the other parental type, or even by one type alone; 2) the vegetative pools initiated by different parental particles in a cell may not mix well; and 3) even if they mix well, the number of matings is randomly distributed (since matings occur at random). Thus the presence of "inert" molecules, with little or no opportunity for mating, causes the **experimentally determined** proportion of recombinants (observed recombinants/total yield) to be lower than the **true** proportion of recombinants in the mating population (observed recombinants/number of molecules with an average opportunity for mating). Since the fraction of double crossovers is based directly on the true proportion of recombinants, the actual value of this fraction is always higher than that calculated from the experimental, apparent proportion of recombinants.

Example: If 50% of the DNA molecules produced have undergone the same number of matings and 50% have not mated at all, the true proportions of recombinants among those that have mated (p_{ac}, etc.) are twice the apparent proportions (p'_{ac}, etc.). Then the relation (1), **which applies to the true proportions,** must be written for these particular circumstances as

$$2p'_{ac} = 2p'_{ab} + 2p'_{bc} - 2(2p'_{ab}) \cdot (2p'_{bc}), \text{ or}$$
$$p'_{ac} = p'_{ab} + p'_{bc} - 4p'_{ab} \cdot p'_{bc} \qquad (2)$$

Comparison of (2) with (1) shows that the actual proportion of double crossovers ($4p'_{ab} \cdot p'_{bc}$) is twice the proportion expected from the apparent proportion of recombinants ($2p'_{ab} \cdot p'_{bc}$).

Distances between markers can be calculated by multiplying the observed recombinant frequencies by a **mapping function** that restores additivity. The deviation of the recombination frequencies from additivity depends on factors that operate in a reproducible fashion, but are too complex to be precisely analyzed; and a mathematical function that restores additivity

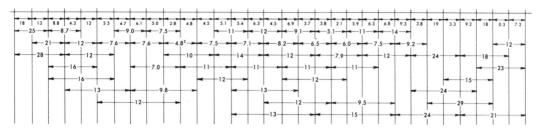

Fig. 23-26 The order of genes in a segment of the T4 genome, determined by three-factor crosses. Each vertical line corresponds to a marker; the observed recombination frequency in each pairwise cross is recorded. Note the consistency of the results: the recombination frequencies between the closest pairs (top row) establish a sequence that yields increasing frequencies, as predicted, in crosses involving more distant pairs. (Modified from R. S. Edgar and I. Lielausis, Genetics 49:649, 1964.)

presumably corrects for these deviations, even though it is discovered by trial and error. By using this mapping function the distances between genes can be established in map units (where one unit corresponds to 1% corrected recombination frequency). In this way the length of the map of phage T4 has been calculated as 2500 map units.

Characteristics of the Act of Recombination in Bacteriophages

Through the use of selection technics that allow the detection of recombination between very closely linked markers, studies in bacteriophages have revealed several important features of recombination, which are now believed to be common to all organisms.

1) **Lack of proportionality between physical and map distances.** As was noted in Chapter 8, Recombination, both in bacteria and in phages the order of mutational sites in a gene is colinear with the amino acid substitutions in the corresponding polypeptide chain. Moreover, the positions of these substitutions can be accurately determined; and so it has become possible to assign absolute values to map distances (in number of amino acid residues) between mutations within a gene. The results have shown that the frequency of recombination per unit distance shows variation at different places, perhaps depending on the local constitution of the DNA. On a larger scale, however, such microscopic inhomogeneity presumably averages out, since cyto-

logical studies in higher organisms, and interrupted mating in bacteria, had earlier supported the classic assumption that recombination frequency is proportional to distance on the chromosome.

This microscopic variability explains the extremely low frequency of recombination (ca. 10^{-6} map units) observed between certain r_{II} mutants of phage T4. This frequency could not be explained in terms of physical distance, since the shortest possible distance is that between adjacent nucleotides, and for this distance the average probability of recombination in T4 would be about 10^{-2} units (calculated as the ratio of total length of the map to total number of nucleotide pairs in a viral DNA molecule, i.e., 2,500:150,000).

2) **Heterozygous DNA.** Cells mixedly infected by two different mutants of the same virus regularly yield some virions that are heterozygous for a given marker. For instance, in the yield of cells infected with a mixture of r and r^+ phage about 1% of the progeny virions can be recognized to be heterozygous at the r locus, because they produce characteristic **mottled plaques** (i.e., with alternating r and r^+ sectors; Fig. 23-20). Since heterozygosity has been characteristic only of diploid organisms this feature in a virus was most unexpected. The nature of the plaques suggests that the heterozygosity is built into a segment of the phage DNA molecule, rather than carried on an accessory fragment; for the regular appearance of similar numbers of r

and r⁺ progeny phages implies that the DNA of heterozygous virions segregates into r and r⁺ vegetative phages at its first replication. Further evidence suggests that **a heterozygous segment contains the genetic information from one parent phage in one strand and that of the other parent in the other strand.**

Thus when heterozygosity was studied in crosses of phage strains differing in several markers (e.g., ABC $\times$ abc) two important properties appeared. 1) Most of the virions that are heterozygous at one site are not heterozygous at the others. However, the probability of heterozygosity is similar for all sites. Detailed studies have shown that each heterozygous segment corresponds to only about 1% of the total genetic map; the particles are therefore **partial heterozygotes.** 2) Virions that are heterozygous at the middle marker are usually **recombinant for the outside markers;** i.e., they have derived the middle marker from both parents, and one of the other markers from each parent (Fig. 23-27). It was concluded that the heterozygous segment might constitute the region where two DNA molecules undergo the exchange that produces recombination; and this result provided the first indication that the act of recombination involves the formation of a short region of overlap of homologous segments from the two parent molecules.

3) **High negative interference.** The heterozygous segments also generate another interesting characteristic of phage recombination first observed with phage, high negative interference: i.e., a very large excess of multiple (double, triple, quadruple) crossovers very close to each other, which are observable in crosses between phages carrying very closely linked markers. This process differs from the statistical negative interference discussed above; its effect on apparent map distances is much more pronounced (hence it name), and it occurs only at very short map distances. High negative interference must be related to the mechanism of recombination itself (in contrast to statistical negative interference, which depends on unequal rounds of matings), because it is also found in fungi and bacteria, where the statistical problems of phage mating do not arise.

The key to understanding this phenomenon was provided by the finding that it takes place within the heterozygous segment: when a heterozygous DNA molecule reproduces it generates a cluster of exchanges within this segment, as shown by the progeny segregated by virions heterozygous for several closely linked r_II mark-

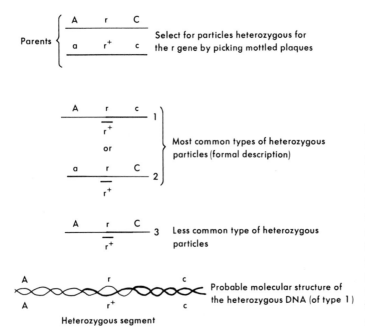

Fig. 23-27 Characteristics of heterozygous particles. Virions are picked for heterozygosity at the central gene and then are scored for the alleles of the other mutant genes. Most heterozygous virions are found to be recombinants for any markers situated on opposite sides of the heterozygous segment. The exceptions can be accounted for by multiple rounds of mating, which have caused a parent of a heterozygote to have undergone a previous recombination, as shown in 3.

ers. This curious behavior of the heterozygous region became understandable with the recent development of a satisfactory model for the molecular mechanism of recombination.

Molecular Mechanism of Phage Recombination

In Chapter 8 we have noted that, according to current ideas, genetic recombination occurs by breakage and reunion of DNA molecules independently of their over-all replication. Much of the evidence for the model presented in Chapter 8 derives from results obtained with bacteriophages. A role of breakage and reunion in phage recombination is suggested by 1) evidence for the fragmentation of DNA molecules (i.e., distribution of label from a parental DNA molecule to many progeny molecules) in the course of multiple rounds of mating (Mode of replication of phage DNA, above); and 2) the parallel extent, in different phages, of genetic exchange and such fragmentation: for instance, both are very frequent with T-even coliphages and relatively infrequent with coliphage λ. 3) In addition, a direct isotopic demonstration of breakage and reunion, in the absence of replication, has been obtained by Meselson and Weigle with bacteriophage λ, in a cross between strains differing in two genetic markers.

In this experiment both the infecting phages contained heavy isotopes in their DNA, and the cells were grown in a medium containing the regular isotopes. Because recombination is too infrequent in λ to cause much fragmentation, the intact progeny virions formed different bands at equilibrium in CsCl, consisting of those containing unreplicated DNA, those containing hybrid DNA, and those containing new DNA. Some **recombinants** were found among the virions carrying a **full complement of parental DNA;** they were clearly formed by unreplicated fragments of the two parental DNAs.

These crosses also yielded an important additional result: within bands of particles of either parental or hybrid density the recombinant particles were slightly lighter than parental-type particles. This shows that **the recombinant molecules had lost a small proportion of the heavy** **(parental) DNA,** presumably replaced by new synthesis.

These results, as well as those relating to the formation of heterozygous segments, are in full agreement with the model of recombination proposed in Chapter 8; indeed, this model requires a heterozygous segment. High negative interference may derive from imperfections of the heterozygous segments (single-strand breaks?, imperfectly paired segments?) which cause many recombinational events. Another possible mechanism is error correction in imperfectly paired regions (Ch. 8, Recombination), which would generate high negative interference because each error-correcting event is formally equivalent to a double crossover (Fig. 23-28).

Organization of the Genetic Material of Phage T4

In bacteria the grouping of the genes in the chromosome has important regulatory aspects, which were discussed in Chapter 9. The question arises whether the much simpler genetic system of viruses possesses a similar organization. This question can best be approached with bacteriophage T4, whose genetic map is more completely known than that of any other organism endowed with genetic continuity. This map presents several important features (Fig. 23-29).

1) **Circularity.** All the genes of phage T4 can be arranged in a unique sequence, showing that they are all linked to each other. This analysis requires many three-factor crosses between markers at relatively close distances (i.e., 20 to 30 units), in order to cover the total length of about 2500 units. The surprising result is that, irrespective of the marker used to initiate the sequence, **the starting marker is closely linked to the marker that terminates the sequence.** Thus the map is represented, in a formal way, by a circle. This result, however, contrasts with the physical evidence that the DNA of the virions is not cyclic.

The apparent contradiction is resolved by the hypothesis that the molecules of T4 DNA present in a population of virions vary as though they were rods obtained by opening

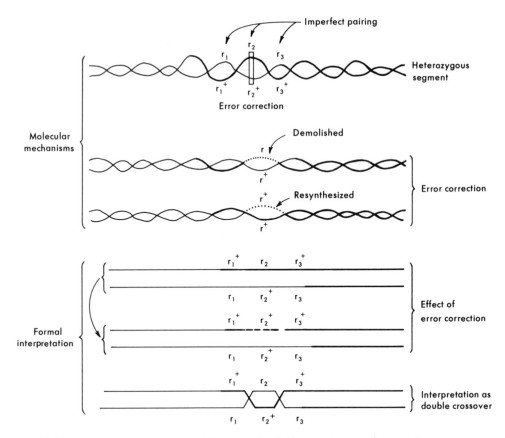

Fig 23-28   Error correction as an explanation for high negative interference. Improper pairing between different alleles would cause demolition of a single-stranded segment and its resynthesis by copying the other strand. The corrected strand would thereby be changed, and would have the same structure as though it had undergone a double exchange with its partner. The symmetric recombinant would not be detected.

a circle at different points (Fig. 23-30); a physical basis for such a relation will be given below. Such rods are said to be **circularly permuted;** in every virus preparation there would be many different types of permuted molecules. Two genes that are at the opposite ends in one molecule would be adjacent to each other in most other molecules. For instance, in the table of Figure 23-30, which represents four such permuted molecules, markers B and C are at opposite ends in the first molecule but adjacent in all other molecules. Since the relation between any two markers is established in crosses involving large populations of phages, the absence of close linkage in a few molecules remains without effect.

The proposed circular permutation not only fits the genetic data, but is directly supported by physical evidence: **on denaturation and renaturation extracted T4 DNA gives rise to cyclic molecules,** recognizable by electron microscopy. These circles presumably arise during renaturation by pairing of complementary strands (resulting from denaturation) with overlapping sequences, as diagrammed in Figure 23-31.

Not all bacteriophages have a circular genetic map. It is striking that coliphage λ has a linear map, although, paradoxically, during intracellular replication it assumes a closed cyclic form, as will be discussed in Chapter 24.

The mechanism by which a large number of permuted molecules is produced in the multipli-

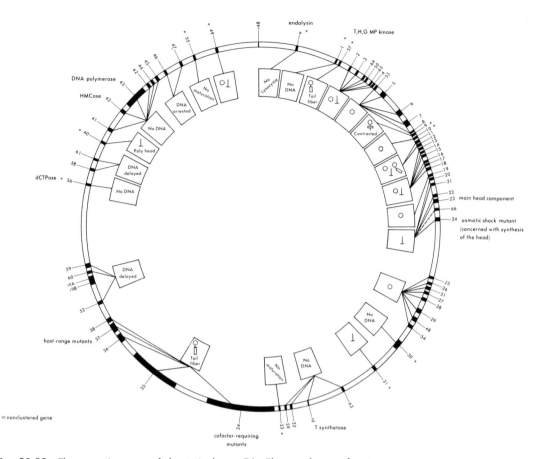

Fig. 23-29 The genetic map of bacteriophage T4. The numbers refer to genes identified by conditionally lethal (*am* or *ts*) mutations, in order of discovery. Dark segments, genes; white segments, empty spaces. The functions indicated on the inside of the circle refer to behavior under restrictive conditions, using the following criteria: 1) absence or delay of viral DNA synthesis; 2) failure of maturation; 3) if maturation is defective, the components synthesized that are recognizable by electron microscopy. Functions indicated on the outside are for genes whose product has been identified; these are few. Genes that are not clustered according to functional relatedness are indicated by a star. (Modified from R. S. Edgar and W. B. Wood, Proc. Nat. Acad. Sc. 55:498, 1966.)

Fig. 23-30 Origin of circularly permuted T4 DNA molecules. In this example, four different permutations are formed by opening the ideal circle of the genetic map at four different points. The letters indicate different loci. The four circularly permuted rods obtained have the following sequences.

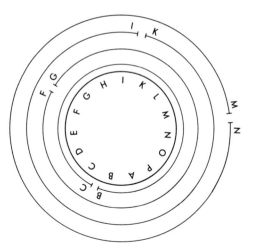

```
C D E F G H I K L M N O P A B   1
G H I K L M N O P A B C D E F   2
K L M N O P A B C D E F G H I   3
N O P A B C D E F G H I K L M   4
```

Each sequence can be obtained by shifting a block of loci from one end to the other. Loci that are at the two opposite ends in one linear molecule (such as B and C in 1) are closely linked in most other molecules.

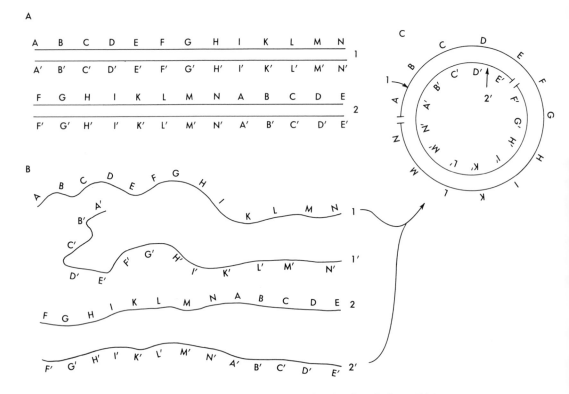

Fig. 23-31 The denaturation and renaturation of permuted molecules of phage T4 in vitro. The letters indicate the sequences of loci on one DNA strand, and the primed letters the corresponding loci on the complementary strand. Denaturation of two differently permuted molecules, 1 and 2 (A) produce the corresponding single strands (B). Renaturation between complementary strands from differently permuted molecules causes the formation of cyclic molecules (C).

cation of a single molecule has not been clarified. It seems to involve, as an intermediate, phage DNA molecules much larger than those present in virions, which can be extracted from cells infected in the presence of chloramphenicol. These large molecules are likely to be equivalent to two or more entire molecules joined together probably lengthwise; from them permuted molecules can be derived by fragmentation, which, as noted above (Mode of replication of phage DNA), does not occur in the presence of chloramphenicol.

2) **Number of genes.** About 70 genes have been identified by intergenic complementation tests in phage T4, and this seems to be the maximal number identifiable by the types of mutations used so far, since essentially all further mutants recently isolated can be assigned to genes previously recognized. There are reasons, how-ever, to suspect the existence of additional genes. First, some genes that are adjacent in the present map give unusually large recombination frequencies, which suggests that they are separated by other, yet unknown genes. Second, T4 DNA, with its 150,000 nucleotide pairs, could contain about 150 genes of 1000 nucleotide pairs, the average gene size. It therefore seems possible that a proportion of the T4 genes has not yet been identified. It is not clear, however, why these genes should fail to be revealed by the powerful mapping tool provided by conditionally lethal (*am* and *ts*) mutants.

General Organization of the Map

T4 genes have been assigned to functional groups by studying, largely with conditionally lethal mutants, the effects of their mutations on the synthesis of phage DNA and of various constituents of the virion's coat (see Maturation, above). The map of these functions (Fig. 23-29) shows that genes tend to be grouped together in clusters according to their functions (e.g., synthesis of early enzymes, or of the head, or of the tail fibers); in fact, only 13 genes are not clustered, and some of them may well be clustered with related genes present in adjacent empty spaces. The clustering recalls the arrangement of genes in bacterial operons (Ch. 9). There is no evidence, however, that these groups in phage constitute operons; for instance, they lack the polarity mutations characteristic of operons (Ch. 9).

Clustering of genes may have an evolutionary significance. As we have seen in the study of phage maturation, the assembly of the complex structure of the phage tail is made of steps that must accurately dovetail with each other. Once the genetic organization to achieve this result has evolved, further mutations may have little evolutionary value because they would tend to disrupt the delicately balanced process of assembly. Evolution may rather occur by exchanging clusters of genes by recombination. This require-ment may even account for the high frequency of recombination with T-even bacteriophages.

Genetic Reactivation of Phage Inactivated by Ultraviolet Light

As already shown (Ch. 8), inactivation of phage by ultraviolet light (UV) is due to lethal chemical damages in the DNA, part of which can be cured by the action of cellular enzymes. Reactivation can also be carried out by genetic exchanges that replace the UV-damaged DNA: cross-reactivation and multiplicity reactivation.

Cross-reactivation occurs in a cell infected simultaneously by one UV-inactivated virion and one or more active virions carrying a different allele of a gene (Fig. 23-32). Whereas the DNA of the active parent multiplies normally, that of the UV-inactivated parent does not multiply; but it can exchange parts with the active DNA. If a piece of DNA carrying the marker of the UV-treated parent but carrying no lethal damage becomes incorporated in a molecule of active DNA, by multiple crossovers, the marker is reactivated.

Such **marker rescue** must occur before the infected cell is destroyed by the multiplication of

Fig. 23-32 Cross-reactivation of UV-inactivated phage in mixed infection with an active phage, carrying a different allele at the r locus. The irradiated DNA cannot multiply, but it still undergoes exchanges with the replicating DNA of the active parent. Cross-reactivation occurs if the marker of the irradiated parent is incorporated in a DNA molecule without UV damage. o, UV damages.

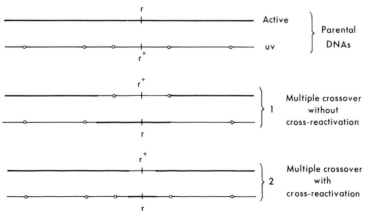

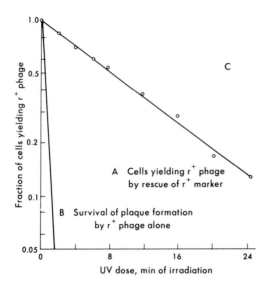

Fig. 23-33 Rescue of the r^+ marker of UV-irradiated T4r^+ by cross-reactivation with active T4r. Curve A shows the surviving fraction of the ability of the cells to yield r^+ phage. Curve B gives the survival of the irradiated phages as plaque formers, a measure of the total target size of the phage DNA. The target size for marker rescue is much smaller than that of the total DNA. (Modified from A. H. Doermann, M. Chase, and F. W. Stahl. J. Cell. & Comp. Physiol. 45:51, 1955, Suppl. 2.)

the active parent; hence its probability decreases when the treated DNA has many lethal damages, which decrease the distance between the marker and the nearest UV damage on either side, and therefore the probability of a reactivating crossover. The requirement for suitable crossovers between marker and UV damages within a certain time period establishes a minimum distance between a marker and adjacent UV damages still compatible with rescue. If any damage falls within this distance, the probability of rescue strikingly decreases. Consequently, according to the theory of inactivation (Ch. 8, Appendix), such a DNA segment is, in the first approximation, the target size for marker rescue; and the probability of cross-reactivation declines as a function of UV dose according to a single-hit type curve, with a slope much smaller (because of the smaller target) than for phage inactivation (Fig. 23-33).

Multiplicity reactivation occurs in cells simultaneously infected with two or more UV-irradiated virions. Though the DNAs of these virions cannot multiply they can exchange parts among themselves (Fig. 23-34). Since in the various parental DNA molecules UV damages are located at random, it may be possible to build an undamaged molecule by piecing together fragments of the various parental molecules; then viral multiplication begins, and a normal phage yield can be produced. The formation of active molecules by this mechanism occurs with great efficiency, since time is not too limiting and a large

Fig. 23-34 Multiplicity reactivation of UV-inactivated bacteriophage DNA. The case of a cell infected by two phage particles is considered. Although UV damages are present in both DNAs they do not coincide; hence it is possible, by multiple exchanges, to obtain molecules without any damaged region.

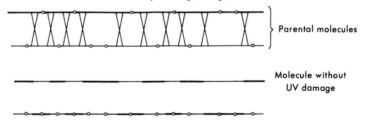

Parental molecules

Molecule without
UV damage

Fig. 23-35 Multiplicity reactivation of UV-irradiated T2. In curve A bacteria were infected with an average of four T2 phages; the curve shows the fraction of the cells able to yield infectious phage, for different UV doses given to the phage. Curve B shows the results obtained when the cells were infected at a low multiplicity (i.e., mostly single infection). (Modified from R. Dulbecco. J. Bact. 63:199, 1952.)

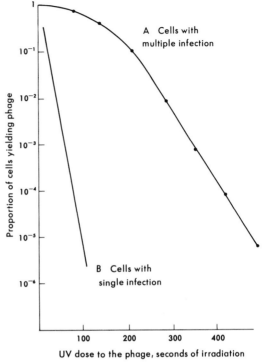

number of exchanges is therefore permissible. However, some early functions must be expressed before exchanges can take place; therefore, the viral DNA molecules infecting the same cell must contain among them at least one undamaged representative of each required early gene.

Measurements of the ability of cells infected by several inactivated virions to produce active virus yield complex curves, which depend on the multiplicity of infection (Fig. 23-35). The curves are of the multiple-hit type (Ch. 8, Appendix) because the cells are multiply infected, and viral multiplication is absent only if **all** the representatives of some required gene are inactivated. In addition, the curves have slopes smaller than those for phage inactivation, since the sum of the required early genes does not encompass the whole genome. The shape of the curves can be precisely accounted for by a mathematical theory based on the requirement both for an undamaged set of the required genes and for formation, by recombination, of a DNA molecule without UV damage.

Cross-reactivation and multiplicity reactivation are very efficient in the T-even bacteriophages, owing to the high frequency of exchanges of the DNA, but are much less efficient in phages with a lower frequency of exchanges.

Since cross-reactivation and multiplicity reactivation occur with UV-damaged molecules that cannot replicate, they show that **recombination is independent of over-all DNA replication.** Multiplicity reactivation also shows that early genes can function in a damaged viral DNA molecule even though they cannot replicate. The same conclusion comes from the study of functional survival (Ch. 8, Functional inactivation). Genes, therefore, are to a considerable extent autonomous in **function,** whereas they are interrelated in **replication.** This difference reflects the autonomy of the synthesis of individual mRNAs, compared with the replication of the DNA molecule as a whole. If replication is interrupted at any point by a damage to the DNA the whole molecule fails to replicate. Thus, **reproductive death** is a property of the whole DNA molecule, whereas **functional death** is a property of the individual functional units (genes or groups of genes).

SELECTED REFERENCES

Books and Review Articles

COHEN, S. S. The biochemistry of viruses. *Ann. Rev. Biochem. 32*:83 (1963).

HAYES, W. *The Genetics of Bacteria and Their Viruses.* Wiley, New York, 1964.

LURIA, S. E. Genetics of bacteriophages. *Ann. Rev. Microbiol. 16*:205 (1962).

STENT, G. *Papers on Bacterial Viruses.* Little, Brown, Boston, 1960.

STENT, G. *Molecular Biology of Bacterial Viruses.* Freeman, San Francisco, 1963.

Specific Articles

BRENNER, S., STREISINGER, G., HORNE, R. W., CHAMPE, S. P., BARNET, L., BENZER, S., and REES, M. W. Structural components of bacteriophage. *J. Molec. Biol. 1*:281 (1959).

DELBRÜCK, M. The growth of bacteriophage and lysis of the host. *J. Gen. Physiol. 23*:643 (1940).

DELBRÜCK, M., and BAILEY, W. T. Induced mutations in bacterial viruses. *Cold Spring Harbor Symp. Quant. Biol. 11*:33 (1946).

EPSTEIN, R. H., BOLLE, A., STEINBERG, C. M., KELLENBERGER, E., BOY DE LA TOUR, E., CHEVALLEY, R., EDGAR, R. S., SUSMAN, M., DENHARDT, G., and LEILAUSIS, A. Physiological studies of conditional lethal mutations of bacteriophage T4D. *Cold Spring Harbor Symp. Quant. Biol. 28*:375 (1963).

HERSHEY, A. D. Nucleic acid economy in bacteria infected with bacteriophage T2. II. Phage precursor nucleic acid. *J. Gen. Physiol. 37*:1 (1953).

HERSHEY, A. D., and CHASE, M. Independent functions of viral protein and nucleic acid in growth of bacteriophage. *J. Gen. Physiol. 36*:39 (1952).

HERSHEY, A. D., and ROTMAN, R. Genetic recombination between host range and plaque type mutants of bacteriophage in single bacterial cells. *Genetics 34*:44 (1949).

KORNBERG, S. R., ZIMMERMAN, S. B., and KORNBERG, A. Glucosylation of deoxyribonucleic acid by enzymes from bacteriophage-infected *E. coli. J. Biol. Chem. 236*:1487 (1961).

LEVINTHAL, C. Recombination in phage T2: Its relation to heterozygosis and growth. *Genetics 39*:169 (1954).

LURIA, S. E. The frequency distribution of spontaneous bacteriophage mutants as evidence for the exponential rate of phage reproduction. *Cold Spring Harbor Symp. Quant. Biol. 16*:463 (1951).

LURIA, S. E., and DULBECCO, R. Genetic recombination leading to production of active bacteriophage from ultraviolet-inactivated bacteriophage particles. *Genetics 34*:93 (1949).

STREISINGER, G., EDGAR, R. S., and DENHARDT, G. H. Chromosome structure in phage T4. 1. Circularity of the linkage map. *Proc. Nat. Acad. Sc. 51*:775 (1964).

VISCONTI, N., and DELBRÜCK, M. The mechanism of genetic recombination in phage. *Genetics 38*:5 (1953).

WYATT, G. R., and COHEN, S. S. The bases of the nucleic acid of some bacterial and animal viruses: The occurrence of 5-hydroxymethylcytosine. *Biochem. J. 55*:774 (1953).

24 LYSOGENY, EPISOMES, AND TRANSDUCING BACTERIOPHAGES

LYSOGENY

The bacteriophages described in the preceding chapters regularly cause lysis of the cells they infect and are therefore defined as **virulent.** Another relation between phages and bacteria is seen in the phenomenon of **lysogeny,** which characterizes many bacterial strains freshly isolated from their natural environment. Such **lysogenic** cultures contain a low concentration of bacteriophage, which can be recognized because it lyses certain other related bacterial strains, known as **sensitive** or

indicator strains.* Lysogeny was recognized in the early twenties; and it was soon realized that lysogenic strains are not simply phage-contaminated bacterial cultures, since the phage could not be eliminated by repeated cloning of the bacteria or by growing the cells in the presence of phage-specific antiserum. Bordet then recognized, in 1925, that the abil-

---

* Sensitive strains either are found by chance or, as noted below, are obtained by "curing" lysogenic strains.

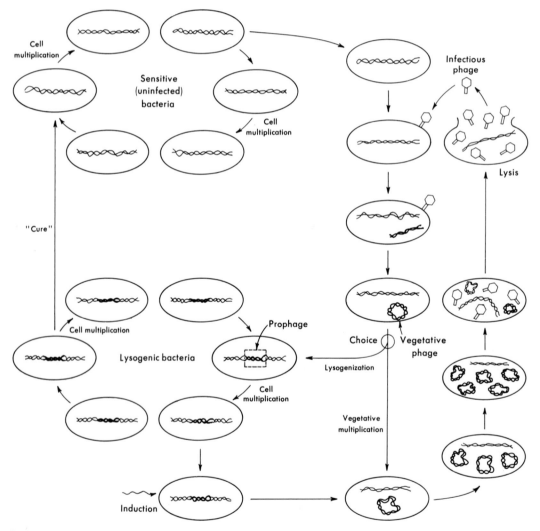

Fig. 24-1   Development of a temperate phage.

ity to produce phage was a hereditary property of the cells. Nevertheless, disruption of the lysogenic cells does not yield infectious phage; hence the phage must be present in the cells in a noninfectious form. Phages capable of such persistent, nonlysing association with a bacterium are known as **temperate** phages.

When a sensitive bacterial strain is infected with a temperate bacteriophage two alternative responses are seen (Fig. 24-1). Some cells are **lysed,** by a process of phage multiplication identical to that described for T phages in the preceding chapter. Other cells are **lysogenized:** they give rise to normally growing cultures in which each cell harbors the phage (in noninfectious form), and the culture forms infectious phage at a low rate. Lysogenic strains thus produced are designated by the name of the sensitive strain followed by that of the lysogenizing phage in parentheses, e.g., *Escherichia coli* K12(λ). Because temperate phages lyse only a fraction of the sensi-

tive cells they infect, they produce **turbid plaques.**

A bacterial strain can be easily recognized as lysogenic by streaking it on a solid medium across a strain sensitive to the phage released; a narrow zone of lysis is seen along the border of the lysogenic strain (Fig. 24-2). Since lysogeny cannot be recognized unless such a sensitive strain is available, many bacterial strains—perhaps most of those known—may be unrecognized as lysogenic. Furthermore, many strains are lysogenic for several different phages.

The systems used most in experimental work on lysogeny are phage λ with *E. coli* K12, and phages P1 and P2 with *Shigella dysenteriae* or with several strains of *E. coli.*

Nature of Lysogeny

The ability of lysogenic cultures to produce virus without obvious lysis remained puzzling until Lwoff, in 1950, patiently observed the

Fig. 24-2 Cross-streaking of lysogenic and sensitive strains of *E. coli* on nutrient agar. **A,** untreated; **B,** exposed to a small dose of ultraviolet light, after streaking, to induce the lysogenic cells. In **A** note the narrow bands of lysis of the sensitive strain (vertical streak) flanking the lysogenic strain (horizontal streak). In **B** note that the inducing treatment, by causing cell lysis, markedly reduces the colony density of the lysogenic streak, and the accompanying release of infectious phage causes pronounced lysis of the sensitive strain in the area of crossing.

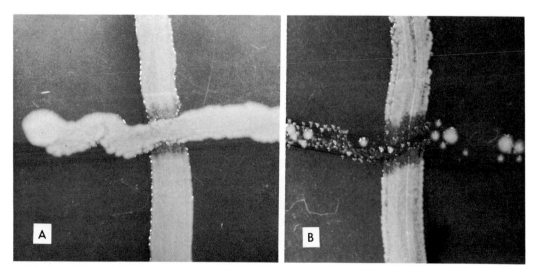

behavior of single cells in microdroplets and showed that phage is produced by a small proportion of the cells, which lyse and release phage in a burst (**induction**),* like *E. coli* B cells infected by phage T2. **The other cells of the culture** do not give rise to a productive infection and are said to be **immune†** to the released phage. The phage adsorbs to the immune cells and injects its DNA, but the DNA does not multiply and does not cause cell lysis. **Immunity, therefore, is different from resistance,** which, as noted in the previous chapter, prevents adsorption and injection.

These experiments made it clear that the noninfectious form of the phage is not some kind of incomplete virus, with an occasional particle becoming completed and "leaking" from the cell. Rather, lysogeny involves a special, stably inherited, noninfectious form of the virus, called **prophage,** whose presence is associated with immunity; and the prophage occasionally shifts abruptly to the **vegetative** form and then reproduces just like a virulent phage. Lwoff further provided a powerful tool for studying lysogeny by showing that the shift from the prophage cycle to the lytic cycle, normally a rare event, could be **induced** in all the cells of a culture by certain environmental influences, such as moderate UV irradiation (Fig. 24-2).

Subsequent studies showed that lysogeny is a special type of virus-cell interaction, based on an intimate association of the viral DNA with the bacterial DNA; and this association is maintained by complex regulatory mechanisms. This interaction of the two genomes has provocative implications for several problems: the origin of viruses, the evolution of bacteria, and the possible relation of some animal viruses to their host cells (especially

tumor-producing viruses). Temperate phages further provide an important mechanism for gene transfer between bacteria (transduction), as has been noted in Chapter 7 and will be expanded later in this chapter.

Characteristics of the Vegetative Multiplication of Phage λ

The lysogenization by bacteriophage λ of *E. coli* K12 cells, which are sensitive to this phage, constitutes an important model for the study of lysogeny. Before considering this process we shall describe the vegetative multiplication of this bacteriophage, which is, on the whole, similar to that of virulent phages, but has certain special features that are relevant for the lysogenic state.

Shapes of Phage DNA. As was previously noted (Ch. 22), molecules of the DNA present in virions of bacteriophage λ are linear, but they can assume in vitro a cyclic shape by base-pairing of the ends (Fig. 24-3). The molecules injected into the cells likewise assume, within a short time, a **ring shape,** as shown by their behavior in zonal centrifugation. (In the latter structure, however, the ends of each strand are joined by covalent bonds in addition to the base-paired end segments, since the two strands do not separate under conditions that cause collapse of the double helical structure of the DNA.) Such ring closure within the cell appears to be essential for vegetative multiplication: if the ability of extracted phage DNA to cyclize is eliminated, by the use of DNA polymerase to convert the single-stranded ends to double strands, the DNA loses its infectivity.

Phage Enzymes. λ DNA resembles host DNA in base ratios. Unlike T-even coliphages, it does not contain unusual bases and hence does not specify the enzymes for their biosynthesis. Phage λ, however does specify a DNase, which in vitro acts on double-stranded DNA (with the peculiar pH optimum of 10). In the cells the action of the enzyme may be restricted to certain specific nucleotide sequences, for the host DNA is **not** broken down in λ-infected cells. Perhaps the enzyme breaks the λ DNA

---

* It should be noted that the term induction here has a different meaning from induction of enzyme synthesis, as used in bacterial regulation.

† This term is totally unrelated to immunity as studied in immunology, since bacteria do not have immunological defenses.

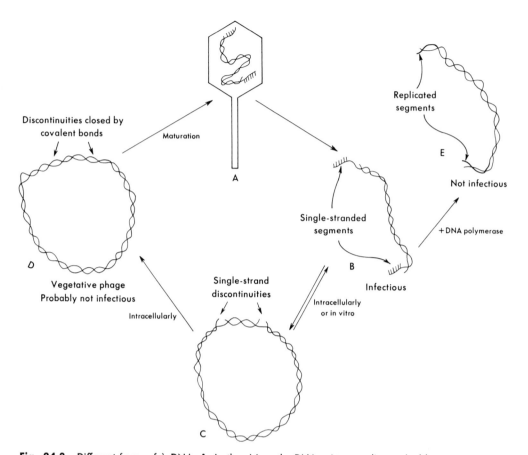

Fig. 24-3 Different forms of λ DNA. **A.** In the virions the DNA exists as a linear double-stranded molecule with short complementary single-stranded segments at the ends. **B.** Under conditions of nucleic acid hybridization, i.e., high temperature and high salt concentration (Ch. 8), the linear molecule can reversibly close into a ring by base-pairing of the single-stranded ends (**C**). **D.** Within the cell the DNA forms completely covalently linked rings. The rings do not convert to **B** when the helical structure collapses. **E.** If the single-stranded ends of **B** are made double-stranded by a polymerase, the molecule can no longer close into a ring. This causes the molecule to lose infectivity, showing that ring closure is essential for the biological function of the DNA.

at specific points, since such a breakage is apparently required for many biological functions of the DNA, as will be discussed below.

The genetics of λ is based on three classes of mutants: 1) conditionally lethal mutants, which are similar to the am mutants of T4 but are called **sus** (suppressor sensitive); 2) plaque-type mutants, such as minute (**m**), host-range (**h**), and clear-plaque (**c**) mutants; and 3) mutants with altered buoyant density, designated as **b** (for buoyancy), which were discovered during purification of the virus by density gradient equilibrium centrifugation; the density is usually lower because of a deletion. The c mutants, and one of the b mutants (b₂), fail to lysogenize the sensitive cells (or c may do so at a very low rate); hence these mutants are especially important in studying the mechanism of lysogenization.

Phage λ undergoes genetic recombination at a considerably lower rate than the T-even coliphages. The genetic map determined during vegetative multiplication of the phage

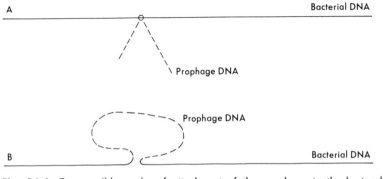

Fig. 24-4 Two possible modes of attachment of the prophage to the host cell DNA. In **A** (hook model) the prophage is attached by a hypothetical linker to the uninterrupted bacterial DNA. In **B** (insertion model) the prophage is linearly inserted in the host DNA.

(**vegetative map**) is linear, with ends corresponding to the ends of the DNA molecules present in the virions. The map obtained by studying recombination between prophages (**prophage map**) is quite different, as will be discussed below.

State of the Prophage in Lysogenic Cells

The prophage is firmly attached to the bacterial chromosome (integrated), since it is transferred with the Hfr chromosome in bacterial crosses, with localization at characteristic sites. In *E. coli* cells prophage λ has a single site located between the gal operon and the biotin locus; prophage P2 can occupy two or more different sites; and prophage Mu-1

can occupy many sites. For prophage P1, however, no site can be located by this method. Since there is evidence from transduction (see below) that this prophage has an attachment site, it may possibly come off during conjugation.

Mechanism of Integration: Insertion

The mode of attachment of prophage to the bacterial DNA has been clarified only recently. It was long believed that the prophage was attached through a point to the bacterial chromosome, the remainder of the molecule hanging free ("hook" model, Fig. 24-4). Evidence against this hypothesis was first provided by Calef in experiments on conjugation between lysogenic strains, in which the pro-

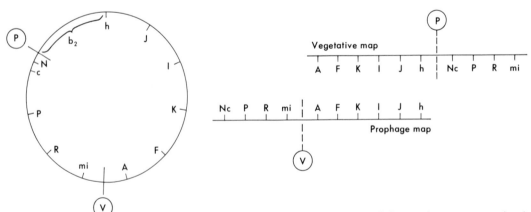

Fig. 24-5 The ring of λ DNA. Both the vegetative and the prophage maps can be derived from the same circle by opening it at different points, V for vegetative multiplication and maturation, and P for prophage insertion. The difference is equivalent to shifting the block of markers NcPRmi from one end of the map to the other. The capital letters refer to sus mutations; h=locus of host range mutations, c=immunity locus (defined by "clear" mutations), mi=locus of minute plaque mutants. The position and size of the b2 deletion are not precisely known.

phages carried different alleles of three loci. The cross produced some bacteria with recombinant prophage. The frequencies of the various recombinant types allowed the ordering of the prophage genes, as in an ordinary three-factor cross, to yield a simple **prophage map.** The striking result was that although the loci had the order h-c-mi in the vegetative map, they had the order c-mi-h in the prophage map. Evidently integration of the phage alters its pattern of linkage.

Campbell explained this **permutation of the map** by suggesting that in lysogenization the viral DNA first becomes attached in cyclic form to the host DNA and then is **inserted linearly** by opening the ring (Fig. 24-5): if the point of opening differs from that used

in vegetative multiplication the prophage map would be a circularly permuted vegetative map (see Ch. 23 for details on the circular permutation of molecules of T4 DNA). Indeed, by the use of phage containing many markers additional evidence was soon obtained for such a regular permutation. Further details of the mechanism of insertion will be discussed below (Fig. 24-7).

Direct evidence for linear insertion of the prophage comes from mapping its genes in respect to bacterial genes (Fig. 24-6). For this purpose a large part of the genome of phage λ, containing many markers, was translocated onto a related prophage that is located adjacent to the $T1^r$ bacterial locus. Deletions of this locus cause

Fig. 24-6 Evidence for linear insertion of the prophage in the bacterial chromosome. *E. coli* cells were lysogenized with a φ80-λ hybrid phage, which contains mostly λ markers, but is localized near the $T1^r$ (T1-resistance) bacterial locus (whose wild-type allele makes the cell T1-sensitive). Many deletions of this locus (phenotypically T1-resistant) were isolated. To determine which prophage markers had also been deleted the cells were induced and then superinfected with a λ phage carrying alleles of all the markers; the appearance (or nonappearance) of various prophage markers in the progeny phage indicated their presence (+) or absence (−) in the partly deleted prophage. From the results given in the table a map of the prophage genes and of the $T1^r$ gene can be constructed. The map shows that the prophage genes and the $T1^r$ gene constitute a unique linear sequence, in agreement with linear insertion of the prophage. (Compare map in Figure 24-5. The relative sequence of the markers in the box was not determined in this experiment.) The continuous line refers to the prophage genome; the dashed line to the bacterial genome. (Modified from N. C. Franklin, W. F. Dove, and C. Yanofsky. *Biochem. & Biophys. Res. Comm.* 18:910, 1965.)

| Prophage markers | | | | | | | | | | Deletion |
c	N	R	A	F	K	I	J	h	$T1^r$	
+	+	+	+	+	+	+	+	−	−	1
+	+	+	+	+	+	+	+	−	−	2
+	+	+	+	+	+	+	−	−	−	3
+	+	+	+	+	+	−	−	−	−	4
+	+	+	+	+	−	−	−	−	−	5
+	+	+	+	−	−	−	−	−	−	6
+	+	+	+	−	−	−	−	−	−	7
+	+	+	−	−	−	−	−	−	−	8

c N R A F K I J h $T1^r$ Try

Prophage map

Bacterial genome   Prophage   Bacterial genome

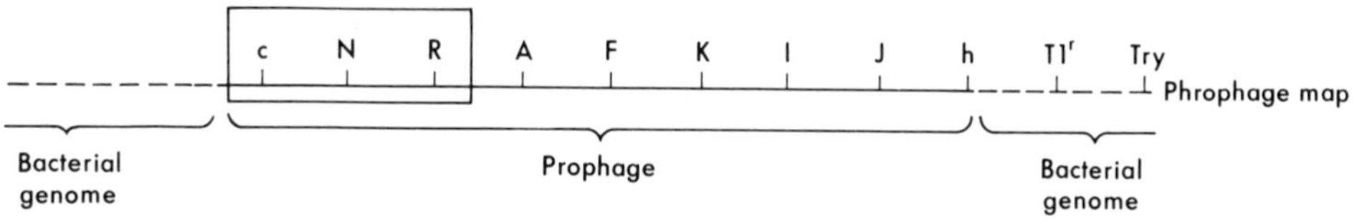

T1 resistance and hence are readily selected. These deletions were found to extend to various distances into the adjacent prophage, thus obliterating different numbers of the translocated λ markers. From the grouping of these deleted markers the prophage genes could be ordered, as shown in Figure 24-6; the results support an insertion model and not a hook model.

Mechanism of Insertion and Recombination

Insertion of the prophage (**integration**) can be best accounted for by a reciprocal crossover between the circular phage DNA and bacterial DNA, employing the same mechanism of breakage and reunion (Fig. 24-7) observed in genetic recombination (Ch. 8). **Detachment (induction)** of prophage would be explained by a reverse of the same process (Fig. 24-7). The breaks may conceivably be produced by the phage-specified nuclease.

The cyclic shape of λ phage DNA is essential for its insertion in the host DNA, since it allows the insertion by a single crossover and without loss of parts. In contrast, the insertion of a linear molecule would require two crossovers, and the ends of the prophage together with a piece of the bacterial DNA would be lost (Fig. 24-7). It is clear that neither of these losses occurs in prophage insertion, since, as discussed below, **both the prophage and the bacterial chromosome** can be recovered intact from the lysogenic cells. Since the cyclic shape is so eminently suited for integration, any cyclic viral DNA may be suspected of being capable of insertion into the DNA of its host cell.

Since recombination between viral and host DNA occurs at precisely defined positions in the bacterial chromosome the two nucleic acids must contain homologous segments. In fact, experiments with DNA hybridization have revealed that about 34% of the λ DNA and 0.2% of the DNA of sensitive host cells are homologous to each other. The DNA of λ phage with a b_2 deletion, which does not produce lysogenic clones, fails to be inserted: presumably the deletion eliminates the segment of the ring that synapses with the bacterial chromosome.

Fairly frequently cells are **doubly lysogenic** for the same prophage, as may be shown by infecting sensitive cells with phages of two strains carrying different genetic markers. In such cells the two prophages are inserted at the same locus in a **tandem linear sequence.** Double lysogeny is unstable, for reasons to be discussed below (Integration of episomes): one of the prophages is lost at a relatively high frequency (0.1 to 1% of the cells at each division).

Multiplication of the Prophage

Whereas the vegetative multiplication of phage DNA is autonomous, i.e., is controlled by phage genes, the replication of the prophage is regulated by the system that controls replication of the bacterial chromosome. Thus there are mutant phages that cannot multiply

Fig. 24-7 Insertion of prophage in lysogenization and its detachment in induction. **A.** The circular phage DNA synapses with the bacterial DNA, using the homology represented by the letters a, b, c, d, e, f. Crossover then takes place, and the prophage becomes inserted (**B**); if the host DNA is stretched (**C**), the linear insertion of the prophage can be recognized.

Detachment occurs by the reverse process. The chromosome forms a loop in which the two homologous segments synapse with each other (**D**). A crossover then occurs between these segments, reconstituting a complete circular phage DNA and an intact bacterial chromosome.

The inset (**H, K**) examines the alternative possibility of insertion of a linear phage DNA by two crossovers. Fragments of both the phage and the host DNA would be lost in this process, which is therefore excluded.

Letters on the phage DNA refer to genetic markers. Capital letters are sus markers, c=a clear plaque marker, h=a host-range marker, GAL=gal locus, and BIO=biotin locus, on the bacterial chromosome.

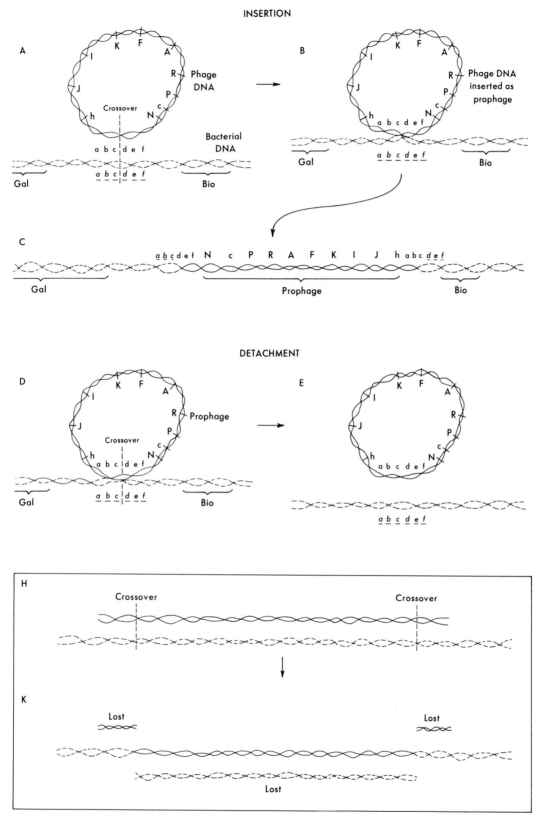

INSERTION

A — Phage DNA / Crossover / Bacterial DNA / Gal / Bio

B — Phage DNA inserted as prophage / Gal / Bio

C — Gal / Prophage / Bio

DETACHMENT

D — Prophage / Crossover / Gal / Bio

E

H — Crossover / Crossover

K — Lost / Lost / Lost

Fig. 24-7 (See legend on facing page)

vegetatively at 40° but are replicated at this temperature as prophages. Presumably these mutants are defective, at the nonpermissive temperature, in some element of the phage replicon required for initiating a round of vegetative replication (Ch. 9, Control of DNA replication); but after integration of the phage the function of this element is not required, and the prophage is replicated as an integral part of the host chromosome.

Further evidence is provided by ascertaining the time at which the prophage replicates in a synchronously growing culture lysogenic for λ. The number of prophages is determined, at various times, by superinfecting the culture with the virulent mutant, λ v, which induces vegetative multiplication of the prophage (see below); doubling of the proportion of λ v^+ to λ v in the yield reveals the time of phophage replication. Comparison with the time of doubling of various bacterial genes, detected by genetic transformation (Ch. 9), shows that the prophage doubles when the growing point of the replicating DNA reaches its locus.

Regulatory Mechanisms Maintaining the Lysogenic State

Repression

A fundamental characteristic of a **prophage** is that it **does not express the function of most of its genes.** Not only does the DNA not multiply autonomously, but it does not cause the synthesis of recognizable viral proteins. Most prophage genes, therefore, must be repressed, presumably by a mechanism similar to that causing the selective repression of bacterial genes (Ch. 9). This conclusion is verified by the virtual absence of phage mRNA in lysogenic cells, in contrast to cells in the lytic cycle of phage multiplication.

Immunity

Immunity and Repression. Jacob, Wollman, and others further demonstrated that this process of phage repression is also responsible for the immunity of lysogenic cells to lytic superinfection by added phage of the same strain. Hence immunity, which originally appeared to be a curious product of the lysogenic state, becomes one of its central features. The main evidence is the following:

1) When prophage is induced the viral genes begin functioning at the same time that immunity to lytic reinfection breaks down. This result suggests that the same repressor influences the activity of both endogenous and exogenous phage DNA. (The breakdown of immunity is revealed by the ability of a suitably marked infecting λ phage to multiply.)

2) When a lysogenic Hfr cell conjugates with a nonlysogenic F^- cell prophage entering the repressor-free F^- cytoplasm is usually induced (**zygotic induction**), just as phage DNA entering by infection usually causes lysis of nonlysogenic cells. In contrast, if the recipient cell is already lysogenic for the same phage the introduced prophage does not exhibit zygotic induction, just as an infecting phage fails to cause lysis.

3) In the conjugation of a lysogenic F^+ (not Hfr) cell with a nonlysogenic F^- cell the repressor reaches the F^- cell and makes it temporarily immune.

The Immunity (c) Locus. There is strong evidence that the synthesis of the λ repressor is under the control of a single phage gene, c_1, belonging to the **clear (c)** locus. In fact, λ phages carrying c_1 mutations fail to lysogenize and therefore produce clear plaques, which suggests failure to produce a functional repressor. These mutants, however, are sensitive to the repressor, since they do not lyse a cell already lysogenic. Another class of mutations of the same gene, called **ind⁻**, causes the prophage to resist induction (hence the name, meaning not inducible); as discussed below, this property suggests the synthesis of a superrepressor. The two classes of mutations appear to be equivalent to the i^- and i^s mutations, respectively, of the β-galactosidase regulator gene (Ch. 9). The product of the c_1 gene has been isolated from λ-infected cells: it is an acidic protein with a molecular weight of 30,000.

The repressor apparently causes immunity by preventing the expression of genes of a superinfecting phage that recognizes the same repressor. Repressors produced by different prophages are usually different, so that each phage recognizes its own repressor and no other; hence cells lysogenic for a certain prophage are not immune to, and are lysogenized by, other temperate phages. Mutants of the same phage, provided they are not altered in the c locus, have the same repressor, i.e., they are **coimmune.** A superinfecting coimmune phage can inject its DNA into immune cells, but the DNA fails to function and to multiply; it persists and is transmitted unilinearly (i.e., from one cell to one of the daughter cells) and remains identifiable by proper genetic tests (**abortive prophage**).

In order to be effective, the repressor must interact with a phage operator. The operator locus is apparently extremely close to the **emitter** locus, responsible for the synthesis of the repressor, because in crosses between λ and a related prophage with a different repressor specificity the two loci cannot be separated by recombination. Thus the two loci are closely linked, and are perhaps located in a segment of DNA where no crossover can occur; such an intimate association may have been stabilized by selection because both emitter and operator must be present in the same phage to ensure temperateness. Recent results suggest that the N locus, adjacent to the c locus, plays an important role in repression. It is not clear, however, whether it contains the operator or produces a product that interacts with the repressor.

Establishment of the Lysogenic State

When a sensitive bacterium is infected by a temperate phage the entering DNA has a "choice" between vegetative multiplication and integration as a prophage. The proportion of infected cells that are lysogenized may vary from a few per cent to nearly 100%, depending on both the system and the conditions employed.

Before the choice is made the injected viral DNA undergoes several rounds of replication (Fig. 24-8). This replication is useful for lysogenization, since it enhances the chance that a DNA molecule will find the site of insertion; in fact, defective phages whose DNA

Fig. 24-8 Rate of synthesis of cellular and viral DNA. *Salmonella typhimurium* was infected by the temperate phage P22, under conditions that permitted essentially all cells to become lysogenic. The graph shows the depression of the rate of cellular DNA synthesis after infection and its subsequent recovery (solid line), as well as the brief viral DNA synthesis (dashed line).

Cellular and viral DNA were separated by zonal sedimentation, the cellular DNA sedimenting faster owing to its larger size. The rate of synthesis is measured from the amount of ^{3}H-thymidine incorporated into DNA in a 2-minute pulse. (Data from H. D. Smith and M. Levine. Virology 25:585, 1965.)

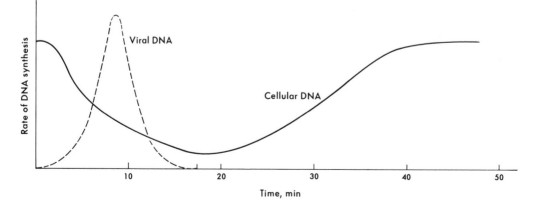

cannot multiply vegetatively lysogenize much less effectively. During this early period of indecision viral messenger RNA is produced (as detected by hybridization with phage DNA) and the viral early functions become expressed.

Among these functions we recognize 1) the sequential functions of the c genes and 2) the function of the nuclease. The c_2 and c_3 genes provide transient functions which are probably responsible for an early inhibition of cellular DNA and RNA synthesis; the c_1 gene finally takes over, causing the continued synthesis of the repressor. All three functions are required for lysogenization. The nuclease probably functions both in vegetative DNA replication and in integration.

The choice between lysogenization and vegetative multiplication appears to result from a competition between repression of phage multiplication and some unknown event that renders repression ineffective; when the synthesis of the repressor wins lysogenization occurs. The balance is critical and is shifted one way or the other by subtle factors. For instance, with some *Salmonella* phages lysogenization is favored by high multiplicity of infection; with coliphage P1 by relatively low temperature (20 to 35°) or the presence of chloramphenicol; and with phage λ by a high concentration of Mg++.

The **repressed viral DNA** constitutes a prophage, whether or not it becomes inserted in the bacterial chromosome. In fact, λ DNA carrying a b_2 deletion, which fails to integrate, remains as abortive prophage in the cells that do not lyse.

It takes about 2 hours before any cells become fully lysogenic (i.e., both immune and inducible). During this time the bacterium undergoes several divisions, occasionally producing sensitive as well as lysogenic progeny, as shown by pedigree analyses of individual cells. The appearance of sensitive cells indicates the existence of a lag between the onset of repression and insertion: during this lag cell division, unaccompanied by phage division, may yield a cell without a prophage.

Induction of a Lysogenic Cell

The transition of prophage into vegetative phage can occur either spontaneously or in response to an inducing stimulus, as already indicated. The first sign of induction is the initiation of synthesis of the phage mRNA. Viral DNA and capsid protein are subsequently synthesized.

Induction represents the failure of repression, which may occur in rare cells as a result of a statistical fluctuation of the interaction between repressor and prophage (**spontaneous induction**); it may occur in a large proportion of the cells if external conditions cause either inactivation of the repressor or cessation of its synthesis (**artificial induction**). Cessation of synthesis can cause induction if the repressor is unstable.

Many prophages are induced by ultraviolet (UV) light, in doses too small to inactivate the phage but sufficient temporarily to halt cellular DNA synthesis. Other prophages are poorly inducible by UV light but can be induced by a variety of other means that inhibit cellular DNA synthesis, e.g., temporary thymine starvation, X-rays, alkylating agents (including the antibiotic mitomycin), and some carcinogens.

Prophage λ can also be induced by infecting the cells with a mutant called λ virulent (v), but the mechanism is unknown. Some prophages cannot be induced at all; they exhibit spontaneous induction, but at a lower frequency than the inducible phages.

The action of mutations of either the phage or the host throws light on the mechanism of artificial induction. 1) *E. coli* cells carrying a certain mutation (called T44) and lysogenic for wild-type prophage, are stable at low temperature but are spontaneously induced at high temperature. This result suggests that induction is the consequence of an upset of cellular metabolism, which can be produced either by an inducing treatment or by a host mutation. Since all inducing treatments have in common a temporary stoppage of DNA synthesis, induction may have as effector an intermediate in DNA synthesis, which accumulates at high temperature in cells with the T44 mutation. Since induction at high temperature in T44 cells is inhibited by addition of guanine or cytosine to the medium and is enhanced by adenine, the effector may be an adenine derivative. The effector may act by neutralizing the repressor. 2) The ind⁻ mutation, discussed above, makes the prophage noninducible, by causing the synthesis of a repressor insensitive to the effector of induction (superrepressor). Moreover, in cells lysogenic for wild-type phage superinfection with ind⁻ phage can prevent induction: apparently the ind⁻ superrepressor replaces the normal repressor, which can be rendered ineffective by induction. 3) Certain phage mutations, by making the repressor thermolabile, cause spontaneous induction at high temperature.

Detachment of the Prophage

In induction the prophage is detached **without replication** from the host chromosome and becomes vegetative phage, as can be shown by growing lysogenic cells in isotopically "heavy" medium and transferring them to "light" medium at the moment of induction. Among the viral progeny of these cells are virions with a full complement of heavy DNA; and these must be detached prophages, because λ DNA does not utilize host DNA as a source of precursors.

Detachment probably occurs by a crossover similar to the one that earlier caused the insertion of the phage DNA in the host chromosome (Fig. 24-7). This reversal reconstitutes a circular λ DNA and a complete cellular chromosome. The detachment is presumably promoted by phage-specified enzymes (the nuclease?) formed as a result of derepression; the same enzymes are believed to be formed in freshly infected cells before repression occurs and to participate in insertion. Once the phage DNA is detached it establishes its own "replicon" (Ch. 9) and starts multiplying independently of the cellular DNA.

Although induction and the ensuing viral multiplication normally kill the cells, **cured** (nonlysogenic) cells are exceptionally obtained after induction. The detached prophage may be inactivated (e.g., by inducing with a large UV dose), while the damages produced in the cell's chromosome are repaired; or the detached viral DNA may fail to initiate autonomous replication until after the cell has divided. Some lysogenic strains spontaneously segregate cured cells, probably by a similar mechanism following spontaneous induction. Cured strains are suitable as indicator strains for the lysogenizing phage.

Defective Prophages

Certain mutations of the prophage prevent synthesis of infectious phage, without interfering with the perpetuation of the prophage; this prophage is then called **defective.** Some of these mutations prevent the autonomous synthesis of the viral DNA; others affect constituents of the coat of the virions. The presence of genetically marked defective prophages is recognized by inducing the cells (to break down immunity) and then superinfecting with a **helper phage,** usually the homologous wild type. The defective prophage uses a function performed by the helper DNA to replace its own missing function; and the progeny includes not only wild-type virions but also virions carrying genes from the defective prophage. The virions produced may also be phenotypically mixed (Ch. 23).

Defective prophages are extremely useful tools for investigation, in the same way as conditionally lethal mutants (Ch. 23): they can be propagated as prophages, and the effects of their defect on vegetative multiplication can be observed after the lysogenic cells have been induced.

Whereas most known defective prophages contain the immunity system, some **extremely defective prophages** of λ and P1 have lost the immunity genes, as well as genes responsible for the detachment of the prophage; hence these prophages persist but the cells are not immune. These prophages are a useful model for understanding the consequence of infection of animal cells with certain tumorigenic DNA-containing viruses.

Effect of Prophage on Host Function

Phage Conversion

Except for transducing phages (see below), which carry genes known to be derived from a recent bacterial host, most prophages exert no discernible effect on the bacterial phenotype other than producing immunity to superinfection. All other phage functions are ordinarily repressed. Certain prophages, however, produce characteristic changes in the bacterial phenotype, called **conversion.** The genes involved are active also, as might be expected, in the vegetative phage.

Among the best known examples of conversion we may recall the change of surface antigens in *Salmonella typhimurium* (which has been carefully analyzed and is discussed in Chapter 20) and the formation of diphtheria toxin by *Corynebacterium diphtheriae.* Another example, of particular importance in the development of fine-structure genetics, is the resistance of *E. coli* K12, when carrying prophage λ, to T-even phages with an rɪɪ mutation (Ch. 23).

Effect on Adjacent Bacterial Genes

An interference by prophage with the regulation of neighboring bacterial genes has been repeatedly observed. The insertion of λ prophage, for instance, affects the function of the adjacent gal operon, increasing its repression. After the prophage is induced by UV radiation the operon is derepressed, and a burst of enzyme synthesis occurs before the cells lyse. Since induction of the prophage depends on a derepression of the prophage, it seems that at least part of the gal operon becomes controlled by the prophage repressor. This effect may arise by insertion of the phage genome between gal genes and their operator, just as "fused operons," created by deletion, place genes of one operon under the control of the operator of another operon (Ch. 9).

Another interesting effect is displayed by prophage Mu-1, which can be inserted at many sites on the host chromosome. In an *E. coli* culture infected by this prophage many different genes in different cells appear to undergo mutation—because they become nonfunctional—in the course of the establishment of lysogenic complexes. Each mutation occurs at a locus adjacent to a prophage localization. It is not known whether these apparent mutations involve an effect of the prophage on the regulation of the genes or on their structure (e.g., splitting the gene by an insertion: Ch. 8, Mutagenesis).

Significance of Lysogeny

Lysogeny indicates a close evolutionary relation between phages and bacteria. Lysogeny,

in fact, depends on a remarkably extensive **homology** between the DNA of the phage and that of the host cells, sometimes at multiple sites; and most phages can lysogenize some bacterial strains. The virulent T coliphages, though long viewed as the prototype phages, are thus exceptional: they represent extreme evolution in the direction of autonomous viral development, leading not only to loss of homology with bacterial DNA, but also to large deviations of biochemical processes.

Prophages give rise to **infectious heredity** in their host cells, i.e., they contribute new genetic characteristics to the lysogenic cells. One way in which this can happen is **conversion,** in which the prophage introduces new characters that persist as long as the lysogenic state persists. This phenomenon raises the question of the origin of the converting genes that remain active in the prophage, i.e., whether viral or, as in transducing phages, cellular. In fact, one cannot say whether converting genes are essential for phage function, advantageous but not essential, or purely adventitious.

Infectious heredity is also seen with **highly defective prophages** that cannot be induced and do not confer immunity; these cannot be distinguished from segments of cellular genetic material. By evolutionary changes the genes of these prophages may acquire genetic significance for the cell and become bona fide cellular genes.

Lysogeny must also be considered in relation to its **survival value for the virus.** As Burnet has pointed out in connection with infectious diseases of higher organisms, the parasites best adapted to their environments are those that do not rapidly kill their hosts and thus deprive themselves of the opportunity to spread.

An important aspect of lysogeny is that it provides an important **model for the study of animal viruses,** mainly because it shows that viruses, as agents of infectious heredity, can modify the hereditary properties of cells. On a more detailed scale, lysogeny has been extremely useful as a guide for the study of tumorigenic animal viruses.

EPISOMES

It has been shown in the preceding section that the DNA of temperate phages can exist in two states in the cells and can shift from one to the other: from vegetative phage to prophage in lysogenization, and from prophage to vegetative phage in induction. The F agent that causes conjugation (Ch. 7), and other sex factors, can similarly be found either in the integrated state, replicating as part of the host chromosome, or separate from the chromosome, and replicating autonomously.

It is now recognized that temperate phages and F factor are two members of a group of elements called **episomes,** which are defined by their **ability to replicate in either the autonomous or the integrated state and to shift between these alternative states.**

The known episomes all have two additional characteristics, which are not required in the original definition of Jacob and Wollman: they govern only properties that are dispensable for the cells and hence are not necessary for cell viability; and they can be transferred from cell to cell, either by viral infection or by conjugation. Transferability is lost, however, in many defective mutants of phage. It is therefore tempting to speculate that cells may carry other, nonlysing episomes that also lack transferability, and therefore cannot be recognized, and that such episomes might alter the properties of the cell on shifting their state, just as various prophage genes become expressed when the prophage is derepressed. Such a mechanism has been suggested for certain high-frequency, abrupt changes in the biosynthetic pattern of a cell, such as phase variation in salmonellae (Ch. 6) or sporulation and germination in bacilli (Ch. 5). There has been no evidence, however, to exclude the more classic mechanism of gene mutation for the former, and a nonepisomal system of gene regulation for the latter.

Structure. It seems reasonable to assume that all episomes capable of integration with the chromosome consist of DNA. With bacteriophages the demonstration is conclusive. With the F agent the small amount per cell has prevented isolation and direct identification, but there is strong evidence for the same structure. This evidence includes 1) inactivation of F by ^{32}P decay or UV irradiation; 2) transfer of tritiated thymidine on transfer of F by conjugation, the amount transferred being 1% of that in the donor cell; 3) appearance in density gradient equilibrium sedimentation of a satellite band of DNA, with the density of *E. coli* DNA, when F infects a species (*Serratia*) with a DNA of a different density; and 4) ability to add bacterial genes, by genetic recombination, to form F′. The F agent and phage λ probably have similar dimensions, since they exhibit much the same degree of sensitivity to ^{32}P decay and to UV irradiation; but F′ can be much larger (Ch. 7).

Integration of Episomes

The **mechanism of integration** of episomes is probably similar to that of phophage λ, discussed above, although direct evidence for the circularity of most episomes is lacking. In this mechanism a part of the episome synapses with a region of the cellular DNA, and then a crossover between the two cyclic molecules leads to the insertion of one into the other.

This mechanism can explain many properties of the F episomes. For instance, the lack of strong homology of F with any region of the bacterial chromosome would account for both the low rate and the variable location of its integration: this process may occur at the sites of weak homologies (involving a small number of nucleotides) which are present, by chance, in otherwise nonhomologous regions of DNA. The F′ agents, in contrast, provide increased homology; the segment of bacterial chromosome carried on the episome thus leads to frequent recombination at the corresponding chromosomal region, just as would occur if the exogenous homologous region were part of a cellular chromosome instead (Fig. 24-9). Conversely, increased homology can also be provided by the addition of a fragment of F to the bacterial chromosome. Thus in some Hfr cells that have lost the F agent, and have become F⁻, reinfection

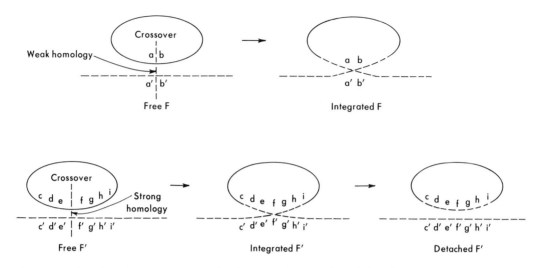

Fig. 24-9 Hypothetical explanation for the difference between F and F' in insertion and in detachment.

F synapses on the basis of its own weak homology for the bacterial DNA (a, b). The probability of insertion is very small, owing to the weakness of the interaction; but once it is inserted the probability of detachment is also small, for the same reason.

F' synapses on the basis of the strong homology of its bacterial segment (c, d, e, f, g, h, i) for the host DNA. Insertion occurs with a high probability because the interaction is strong, and for the same reason detachment also occurs frequently.

Dashed line = DNA of bacterial origin; continuous line = episomal DNA.

with normal F results in immediate formation of Hfr cells with the origin at the **same** locus as before. Evidently the earlier loss of the F episome was incomplete, and the residual segment provides a **sex-factor-attracting** locus in the bacterial chromosome.

As we have seen with prophage λ, the **mechanism that detaches an episome** is exactly the reverse of that causing insertion, and depends on synapsis by loop formation, followed by crossing over. Since the efficiency of this process depends on the degree of homology, this mechanism may also account for differences in the frequency of reversion of different Hfr strains to F^+. Presumably strains with a high degree of homology revert more easily. The extreme case is that of strains containing an integrated F': the very high homology between the bacterial component of the F' and the corresponding segment belonging to the bacterial chromosome accounts for the high reversion rate seen in the "intermediate donors" described in Chapter 7 (Modification of F agent).

The formation of F' from F can be considered as the detachment of a loop consisting of an intact F together with a contiguous bacterial segment. This process must involve a crossover between regions of bacterial DNA that are not particularly homologous, which explains the rarity of the events. According to the insertion model for integration the relation between the episome and the bacterial chromosome is symmetrical, except for the size of the units. Indeed, as was noted in Chapter 7, the Hfr chromosome can be considered either as a bacterial chromosome that has incorporated the episome, or alternatively, as a glorified F', with the entire bacterial chromosome inserted into the transmissible F agent.

Resistance-Transfer Factors (RTF)

Resistance-Transferring Episomes (R Factors). An episome of unusual medical interest was discovered in 1959 in Japan as a consequence of widespread chemotherapy of bacillary dysentery (Ch. 20, Shigellosis), which favored the selection of resistant *Shigella* strains. Strains that were simultaneously resistant to some or all of the four widely used drugs (sulfonamides, streptomycin, chloramphenicol and tetracyclines) began to appear with high frequency; and, moreover, nonpathogenic *E. coli* strains were found with the same property. This unexpected development became understandable when it was found that this heritable multiple resistance could be transferred from these resistant organisms to sensitive strains of a variety of Enterobacteriaceae in mixed cultures, both in vitro and in the mammalian gastrointestinal tract.

The agents responsible, called R factors (RF), have been extensively investigated in Japan, particularly by Watanabe and by Mitsuhashi. They proved to be episomes that closely resemble an F′ agent in many respects. Each consists of two distinguishable parts: a transfer agent (analogous to F), called the **resistance-transfer factor** (RTF), together with attached genes for drug resistance (R genes), which have apparently been picked up from bacterial hosts. Transfer is by conjugation, since it requires cell contact and can be interrupted mechanically. Moreover, the agent can be integrated, but it is usually transferred without accompanying chromosomal genes; and it can be eliminated from a cell by acriflavin. It can also be transferred by generalized transducing phages, indicating that the size of the R genome is similar to or smaller than that of the phage genome.

The Transfer Factor (RTF). RTF carrying various genes for resistance can lose them separately or in groups; and from the patterns of segregation and linked transduction observed the genes can be mapped on the episome. Moreover, the presence of a "naked" RTF, without resistance genes, can be demonstrated, and may be very widespread, in *Salmonella;* a considerable proportion of sensitive strains of *Salmonella,* when mixed with nontransmitting multiple-resistance strains, cause the production of complete, detectable resistance-transmitting factors (RF). It is in-

ferred that in these mixtures the required RTF, without R genes, is provided by the sensitive strain to the resistant strain, in which the genes are present but the transfer factor is absent or defective.

It is believed that the RTF has become an RF for multiple resistance by picking up individual genes for resistance to different agents from various hosts. Such successive pick-ups are perhaps surprising, since we know that an F′ will no longer integrate at random in the chromosome, but will be directed, at least most of the time, to the region homologous to its segment of recent bacterial origin. However, the selective pressures in the flora of a drug-treated human population act on so large a scale that they can probably select for recombinants that are too rare to produce in the laboratory.

This view is supported by the appearance, in the flora of patients, of RFs with resistance to an increasing number of drugs, as additional drugs (e.g., kanamycin, neomycin) have been introduced. The RTF can presumably pick up other kinds of genes as well, but they have not been observed, for lack of suitable selective pressures and ready means of detection. Additional evidence for multiple pick-up is that RFs with different patterns of resistance exhibit different DNA density patterns, suggesting that different segments have originated from different bacterial species.

The mechanism of action of the resistance genes is discussed in Chapter 10 (Drug resistance).

Comparison with the F Agent. Cells **freshly infected** with the R factor transfer it at a high frequency, resulting in an explosive spread in a mixed culture. In contrast, cultures **infected for several generations** (including stock R cultures) transfer R with a much lower frequency (10^{-2} to 10^{-7} per donor cell), depending on donor and recipient. The basis for the change in transferability is not certain, but it probably involves the establishment by RTF of a repression system that impairs the production of the apparatus for its transmission.

Evidence for this view is provided by the relation of RTF strains to the F agent. At the stage of high fertility (i.e., after fresh infection) most strains produce the same kind of special conjugation pili as the F agent: these pili are demonstrated by their adsorption of the male-specific f phage (Ch. 7). Moreover, if an F+ cell is infected by such an RTF strain the subsequent development of low fertility for RTF (by further cultivation) also applies to the F agent, and the vast majority of the cells no longer possess F pili. In other words, these strains of RTF are epistatic* to F, as would be expected if they made a repressor acting on both systems. RTF strains with this property are called fi+ (for F-inhibiting), and may well be mutants of the F agent.

A second group of RTF isolates have no effect on F, and do not produce f-specific pili; they are called fi⁻, and may be phylogenetically much more remote from F. It is thus evident that the RTFs comprise a mixed group of sex factors.

The RTF agents differ from F not only in producing a low level of fertility (in terms of their own transfer), but also in producing an even lower frequency of chromosomal transfer (ca. 10^{-8}); no Hfr-type derivatives have been isolated, suggesting that chromosomal integration is unstable.

Bacteriocins and Bacteriocinogens

In 1925 Gratia in Belgium discovered that filtrates of a particular strain of *E. coli* inhibited the growth of another strain of the same species. The inhibitory substance was later shown to be lethal and was named **colicin.** Some 20 colicins were subsequently recognized and were labeled A to V. Each was specific for a limited variety of strains of several species of Enterobacteriaceae, and they could be distinguished by this host range (antimicrobial spectrum). Similar agents have since been isolated from strains of *Pseudomonas pyocyaneus* (pyocins) and *Bacillus megaterium* (megacins); each acts only on organisms closely related to the one that produces it.

The group as a whole are now called **bacteriocins.** Their formation is widespread: 20%

of a random group of enteric bacteria (including *Shigella* and *Salmonella*) yielded colicins against a single test strain of *E. coli*. Bacteriocins differ from antibiotics (Ch. 10): they are proteins, have a much narrower antimicrobial spectrum, and are generally much more potent. Bacteriocins are detected and titrated by placing a drop of culture filtrate on a lawn of freshly inoculated indicator bacteria; titers are usually expressed in terms of the highest dilution yielding a clear spot. A more satisfactory assay is available for some colicins which, when added to an excess of sensitive bacteria, kill a number of them that is directly proportional to the amount of colicin. This finding shows that one molecule of these colicins is sufficient to kill a bacterium; and the number of bacteria killed measures the number of colicin molecules.

Mechanism of Action of Bacteriocins

Colicins apparently attach to specific cell wall receptors: a given colicin will cause the selection of resistant bacterial mutants which can no longer adsorb it. This specificity suggests that colicins are similar to the components of phage (such as tail fibers) that are responsible for phage adsorption to the host cells (Ch. 23). Indeed, certain colicins and certain phages (e.g., colicin K and phage T6) appear to share the same receptors, since mutants selected for resistance to either are resistant to the other.

Megacins can damage osmotically sensitive protoplasts of sensitive strains, suggesting that they attack the cell membrane. Various colicins, in contrast, interfere with various classes of macromolecule synthesis, without apparent membrane damage. The effect of some bacteriocins is thus similar to that of the coat protein of bacteriophages, which can kill the host cell even without DNA injection (Ch. 23). It is not clear how one molecule, apparently nonreplicating, can exert such extensive effects.

Bacteriocinogens

The formation of bacteriocins bears a strong resemblance to that of temperate bacteriophages. The ability to form a bacteriocin ap-

---

* Gene A is called **epistatic** to gene B in the same cell if the expression of A prevents or reduces the expression of B. The phenomenon is analogous to dominance, except that the two genes are not allelic and may be on the same chromosome.

pears to be due to a special genetic determinant (**bacteriocinogen,** bacteriocin factor), and not to an ordinary chromosomal gene, for when the property is lost it cannot be restored by back-mutation but requires reintroduction of a bloc of genetic material from bacteriocinogenic cells. The bacteriocinogen behaves like a prophage. In fact, **most cells in a bacteriocinogenic culture do not contain or produce bacteriocin;** and the low level of bacteriocin normally found in the cultures is probably produced by a small proportion of the cells. Furthermore, the cells of some bacteriocinogenic strains can be induced to form bacteriocin, by using the same agents that induce certain lysogenic strains to form infectious phage (e.g., light UV irradiation, chemical mutagens, thymine deprival, etc.). The induced cells go on to die, and in at least some systems to lyse. Bacteriocinogens, therefore, **behave like defective prophages,** which on induction cause the production of only one protein, the colicin.

Bacteriocinogenic strains are relatively immune to bacteriocin of their own type, and are unaffected by the levels ordinarily found in their cultures. The nature of the immunity is not clear.

The Genetics of Colicinogens. Among bacteriocinogens only colicinogens have been subject to much genetic study. Their behavior is quite heterogeneous but clearly justifies their inclusion among the episomes.

1) **Colicinogens as autonomous episomes.** Fredericq discovered that certain colicinogens, such as E1 (abbreviated **Col E1**), can be transferred from F$^+$ to F$^-$ cells with high frequency, but not at all from F$^-$ cells. The characteristics of transfer are similar to those of the autonomous F agent (Ch. 7). This colicinogen thus appears to replicate autonomously and to be able to cross the conjugation bridge formed by F. Like other episomes, it can also be transferred by transduction.

2) **Integrated colicinogens.** While transfer of Col E1 by conjugation requires the presence of a sex factor, the transfer of Col I does not. Indeed, Col I is itself a sex factor: it is readily transferred in mixed cultures from one F$^-$ strain of *E. coli* to another; it can mediate the transfer of Col E1 as well; and **it can mediate chromosomal transfer,** though at low frequency. Col I must therefore be capable of integration.

Col I, like the RTF factor, is transferred with much higher efficiency by cells in which it has been freshly introduced than by cells that have carried it for many generations. Hence the spread in a freshly mixed culture of colicinogenic and sensitive cells is "epidemic."

Some bacteriocinogens thus appear to be capable of assuming **three** distinct forms in the cell: integrated (like prophage or Hfr), autonomous but nonlethal (like F$^+$), and induced (lethally producing bacteriocins, like vegetative phage). Furthermore, there is some evidence for the simultaneous presence of autonomous and integrated colicinogen in the same cell. This pattern could explain several anomalous findings: 1) Hfr(Col E1)$^-$ $\times$ F$^-$(Col E1)$^+$ crosses fail to yield Col E1$^-$ segregants, presumably owing to absence of segregation of bacteriocinogens when in the autonomous state; 2) probably for the same reason zygotes receiving Col E1 from Hfr (Col E1)$^+$ donors transmit it to **all** their progeny, without yielding the segregants expected of chromosomal genes; and 3) Col I is not lost as easily as the autonomous F factor on prolonged storage or on acridine treatment, perhaps because in many cells it exists in an integrated state. Other colicinogens exhibit a variety of episomal patterns, not always identical with either of those described for Col E1 and Col I.

It is tempting to postulate an evolutionary relation between bacteriocinogens and bacteriophages. Bacteriocinogens might be degraded viral genomes that have lost most of their morphogenetic capacities; or they might be an intermediate stage in the evolution of viruses, which is maintained because of the selective advantage it provides for a strain competing with bacteriocin-sensitive neighbors.

Phylogeny of Episomes

Both the RTF and the F agents can be transferred by conjugation to, and can be recovered from, bacterial species that are phylogenetically fairly distant from their usual hosts (the *Escherichia-Salmonella-Shigella* group), and that differ markedly in the base ratio of their DNA (e.g., *Proteus, Serratia,* and *Vibrio*). However, though these episomes can undergo autonomous replication in these organisms there is no evidence that they undergo integration. This finding suggests the possibly widespread distribution of genetic elements that can induce their own transfer by conjugation but cannot be integrated. One example, F_0-lac, was discovered in an otherwise classic *S. typhosa,* and gave this pathogenic organism the diagnostically confusing property of being lac$^+$. Though such an agent probably derives from an episome, it cannot itself be considered an episome for lack of integration; rather, it may bear the same relation to episomes that virulent phages bear to temperate phages.

Cytoplasmic Inheritance: Implications for Higher Organisms

Episomes may well extend beyond bacteria. In the cells of higher organisms a number of cytoplasmic organelles, called **plasmids,** can apparently reproduce only from preexisting identical structures; these include chloroplasts, centro-somes, and mitochondria. Mutations in plasmids exhibit non-Mendelian (cytoplasmic, nonchromosomal) inheritance, in which the progeny inherit only the maternal character (rather than the familiar Mendelian inheritance, with segregation of paternal and maternal characters). The possible generality of such cytoplasmic inheritance has long been a subject of debate. In bacteria episomes now provide a link between chromosomal and cytoplasmic inheritance, and between infection and heredity; and episomes can acquire initially chromosomal genes by recombination. The dividing lines between these types of inheritance are therefore no longer sharp.

It would not be surprising if mammalian cells should also take advantage of the genetic flexibility provided by episomes, e.g., in differentiation. Episomes may also play a role in neoplasia. If so, the viral and the mutational theories of the origin of neoplasias would no longer be mutually exclusive, because a chromosomal mutation can be transferred via an episome. However, it will not be possible to test for episomes in mammals until methods have been developed for the genetic analysis of somatic cells.

PHAGES AS TRANSDUCING AGENTS

As was pointed out in Chapter 7, phage can mediate transfer of bacterial genetic material from one cell to another, and this process of transduction has been extensively used for mapping the bacterial chromosome. We shall consider here only the virological aspects of the phenomenon.

Two types of transduction can be distinguished: generalized transduction, which transfers any bacterial genes, and restricted (specialized) transduction, which can transfer genes from only a very small region of the host chromosome.

Generalized Transduction

This type of transduction was discovered by Zinder and Lederberg during a search for conjugation in *Salmonella.* It was found that a cross of strain L-22 and strain L-2, each carrying a different pair of auxotrophic mutations, produced rare prototrophic recombinants. The process appeared to involve conjugation, since the filtrate of either strain did not transform the other. When, however, L-22 and L-2 were grown together, the bacteria-free filtrate of the mixed culture caused a fresh culture of L-22 also to yield prototrophs. The filtrable agent was resistant to DNase and was soon recognized to be a phage.

The events occurring in the mixed culture are complex (Fig. 24-10). Strain L-22 proved to be lysogenic for a phage, which was named P22; the particles that are occasionally released infect L-2 cells. Most of these cells lyse, releasing regular phage particles and also rare particles containing adventitious bits of L-2 DNA. When the latter type infect L-22 cells

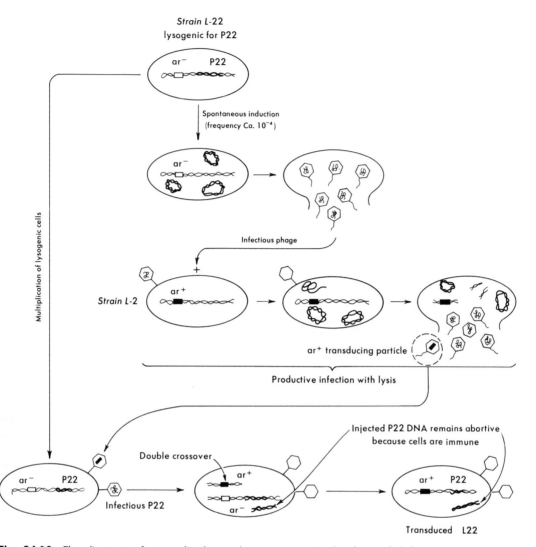

Strain L-22
lysogenic for P22

Fig. 24-10 The discovery of generalized transduction. In a mixed culture of *Sal-monella* strain L-22 (lysogenic for P22, aromatic⁻) and L-2 (nonlysogenic, aromatic⁺) P22, released from L-22 cells by spontaneous induction, infects L-2 cells and lyses most of them. In the lysate, among a large excess of regular infectious P22 particles, there is a small proportion of particles carrying various fragments of L-2 DNA. One such transducing particle, carrying the DNA of the ar⁺ gene of L-2, injects its DNA into an L-22 cell. By a double crossover, this DNA replaces the ar⁻ DNA of the L-22 cell, causing transduction. (The L-22 cells are not lysed by the infectious P22 present because they are lysogenic for P22 and therefore immune.)

they transfer the wild-type alleles of genes for which L-22 is auxotrophic, and proto-trophs are formed by recombination.

The lysogenic character of L-22 was accidental in the experiment, but was instrumental in the discovery of transduction because it provided a source of phage to which L-2 was sensitive. Furthermore, L-22 cells, being lysogenic, were immune to the phage released from L-2 cells, although they permitted injection of its DNA; hence they could accept the L-2 DNA present in occasional phage particles without being destroyed by the large excess of regular infectious phage particles.

Distribution and Scope

Transduction can apparently occur for any markers of the donor bacterium. Only closely linked markers, however, can be **cotransduced** by the same phage particle (Ch. 7), because the piece of bacterial DNA carried by a phage must fit inside the phage head and therefore is similar in size to the phage DNA (i.e., ca. 1 to 2% of the bacterial DNA).

In addition to Salmonella, transduction has been reported with different phages for genera as varied as *Escherichia, Shigella, Pseudomonas, Staphylococcus, Bacillus,* and *Proteus.* Phage P1 is now widely used in genetic studies on *Salmonella, E. coli,* and *Shigella.* Transduction is usually carried out with a high-titer phage preparation obtained from the donor strain **either by lytic infection or by induction of lysogenic cells.** Any remaining viable bacteria are killed by addition of chloroform. With a recipient culture infected at multiplicity of about 5, the frequency of transduction of a given character ranges from 10^{-5} to 10^{-8} per cell. With *E. coli* the linkage groups obtained by transduction and by conjugation are in gratifying agreement.

Mechanism of Generalized Transduction: Role of Defective Phage

Transducing particles are ordinarily defective, but this feature was not immediately clear after the discovery of transduction. Since the recipient cells were infected at high multiplicity, in order to promote a good yield of transductants, those cells that received a transducing phage particle also received several regular particles and thus usually became lysogenic. The study of phage structure, however, led eventually to the realization that a phage cannot carry into the cell both its own DNA and a large piece of foreign DNA. (For instance, P1 DNA, of M.W. ca. 60×10^6, can transduce the entire prophage λ of M.W. 30×10^6, together with adjacent gal markers, or can even transduce two λ prophages when the donor cells are doubly lysogenic.)

The defectiveness of the transducing particles was demonstrated by Luria by the simple device of using a low over-all multiplicity of infection: then none of the transduced cells were lysogenic. Indeed, the bulk of the transductants contained no detectable phage genes, suggesting that in generalized transducing phages the defective phage component either was absent or had a very low probability of integration.

The composition of the transducing particles has been clarified by the following physical studies. 1) In a CsCl gradient at equilibrium transducing particles form a band that coincides with that of the infectious particles; hence the two types of particles have the same DNA/protein ratio and thus the same amount of DNA (since the amount of protein per particle does not seem to vary). 2) After cells were grown in a medium containing both 5-bromouracil (which makes DNA heavy) and nonradioactive phosphate they were transferred to a medium containing thymine and $^{32}PO_4$, and were immediately infected with a virulent mutant of P1 (which blocks the synthesis of bacterial DNA after infection). The transducing particles among the progeny were found to have heavy, nonradioactive DNA; thus they contain only cellular DNA, synthesized before infection. It follows that these transducing particles contain DNA derived from the host cell, **adventitiously enclosed** in the phage head, and without any phage DNA. It seems likely that this is true for most phages causing generalized transduction.

With separated transducing particles, obtained as in experiment 2, described above, the extracted DNA is found to be a single piece of rather uniform length (which in P1 corresponds to about 2% of the *E. coli* chromosome). This finding explains why generalized transduction is well suited for mapping bacterial genetic markers.

We do not know how a regular fragment of host DNA, of the same size as phage DNA, is cut out at random. One possibility is that during phage assembly the cellular DNA may fold and become enclosed in the capsid of the phage head, the unenclosed segments then being destroyed by nucleases.

Complete and Abortive Transduction (Fig. 24-11)

We call **complete** the transduction that causes the fragment of the donor bacterial chromosome brought in by the phage (the **exogenote**) to be inserted, by recombination, into the chromosome of the recipient cell. The transductants then transmit the transduced markers regularly to all their progeny. In **abortive** transduction, in contrast, the exogenotic fragments are introduced into the cell but for unknown reasons they do not become inserted into the bacterial chromosome. The exogenote behaves in the cell like an abortive prophage: it does not replicate and is transmitted unilinearly from a cell to only one of its daughters. However, it expresses the function of its genes.

Recognition of abortive transduction is facilitated when genes of the exogenote specify the synthesis of enzymes required for growth on a selective medium, for though unilinear inheritance deprives one daughter cell, at each division, of the exogenote, this cell receives a normal complement of any enzyme specified by the exogenote. The cell lineage can thus go on dividing for a limited number of times until the initial dowry of enzyme received from the progenitor carrying the exogenote is exhausted. Meanwhile, the cell line that inherits the exogenote creates a similar abortive clone at each generation. In this way abortive transductants for a prototrophic gene can make microcolonies on minimal medium, which are detectable only with magnification.

The numbers of microcolonies formed reveal that abortive transduction is several times as frequent as the corresponding complete transduction; furthermore, the abortive exogenote, in spite of its indefinite survival, never becomes incorporated in the host genome. Hence the exogenote that becomes incorporated in the bacterial chromosome probably has some special, yet unidentified, characteristic.

Abortive transduction is a useful tool in **complementation tests** for determining whether or not two auxotrophic mutations affecting the same character are allelic (i.e., located in the same gene; Ch. 8). For this purpose one of the mutants is used as donor and the other as recipient in a transduction experiment; the cells are plated on minimal medium. The formation of large prototrophic colonies (complete transduction) by recombination between the two mutations occurs whether or not they are allelic. In contrast, the additional formation of microcolonies (abortive transduction) indicates that the two mutations are not allelic: the mutation of the exogenote complements that of the recipient cell (see, however, Ch. 8, Intragenic complementation).

Specialized Transduction

Low-Frequency Transduction

The Lederbergs discovered that phage λ can give rise to transduction in quite a different manner. It transfers only a restricted group of genes (the gal region), which has been shown by conjugation mapping to be located near the site of insertion of the prophage. Moreover, **restricted transduction is possible only with lysates produced by induction of prophage,** and not (in contrast to generalized transduction) with lysates produced by lytic infection. These features suggest that the transduced genes are incorporated into the phage genome while it is a prophage.

Thus in an *E. coli* strain lysogenic for λ the prophage will undergo exchange, in an occasional cell, with the nearby gal segment of the bacterial DNA (Fig. 24-12). On induction such a cell yields particles, defective as phage, that transduce gal genes. These particles, called λ**dg** (for λ-defective-gal), constitute a minute fraction of the particles in the lysate, which is called a **low-frequency-transduction** (LFT) lysate.

High-Frequency Transduction

In a λ-sensitive culture exposed to such an LFT lysate a rare cell will receive the DNA of a λdg particle, and the integration of this material yields a clone of cells that are **heterogenotes** for gal (i.e., gal$^-$/λdg gal$^+$, when the phage is from a gal$^+$ donor and the recipient

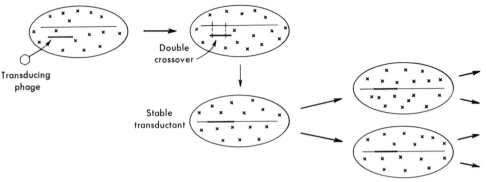

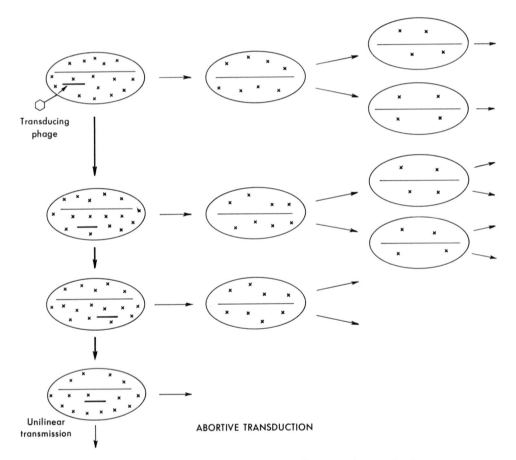

Fig. 24-11 Complete and abortive transduction. In complete transduction the fragment of bacterial DNA (exogenote) introduced by the transducing phage (heavy line) becomes inserted in the DNA of the recipient bacterium (thin line). In abortive transduction the exogenote is not integrated and is transmitted unilinearly (gray arrow). A gene contained in the exogenote makes a cytoplasmic product (indicated by x), whether integration occurs or not. In abortive transduction the gene product is transmitted to both daughter cells, but in those that do not receive the exogenote it is progressively diluted out as cell multiplication proceeds.

Fig. 24-12 Possible mechanism of formation of defective transducing λdg prophage by two crossovers between the prophage DNA (solid line) and the bacterial genome (dashed line). In the exchange the prophage loses a large fraction of its own genetic information and becomes defective.

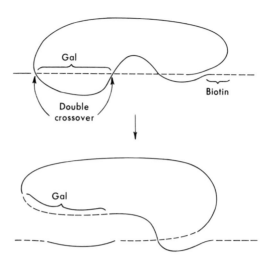

The length of the exchanged segment may vary, yielding particles that transduce different numbers of genes of the gal operon. Moreover, the amount of cellular DNA acquired does not exactly compensate for the amount of phage DNA lost; hence different HFT clones of λdg differ in buoyant density in CsCl (the amount of protein per particle apparently being constant).

Exchange could also occur by a single crossover, as in Fig. 24-7, but outside the regular area of homology. Detached ring would contain both bacterial and phage DNA, in different amounts at each occurrence.

is gal⁻). These cells are usually doubly lysogenic (when formed by high-multiplicity infection), containing regular λ as a second prophage. When such cells are induced the regular λ genome acts as helper to provide the functions of genes missing in λdg; and the cells yield a **high-frequency-transduction** (HFT) lysate, in which about half the particles are λdg and half are derived from the helper phage. Cells can also be lysogenized by λdg alone, but then they require superinfection by regular λ to produce an HFT lysate (Fig. 24-13). The HFT lysate, on lysogenizing sensitive cells, will yield heterogenotes that again will form an HFT lysate on induction.

The act of transduction by the lysate is thus identical in LFT and HFT. LFT and HFT lysate differ, however, both in the **proportions** and **kinds** of transducing particles they contain. In LFT lysates the transducing particles are a minute proportion and are of different types, since they have arisen from many independent exchanges between prophage and bacterial DNA (Fig. 24-12). In HFT lysates, in contrast, the transducing particles are in high proportion and are uniform, both in genetic constitution and in buoyant density, because they belong to the same clone.

Genetic Changes in Heterogenotes. Heterogenotes obtained by transduction mostly breed true, with unchanged characteristics. A small

proportion of the cells, however, show genetic changes of the following types (Fig. 24-13B).

1) **Loss of the λdg.** This loss is revealed by the segregation in about 1 in 10³ cells of completely stable haploid cells with the old gal genes (i.e., those present in the original sensitive cells before their lysogenization by λdg). Since the defective prophage and the carried gal genes are lost together, they must be attached together in the heterogenote.

2) **Replacement of the original bacterial gal genes by those carried by λdg.** This rarer phenomenon is revealed by the segregation of stable bacterial strains with the new gal genes (i.e., those present in λdg). The stability, i.e., lack of segregation indicated by (1) above, shows that the new genes are no longer associated with λdg. The substitution probably occurs by exchange of a segment between the prophage-carried gal region and the homologous part of the bacterial chromosome, followed by loss of the prophage. The transduced genes can no longer be transduced at high frequency, but must be recaptured by a λ prophage, i.e., one would again have low-frequency transduction.

Defectiveness of λdg. The defectiveness of these transducing particles is demonstrated, as with generalized transducing phage, by working at multiplicities of infection low enough to produce only singly infected cells. The resulting transductant clones are defectively lysogenic: they exhibit immunity and lyse upon induction, but they do not yield infectious particles. When transduction is carried out at such a low multiplicity its efficiency per λdg phage is reduced

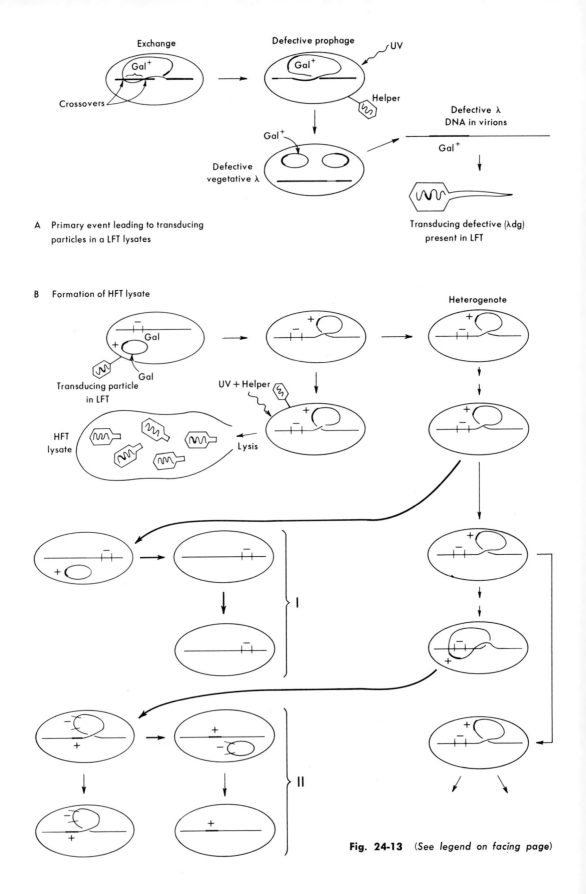

A   Primary event leading to transducing particles in a LFT lysates

B   Formation of HFT lysate

Fig. 24-13 (See legend on facing page)

30-fold, presumably because the infecting, defective DNA cannot multiply and so the probability of its integration decreases (see above, Establishment of the lysogenic state). As already noted, transductants formed at high multiplicity of infection mask the defectiveness because they are mostly doubly lysogenic, containing a regular prophage as well as the transducing phage.

Nondefective Transducing Phage. Though most transducing phages are defective, strains of nondefective HFT phage have been detected. Thus, λ can transduce the biotin locus (at the other side of the prophage with respect to gal, Fig. 24-12) and remain infectious. Similarly, a transducing but infectious strain of P1 has been isolated that confers chloramphenicol resistance on bacterial strains that it lysogenizes. It appears to have arisen by recombination with the resistance-transfer episome (RTF). Possibly the added DNA required in these cases is small and could fit in the phage head together with the whole of the phage DNA; but conservation of phage infectivity may be due to some more profound reason which escapes detection. Whatever the mechanism, such modified infectious phages are indistinguishable, except in their history, from **converting phages** (see above, Phage conversion), and they suggest that the latter, which modify the host phenotype in various ways, have derived the responsible genes from unknown previous bacterial hosts.

Specialized Transduction by a Generalized Transducing Phage. We have seen above that phage P1 carries out generalized transduction by enclosing a block of DNA of bacterial origin in the phage coat. However, in a rare P1 transducing particle the DNA will be a product of recombination between phage and host, as in specialized transduction.

Thus from P1 lysates of a lac+ strain of *E. coli* a defective strain called P1dl (analogous to λdg) has been recovered, in which lac genes are attached to phage genes. On infecting a lac⁻ point mutant of *E. coli* P1dl undergoes genetic exchange in the lac region, yielding the nonlysogenic, stable lac+ transductants typical of generalized transduction. In contrast, when these particles infect a cell that has no lac region (e.g., *E. coli* mutants with a lac deletion, or the lac⁻ species *Shigella dysenteriae*), the lac+ transductants that they yield can be shown to be lac⁻/P1dl-lac+ heterogenotes, as in specialized transduction: they yield HFT lysates for P1dl, and they show frequent segregation of lac⁻ cells. Apparently when no region of strong homology is present the weak homology between P1 DNA and bacterial DNA leads to integration; but when a bacterial lac region is present its much stronger homology with the lac segment of P1dl provides the favored sites of synapsis and recombination. P1dl thus resembles F'-lac (see above, Integration of episomes) in interacting differently with recipients that do or do not possess a lac region.

The nature of the transductants formed thus depends not only on the composition of the transducing particles (Table 24-1), but also on the degree of homology between the bacterial DNA and the components of the exogenote DNA.

Range of Transducing Phage

Transducing phages vary widely in defectiveness. Some biotin-transducing λ strains, as noted, are not defective; and λdg of independent isolates are defective to a varying extent, since they have lost a variable number of phage markers—although all lysogenize,

Fig. 24-13 Specialized transduction. **A.** LFT lysate. In rare cells of a culture lysogenic for λ a piece of prophage DNA is exchanged for the gal segment of the bacterial DNA, thus generating a defective transducing prophage. On induction such a cell yields transducing particles (λdg), presumably with the help of regular λ virions produced in the culture. **B.** HFT lysate. Infection by a λdg particle causes the formation of a heterogenote, containing both the gal⁻ gene preexisting in the bacterium and the gal+ introduced by λdg. When the cells of a clone deriving from such a heterogenote are induced, and are infected with regular λ as helper phage, they lyse and produce the HFT lysate.

Rarely the heterogenote segregates, by loss of the prophage, a nonlysogenic cell with the original gal⁻ gene (I); even more rarely it segregates, by exchange, a nonlysogenic cell with the gal+ gene of the transducing prophage (II).

TABLE 24-1. COMPARISON OF TRANSDUCING PHAGES

	Specialized	Generalized
	Example: *E. coli* K12 phage λdg	Example: *Salmonella* phage P22
Genes transduced	Only gal	Any selectable marker
Localization of prophage	Locus closely linked to gal	Unknown
Source of transducing phage	Induction only	Induction or lytic infection
Capacity of the transducing particles to produce infectious viral progeny	Defective (multiply with helper)	No multiplication
Characteristics of the clones of transduced cells	Unstable heterogenotes, segregating stable haploids	Stable haploids
Efficiency of transduction per phage particle	LFT 10^{-6} (from haploid) to HFT 10^{-1} (from heterogenote)	10^{-5} to 10^{-6}

produce immunity, and in the presence of a helper phage give rise to a viral progeny. Particles of P1dl have been observed with even a wider range of defectiveness: some can lysogenize and can cause lysis on induction, but without yielding infectious particles; some do not cause lysis; some do not cause immunity; and some give rise to prophages that can no longer detach but are recognizable by rescuing their genes by recombination.

The most defective of these specialized transducing particles may be similar in structure to those causing generalized transduction. Thus there is an almost uninterrupted spectrum between DNA molecules with completely viral specificity and those with exclusively bacterial specificity, without a clear demarcation between the two. When much of the DNA is viral the phage DNA tends to interact with the bacterial chromosome at a site specified by the homology between bacterial and viral DNA; when most of the DNA is bacterial the interaction occurs at sites specified by the homology of the transduced bacterial DNA and the DNA present in the cell. The demarcation between "viral" and "bacterial" properties is further confused by the converting phages, which have bacterial functions although they are not known to carry bacterial genes, and by the very similar infectious transducing phages, which carry genes of known bacterial origin. Finally, in abortive transduction a bacterial fragment remains nonreplicating and nonintegrating in the cell.

The distinction between phage genes and bacterial genes is thus blurred, in respect to both function (as in conversion) and heredity (as in defective lysogenization). It is conceivable that much of the heredity of bacteria is of viral origin, since many unknown defective proviruses may exist in Nature; and on the other hand, phages may be fragments of bacterial DNA that have acquired the capacity for independent reproduction. Indeed, with a history of mutual interaction of viruses and bacteria in the course of evolution, the question of sharply distinguishing their genes may be meaningless except for recent, observed exchanges.

SELECTED REFERENCES

Books and Review Articles

ARBER, W. Bacteriophage lysogeny. *Symp. Soc. Gen. Microbiol. 13* (1963).

CAMPBELL, A. Episomes. *Advances Genet. 11*:101 (1962).

DATTA, N. Infectious drug resistance. *Brit. M. Bull. 21*:260 (1965).

LWOFF, A. Lysogeny. *Bact. Rev. 17*:269 (1953).

SCAIFE, J. Episomes. *Ann. Rev. Microbiol.* (1967).

STENT, G. *Molecular Biology of Bacterial Viruses.* Freeman, San Francisco, 1963.

WATANABE, T. Infective heredity of multiple drug resistance in bacteria. *Bact. Rev. 27*:87 (1963).

Specific Articles

BERTANI, G., and SIX, E. Inheritance of prophage P2 in bacterial crosses. *Virology 6*:357 (1958).

CAMPBELL, A. Segregants from lysogenic heterogenotes carrying recombinant λ prophages. *Virology 20*:344 (1963).

COWIE, D. B., and MCCARTHY, B. J. Homology between bacteriophage λ DNA and *E. coli* DNA. *Proc. Nat. Acad. Sc. 50*:537 (1963).

FISCHER-FANTUZZI, L., and CALEF, E. A type of λ prophage unable to confer immunity. *Virology 23*:209 (1964).

GREEN, M. H. Complementarity between lambda (λ) phage and *Escherichia coli. Proc. Nat. Acad. Sc. 50*:1177 (1963).

HERSHEY, A. D., BURGI, E., and INGRAHAM, L. Cohesion of DNA molecules isolated from phage lambda. *Proc. Nat. Acad. Sc. 49*:748 (1963).

KAISER, A. D., and JACOB, F. Recombination between related temperate bacteriophages and the genetic control of immunity and prophage localization. *Virology 4*:509 (1957).

LURIA, S. E., FRASER, D. K., ADAMS, J. N., and BURROWS, J. W. Lysogenization, transduction and genetic recombination in bacteria. *Cold Spring Harbor Symp. Quant. Biol. 23*:71 (1958).

LWOFF, A., SIMINOVITCH, L., and KJELDGAARD, N. Induction de la production de bacteriophages chez une bacterie lysogène. *Ann. Inst. Pasteur 79*:815 (1950).

MORSE, M. L., LEDERBERG, E. M., and LEDERBERG, J. Transduction in *Escherichia coli* K-12. *Genetics 41*:142 (1956).

NOMURA, M. Mode of action of colicines. *Cold Spring Harbor Symp. Quant. Biol. 28*:315 (1963).

PTASHNE, M. The detachment and maturation of conserved lambda prophage DNA. *J. Molec. Biol. 11*:90 (1965).

PTASHNE, M. Isolation of the λ phage repressor. *Proc. Nat. Acad. Sc. 57*:306 (1967).

SLY, W. S., ECHOLS, H., and ADLER, J. Control of viral messenger RNA after lambda phage infection and induction. *Proc. Nat. Acad. Sc. 53*:378 (1965).

TAYLOR, A. L. Bacteriophage-induced mutation in *Escherichia coli. Proc. Nat. Acad. Sc. 50*:1043 (1963).

WEISSBACH, A., and KORN, D. The effect of lysogenic induction on the deoxyribonucleases of *Escherichia coli* K-12 λ. *J. Biol. Chem. 5*:237, PC3312 (1962).

YARMOLINSKY, M. B., and WEISMEYER, H. Regulation by coliphage lambda of the expression of the capacity to synthesize a sequence of host enzymes. *Proc. Nat. Acad. Sc. 46*:1626 (1960).

MULTIPLICATION

The multiplication of animal viruses follows the pattern of bacteriophage multiplication described in the preceding two chapters, but with differences related to the constitution of the viruses and of their host cells. Some animal viruses, for instance, contain RNA, whose replication differs somewhat from that of DNA. (RNA-containing phages, which have not been discussed before, will accordingly also be dealt with in this chapter.) Moreover, animal viruses differ from bacteriophages in their interaction with the surface of the host cells (which do not have rigid walls) and in the mechanism of release of their nucleic acid in the cell. These differences, however, tend to affect the details rather than the basic events.

Like bacteriophages, animal viruses can be differentiated into two main classes: **virulent** viruses, which correspond to the virulent bacteriophages, and **moderate** viruses, which resemble temperate bacteriophages in being able to establish stable complexes with the host

cells. These complexes, however, appear to differ from lysogenic cells, and so the term temperate is reserved for bacteriophages that can lysogenize. The differentiation between virulent and moderate animal viruses is less sharp than that between virulent and temperate bacteriophages: there are different degrees of virulence, and it is difficult to decide whether some viruses are virulent or moderate.

As a background for understanding the results obtained in experimental work with animal viruses we shall first review the salient features of the host cells, especially in cultures.

Host Cells for Animal Viruses

The Chick Embryo

Chick embryos have contributed in an important way to the development of virology by providing conveniently a variety of cell types susceptible to many viruses. Although

Fig. 25-1 The chicken embryo (10 to 12 days old) and routes of inoculation. For chorioallantoic membrane inoculation a hole is first drilled through the egg shell and shell membrane; the shell over the air sac is then perforated, causing air to enter between the shell membrane and the chorioallantoic membrane and then creating an artificial air sac, where the sample is deposited. The sample comes in contact with the chorionic epithelium. Yolk sac inoculation is usually carried out in younger (6-day-old) embryos, in which the yolk sac is larger.

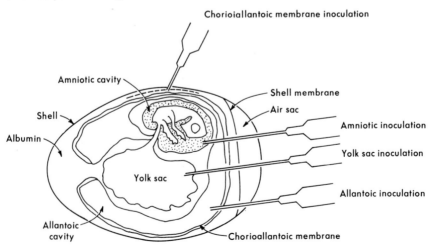

chick embryos are now being increasingly replaced by tissue cultures, they are still valuable for a variety of purposes.

Various cell types can be reached by inoculating the chick embryo by different routes (Fig. 25-1): the chorionic epithelium of the chorionic membrane; the allantoic epithelium lining the allantoic cavity; the amniotic epithelium lining the amniotic cavity; the cells of the yolk sac; the cells of the embryonic body. The use of these various cells will be discussed in chapters dealing with individual viruses.

Animal Cell Cultures

The recent development of improved methods for cultivating animal cells in vitro has contributed enormously to the progress of animal virology. In fact, cultures of animal cells are so similar to cultures of microorganisms that they have made possible quantitative technics for studying animal viruses comparable to those used for bacteriophages. Animal cells in culture, however, are much less stable, both in transferability and in genetic properties, than most bacteria. Thus primary cultures of the separated cells of a tissue may die out on repeated secondary cultivation or may give rise to altered but still diploid cell **strains**. These, in turn, will also eventually die out unless they give rise to more radically altered but permanent cell **lines**. These several types of cultures are all valuable for studies in virology as well as in cell physiology and genetics; their origin and properties will now be described.

Primary and Secondary Cultures. To propagate separated animal cells a tissue fragment is first dispersed into its constituent cells, usually with the aid of **trypsin**. After removal of the trypsin the suspension is placed in a flat-bottomed glass or plastic container (a Petri dish, bottle, or test tube), together with a liquid medium containing required ions at isosmotic concentration, a number of amino acids and vitamins, and an animal serum in a proportion varying from a few per cent to 50%. A widely used medium devised by Eagle is given as an example in Table 25-1. Bicarbonate is commonly used as a buffer,

TABLE 25-1. COMPOSITION OF EAGLE'S MEDIUM FOR CULTIVATION OF ANIMAL CELLS IN VITRO

	Concentration	
	Mg/1000 ml	Approx. equiv. in Mmoles
L-Arginine	17·4	0·1
L-Cystine	6·0	0·05
L-Histidine	3·2	0·02
L-Isoleucine	26·2	0·2
L-Leucine	13·1	0·1
L-Lysine	18·2	0·1
L-Methionine	7·5	0·05
L-Phenylalanine	8·3	0·05
L-Threonine	11·9	0·1
L-Tryptophan	2·0	0·01
L-Tyrosine	18·0	0·1
L-Valine	11·7	0·1
L-Glutamine	146·0	1·0
Choline	1·0	
Nicotinic acid	1·0	
Pantothenic acid	1·0	
Pyridoxal	1·0	
Riboflavin	0·1	
Thiamine	1·0	
i-Inositol	1·0	
Biotin	1·0	
Folic acid	1·0	
Glucose	2000·0	
NaCl	8000·0	
KCl	400·0	
CaCl$_2$	140·0	
MgSO$_4$ · 7H$_2$O	100·0	
MgCl$_2$ · 6H$_2$O	100·0	
Na$_2$HPO$_4$ · 2H$_2$O	60·0	
KH$_2$PO$_4$	60·0	
NaHCO$_3$	350·0	
Phenol red	20·0	
Penicillin	0·50	

From J. Paul. Cell and Tissue Culture, 2nd ed., p. 95. Williams & Wilkins, Baltimore, 1960.

in equilibrium with CO_2 in the air above the medium. After a variable lag the cells attach and spread on the bottom of the container and then start dividing mitotically, giving rise to a **primary culture.**

In the primary cultures the cells retain some of the characteristics of the tissue from which they derived, and are mainly of two types: thin and elongated (**fibroblast-like**), or polygonal and tending to form sheets (**epithelium-like**). In addition, certain cells have a roundish outline and resemble epithelial cells but do not form sheets (**epithelioid** cells). The cells multiply to cover the bottom of the container with a continuous but thin layer, often one cell thick (**monolayer**); if they are fibroblastic they are **regularly oriented** parallel to each other. Primary cell cultures obtained from **cancerous tissues** usually differ from those of normal cells in two ways: they tend to form **thick layers**, and the cells are **randomly oriented.**

The cells of primary cultures can be detached from the vessel wall by either trypsin or the chelating agent EDTA, and can then be used to initiate new **secondary** cultures. From a confluent primary culture of normal cells usually only two subcultures are started. A subdivision into a larger number of subcultures is often unsuccessful: apparently for survival and multiplication of recently isolated cells the medium must contain adequate concentrations of unknown factors produced by the cells themselves. Cancer cells usually withstand a much greater dilution than normal cells.

Cell Strains and Cell Lines. Cells from primary cultures can often be transferred serially a number of times (Fig. 25-2). This process usually causes a selection for some cell type, which becomes predominant. The cells may then continue to multiply at a constant rate over many successive transfers, and the primary culture is said to have originated a **cell strain** (often called a diploid cell strain). The transferability of cell strains is limited: for instance, with cultures of human cells the growth rate declines after about 50 transfers, and the cells appear morphologically altered. Soon multiplication ceases and the life of the strain comes to an end. Although it is not known why strains die, two hypotheses are generally considered: either the cells have a limited inherent potential life span in terms of number of cell generations, characteristic for certain cells and certain organisms; or imperfect conditions of cultivation cause the accumulation of damages, which finally become lethal.

During the multiplication of a cell strain, some

Fig. 25-2 Diagram representing the multiplication of cultures of cells derived from normal tissues. The primary culture gives rise to a cell **strain**, whose cells grow actively for many cell generations; then growth declines and finally the culture stops growing and dies. During the multiplication of the cell strain altered cells may be produced, which continue to grow indefinitely and originate a cell **line**. The cumulative number of cells is calculated as if all cells derived from the original culture had been kept at every transfer. (Modified from L. Hayflick. *Analytic Cell Culture.* National Cancer Institute Monograph, No. 7, p. 63. 1962.)

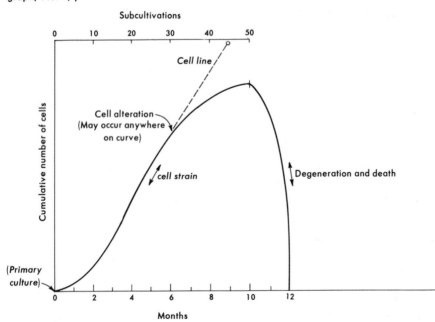

cells become altered: they acquire a different morphology, grow faster and often become neoplastic (i.e., they produce a cancer if transplanted into animals). The clone derived from one such cell, in contrast to the cell strain in which it originated, **has unlimited life,** and is designated a **cell line.** The cause of such spontaneous transformation during cultivation is unknown. Cell lines can be obtained also directly from the cultivation of neoplastic tissue or can be generated from normal primary cultures or cell strains by infection with oncogenic viruses.

During repeated serial transfers the composition of cell lines undergoes extensive further change, owing to the emergence and selection of variants. In this process greatly altered cells are often encountered which show little adhesion to the bottom of the container; they can be easily propagated in suspension by using a medium poor in divalent ions and stirring constantly. Such **suspension cultures** are very useful for experimental virology.

Although cell strains and lines change continually on repeated cultivation, by preserving cells in the frozen state it is possible to work with cells of constant characteristics. For this purpose large batches of cells are mixed with glycerol or dimethylsulfoxide and subdivided in a number of ampules, which are then sealed and frozen, the temperature being lowered in a programmed way. The additives allow the cells to survive freezing. The frozen cells can be maintained in liquid nitrogen for years with unchanged characteristics; when the ampules are thawed most of the cells are viable and can initiate new cultures.

Cloning of Animal Cells. Cell clones can be obtained from most cell strains or lines by transferring cells to a new culture at a very high dilution. The proportion of cells that survive and give rise to colonies (**efficiency of plating**) under these conditions is usually small. Puck showed that the efficiency of plating can be greatly increased if the cells are mixed with a larger number of similar cells made incapable of multiplication by a large dose of X-ray. The X-rayed cells in a sparse **feeder layer** are still metabolically active and supply factors that enable the unirradiated cells to survive and multiply. The efficiency of plating can also be increased by Earle's

technic of introducing individual cells into very small volumes of medium, as in sealed capillary tubes or in small drops of medium surrounded by paraffin oil. The cell-produced factors thus reach an adequate concentration, permitting the survival and multiplication of the cell without a feeder layer.

The Karyotype of Cultured Cells

The numbers and types of chromosomes (the karyotype) present in cultured cells have been actively studied, especially since it became clear that karyotype anomalies of the body's cells are associated with certain human diseases. In the study of cell cultures the karyotype is an indication of the degree of abnormality the cells have attained during their cultivation.

In **young cell strains** most cells tend to maintain the chromosome number characteristic of the animal, i.e., they are **diploid** ($2n$). If the individual chromosomes are recognizable by their distinctive features, it can usually be ascertained that at this stage the types of chromosomes are also normal, and the cells are said to be **euploid.** The cells of **older strains** and cell **lines,** in contrast, always contain deviations from the euploid chromosome number and distribution (**aneuploid cells**).

The number of chromosomes may be different from diploid (**heteroploid**), either higher (usually between $3n$ and $4n$—**hypertriploid**) or lower (**hypodiploid**). In some cases the number of chromosomes is $2n$, but the distribution of chromosome types is abnormal; for example, a chromosome of a pair may be missing and replaced by an extra chromosome of another pair (**quasidiploid cells**). In addition, **chromosomal aberrations** (e.g., translocations and deletions) often involve highly characteristic morphological abnormalities in individual chromosomes, which are useful as **markers** for cell identification.

Although in some cell lines most cells are diploid, the majority of cell lines are constituted of heteroploid, especially hypertriploid cells. Individual lines are heterogeneous, with various cells containing different numbers of chromosomes. The most frequent (modal) number remains constant if the cells are grown under a constant set of conditions, but changing the conditions often results in selection of a type with a different modal number. Heteroploid cultures show a great deal of variability, probably accounted for by the great variety of karyotypes they continually produce by unequal segregation of chromosomes at mitosis.

Cell Hybridization. For special purposes, such as studies of tumor induction by viruses, it would be desirable to study the genetic properties of cultured animal cells. This possibility long seemed remote, because tissue culture cells could not be induced to mate with each other. Recently, however, both Barski and Ephrussi have demonstrated spontaneous mating of cultured animal cells, resulting in cytoplasmic and nuclear fusion; and Harris has obtained hybridization at high frequency of many kinds of cells by infecting them with a fusion-promoting virus that does not damage the cells (a paramyxovirus). The hybrid cells are clearly recognizable cytologically because they contain the marker chromosomes or biochemical markers present in the two cells that fused. These cells multiply well, but their mitosis is often irregular and gives rise to cells with fewer and fewer chromosomes, producing a large number of possible karyotypes.

This process holds much promise for genetic work with cultured cells.

Use of Cell Strains and Cell Lines in Virology

Every type of animal cell culture has found application in virology. The choice of species and tissue of origin and type of culture (primary, cell strains, or cell lines) depends on the virus and the experimental objectives. The systems used for the individual viral families will be given in the appropriate chapters. The origin and the characteristics of the most widely used cell lines are summarized in Table 25-2.

In the **production of viral vaccines** for human use the permanent cell **lines** are not employed, even though they can be grown in large amounts. The reason is the fear that the viruses propagated in them may acquire genetic determinants of malignancy, since these cell lines roughly resemble malignant cells in their cultural pattern and their aneuploidy.

Thus, only primary cultures are used; on the other hand, these often contain a variety of latent viruses which may also constitute a health hazard.

Infection

Infection as a Function of the Nucleic Acid

That cells of higher organisms can be infected by naked viral nucleic acid was first shown for tobacco mosaic virus RNA by Gierer and Schramm. This discovery was soon generalized to show that the highly purified RNA or DNA of many animal viruses is infectious and gives rise to synthesis of normal virions. In conjunction with the Hershey and Chase experiment with bacteriophage (Ch. 23, Separation of nucleic acid from coat), this result provided proof for the exclusive genetic role of the viral nucleic acid.

Infectious nucleic acid has been isolated, by deproteinization with phenol or other agents, from viruses of various types, provided their nucleic acid molecule is small (e.g., picornaviruses and arboviruses among the RNA viruses, and polyoma and papilloma viruses among the DNA viruses). Larger nucleic acids lack infectivity either because they are broken during extraction or because they are attacked by nucleases during their penetration into the cells. The RNA of enveloped helical viruses (e.g., myxoviruses) cannot be regularly extracted in infectious form, in spite of its small size, for reasons that are not yet known.

There are several important differences between infections by nucleic acid and by virions.

1) **The efficiency of infection with the nucleic acid is much lower,** showing that the viral coat plays an important role in getting the intact nucleic acid into the cell. In ordinary media the efficiency of infection of cell cultures by viral nucleic acids is 10^{-6} to 10^{-8} that of the corresponding virions. It increases by several orders of magnitude in hypertonic solutions (e.g., 1 M NaCl or 2 M Na_2SO_4)

TABLE 25-2. CELL LINES IN COMMON USE IN VIROLOGY: ALL EXCEPT THE LAST TWO WERE CERTIFIED BY THE CELL CULTURE COLLECTION COMMITTEE IN 1964 AND ARE MAINTAINED FROZEN BY THE AMERICAN TYPE TISSUE CULTURE COLLECTION

Name of cell line	Species of origin	Tissue of origin	Morphology*	Ploidy†	Karyology	
					Modal No.	Markers
NCTC, clone 929	Mouse	Connective	FB-L	Aneu	66	Yes
HeLa	Human	Carcinoma, cervix	EP-L	Aneu	79	
Detroit-6	Human	Sternal bone marrow	EP-L	Aneu	64	
Minnesota-EE	Human	Esophageal epithelium	EP-L	Aneu	67	Yes
L-132	Human	Embryonic lung	EP-L	Aneu	71	
Intestine 407	Human	Embryonic intestine	EP-L	Aneu	76	
LLC-MK$_2$	Monkey‡	Kidney	EP-L	Aneu	70	
CCRF S-180 II	Mouse	Sarcoma 180	FB-L	Aneu	86	Yes
NCTC, clone 2472	Mouse	Connective tissue	FB-L	Aneu	52	Yes
NCTC, clone 2555	Mouse	Connective tissue	FB-L	Aneu	56	Yes
Chang liver	Human	Liver	EP-L	Aneu	70	
B14-FAF-G3	Ch. hamster§	Peritoneal cells	FB-L	Quasidi	22	
HaK	Syr. hamster‖	Kidney	EP-L	Aneu	57	
Don	Ch. hamster§	Lung	FB-L	Eu	22	
KB	Human	Carcinoma, oral	EP-L	Aneu	77	
Detroit-98	Human	Sternal bone marrow	EP-L	Aneu	63	
AV$_3$	Human	Amnion	EP-L	Aneu	74	
Hep-2	Human	Carcinoma, larynx	EP-L	Aneu	76	Yes
J-111	Human	Peripheral blood #	EP-L	Aneu	111	Yes
WISH	Human	Amnion	EP-L	Aneu	74, 75	
BHK	Hamster	Kidney	FB-L	Eu		
BS-C-1	Monkey**	Kidney	EP-L	Hypodip?		

* *FB-L, fibroblast-like; EP-L, epithelium-like.*
† *Aneu, aneuploid; Di, diploid; Eu, euploid.*
‡ Macaca mulatta.
§ Cricetulus griseus.
‖ Mesocricetus auratus.
Monocytic leukemia.
** Cercopithecus aethiops.

or in the presence of basic proteins (e.g., protamine or histone). These additions appear to act by protecting the nucleic acid against nucleases, by increasing its uptake by the cells (perhaps through promoting phagocytosis), and by affecting its over-all charge and secondary structure. Even under the most favorable conditions, however, the efficiency of infection is less than 1% that of the corresponding virions.

2) **The host range is much wider with nucleic acids.** Many animal cells resistant to a given virus can be infected by its nucleic acid. For instance, chicken cells, which are resistant to poliovirus, are susceptible to its RNA; only a single cycle of viral multiplication, however, takes place because these cells cannot be infected by the progeny virions. This result shows that the limitation in host range of a given virus often derives from the restraints imposed by its interaction with the cell surface, rather than from biosynthetic differences of the cells.

3) **Infectious nucleic acid can be extracted even from heat-inactivated viruses,** in which the protein of the capsid has been denatured; the nucleic acid can withstand much higher temperatures than the protein.

4) Finally, **the infectivity of nucleic acid is unaffected by virus-specific antibodies,** which

suggests that this form of a virus could be an effective infectious agent, even in the presence of immunity. However, nucleases in body fluids probably greatly limit its role, because a single complete break in a molecule abolishes its infectivity; it is not clear whether naked viral nucleic acid plays any role in natural infection. In the preparation of viral vaccines, the ability of nucleic acid infectivity to survive damage to the viral coat is a factor to be considered.

Release of the Nucleic Acid

In ordinary infection entry of the viral nucleic acid into a cell follows the main steps observed with bacteriophages, i.e., adsorption of the virions to the cells, followed by release of the nucleic acid. The major difference is that the entry of animal viruses involves phagocytosis, which is absent in bacteria.

Adsorption. Animal viruses generally do not appear to possess an adsorption organ corresponding to the tail fibers of bacteriophages; it is likely that adsorption occurs through specific sites distributed over the surface of the virion, such as the spikes of enveloped viruses or the capsomers of icosahedral viruses. A more specialized structure may be the fibers located at the corners of the icosahedral capsid of adenoviruses, which give rise to neutralizing antibody and therefore are clearly involved in adsorption.

The virions are adsorbed to specific **receptors:** for myxoviruses they are mucoproteins similar to the red cell receptors involved in hemagglutination (Ch. 22), and for poliovirus they are lipoproteins. Receptors for a given virus are present only on cells of certain species and belonging to certain tissues; with poliovirus their presence correlates fairly well with the susceptibility of the cells to infection (Ch. 27). The presence of these receptors also depends on the state of the cells. Thus, receptors for poliovirus are absent in human kidney, testis, and amnion, but appear within several days in primary cultures of cells of these organs.

The adsorption of virions to animal cells is favored by optimal concentration of cations in the medium, and is at first **reversible,** since the adsorbed virions can be recovered from the cells in infectious form. Adsorbed poliovirus, for instance, can be freed by detergents, low pH, or high salt concentrations; myxoviruses by neuraminidase; and certain ECHO viruses by chymotrypsin.

Eclipse. After incubation at 37° for some time the adsorbed virions become eclipsed, i.e., cannot be recovered from the cells in infectious form. Similarly, while antibodies added shortly after virus adsorption prevent the adsorbed virions from initiating infection (Ch. 26), the proportion of cells sensitive to antibodies progressively decreases at 37° (Fig. 25-3), presumably reflecting penetration of the total virion or its nucleic acid into the cell. Since the two effects have the same time course, eclipse can be conveniently studied by following the changes in the susceptibility of absorbed virions to neutralization by antibodies.

The **mechanism of eclipse** has been studied particularly with poliovirus adsorbed to receptor-containing particulate fractions obtained from disrupted cells. Eclipse of this virus has a high temperature coefficient and involves modification of the viral capsid, through either thermal or enzymatic action, since the capsid becomes attackable by proteolytic enzymes. The altered capsid, however, still holds the viral RNA and protects it from RNase. Within 1 hour after infection of whole cells with poliovirus about half the adsorbed virions slough off the cell in an altered state, probably attached to pieces of the cell membrane. With influenza virions adsorbed to fragments of the cell membrane the envelope appears to disintegrate rapidly at 37°, as shown by electron microscopic observations, but it is not known whether this phenomenon is related to the regular eclipse.

These observations with cell-free systems suggest that viral eclipse is the consequence of alterations of the outer coat of the virions.

Phagocytosis. The plasma membrane of cultured animal cells continuously carries out active movements which cause droplets of

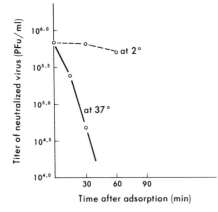

Fig. 25-3 Eclipse of poliovirus in HeLa cells determined from loss of sensitivity to neutralizing antibody. Eclipse occurs at 37° but not at 2°. The virus was allowed to adsorb for 20 minutes at 2°; the cells were then washed and resuspended in fresh medium at either temperature. At the indicated times samples were taken, mixed with antipoliovirus serum, and incubated to allow virus neutralization to occur. The infected cells were then diluted as required and plated on cell monolayers, where productive cells (whose virus was not neutralized) produce a plaque. The titer of neutralized virus plotted in the figure is obtained as the difference between the concentration of productive cells not exposed to antibody and the titer resulting after exposure to antibody. (Data from B. Mandel. Cold Spring Harbor Sypm. Quant. Biol. 27:123, 1962.)

medium and particles to be engulfed into the cells, where they remain for a while within membrane-bound vacuoles. Extensive electron microscopic evidence, from cells sectioned at various times after infection, has clearly demonstrated that **animal virions of all morphological types are engulfed by phagocytosis;** undoubtedly this is an important step in infection, although it has not been shown to be required. In fact, if the interaction of the viral coat with the plasma membrane plays an important role, eclipse could occur on both the outer cell membrane and that surrounding the vacuoles. In any case, phagocytosis would at least enhance the rate of cell infection in

various ways: by preventing the flaking off of eclipsed virus with pieces of membrane, as noted with poliovirus; by allowing the cytoplasmic enzymes (e.g., from lysosomes) to act on the virions; and by favoring the passage of virions, or their components, into the cytoplasmic matrix.

Uncoating of the Nucleic Acid. The viral nucleic acid is ultimately set free in the cells, as can be shown by studying cells infected by virions labeled in the nucleic acid: if these cells are homogenized after viral eclipse and treated with a suitable nuclease the viral nucleic acid is broken down, whereas that of intact virions is not. Moreover, uncoating of the nucleic acid is the consequence of breakdown of the viral coats, for if viruses are radioactively labeled in their protein or phospholipids, they yield radioactive fragments in the cells that they infect.

Many aspects of the process of uncoating are obscure. Fragmentary evidence is available for some viruses, and it is not clear how much it can be generalized. With viruses possessing more than one coat (enveloped or complex virions) uncoating appears to be a stepwise process. Electron microscopic observations of cells infected by **poxviruses** show that the outermost coat is lost in cytoplasmic vacuoles, and the other coats are removed after the partly uncoated particles penetrate into the cell's matrix. In these cells a special **uncoating enzyme,** which removes the inner coats, makes its appearance after infection.

It is likely that enveloped virions also lose their envelope by interaction with the cell's membrane (in vacuoles or at the outer surface), but we do not know where their capsid is removed. Also uncertain is the site of uncoating of **icosahedral virions;** although the capsid of poliovirus undergoes modification in contact with the cell's receptors, the particles are not uncoated there; and other icosahedral viruses (adenoviruses) fail even to show capsid alteration in contact with receptors. The penetration of a few virions into the cytoplasmic matrix has been revealed by electron microscopy, and it is thus likely that they are uncoated there.

One-Step Multiplication Curves

In cultures of cells growing in suspension multiplication curves for animal viruses are obtained, as for bacteriophages; and in infected monolayer cultures dispersal by trypsin into suspension of single cells can be followed by similar procedures. Moreover, for viruses whose cell receptors can be easily destroyed (e.g., myxoviruses, polyoma virus) one-step multiplication curves can be obtained even without dispersing the monolayers: the infected monolayer cultures are washed free of unadsorbed virus and then covered with a nutrient medium containing receptor-destroying enzyme, which prevents further adsorption of virus to the cells. Finally, for viruses that are not readily released from cells (e.g.,

poxvirus, adenovirus, herpesvirus) the mere washing of the monolayers, after infection, with viral antibody creates approximate one-step conditions.

It is difficult in some cases to obtain rigorous one-step conditions. Approximate one-step conditions are then realized by infecting monolayer cultures with a large inoculum, which leaves no uninfected cells; the unadsorbed virus is then removed by washing the cultures. Since all cells are infected at once, multiplication is necessarily confined to a single cycle. The method has two drawbacks: high multiplicity of infection, which may cause an abnormal multiplication; and extensive readsorption of progeny virions to cell debris.

One-step multiplication curves of animal

Fig. 25-4 One-step multiplication curves of two viruses with intracellular accumulation periods of different length. **A.** Western equine encephalitis virus (arbovirus) multiplies in cultures of chick embryo cells with an extremely short accumulation period (about 1 minute). **B.** Poliovirus multiplies in cultures of monkey kidney cells with a long accumulation period (about 3 hours). The relation between the titers of intracellular and extracellular virus in one curve are the inverse of the other. (**A.** from data of H. Rubin, M. Baluda, and J. Hotchin. J. Exp. Med. 101:205, 1955; **B.** from data of M. Reissig, D. W. Howes, and J. L. Melnick. J. Exp. Med. 104:289, 1956.)

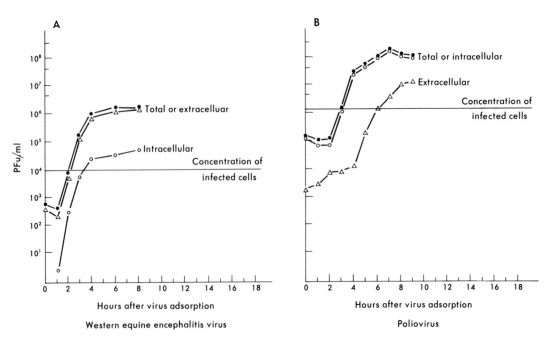

viruses (Fig. 25-4) show the same periods identified with bacteriophages (Ch. 23). However, the length of the **intracellular accumulation period** varies over a wide range with different viruses (Table 25-3); it is very long with some because the progeny virions tend to remain within the cells, and is very short with others which mature and are released in the same act (e.g., acquisition of an envelope at the cell surface). If the accumulation period is very short the intracellular virus is at any time a small fraction of the total virus, as in Figure 25-4A.

Intracellular virus is often measured as **cell-associated virus,** i.e., the virus released by disrupting the cells after they have been washed free of extracellular virus. Cell-associated virus, however, includes both true intracellular virus and extracellular virus that has become secondarily adsorbed to cellular receptors, and its titer is often much larger than that of true intracellular virus (e.g., myxoviruses).

Synthesis of DNA Viruses

Effect on Synthesis of Host Macromolecules

The effect on the synthesis of host cell DNA can be studied with viruses whose DNA is distinguishable from that of the host cells. Among these are vaccinia virus, whose DNA is made in the cytoplasm; herpesviruses and adenoviruses, whose DNA has a higher buoyant density than cellular DNA; and polyoma virus, whose DNA can be separated chromatographically owing to its small size.

When **virulent** viruses (e.g., vaccinia, herpes, and adenoviruses) infect actively growing cultures they always **inhibit,** to a varying extent, the synthesis of host DNA. The inhibition appears to be mediated by a virus-specified protein, since it is arrested by the addition of puromycin at the time of infection. The cellular DNA is not broken down, and therefore it does not serve as a

TABLE 25-3. AVERAGE ACCUMULATION PERIOD OF REPRESENTATIVE VIRUSES

Virus	Cells	Hours
Western equine encephalomyelitis (arbovirus)	Chick embryo (secondary cultures)	0
Venezuelan equine encephalomyelitis (arbovirus)	KB cells	0
Newcastle disease virus (paramyxovirus)	HeLa cells	2
Fowl plague (myxovirus)	Chick embryo (secondary cultures)	ca. 2
Poliovirus (picornavirus)	Rhesus monkey kidney (primary cultures)	3
Foot-and-mouth disease (picornavirus)	Bovine kidney (primary cultures)	0.75
Mengovirus (picornavirus)	L cells	1.5
Polyoma virus	Mouse embryo (secondary culture)	20
Reovirus	Monkey kidney cells (primary cultures)	6–8
	L cells	4
Adenovirus	HeLa cells	Very long
GAL (chicken adenovirus)	Chick embryo liver (primary cultures)	ca. 8
Vaccinia virus (poxvirus)	KB cells	6

source of precursors for the synthesis of the viral DNA.

In contrast, **moderate** viruses (e.g., polyoma virus) may **stimulate** host DNA synthesis. This phenomenon is of considerable interest for viral carcinogenesis.

Expression and Replication of Viral DNA

According to fragmentary evidence, the expression and replication of the DNA of animal viruses take place along lines similar to those reviewed in Chapter 23 for bacteriophages.

Messenger RNA. The synthesis of mRNA by vaccinia virus has been recognized by its cytoplasmic location (which contrasts with the nuclear synthesis of cellular mRNA). The mRNA of adenovirus and polyoma virus has been demonstrated by hybridization (Ch. 8) with viral DNA. Finally, poxvirus mRNAs extracted early and late in infection have different base ratios, suggesting that there are two distinct groups of messengers, the early and the late ones, as in bacteria infected by T-even bacteriophages.

New Enzymes. Several new enzymes are induced by various viruses. For example, herpesvirus and poxvirus induce a marked increase of the activity of **thymidine kinase,** which phosphorylates thymidine to thymidylic acid; and this enzyme is probably virus-specified, because it differs immunologically from the enzyme present in uninfected cells and because it is not made in cells infected by certain viral mutants. The role of this enzyme, however, is not clear, since it is not part of the normal pathway to thymidylic acid. **DNA polymerase** and **DNase** activity similarly increase in cells infected by certain viruses.

Some viral infections induce the synthesis of enzymes specified by **cellular genes,** e.g., several enzymes induced by polyoma virus.

Regulation of Synthesis of Viral Enzymes. Studies with the thymidine kinase of vaccinia virus show that this enzyme is an "early" protein, whose synthesis is terminated by the expression of a "late" gene. This termination apparently involves the formation of an inhibitory protein (Fig. 25-5), since it is prevented by adding actinomycin D (which stops mRNA syn-

thesis) shortly before termination would normally occur and it is postponed by a period of incubation with puromycin (which reversibly stops protein synthesis) at the time of normal termination.

DNA replication has been studied with viruses whose DNA can be separated from host DNA, owing either to its high G + C content and therefore high buoyant density in CsCl (e.g., herpesvirus, adenovirus) or to its small size (e.g., polyoma virus). Viral DNA is found to be synthesized from precursors present in the medium. Synthesis begins in the middle of the eclipse period and continues beyond the end of this period (Fig. 25-6). At the end of the multiplication cycle a considerable amount of unused viral DNA remains in the infected cells, in contrast to bacteriophage infection, where most of the viral DNA is utilized for virion formation. The difference may reflect the topographical disadvantage of virion assembly in large animal cells.

The replication of the DNA of animal viruses, like that of bacteriophages, depends on new proteins, since it is prevented by inhibitors of protein synthesis added to the medium shortly after infection; if the inhibitor is added somewhat later, DNA replication is partly inhibited. After the first half of the eclipse period the addition of the inhibitor has no effect.

As with bacteriophages, the newly synthesized viral DNA enters a pool; thus, if the infected cells are exposed to a short pulse of a radioactive DNA precursor at any time during the eclipse period, the label is distributed among virions finished at any subsequent time.

The mode of replication of the viral DNA has been shown to be semiconservative in studies with a herpesvirus. The infected cells were first kept in a medium containing 5-bromodeoxyuridine, whose incorporation in DNA makes it "heavy," and were then transferred to thymidine-containing medium, which causes the subsequently synthesized DNA strands to be "light." As shown in

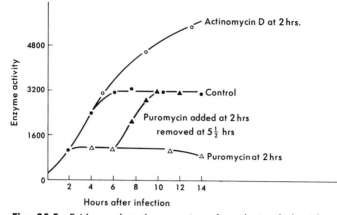

Fig. 25-5 Evidence that the cessation of synthesis of thymidine kinase in cells in-fected by vaccinia virus (a poxvirus) is controlled by the expression of a gene (probably viral). The evidence derives from the effect of actinomycin D and puromycin. In the control cells, i.e., not exposed to any inhibitor, synthesis of the enzyme stops at about 5½ hours after infection; but earlier addition of actinomycin D allows synthesis to continue, showing that the block in this specific synthesis requires new RNA synthesis. Puromycin at 2 hours interrupts all enzyme synthesis, but after its removal at 5½ hours synthesis of thymidine kinase resumes, although it has stopped in the control; this result shows that synthesis of the enzyme stops only after some required protein synthesis. (Modified from B. McAuslan. Virology, 21:383, 1963.)

Figure 25-7, viral DNA extracted after the transfer contained a hybrid band of inter-mediate density, in agreement with semicon-servative replication (Ch. 8). Breakage and reunion do not appear to play a major role in the replication of the DNA of herpesvirus, in agreement with its observed low frequency of genetic recombination.

Site of Replication. The DNA of all ani-mal viruses (except poxviruses, whose DNA is made in the cytoplasm) is synthesized in the cell nucleus. This is shown by radio-autographic observations after a pulse of ³H-thymidine.

Synthesis of RNA Viruses (Including RNA Phages)

Replication of single-stranded RNA does not occur in uninfected cells, which appar-ently lack the required enzymes; hence an infecting single-stranded viral RNA must cause the synthesis of such an enzyme before it can replicate, and it must therefore act as messenger. Since a single molecule of viral

Fig. 25-6 Time course of the synthesis of the DNA and protein of polyoma virus (an icosahedral virus synthesized in the nucleus) in cultures of mouse kidney cells. Total viral DNA was determined by infectivity after phenol extraction, viral protein by hemagglu-tination; the amounts are given in arbitrary units. (Data from R. Dulbecco, L. H. Hartwell, and M. Vogt. Proc. Nat. Acad. Sc. 53:403, 1965.)

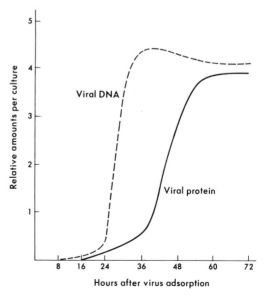

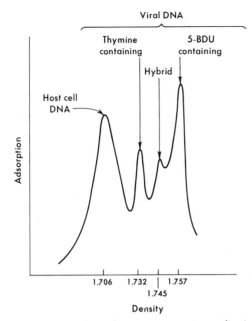

Fig. 25-7 Evidence for semiconservative replication of the DNA of pseudorabies virus (a herpesvirus). The infected cells were transferred from a medium containing thymidine to one containing the heavy precursor, 5-bromodeoxyuridine (5-BDU), where synthesis was allowed to continue. The DNA later extracted and analyzed by density gradient equilibrium centrifugation shows four density peaks, one of cellular DNA and three of viral DNA; one of the latter has a hybrid density, proving semiconservative replication. (Modified from A. S. Kaplan. Virology 24:19, 1964.)

RNA in a cell is sufficient to initiate infection, the same molecule that acts as messenger must serve later as template for multiplication. **Viral infectious RNA,** therefore, has the unique characteristic of being both messenger and template. We shall discuss together the very similar syntheses of phages and animal viruses containing RNA.

Effect on Synthesis of Host Macromolecules

Infection of cells with highly virulent picornaviruses (e.g., poliovirus, mengovirus) causes rapid inhibition of host synthesis of both RNA and protein (Fig. 25-8). The inhibition of host RNA synthesis does not take place in the presence of high concentrations of puromycin (which inhibits protein synthesis), showing that it is caused by a new protein, probably specified by viral genes. The rapid inhibition of host protein synthesis apparently results from disaggregation of cellular polyribosomes (Fig. 25-9); the mechanism is unknown, but it must differentiate between host and viral polyribosomes. These effects of infection favor viral multiplication by freeing ribosomes for the synthesis of viral proteins.

Expression of Viral RNA

Viral RNA as a Messenger. The RNAs of various viruses (poliovirus, tobacco mosaic virus, and coliphage f2) have been found to stimulate the incorporation of radioactive amino acids into proteins in vitro by cell-free protein-synthesizing systems derived from *Escherichia coli* (which contain ribosomes and various required molecules). Among the products formed by phage MS2 RNA, whole protein molecules of the viral capsid have been identified. They are recognizable because

Fig. 25-8 Inhibition of cellular RNA and protein synthesis in L cells infected with mengovirus (a picornavirus). The decline in the incorporation of radioactive precursors begins immediately after infection. The resumption of synthesis at about 3 hours is due to synthesis of viral RNA and proteins. (Modified from R. M. Franklin and D. Baltimore. Cold Spring Harbor Symp. Quant. Biol. 27:175, 1962.)

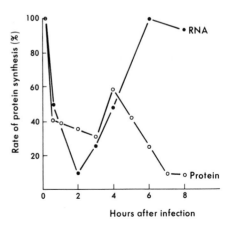

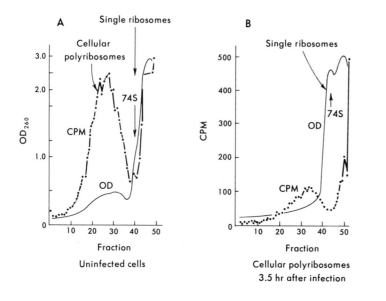
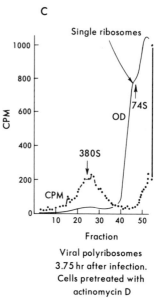

Fig. 25-9 Effect of poliovirus infection on polyribosomes of HeLa cells. Polyribosomes are studied by exposing the cells briefly to radioactive amino acids, then disrupting the cells and sedimenting the cytoplasmic extract through a sucrose gradient. Single ribosomes (74S) constitute a peak recognizable by optical density (thin line), which is used as a reference; the polyribosomes are identified by their high sedimentation rate and by the radioactivity of the attached polypeptides. The normal polyribosomes present in uninfected cells (most frequent sedimentation rate 200S; diagram **A**) tend to disappear after infection (diagram **B**). Although viral polyribosomes around 380S must start forming very early in infection, they are recognizable as a peak only when the synthesis of viral protein is well under way (diagram **C**, obtained in cells treated with actinomycin D to prevent the formation of cellular polyribosomes). (Modfield from S. Penman, K. Scherrer, Y. Becker, and J. E. Darnell. Proc. Nat. Acad. Sc. 49: 657, 1963.)

they yield characteristic peptides upon trypsin digestion. Moreover, from cells infected by poliovirus, which have lost their cellular messenger, polyribosomes can be extracted which contain viral RNA, as shown by its length and its base ratios.

RNA Synthetase.* In addition to other new proteins, a well studied enzyme makes its appearance after infection with RNA

---

* Since this enzyme synthesizes RNA by using RNA as template, it could be called "RNA-dependent RNA polymerase." We have adopted the name "RNA synthetase," used by many workers in the field, because it is simpler and avoids confusion with the cellular "DNA-dependent RNA polymerase." The virus-induced enzyme is also called "RNA replicase."

viruses: RNA synthetase, which replicates the viral RNA (Fig. 25-10). This enzyme is present both in animal cells infected by RNA viruses (e.g., the picornaviruses poliovirus and mengovirus) and in bacteria infected by RNA phages. It is detected by its ability to cause the incorporation of a labeled ribonucleoside, provided as the triphosphate, into single-stranded RNA. The incorporation requires the presence of all four ribonucleoside triphosphates (guanosine, adenosine, cytidine, and uridine); suitable ionic conditions; and, with purified enzymes, a template.

The RNA synthetase made by several RNA bacteriophages has been extensively purified.

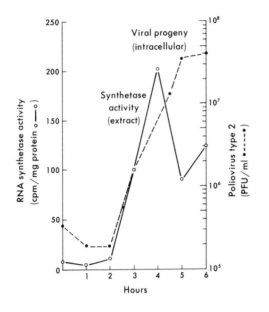

Fig. 25-10 Appearance of RNA synthetase activity in Hela cells infected by poliovirus. Extracts prepared at various times after infection show the appearance of ability to incorporate ^{14}C-labeled guanosine triphosphate into RNA (solid line), beginning near the time of synthesis of the viral progeny in the cells (dotted line). (Modified from D. Baltimore, H. J. Eggers, R. M. Franklin, and I. Tamm. Proc. Nat. Acad. Sc. 49:843, 1963.)

in large excess over the amount of template supplied. This outstanding result shows how far the art of synthesizing biological polymers in vitro has progressed.

The synthetase is quite different from the cellular DNA-dependent RNA polymerase (which synthesizes mRNAs by using double-stranded DNA as template), since it does not recognize DNA as template and has a different ionic requirement (Mn^{++} stimulates the polymerase but inhibits the synthetase). Whether these properties are shared by the RNA synthetases of animal viruses is unknown, because these enzymes have not yet been purified.

In infected animal cells the activity of the synthetase drops rapidly upon addition of an inhibitor of protein synthesis, puromycin, suggesting that **the enzyme is unstable in the cells.** This finding explains the dependence of viral RNA synthesis on **continuing** protein synthesis: RNA synthesis can be interrupted at any stage (Fig. 25-11) by adding puromycin or the amino acid analog p-fluorophenylalanine (Ch. 10).

It requires **homologous single-stranded** viral RNA as external template, and is almost totally inactive with other RNAs of both viral and cellular origin. This specificity is remarkable, and accounts for the ability of the cell to avoid replication of cellular RNAs. RNA synthetase can give rise to **net synthesis** in vitro of a product with all the properties of **viral RNA, including infectivity,** i.e., synthesis

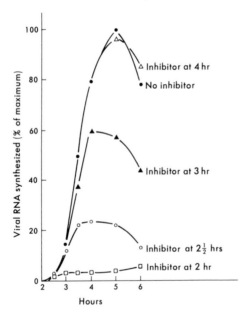

Fig. 25-11 Inhibition of the synthesis of poliovirus RNA by inhibitors of protein synthesis. Puromycin or p-fluorophenylalanine were added at various times after infection. The synthesis of viral RNA is detected from the incorporation of labeled uridine into RNA in the presence of actinomycin D, which prevents the synthesis of cellular RNA but not of viral RNA. (Modified from M. D. Scharff, M. M. Thoren, N. F. McElvain, and L. Levintow. Biochem. & Biophys. Res. Comm. 10:127, 1963.)

The formation of an active RNA synthetase in cells infected by various enteroviruses (e.g., poliovirus) is specifically prevented by two inhibitors: guanidine and 2-(α-hydroxybenzyl)-benzimidazole. This property, which will be discussed further in Chapter 26, is of considerable help for research with these viruses.

Synthesis of Viral RNA

Time Course. The synthesis of the RNA of many animal viruses can be studied by blocking the synthesis of cellular RNA by actinomycin D; then only viral RNA is synthesized (Fig. 25-12). Such experiments show that the appearance of the RNA of **naked icosahedral** viruses, measured either chemically or by infectious titer, is followed shortly by mature virus: for poliovirus the time difference is 30 to 60 minutes, varying with the experimental procedure. The synthesis of the RNA of **enveloped viruses** precedes the appearance of finished virions by a longer time interval (e.g., 2 hours for Western equine encephalomyelitis, an arbovirus). However,

the synthesis of this RNA appears to be followed shortly by its assembly in the nucleocapsid, the extra time probably being spent in adding the envelope to the nucleocapsid.

The fairly close temporal connection between synthesis and assembly has probably evolved because of the inherent instability of the viral RNA in the cells when not protected by the capsid; in fact, in the presence of puromycin the unassembled RNA rapidly loses its infectivity.

Double-Stranded Intracellular Viral RNA. The replication of single-stranded viral RNA would be expected, like that of single-stranded phage DNA (Ch. 23, Multiplication of bacteriophage ϕX174), to employ as intermediate **a double-stranded replicative form.** Indeed, in extracts of animal cells infected with a picornavirus double-stranded RNA was demonstrated by zonal centrifugation (Fig. 25-13), which was found to separate the infectivity of the extracted RNA into two components. The major component had the high sedimen-

Fig. 25-12 Lack of inhibition of the synthesis of Newcastle disease virus (a paramyxovirus) by actinomycin D. **A** shows that the drug (2 μg/ml) does not inhibit formation of infectious virus in HeLa cells. **B** shows that the drug (present for both curves) inhibits the synthesis of RNA in uninfected cells but not in infected cells (where viral RNA is being made). (From E. F. Wheelock. Proc. Soc. Exp. Biol. & Med. 114:56, 1963.)

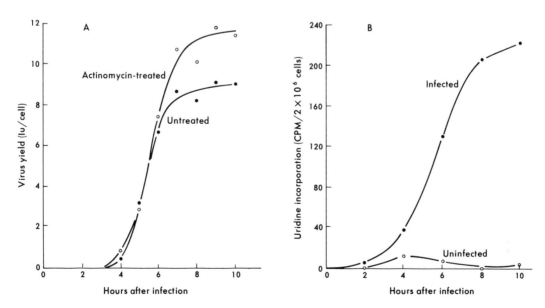

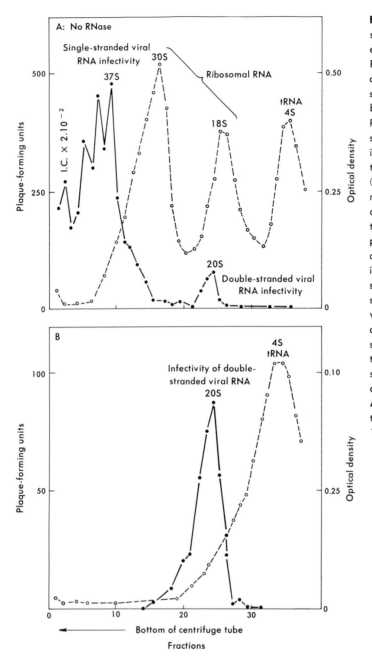

Fig. 25-13 Evidence for a double-stranded intracellular form of encephalomyocarditis virus RNA. RNA extracted from the infected cells 6 hours after infection was sedimented in a sucrose gradient both before (**A**) and after (**B**) a brief RNase treatment to destroy single-stranded RNA. The viral RNA was identified by its infectivity (continuous line); the bulk of the RNA (in which the viral contribution is negligible) was identified by its optical density (dashed line). In **A** the optical density reveals the 4S peak of transfer RNA and the 18S and 30S peaks of ribosomal RNA; infectivity reveals the 37S peak of single-stranded viral RNA and a small 20S peak of double-stranded viral RNA. RNase under these conditions did not attack the double-stranded viral RNA and the cellular tRNA (which is also largely double-stranded; see Ch. 8). (Note the difference of ordinate scale between **A** and **B**.) (Modified from L. Montagnier and F. K. Saunders. Nature 199:664, 1963.)

tation velocity (S = 37) and RNase sensitivity characteristic of the ordinary viral RNA; while the minor component had a lower sedimentation velocity (S = 20), was resistant to RNase, and had a steep melting curve, suggesting that it was made up of double-stranded RNA (Ch. 8, Physical properties of nucleic acids). (The much higher sedimentation velocity of the single-stranded form can be attributed to its more compact conformation.)* Subsequently, a double-

---

* Since double-stranded RNA lacks messenger functions, its infectivity suggests that it is transcribed into single-stranded RNA by a cellular enzyme.

stranded component was found in cells infected by other viruses containing single-stranded RNA, including bacteriophages and plant viruses.

Whether this double-stranded RNA is the expected intermediate in replication is not yet clear, however, since it is produced in abundance only in late stages of infection when the synthesis of viral RNA has ceased. Similar kinetics are observed during in vitro synthesis, using a highly purified synthetase. Hence, the double-stranded material may conceivably be an abnormal product rather than an intermediate. This problem has been partly clarified by the discovery of a probably related replicative form.

Replicative Form. The notion of a special replicative form derives from work with cells infected by either an RNA phage or poliovirus, which were exposed to a radioactive RNA precursor for a very short time, comparable to that required for the synthesis of a molecule of viral RNA. The label was incorporated, not in double-stranded RNA, but in an unusual RNA, which has properties characteristic of both double-stranded and single-stranded molecules. In zonal sedimentation it forms a broad band at a position intermediate between those of double- and single-stranded RNA; like single-stranded RNA, it is insoluble in 2 M LiCl, but like double-stranded RNA, it is partially resistant to RNase. This RNA contains a polynucleotide chain ("minus" chain) complementary to that present in virions ("plus" chain), because it forms with it hybrid molecules (Ch. 8, Nucleic acid hybridization); but most of the label is in chains of the plus type. It thus appears that this replicative form is constituted by a minus chain attached to many growing plus chains; a segment of each plus chain would form a double helix with the minus chain, but the remainder would be in the form of a random coil; thus the replicative form could have a discontinuous double-stranded backbone from which hang many single-stranded tails (Fig. 25-14A).

A model of the replication of the viral RNA, given in Figure 25-14B, can be deduced from these findings and from the additional observation that the **infecting** RNA does not end up in viral progeny.

Site of Replication of Viral RNA

Cytoplasmic synthesis has been reasonably well demonstrated for certain RNA viruses, while nuclear synthesis is suspected for others.

Cytoplasmic Synthesis. This has been demonstrated by **radioautography** of cells infected by certain highly virulent RNA viruses (e.g., the picornaviruses poliovirus or mengovirus, or the paramyxovirus Newcastle disease virus). If such cells are given a brief pulse of tritiated uridine, after the synthesis of cellular RNA has been inhibited, labeled RNA is found exclusively in the cytoplasm (Fig. 25-15). Since the pulse of radioactive precursor has been very short and the cells have been fixed immediately, the possibility is minimized that the RNA has been synthesized in the nucleus and then transported to the cytoplasm.

Cytoplasmic synthesis of the viral RNA is also supported by **microsurgical** experiments, in which small bits of cytoplasm are separated from the cell body. If these bits are infected by poliovirus they synthesize RNA, which is labeled by a radioactive precursor and detected by radioautography; in contrast, no RNA synthesis occurs in uninfected bits. Since the infected fragments also synthesize poliovirus protein, recognizable by immunofluorescence, it is likely that the RNA they make is viral.

Nuclear Synthesis. In cells infected by certain myxoviruses (influenza or fowl plague virus) the capsid protein is recognizable by immunofluorescence first in the nucleus (Fig. 25-16); later it appears in the cytoplasm, where the protein of the viral envelope (i.e., the hemagglutinin) also appears. These observations suggest that the viral RNA is synthesized in the nucleus, but the possibility is not ruled out that the nucleocapsids are synthesized in the cytoplasm and then accumulate in the nucleus.

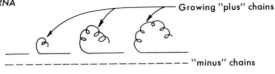

A *Replicative form of the viral RNA*

Growing "plus" chains

"minus" chains

B *Model of RNA replication*

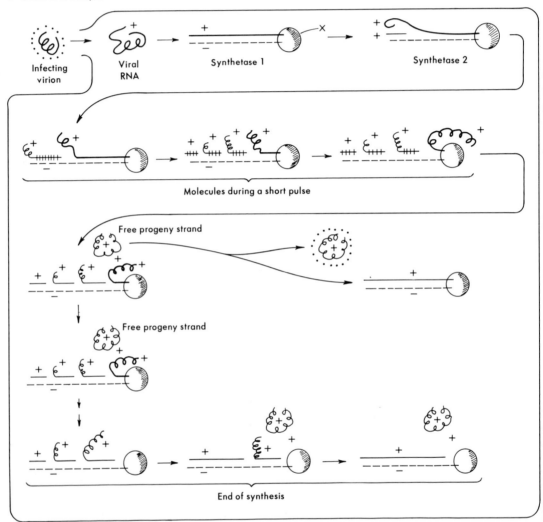

Infecting
virion

Viral
RNA

Synthetase 1

Synthetase 2

Molecules during a short pulse

Free progeny strand

Free progeny strand

End of synthesis

Fig. 25-14 (See legend on facing page)

Effect of Inhibitors Acting on Cellular DNA

To test whether cellular DNA has any role in the replication of viral RNA, various inhibitors have been employed: actinomycin D, which inhibits transcription of DNA to RNA; mitomycin C, which alkylates DNA; 5-bromodeoxyuridine, whose incorporation into the DNA of animal cells appears to alter its function and reproductive ability; 5-fluoro-deoxyuridine and amethopterin, which prevent the synthesis of new DNA (Ch. 10). The different RNA viruses tested can be subdivided into three groups on the basis of their response.

1) Some viruses multiply normally in the

Fig. 25-14 A. Probable structure of the replicative form of the single-stranded viral RNA. **B.** Hypothetical model for the replication of the RNA. Upon entering the cells the + (parental) RNA becomes associated with a cellular structure (x) and gives rise to a double-stranded form, which is immediately used for the synthesis of single + (progeny) strands. Most of the intermediate molecules are largely double-stranded with several newly formed single-stranded tails, and the single parental strand, sticking out. The single-stranded tails cause the low solubility of the molecules in high salt. Every progeny strand is attached to the replicative form by a short segment which moves along the minus strand during growth, being displaced by new synthesis. When growth reaches the end of the chain the strand is released, and it can either become incorporated in a progeny virion or give rise to a new replicative form. During a short pulse of labeled precursors the cross-hatched segments are labeled; most of the label is therefore in double-stranded molecules and RNase resistant.

Two synthetases are postulated to carry out the two different syntheses (of either − or + strand). When synthesis slows down all replicative forms become double-stranded molecules; presumably the last + strand to be initiated is completed, but it is no longer detached from the − strand by the new synthesis of additional + strands.

Fig. 25-15 Effect of infection with mengovirus on the distribution of RNA synthesis in the cell. An uninfected L cell (**A**) and one infected 6 hours earlier (**B**) were radioautographed after exposure for 3 minutes to ^{3}H-uridine. In the uninfected cell the silver grains produced by the β-radiation of decaying ^{3}H atoms is concentrated over the nucleus; in the infected cells there are only a few grains over the nucleus, because the synthesis of cellular RNA is inhibited, and many grains over the cytoplasm, due to synthesis of viral RNA. (From R. M. Franklin and D. Baltimore. Cold Spring Harbor Symp. Quant. Biol. 27:175, 1962.)

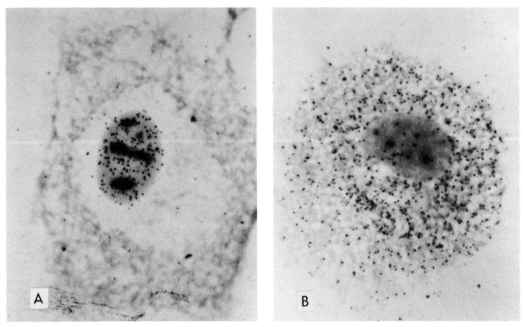

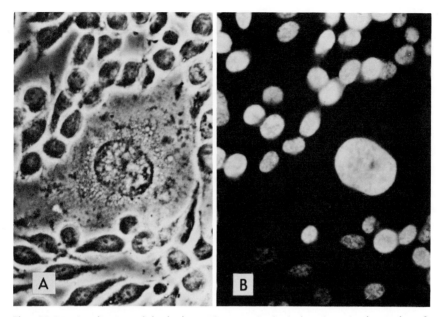

Fig. 25-16 Localization of fowl plague (a myxovirus) viral antigen in the nucleus 3 hours after infection of a culture of L cells. The cells were fixed and treated with fluorescent antibody to the viral antigen. **A.** Phase contrast micrograph; **B.** Micrograph of the same field in ultraviolet light, where only the antibody bound to the viral antigen is visible. The absence of fluorescence in the cytoplasm is especially evident in the giant cell. (From R. Franklin and P. Breitenfeld. Virology 8:293, 1959.)

presence of any of these inhibitors: picornaviruses (poliovirus and mengovirus), paramyxoviruses (Newcastle disease virus), tobacco mosaic virus, and the coliphage f2 (Fig. 25-12).

2) Myxoviruses (influenza and fowl plague viruses) are inhibited by actinomycin D but not by the other compounds. Actinomycin inhibits if added to the cells either before infection or shortly afterwards; if added toward the end of the eclipse period, it is without effect on viral multiplication. These results suggest that a function of cellular DNA is required for the initiation of myxovirus replication.

3) The leucosis viruses of chickens are inhibited by all the above agents. This result suggested a DNA-containing intermediate in the replication of the RNA of these tumor viruses.

Double-Stranded RNA Viruses

In contrast to single-stranded viral RNA, double-stranded RNA (i.e., that of reovirus

virions) does not function as a messenger in vitro. It is probably transcribed into mRNA by a cellular enzyme.

If reovirus with labeled RNA is used to infect cells, part of the label is found in **cytoplasmic** foci surrounding tubules of the mitotic spindle. These foci, which are known to be the sites of assembly of progeny virions, may therefore also be the sites of replication of the RNA.

Maturation and Release of Animal Viruses

Maturation of naked, enveloped, and complex viruses has different characteristics; furthermore, for some enveloped viruses it occurs simultaneously with release. It will therefore be useful to consider these several groups of viruses separately.

Naked Icosahedral Viruses

Maturation. DNA of icosahedral viruses begins to be synthesized a considerable time before the capsid protein. This DNA may become associated early, however, with non-capsid protein, as shown by changes in its properties, including altered solubility and resistance to attack by DNase. This process may be equivalent to the formation of DNA condensates in bacteriophage infection (Ch. 23, Maturation). The **capsid protein** appears first, like the DNA, in the nucleus.

With the complex poxviruses, in contrast, the coat protein, like the DNA, appears in cytoplasmic foci.

With **icosahedral RNA viruses** the viral RNA becomes rapidly associated with the capsid protein, which begins to be synthesized at almost the same time. Both components are made in the cytoplasm, in **foci** intimately associated with membranes. This topographical connection between RNA and protein synthesis has an evident function, since these foci have been shown to contain many polyribosomes with the viral RNA as messenger (Fig. 25-17).

Capsids are formed by **self-assembly** of monomers into capsomers, and of capsomers into capsids. The nucleic acid is not required, for with many viruses capsids empty of nu-

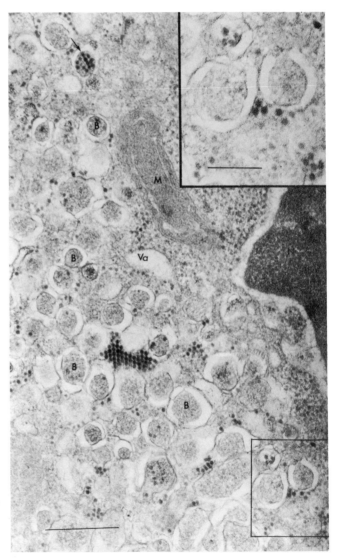

Fig. 25-17 Electron micrograph of part of the cytoplasm of a HeLa cell infected by poliovirus (an RNA virus), showing a focus of viral reproduction. Many viral particles are present in the cytoplasmic matrix (some in small crystals) around or within characteristic bodies (B; also arrows) and vacuoles (Va). The inset reproduces a detail at greater enlargement. (From S. Dales, H. J. Eggers, I. Tamm, and G. Palade. Virology 26:379, 1965.)

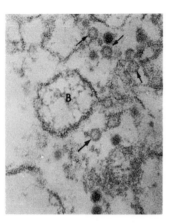

Fig. 25-18 A detail from a focus of viral multiplication in a HeLa cell infected by poliovirus, similar to that of Figure 25-17, showing the presence of empty capsids (arrow). Complete viral particles can be distinguished nearby. B is a characteristic body similar to those of Figure 25-17. (From S. Dales, H. J. Eggers, I. Tamm, and G. Palade. Virology 26:379, 1965.)

cleic acid can be recognized in thin sections of the infected cells (Fig. 25-18), and it is unlikely that they arise by secondary loss of the nucleic acid.

Icosahedral viruses are often concentrated in large numbers at the site of maturation and tend to form intracellular **crystals** (Fig. 25-19), frequently observed in thin sections of infected cells.

Release. The release of naked icosahedral virions has different characteristics for different viruses. Poliovirus, a highly virulent, cytoplasmic **RNA** virus, causes rapid death of the infected cells and is also **rapidly released.** The study of single infected cells, contained in small drops of medium under paraffin oil (Fig. 25-20), shows a total yield of about 100 plaque-forming units (more than 10^4 viral particles) released over a period of 1/2 hour. During release the cells show rupture of surface vacuoles and surface bubbling with detachment of small cytoplasmic blebs.

In contrast, icosahedral DNA viruses which mature in the nucleus do not reach the cell surface as rapidly, and are released when the

Fig. 25-19 A crystal of poliovirus particles in infected HeLa cells. Va, vacuoles similar to those of Figure 25-17. (From S. Dales, H. J. Eggers, I. Tamm, and G. Palade. Virology 26:379, 1965.)

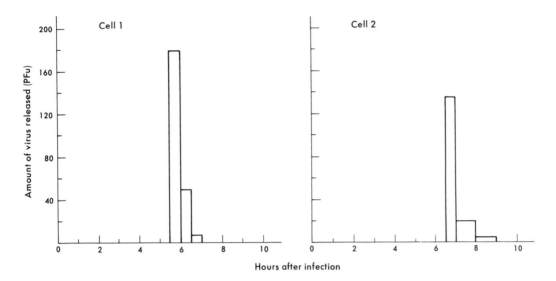

Fig. 25-20 The viral yield from two single monkey kidney cells infected by poliovirus. The cells were obtained by disrupting a monolayer of monkey kidney cells by trypsin; after being infected with poliovirus each was introduced into a separate small drop of medium immersed in paraffin oil. Every ½ hour the medium of each drop was removed, replaced with fresh medium, and assayed for infectivity by plaque assay. Note that with either cell the release was rapid (most virus came out in ½ hour), and note also the difference in latent peirod. (Data from A. Lwoff, R. Dulbecco, M. Vogt, and M. Lwoff. Virology 1:128, 1955.)

cells undergo autolysis. They thus tend to remain for a long time within the infected cells, causing a **long accumulation period.**

Enveloped Viruses

Synthesis of Coat Components. In the maturation of enveloped viruses a capsid must first be assembled around the nucleic acid to form the nucleocapsid, which is then surrounded by the envelope. The assembly of the capsid appears probably to occur in the same way as with naked viruses.

With paramyxoviruses (e.g., Newcastle disease virus) the **capsid protein** is first detected by immunofluorescence 3 hours after infection, in a perinuclear zone of the cytoplasm. In contrast, with myxoviruses (e.g., influenza and fowl plague virus) the capsid protein is recognizable 3 hours after infection in the nucleus and 1 hour later in the cytoplasm (Fig. 25-16); but as noted above in connection with the site of RNA synthesis, the sequence of events is not altogether clear. With both

groups of viruses the envelope antigen appears in the cytoplasm about 1 hour after the capsid antigen.

The virus-specified proteins of the viral envelope are synthesized de novo after infection. In contrast, the lipids (Ch. 22), which resemble in composition those of the uninfected host cell membrane, derive from lipids preexisting in the cells before infection. In fact, when cells labeled with ^{32}P were infected with influenza or Sindbis virus (an arbovirus) in unlabeled medium, the individual phosphatides of the progeny virus had about the same specific activity as those of the uninfected control cells. Evidently the lipoprotein of the viral membrane is formed by aggregation of new protein with old lipids.

Formation and Release of Virions. Envelopes are formed around the nucleocapsids by **budding of cellular membranes,** either at the cell's surface or in vacuoles (Fig. 25-21). When the nucleocapsid has become surrounded by the envelope the bud detaches

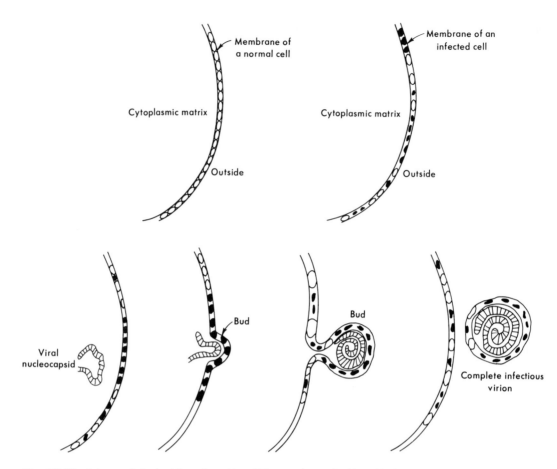

Fig. 25-21 Scheme of the budding of a virion. White circles O, building blocks of the normal cellular membrane (specified by cellular genes); black circles ●, viral hemagglutinins (specified by a viral gene), which became incorporated in the cell membrane before budding of viral particles begins.

from the membrane and the virion is formed. If the process occurs on the surface membrane, release occurs at the same time. If budding occurs in a vacuole, release requires subsequent fusion of the vacuole with the cell membrane. Either method of release is compatible with cell survival and can be very efficient, allowing thousands of viral particles to be released from each cell per hour for many hours.

Studies with myxo- and paramyxoviruses have shown that the budding occurs in regions of membranes containing the virus-specified building blocks of the envelope (e.g., the hemagglutinins). These viral constituents become incorporated in the membranes before budding begins and are recognizable from the appearance of novel properties of the cell surface: hemadsorption (Fig. 25-22); the abil-

Fig. 25-22 Hemadsorption of HeLa cells infected by Newcastle disease virus. The cells used had been heavily irradiated with X-ray several days before infection; they stopped multiplying but increased in size and became giant cells. facilitating observations. The virus multiplies regularly in these cells. **A.** A cell 5 hours after infection. The ability to adsorb chicken erythrocytes begins to appear at two opposite regions of the cell surface. At these regions new cell membrane appears to be laid down, allowing viral components to become incorporated together with the cellular components. **B** and **C.** Nine hours after infection, cells at different magnification, showing that the entire cellular membrane has developed the capacity for hemadsorption. The erythrocytes are firmly attached to the cells and are not removed by repeated washing. (From P. Marcus. Cold Spring Harbor Symp. Quant. Biol. 27:351, 1962.)

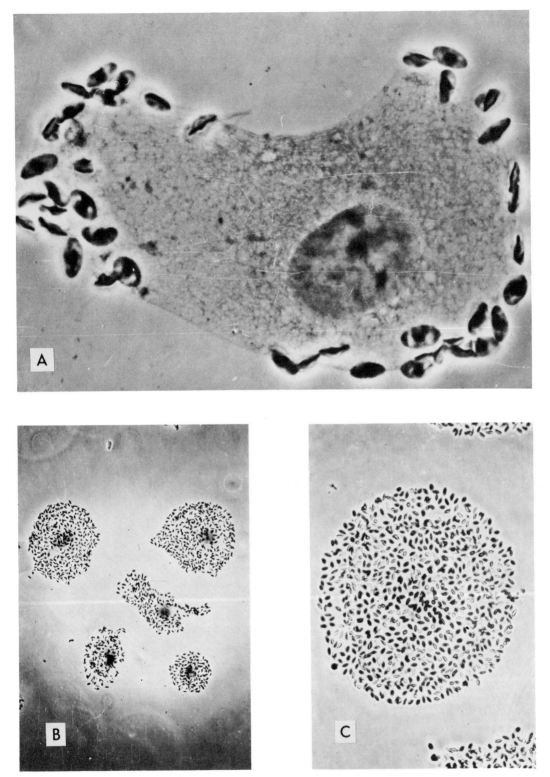

Fig. 25-22 (See legend on facing page)

ity to bind antiviral antibodies (as shown by the electron microscope with ferritin-conjugated antibodies); and the ability to fuse with the surface of uninfected cells to form multinucleated syncytia, called polykaryocytes (Fig. 25-23).

Budding can be considered the result of an intimate adhesion between the nucleocapsid and the cytoplasmic side of the cell membrane, which causes the membrane to curve into a protruding sphere, connected by a collar to the membrane (Fig. 25-21). Complete separation may be caused by fusion of the membranous collar in the same way as in phagocytosis, in which the invaginated plasma membrane gives rise to a closed vesicle. Thus the completion of the envelope, like the assembly of other viral components, would

occur spontaneously (i.e., be like crystallization).

With some myxoviruses a deviation from the normal pattern of maturation leads to the formation of **filaments** instead of round particles. The filaments are cylindrical, with a diameter similar to that of the spherical particles, but of variable length. They are surrounded by an envelope similar to that of the virions, and they are also infectious. Their formation depends on many factors, such as genetic properties of the virus, type of host cell, and environment (e.g., it is greatly enhanced in the presence of vitamin A alcohol, or surfactants).

Complex Viruses

The maturation of **poxviruses** can be inferred by ordering electron microscopic

Fig. 25-23 Formation of multinucleated syncytia (polykaryocytes) by Hep-2 cells infected by herpes simplex virus. Five cells have fused completely, and several others partly, into a central mass. The cells were stained with the fluorescent dye, acridrine orange, and photographed in a dark field. (From B. Roizman. Cold Spring Harbor Symp. Quant. Biol. 27:327, 1962.)

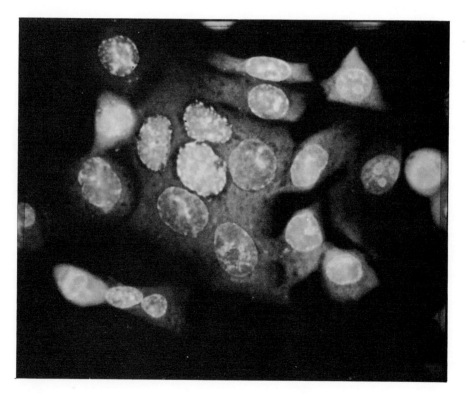

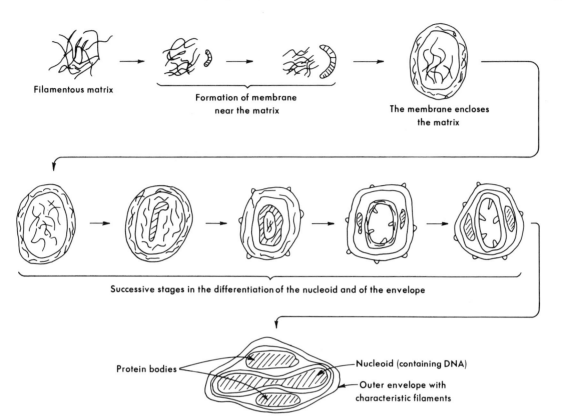

Filamentous matrix

Formation of membrane
near the matrix

The membrane encloses
the matrix

Successive stages in the differentiation of the nucleoid and of the envelope

Protein bodies

Nucleoid (containing DNA)

Outer envelope with
characteristic filaments

Finished virions

Fig. 25-24 Diagram of the development of vaccinia virus, reconstructed from electron micrographs of thin sections of infected cells. (Modified from A. A. Avakyan and A. F. Byckovsky. J. Cell Biol. 24:337, 1965.)

images (Fig. 25-24) in a reasonable time sequence. Synthesis of the viral constituents takes place in cytoplasmic foci called **factories.** At the beginning of maturation these foci contain fibrils 20 to 25 A in diameter, of which some are presumably DNA. A parcel of the fibrous material becomes surrounded by heavy multilayered membranes, within which it differentiates into an inner membrane and the characteristic nucleoid, while the external membrane acquires the characteristic pattern recognizable with negative staining on the surface of poxvirus virions (Ch. 22).

The maturation of these viruses has important differences from the maturation of simpler viruses, since the virion differentiates **after** the precursors have been enclosed within the primitive membrane. This pattern represents a step toward a cellular organization, where differentiation is all internal. A further step in the same direction can be observed in the development of bedsoniae. Thus **poxviruses may be transition forms toward bacteria.**

Phenotypic Mixing

In a cell simultaneously infected by certain pairs of related viruses that differ in capsid antigens, such as poliovirus types 1 and 2, phenotypic mixing can occur, as with bacteriophage (Ch. 23), because capsids made by building blocks of either organism (or both) may enclose the same genome. Indeed, when a part of the capsid has type 1 specificity and another part type 2, the particles are usually neutralized by antiserum to either antigen. Hence a mixture of polioviruses of types 1 and 2 yields six classes of virions, with different combinations of genotype (RNA) and phenotype (protein), as shown in Figures 25-25 and 25-26.

Such phenotypic mixing shows that with animal viruses, as with bacteriophage, building blocks are more or less randomly assembled from pools. Moreover, it can be shown that these building blocks are specified not solely by the nucleic acid of the infecting virions, but also by that of the progeny: thus if one genotype in a mixedly infected cell

Fig. 25-25 Mechanism underlying phenotypic mixing of the antigenic specificity of poliovirus. Cells mixedly infected by types 1 and 2 produce virions of six genotype and phenotype combinations. Cloning of these by plaque formation yields unmixed virions, with phenotype determined by the genotype of the initiating virion, irrespective of the latter's phenotype (see Fig. 25-26.)

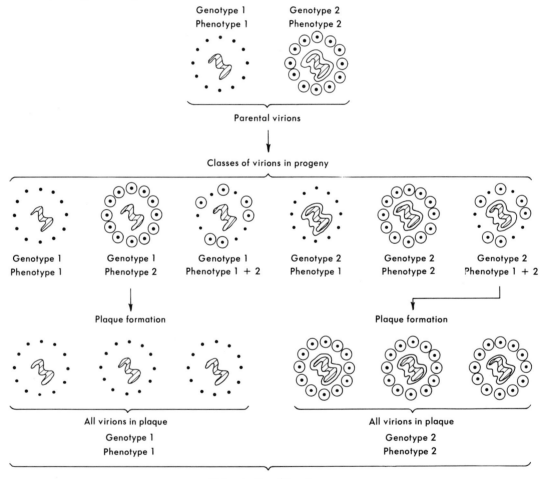

Genotype = the genetic information residing in the nucleic acid

Phenotype = the immunological characteristics residing in the capsid protein

multiplies preferentially, the proportion of the two types of proteins made varies with the proportion of the genotypes.

Host-Induced Modification

The type of host-induced modification found in bacteriophages, involving chemical alteration of bases in DNA, has never been observed with animal viruses. Another kind, however, occurs with enveloped viruses (e.g., myxoviruses and paramyxoviruses), and appears to be caused by the **incorporation of constituents of the host cell membrane in the viral envelope.** Virions made in different

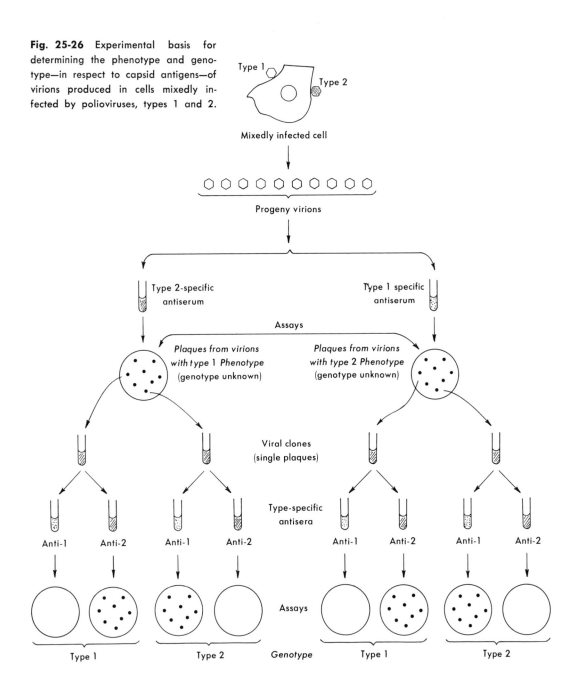

Fig. 25-26 Experimental basis for determining the phenotype and genotype—in respect to capsid antigens—of virions produced in cells mixedly infected by polioviruses, types 1 and 2.

kinds of host cells have been found to differ in several respects: buoyant density, kinetics of heat inactivation, and hemolytic activity. Since such changes appear after a single cycle of multiplication in a new cell type, and since they affect all the progeny virions, they cannot result from the selection of mutants.

Steady-State Viral Infections

Endosymbiotic Infection. In certain virus-cell systems the infected cells multiply for many generations, although they continue to release virus. These cells generate populations in which all or most individuals are infected (as shown either by release of virus or by the presence of viral antigens), even when external reinfection is prevented by the presence of strong antiviral serum. The cells may be functionally normal: for instance, chick em-

ENDOSYMBIOTIC INFECTION

All or most cells infected
Intracellular transmission of infection
Infection cannot be cured by viral antibody
Caused by viruses that can be released without killing cell

bryos carrying certain tumor viruses (Avian leucosis viruses) develop normally.

Such endosymbiotic infection is caused by many viruses, both in the animal and in tissue cultures, and by the very small bacteriophage fd in bacteria. Although this type of persistent infection is superficially similar to lysogeny, it is maintained by quite a different mechanism. There is no evidence for association of the viral nucleic acid with the cellular chromosome, or for the operation of a specific regulatory mechanism leading to immunity. The infection persists because 1) the rate of multiplication of virus must be low enough to permit the cells to survive and multiply, and 2) there is a sufficient number of viral nucleic acid molecules, or viral particles, in each cell, to ensure infection of most daughter cells by random segregation at mitosis.

Carrier State. The steady-state infection must be distinguished from the carrier state,

often observed in virus-infected cultures of animal cells. This state also causes a persistent viral infection of a cell population, but it is based on the infection of a **small proportion** of the cells: in these a regular viral multiplication cycle takes place, usually terminating in cell death, but the released virus infects only a small number of the other cells. This limited reinfection depends on special conditions of the culture, e.g., partial resistance of the cells to infection, the presence in the medium of antiviral agents such as weak antibody or interferon, or cell-to-cell transmission of virus without release into the medium. If the continuing reinfection is prevented, as by adding strong antiviral antibodies, the culture is often cured of the infection.

In summary, the differences between **endosymbiotic infection** and the carrier state are the following:

CARRIER-STATE INFECTION

Small proportion of cells infected (1% or less)
Usually extracellular, occasionally intracellular, transmission of infection
Infection can often be cured by viral antibody
Caused by any virus

Abortive Infection

Viral infection of cells does not always result in the synthesis of infectious progeny virions (**productive infection**). Under some special circumstances the infection is **abortive**: although viral constituents are synthesized, either no viral particles or only noninfectious particles are produced.

Abortive infection occurs regularly in certain virus-cell systems (e.g., influenza virus in HeLa cells, fowl plague or Newcastle disease virus in L cells, or herpes simplex virus in dog kidney cells). Viral mutants, however, may be capable of productive infection in the same type of cell. In the abortive infection the viral nucleic acid and proteins of the viral coat may be synthesized but **are not assembled,** probably because some component, for unknown reasons, is either missing or faulty.

A special and interesting class of abortive

infections is due to genetically **defective viruses,** which are unable to cause the synthesis of some product essential for their own reproduction. These viruses, like defective bacteriophages (Ch. 24), can produce infectious progeny in cells infected at the same time by a **helper** virus, which provides the missing product. Examples are known among the tumor-producing viruses.

Acridine derivatives, such as proflavin, have caused abortive infection with both icosahedral viruses (poliovirus) and enveloped viruses (fowl plague virus), as well as with bacteriophages.

With both types of animal viruses the capsid protein is synthesized at a nearly normal rate in the presence of the drug, but no infectious virions are formed. The reasons for this abnormal reproduction are unknown.

The infection of susceptible cells by certain enveloped viruses (influenza or fowl plague) at **high multiplicity** causes abnormal multiplication (Von Magnus effect). The infection is only partially abortive, since the viral progeny contains small proportions of infectious virions, together with many noninfectious hemagglutinating particles. The noninfectious particles are much more irregular in size and shape than infectious virions, contain little RNA, and often are only empty envelopes.

GENETICS OF ANIMAL VIRUSES

The genetics of animal viruses is much less known than that of bacteriophages, largely for lack of suitable technics for selecting and identifying mutants or recombinants, and also because of the low frequency of recombination.

Mutations

Mutations of animal viruses occur spontaneously and can be induced by various mutagenic treatments. The known mutant phenotypes are numerous and cover a larger range than bacteriophage mutations, because there are more ways for studying their properties: for instance, the various effects on animals. **Conditionally lethal** mutants have also been isolated for both DNA-containing viruses (poxviruses and polyoma virus) and RNA-containing viruses (poliovirus and Sindbis virus), but their study is only beginning.

Mutant Types

The known mutations affect a variety of viral properties. 1) **Plaque size or type** (Fig. 25-27). These mutants are not as diverse as the corresponding phage mutants because

animal virus plaques have less detail (they affect fewer and larger cells). Differences of plaque size may depend on differences either in parameters of the multiplication cycle or in the surface charges of the virus. Small charge differences affect plaque size because agar contains a sulfated polysaccharide which absorbs the more highly charged virions, especially at certain pHs. 2) **Pock type.** Some poxvirus types produce white smooth pocks on the chorioallantoic membrane of the chick embryo, while others produce red, ulcerated pocks (*u* character). 3) **Surface properties** detected by physical methods. 4) **Antigenic properties.** 5) **Hemagglutination,** or the neuraminidase activity (in myxoviruses). 6) **Resistance to inactivation** by a variety of agents. 7) **Resistance toward or dependence on inhibitory substances during multiplication.** 8) **Pathogenic effect** for organisms. 9) **Host range.** 10) **Functions of certain viral genes in the infected cells,** such as production of thymidine kinase or induction of interferon.

Pleiotropism or Covariation

Mutants selected for a certain phenotypic alteration are often found to be changed in

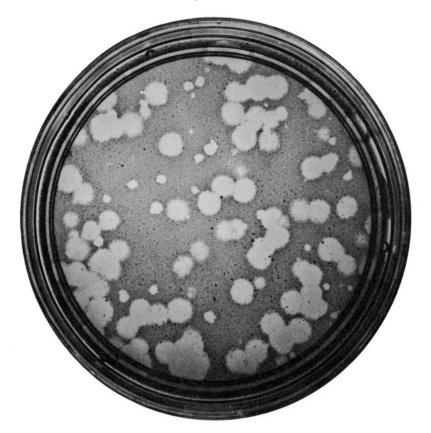

Fig. 25-27 Two plaque-type mutants of fowl plague virus on a monolayer of chick embryo cells. The wild type produces large round plaques with fuzzy edges; a small plaque mutant produces small plaques with irregularly indented outline and sharp edges. (Courtesy of H. R. Staiger.)

other properties. For instance, poliovirus mutants with altered chromatographic properties often, but not always, have decreased neurovirulence for monkeys. This pleiotropism reflects the effect of a single viral protein on several properties of the virus. The variable connection between the properties is readily understood: for example, mutations can modify different charged groups of the viral capsid, with similar effects on chromatographic adsorption but different effects on the more specific adsorption to certain cells.

Pleiotropism is useful in certain applications of viral genetics. Thus by employing characters that are detectable in vitro and show covariation with virulence it is easy to select attenuated (i.e., nonvirulent) strains for use

as live vaccines, reserving the more cumbersome animal testing for final characterization. This approach has been used in the selection of poliovirus vaccines.

Distribution of Mutants in the Yields of Single Cells

With animal viruses, as with bacteriophages, the mode of replication of the viral nucleic acid has been analyzed by studying the distribution of the number of spontaneous mutants in the yields of individual cells (Ch. 23). This approach is especially interesting for **viral RNA,** whose mode of replication cannot be deduced from the biochemical information available. Experiments with poliovirus suggest that **viral RNA,** like viral DNA,

replicates geometrically. The validity of this interpretation, however, is weakened by the large particles/infectivity ratio (Ch. 22).

Complementation

Complementation of temperature-sensitive mutants of poliovirus at a restrictive temperature (Ch. 8) has been studied to determine the functional organization of the viral genome. A number of mutants displayed complementation with one another: surprisingly, however, the viral yield from mixedly infected cells was at best only 1/100 the yield from wild-type viruses under the same circumstances.

Similar results have been obtained with Sindbis virus (an arbovirus). Since at least some of the various complementing groups of mutants display different functional alterations, they must represent different genes. The low efficiency of complementation may be attributed to poor diffusion of viral proteins from one to another part of the same cell, owing to partitioning by membranes.

Genetic Recombination

DNA Viruses

Among DNA viruses recombination has been studied largely with poxviruses, employing mutations affecting the type of pocks on the chorioallantoic membrane of the chicken embryo (u; see above, Mutations). Strains carrying independent mutations were crossed by mixed infection of tissue culture cells; the yield was then assayed on the chorioallantoic membrane, where the proportion of wild-type recombinants could be determined. In this way, 18 u markers have been arranged in a linear order, using the semiqualitative criterion that closely linked markers produce fewer recombinants than distant ones. The relation of recombinant frequency to map distance, however, was obscured by strong selection, during intracellular multiplication, for the wild type and for certain mutant genotypes, as demonstrated in control mixed infections. Genetic recombination has also been observed with herpes simplex virus.

RNA Viruses

Genetic recombination with an RNA virus, and indeed with any animal virus, was first observed with influenza virus by Burnet in 1951. Recombination was later found also with another myxovirus (that of fowl plague) and picornaviruses (poliovirus, foot-and-mouth disease virus). In the poliovirus crosses the proportion of recombinants in the yield was found to increase with the time between infection and collection of the sample, as with bacteriophages, with early and late samples differing by more than a factor or two (Fig. 25-28). This finding suggests that, like phage DNA (Ch. 23), the RNA molecules mate throughout their period of multiplication.

With most RNA viruses the proportion of recombinants is low (between 0.2 and 0.4% of the total yield), irrespective of the markers used. The uniformity of the results with different viruses and different markers suggests that the low value does not depend on selection during viral multiplication, and that the maximal recombination frequency of these viruses is less than 1%. With influenza virus, however, the proportion of recombinants is much higher; in some crosses up to 50% of the progeny virions may be recombinants. The recombination frequencies in different animal viruses are similar to the range obtained with phages after normalizing the different lengths of the nucleic acid.

Thus, in T-even bacteriophages the map is about 2500 units long (a unit being defined as the distance that yields 1% frequency of recombinants), and since the DNA has 150,000 nucleotide pairs, about 75 nucleotides correspond to a map unit. A comparable value, i.e., 120 nucleotides per map unit, is found for influenza virus, assuming a map length of 50 units. On the other hand, in phage λ the map is less than 20 units with about 40,000 nucleotide pairs, and thus there are about 2000 nucleotides to a map unit. And in poliovirus, with 6000 nucleotides, the total map length appears to be 1 unit: hence,

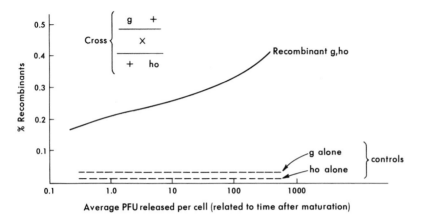

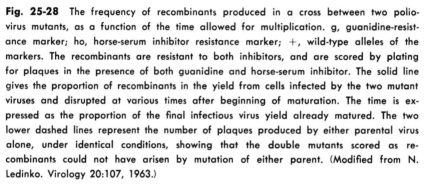

Fig. 25-28 The frequency of recombinants produced in a cross between two polio-virus mutants, as a function of the time allowed for multiplication. g, guanidine-resist-ance marker; ho, horse-serum inhibitor resistance marker; +, wild-type alleles of the markers. The recombinants are resistant to both inhibitors, and are scored by plating for plaques in the presence of both guanidine and horse-serum inhibitor. The solid line gives the proportion of recombinants in the yield from cells infected by the two mutant viruses and disrupted at various times after beginning of maturation. The time is ex-pressed as the proportion of the final infectious virus yield already matured. The two lower dashed lines represent the number of plaques produced by either parental virus alone, under identical conditions, showing that the double mutants scored as re-combinants could not have arisen by mutation of either parent. (Modified from N. Ledinko. Virology 20:107, 1963.)

the number of nucleotides per map unit is three times that of λ.

The striking frequency of recombination of influenza virus compared with other viruses with an RNA of similar size may be correlated with another special property of influenza virus: its frequently defective replication. Both character-istics may derive from extensive fragmentation of the viral RNA during replication, which could promote union of some of the fragments to form recombinant molecules, as with the T-even bacteriophages.

Heterozygosity. In contrast to myxoviruses (influenza and fowl plague virus), a paramyxo-virus (Newcastle disease virus) has failed to dis-play recombination, in spite of extensive search. This virus, however, exhibits a peculiar genetic property: in the yield of cells mixedly infected by two genetically marked strains about half the virions are composed of heterozygous particles, which on further multiplication produce virions of the two parental types, as well as their own type. These particles differ from phage hetero-zygotes in two respects: 1) they are **complete** heterozygotes, i.e., for all the markers present;

2) they continue to give rise to a high propor-tion of heterozygous virions during their multi-plication. These two properties have led to the speculation that a high proportion of the New-castle disease virions are **diploid,** i.e., contain two RNA molecules, and that heterozygous virions have one complete molecule from each parent. Since the virion is surrounded by a floppy en-velope, with an outer diameter much larger than that of influenza virus, it could even contain two entire nucleocapsids. When a heterozygous virion replicates it would produce about 50% heterozygous virions if all progeny virions are again diploid, with RNA molecules selected at random (Fig. 25-29).

General Remarks About Recombination

The results obtained are of interest for un-derstanding certain aspects of the biology of animal viruses. For example, cytological stud-ies have suggested that poxviruses multiply in separate "factories," each populated with the progeny of only one particle; but since there

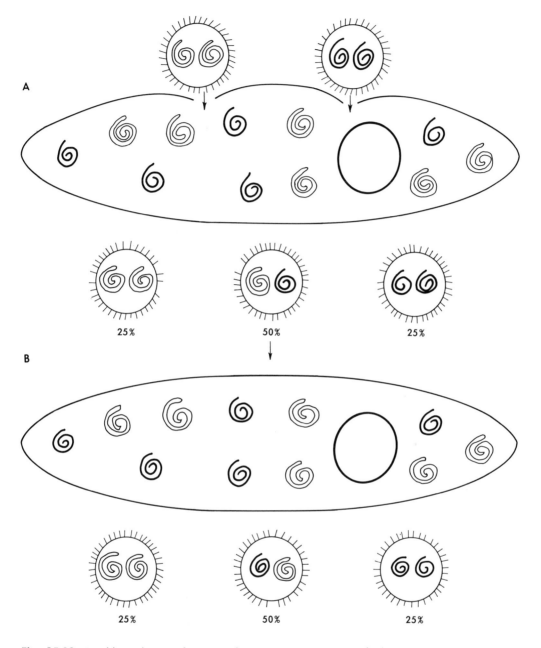

Fig. 25-29 Possible mechanism of persistent heterozygosity with Newcastle disease virus. In **A** a cell is infected by two viral particles of different genotypes; each particle is pictured with two nucleocapsids (i.e., two genomes). Both nucleic acids multiply in the cells, and when the progeny virions are formed most of them contain again two nucleocapsids, selected at random; the heterozygous particles then represent about 50% of the progeny. When a heterozygous particle multiplies (**B**) it again produces two types of nucleocapsids, and if they are again enclosed in randomly selected pairs in progeny particles, the proportion of heterozygous particles in the progeny is again 50%. The observed values are somewhat below 50%—probably because some particles have a single capsid.

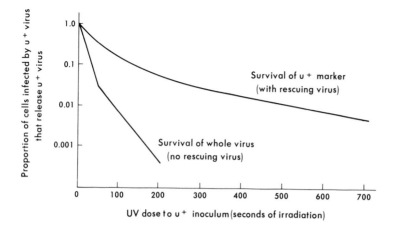

Fig. 25-30 Rescue of u^+ markers from UV-irradiated rabbit poxvirus. KB cells were simultaneously infected by variously UV-irradiated u^+ virus, at a multiplicity of 0.1 IU per cell (determined before irradiation), and with active u virus at high multiplicity. The infected cells were plated for plaque formation on monolayers of chicken embryo cells, where only the u^+ virus forms distinct plaques (on these cells u virus forms minute, often invisible plaques). The u^+ plaques formed measure the number of infected cells able to release at least one u^+ infectious unit, which was used as a measure of the survival of the u^+ markers. Parallel cultures, infected only with the irradiated u^+ virus, were used to determine the survival of its infectivity in singly-infected cells. (Data from P. Abel. Virology 17:511, 1962.)

is recombination, there must be mixing, presumably when the factories grow sufficiently large and fuse. Similarly, the occurrence of recombination in RNA viruses, both icosahedral and helical, excludes their replication in entirely separate factories. Finally, the suggestion that recombination of RNA, like that of DNA, may occur by breakage and reunion provides strong further evidence for a double-stranded intermediate in RNA replication, since single strands broken at the same site could not find and recognize each other.

With animal viruses, as with phage, recombination may contribute to genetic variability. For instance, it may contribute to the high antigenic variability of influenza virus by combining antigenic sites that have evolved by independent mutation.

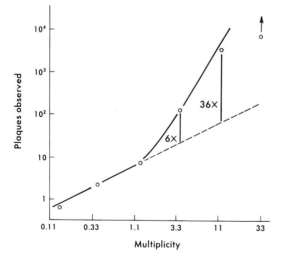

Fig. 25-31 Multiplicity reactivation with vaccinia virus. The virus was heavily irradiated with UV light and plated onto monolayers of $10^{6.4}$ L cells at various multiplicities. In the absence of multiplicity reactivation the number of plaques should increase proportionally to the multiplicity of infection with particles (dotted line), since the number of infectious units is so low. In the experiments (solid line), however, the number of plaques increased faster than multiplicity (in the range of multiplicities above 1). The encircled numbers correspond to the factor by which the number of plaques increased over the expected number, owing to multiplicity reactivation. (From G. J. Galasso and D. G. Sharp. J. Bact. 85: 1307, 1963.)

Cross-Reactivation

With viruses that give rise to recombination (vaccinia, influenza) markers from a strain inactivated with ultraviolet (UV) light can be rescued in cells simultaneously infected by active virus. This approach could theoretically be generalized for introducing desirable characters into viruses, as in the production of vaccine strains. The curve relating the frequency of rescue to the UV dose has a much smaller slope than that for the survival of the whole virus (Fig. 25-30), as already seen with phages (Ch. 23).

Multiplicity Reactivation

Like bacteriophages, animal viruses capable of recombination also display **multiplicity reactivation** when UV-inactivated. In this phenomenon as multiplicity of infection is raised the proportion of cells yielding infectious virus increases excessively (Fig. 25-31).

SELECTED REFERENCES

Books and Review Articles

Basic mechanisms in animal virus biology. *Cold Spring Harbor Symp. Quant. Biol. 27* (1962).

FENNER, F., and SAMBROOK, J. F. The genetics of animal viruses. *Ann. Rev. Microbiol. 18*:47 (1964).

HARRIS, M. *Cell Culture and Somatic Variation.* Holt, New York, 1964.

LEVINTOW, L. The biochemistry of virus replication. *Ann. Rev. Biochem. 34*:487 (1965).

SCHAFER, W. Structure of some animal viruses and significance of their components. *Bact. Rev. 27*:1 (1963).

Specific Articles

BISHOP, J. M., SUMMERS, D. F., and LEVINTOW, L. Characterization of ribonuclease-resistant RNA from poliovirus-infected HeLa cells. *Proc. Nat. Acad. Sc. 54*:1273 (1965).

DALES, S., and SIMINOVITCH, L. Development of vaccinia virus in Earle's L strain cells as examined by electron microscopy. *J. Biophys. & Biochem. Cytol. 10*:475 (1961).

ERIKSON, R. L., FENWICK, M. L., and FRANKLIN, R. M. Replication of bacteriophage RNA: Some properties of the parental-labeled replicative intermediate. *J. Molec. Biol. 13*:399 (1965).

HARUNA, I., and SPIEGELMAN, S. Autocatalytic synthesis of a viral RNA *in vitro. Science 150*:884 (1965).

HOTCHIN, J. E., COHEN, S. M., RUSKA, H., and RUSKA, C. Electron microscopical aspects of hemadsorption in tissue cultures infected with influenza virus. *Virology 6*:689 (1958).

JOKLIK, W. K. The intracellular uncoating of poxvirus DNA. I and II. *J. Molec. Biol. 8*:263, 277 (1964).

KRUG, R. M., and FRANKLIN, R. M. Studies on the synthesis of mengovirus ribonucleic acid and protein. *Virology 22*:48 (1964).

MOUNTAIN, I. M., and ALEXANDER, H. E. Infectivity of ribonucleic acid (RNA) from Type 1 poliovirus in embryonated egg. *Proc. Soc. Exp. Biol. & Med. 101*:527 (1959).

PFEFFERKORN, E. R., and HUNTER, H. S. The source of the ribonucleic acid and phospholipid of Sindbis virus. *Virology 20*:446 (1963).

ROTT, R., and SCHOLTISSEK, C. Investigations about the formation of incomplete forms of fowl plague virus. *J. Gen. Microbiol. 33*:303 (1963).

SCHAFER, W. Some observations concerning the reproduction of RNA-containing animal viruses. *Symp. Soc. Gen. Microbiol. 9*:61 (1959).

SCHARFF, M. D., and LEVINTOW, L. Quantitative studies of the formation of poliovirus antigens in infected HeLa cells. *Virology 19*:491 (1963).

SIMON, E. H. Evidence for the nonparticipation of DNA in viral RNA synthesis. *Virology 13*:105 (1961).

WECKER, E., and SCHONNE, E. Inhibition of viral RNA synthesis by parafluorophenylalanine. *Proc. Nat. Acad. Sc. 47*:278 (1961).

ZIMMERMAN, E. F., HEETER, M., and DARNELL, J. E. RNA synthesis in poliovirus-infected cells. *Virology 19*:400 (1963).

26 INTERFERENCE WITH VIRAL MULTIPLICATION AND INFECTIVITY

VIRAL INTERFERENCE

When virions of more than one type infect the same cell each may multiply undisturbed by the presence of the others, except for possible recombination or phenotypic mixing. In certain combinations, however, the multiplication of one type of virion may be inhibited to a varying extent, whereas that of the other types is normal. This inhibition is called **viral interference.**

The notion of interference developed first from observations with a plant virus, ring spot virus, which causes characteristic ring-shaped lesions in tobacco plants. The lesions then regress but the virus persists without obvious symptoms; and if the plant is reinoculated with the same virus no new lesions develop. Thus the first infection interferes with the expression of the second infection. Subsequently, a similar phenomenon was observed with animal viruses. It was found that in monkeys infection with a neurotropic strain of yellow fever virus (which by itself causes a mild disease) can prevent the usually lethal disease caused by the pantropic strain of the same virus. Protection is not caused by antibody, because the same effect is obtained if an antigenically unrelated virus (Rift Valley fever) is used instead of the neurotropic strain of yellow fever. Interference was later found also with bacteriophages, thus opening the way for quantitative studies.

The study of interference with animal viruses took an important turn when Isaacs and Lindenmann, in 1957, discovered that interference can be mediated by a substance produced by virus-infected cells, called **interferon.** Much work since then has shown that interferon accounts for many, but not all, observed instances of viral interference.

Demonstration of Interference with Animal Viruses

Interference has been studied especially in the allantoic epithelium of the chick embryo infected with influenza viruses. A typical experiment consists in inoculating the allantoic cavity with influenza A virus, **as interfering virus,** followed 24 hours later by influenza B virus, **as challenge virus:** the multiplication of the second inoculum is partially or totally inhibited. The experiments can be simplified by using inactivated interfering virus which does not multiply: interference can then be determined by measuring the yield of the challenge virus, without the need to distinguish it from the interfering virus.

With two active viruses interference occurs if the interfering virus has a quantitative advantage over the challenge virus, being inoculated either in advance or in considerable excess. These conditions ensure that the interfering virus infects all the cells (either immediately or after several multiplication cycles) **before** the challenge virus. A time interval is regularly required before maximal interference is established.

A pair of viruses that exhibit interference with a certain regimen of infection, as exemplified above, may not demonstrate interference with a different regimen. For instance, influenza A and B inoculated **simultaneously** at equal multiplicity in the allantoic cavity can multiply concurrently in the same cells, as shown by the production of progeny particles that are phenotypically mixed (Chs. 23 and 25). Even viruses of different families can multiply under proper circumstances in the same cells, as shown in various ways. Thus electron microscopy reveals adenovirus and simian virus 40 virions, which have a different size, in the same nucleus; immunofluorescence demonstrates the unrelated antigens of Newcastle disease virus and parainfluenza virus 3 in the same cytoplasm; and the same cell may contain characteristic inclusions of herpes simplex in the nucleus and vaccinia in the cytoplasm.

We shall first consider in some detail the role of interferon in viral interference, and shall then consider a heterogeneous group of examples of interference in which interferon plays no demonstrable role.

Interferon

Interferon was discovered in the course of studying the effect of influenza virus inactivated by ultraviolet (UV) light on fragments of the chick chorioallantoic membrane, maintained in an artificial medium. The supernatants, although devoid of viral particles, inhibited the multiplication of active influenza virus in fresh fragments; and the inhibitor was found to be a soluble substance. Substances of this class, called interferons, were subsequently shown to be produced by cells infected by almost any animal virus, either DNA- or RNA-containing, in tissue culture or in the animal.

Characteristics

Purified interferons from various sources consist of small proteins unusually stable at low pH (they resist a long exposure to pH 2 in the cold), and fairly resistant to heat (mouse interferon loses half its activity after 1 hour at 50°, chick interferon at 70°).

Interferons are not **virus-specific,** but **cell-specific,** in both their production and their effects; indeed, interferons produced in different species after infection with the same virus differ in both antigenic specificity and molecular weight (e.g., chick interferon, M.W. 38,000; mouse and human interferon, M.W. 26,000). Furthermore, a given interferon inhibits viral multiplication most effectively in cells of the species in which it was produced. For instance, purified interferon of chick origin is less than 0.1% as effective in mouse cells as in chick cells. (Interferon produced in monkey kidney cells, however, is effective in human as well as in monkey cells.) The basis for species specificity is unknown; it does not depend on a difference in uptake, since both mouse and chicken cells take up mouse interferon at a similar rate.

Since interferons are produced only in small amounts they are difficult to obtain in pure form, and crude preparations are almost invariably used. These consist of the fluids surrounding the infected cells (e.g., tissue culture fluid, allantoic fluid) or homogenized tissue suspensions in which viral particles are inactivated at pH 2 and often removed by centrifugation. Any interfering activity of these preparations is attributed to interferon if it is 1) nondialyzable, 2) destroyed by proteolytic enzymes, and 3) cell-specific but not virus-specific.

Interferon is **assayed** by determining its effect on plaque production by a test virus (usually vesicular stomatitis virus, because it is very sensitive to interferon and produces plaques on cells of many vertebrate species). Serial dilutions are added to the agar overlay, and the endpoint is a 50% reduction of the number of plaques.

Production

Relation to Viral Multiplication. Interferon is produced by cells infected with complete virions, either infectious or inactivated. The amounts produced in different systems differ widely. Viruses that multiply very rapidly and produce early cytopathic alteration of the cells tend to be poor producers of interferon, while viruses that multiply slowly and do not damage the cells markedly are the best producers. Notable exceptions are many arboviruses, which produce large amounts of interferon even though they multiply rapidly and have a pronounced cytopathic effect.

The relation between viral multiplication and interferon production may be illustrated by considering some specific instances. For example, an attenuated mutant of poliovirus is a much better interferon producer than the wild type, which multiplies better; and the paramyxovirus of Newcastle disease multiplies well in chick embryo cells but produces little interferon, while in human cells it causes a defective infection but produces abundant interferon.

Many viruses that multiply rapidly and produce little interferon become good producers after inactivation by UV light or heat (e.g., Newcastle disease virus in chick embryo cells, Fig. 26-1). This rule is not general, however,

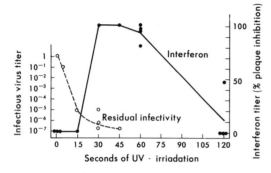

Fig. 26-1 Effect of UV light on the ability of Newcastle disease virus to induce interferon production in chick embryo cell cultures. Virus receiving no or little irradiation (less than 15 seconds) produces almost no interferon; at intermediate UV doses the ability to induce interferon production appears; and the ability is lost at higher doses. Note that maximal inducing ability is attained when infectivity is almost entirely lost. (Modified from M. Ho and M. K. Breinig. Virology 25:331, 1965.)

since arboviruses often lose their ability to produce interferon after heat inactivation.

Kinetics of Formation. Under one-step conditions of viral multiplication the synthesis of interferon begins after viral maturation is initiated; if not interrupted by an early cytopathic effect it continues at the same rate for 20 to 50 hours, then stops (Fig. 26-2). The interferon is mostly released extracellularly. If the cells survive for a longer time, as after infection by UV-inactivated virus, they cannot produce interferon again, in response to reinfection, until they have divided at least twice.

Viral strains capable of high interferon production give rise to **autointerference:** in endpoint assays for infectivity the dilutions containing much virus are less effective than those containing less virus. This effect results from the presence in the larger inoculum of enough interferon to block the further cycles of viral multiplication.

Mechanism of Production. There is strong evidence that interferon production results

from the expression of a **cellular gene.** Thus in cells infected by RNA viruses actinomycin D prevents the expression of cellular, but not of viral, genes; and when added to the cells before infection the drug prevents the formation of interferon, showing that this function depends on the synthesis of a novel cellular mRNA (Fig. 26-3A). However, if the drug is added several hours after infection interferon production is normal, suggesting that the required mRNA is synthesized before that time and persists afterward. The virus, therefore, apparently induces the activation of a cellular gene.

Production of interferon is inhibited by puromycin, as would be expected since interferon is a protein. It is also inhibited by cortisone and certain carcinogenic hydrocarbons, but the mechanisms are not known.

The requirement of cellular mRNA for interferon synthesis affords a tentative explanation for the different "interferogenic" potency of different viral strains: **viruses that**

Fig. 26-2 The time course of viral multiplication and interferon synthesis in the allantoic membrane of the chick embryo infected with influenza virus. Owing to the low multiplicity of infection several cycles of viral growth were required before progeny virus could be detected; hence the lag observed is much longer than the regular eclipse period of the virus. Note the considerable delay in the synthesis of interferon. (Modified from K. M. Smart and E. D. Kilbourne. J. Exp. Med. 123:309, 1966.)

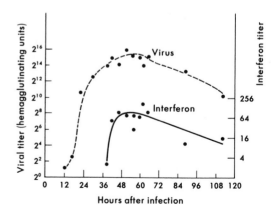

block cellular mRNA synthesis are necessarily poor inducers of interferon production. Also certain interactions between viruses become understandable. For instance, in cells simultaneously infected by a good inducer and a poor inducer interferon synthesis fails; this can be attributed to a block of host RNA synthesis by the poor inducer (Fig. 26-3B). Interactions of this type, often observed in tissue culture, presumably also occur in animals, where they may influence the pathogenesis of viral infections.

The **nature of the stimulus** that activates the cellular gene is uncertain. It probably does not involve the function of a viral gene, since interferon production is induced by many different viruses, containing either DNA or RNA. Moreover, specific gene functions (e.g., the initiation of viral RNA synthesis) are inactivated by UV light in doses that do not influence the ability to induce interferon production. Interferon induction does require the viral nucleic acid, since coreless viral particles are inactive; a moderate response can be in-

duced also by cellular RNAs of a heterologous animal species, and even by nucleotides. Interferon production may thus represent a response to **foreign nucleic acids** in the cell.

Brucella and *E. coli* endotoxins also induce production of substances resembling viral interferons, but these are probably different from those induced by viruses because they are less resistant to both acid pH and heat; this suggests that a cell can produce more than one type of interferon. The search for chemicals able to induce even more effective interferon production is one of the current approaches to antiviral chemotherapy. Interferon production is induced, for example, by a crude microbial product endowed with antiviral activity (Statolon; see below, Antiviral chemotherapy), which contains polyanionic polysaccharides and probably also RNA.

Mechanism of Action

Interferon specifically interferes with viral synthesis: in uninfected cells it causes only a mild and transient decrease in the rate of

Fig. 26-3 Inhibition of interferon production by actinomycin D or vesicular stomatitis virus (VSV). Erlich ascites cells (a transplantable mouse cancer) were infected, at a multiplicity of 5 infectious units per cell, with Newcastle disease virus. Although the virus does not undergo a regular multiplication cycle in these cells it elicits interferon production. Either actinomycin D or vesicular stomatitis virus (which by itself does not elicit interferon production) prevents interferon synthesis if added within 4 hours; later additions have progressively less effect. (Modified from R. R. Wagner and A. S. Huang. Virology 28:1, 1966.)

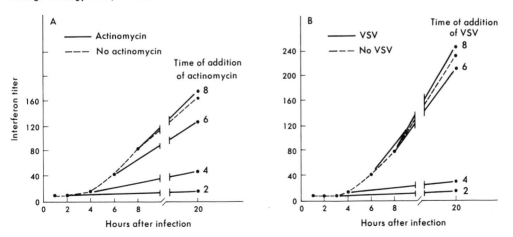

RNA synthesis and a temporary delay in multiplication. Viruses are not equally inhibited: among the most sensitive are many arboviruses, myxoviruses, vaccinia virus, and vesicular stomatitis virus; among the least sensitive are adenoviruses and Newcastle disease virus (a paramyxovirus). Interferon does not affect the virions or hinder their adsorption to cells, but it interferes with the combination of viral messenger RNA with cellular ribosomes to form functional polysomes, on which the viral proteins are normally synthesized. As a result the proteins required for the replication of the viral nucleic acid are not made, and the viral nucleic acid is not replicated. Interferon thus acts at an early stage of viral multiplication; and, indeed, in cells infected by mengovirus (a picornavirus) interferon even prevents the early inhibition of host RNA synthesis (Ch. 25).

Interferon apparently does not affect directly the viral polysomes, but induces a cellular gene to produce an inhibitor that interferes with their function. Thus when cells are infected in the presence of actinomycin D with a virus insensitive to the drug, interferon added at the time of infection has no effect.

A single molecule of interferon appears to be sufficient to initiate the inhibitor. In fact, in cells infected at low multiplicity the inhibition of viral multiplication by interferon appears to be an all-or-none effect, since some cells fail to produce virus while others produce it normally. The proportion of inhibited cells varies with the time of action and the concentration of the interferon, according to single-hit kinetics (although the curve may display a multicomponent character if some cells are more sensitive than others; Ch. 8, Appendix).

After removal of exogenous interferon the inhibition persists for a considerable period, whose length depends on interferon concentration; inhibition may even persist after cell division. The degree of inhibition decreases if the multiplicity of the challenge virus is high; presumably the entry of a large number of molecules of viral nucleic acid into the cell increases the probability of formation of functional polysomes.

Protective Role in Viral Infections

Experimental evidence on the protective role of endogenous interferon in viral infection comes from studies in both tissue cultures and animals. In **tissue cultures** this role is demonstrated by the establishment of **carrier cultures,** in which most of the cells are made resistant by interferon produced in the culture and only a small proportion are infected at any time (Ch. 25). Interferon production prevents such cultures from being rapidly destroyed by viral multiplication; the inhibition is also too limited to wipe out the infection.

In **animals** many studies have been concerned with **relating the course** of a viral disease to endogenous **interferon production.** The following observations support a **protective role.** 1) In children receiving live measles vaccine and, at the peak of the circulating interferon titer, live smallpox vaccine, the smallpox vaccination did not "take." 2) In mice recovering from influenza virus infection the titer of interferon was found maximal at the time when the virus titer began to decrease. Furthermore, at this stage the animals exhibited significant protection against the lethal action of an arbovirus injected intraperitoneally, showing that the interferon concentration was sufficient to prevent a generalized infection. 3) When the dermal tissue of the rabbit is infected with herpes simplex virus there is an early but transient production of interferon, during which viral multiplication is limited (Fig. 26-4). Viral multiplication intensifies later, when interferon is no longer demonstrable, and permanently declines only when antibody formation begins. 4) Suckling mice, which are susceptible to coxsackie B1 virus, produce little interferon in response to this virus; whereas adult mice, which are resistant, produce large amounts.

In other situations, however, any protective role of interferon is masked by other phenomena. 1) Newborn mice produce large amounts of interferon after infection by ar-

Fig. 26-4 The multiplication of herpes simplex virus in the dermal tissue of the rabbit, together with the interferon titers in the tissue and the antibody titers in the serum. Note that viral multiplication reaches a peak after interferon production subsides. (Modified from E. E. Force, R. C. Stewart, and R. F. Haff. Virology 25:322, 1965.)

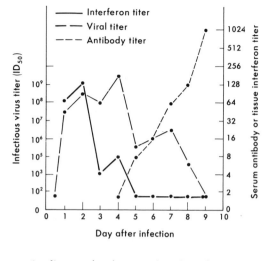

boviruses to which they are very susceptible; whereas adult mice, which are much more resistant to these viruses, produce less interferon when infected. 2) Mice of strains genetically susceptible to West Nile virus (another arbovirus) produce much larger amounts of interferon following infection by this virus than do genetically resistant mice. In both cases interferon production appears to reflect the extent of viral multiplication, which is limited by other factors.

These studies suggest that interferon has a major protective role in some, but not all, viral infections. The protection afforded appears to be especially useful because it develops more promptly than antibody production.

Possible Therapeutic Use. Interferon could theoretically be an ideal antiviral agent, since it acts on many different viruses, lacks serious toxic effect on the host cells, and has high activity.* However, its therapeutic value is limited by various factors: interferon is effective only during relatively short periods, has a reversible action, and has no effect on viral synthesis once it is initiated in a cell. Moreover, interferon is difficult to produce in large amounts.

Studies on the therapeutic value of exogenous interferon have had some limited success. Influenza in mice was delayed and rendered less severe by injecting large amounts of interferon before infection. Rabbits could be protected against intradermal vaccinia virus infection by interferon prepared in rabbit kidney cells. Some protective effect has also been observed in man: interferon prepared in monkeys inhibited the local development of vaccinia lesions in primary vaccination and inhibited certain stages of vaccinial keratitis.

Interference Not Mediated by Interferon

Inability to detect interferon does not exclude its participation in an instance of interference, because the detection methods are insensitive. But if, in addition, interference is established **early** in the infectious cycle, the participation of interferon can be considered unlikely because its production usually begins later.

A more direct, competitive interference between different viruses, not involving interferon, has been studied with both bacteriophages and animal viruses; it seems to include several different mechanisms, mostly not understood.

Bacteriophage

Homologous Phages. Within the T-even groups of coliphages homologous phages (such as two mutants of the same strain) can

---

* As little as 4×10^{-3} μg of purified interferon inhibits 100 infective units of Eastern equine encephalitis virus (an arbovirus) in cultures of chick embryo cells; thus on a weight basis the antiviral activity of interferon is greater than the antibacterial activity of effective antibotics.

replicate more or less equally in the same cell if both infect it simultaneously. If they infect at different times the phage infecting first multiplies normally and interferes with the multiplication of the phage infecting later; indeed, this challenge phage is almost completely excluded when it infects after the middle of the eclipse period of the interfering phage. Exclusion appears to result from a **change in the bacterial plasma membrane,** which prevents speedy penetration of the DNA of the challenge phage and even causes its degradation, presumably by nucleases of the plasma membrane, as shown with radioactively labeled challenge phage.

If the challenge phage is used at a very high multiplicity the many DNA molecules simultaneously released saturate the nucleases. Some intact molecules can then penetrate into the cells, where they enter the DNA pool of the interfering phage and immediately start replication. Genetic markers of the challenge phage appear in the viral progeny in a proportion that depends on the size of the DNA pool at the time of challenge (Ch. 23).

Heterologous Bacteriophages. The consequences of mixed infections vary with the degree of relatedness of the phages. Simultaneous infection with **related** T-even bacteriophages (e.g., T2 and T4) still allows the production of mixed yields, in which, however, T4 prevails over T2. The preference appears to be related to the greater resistance of T4 DNA to nucleases because it is more extensively glucosylated (Ch. 23, Host-induced modification).

Mixed infection with **unrelated** phages usually results in exclusion; which phage is excluded depends on several factors. When infection is simultaneous certain phages regularly exclude others: T-even bacteriophages, for instance, exclude coliphages T1, T3, and λ. In these cases exclusion can be attributed to profound biological differences between the phages; the T-even phages destroy the host cell DNA, whereas the more readily excluded phages do not destroy it, and may even depend on certain of its functions for their multiplication. In nonsimultaneous infection the challenge phage is regularly excluded if it injects its DNA after the interfering phage has taken control of the whole cell machinery.

Animal Viruses

Animal viruses may interfere with each other at different stages of infection. For example, Newcastle disease virus (a paramyxovirus) inhibits **adsorption** as a consequence of destruction of the cellular receptors; certain chicken leukosis viruses inhibit a step in viral eclipse. Interference between infectious poliovirus strains of different antigenic types (such as type 1 and 2) occurs at a later stage; it appears to depend on multiplication of the RNA of the interfering virus, because it can be reversed if this process is stopped (e.g., by guanidine). This type of interference may be based on competition of the RNA of the two viruses for critical substrates or for limiting replication sites.

Significance of Viral Interference

Interference appears to play a role in several aspects of viral infection in animals and man. It clearly can be important when **a live vaccine** is administered for prophylactic immunization. For instance, in human vaccination with attenuated poliomyelitis viruses the three strains must be administered in a precise sequence or at specified concentration ratios in order to avoid loss of effectiveness of one strain through interference by the others. Similarly, the presence of various enteroviruses in the normal intestinal flora may hinder the establishment of infection by the vaccine strains. Interference by viruses already present in the organism may also influence the response to an **infecting virus.** An example is the mildness of dengue virus infection in man in the presence of an attenuated strain of yellow fever virus. Therefore, interference may provide protection against infection; but it also represents an obstacle for simultaneous vaccination with different "live" vaccines.

Interferon may play an important role in **initiating recovery from viral infections,** particularly in the light of the uncertain role of antibodies. Thus recovery often occurs before there is a pronounced increase in antibody level; furthermore, recovery usually occurs without delay in agammaglobulinemic individuals. Since, however, small amounts of antibodies may be present in both cases there is no strong basis for concluding that recovery may be produced by interference alone.

Finally, in **antiviral therapy,** it seems unlikely that the use of interferon will become a general method in the immediate future, except for the control of local superficial infections. However, chemicals or viruses able to induce the formation of interferon may become important for bolstering the defenses of the organism against viruses.

CHEMICAL INHIBITION OF VIRAL MULTIPLICATION: ANTIVIRAL CHEMOTHERAPY

Because bacterial and mammalian cells differ metabolically in many ways, it has been possible to develop a variety of antibacterial agents with an extraordinarily selective effect on the parasite (Ch. 10). Viruses, in contrast, depend for their multiplication on biosynthetic processes of the host cell; this severely limits the possibilities for such selective inhibition, and only a few modest successes have been achieved. However, with RNA viruses the special features of RNA replication offer a potential site for chemotherapeutic attack distinct from host cell metabolism; also we have noted above the possibilities implicit in the induction of interferon production by noninfecting agents.

The prospects for general antiviral chemotherapy, however, are not necessarily discouraging, in view of the evidence that effective antibacterial chemotherapy does not always depend on "private" biochemical reactions of the parasite, such as those involved in cell wall biosynthesis. Thus, selectivity can also depend on quantitative differences in the sensitivity of a component common to different organisms, such as the ribosomes (Ch. 10, Chloramphenicol) or the PAB-incorporating enzyme in different bacteria (Ch. 10, p-Aminosalicylic acid). Indeed, such subtle differences appear to underlie the action of several groups of compounds, reviewed below, that selectively inhibit the multiplication of certain viruses. It may be pointed out that the most characteristic viral property, i.e., adsorption to cellular receptors, has not yet been successfully exploited for chemotherapeutic purposes, although it would appear a priori as perhaps the most logical point of attack.

Inhibitors of Known Chemical Constitution (Fig. 26-5)

Substituted Benzimidazole and Guanidine

A substituted benzimidazole and guanidine each affects only certain picornaviruses. The benzimidazole [2-(α-hydroxybenzyl)-benzimidazole, or HBB] inhibits multiplication of certain enteroviruses in this group; guanidine inhibits multiplication of the same viruses and a few more.

These two compounds inhibit viral, but not host, RNA synthesis, by preventing formation of a functional virus-induced RNA synthetase. Since these compounds do not inhibit protein synthesis, or diminish activity of RNA synthetase in vitro, they may act by modifying the configuration of the synthetase during its formation.

In spite of their marked effect in vitro, neither HBB nor guanidine has shown promise as a chemotherapeutic agent in animals, owing to the rapid emergence of **resistant** viral mutants. Viruses can also mutate to **dependence** on these drugs; and the mutations to resistance or dependence may affect the response to only one drug or to both (covariation).

Sensitivity and dependence are produced by closely related mechanisms: with sensitive virus in the presence of guanidine, as with dependent virus in its absence, formation of RNA syn-

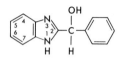

2-(α-Hydroxybenzyl)-
benzimidazole
(HBB)

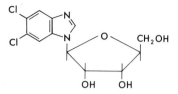

5, 6-dichloro 1-β-D-ribofuranosyl
benzimidazole(DRB)

Guanidine·HCl

Isatin β -thiosemicarbazone

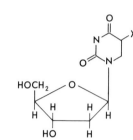

5-Substituted deoxyuridines

X = CH₃ : Thymidine

F : 5-Fluorodeoxyuridine (FUDR)

Br : 5-Bromodeoxyuridine (BUDR)

I : 5-Iododeoxyuridine (IUDR)

1-Adamantanamine

Fig. 26-5 Chemical constitution of some antiviral inhibitors.

thetase is specifically impaired. Moreover, most substances that inhibit, to a varying degree, guanidine-sensitive strains, also support the multiplication of dependent strains. Hence, the drug evidently has the same target when inhibiting a susceptible system or activating a dependent one. A useful model is provided by streptomycin and bacteria, for which it has been shown that sensitivity, dependence, and resistance involve alternative configurations of the ribosome (Ch. 10). The comparable target for guanidine or HBB is not known.

It should be remarked that the mode of action of HBB is completely different from that of another substituted benzimidazole, **5,6-dichloro-1-β-D-ribofuranosyl benzimidazole (DRB)**, an analog of purine nucleosides. DRB inhibits the synthesis of RNAs of both viral and cellular origin, including mRNA of DNA viruses; hence it inhibits the multiplication of all viruses. Its selectivity for viral syntheses, however, is too low, and DRB does not qualify as a useful antiviral agent.

Isatin β-Thiosemicarbazone

Isatin β-thiosemicarbazone inhibits multiplication of poxviruses but not other DNA-containing viruses. This compound does not reduce synthesis of viral DNA, RNA, or early proteins, but it selectively inhibits synthesis of late viral structural proteins, apparently by causing a change of the late viral mRNAs after their synthesis, and thus preventing their combination with ribosomes to form polyribosomes. Failure to synthesize late proteins, which participate in the formation of the viral coats, leads to the production of defective particles which are nearly spherical and without the characteristic internal differentiation.

The β-thiosemicarbazone drugs are of considerable practical use for the control of smallpox; indeed, one of the most active derivatives, N-methylisatin-β-thiosemicarbazone, had an impressive **prophylactic** success in preventing the spread of smallpox to contacts in an epidemic in Madras, India, in 1963.

Oral treatment of household contacts of hospitalized patients was begun 1 day after admission of the patients to the hospital. Among 1101 contacts treated with N-methylisatin-β-thiosemicarbazone and vaccinated 3 mild cases of smallpox occurred; in contrast, among 1126 vaccinated contacts not treated with the drug 78 contracted smallpox and 12 died. The much greater prophylactic effect of the drug can be attributed to its immediate effect on viral multiplication, whereas the effect of vaccination has to wait for the development of antibodies.

In contrast to this brilliant **prophylactic** success, N-methylisatin-β-thiosemicarbazone failed as a **therapeutic** agent in patients already suffering from smallpox. This failure is understandable on the basis of the pathogenesis of smallpox, because the disease appears only after viral multiplication has reached a maximum. This failure points to one of the major difficulties of viral chemotherapy; **in most viral diseases symptoms appear after extensive viral multiplication** has taken place. Prophylaxis may therefore offer a much more effective approach than therapy to the control of viral diseases.

Analogs That Interfere with DNA Synthesis

Halogenated Derivatives of Deoxyuridine. The hydrogen atom in the position 5 of uracil can be substituted by halogens, yielding 5-fluorouracil, 5-bromouracil, and 5-iodouracil. The deoxyribosyl derivatives of these compounds (ie., the deoxynucleosides) are taken up by cells and, after phosphorylation to the 5′-monophosphates by thymidine kinase, interfere with normal DNA synthesis. They thus interfere with the development of DNA viruses, sometimes causing the synthesis of noninfectious, empty viral particles.

5-Fluorodeoxyuridine (FUDR) is inhibitory because its 5′-monophosphate inhibits thymidylic acid synthetase (which converts deoxyuridylic to thymidylic acid), thus stopping DNA synthesis for lack of thymidine triphosphate. 5-Bromo- and 5-iododeoxyuridine (BUDR, IUDR) not only interfere with enzymes synthesizing DNA precursors but also are converted to the triphosphates, and then are incorporated into DNA instead of thymidine; the DNA resulting can continue to replicate, but causes the synthesis of nonfunctional proteins. Indeed in cells infected by herpesvirus in the presence of IUDR the viral DNA replicates, but viral maturation fails, owing to defects of the capsid protein. If the drug is later removed, virions are formed; they contain DNA replicated in the presence of the drug, in which iodouracil replaces thymine. The inhibition of viral multiplication resulting from this mechanism is especially effective for BUDR and IUDR, but not FUDR. BUDR and IUDR are especially valuable for their inhibitory action on herpes simplex virus and vaccinia virus in surface lesions (e.g., keratitis).

The question whether these analogs have a selective effect on infected in comparison with uninfected cells can be answered only tentatively. In cultures the same effect on the rate of DNA synthesis has been seen in uninfected and in virus-infected cells. However, **in animals** the situation may be different, because many uninfected cells are in a resting stage, with a low level of thymidine kinase activity and with no DNA synthesis; these cells are therefore resistant to the inhibitors. Herpes simplex and vaccinia viruses cause the formation of a thymidine kinase, probably virus-specified (Ch. 25), which phosphorylates both BUDR and IUDR and converts them into their inhibitory monophosphates. This step is required for the incorporation of the analogs in DNA and the lethal effect. A differential effect may therefore be created by the ability of the virus to cause the formation of this enzyme.

IUDR-resistant herpes simplex strains have been formed in Nature; they are not deficient in thymidine kinase production, and the mechanism of resistance is unknown.

Arabinosyl cytosine (commonly called cytosine arabinoside) similarly inhibits the multiplication of DNA viruses by interfering with DNA synthesis. Apparently the analog inhibits the reduction of cytidylic to deoxycytidylic acid. It differentiates less between infected and normal cells, perhaps because no virus-specified enzyme phosphorylates arabinosyl cytidine. **5-Iodo-2′-deoxycytidine** has a similar action. Viruses resistant to IUDR are still sensitive to these compounds.

Clinical Application. The analogs interfering with normal DNA synthesis have scored the most spectacular success of antiviral chemotherapy by controlling herpes simplex keratitis. IUDR is mostly used; even after keratitis has appeared, the drug, dropped directly into the eye every 1 to 2 hours, drastically reduces the period of clinical disease and prevents the formation of corneal scars. Arabinosyl cytosine and 5-iodo-2′-deoxycytidine are also effective.

The chemotherapeutic value of these drugs is unfortunately limited to superficial infections, which can be exposed to the drugs without systemic involvement, for even if DNA is damaged in the neighboring, uninfected superficial cells, almost no damage results because these cells are normally desquamated. If the inhibitor were administered internally, in contrast, it would not have a differential action, because it would affect DNA synthesis of essential, rapidly dividing cells (e.g., blood cells).

1-Adamantanamine

This compound, of peculiar structure (Fig. 26-5), inhibits the multiplication of several myxoviruses. It appears to interfere with an early step in virus-cell interaction after adsorption—perhaps a step required for the release of the viral nucleic acid in the cells. It has not yet been used for therapeutic purposes.

Agents of Microbial Origin

A number of products of poorly known constitution derived from bacteria or molds have antiviral activity in vitro and in experimental animals.

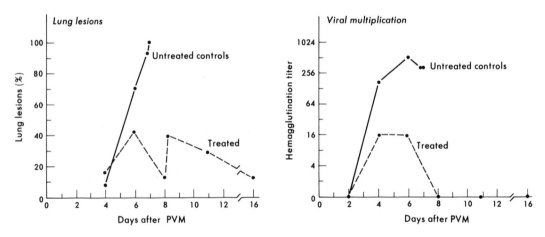

Fig. 26-6 Recovery of mice from pneumonia produced by pneumonia virus of mice (PVM) when treated with a purified capsular polysaccharide from *K. pneumoniae* 2 days after viral infection. The treatment markedly reduced both the extent of viral multiplication and the number of lesions formed in the lungs. Whereas untreated animals all died by the seventh day, the treated animals recovered. In spite of these striking results, the effect is of no practical value; furthermore it is not theoretically understood. (Modified from H. S. Ginsberg and F. L. Horsfall, Jr. *J. Exp. Med.* 93:161, 1951.)

Purified Capsular Polysaccharide from K. pneumoniae

This material can inhibit multiplication of mumps virus or pneumonia virus of mice (PVM, an unclassified virus) although the mechanism of action is unknown. In cultures it does not prevent viral adsorption or eclipse, but it inhibits viral multiplication if given during the first half of the viral eclipse period. In mice it is effective even after lesions have become detectable in the lungs.

Figure 26-6 summarizes the results of administering a single small dose of polysaccharide intranasally 4 days after infection with PVM, when considerable infectious virus had been produced and pneumonic lesions had appeared. Viral multiplication was stopped rapidly, and within 2 days the pneumonia ceased to progress. The treated mice survived, whereas untreated mice died.

Products from Penicillium Molds

Four ill-defined products endowed with antiviral activity have been obtained: Helenine, M-8450, Statolon, and Cyclopin. The two former products contain protein and probably RNA; Statolon contains a polyanionic polysaccharide, and probably also protein and RNA.

Helenine, M-8450, and Statolon inhibit the multiplication of several picornaviruses and one arbovirus, provided the cells are treated before infection. The most interesting observation concerning these products is that Statolon induces interferon synthesis, which may be the mechanism of its chemotherapeutic action. If so, it would open a new approach for antiviral chemotherapy. This cannot be the whole story, however, since the range of action of these products is much more limited than that of interferon.

INACTIVATION BY PHYSICAL AND CHEMICAL AGENTS

Inactivation is the permanent loss of infectivity of viral particles as the consequence of their exposure to chemical or physical **inactivating agents.** The purpose of inactivation may be simply sterilization, or it may be destruction of infectivity with retention of other viral properties, such as immunogenic specificity for preparing killed vaccines.

Two general problems arise in viral inactivation: the determination of **degree of inactivation,** and the **consequences of inactivation** for the various components of the virions.

The Degree of Inactivation

The exposure of a population of virions to an inactivating agent at a defined concentration for a limited time results in the inactivation of a proportion of the virions; the others retain infectivity. The extent of inactivation (i.e., the proportion of virions that are inactivated) is related to the product: time $\times$ concentration of the agent. This product may be called the **dose.** The mathematical relation between the extent of inactivation and the dose of the agent resembles that described for the action of radiations in Chapter 8, Appendix.

The inactivation of viruses by any agent yields similar **survival curves.** These curves are useful for two reasons: from their shapes it is possible to gain **information about the mechanism** of inactivation; and once the shape is known, it is possible to **calculate the dose of the agent required** in order to obtain a certain degree of inactivation. This information is essential to define the conditions of inactivation either for sterilization or for preparing inactivated vaccines. The calculation of the dose usually requires a prediction based on the experimental data available.

What is the required degree of inactivation? As shown in Chapter 8, Appendix, in the usual semilogarithmic plot the survival curves have a variable shape at low doses of the inactivating agents and become straight lines at higher doses. Since in these curves the logarithm of the surviving fraction of virions is plotted versus the dose, a survival equal to zero is never reached (since the logarithm of zero is negative infinity). In practice, the sample exposed to inactivation contains a finite number of virions, and therefore a dose can be reached at which less than a single surviving virion exists on the average in the whole sample. **Even at these doses, however, it cannot be stated that the sample is totally inactivated; and a survival corresponding to a fraction of a virion must be interpreted in probability terms.** For instance, if the theoretical survival is 1/2 a virion, there is a chance of 1/2 that a surviving virion will remain in the sample; and if many similar samples are inactivated in the same way, half of them will contain an active virion; if the theoretical survival is 1/10, 1 out of 10 similarly treated samples will contain an active virion.

Although **total** inactivation cannot be reached, it is possible to achieve a **safe** inactivation. The corresponding degree of theorectical inactivation required varies for different purposes; it depends on the **acceptable risk** of an active virion and on the **total amount of the virus** to be inactivated. In the preparation of killed vaccines, the theoretical inactivation depends on the number of individuals to be inoculated, since conditions of inactivation that give an acceptable risk of surviving infectivity for a single dose may be unacceptable for a large number of doses.

Example: A vaccine of inactivated virus is prepared, starting with a virus of titer 10^7 infectious units per milliliter, of which 0.1 ml is inoculated per individual; a 1% risk of infectious virus surviving in the inoculum is acceptable. A theoretical survival of 10^{-8} would be satisfactory for a single dose of vaccine. If a million individuals are to be inoculated, the same survival would cause 10^4 individuals to receive an infectious dose, and the risk would be unacceptable. For a million doses, the theoretical survival should become 10^{-14}, which would lower the risk to a 1% chance of one case **for the total inoculated population.**

Predictions Based on Survival Curves. Such low theoretical survivals cannot be determined experimentally, but can only be inferred by extrapolating survival curves determined experimentally for much higher survivals. **Extrapolation always involves a risk** because it is never quite sure that the shape of the survival curve in the undetermined

segment follows a predictable behavior. Barring unforeseeable events, however, extrapolation is justified if the survival curve is sufficiently well defined in the part that can be determined; faulty extrapolations usually derive from inadequate data in this region. Errors occur especially when the survival curve is not of a single-hit type, but is either of the **multiple-hit** or the **multicomponent** type (Ch. 8, Appendix), and it is erroneously assumed that the slope of the lower part is known.

The errors that can arise are of two types, as shown in Figure 26-7. If the survival curve is of the multiple-hit type (case A), the dose of inactivating agent required for achieving an acceptable level of infectivity is overestimated; if the survival curve is of the multicomponent type (case B) the dose is underestimated. Both errors should be avoided. In case A the error leads to an excessive dose, which may cause undesirable changes of the virus (e.g., decrease in immunogenicity of the vaccine); in case B a dangerously high level of infectious virus could remain. Errors of type B are more likely because multicomponent-type survival curves are common; the consequences of these errors may also be much more serious.

Inactivating Agents: Mechanisms of Action

Some agents are relatively selective, i.e., show a more pronounced action on one viral component than on another. Since this selectivity is important for practical applications, the agents are grouped according to their main target as nucleotropic, proteotropic, lipotropic, and universal (unselective) agents. Since selectivity is usually incomplete, the results vary with the composition of the virus; for instance, a nucleotropic agent will affect almost only the nucleic acid when acting on bacteriophages, which contain 50% nucleic acid, but will also damage other components when acting on influenza virus, which contains only 1% nucleic acid. The various inactivating agents are listed below.

Nucleotropic agents: Ultraviolet light of

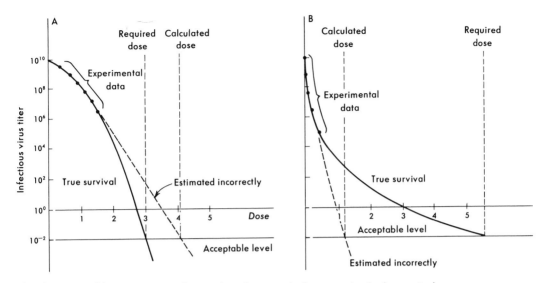

Fig. 26-7 Possible errors in predictions based on survival curves. In **A** the survival curve is multiple-hit and in **B** it is multicomponents; in both inadequately determined curves lead to erroneous extrapolations. The estimated dose for acceptable inactivation is too large in **A**, while in **B** it is only about 20% that required, and the corresponding survival is about 10^4 times the acceptable level.

260 mμ wave length; formaldehyde; nitrous acid; hydroxylamine; decay of radioactive elements which are incorporated in nucleic acid, such as ^{32}P in viruses without phospholipids, or ^{3}H incorporated as thymidine in DNA

Proteotropic agents: Ultraviolet light of 235 mμ wave length; heat; proteolytic enzymes; mild acid pH; sulfhydryl-containing or sulfhydryl-reactive compounds

Lipotropic agents: Lipolytic enzymes, lipid solvents

Universal agents: X-rays; alkylating agents; photodynamic action

The properties of some inactivating agents will be briefly analyzed in the following paragraphs.

Ultraviolet light of 260 mμ wave length acts mainly on nucleic acids. The mode of action has been discussed in Chapter 8. This agent is not well suited for viral inactivation because its damage to nucleic acids can be repaired by a variety of enzymatic and genetic mechanisms, causing reactivation (Chs. 8, 23, and 25). If this agent is used the inactivation should be measured allowing maximal reactivation by the vari-

ous mechanisms. UV is also inconvenient because it is absorbed by many substances in biological media, and shadows are projected by opaque particles; the risk of virions escaping inactivation by these mechanisms is high.

Ultraviolet light at 235 mμ wave length acts strongly on proteins, as shown, for instance, by alterations of the tail structure of bacteriophages, which prevent injection of the phage DNA into the cell.

X-rays cause the production of highly reactive and short-lived chemicals within and around the virions; these unstable products interact with various viral components (**direct effect**). The reactive chemicals also cause changes in components of the medium that produce long-lived inactivating poisons (**indirect effect**); this effect is minimized by using a medium rich in organic molecules, especially amino acids. The direct effect results in one-hit survival curves; the indirect effect results in multiple-hit curves.

Formaldehyde in the form of a water solution (formalin) is widely used for the production of killed vaccines. It reacts mainly with amino groups in nucleic acids and proteins. The amino groups of single-stranded nucleic acids are readily accessible to this agent, whereas those of double-stranded nucleic acids are not, under ordinary conditions. Thus, in virions with double-stranded nucleic acids inactivation results mostly from modification of the protein. The amino groups of double-stranded nucleic acids become available to formaldehyde if the helical structure is melted, e.g., at high temperature. This property can be used in the preparation of vaccines, since helical DNA can melt at relatively low temperatures in the presence of certain molecules, including formaldehyde. The survival curve of formaldehyde inactivation is of the multicomponent type, as shown in Figure 26-8; hence the prediction of the dose required for attaining a certain degree of inactivation is especially difficult, as previously discussed (Fig. 26-7).

Heat inactivation is caused mostly by denaturation of the capsid protein, since infectious nucleic acid can be extracted from heat-inactivated virus. Viruses vary greatly in their sensitivity to heat inactivation. The sensitivity is usually defined by the half life at a certain temperature, i.e., the time required for the infectious titer to decrease by 1/2. The greater the slope of the inactivation curve (and therefore the greater the sensitivity of the virions), the shorter

is the half life. Very unstable viruses, such as the Rous sarcoma virus, have a half life of 1 or 2 hours at 37°. The half life decreases rapidly as the temperature is raised.

Usually the half life is shortest in distilled water, and it is increased by adding salts or small amounts of protein. The half life of poliovirus is markedly increased by high concentration of cations, especially Mg^{++}, and by suitable concentrations of cystine or polysulfides. The agents that increase resistance stabilize the tertiary structure of the protein by a variety of mechanisms.

The survival curves for heat inactivation are usually of the multicomponent type. With poliovirus they clearly differentiate two components, the major one with rapid inactivation according to a one-hit curve, and the minor one with slower inactivation. The minor component is probably **free viral RNA.** Apparently heating causes a breakdown of the virions and release of RNA, which can produce plaques, but with much lower efficiency than intact virions (Ch. 25).

Nitrous acid deaminates purines and pyrimidines, in both single-stranded and double-stranded nucleic acids. It also deaminates protein.

Hydroxylamine acts mainly by the deamination of cytosine in nucleic acids.

Alkylating agents substitute alkyl groups in both nucleic acids and proteins. In nucleic acids they preferentially attack the 7 position of the guanine ring. Bifunctional alkylating agents cause cross-linking of the DNA.

Enzymes. Most viruses are resistant to the action of trypsin; some, however, are inactivated by this enzyme (e.g., some arboviruses and, under special conditions, some myxoviruses). Viruses are more readily inactivated by proteolytic enzymes of broader specificity, such as pronase. Enveloped viruses may be inactivated by some lipolytic enzymes: some arboviruses are inactivated by phospholipase A; and influenza virus treated with phospholipase C becomes susceptible to inactivation by a proteinase.

Photodynamic inactivation. The presence of certain dyes, such as acridine orange, proflavin, methylene blue, and neutral red can render virions of most viruses susceptible to inactivation by exposure to visible light of the wave length absorbed by the dye. In most cases virions become photosensitive simply on being mixed with the dye. In other cases (e.g., poliovirus) photo-

Fig. 26-8 Time course of the inactivation of type 2 poliovirus by formaldehyde, showing the marked multicomponent character of the survival curve. (Modified from S. Gard. In *The Nature of Viruses* (CIBA Foundation Symposium; G. E. W. Wolstenholme and E. C. P. Millar, eds.) Little, Brown, Boston, 1957.)

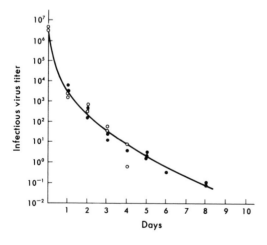

sensitivity results only when the virus is grown in the presence of the dye. Photosensitive poliovirus retains its sensitivity to light in the absence of external dye, since a certain amount of dye remains within the capsid; and photosensitivity is lost when the virus infects a cell and the nucleic acid is released from the capsid.

Lipid solvents. Viruses containing lipids in their outer coat (enveloped viruses) are readily inactivated by ether added (usually at 20% concentration) to a suspension of virions. Naked viruses, on the contrary, are unaffected. Thus ether sensitivity is a simple and useful criterion for characterizing viruses.

SELECTED REFERENCES

Books and Review Articles

HILLEMAN, M. R. Interferon in prospect and perspective. *J. Cell. & Comp. Physiol. 62*:337 (1963).

ISAACS, A. Interferon. *Advances Virus Res. 10*:1 (1963).

TAMM, I., and EGGERS, H. J. Selective Inhibition of Viral Reproduction. In (F. L. Horsfall and I. Tamm, eds.) *Viral and Rickettsial Infections of Man.* p. 305. Lippincott, Philadelphia, 1965.

WAGNER, R. R. The interferons: Cellular inhibition of viral infection. *Ann. Rev. Microbiol. 17*:285 (1963).

WAGNER, R. R. Interferon: A review and analysis of recent observations. *Am. J. Med. 38*:726 (1965).

Specific Articles

BALTIMORE, D., EGGERS, J. H., FRANKLIN, R. M., and TAMM, I. Poliovirus-induced RNA polymerase and the effects of virus-specific inhibitors on its production. *Proc. Nat. Acad. Sc. 49*:843 (1963).

BAUER, D. J., ST. VINCENT, L., KEMPE, C. H., and DOWNIE, A. W. Prophylactic treatment of smallpox contacts with N-methylisatin-β-thiosemicarbazone. *Lancet 2*:494 (1963).

CANTELL, K., and TOMMILA, V. Effect of interferon on experimental vaccinia and herpes simplex virus infections in rabbits' eyes. *Lancet 2*:682 (1960).

DESOMER, P., PRINZIE, A., DENYS, P., and SCHONNE, E. Mechanism of action of interferon. I. Relationship with viral ribonucleic acid. *Virology 16*:63 (1962).

ISAACS, A., and LINDENMANN, J. Virus interference. I. The interferon. *Proc. Roy. Soc. London S.B. 147*:258 (1957).

JOKLIK, W. K., and MERIGAN, T. C. Concerning the mechanism of action of interferon. *Proc. Nat. Acad. Sc. 56*: 558 (1966).

JONES, B. R., GALBRAITH, J. E. K., KHALAF, A., and HUSSAINI, M. Vaccinal keratitis treated with interferon. *Lancet 1*:875 (1962).

KAUFMAN, H. E. Clinical Cure of Herpes Simplex and Vaccinia Keratitis by 5-Iodo-2'-Deoxyuridine. In *Perspectives in Virology III,* p. 90. (M. Pollard, ed.) Hoeber, New York, 1963.

MERIGAN, T. C. Purified interferons: Physical properties and species specificity. *Science 145*:811 (1964).

WOODSON, B., and JOKLIK, W. K. The inhibition of vaccinia virus multiplication by isatin-β-thiosemicarbazone. *Proc. Nat. Acad. Sc. 54*:946 (1965).

27 VIRAL IMMUNOLOGY AND PATHOGENESIS

The immunological properties of viruses are of great importance to essentially every area of virology. In fundamental virology they are used to identify, quantitate, and isolate both virions and some of their unassembled components. In medical virology they afford criteria for classification and identification of viruses and for serological diagnosis of viral diseases; they provide the key to defense against viral infection through either natural or artificially induced immunity. Immunological methods are useful because they are both exquisitely specific and simple, and can be carried out with crude preparations of either antibody or virus.

INTERACTION BETWEEN VIRIONS AND ANTIBODY

While viral immunology is based on the same principles as immunology in general, there are special features to consider, especially in the quantitative aspects of virus neutralization by antibodies.

The immunological characteristics of viruses reflect the multimeric structure of the virion coat. Since the monomers are all alike, or at most consist of a small number of different types (Ch. 22), identical antigenic sites are regularly repeated many times on the surface of the virions, and this feature has important consequences for the characteristics of the antibody-virion interaction, as discussed below. In addition, certain antigenic sites are hidden by the reciprocal attachment of the monomers, but can be unmasked if the structure of the capsid is altered, as by heating or by incomplete assembly (empty capsids).

Detection of the Interaction of Viruses with Antibody

Viral antigens are studied by their reactions with the corresponding antisera, by employing both the usual immunological tests and some special ones, such as hemagglutination inhibition and neutralization. Various tests are used for different purposes. **Precipitation** is used mostly to isolate viral proteins from crude preparations, such as extracts of infected cells. **Neutralization, complement fixation (CF),** and **hemagglutination inhibition (HI)** find widespread diagnostic and epidemiological application, but are also important for research. Immunofluorescence is employed in research and diagnostically for the detection and the localization of viral antigens in cells.

Viral antigens behave in different ways in these procedures.

1) With intact virions antigens located on the **surface** participate in precipitation, complement fixation, hemagglutination inhibition, and neutralization.

2) Antigens located **deep** within the virion (capsids of enveloped viruses; certain proteins of complex virions, such as the internal head protein of T-even bacteriophages) are detected by precipitation and complement fixation after rupture of the outer coat.

3) **Unassembled** viral protein components in infected cells can be detected cytologically by immunofluorescence or, after extraction, by precipitation, complement-fixation, or hemagglutination-inhibition tests. Components that would be involved in neutralization can also be studied by their **serum blocking power,** i.e., they absorb neutralizing antibodies and consequently reduce the serum's neutralizing power.

The interaction that leads to neutralization is particularly characteristic of viruses and has widespread application. For these reasons we shall consider it in detail.

Neutralization

Viral neutralization consists in the decrease of infectious titer of a viral preparation following exposure to antibodies. Several features of this interaction are noteworthy. As with other antigen-antibody complexes, the components can be dissociated and recovered in their original forms. Moreover, the reversibility of the association often decreases with time. Finally, the host cell influences the effectiveness of the interaction: a virion that is neutralized for one kind of host cell may be infectious for another.

Readily Reversible and Stable Virion-Antibody Complexes. These two classes of complexes are distinguished by an experiment of the following kind. Antibody is added to a preparation of influenza virus of known titer at 0° to form a neutralization mixture; 1/2 hour later a sample of the mixture is added, **without dilution,** to the viral assay system (e.g., the allantoic cavity of chicken embryos or cell cultures). A decrease of the viral titer in comparison with untreated virus shows that a proportion of the virus is neutralized. If, however, the neutralization mixture is **diluted** by a large factor before it is added to the assay system, the original titer of the virus is restored. This finding shows that the combination between virions and antibody molecules under these conditions is freely reversible, i.e., there is an equilibrium between dissociation and reformation of the antibody-virion complexes. Dilution decreases the concentration of the reactants, thus diminishing the rate of re-formation of the complexes (but not their rate of dissociation).

If, however, the assays are made **several hours after the virus has been mixed** with the antibodies, neutralization persists after dilution. Hence with time the virus-antibody complexes become more stable and are no longer reversed on dilution (at neutral pH and physiological ionic strength).

Results of this type with several viruses show that virions unite with antibodies in at least two steps:

$$V(\text{virions}) + A(\text{antibody molecules}) \overset{(1)}{\rightleftharpoons}$$
$$(VA)_r \overset{(2)}{\rightarrow} (VA).$$

$(VA)_r$ represents virions complexed with antibodies in a freely reversible way; (VA) represents virions complexed with antibodies

in an essentially irreversible way, as defined above.

The equilibrium of step (1) is reached very rapidly and shows little temperature dependence, like many antibody-antigen combinations; it merely reflects the attachment of antibody molecules to exposed antigenic sites of the virion. Step (2), however, is markedly dependent on temperature: at 0° it occurs very slowly, but at higher temperature (37°) it occurs rapidly, so that within minutes most of the antibody-virion complexes formed are stable.

The reenforcement of the antigen-antibody union with time is not a property of viruses exclusively; it can be observed with ordinary protein antigens (Ch. 13, Danysz phenomenon).

Reactivation of Stably Neutralized Virus. Stabilization of the virus-antibody complex is not associated with a permanent change of either reactant, since the unchanged components can be recovered. Dissociation can be accomplished either by a physicochemical alteration of the antibody-antigen complexes or by competition with a large excess of inactivated virions of similar antigenic specificity. Commonly employed dissociating agents are acid or alkaline pH (Fig. 27-1), sonic vibration, and extraction with fluorocarbon.

Physicochemical Events Leading to a Stable Association Between Antibody and Virions. Since the combination of antibodies with haptens and soluble antigens is usually readily reversible, except when large complexes are formed (as in the Danysz phenomenon), the firm combination with individual virions probably originates from the multimeric nature of their coat. A single antibody molecule can establish two specific bonds with two sites on a single virion; and the specific bonds may be reenforced by nonspecific bonds between antibody molecules and virions. Although each individual bond may be weak, the collaboration of several may produce considerable stability. Indeed, whenever one of the bonds dissociates the others would hold, and the dissociated one would have time to be-

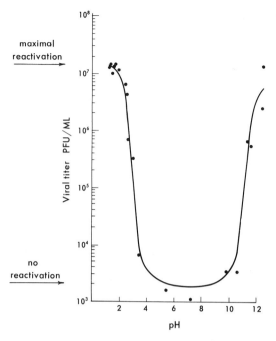

maximal
reactivation →

no
reactivation →

Viral titer PFU/ML

pH

Fig. 27-1 Reactivability of neutralized Newcastle disease virus (a myxovirus) at different pHs, showing the dissociability of the virus-antibody complexes at acid and alkaline pHs. Virus and antibodies were incubated together until a relative infectivity of about 10^{-4} was obtained (assayed after dilution). Aliquots of the mixture were then diluted 1:100 in cold buffer at various pH values, and after 30 seconds the pH was returned to 7 by dilution into a neutral buffer. The samples were then assayed. (From A. Granoff. Virology 25:38, 1965.)

come reestablished. In order to dissociate the complex **all** the individual bonds would have to dissociate by independent activation within a short time, and the probability of such simultaneous dissociation is small.

Since the stabilization of the complexes has a high temperature coefficient it probably involves structural modifications of the interacting proteins. We know that macromolecules are constantly "wiggling," the rate and extent of the changes in conformation being markedly dependent on temperature. When

Fig. 27-2 Electron micrograph of an influenza virion with antibody molecules attached to the spikes, some of them forming bridges between two spikes (arrows). (From K. J. Lafferty. Virology 21:91, 1963.)

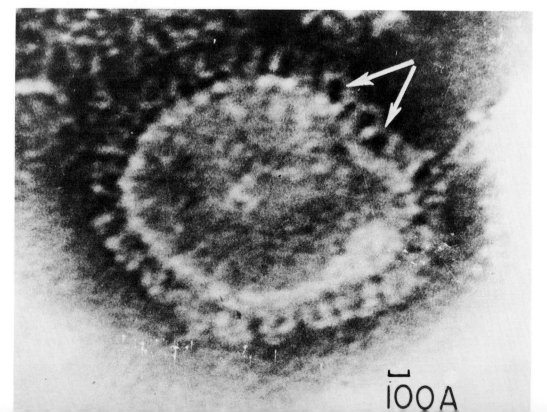

100 Å

such wiggling brings complementary groups of the two proteins into close proximity a new bond may be established. It is likely that in this way more and more bonds are formed after the establishment of a primary specific bond.

Electron micrographs of influenza virion-antibody complexes afford evidence that an antibody molecule can form two, probably specific, bonds, since antibody molecules can be seen bridging two spikes (Fig. 27-2). These bridges may be required for stable neutralization of this virus because monovalent antibody fragments produced by papain digestion (Ch. 14), which cannot form bridges, do not form stable complexes, even though they can combine specifically with the virions and cause reversible neutralization. With poliovirus, however, stabilization may occur even without bridge formation, since it has been reported that monovalent antibody fragments form stable neutralizing complexes with the virions.

Role of the Host Cells in Neutralization. It has recently been recognized that the host cells play a role in neutralization. Their interaction with neutralized virus has therefore been studied in some detail.

1) **Interaction between neutralized virions and host cells.** Neutralized virions adsorb to the host cells, provided the number of neutralizing antibody molecules per virion is small. The particles **that are adsorbed, however, do not release their nucleic acid into the cells.** The primary characteristic of neutralized virus, therefore, is failure to infect the cells rather than failure to adsorb; the latter occurs only when the virion is heavily covered with antibody molecules.

2) **Influence of host cells on the infectivity of antibody-virion complexes.** The same antibody-virus mixture can exhibit different levels of residual infectivity when assayed on different host cells under otherwise identical conditions (Fig. 27-3). This finding is of considerable interest for understanding the mechanism of neutralization. It must mean that neutralization is not the inevitable consequence of certain antibody-virion complexes, but results from a triple interaction of antibody, virion, and host cell. Virions that are scored as neutralized on certain cells, but not on others, will be called **conditionally neutralized.**

Mechanism of Neutralization

The observations reported above permit the development of a model of neutralization which, although hypothetical, aids understanding of other aspects of viral immunology that will be discussed later. The model is

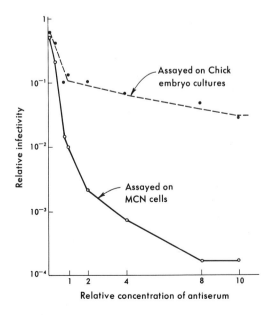

Fig. 27-3 A marked effect of the host cells used in the assay on the residual infectivity in neutralization. Vesicular stomatitis virus was mixed with antiserum at various dilutions at 37°, and after 2 hours the mixtures were appropriately diluted and plated for residual infectivity. This was done by plaque formation on cultures of either chick embryo cells or MCN cells (a line of cells derived from human leucemic bone marrow). The titer of untreated virus is the same on either cell type. (Modified from L. E. Kjellen an R. W. Schlesinger. Virology 7:236, 1959.)

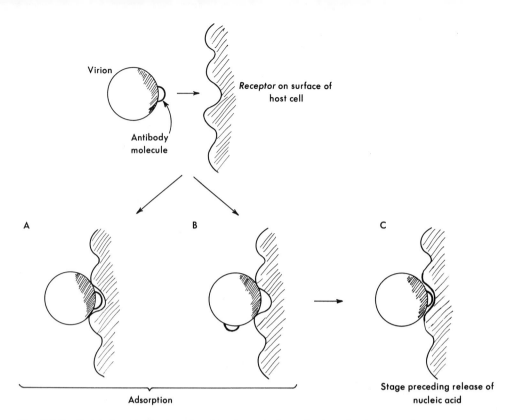

Fig. 27-4 Model of neutralization of a virion by a single antibody molecule. Neutralization occurs at a stage following adsorption and preceding release of the viral nucleic acid into the cell; the antibody is believed to hinder sterically the intimate adhesion of the virus to the cell surface (**C**). Virions adsorbed as in **B**, or neutralized after adsorption, may move around until they also reach position **C** (similar to **A**).

based on recognizing that neutralization does **not** require **saturation** of the surface of the virion with antibody molecules. Thus, cell-adsorbed virions can be neutralized, and phenotypically mixed virions with two types of monomers, produced by double infection (Chs. 23 and 25), can be neutralized by antisera specific for **either** monomer. Indeed, kinetic evidence, which will be discussed below, shows that neutralization can be produced by **a single antibody molecule.** The problem is how one antibody molecule prevents the whole virion, with its many identical monomers, from infecting the cell.

The following model offers an explanation of these seemingly conflicting facts. A virion carrying a single **neutralizing antibody molecule** adsorbs to cellular receptors in either position A or position B (Fig. 27-4). Since adsorbed virions appear to move around on the receptors (according to evidence obtained

in studies of receptor destruction by influenza virus), a particle in position B may also reach position A. This particle does not infect (i.e., it does not release its nucleic acid to the cell), perhaps because interposition of the antibody molecule prevents the required intimate contact of the virion and the cell surface (Ch. 25). This model can also account for conditional neutralization, which may derive from attachment of antibody molecules to sites of the virion that are required for infection in some cells but not in others.

Quantitative Aspects of Neutralization

Kinetics of Neutralization. Much information on the nature of the antibody-virion interaction leading to neutralization is afforded by studying the kinetics (i.e., the time course) of neutralization. A virus preparation and serum are mixed, and the mixture is then assayed for infectivity at regular intervals. The results are plotted as the logarithm of the fraction of the initial infectious titer that remains unneutralized (**relative infectivity**) versus the time of sampling.

1) **Relation of the kinetics of neutralization to the stability of the complexes.** The stability of the antibody-virion complexes affects the kinetics of neutralization as revealed by an experiment of the following type. A virus-serum mixture is made and part is immediately diluted (e.g., fivefold); the kinetic curve is determined for the two mixtures by carrying out the assay without further dilution. (It is assumed that the concentration of antibody in the mixture is sufficiently low and will not interfere with the infectivity assay.) In the undiluted and the diluted mixtures the relative concentrations of virus and antibody are equal, but the absolute concentrations differ by a factor of five. The curve obtained with readily reversible antibody-virion complexes begins without a shoulder, then decreases in slope and tends to a horizontal line (**plateau**), which is reached when the rate of dissociation of virion-antibody complexes equals that of their formation (equilibrium) (Fig. 27-5). If the undiluted mixture is diluted fivefold after reaching equilibrium (time A in the figure), its equilibrium shifts to that of the originally diluted mixture.

The curves obtained with the more stable complexes also begin without a shoulder and then tend to a plateau. In contrast to the previous case, however, the final relative infectivity is equal in the two mixtures. Since every antibody-virion complex, once formed, persists, the plateau is reached when no more antibodies combine; and the residual infectivity depends on the ratio of antibody concentration to virion concentration, which is the same in the two mixtures. In the diluted mixture, however, the horizontal part of the curve is reached more slowly because collisions between reactants are fewer per unit time. If the mixtures are now diluted their relative infectivity does not change, since the antibody molecules do not dissociate appreciably from the virions.

When the antibody complexes are relatively stable, as is usual in neutralization carried out at 37° with hyperimmune or convalescent serum, the virus-serum mixture can be diluted for assay without altering the results, and so kinetic curves can be obtained for mixtures in which antibody is in large excess over the virions. The curves obtained closely approach straight lines passing through the origin; the slopes are proportional to the concentration of the antibody and to its tendency to combine with the virions and are

Fig. 27-5 A diagrammatic representation of the time course of neutralization in a virus-antibody mixture with readily reversible antibody-antigen combinations. One mixture is undiluted; the other is diluted fivefold. Note the different equilibrium values reached. If at time A the undiluted mixture is diluted fivefold the viral titer, corrected for dilution, increases, owing to dissociation of virus-antibody complexes, and reaches the same equilibrium value as the mixture originally diluted.

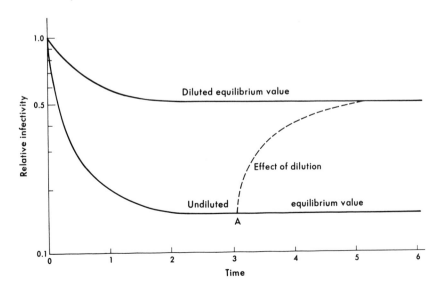

independent of the virion's concentration (Fig. 27-6). These curves follow the equation:*

$$I = e^{-ktD} \qquad (1)$$

and, taking the logarithm of both sides: ln $I = -ktD$

$$k = \frac{-\ln I}{tD} \qquad (2)$$

where I is relative infectivity; t, time after mixing the virus and the antibody (in minutes); D, dilution of the serum; and k, a constant proportional to the concentration and combining power of the antibody in the serum.

2) **The residual relative infectivity.** Kinetic curves of neutralization tend to a plateau of residual infectivity as the time after mixing virus and antibodies increases. This plateau is caused

---

* This equation is equivalent to that used in Chapter 8, Appendix. ktD is the average number of neutralizing antibody molecules per virion after time t, since molecules of antibody (which is in large excess) continue to attach to the virions at a constant rate. Thus I is the fraction of virions that have **no neutralizing molecule.** As discussed in Chapter 8, Appendix, equation (1) generates single-hit curves and is valid if a single antibody molecule is sufficient to produce neutralization; otherwise the curve would have an initial shoulder (i.e., it would be a multiple-hit curve).

by attainment of equilibrium if the antibody-virion complexes are readily dissociable, and by exhaustion of free antibody if the complexes are stable. In either case the residual relative infectivity corresponding to the plateau is a function of the quantities of virus and antibodies in the mixture.

If the **complexes are reversible** (and are tested without dilution), the **percentage law** established by Andrewes and Elford in 1933 applies: under conditions of antibody excess the proportion (percentage) of virus neutralized by a given antiserum is constant, irrespective of the virus titer. This law can be deduced from the mass law

$$V + A \underset{k_2}{\overset{k_1}{\rightleftharpoons}} VA; \quad \frac{k_1}{k_2} = \frac{(\overline{VA})}{(V)(A)}; \quad k(A) = \frac{(\overline{VA})}{(V)}$$

where V indicates the free virus; A, the free antibody (assumed to have a much higher concentration than bound antibody); and $\overline{VA}$, the antibody-virion complexes.

3) **The persistent fraction.** If the **complexes are stable** the residual relative infectivity, determined after dilution of the virus-serum mixture (Fig. 27-7), theoretically obeys the relationship

$$R = e^{-c(A/V)} \qquad (3)$$

where c is a constant, A denotes the total amount

Fig. 27-6 Kinetic curves of neutralization of poliovirus with stable antibody-virion complexes and antibody excess. Note the linearity of the curves in the semilogarithmic plot **A**, with different slopes corresponding to different relative concentration of antibodies (given by the numbers near each line). In **B** the slopes of the curves of **A** are plotted versus the concentration of the antiserum (in relative values), yielding a straight line. The linearity of the two types of curves implies that a single antibody molecule is sufficient to neutralize a virion. (From R. Dulbecco, M. Vogt, and A. G. R. Strickland. Virology 2:162, 1956.)

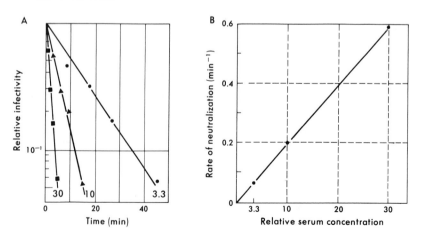

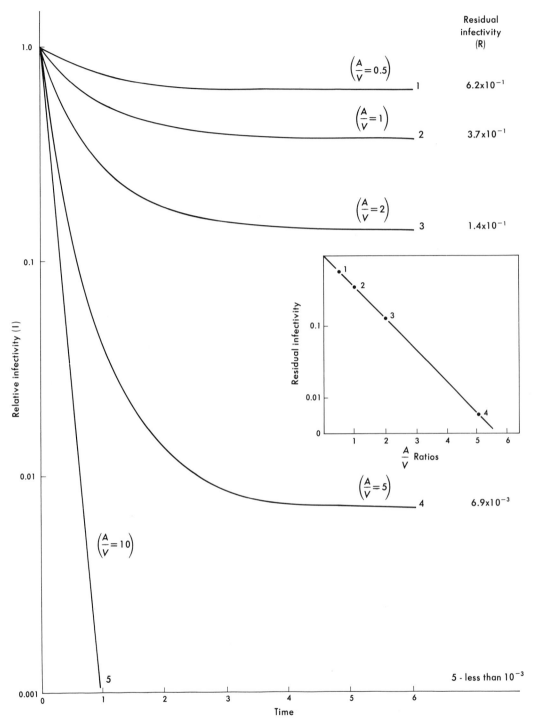

Fig. 27-7 Theoretical kinetic curves at different ratios of total antibody (A) to total virus (V) for stable antibody-virion complexes. All the curves tend to plateaus, the relative infectivity of which is a function of the ratio A/V (in arbitrary units). When the residual infectivity values are plotted semilogarithmically versus the A/V ratio they generate a straight line; this result affords additional evidence that neutralization of a virion requires only the binding of a single antibody molecule.

of antibody, and V the total amount of virus.* The problem is quite parallel to that of determining the proportion of uninfected cells at different multiplicities of infection (Ch. 23).

The kinetic curves actually obtained with a large excess of antibodies, however, show an abrupt plateau not justifiable on the basis of the A/V ratio (Fig. 27-8). The fraction of virus that is not neutralized is different in character from the residual infectivity of dissociable antibody-virion complexes at equilibrium, because it is not affected either by dilution or by addition of a fresh charge of antibody. The presence of this **persistent fraction** obscured the study of neutralization of animal viruses for a long time; since it was erroneously attributed to equilibrium, it prevented the recognition of the stable complexes. The persistent fraction was eventually shown to be caused by interaction of virions with **antibody molecules that do not produce neutralization but prevent neutralization by the conventional interaction.** These inhibitory molecules appear to be of two classes: 1) readily dissociable molecules, whose action is duplicated by univalent antibody fragments; and 2) antibody causing conditional neutralization, which is ineffective with the cells used for determining the residual infectivity.

Measurement of Neutralizing Antibodies

This measurement rests on the relations derived above. If the serum-virus mixtures are assayed **without dilution** the relative concentration of antibody is derived from the proportion of neutralized virus, according to the **percentage law.** This method is simple to perform and measures both reversible and stable antibody-virion complexes. The method is unsuitable for accurate measurement, but is adequate and is widely used for diagnostic purposes.

If, alternatively, the serum-virus mixtures are assayed **with dilution** the relative concentration and combining power of the antibody can be calculated either from the **slope of kinetic curves,** according to equations (1) and (2), or from the **residual relative infectivity,** according to equa-

---

*This equation is derived similarly to equation (1) above, except that the average number of neutralizing antibody molecules per virion is $c(A/V)$. Again this equation requires that a single antibody molecule is sufficient for neutralization; otherwise the curve would have an initial shoulder.

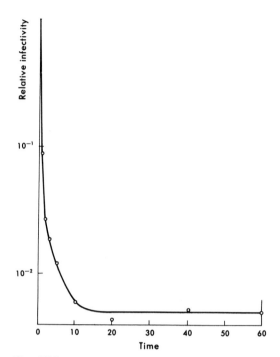

Fig. 27-8 Kinetic curve of neutralization of Western equine encephalitis virus (an arbovirus), showing the rather abrupt change into a plateau as the time of incubation increases. This plateau is not justified by the A/V ratio employed, which would have allowed a far greater neutralization. The plateau corresponds to the persistent fraction. (From R. Dulbecco, M. Vogt, and A. G. R. Strickland. Virology 2:162, 1956.)

tion (3). Although these methods measure mostly stably bound antibody, they yield results of far greater precision than the first method.

Hemagglutination Inhibition

With virions having hemagglutinating activity hemagglutination inhibition can be detected as a decrease of the hemagglutinating titer when the appropriate antibodies are added to the virus before the red cells. The mechanism is basically simple and consists of the attachment of antibody molecules to the adsorption sites of the virions, thus creating a steric hindrance to the adsorption to the red cells.

Hemagglutination inhibition differs from neutralization in several ways. In the former antibodies interfere with the adsorption of the virions; in neutralization they interfere with cell infection and not necessarily with adsorption. Moreover, there is no evidence for a special role of stable antibody-virion complexes in hemagglutination inhibition, since it is effectively carried out by univalent antibody fragments. Finally, though the number of antibody molecules per virion required to produce hemagglutination inhibition has not been determined, it may have to be high enough to cover all the sites of the virion involved in adsorption.

SPECIAL USES OF IMMUNOLOGY

Relatively simple but precise immunological tests have been utilized not only to identify viruses and to measure the development of specific antibodies but also to investigate the more general problems of viral classification and evaluation of viral antigens. The diagnostic uses of immunology have been discussed in detail in the parent volume.* The more general aspects will be considered here.

Antigenic Classification of Viruses

Because of their high resolution, immunological methods can differentiate not only between viruses of different families but also between closely related viruses of the same family or subfamily. By these means families may be identified, the members of which share a **family antigen;** each family or subfamily may be subdivided into **types** (species) on the basis of **type-specific antigens;** some types can even be subdivided into strains (intratypic differentiation). The levels in this classification are obviously somewhat arbitrary.

Different immunological tests are generally used for identifying viral families and types within different families, because the degree of cross-reaction of an antiserum with related viruses depends on the test method. Usually antibodies detected by neutralization tend to be less cross-reactive, and thus are useful to define the immunological type, whereas those detected by complement fixation tend to be more cross-reactive and are useful to define the family. By proper procedures, however, such as immunization with purified antigens, complement-fixing antibodies as specific as neutralizing antibodies can be prepared. These differences in the specificities of neutralizing and other antibodies are of theoretical interest because they allow some insight into the evolution of viral antigens.

Evolution of Viral Antigens

The great selectivity of neutralization can be understood on the basis of the structure, genetics, and evolution of viruses. Animal viruses that have evolved in the ecology of the mammalian organisms have been opposed by the immunological defenses, i.e., the neutralizing antibodies, which are able to block viral reproduction. Viral evolution must tend to select for mutations changing the antigenic determinants involved in neutralization, since such changes would improve the ability of the mutants to multiply in hosts immunized by previous infection with the original type. In contrast, other antigenic sites, detectable by complement fixation but not by neutralization, would tend to remain unchanged, because mutations affecting them would not be selected for. This process would thus force a virus to evolve from a single original type to a variety of types, different in neutralization tests (and sometimes in hemagglutination-inhibition tests), but all retaining some of the original mosaic of antigenic determinants recognizable by complement fixation.

The evolution of antigenic variation appears to have been extensive with some viruses but

* Davis, B. D., Dulbecco, R., Eisen, H. N., Ginsberg, H. S., and Wood, W. B., Jr. "Microbiology," New York, Hoeber Medical Division, Harper & Row, 1967.

not with others. These differences derive in part from the nature of evolutionary changes, which must always occur in small steps to avoid disrupting the orderly process of viral multiplication; they also derive from the structure of virions and from their habitat. The structure of the virions determines the amount of variability they can tolerate without losing fundamental attributes, such as stablity or ability to infect cells. The habitat determines the extent of immunological attack to which the virus is exposed, and this should influence the selective pressure on immunological variants.

CELLULAR AND VIRAL FACTORS IN PATHOGENESIS

The effects of viral infection on cells depend on both the characteristics of the virus (including its virulence) and the susceptibility of the cells.

Viral Virulence

Virulent viruses can produce **attenuated mutants,** with reduced virulence. Moreover, successive mutations can have an additive effect on virulence; and influenza strains that differ considerably in virulence can yield recombinants of intermediate virulence. This polygenic control of viral virulence is similar to that of bacterial virulence (Ch. 19, Pathogenic properties of bacteria).

Adaptation. A virus that has lost virulence for some cells may retain or even increase its virulence for others: for instance, attenuated strains of poliovirus, which are not virulent for cells of the nervous system of the monkey, are still highly virulent for cultures of monkey kidney cells. Serial propagation of a virus in a given host tends to select for **adapted** variants, with high virulence for that host but often less virulence for another host. This process may be used to isolate attenuated strains: for instance, poliovirus attenuated for human neurovirulence has been obtained by serial passages either in monkey kidney cultures or in the brains of cotton rats. There are no fixed rules, however, on the selection of attenuated strains, and this method is often unsuccessful.

Cell Alterations Produced by Viral Infection

Cells can respond in four different ways to viral infection: 1) no apparent change, as in some endosymbiotic infections (Ch. 25); 2) cytopathic effect and death, as with many virulent viruses; 3) hyperplasia followed by death, as in the pocks of poxviruses on the chorioallantoic membrane of the chicken embryo; and 4) hyperplasia alone, as in viral transformation to cancer cells.

Cytopathic Effect

The cytopathic effect consists in morphological alterations of the cells, usually resulting in death. There are various types, of which the following are typical. With many adenoviruses the cells round up and aggregate in grape-like clusters; with polioviruses they round up and then shrink and lyse, leaving cellular debris; with respiratory syncytial viruses they fuse, producing large syncytia; varicella-zoster virus produces large foci of round cells.

The causes of the various cytopathic effects are not precisely known, but several factors appear to contribute to their development.

Effects on Synthesis of Cellular Macromolecules. Many virulent viruses cause early depression of cellular syntheses. As noted in Chapter 25, DNA-containing viruses inhibit synthesis of host cell DNA, but not of host cell RNA and protein until late in the multiplication cycle. Many RNA viruses, in contrast, inhibit host cell RNA and protein synthesis early in the multiplication cycle.

Alterations of Lysosomes. These cellular organelles contain hydrolytic enzymes, whose release into the cytoplasm after alteration of the lysosomal membrane can cause cell destruction. Various types of lysosome alterations are observed in virus-infected cells. 1) A reversible increase in permeability of the lysosomes is shown by an increased ability to bind neutral red, the dye commonly used to stain the live cells in the plaque assay. The cells appear hyperstained and form "red plaques." 2) An irreversible damage results in disruption of the organelles and discharge of their enzymes into the cytoplasm. The cells lose their ability to be stained with neutral red and form the usual "white plaques."

Alterations of the Cell Membranes. Cells infected by many of the enveloped viruses incorporate viral proteins into cell membranes, preliminary to the formation of the viral envelope (Ch. 25). The cell membrane acquires antigenic characteristics of the virions and also, in some instances (myxo-, paramyxoviruses), the ability to adsorb red blood cells (hemadsorption). These and other effects on membranes probably play a large role in altering the cell shape. In a striking effect (observed with paramyxoviruses and herpesviruses) the infected cells fuse with adjacent uninfected cells and, after dissolution of the common cytoplasmic membranes, form giant cells (polykaryocytes).

Cytopathic Effect Without Synthesis of Progeny Virus. A high concentration of virions or of viral coat protein may initiate cytopathic changes without replication of infectious virus (**toxic effect**). For instance, vaccinia virus at high concentration can rapidly kill cultures of macrophages and other cells; mumps virus lyses erythrocytes and induces syncytial formation in cell cultures of various types; and the cytopathic effect of adenovirus is reproduced by a purified capsid protein, the penton antigen. Moreover, the cytopathic effect of poliovirus is greatly delayed if the synthesis of the capsid protein is prevented by late addition of guanidine. Such cytopathic effects, apparently produced by the viral coat (or by some lytic agent associated with it), may be the equivalent of "lysis from without" with bacteriophages (Ch. 23).

Cytopathic effects may also be caused by **incomplete viral synthesis:** for example, influenza viruses in cultured HeLa cells synthesize viral antigens and damage the cells but do not form infectious virions.

Viral toxic effects occur also in animals. In mice, for example, the intravenous injection of highly concentrated preparations of certain viruses (influenza, mumps, and vaccinia viruses) causes death within 24 hours, with hemorrhages and cellular necrosis in various organs but without much viral multiplication; intracerebral inoculation of large numbers of influenza virus particles produces necrosis of brain cells accompanied by synthesis only of incomplete viral particles; and the intranasal inoculation of large amounts of Newcastle disease virus produces extensive pneumonia, without detectable multiplication of the virus.

Development of Inclusion Bodies

Inclusion bodies, i.e., intracellular masses of new material, are formed by two mechanisms. 1) Some arise as a consequence of the accumulation of virions and unassembled viral subunits (nucleic acid and protein), in the nucleus (e.g., adenovirus), in the cytoplasm (e.g., rabies virus, Negri bodies), or in both the nucleus and the cytoplasm (e.g., measles). These large accumulations of viral materials appear to disrupt the structure and function of the cells and to cause their death. 2) Other inclusion bodies develop at the sites of earlier viral synthesis but do not contain detectable virions or their components: thus the eosinophilic intranuclear inclusion bodies in cells infected by herpes simplex virus are "scars" left by earlier viral multiplication.

Induction of Chromosomal Aberrations

Cells of **primary cultures** infected by a variety of viruses commonly show chromosomal aberrations, such as breaks or constrictions. Such effects have been reported for measles virus, several herpesviruses, oncogenic adenoviruses, polyoma virus, simian virus 40, and Rous sarcoma virus. Measles virus produces similar chromosomal abnormalities in peripheral leucocytes during **natural infections.** The alterations often appear to be an early expression of the cytopathic effect in cells that will die later. Some of these aberrations, however, have characteristic features; e.g., herpesvirus induces chromatid breaks only at certain sites of two specific chromosomes. It is also noteworthy that chromatid breaks may continue to occur during the multiplication of cells surviving infection by herpes simplex or polyoma virus, suggesting a persistent infection of the cell clones.

These chromosomal alterations may conceivably result from lysosomal enzymes mobilized in the cells, from virus-specified enzymes, or even from metabolic disturbances. The latter possibility is suggested by the occurrence of chromatid breaks in uninfected cells during drug-induced thymidine starvation.

Cell Transformation

A perplexing consequence of infection by certain moderate viruses is the production of tumors or leucemia. Tumor-producing viruses may have several effects on the cells: stimulation of the synthesis of cellular DNA (e.g., polyoma virus); surface alterations recognizable by the incorporation of new antigenic specificities, distinct from those of virion subunits; chromosomal aberrations; and alterations of the growth properties of the cells. This conversion of a normal cultured cell to one resembling a malignant cell has been termed **transformation.**

Cell Susceptibility

The Expression of Susceptibility

The susceptibility of the cells plays a critical role in viral infection. Differences in cell susceptibility generally depend on early steps in the virus-cell interaction, such as the attachment of the virions or the release of their nucleic acids in the cells: as noted in Chapter 25, cells resistant to a virion may be susceptible to its extracted nucleic acid.

With animal viruses, just as was observed earlier with bacteriophages (Ch. 23), resistance of cells is often caused by **failure of adsorption.** Indeed, susceptibility to poliovirus and coxsackieviruses correlates with presence of receptors for viral adsorption on the cell surface: in several animal hosts homogenates of susceptible organs adsorb the virions, whereas homogenates of insusceptible organs do not. In species in which viral susceptibility varies markedly with age the ability of the organs to adsorb the virus often also varies in a parallel way.

The presence or absence of receptors for viral adsorption on the cell surface depends on both physiological and genetic factors.

Physiological Factors

Cultivation in vitro may markedly alter the viral susceptibility of cells from that in the original organ. For instance, polioviruses do not multiply in the kidney of a living monkey, but multiply well in cultures derived from the kidneys, and this difference is paralleled by the presence of receptor activity in the homogenates of the cultivated cells but not of the intact kidney. Hence it is possible to propagate many viruses in cells that are readily cultured, without having to use cells that are difficult to grow in vitro; e.g., polioviruses can be propagated in human amnion or monkey kidney cells, without requiring cells of nervous tissues.

Marked changes in susceptibility accompany the **maturation** of animals. Many viruses are much more virulent toward newborn than toward adult animals (e.g., coxsackieviruses, herpes simplex virus); while some viruses (e.g., polioviruses, lymphocytic choriomeningitis virus) are more virulent for older animals. With coxsackieviruses and mice the change correlates with receptor activity, although it may also depend on changes in interferon and antibody production (Ch. 26). In contrast, with foot-and-mouth disease virus the change involves rate of viral multiplication rather than adsorption, suggesting that a step following adsorption varies with age. The age-dependence of lymphocytic choriomeningitis arises by an entirely different mechanism (i.e., when infected *in utero,* mice develop immune tolerance and infection is asymptomatic; when infected late in life, mice may develop a fatal illness owing to an apparently allergic reaction to the virus).

Genetic Factors

Genetic control of cell susceptibility has been demonstrated in mice with hereditarily altered susceptibility to some arboviruses, to mouse hepatitis virus, or to influenza virus, and in chickens with altered susceptibility to Rous sarcoma virus. In crosses between resistant and susceptible animals the hetero-zygous first-generation (F_1) progeny are usually of uniform susceptibility, depending on which allele is dominant. (Resistance is dominant with arboviruses, whereas susceptibility is dominant with mouse hepatitis and Rous sarcoma viruses.) Moreover, back-crosses of the F_1 individuals to the parent carrying the recessive allele yield 50% susceptible and 50% resistant animals. These results imply a difference at a single gene.

With arboviruses and mouse hepatitis virus the state of susceptibility of the mice is correlated with that of their macrophages and, therefore, can be studied in vitro; with Rous sarcoma virus resistance is also expressed at the cellular rather than the immunological level, since it is present in cultured cells. Since a single gene can thus control cell susceptibility its product may have receptor functions.

SELECTED REFERENCES

Books and Review Articles

HOLLAND, J. J. Enterovirus entrance into specific host cells and subsequent alterations of cell protein and nucleic acid synthesis. *Bact. Rev. 28*:3 (1964).

Mechanism of Virus Infection. (W. Smith, ed.) Academic Press, New York, 1963.

Specific Articles

ALLISON, A. C., SANDELIN, B. M., and SANDELIN, K. Activation of lysosomal enzymes in virus-infected cells and its possible relationship to cytopathic effects. *J. Exp. Med. 117*:879 (1963).

BANG, F. B., and WARWICK, A. Mouse macrophages as host cells for the house hepatitis virus and the genetic basis of their susceptibility. *Proc. Nat. Acad. Sc. 46*:1065 (1960).

HOLLAND, J. J. Receptor affinities as major determinants of enterovirus tissue tropisms in humans. *Virology 15*:312 (1961).

JERNE, N. K., and AVEGNO, P. The development of the phage-inactivating properties of serum during the course of specific immunization of an animal: Reversible and irreversible inactivation. *J. Immunol. 76*:200 (1956).

MCBRIDE, W. D. Antigenic analysis of polioviruses by kinetic studies of serum neutralization. *Virology 7*:45 (1959).

MANDEL, B. Reversibility of the reaction between poliovirus and neutralizing antibody of rabbit origin. *Virology 14*:316 (1961).

SUPPLEMENTARY REFERENCES

CHAPTER 1

ANFINSEN, C. B. *The Molecular Basis of Evolution*. Wiley, New York, 1959.

HEDEN, C. G. Defences against biological warfare. *Ann. Rev. Microbiol.* 21:639 (1967).

HOROWITZ, N. H. On the evolution of biochemical syntheses. *Proc. Nat. Acad. Sc. 31*:153 (1945).

HOROWITZ, N. H., and MILLER, S. L. Current theories on the origin of life. *Fortschr. Chem. Org. Naturstoffe* 20:423 (1962).

MILLER, S. L., and UREY, H. C. Organic compound synthesis on the primitive earth. *Science 130*:245 (1959).

PATTEE, H. H. Experimental approaches to the origin of life problem. *Advances Enzymol.* 27:381 (1965).

Phage and the Origins of Molecular Biology. (Cairns, J., Stent, G. S., and Watson, J. D., eds.) *Cold Spring Harbor Lab. Quant. Biol.*, 1966. A series of essays by pioneers in this new field.

Prebiological Systems. (S. W. Fox, ed.). Academic Press, New York, 1964.

CHAPTER 2

BAYER, M. E. Response of cell walls of *Escherichia coli* to a sudden reduction of the environmental osmotic pressure. *J. Bact. 93*:1104 (1967).

BURGE, R. E., and DRAPER, J. C. The structure of the cell wall of the gram-negative bacterium *Proteus vulgaris. J. Mol. Biol.* 28:173, 189, 205 (1967).

COHEN-BAZIRE, G., PFENNIG, N., and KUNISAWA, R. The fine structure of green bacteria. *J. Cell. Biol.* 22:207 (1964).

HOFFMAN, H., and FRANK, M. E. Time-lapse photomicrography of cell growth and division in *Escherichia coli. J. Bact. 89*:212 (1965).

KNOX, K. W., VESK, M., and WORK, E. Relation between excreted lipopolysaccharide complexes and surface structures of a lysine-limited culture of *Escherichia coli. J. Bact. 92*:1206 (1966).

MCCARTHY, B. J. The evolution of base sequences in polynucleotides. *Progr. Nucleic Acid Res. and Molec. Biol.* 4:129 (1965).

MEYNELL, G. G., and LAWN, A. M. Inheritance of capsule and the manner of cell wall formation in *Bacillus anthracis. J. Gen. Microbiol. 39*:423 (1965).

MOROWITZ, H. J. The Minimum Size of Cells. In *Principles of Biomolecular Organization* (Ciba Foundation Symposium: G. E. W. Wolstenholme and M. O'Connor, eds.). Churchill, London, 1966.

SALTON, M. R. J. Structure and function of bacterial cell membranes. *Ann. Rev. Microbiol. 21*:417 (1967).

SHARON, N. The chemical structure of lysozyme substrates and their cleavage by the enzyme. *Proc. Roy. Soc. B167*:402 (1967).

WEIDEL, W., and PELZER, H. Bagshaped macromolecules—a new outlook on bacterial cell walls. *Advances Enzymol.* 26:193 (1964).

CHAPTER 3

ALEEM, M. I. H., HOCH, G. E., and VARNER, J. E. Water as the source of oxidant and reductant in bacterial chemosynthesis. *Proc. Nat. Acad. Sc.* *54*:869 (1965).

Bacterial Photosynthesis (Symposium: H. Gest, A. San Pietro, and L. P. Vernon, eds.). Antioch Press, Yellow Springs, Ohio, 1963.

BASSHAM, J. A. Photosynthesis: energetics and related topics. *Advances Enzymol.* *25*:39 (1963).

BROWN, H. The carbon cycle in nature. *Fortschr. Chem. Org. Naturstoffe* *14*:317 (1957).

COHEN-BAZIRE, G., SISTROM, W. R., and STANIER, R. Y. Kinetic studies of pigment synthesis by non-sulfur purple bacteria. *J. Cell. Comp. Physiol.* *49*:25 (1957).

DAWES, E. A., and RIBBONS, D. W. Some aspects of the endogenous metabolism of bacteria. *Bact. Rev.* *28*:126 (1964).

FRAENKEL, D. G., and LEVISOHN, S. R. Glucose and gluconate metabolism in an *Escherichia coli* mutant lacking phosphoglucose isomerase. *J. Bact.* *93*:1571 (1967).

LERNER, S. A., WU, T. T., and LIN, E. C. C. Evolution of a catabolic pathway in bacteria. *Science* *146*:1313 (1964).

MERRICK, J. M., and DOUDOROFF, M. Depolymerization of poly-β-hydroxybutyrate by an intracellular enzyme system. *J. Bact.* *88*:60 (1964).

PFENNIG, N. Photosynthetic bacteria. *Ann. Rev. Microbiol.* *21*:285 (1967).

STADTMAN, T. Methane fermentation. *Ann. Rev. Microbiol.* *21*:121 (1967).

CHAPTER 4

ATTARDI, G. The mechanism of protein synthesis. *Ann. Rev. Microbiol.* *21*:383 (1967).

BEADLE, G. W., and TATUM, E. L. Genetic control of biochemical reactions in Neurospora. *Proc. Nat. Acad. Sc.* *27*:499 (1941).

BOREK, E., and SRINIVASAN, P. R. The methylation of nucleic acids. *Ann. Rev. Biochem.* *35*:275 (1966).

CAMPBELL, P. N., and SARGENT, J. R., (eds.). *Techniques in Protein Biosynthesis.* Academic Press, New York, Vol. I, 1967.

CAPECCHI, M. R. Polypeptide chain termination in vitro: isolation of a release factor. *Proc. Nat. Acad. Sc.* *58*:1155 (1967).

CUNDLIFFE, E., and MCQUILLEN, K. Bacterial protein syntheses: the effects of antibiotics. *J. Mol. Biol.* *30*:137 (1967).

DAVIS, B. D. Studies on nutritionally deficient bacterial mutants isolated by means of penicillin. *Experientia* *6*:41 (1950).

EISENSTADT, J. M., and BRAWERMAN, G. The role of the native subribosomal particles of *Escherichia coli* in polypeptide chain initiation. *Proc. Nat. Acad. Sc.* *58*:1560 (1967).

EVANS, M. C. W., BUCHANAN, B. B., and ARNON, D. I. A new ferredoxin-dependent carbon reduction cycle in a photosynthetic bacterium. *Proc. Nat. Acad. Sc.* *55*:928 (1966).

GILVARG, C., and DAVIS, B. D. The role of the tricarboxylic acid cycle in acetate oxidation in *Escherichia coli*. *J. Biol. Chem.* *222*:307 (1956).

HIRSCH, C. A., RASMINSKY, M., DAVIS, B. D., and LIN, E. C. C. A fumarate reductase in *Escherichia coli* distinct from succinate dehydrogenase. *J. Biol. Chem.* *238*:3770 (1963).

KAEMPFER, R. O. R., MESELSON, M., and RASKAS, H. J. Cyclic dissociation into stable subunits and reformation of ribosomes during bacterial growth. *J. Mol. Biol.*, 1968, in press.

KORNBERG, A. Biologic synthesis of deoxyribonucleic acid (Nobel lecture). *Science* *131*:1503 (1960).

KORNBERG, H. L., and ELSDEN, S. R. The metabolism of 2-carbon compounds by microorganisms. *Advances Enzymol.* *23*:401 (1961).

KREBS, H. A., and LOWENSTEIN, J. M. The Tricarboxylic Acid Cycle. In *Metabolic Pathways* (D. M. Greenberg, ed.). Academic Press, New York, Vol. 1, 1960.

MONROE, R. E., and VASQUEZ, D. Ribosome-catalyzed peptidyl transfer: effect of some inhibitors of protein synthesis. *J. Mol. Biol.* *28*:121 (1967).

NIKAIDO, H., NIKAIDO, K., and MAKELA, P. H. Genetic determination of enzymes synthesizing O-specific sugars of *Salmonella* lipopolysaccharides. *J. Bact.* *91*:1126 (1966).

NOMURA, M., and LOWRY, C. V. The role of 30S ribosomal subunits in initiation of protein synthesis. *Proc. Nat. Acad. Sc. 58*:946 (1967).

SABLE, H. Z. Biosynthesis of ribose and deoxyribose. *Advances Enzymol. 28*:391 (1966).

OSAWA, S. Biosynthesis of ribosomes in bacterial cells. *Progr. Nucleic Acid Res. and Molec. Biol. 4*:161 (1965).

ROBBINS, P. W., BRAY, D., DANKERT, M., and WRIGHT, A. Direction of chain growth in polysaccharide synthesis. *Science 158*:1536 (1967).

SRINIVASAN, P. R., and BOREK, E. Enzymatic alteration of macromolecular structure. *Progr. Nucleic Acid Res. and Molec. Biol. 5*:157 (1966).

Synthesis and Structure of Macromolecules. *Cold Spring Harbor Symp. Quant. Biol. 28*, 1963.

TRAUT, R. R., MOORE, P. B., DELIUS, H., NOLLER, H., and TISSIÈRES, A. Ribosomal proteins of *Escherichia coli.* I. Demonstration of different primary structures. *Proc. Nat. Acad. Sc. 57*:1294 (1967).

WOOD, H. G., and UTTER, M. F. The Role of CO_2 Fixation in Metabolism. In *Essays in Biochemistry* (P. N. Campbell and G. D. Greville, eds.). Academic Press, New York, Vol. 1, 1965.

WRIGHT, A., DANKERT, M., FENNESSEY, P., and ROBBINS, P. W. Characterization of a polyisoprenoid compound functional in O-antigen biosynthesis. *Proc. Nat. Acad. Sc. 57*:1798 (1967).

CHAPTER 5

ADLER, J. Chemotaxis in bacteria. *Science 153*:708 (1966).

DREYFUSS, J., and PARDEE, A. B. Regulation of sulfate transport in *Salmonella typhimurium. J. Bact. 91*:2275 (1966).

FALASCHI, A., and KORNBERG, A. Biochemical studies of bacterial sporulation. II. DNA polymerase in spores of *Bacillus subtilis. J. Biol. Chem. 241*:1478 (1966).

FARRELL, J., and ROSE, A. Temperature effects on microorganisms. *Ann. Rev. Microbiol. 21*:101 (1967).

FINSTEIN, M. S., and DELWICHE, C. C. Molybdenum as a micronutrient for Nitrobacter. *J. Bact. 89*:123 (1965).

HELMSTETTER, C. E., and CUMMINGS, D. J. Bacterial synchronization by selection of cells at division. *Proc. Nat. Acad. Sc. 50*:767 (1963). See also *Biochim. Biophys. Acta 82*:608 (1964).

HEPPEL, L. A. Selective release of enzymes from bacteria. *Science 156*:1451 (1967).

KABACK, H. R., and STADTMAN, E. R. Proline uptake by an isolated cytoplasmic membrane preparation of *Escherichia coli. Proc. Nat. Acad. Sc. 55*:920 (1966).

KELLER-SCHIERLEIN, W., PRELOG, V., and ZÄHNER, H. Siderochrome. (Natürliche Eisen (III)-trihydroxamat-Komplexe). *Fortschr. Chem. Org. Naturstoffe 22*:279 (1964).

LARSEN, H. Biochemical aspects of extreme halophilism. *Advances Microb. Physiol. 1*:97 (1967).

MURRELL, W. G. The biochemistry of the bacterial endospore. *Advances Microb. Physiol. 1*:133 (1967).

NOVICK, A., and SZILARD, L. Experiments with the Chemostat on the Rates of Amino Acid Synthesis in Bacteria. In *Dynamics of Growth Processes*. Princeton University Press, 1954.

O'DONOVAN, G. A., and INGRAHAM, J. L. Cold-sensitive mutants of *Escherichia coli* resulting from increased feedback inhibition. *Proc. Nat. Acad. Sc. 54*:451 (1965).

POSTGATE, J. R. Viability 'measurements of the survival of microbes under minimum stress. *Advances Microb. Physiol. 1*:1 (1967).

SCHAEFFER, P., MILLET, J., and AUBERT, J.-P. Catabolic repression of bacterial sporulation. *Proc. Nat. Acad. Sc. 54*:704 (1965).

SCHLEGEL, H. G., and JANNASCH, H. W. Enrichment cultures. *Ann. Rev. Microbiol. 21*:49 (1967).

TANAKA, S., and LIN, E. C. C. Two classes of pleiotropic mutants of *Aerobacter aerogenes* lacking components of a phosphoenopyruvate-dependent phosphotransferase system. *Proc. Nat. Acad. Sc. 57*:913 (1967). (Reinterprets the apparent active transport of a number of sugars.)

TONO, H., and KORNBERG, A. Biochemical studies of bacterial sporulation. IV. Inorganic pyrophosphotase of vegetative cells and spores of *Bacillus megaterium. J. Bact. 93*:1819 (1967).

TREVITHICK, J. R., and METZENBERG, R. L. Molecular sieving by *Menospora* cell walls during secretion of invertase enzymes. *J. Bact. 92*:1010 (1966).

CHAPTER 6

FINCHAM, J. R. S., and DAY, P. R. *Fungal Genetics*. Blackwell, Oxford, 1963.

PEARCE, U. B., and STOCKER, B. A. D. Phase variation of flagellar antigens in Salmonella: abortive transduction studies. *J. Gen. Microbiol.* 49:335 (1967).

CHAPTER 7

ADELBERG, E. A., and BURNS, S. N. Genetic variation in the sex factor of *E. coli*. *J. Bact.* 79:321 (1960).

CLARK, D. J., and MAALOE, O. DNA replication and the division cycle in *Escherichia coli*. *J. Mol. Biol.* 23:99 (1967).

DATTA, N., LAWN, A. M., and MEYNELL, E. The relationship of F type piliation and F phage sensitivity to drug resistance transfer in R^+F^- *Escherichia coli* K12. *J. Gen. Microbiol.* 45:365 (1966).

GUTHRIE, G. D., and SINSHEIMER, R. L. Infection of protoplasts of *Escherichia coli* by subviral particles of Bacteriophage ϕx174. *J. Mol. Biol.* 2:297 (1960).

HAYES, W. Recombination in *Bact. coli* K-12: unidirectional transfer of genetic material. *Nature* 169:118 (1952).

HAYES, W. The kinetics of the mating process in *Escherichia coli*. *J. Gen. Microbiol.* 16:97 (1957).

HIROTA, Y. Mutants of the sex factor in *E. coli* K12. *Genetics* 44:515 (1959).

HOTCHKISS, R. D. Gene, Transforming Principle, and DNA. In *Phage and the Origins of Molecular Biology* (J. C. Cairns, G. S. Stent, and J. D. Watson, eds.). *Cold Spring Harbor Lab. Quant. Biol.*, 1966.

JACOB, F. Genetics of the bacterial cell (Nobel lecture). *Science* 152:1470 (1966).

LACKS, S., GREENBERG, B., and CARLSON, K. Fate of donor DNA in pneumococcal transformation. *J. Mol. Biol.* 29:327 (1967).

LEDERBERG, J. Aberrant heterozygotes in *Escherichia coli*. *Proc. Nat. Acad. Sc.* 35:178 (1949).

MAAS, W. K., and CLARK, A. J. Studies on the mechanism of repression of arginine biosynthesis in *Escherichia coli*. II. Dominance of repressibility in diploids. *J. Mol. Biol.* 8:365 (1964).

ROWND, R., NAKAYA, R., and NAKAMURA, A. Molecular nature of the drug-resistance factors of the Enterobacteriaceae. *J. Mol. Biol.* 17:376 (1966).

TOMASZ, A., and HOTCHKISS, R. D. Regulation of the transformability of pneumococcal cultures by macromolecular cell products. *Proc. Nat. Acad. Sc* 51:480 (1964).

ZINDER, N., and LEDERBERG, J. Genetic exchange in Salmonella. *J. Bact.* 64:679 (1952).

CHAPTER 8

ANDOH, T., and GAREN, A. Fractionation of a serine transfer RNA containing suppressor activity. *J. Mol. Biol.* 24:129 (1967).

BRAMMER, W. J., BERGER, H., and YANOFSKY, C. Altered amino acid sequences produced by reversion of frameshift mutants of tryptophan synthetase A gene of *E. coli*. *Proc. Nat. Acad. Sc.* 58:1499 (1967).

BRENNER, S., BARNETT, L., KATZ, E. R., and CRICK, F. H. C. UGA: A third nonsense triplet in the genetic code. *Nature* 213:449 (1967).

CAIRNS, J., and DAVERN, C. I. Effect of ^{32}P decay upon DNA synthesis by a radiation-sensitive strain of *Escherichia coli*. *J. Mol. Biol.* 17:418 (1966).

CAPRA, J. D., and PETERKOFSKY, A. The coding properties of methyldeficient leucyl-transfer RNA. *J. Mol. Biol.* 21:455 (1966).

CHAI, N., and LARK, K. G. Segregation of deoxyribonucleic acid in bacteria: association of the segregating unit with the cell envelope. *J. Bacteriol.* 94:415 (1967).

CLARK, A. J., CHAMBERLIN, M., BOYCE, R. P., and HOWARD-FLANDERS, P. Abnormal metabolic response to ultraviolet light of a recombination deficient mutant of *Escherichia coli* K12. *J. Mol. Biol.* 19:442 (1966).

CLARK, B. F. C., and MARCKER, K. A. N-formyl-methionyl-s ribonucleic acid and chain initiation in protein biosynthesis. Polypeptide synthesis directed by a bacteriophage ribonucleic acid in a cell-free system. *Nature 211*:378 (1966).

CRICK, F. H. C. Codon-anticodon pairing: the wobble hypothesis. *J. Mol. Biol. 19*:548 (1966).

CRICK, F. H. C., and BRENNER, S. The absolute sign of certain phase-shift mutants in bacteriophage T4. *J. Mol. Biol. 26*:361 (1967).

FITCH, W. M. Evidence suggesting a partial, internal duplication in the ancestral gene for heme-containing globins. *J. Mol. Biol. 16*:17 (1966).

FULLER, W., and HODGSON, A. Conformation of the anticodon loop in t-RNA. *Nature 215*:817 (1967).

GUEST, J. R., and YANOFSKY, C. Relative orientation of gene, messenger and polypeptide chain. *Nature 210*:799 (1966).

HOWARD-FLANDERS, P., BOYCE, R. P., and THERIOT, L. Three loci in *Escherichia coli* K-12 that control the excision of pyrimidine dimers and certain other mutagen products from DNA. *Genetics 53*:1119 (1966).

KELLOGG, D. A., DOCTOR, B. P., LOEBEL, J. E., and NIRENBERG, M. W. RNA codons and protein synthesis. IX. Synonym codon recognition by multiple species of valine-, alanine-, and methionine-s RNA. *Proc. Nat. Acad. Sc. 55*:912 (1966).

KLOTZ, I M. Protein subunits: a table. *Science 155*:697 (1967).

LEDER, P., and NAU, M. M. Initiation of protein synthesis. III. Factor-GTP-codon-dependent binding of F-MET-tRNA to ribosomes. *Proc. Nat. Acad. Sc. 58*:774 (1967).

MARSHALL, R. E., CASKEY, C. T., and NIRENBERG, M. Fine structure of RNA codewords recognized by bacterial, amphibian, and mammalian transfer RNA. *Science 155*:820 (1967) .

SALSER, W., GESTELAND, R. F., and BOLLE, A. *In vitro* synthesis of bacteriophage lysozyme. *Nature 215*:588 (1967).

SARABHAI, A., and BRENNER, S. A mutant which reinitiates the polypeptide chain after chain termination. *J. Mol. Biol. 27*:145 (1967).

TERZAGHI, E., OKADA, Y., STREISINGER, G., EMRICH, J., INOUYE, M., and TSUGITA, A. Change of a sequence of amino acids in phage T4 lysozyme by acridine-induced mutations. *Proc. Nat. Acad. Sc. 56*:500 (1966).

WITKIN, E. M. Radiation-induced mutations and their repair. *Science 152*:1345 (1966).

YANOFSKY, C., COX, E. C., and HORN, V. The unusual mutagenic specificity of an *E. coli* mutator gene. *Proc. Nat. Acad. Sc. 55*:274 (1966).

YANOFSKY, C., DRAPEAU, G. R., GUEST, J. R., and CARLTON, B. C. The complete amino acid sequence of the tryptophan synthetase A protein (α subunit) and its colinear relationship and the genetic map of the A gene. *Proc. Nat. Acad. Sc. 57*:296 (1967).

ZIPSER, D. Orientation of nonsense codons on the genetic map of the lac operon. *Science 157*:1176 (1967).

CHAPTER 9

AMES, B. N., and HARTMAN, P. E. The histidine operon. *Cold Spring Harbor Symp. Quant. Biol. 28*:349 (1963).

ATKINSON, D. E. Regulation of enzyme activity. *Ann. Rev. Biochem. 35*:85 (1966).

BERBERICH, M. A., KOVACH, J. S., and GOLDBERGER, R. F. Chain initiation in a polycistronic message: sequential versus simultaneous depression of the enzymes for histidine biosynthesis in *Salmonella typhimurium*. *Proc. Nat. Acad. Sc. 51*:1857 (1967).

CAPECCHI, M. R. Polarity in vitro. *J. Mol. Biol. 30*:213 (1967).

DAS, H. K., GOLDSTEIN, A., and LOWNEY, L. Attachment of ribosomes to nascent messenger RNA in *Escherichia coli*. *J. Mol. Biol. 24*:231 (1967).

DATTA, P., and GEST, H. Control of enzyme activity by concerted feedback inhibition. *Proc. Nat. Acad. Sc. 52*:1004 (1964).

ENGLESBERG, E., IRR, J., POWER, J., and LEE, N. Positive control of enzyme synthesis by gene C in the L-arabinose system. *J. Bac. 90*:946 (1965).

The Genetic Code. *Cold Spring Harbor Symp. Quant. Biol. 31*, 1966. Especially sections on Polarity, Punctuation, and Control of Gene Expression.

GILBERT, W., and MÜLLER-HILL, B. Isolation of the Lac repressor. *Proc. Nat. Acad. Sc. 56*:1891 (1966).

HAROLD, F. M., and HAROLD, R. L. Degradation of inorganic polyphosphate in mutants of *Aerobacter aerogenes*. *J. Bact. 89*:1262 (1965).

HAYASHI, M., SPIEGELMAN, S., FRANKLIN, N., and LURIA, S. E. Separation of the RNA message transcribed in response to a specific inducer. *Proc. Nat. Acad. Sc. 49*:729 (1963).

HAYASHI, S., and LIN, E. C. C. Product induction of glycerol kinase in *Escherichia coli*. *J. Mol. Biol. 14*:515 (1965).

JACOB, F., BRENNER, S., and CUZIN, F. On the regulation of DNA synthesis in bacteria. *Cold Spring Harbor Symp. Quant. Biol. 28*:329 (1963).

JENSEN, R. A., NASSER, D. S., and NESTER, E. W. Comparative control of a branch-point enzyme in microorganisms. *J. Bact. 94*:1582 (1967).

KAEMPFER, R. O. R., and MAGASANIK, B. Mechanism of β-galactosidase induction in *Escherichia coli*. *J. Mol. Biol. 27*:475 (1967).

KJELDGAARD, N. O., Regulation of nucleic acid and protein formation in bacteria. *Advances Microb. Physiol. 1*:39 (1967).

KUBITSCHEK, H. E., BENDIGKEIT, N. E., and LOKEN, M. R. Onset of DNA synthesis during the cell cycle in chemostat cultures. *Proc. Nat. Acad. Sc. 57*:1611 (1967).

LARK, K. G. Regulation of chromosome replication and segregation in bacteria. *Bact. Rev. 30*:3 (1966).

LOOMIS, W. F., JR., and MAGASANIK, B. The catabolite repression gene of the *lac* operon in *Escherichia coli*. *J. Mol. Biol. 23*:487 (1967).

MARTIN, R. G., SILBERT, D. F., SMITH, D. W. E., and WHITFIELD, H. J., JR. Polarity in the histidine operon. *J. Mol. Biol. 21*:357 (1966).

MONOD, J., WYMAN, J., and CHANGEUX, J.-P. On the nature of allosteric transitions: a plausible model. *J. Mol. Biol. 12*:88 (1965).

NEWTON, W. A., BECKWITH, J. R., ZIPSER, D., and BRENNER, S. Nonsense mutants and polarity in the *lac* operon of *Escherichia coli*. *J. Mol. Biol. 14*:290 (1965).

OISHI, M., YOSHIKAWA, H., and SUEOKA, N. Synchrononous and dichotomous replications of the *Bacillus subtilis* chromosome during spore germination. *Nature 204*:1069 (1964).

PTASHNE, M. Isolation of the phage repressor. *Proc. Nat. Acad. Sc. 57*:306 (1967).

Regulation of Nucleic Acid and Protein Biosynthesis (Internat. Symp.: V. V. Koningsberger and L. Bosch, eds.). Elsevier, New York, 1967.

ROSSET, R., JULIEN, J., and MONIER, R. Ribonucleic acid composition of bacteria as a function of growth rate. *J. Mol. Biol. 18*:308 (1966).

ROTH, J. R., ANTON, D. N., and HARTMAN, P. E. Histidine regulatory mutants in *Salmonella typhimurium*. *J. Mol. Biol. 22*:305 (1966).

SADLER, J. R., and NOVICK, A. The properties of repressor and the kinetics of its action. *J. Mol. Biol. 12*:305 (1965).

SCHLEIF, R. Control of production of ribosomal protein. *J. Mol. Biol. 27*:41 (1967).

SHEPPARD, D. E., and ENGLESBERG, E. Further evidence for positive control of the L-arabinose system by Gene *ara*C. *J. Mol. Biol. 25*:443 (1967).

SINGER, M. F., and LEDER, P. Messenger RNA: an evaluation. *Ann. Rev. Biochem. 35*:195 (1966).

STADTMAN, E. R. Allosteric regulation of enzyme activity. *Advances Enzymol. 28*:41 (1966).

VOGEL, H. J., and VOGEL, R. H. Regulation of protein synthesis. *Ann. Rev. Biochem. 36*:519 (1967).

WU, H. C. P. Role of the galactose transport system in the establishment of endogenous induction of the galactose operon in *Escherichia coli*. *J. Mol. Biol. 24*:213 (1967).

YANOFSKY, C., and ITO, J. Nonsense codons and polarity in the tryptophan operon. *J. Mol. Biol. 21*:313 (1966).

CHAPTER 10

ANDERSON, P., DAVIES, J., and DAVIS, B. D. Effect of spectinomycin on polypeptide synthesis in extracts of *Escherichia coli*. *J. Mol. Biol. 29*:203 (1967).

BATCHELOR, F. R., CHAIN, E. B., and ROLINSON, G. N. 6-Aminopenicillanic acid. *Proc. Roy. Soc. London B154*:478 (1961). See also pp. 490, 498, 509, 514, 522.

CITRI, N., and POLLOCK, M. R. The biochemistry and function of β-lactanase (penicillinase). *Advances Enzymol. 28:237* (1966).

DAVIES, J., GILBERT, W., and GORINI, L. Streptomycin, suppression, and the code. *Proc. Nat. Acad. Sc. 55:883* (1964).

DEITZ, W. H., COOK, T. M., and GOSS, W. A. Mechanism of action of nalidixic acid. *J. Bact. 91:768, 774* (1966).

FOX, J. J., WATANABE, K. A., and BLOCH, A. Nucleoside antibiotics. *Progr. Nucleic Acid Res. and Mol. Biol. 5:251* (1966).

JACOBY, G. A., and GORINI, L. Mechanism of Action of Aminoglycosides. In *Mechanism of Action and Biosynthesis of Antibiotics* (D. Gottlieb and P. Shaw, eds.). Springer-Verlag, Berlin, 1967.

LEON, S. A., and BROCK, T. D. Effect of streptomycin and neomycin on physical properties of the ribosome. *J. Mol. Biol. 34:391* (1967).

LIKOVER, T. E., and KURLAND, C. G. Ribosomes from a streptomycin-dependent strain of *Escherichia coli*. *J. Mol. Biol. 25:497* (1967).

OKAMOTO, S., and SUZUKI, Y. Chloramphenicol, dehydrostreptomycin-, and kanamycin-inactivating enzymes from multiple drug-resistant *Escherichia coli* carring episome "R." *Nature 208:1301* (1965).

PESTKA, S., MARSHALL, R., and NIRENBERG, M. Effect of streptomycin on the formation of ribosome-sRNA complexes. *Proc. Nat. Acad. Sc. 53:639* (1965).

SIEWERT, G., and STROMINGER, J. L. Bacitracin: an inhibitor of the dephosphorylation of lipid pyrophosphate, an intermediate in the biosynthesis of the peptidoglycan of bacterial cell walls. *Proc. Nat. Acad. Sc. 57:767* (1967).

SILVER, S., and WENDT, L. Mechanism of action of phenethyl alcohol: breakdown of the cellular permeability barrier. *J. Bact. 93:560* (1967).

SMITH, D. H., and DAVIS, B. D. Mode of action of novobiocin in *Escherichia coli*. *J. Bact. 93:71* (1967).

SPOTTS, C. R., and STANIER, R. Y. Mechanism of streptomycin action on bacteria: a unitary hypothesis. *Nature 192:633* (1961).

STAEHELIN, T., and MESELSON, M. Determination of streptomycin sensitivity by a subunit of the 30 S ribosome of *Escherichia coli*. *J. Mol. Biol. 19:207* (1966).

TRAUB, P., HOSOKAWA, K., and NOMURA, M. Streptomycin sensitivity and the structural components of the 30 S ribosomes of *Escherichia coli*. *J. Mol. Biol. 19:211* (1966).

WATANABE, T. Infectious drug resistance. *Sci. Amer. 217,* No. 6, p. 19 (Dec., 1967).

WEBB, J. L. *Enzyme and Metabolic Inhibitors*. Academic Press, New York, Vol. 2, 1966. Especially: Ch. 2, Analogs of Enzyme Reaction Components.

CHAPTER 11

DAVIES, D. R., and EVANS, K. J. The role of genetic damage in radiation-induced cell lethality. *Advances Radiation Biol. 2:243* (1966).

FRY, R. M. Freezing and Drying of Bacteria. In *Cryobiology* (H. T. Meryman, ed.). Academic Press, New York, 1966.

CHAPTER 22

ABELSON, J., and THOMAS, C. A., JR. The anatomy of the T5 bacteriophage DNA molecule. *J. Mol. Biol. 18:262* (1966).

AGRAWAL, H. O., and BRUENING, G. Isolation of high-molecular-weight, P^{32}-labeled influenza virus ribonucleic acid. *Proc. Nat. Acad. Sc. 55:818* (1966).

HYDE, J. M., GAFFORD, L. G., and RANDALL, C. C. Molecular weight determination of fowlpox virus DNA by electron microscopy. *Virology 33:112* (1967).

KINGSBURY, D. W. Newcastle disease virus RNA. I. Isolation and preliminary characterization of RNA from virus particles. *J. Mol. Biol. 18:195* (1966).

ROBERTS, J. W., and STEITZ, J. E. A. The reconstitution of infective bacteriophage R17. *Proc. Nat. Acad. Sc. 58:1416* (1967).

STRAUSS, J. H., JR., and SINSHEIMER, R. L. Characterization of an infectivity assay for the ribonucleic acid of bacteriophage MS2. *J. Virology 1*:711 (1967).

TOVELL, D. R., and COLTER, J. S. Observations on the assay of infectious viral ribonucleic acid: effects of DMSO and DEAE-dextran. *Virology 32*:84 (1967).

CHAPTER 23

ANDRAKU, N., and TOMIZAWA, J. Molecular mechanisms of genetic recombination of bacteriophage. V. Two kinds of joining of parental DNA molecules. *J. Mol. Biol. 12*:805 (1965).

BRADLEY, D. E., and DEWAR, C. A. Intracellular changes in cells of *Escherichia coli* infected with a filamentous bacteriophage. *J. Gen. Virol. 1*:179 (1967).

BURTON, A., and SINSHEIMER, R. L. The process of infection with bacteriophage φX174. VII. Ultracentrifugal analysis of the replicative form. *J. Mol. Biol. 14*:327 (1965).

DENHARDT, D. T., and SILVER, R. B. An analysis of the clone size distribution of φX174 mutants and recombinants. *Virology 30*:10 (1966).

DENHARDT, D. T., and SINSHEIMER, R. L. The process of infection with bacteriophage φX174. IV. Replication of the viral DNA in a synchronized infection. *J. Mol. Biol. 12*:647 (1965).

DRAKE, J. W. The length of the homologous pairing region for genetic recombination in bacteriophage T4. *Proc. Nat. Acad. Sc. 58*:962 (1967).

EBISUZAKI, K. Ultraviolet sensitivity and functional capacity in bacteriophage T4. *J. Mol. Biol. 20*:545 (1966).

EDGAR, R. S., and WOOD, W. B. Morphogenesis of bacteriophage T4 in extracts of mutant-infected cells. *Genetics 55*:498 (1966).

FRANKEL, F. R. Studies on the nature of the replicating DNA in *Escherichia coli* infected with certain *amber* mutants of phage T4. *J. Mol. Biol. 18*:144 (1966).

KELLENBERGER, E., BOLLE, A., DE LA TOUR, E. B., EPSTEIN, R. H., FRANKLIN, N. C., JERNE, N. K., REALE-SCAFATI, A., and SÉCHAUD, J. Functions and properties related to the tail fibers of bacteriophage T4. *Virology 26*:419 (1965).

KOZINSKI, A. W., and KOZINSKI, P. B. Early intracellular events in the replication of T4 phage DNA. II. Partially replicated DNA. *Proc. Nat. Acad. Sc. 54*:634 (1965).

LEIBY, P. D. Recombination in bacteriophage T4: a mechanism. *Science 150*:760 (1965).

MOSIG, G. Distances separating genetic markers in T4 DNA. *Proc. Nat. Acad. Sc. 56*:1177 (1966).

PÈNE, J. J., and MARMUR, J. Deoxyribonucleic acid replication and expression of early and late bacteriophage functions in *Bacillus subtilis*. *J. Virology 1*:86 (1967).

RAY, D. S., PREUSS, A., and HOFSCHNEIDER, P. H. Replication of the singlestranded DNA of the male-specific bacteriophage M13. *J. Mol. Biol. 21*:485 (1966).

SIEGEL, J. E. D., and HAYASHI, M. Complementary strand infectivity in φX174 replicative form DNA. *J. Mol. Biol. 27*:443 (1967).

STAHL, F. W., MURRAY, N. E., NAKATA, A., and CRASEMANN, J. M. Intergenic *cis-trans* position effects in bacteriophage T4. *Genetics 54*:223 (1966).

STREISINGER, G., EMRICH, J., and STAHL, M. M. Chromosome structure in phage T4. III. Terminal redundancy and length determination. *Proc. Nat. Acad. Sc. 57*:292 (1967).

WOOD, W. B. Host specificity of DNA produced by *Escherichia coli*: bacterial mutations affecting the restriction and modification of DNA. *J. Mol. Biol. 16*:118 (1966).

CHAPTER 24

BERTANI, G., TORHEIM, B., and LAURENT, T. Multiplication in *Serratia* of a bacteriophage originating from *Escherichia coli*: lysogenization and host-controlled variation. *Virology 32*:619 (1967).

BERTANI, L. E. Limited multiplication of phages superinfecting lysogenic bacteria and its implication for the mechanism of immunity. *Virology 27*:496 (1965).

BROOKS, K., and CLARK, A. J. Behavior of λ bacteriophage in a recombination deficient strain of *Escherichia coli*. *J. Virology 1*:283 (1967).

CAMPBELL, A. The steric effect in lysogenization by bacteriophage lambda. II. Chromosomal attachment of the b$_2$ mutant. *Virology 27*:340 (1965).

DOVE, W. F. Action of the lambda chromosome. I. Control of functions late in bacteriophage development. *J. Mol. Biol. 19*:187 (1966).

EISEN, H. A., FUERST, C. R., SIMINOVITCH, L., THOMAS, R., LAMBERT, L., DASILVA, L. P., and JACOB, F. Genetics and physiology of defective lysogeny in K12 (λ): studies of early mutants. *Virology 30*:224 (1966).

FALKOW, S., CITARELLA, R. V., WOHLHIETER, J. A., and WATANABE, T. The molecular nature of R-factors. *J. Mol. Biol. 17*:102 (1966).

FISCHER-FANTUZZI, L. Integration of λ and λ b2 genomes in nonimmune host bacteria carrying a λ cryptic prophage. *Virology 32*:18 (1967).

GREEN, M. H. Inactivation of the prophage lambda repressor without induction. *J. Mol. Biol. 16*:134 (1966).

HERSCHMAN, H. R., and HELINSKI, D. R. Comparative study of the events associated with colicin induction. *J. Bacteriol. 94*:691 (1967).

HICKSON, F. T., ROTH, T. F., and HELINSKI, D. R. Circular DNA forms of a bacterial sex factor. *Proc. Nat. Acad. Sc. 58*:1731 (1967).

KAISER, A. D., and INMAN, R. B. Cohesion and the biological activity of bacteriophage lambda DNA. *J. Mol. Biol. 13*:78 (1965).

KAYAJANIAN, G., and CAMPBELL, A. The relationship between heritable physical and genetic properties of selected gal$^-$ and gal$^+$ transducing λ dg. *Virology 30*:482 (1966).

KONDO, E., and MITSUHASHI, S. Drug resistance of enteric bacteria. IV. Active transducing bacteriophage P1 CM produced by the combination of R factor with bacteriophage P1. *J. Bacteriol. 88*:1266 (1964).

LIEB, M. Studies of heat-inducible λ phage. III. Mutations in cistron N affecting heat induction. *Genetics 54*:835 (1966).

LIEDKE-KULKE, M., and KAISER, A. D. Genetic control of prophage insertion specificity in bacteriophages λ and 21. *Virology 32*:465 (1967).

LWOFF, A. Interaction among virus, cell, and organism. *Science 152*:1216 (1966).

MAEDA, A., and NOMURA, M. Interaction of colicins with bacterial cells. *J. Bacteriol. 91*:685 (1966).

MEYNELL, E., and DATTA, N. Mutant drug resistant factors of high transmissibility. *Nature 214*:885 (1967).

MEYNELL, G. G., and LAWN, A. M. Sex pili and common pili in the conjugational transfer of colicin factor Ib by *Salmonella typhimurium*. *Genet. Res., Camb. 9*:359 (1967).

PEARCE, U., and STOCKER, B. A. D. Variation in composition of chromosome fragments transduced by phage P22. *Virology 27*:290 (1965).

PTASHNE, M. Specific binding of the λ phage repressor to λ DNA. *Nature 214*:232 (1967).

SATO, K., and MATSUSHIRO, A. The tryptophan operon regulated by phage immunity. *J. Mol. Biol. 14*:608 (1965).

SHAW, W. V. The enzymatic acetylation of chloramphenicol by extracts of R factor-resistant *Escherichia coli*. *J. Biol. Chem. 242*:687 (1967).

TAYLOR, K., HRADECNA, Z., and SZYBALSKI, W. Asymmetric distribution of the transcribing regions on the complementary strands of colliphage λ DNA. *Proc. Nat. Acad. Sc. 57*:1618 (1967).

THOMAS, R. Control of development in temperate bacteriophages. I. Induction of prophage genes following hetero-immune super-infection. *J. Mol. Biol. 22*:79 (1966).

WATANABE, T. Evolutionary relationships of R factors with other episomes and plasmids. *Fed. Proc. 26*: 23 (1967).

ZISSLER, J. Integration-negative (int) mutants of phage λ. *Virology 31*:189 (1967).

CHAPTER 25

BALTIMORE, D., and GIRARD, M. An intermediate in the synthesis of poliovirus RNA. *Proc. Nat. Acad. Sc. 56*:741 (1966).

BRATT, M. A., and ROBINSON, W. S. Ribonucleic acid synthesis in cells infected with Newcastle disease virus. *J. Mol. Biol. 23*:1 (1967).

BUCK, C. A., GRANGER, G. A., TAYLOR, M. W., and HOLLAND, J. J. Efficient, inefficient, and abortive infection of different mammalian cells by small RNA viruses. *Virology 33*:36 (1967).

BURGE, B. W., and PFEFFERKORN, E. R. Temperature-sensitive mutants of Sindbis virus: biochemical correlates of complementation. *J. Virology 1*:956 (1967).

EDGELL, M. H., and GINOZA, W. The fate during infection of the coat protein of the spherical bacteriophage R17. *Virology 27*:23 (1965).

ERIKSON, R. L., and GORDON, J. A. Replication of bacteriophage RNA: purification of the replicative intermediate by agarose column chromatography. *Biochem. Biophys. Res. Com. 23*:422 (1966).

GRANBOULAN, N., and FRANKLIN, R. M. Electron microscopy of viral RNA, replicative form and replicative intermediate of the bacteriophage R17. *J. Mol. Biol. 22*:173 (1966).

HAY, J., KOTELES, G. J., KEIR, H. M., and SHARPE, H. S. Herpes virus specified ribonucleic acids. *Nature 210*: 387 (1966).

IGLEWSKI, W. J., and FRANKLIN, R. M. Denaturation and renaturation of viral RNA. III. Purification of the complementary strand of R17 RNA. *Proc. Nat. Acad. Sc. 58*:1019 (1967).

JUNGWIRTH, C., and JOKLIK, W. K. Studies on "early" enzymes in HeLa cells infected with vaccinia virus. *Virology 27*:80 (1965).

KATES, J. R., and MCAUSLAN, B. R. Messenger RNA synthesis by a "coated" viral genome. *Proc. Nat. Acad. Sc. 57*:314 (1967).

KEIR, H. M., SUBAK-SHARPE, H., SHEDDEN, W. I. H., WATSON, D. H., and WILDY, P. Immunological evidence for a specific DNA polymerase produced after infection by herpes simples virus. *Virology 30*:154 (1966).

KINGSBURY, D. W. Newcastle disease virus complementary RNA: its relationship to the viral genome and its accumulation in the presence or absence of actinomycin D. *Virology 33*:227 (1967).

LODISH, H. F., and ZINDER, N. D. Mutants of the bacteriophage f2. VIII. Control mechanisms for phage-specific syntheses. *J. Mol. Biol. 19*:333 (1966).

LODISH, H. F., and ZINDER, N. D. Semi-conservative replication of bacteriophage f2 RNA. *J. Mol. Biol. 21*: 207 (1966).

MAIZEL, J. V., JR., PHILLIPS, B. A., and SUMMERS, D. F. Composition of artificially produced and naturally occurring empty capsids of poliovirus type 1. *Virology 32*:692 (1967).

MANDEL, B. The relationship between penetration and uncoating of poliovirus in HeLa cells. *Virology 31*: 702 (1967).

MCAUSLAN, B. R., HERDE, PAMELA, PETT, D., and ROSS, J. Nucleases of virus-infected animal cells. *Biochem. Biophys. Res. Com. 20*:586 (1965).

ODA, K., and JOKLIK, W. K. Hybridization and sedimentation studies on "early" and "late" vaccinia messenger RNA. *J. Mol. Biol. 27*:395 (1967).

PACE, N. R., BISHOP, D. H. L., and SPIEGELMAN, S. The kinetics of product appearance and template involvement in the *in vitro* replication of viral RNA. *Proc. Nat. Acad. Sc. 58*:711 (1967).

SALZMAN, N. P., and SEBRING, E. D. Sequential formation of vaccinia virus proteins and viral deoxyribonucleic acid replication. *J. Virology 1*:16 (1967).

SAMBROOK, J. F., PADGETT, B. L., and TOMKINS, J. K. N. Conditional lethal mutants of rabbitpox virus. I. Isolation of host cell-dependent and temperature-dependent mutants. *Virology 28*:592 (1966).

SIMON, L. D., and ANDERSON, T. F. The infection of *Escherichia coli* by T2 and T4 bacteriophages as seen in the electron miscroscope. II. Structure and function of the baseplate. *Virology 32*:298 (1967).

SUGIURA, A., and KILBOURNE, E. D. Genetic studies of influenza viruses. III. Production of plaque-type recombinants with A_0 and A_1 strains. *Virology 29*:84 (1966).

SUGIYAMA, T., and NAKADA, D. Control of translation of MS2 RNA cistrons by MS2 coat protein. *Proc. Nat. Acad. Sc. 57*:1744 (1967).

SUMMERS, D. F., MAIZEL, J. V., JR., and DARNELL, J. E., JR. Evidence for virus-specific noncapsid proteins in poliovirus-infected HeLa cells. *Proc. Nat. Acad. Sc. 54*:505 (1965).

WEISSMANN, C., FELIX, G., SLOR, H., and POLLET, R. Replication of viral RNA. XIV. Single-stranded minus strands as template for the synthesis of viral plus strands *in vitro*. *Proc. Nat. Acad. Sc. 57*:1870 (1967).

WILLEMS, M., and PENMAN, S. The mechanism of host cell protein synthesis inhibition by poliovirus. *Virology 30*:355 (1966).

CHAPTER 26

BABLANIAN, R., EGGERS, H. J., and TAMM, I. Inhibition of enterovirus cytopathic effects by 2-(α-hydroxybenzyl)-benzimidazole. *J. Bacteriol. 91*:1289 (1966).

BRYANS, J. T., ZENT, W. W., GRUNERT, R. R., and BOUGHTON, D. C. I-adamantanamine hydrochloride prophylaxis for experimentally induced A/equine 2 influenza virus infection. *Nature 212*:1542 (1966).

FIELD, A. K., TYTELL, A. A., LAMPSON, G. P., and HILLEMAN, M. R. Inducers of interferon and host resistance. II. Multistranded synthetic polynucleotide complexes. *Proc. Nat. Acad. Sc. 58*:1004 (1967).

FINTER, N. B. Interferon in mice: protection against small doses of virus. *J. Gen. Virol. 1*:395 (1967).

KAPLAN, A. S., and BEN-PORAT, T. Mode of antiviral action of 5-iodouracil deoxyriboside. *J. Mol. Biol. 19*:320 (1966).

MARCUS, P. I., and SALB, J. M. Molecular basis of interferon action: inhibition of viral RNA translation. *Virology 30*:502 (1966).

MERIGAN, T. C., and KLEINSCHMIDT, W. J. Different molecular species of mouse interferon induced by statolon. *Nature 208*:667 (1965).

MERIGAN, T. C., WINGET, C. A., and DIXON, C. B. Purification and characterization of vertebrate interferons. *J. Mol. Biol. 13*:679 (1965).

TYTELL, A. A., LAMPSON, G. P., FIELD, A. K., and HILLEMAN, M. R. Inducers of interferon and host resistance. III. Double-stranded RNA from reovirus type 3 virions (Reo 3-RNA). *Proc. Nat. Acad. Sc. 58*:1719 (1967).

ZEMLA, J., COTO, C., and KAPLAN, A. S. Differential incorporation of iododeoxyuridine into the DNA of pseudorabies virus-infected and noninfected cells. *Virology 31*:734 (1967).

CHAPTER 27

ASHE, W. K., and NOTKINS, A. L. Neutralization of an infectious herpes simplex virus-antibody complex by anti-δ-globulin. *Proc. Nat. Acad. Sc. 56*:447 (1966).

PHILIPSON, L. Interaction between poliovirus and immunoglobulins. II. Basic aspects of virus-antibody interaction. *Virology 28*:35 (1966).

PHILIPSON, L., and BENNICH, H. Interaction between poliovirus and immunoglobulins. III. The effect of cleavage products of rabbit δG-globulin on infectivity and distribution of virus in polymer phase systems. *Virology 29*:330 (1966).

PHILIPSON, L., KILLANDER, J., and ALBERTSSON, P. Interaction between poliovirus and immunoglobulins. I. Detection of virus antibodies by partition in aqueous polymer phase systems. *Virology 28*:22 (1966).

INDEX

Page numbers in *italics* refer to illustrations.

E

Eagle's medium, animal cells in, 749
Eberthella typhosa, 47
Eclipse: in nucleic acid infection, 754
transformation and, 189
Ecological criteria, 47
Edema, hereditary angioneurotic, 523
EDTA (ethylenediaminetetraacetic acid), cell permeability and, 34
Effectors, gene, 268
Efflux rate, in membrane transport, 163
Electron microscope, 23, 32–33, 29–30, 36–37, 126
DNA and, 212
negative staining, 635
shadowcasting in, 634
Electron transport system, 35, 66–72
Electrophoresis, 634, 435
Embden-Meyerhof pathway, 63, 75, 60, 64
Emphysema, as allergic response, 527, 530
Encephalomyocarditis, 764
Endocarditis, 307
Endoplasmic reticulum, of yeasts and molds, 611
Endospores, 5
Endotoxins, 578, 581–582, 600
Endpoint method, of viral assay, 664–665
Endproduct inhibition, 283–285
Energy: chemical bond, 57
sources of, 57
production of, 55–57, 70
Enrichment cultures, 6, 74
Enteric bacilli, 590–603
antigenic structure of, 593–600
antisera of, 595
conjugation in, 601–602
fermentation reactions in, 592
flagella of, 594
general properties of, 590–603
genetic interrelations in, 601–602
groups, genera, and species in, 590
metabolic characteristics of, 592, 593, 601
mutations in, 601
physiological characteristics of, 591
primary isolation of, 593
resistance to dyes, 593
screening of, 592
transduction in, 601, 594
Enterobacteriaceae, 45, 48, 65, 119, *See also* Enteric bacilli
Enthalpy, defined, 373
Entner-Doudoroff pathway, 63, 64

Entropy change, 373
Entry, nonspecific, in membrane transport, 162–165
Envelope, of virions, 636
Environmental influences, 110–111, 311
Enzymes, 65–67
adaptive, 76, 264
allosteric, 285–286, 286
amino acids, and, 113, 229
aminoacyl transfer of, 128–130
in antibody-antigen reactions, 369, 507
as antiviral agents, 802
and bacterial invasiveness, 576–578
in bacterial systems, 130
and basal wall, 114
biosynthesis and, 80–81, 113, 115–116
cell size and, 289
chromosomes and, 41
coenzymes and, 59
constitutive, 76, 266
coordinate synthesis of, 270
crypticity of, 161
digestion by, 216–217
differential rate of synthesis in, 265
in DNA synthesis, 684–685
DPN and, 90
extracellular, 140, 577
fibrinolytic, 577
fractionation of, 82
glucosylating, 601
inducible, 76, 264–268
O gene and, 562
phage, 720, 685
polymerizing, 120
reactions of, 80
receptor-destroying (RDE), 660
regulation of, 283–288
replicating, 227
reserve capacity for, 297
respiration and, 56
"salvage," 102
soluble, 42
in spores, 156–157
surface, 140
temperature-sensitive, 291
transcribing, 228–229
uncoating, 755
viral, 758
yellow, 68
Enzyme formation; induced, 264–268, 265
Enzyme repression, 264–268
Eosin-methylene blue, 149
Epidemiology, science of, 7
Epigenetics, 282
Episomes, 601, 731–736
conjugation through, 602
cure by, 193, 318
cytoplasmic inheritance and; 736
defined, 731

F and F' formation in, 733, 732
integration of, 731–732
phylogeny of, 735–736
resistance-transferring, 732–734
structure of, 731
Epithelial cells, 484, 485–486
Epithelium, intestinal, 492
Equilibrium density centrifugation, see Centrifugation
Equilibrium dialysis, 367
Equivalence point and zone, in antibody-antigen reactions, 380–383
Ergotamine, 621
Error correction, in genetic code, 256
Erwinia, 47
Erythema, *see* Wheal-and-erythema response
Erythroblastosis fetalis, 564
Erythrocytes, blood groups and, 556, 563
Erythromycin, 320
Escherichia coli, 47, 58, 63, 65, 77, 103, 118, 123, 27, 32–33, 682
bacteriophage and, 677
biosynthesis in, 94
in branched pathway, 284–285
chromosome replication in, 292
chromosomes of, 225–226
comparative size of, 631
diauxic growth of, 77
DNA in, 122, 212
drug-resistant strains, 602
enteric, 591
genetic map of, 199–200
Hfr strain in, 204
interferon and, 791
lethal phage mutants and, 702
lysogenic and sensitive strains of, 719
mutants and, 187, 702
polysome of, 278
primary response in, 461
radiation of, 341
radioautographs of, 223
temperature and, 135
T-phages of, 674
viral RNA and, 760
Essential metabolites, 80, 306
Essential nutrients, 80, 306
Ethylene oxide, uses of, 347
Eubacteria, 24, 48
cell of, 22
Eubacteriales, 26
Eucaryotes, 16–17
Eucaryotic cells, 16, 35, 38
Euglobulin, 514
Eumycetes, 15
Evans blue, in anaphylaxis, 530, 531
Evolution: genetic diversity and, 184
human, 14–15